Instructor's Solutions Manual

Kevin Bodden
Randy Gallaher
Lewis and Clark Community College

Elementary and Intermediate Algebra
for College Students

■ Third Edition

Allen R.
Angel

PEARSON

Prentice
Hall

Upper Saddle River, NJ 07458

Vice President and Editorial Director, Mathematics: Christine Hoag
Executive Editor: Paul Murphy
Project Manager, Editorial: Dawn Nuttall
Editorial Assistant: Georgina Brown
Senior Managing Editor: Linda Mihatov Behrens
Project Manager, Production: Kristy Mosch
Supplement Cover Manager: Paul Gourhan
Supplement Cover Designer: Victoria Colotta
Operations Specialist: Ilene Kahn
Senior Operations Supervisor: Diane Peirano

© 2008 Pearson Education, Inc.
Pearson Prentice Hall
Pearson Education, Inc.
Upper Saddle River, NJ 07458

Pearson Prentice Hall™ is a trademark of Pearson Education, Inc.

The author and publisher of this book have used their best efforts in preparing this book. These efforts include the development, research, and testing of the theories and programs to determine their effectiveness. The author and publisher make no warranty of any kind, expressed or implied, with regard to these programs or the documentation contained in this book. The author and publisher shall not be liable in any event for incidental or consequential damages in connection with, or arising out of, the furnishing, performance, or use of these programs.

Printed in the United States of America

10 9 8 7 6 5 4 3 2 1

ISBN 13: 978-0-13-233725-0

ISBN 10:   0-13-233725-8

Pearson Education Ltd., London
Pearson Education Australia Pty. Ltd., Sydney
Pearson Education Singapore, Pte. Ltd.
Pearson Education North Asia Ltd., Hong Kong
Pearson Education Canada, Inc., Toronto
Pearson Educación de Mexico, S.A. de C.V.
Pearson Education—Japan, Tokyo
Pearson Education Malaysia, Pte. Ltd.

Table of Contents

Chapter 1

Exercise Set 1.1

1 – 10. Answers will vary.

11. To prepare properly for this class, you need to do all the homework carefully and completely; preview the new material that is to be covered in class.

12. Answers will vary.

13. At least 2 hours of study and homework time for each hour of class time is generally recommended.

14. A mathematics text should be read slowly and carefully; do not just skim the text.

15. a. You need to do the homework in order to practice what was presented in class.

    b. When you miss class, you miss important information. Therefore it is important that you attend class regularly.

16. It is important to know why you follow the specific steps to solve a problem so that you will be able to solve similar types of problems.

17. Answers will vary.

18. 1. Carefully write down any formulas or ideas that you need to remember.

    2. Look over the entire exam quickly to get an idea of its length. Also make sure that no pages are missing.

    3. Read the test directions carefully.

    4. Read each question carefully. Show all of your work. Answer each question completely, and make sure that you have answered the specific question asked.

    5. Work the questions you understand best first; then go back and work those you are not sure of. Do not spend too much time on any one problem or you may not be able to complete the exam. Be prepared to spend more time on problems worth more points.

    6. Attempt each problem. You may get at least partial credit even if you do not obtain the correct answer. If you make no attempt at answering the question, you will lose full credit.

    7. Work carefully step by step. Copy all signs and exponents correctly when working from step to step, and make sure to copy the original question from the test correctly.

    8. Write clearly so that your instructor can read your work. If your instructor cannot read your work, you may lose credit. Also, if your writing is not clear, it is easy to make a mistake when working from one step to the next. When appropriate, make sure that your final answer stands out by placing a box around it.

    9. If you have time, check your work and your answers.

    10. Do not be concerned if others finish the test before you or if you are the last to finish. Use any extra time to check your work.

Exercise Set 1.2

1. understand, translate, calculate, check, state answer

2. An expression is a collection of numbers, letters, grouping symbols, and operations.

3. The symbol $\approx$ means "is approximately equal to."

4. Substitute smaller or larger numbers so that the method becomes clear.

5. Rank the data. The median is the value in the middle.

6. We usually think of the mean as the average.

7. Divide the sum of the data by the number of pieces of data.

8. The mean is greater since it takes the value of 30 into account.

9. A mean average of 80 corresponds to a total of 800 points for the 10 quizzes. Walter's mean average of 79 corresponds to a total of 790 points for the 10 quizzes. Thus, he actually missed a B by 10 points.

10. The median will not change since the two middle values in the ranked data will still be 3 and 4. The mean will change since the total of the data will change.

11. a. $\dfrac{78+97+59+74+74}{5} = \dfrac{382}{5} = 76.4$

   The mean grade is 76.4.

   b. 59, 74, 74, 78, 97
   The middle value is 74.
   The median grade is 74.

12. a. $\dfrac{161+131+187+163+145}{5} = \dfrac{787}{5} = 157.4$

   The mean score is 157.4.

   b. 131, 145, 161, 163, 187
   The middle value is 161.
   The median score is 161.

13. a. $\dfrac{96.56+108.78+87.23+85.90+79.55+65.88}{6}$

   $= \dfrac{523.90}{6} \approx 87.32$

   The mean bill is about \$87.32.

b. \$65.88, \$79.55, \$85.90, \$87.23, \$96.56, \$108.78
   The middle values are \$85.90 and \$87.23.
   $\dfrac{85.90+87.23}{2} = \dfrac{173.13}{2} = 86.57$
   The median bill is about \$86.57.

14. a. $\dfrac{204.83+153.85+210.03+119.76+128.38}{5}$

   $= \dfrac{816.85}{5} = 163.37$

   The mean bill is \$163.37.

   b. \$119.76, \$128.38, \$153.85, \$204.83, \$210.03
   The middle value is \$153.85.
   The median bill is \$153.85.

15.a. $\dfrac{10.63+10.67+10.68+10.83+11.6+11.76+11.87+12.18+12.8+12.91}{10} = \dfrac{115.93}{10} = 11.593$

   The mean inches for rainfall for the 10 years is 11.593.

   b. 10.63, 10.67, 10.68, 10.83, 11.6, 11.76, 11.87, 12.18, 12.8, 12.91
   The middle values are 11.6 and 11.76.

   $\dfrac{11.6+11.76}{2} = \dfrac{23.36}{2} = 11.68$

   The median inches for rainfall for the 10 years is 11.68.

16. a. $\dfrac{124,000+175,900+142,300+164,800+146,000+210,000+112,200+153,600}{8} = \dfrac{1,228,900}{8} = 153612.5$

   The mean sale price for homes is \$153,612.50.

   b. 112,200, 124,100, 142,300, 146,000, 153,600, 164,800, 175,900, 210,000
   The middle values are 146,000 and 153,600.
   $\dfrac{146,000+153,600}{2} = \dfrac{299,600}{2} = 149,800$
   The median sale price of homes is \$149,800.

17. Barbara's earnings = 5% of sales
   Barbara's earnings = 0.05(9400) = 470
   Her week's earnings were \$470.

18. feet per meter =
   $\dfrac{\text{number of feet}}{\text{number of meters}} = \dfrac{1454}{443} \approx 3.28$
   There are about 3.28 feet in a meter.

19. a. sales tax = 8% of price
   sales tax = 0.08(16,700) = 1336
   The sales tax was \$1,336.

   b. Total cost = price + tax
   Total cost = 16,700 + 1,336 = 18,036
   The total cost was \$18,036.

20. New balance = old balance – (number of disks) (cost of each disk)
New balance = 312.60 – 5(17.11)
$$= 312.60 - 85.55$$
$$= 227.05$$
Her new balance is $227.05.

21. operations performed = (number of operations in billions)(amount of time in seconds)
$$= (2.3)(0.7)$$
$$= 1.61 \text{ billion}$$
In 0.7 seconds, 1,610,000,000 operations can be performed.

22. a. total cost with payments = down payment + (number of months)(monthly payment)
total cost with payments = 200 + 24(33)
$$= 200 + 792$$
$$= 992$$
Making monthly payments, it costs $992.

b. savings = total cost with payments – total cost at purchase
savings = 992 – 950 = 42
He saves $42 by paying the total at the time of purchase.

---

23. a. time to use energy $= \dfrac{\text{kJ in hamburger}}{\text{kJ/min running}}$

$$= \dfrac{1550}{80}$$

$$= 19.375$$

It takes 19.375 minutes to use up the energy from a hamburger by running.

b. time to use energy $= \dfrac{\text{kJ in milkshake}}{\text{kJ/min walking}}$

$$= \dfrac{2200}{25}$$

$$= 88$$

It takes 88 minutes to use up the energy from a chocolate milkshake by walking.

c. time to use energy

$= \dfrac{\text{kJ in glass of skim milk}}{\text{kJ/min cycling}}$

$= \dfrac{350}{35}$

$= 10$

It takes 10 minutes to use up the energy from a glass of skim milk by cycling.

24. Cost at Don's
$= 20.00$ (number of 30 min intervals)
$= 20.00(6)$
$= \$120$

Cost at Carol's
$= 50$ (number of hours)
$= 50(3)$
$= \$150$

a. Don's is the better deal.

b. savings = cost at Carol's – cost at Don's
savings = 150 – 120= 30
You would save $30.

25. miles per gallon $= \dfrac{\text{number of miles}}{\text{number of gallons}}$

$$= \dfrac{16,935.4 - 16,741.3}{10.5}$$

$$= \dfrac{194.1}{10.5}$$

$$\approx 18.49$$

His car gets about 18.49 miles per gallon.

26. a. taxes = 1460 + 15% in excess of 14,600

taxes = 1460 + 0.15(34,612 − 14,600)

$\quad = 1460 + 0.15(20,012)$

$\quad = 1460 + 3001.80$

$\quad = 4461.80$

Their taxes were $4461.80

b. taxes

$= 8180 + 25\%$ in excess of 59,400

$= 8180 + 0.25(75,610 - 59,400)$

$= 8180 + 0.25(16,210)$

$= 8180 + 4052.50$

$= 12,232.50$

Their taxes were $12,232.50.

27. savings = local cost − mail order cost

local cost $= 425 + (0.08)(425)$

$\quad = 425 + 34$

$\quad = 459$

mail cost $= 4(62.30 + 6.20 + 8)$

$\quad = 4(76.50)$

$\quad = 306$

savings $= 459 - 306$

$\quad = 153$

Eric saved $153.

28. Martinez' salary per inning

$= \dfrac{\text{total amount paid}}{\text{number of innings pitched}}$

$= \dfrac{17.5 \text{ million}}{217 \text{ innings}}$

$\approx 80,645.16$ per inning

Ramirez' salary per bat

$= \dfrac{\text{total salary}}{\text{number of at bats}}$

$= \dfrac{22.5 \text{ million}}{568 \text{ at bats}}$

$\approx 39,612.67$ per bat

$80,645.16 - 39,612.67 \approx 41,032.49$

Martinez received about $41,032.49 more per inning than Ramirez did at bat.

29. A single green block should be placed on the 3 on the right. This is required for

$-6 + (-4) + 2(-2) + 3(3) + 5$

$= -6 + (-4) + (-4) + 9 + 5$

$= -10 + (-4) + 9 + 5$

$= -14 + 9 + 5$

$= -5 + 5$

$= 0$

30. Note: 3 miles = 12 quarter miles and 90 seconds = 3 thirty-second intervals.

Cost = Flat Fee + 0.30 (each quarter mile traveled)

$\qquad + 0.20$ (each 30 seconds stopped in traffic)

$= 2.00 + 0.30(12) + 0.20(3)$

$= 2.00 + 3.60 + 0.60$

$= 6.20$

David's taxi ride cost $6.20.

31. a. gallons per year = 365(gallons per day)

$\qquad = 365(11.25 \text{ gallons})$

$\qquad = 4106.25$

There are 4106.25 gallons of water wasted each year.

b. additional money spent

= (cost)(gallons wasted)

$= \dfrac{5.20}{1000 \text{ gallons}} \cdot 4106.25 \text{ gallons}$

≈ 21.35

About $21.35 extra is spent because of the wasted water.

32. a. $\dfrac{1 \text{ mile}}{1 \text{ hour}} = \dfrac{1 \text{ mile}}{1 \text{ hour}} \cdot \dfrac{5280 \text{ feet}}{1 \text{ mile}}$

$= 5280$ feet per hour

b. $\dfrac{1 \text{ mile}}{1 \text{ hour}} = \dfrac{1 \text{ mile}}{1 \text{ hour}} \cdot \dfrac{5280 \text{ feet}}{1 \text{ mile}} \cdot \dfrac{1 \text{ hour}}{60 \text{ min}} \cdot \dfrac{1 \text{ min}}{60 \text{ sec}}$

$= \dfrac{5280}{3600}$ feet per second

≈ 1.47 feet per second

c. $\dfrac{60 \text{ miles}}{1 \text{ hour}} = \dfrac{60 \text{ miles}}{1 \text{ hour}} \cdot \dfrac{5280 \text{ feet}}{1 \text{ mile}} \cdot \dfrac{1 \text{ hour}}{3600 \text{ sec}}$

≈ 88.0 feet per second

33. a. cost

$= \text{deductible} + 20\%\left(\text{doctor bill} - \text{deductible}\right)$

$= 150 + 0.20\left(365 - 150\right)$

$= 150 + 0.20(215)$

$= 150 + 43$

$= 193$

Mel will be responsible for $193.

b. The insurance company would be responsible for the remainder of the bill which would be 365 − 193 = $172.

34. a. premiums savings

= (number of years)(savings per year)

= 7(10% of 630)

$= 7(63)$

$= 441$

He would save $441.

b. savings after course = savings − cost of course

$= 441 - 70$

$= 371$

His net savings is $371.

35. a. Hong Kong-China; 550

b. Mexico; 385

c. 550 − 385 = 165

36. a. 0.7 billion

b. 1.0 billion

c. $\dfrac{1.0}{0.7} \cdot 100 \approx 1.429 \cdot 100 \approx 1.43$ times greater

37. a. 1992: 275,000
2004: 1,050,000

b. 1,050,000 − 275,000 = 775,000

c. $\dfrac{1,050,000}{275,000} \approx 3.818$

≈ 3.82 times greater

38. a. 1997-1998 and 1999-2000

b. 2003-2004

c. 2001-2002

39. a. 82% of 1.7 million = 0.82(1.7 million)

=1.394 million

b. 15% of 1.7 million = 0.15(1.7 million)

=0.255 million

c. 3% of 1.7 million = = 0.03(1.7 million)

=0.051 million

40. a. 83.125% of 160 = 0.83125(160) = 133

He answered 133 questions correctly.

b. 160 − 133 = 27

He answered 27 questions incorrectly.

41. a. $\text{mean} = \dfrac{\text{sum of grades}}{\text{number of exams}}$

$60 = \dfrac{50 + 59 + 67 + 80 + 56 + \text{last}}{6}$

$360 = 312 + \text{last}$

$\text{last} = 360 - 312$

$= 48$

Lamond needs at least a 48 on the last exam.

b. $70 = \dfrac{312 + \text{last}}{6}$

$420 = 312 + \text{last}$

$\text{last} = 420 - 312$

$= 108$

Lamond would need 108 points on the last exam, so he cannot get a C.

42. a. To earn a B she would need to accumulate 5(80) = 400 points.

minimum grade on the fifth exam

= 400 − the sum of the first four exams

= 400 − (95 + 88 + 82 + 85)

= 400 − 350

= 50

Heather needs to earn a minimum of 50 on the next exam.

b. To earn a A she would need to accumulate 5(90) = 450 points.

minimum grade on the fifth exam

= 450 − the sum of the first four exams

= 450 − (95 + 88 + 82 + 85)

= 450 − 350

= 100

Heather needs to earn a 100 on the next exam.

43. bachelor's degree
$$\frac{49,900}{21,600} \approx 2.3$$

44. $6(78) = 468$

45. Answers will vary.
One possible solution is:
50, 60, 70, 80, 90
$$\text{mean} = \frac{50+60+70+80+90}{5} = \frac{350}{5} = 70$$

46. **a.** The meter reading is 16504.

   b. electrical cost
= (number of kilowatt hour used)(cost per kilowatt hour)
= (16,504 − 16064)(.243)
= 440(.243)
= 106.92
Your electrical cost would be $106.92.

Exercise Set 1.3

1. **a.** Variables are letters that represent numbers.

   b. Letters often used to represent variables are x, y, and z.

2. Factors are numbers or variables that are multiplied together.

3. **a.** The top number is the numerator.

   b. The bottom number is the denominator.

4. $5(x)$, $(5)x$, $(5)(x)$, $5x$, $5 \cdot x$

5. Divide out factors that are common to both the numerator and the denominator.

6. **a.** ellipsis

   b. numbers continue in the same manner

7. **a.** The least common denominator is the smallest number divisible by the two denominators.

   b. Answers will vary.

8. The LCD is 40 because it is the smallest number that both 8 and 10 divide into evenly.

9. Part b) shows simplifying a fraction. In part a) common factors are divided out of two fractions.

10. Part a) shows simplifying a fraction. In part b) common factors are divided out of two fractions.

11. Part a) is incorrect because you cannot divide out common factors when adding.

12. Part b) is incorrect because you cannot divide out common factors when adding.

13. c) $\frac{4}{5} \cdot \frac{1}{4} = \frac{1}{5} \cdot \frac{1}{1} = \frac{1}{5}$. Divide out the common factor, 4. This process can be used only when multiplying fractions and so cannot be used for a) or b). Part d) becomes $\frac{4}{5} \cdot \frac{4}{1}$ so no common factor can be divided out.

14. b) $6 \cdot \frac{5}{12} = \frac{6}{1} \cdot \frac{5}{12} = \frac{5}{2}$. Divide both 6 and 12 by 6. This process can be used only when multiplying fractions and so cannot be used for a) or c). Part d) becomes $\frac{6}{1} \cdot \frac{12}{5}$ so no common factor can be divided out.

15. Multiply numerators and multiply denominators.

16. Invert the divisor, then multiply.

17. Write fractions with a common denominator, add or subtract numerators, keep the common denominator.

18. Answers will vary. One example is $3\frac{1}{2}$.

19. Yes, it is simplified because the greatest common divisor of the numerator and denominator is 1.

20. Yes, it is simplified because the greatest common divisor of the numerator and denominator is 1.

21. Yes, it can be written as a mixed number.
$$\frac{13}{5} = \frac{10}{5} + \frac{3}{5} = 2\frac{3}{5}$$

22. Yes, it can be written as a mixed number.
$$\frac{8}{3} = \frac{6}{3} + \frac{2}{3} = 2\frac{2}{3}$$

23. The greatest common factor of 10 and 15 is 5.
$$\frac{10}{15} = \frac{10 \div 5}{15 \div 5} = \frac{2}{3}$$

24. The greatest common factor of 40 and 10 is 10.

$$\frac{40}{10} = \frac{40 \div 10}{10 \div 10} = \frac{4}{1} = 4$$

25. The greatest common factor of 3 and 12 is 3.

$$\frac{3}{12} = \frac{3 \div 3}{12 \div 3} = \frac{1}{4}$$

26. 19 and 25 have no common factors other than 1. Therefore, the fraction is already simplified.

27. The greatest common factor of 36 and 76 is 4.

$$\frac{36}{76} = \frac{36 \div 4}{76 \div 4} = \frac{9}{19}$$

28. The greatest common factor of 16 and 72 is 8.

$$\frac{16}{72} = \frac{16 \div 8}{72 \div 8} = \frac{2}{9}$$

29. The greatest common factor of 9 and 21 is 3.

$$\frac{9}{21} = \frac{9 \div 3}{21 \div 3} = \frac{3}{7}$$

30. The greatest common factor of 60 and 105 is 15.

$$\frac{60}{105} = \frac{60 \div 15}{105 \div 15} = \frac{4}{7}$$

31. 18 and 49 have no common factors other than 1. Therefore, the fraction is already simplified.

32. The greatest common factor of 100 and 144 is 4.

$$\frac{100}{144} = \frac{100 \div 4}{144 \div 4} = \frac{25}{36}$$

33. 12 and 25 have no common factors other than 1. Therefore, the fraction is already simplified.

34. The greatest common factor of 42 and 138 is 6.

$$\frac{42}{138} = \frac{42 \div 6}{138 \div 6} = \frac{7}{23}$$

35. $2\frac{13}{15} = \frac{30 + 13}{15} = \frac{43}{15}$

36. $5\frac{1}{3} = \frac{15 + 1}{3} = \frac{16}{3}$

37. $7\frac{2}{3} = \frac{21 + 2}{3} = \frac{23}{3}$

38. $4\frac{3}{4} = \frac{16 + 3}{4} = \frac{19}{4}$

39. $3\frac{5}{18} = \frac{54 + 5}{18} = \frac{59}{18}$

40. $6\frac{2}{9} = \frac{54 + 2}{9} = \frac{56}{9}$

41. $9\frac{6}{17} = \frac{153 + 6}{17} = \frac{159}{17}$

42. $3\frac{3}{32} = \frac{96 + 3}{32} = \frac{99}{32}$

43. $\frac{7}{4} = 1\frac{3}{4}$ because $7 \div 4 = 1$ R 3

44. $\frac{18}{7} = 2\frac{4}{7}$ because $18 \div 7 = 2$ R 4

45. $\frac{13}{4} = 3\frac{1}{4}$ because $13 \div 4 = 3$ R 1

46. $\frac{9}{2} = 4\frac{1}{2}$ because $9 \div 2 = 4$ R 1

47. $\frac{32}{7} = 4\frac{4}{7}$ because $32 \div 7 = 4$ R 4

48. $\frac{110}{20} = 5\frac{10}{20} = 5\frac{1}{2}$ because $110 \div 20 = 5$ R 10

49. $\frac{86}{14} = 6\frac{2}{14} = 6\frac{1}{7}$ because $86 \div 14 = 6$ R 2

50. $\frac{72}{14} = 5\frac{2}{14} = 5\frac{1}{7}$ because $72 \div 14 = 5$ R 2

51. $\frac{2}{3} \cdot \frac{4}{5} = \frac{2 \cdot 4}{3 \cdot 5} = \frac{8}{15}$

52. $\frac{6}{13} \cdot \frac{7}{17} = \frac{6 \cdot 7}{13 \cdot 17} = \frac{42}{221}$

53. $\frac{5}{12} \cdot \frac{4}{15} = \frac{\cancel{5}^{1}}{\cancel{12}_{3}} \cdot \frac{\cancel{4}^{1}}{\cancel{15}_{3}} = \frac{1 \cdot 1}{3 \cdot 3} = \frac{1}{9}$

54. $\dfrac{36}{48} \cdot \dfrac{16}{45} = \dfrac{\overset{1}{\cancel{3}}}{\cancel{4}_1} \cdot \dfrac{\overset{4}{\cancel{16}}}{\cancel{45}_{15}} = \dfrac{1 \cdot 4}{1 \cdot 15} = \dfrac{4}{15}$

55. $\dfrac{3}{4} \div \dfrac{1}{2} = \dfrac{3}{\cancel{4}_2} \cdot \dfrac{\cancel{2}^1}{1} = \dfrac{3}{2} \cdot \dfrac{1}{1} = \dfrac{3}{2}$ or $1\dfrac{1}{2}$

56. $\dfrac{15}{16} \cdot \dfrac{4}{3} = \dfrac{\overset{5}{\cancel{15}}}{\cancel{16}_4} \cdot \dfrac{\cancel{4}^1}{\cancel{3}_1} = \dfrac{5 \cdot 1}{4 \cdot 1} = \dfrac{5}{4}$ or $1\dfrac{1}{4}$

57. $\dfrac{3}{8} \div \dfrac{3}{4} = \dfrac{\overset{1}{\cancel{3}}}{\cancel{8}_2} \cdot \dfrac{\cancel{4}^1}{\cancel{3}_1} = \dfrac{1 \cdot 1}{2 \cdot 1} = \dfrac{1}{2}$

58. $\dfrac{3}{8} \cdot \dfrac{10}{11} = \dfrac{3}{\cancel{8}_4} \cdot \dfrac{\overset{5}{\cancel{10}}}{11} = \dfrac{3 \cdot 5}{4 \cdot 11} = \dfrac{15}{44}$

59. $\dfrac{10}{3} \div \dfrac{5}{9} = \dfrac{\overset{2}{\cancel{10}}}{\cancel{3}_1} \cdot \dfrac{\overset{3}{\cancel{9}}}{\cancel{5}_1} = \dfrac{2 \cdot 3}{1 \cdot 1} = \dfrac{6}{1} = 6$

60. $\dfrac{5}{9} \div 30 = \dfrac{\overset{1}{\cancel{5}}}{9} \cdot \dfrac{1}{\cancel{30}_6} = \dfrac{1 \cdot 1}{9 \cdot 6} = \dfrac{1}{54}$

61. $\dfrac{15}{4} \cdot \dfrac{2}{3} = \dfrac{\overset{5}{\cancel{15}}}{\cancel{4}_2} \cdot \dfrac{\cancel{2}^1}{\cancel{3}_1} = \dfrac{5 \cdot 1}{2 \cdot 1} = \dfrac{5}{2}$ or $2\dfrac{1}{2}$

62. $\dfrac{5}{12} \div \dfrac{4}{3} = \dfrac{5}{\cancel{12}_4} \cdot \dfrac{\cancel{3}^1}{4} = \dfrac{5 \cdot 1}{4 \cdot 4} = \dfrac{5}{16}$

63. $5\dfrac{3}{8} \div 1\dfrac{1}{4}$

$5\dfrac{3}{8} = \dfrac{40+3}{8} = \dfrac{43}{8}$

$1\dfrac{1}{4} = \dfrac{4+1}{4} = \dfrac{5}{4}$

$5\dfrac{3}{8} \div 1\dfrac{1}{4} = \dfrac{43}{8} \div \dfrac{5}{4} = \dfrac{43}{\cancel{8}_2} \cdot \dfrac{\cancel{4}^1}{5} = \dfrac{43 \cdot 1}{2 \cdot 5} = \dfrac{43}{10}$ or $4\dfrac{3}{10}$

64. $\left(2\dfrac{1}{5}\right)\dfrac{7}{8}$

$2\dfrac{1}{5} = \dfrac{10+1}{5} = \dfrac{11}{5}$

$\left(2\dfrac{1}{5}\right)\dfrac{7}{8} = \left(\dfrac{11}{5}\right)\dfrac{7}{8} = \dfrac{11 \cdot 7}{5 \cdot 8} = \dfrac{77}{40}$ or $1\dfrac{37}{40}$

65. $\dfrac{28}{13} \cdot \dfrac{2}{7} = \dfrac{\overset{4}{\cancel{28}}}{13} \cdot \dfrac{2}{\cancel{7}_1} = \dfrac{4 \cdot 2}{13 \cdot 1} = \dfrac{8}{13}$

66. $4\dfrac{4}{5} \div \dfrac{8}{15}$

$4\dfrac{4}{5} = \dfrac{20+4}{5} = \dfrac{24}{5}$

$4\dfrac{4}{5} \div \dfrac{8}{15} = \dfrac{24}{5} \div \dfrac{8}{15} = \dfrac{\overset{3}{\cancel{24}}}{\cancel{5}_1} \cdot \dfrac{\overset{3}{\cancel{15}}}{\cancel{8}_1} = \dfrac{3 \cdot 3}{1 \cdot 1} = 9$

67. $\dfrac{3}{8} + \dfrac{2}{8} = \dfrac{3+2}{8} = \dfrac{5}{8}$

68. $\dfrac{18}{36} - \dfrac{1}{36} = \dfrac{18-1}{36} = \dfrac{17}{36}$

69. $\dfrac{3}{14} - \dfrac{1}{14} = \dfrac{3-1}{14} = \dfrac{2}{14} = \dfrac{1}{7}$

70. $\dfrac{1}{4} + \dfrac{3}{4} = \dfrac{1+3}{4} = \dfrac{4}{4} = 1$

71. $\dfrac{4}{5} + \dfrac{6}{15}$

$\dfrac{4}{5} = \dfrac{4}{5} \cdot \dfrac{3}{3} = \dfrac{12}{15}$

$\dfrac{4}{5} + \dfrac{6}{15} = \dfrac{12}{15} + \dfrac{6}{15} = \dfrac{12+6}{15} = \dfrac{18}{15} = \dfrac{6}{5}$ or $1\dfrac{1}{5}$

72. $\dfrac{7}{8} - \dfrac{5}{6}$

$\dfrac{7}{8} = \dfrac{7}{8} \cdot \dfrac{3}{3} = \dfrac{21}{24}$

$\dfrac{5}{6} = \dfrac{5}{6} \cdot \dfrac{4}{4} = \dfrac{20}{24}$

$\dfrac{7}{8} - \dfrac{5}{6} = \dfrac{21}{24} - \dfrac{20}{24} = \dfrac{21-20}{24} = \dfrac{1}{24}$

73. $\dfrac{8}{17} + \dfrac{2}{34}$

$\dfrac{8}{17} = \dfrac{8}{17} \cdot \dfrac{2}{2} = \dfrac{16}{34}$

$\dfrac{8}{17} + \dfrac{2}{34} = \dfrac{16}{34} + \dfrac{2}{34} = \dfrac{16+2}{34} = \dfrac{18}{34} = \dfrac{9}{17}$

74. $\dfrac{3}{7}+\dfrac{17}{35}$

$$\frac{3}{7}=\frac{3}{7}\cdot\frac{5}{5}=\frac{15}{35}$$

$$\frac{3}{7}+\frac{17}{35}=\frac{15}{35}+\frac{17}{35}=\frac{15+17}{35}=\frac{32}{35}$$

75. $\dfrac{1}{3}+\dfrac{1}{4}$

$$\frac{1}{3}=\frac{1}{3}\cdot\frac{4}{4}=\frac{4}{12}$$

$$\frac{1}{4}=\frac{1}{4}\cdot\frac{3}{3}=\frac{3}{12}$$

$$\frac{1}{3}+\frac{1}{4}=\frac{4}{12}+\frac{3}{12}=\frac{4+3}{12}=\frac{7}{12}$$

76. $\dfrac{1}{6}-\dfrac{1}{18}$

$$\frac{1}{6}=\frac{1}{6}\cdot\frac{3}{3}=\frac{3}{18}$$

$$\frac{1}{6}-\frac{1}{18}=\frac{3}{18}-\frac{1}{18}=\frac{3-1}{18}=\frac{2}{18}=\frac{1}{9}$$

77. $\dfrac{7}{12}-\dfrac{2}{9}$

$$\frac{7}{12}=\frac{7}{12}\cdot\frac{3}{3}=\frac{21}{36}$$

$$\frac{2}{9}=\frac{2}{9}\cdot\frac{4}{4}=\frac{8}{36}$$

$$\frac{7}{12}-\frac{2}{9}=\frac{21}{36}-\frac{8}{36}=\frac{21-8}{36}=\frac{13}{36}$$

78. $\dfrac{3}{7}+\dfrac{5}{12}$

$$\frac{3}{7}=\frac{3}{7}\cdot\frac{12}{12}=\frac{36}{84}$$

$$\frac{5}{12}=\frac{5}{12}\cdot\frac{7}{7}=\frac{35}{84}$$

$$\frac{3}{7}+\frac{5}{12}=\frac{36}{84}+\frac{35}{84}=\frac{36+35}{84}=\frac{71}{84}$$

79. $3\dfrac{1}{8}-\dfrac{5}{12}$

$$3\frac{1}{8}=\frac{24+1}{8}=\frac{25}{8}\cdot\frac{3}{3}=\frac{75}{24}$$

$$\frac{5}{12}=\frac{5}{12}\cdot\frac{2}{2}=\frac{10}{24}$$

$$3\frac{1}{8}-\frac{5}{12}=\frac{75}{24}-\frac{10}{24}=\frac{75-10}{24}=\frac{65}{24}\text{ or }2\frac{17}{24}$$

80. $5\dfrac{6}{7}+4\dfrac{5}{8}$

$$5\frac{6}{7}=\frac{35+6}{7}=\frac{41}{7}\cdot\frac{8}{8}=\frac{328}{56}$$

$$4\frac{5}{8}=\frac{32+5}{8}=\frac{37}{8}\cdot\frac{7}{7}=\frac{259}{56}$$

$$5\frac{6}{7}+4\frac{5}{8}=\frac{328}{56}+\frac{189}{56}=\frac{328+259}{56}$$

$$=\frac{587}{56}\text{ or }10\frac{27}{56}$$

81. $6\dfrac{1}{3}-3\dfrac{1}{2}$

$$6\frac{1}{3}=\frac{18+1}{3}=\frac{19}{3}\cdot\frac{2}{2}=\frac{38}{6}$$

$$3\frac{1}{2}=\frac{6+1}{2}=\frac{7}{2}\cdot\frac{3}{3}=\frac{21}{6}$$

$$6\frac{1}{3}-3\frac{1}{2}=\frac{38}{6}-\frac{21}{6}=\frac{38-21}{6}=\frac{17}{6}\text{ or }2\frac{5}{6}$$

82. $2\dfrac{3}{8}+3\dfrac{3}{4}$

$$2\frac{3}{8}=\frac{16+3}{8}=\frac{19}{8}$$

$$3\frac{3}{4}=\frac{12+3}{4}=\frac{15}{4}\cdot\frac{2}{2}=\frac{30}{8}$$

$$2\frac{3}{8}+3\frac{3}{4}=\frac{19}{8}+\frac{30}{8}=\frac{19+30}{8}=\frac{49}{8}\text{ or }6\frac{1}{8}$$

83. $9\dfrac{2}{5}-6\dfrac{1}{2}$

$$9\frac{2}{5}=\frac{45+2}{5}=\frac{47}{5}\cdot\frac{2}{2}=\frac{94}{10}$$

$$6\frac{1}{2}=\frac{12+1}{2}=\frac{13}{2}\cdot\frac{5}{5}=\frac{65}{10}$$

$$9\frac{2}{5}-6\frac{1}{2}=\frac{94}{10}-\frac{65}{10}=\frac{94-65}{10}=\frac{29}{10}\text{ or }2\frac{9}{10}$$

84. $4\dfrac{5}{9} - \dfrac{7}{8}$

$$4\dfrac{5}{9} = \dfrac{36+5}{9} = \dfrac{41}{9} \cdot \dfrac{8}{8} = \dfrac{328}{72}$$

$$\dfrac{7}{8} \cdot \dfrac{9}{9} = \dfrac{63}{72}$$

$$4\dfrac{5}{9} - \dfrac{7}{8} = \dfrac{328}{72} - \dfrac{63}{72} = \dfrac{328-63}{72} = \dfrac{265}{72} = 3\dfrac{49}{72}$$

85. $5\dfrac{9}{10} + 3\dfrac{1}{3}$

$$5\dfrac{9}{10} = \dfrac{50+9}{10} = \dfrac{59}{10} \cdot \dfrac{3}{3} = \dfrac{177}{30}$$

$$3\dfrac{1}{3} = \dfrac{9+1}{3} = \dfrac{10}{3} \cdot \dfrac{10}{10} = \dfrac{100}{30}$$

$$5\dfrac{9}{10} + 3\dfrac{1}{3} = \dfrac{177}{30} + \dfrac{100}{30} = \dfrac{177+100}{30} = \dfrac{277}{30} \text{ or } 9\dfrac{7}{30}$$

86. $8\dfrac{2}{7} - 3\dfrac{1}{3}$

$$8\dfrac{2}{7} = \dfrac{56+2}{7} = \dfrac{58}{7} \cdot \dfrac{3}{3} = \dfrac{174}{21}$$

$$3\dfrac{1}{3} = \dfrac{9+1}{3} = \dfrac{10}{3} \cdot \dfrac{7}{7} = \dfrac{70}{21}$$

$$8\dfrac{2}{7} - 3\dfrac{1}{3} = \dfrac{174}{21} - \dfrac{70}{21} = \dfrac{174-70}{21} = \dfrac{104}{21} \text{ or } 4\dfrac{20}{21}$$

87. $\dfrac{5}{6} - \dfrac{3}{8}$

$$\dfrac{5}{6} \cdot \dfrac{4}{4} = \dfrac{20}{24}$$

$$\dfrac{3}{8} \cdot \dfrac{3}{3} = \dfrac{9}{24}$$

$$\dfrac{5}{6} - \dfrac{3}{8} = \dfrac{20}{24} - \dfrac{9}{24} = \dfrac{20-9}{24} = \dfrac{11}{24}$$

It is $\dfrac{11}{24}$ mile larger.

88. $\dfrac{1}{5} - \dfrac{1}{7}$

$$\dfrac{1}{5} \cdot \dfrac{7}{7} = \dfrac{7}{35}$$

$$\dfrac{1}{7} \cdot \dfrac{5}{5} = \dfrac{5}{35}$$

$$\dfrac{7}{35} - \dfrac{5}{35} = \dfrac{7-5}{35} = \dfrac{2}{35}$$

It is $\dfrac{2}{35}$ meter larger.

89. $55\dfrac{3}{16} - 46\dfrac{1}{4}$

$$55\dfrac{3}{16} = \dfrac{880+3}{16} = \dfrac{883}{16}$$

$$46\dfrac{1}{4} = \dfrac{184+1}{4} = \dfrac{185}{4} = \dfrac{185}{4} \cdot \dfrac{4}{4} = \dfrac{740}{16}$$

$$53\dfrac{3}{16} - 46\dfrac{1}{4} = \dfrac{883}{16} - \dfrac{740}{16} = \dfrac{143}{16} = 8\dfrac{5}{16}$$

Rebecca has grown $8\dfrac{5}{16}$ inches.

90. $2\dfrac{1}{4} + 2\dfrac{7}{8} + 1\dfrac{3}{4}$

$$2\dfrac{1}{4} = \dfrac{8+1}{4} = \dfrac{9}{4} = \dfrac{9}{4} \cdot \dfrac{2}{2} = \dfrac{18}{8}$$

$$2\dfrac{7}{8} = \dfrac{16+7}{8} = \dfrac{23}{8}$$

$$1\dfrac{3}{4} = \dfrac{4+3}{4} = \dfrac{7}{4} = \dfrac{7}{4} \cdot \dfrac{2}{2} = \dfrac{14}{8}$$

$$2\dfrac{1}{4} + 2\dfrac{7}{8} + 1\dfrac{3}{4} = \dfrac{18}{8} + \dfrac{23}{8} + \dfrac{14}{8} = \dfrac{55}{8} = 6\dfrac{7}{8}$$

From June through August, $6\dfrac{7}{8}$ miles of highway was paved.

91. $1 - \dfrac{31}{50} = \dfrac{50}{50} - \dfrac{31}{50} = \dfrac{50-31}{50} = \dfrac{19}{50}$

The fraction of putts not made were $\dfrac{19}{50}$.

92. $1 - \dfrac{7}{9} = \dfrac{9}{9} - \dfrac{7}{9} = \dfrac{9-7}{9} = \dfrac{2}{9}$

The probability that global warming is not occurring is $\dfrac{2}{9}$.

93. $1 - \dfrac{37}{40} = \dfrac{40}{40} - \dfrac{37}{40} = \dfrac{40-37}{40} = \dfrac{3}{40}$

There were $\dfrac{3}{40}$ people unemployed.

94. $1 - \dfrac{313}{1000} = \dfrac{1000}{1000} - \dfrac{313}{1000} = \dfrac{1000-313}{1000} = \dfrac{687}{1000}$

$\dfrac{687}{1000}$ homes did not use electricity.

95. 15 feet $2\dfrac{1}{2}$ in. $-$ 3 feet $3\dfrac{1}{4}$ in.

$= 14$ feet $14\dfrac{2}{4}$ in. $-$ 3 feet $3\dfrac{1}{4}$ in.

$= 11$ feet $11\dfrac{1}{4}$ in.

Now convert to inches,

$11(12) + 11\dfrac{1}{4} = 132 + 11\dfrac{1}{4} = 143\dfrac{1}{4}$ in.

Now convert to feet.

$143\dfrac{1}{4} \div 12 = \dfrac{572+1}{4} \cdot \dfrac{1}{12} = \dfrac{573}{48} \approx 11.94$ft.

96. $1\dfrac{5}{16} = \dfrac{16+5}{16} = \dfrac{21}{16}$

$1\dfrac{5}{16} \div 6 = \dfrac{21}{16} \cdot \dfrac{1}{6} = \dfrac{7}{16} \cdot \dfrac{1}{2} = \dfrac{7}{32}$

Each person will get $\dfrac{7}{32}$ pounds of pie.

97. $10\dfrac{1}{2} - 8\dfrac{2}{5} =$

$10\dfrac{1}{2} = \dfrac{21}{2} \cdot \dfrac{5}{5} = \dfrac{105}{10}$

$8\dfrac{2}{5} = \dfrac{42}{5} \cdot \dfrac{2}{2} = \dfrac{84}{10}$

$\dfrac{105}{10} - \dfrac{84}{10} = \dfrac{105-84}{10} = \dfrac{21}{10} = 2\dfrac{1}{10}$

She improved by $2\dfrac{1}{10}$ minutes.

98. $13\dfrac{1}{2} = \dfrac{26+1}{2} = \dfrac{27}{2}$

$22\left(13\dfrac{1}{2}\right) = \dfrac{\overset{11}{\cancel{22}}}{1} \cdot \dfrac{27}{\underset{1}{\cancel{2}}} = \dfrac{11 \cdot 27}{1 \cdot 1} = \dfrac{297}{1} = 297$

The turkey should be baked for 297 minutes or 4 hours and 57 minutes.

99. $3\dfrac{1}{8} = \dfrac{24+1}{8} = \dfrac{25}{8}$

$3\dfrac{1}{8} \div 2 = 3\dfrac{1}{8} \div \dfrac{2}{1} = \dfrac{25}{8} \cdot \dfrac{1}{2} = \dfrac{25}{16}$ or $1\dfrac{9}{16}$

Each piece is $1\dfrac{9}{16}$ inches long.

100. $28\dfrac{3}{8} = \dfrac{28 \cdot 8 + 3}{8} = \dfrac{227}{8}$

$30 = \dfrac{30}{1} \cdot \dfrac{8}{8} = \dfrac{240}{8}$

$30 - 28\dfrac{3}{8} = \dfrac{240}{8} - \dfrac{227}{8} = \dfrac{13}{8}$ or $1\dfrac{5}{8}$

The pants will need to be shortened by $1\dfrac{5}{8}$ inches.

101. $\dfrac{1}{16} \cdot 80 = \dfrac{1}{16} \cdot \dfrac{80}{1} = \dfrac{1}{1} \cdot \dfrac{5}{1} = 5$

Mr. Krisanda should be given 5 milligrams of the drug.

102. $5\dfrac{1}{2} = \dfrac{10+1}{2} = \dfrac{11}{2}$

$5\dfrac{1}{2} \cdot \dfrac{1}{4} = \dfrac{11}{2} \cdot \dfrac{1}{4} = \dfrac{11 \cdot 1}{2 \cdot 4} = \dfrac{11}{8}$ or $1\dfrac{3}{8}$

$1\dfrac{3}{8}$ cups of chopped onions are needed.

103. $15 \div \dfrac{3}{8} = \dfrac{15}{1} \cdot \dfrac{8}{3} = \dfrac{5}{1} \cdot \dfrac{8}{1} = \dfrac{5 \cdot 8}{1 \cdot 1} = \dfrac{40}{1} = 40$

Tierra can wash her hair 40 times.

104. a. $16\dfrac{2}{3} = \dfrac{48+2}{3} = \dfrac{50}{3} = \dfrac{50}{3} \cdot \dfrac{8}{8} = \dfrac{400}{24}$

$22\dfrac{2}{3} = \dfrac{66+2}{3} = \dfrac{68}{3} = \dfrac{68}{3} \cdot \dfrac{8}{8} = \dfrac{544}{24}$

$14\dfrac{1}{8} = \dfrac{112+1}{8} = \dfrac{113}{8} = \dfrac{113}{8} \cdot \dfrac{3}{3} = \dfrac{339}{24}$

$16\dfrac{2}{3} + 22\dfrac{2}{3} + 14\dfrac{1}{8} = \dfrac{400}{24} + \dfrac{544}{24} + \dfrac{339}{24}$

$= \dfrac{400+544+339}{24}$

$= \dfrac{1283}{24}$ or $53\dfrac{11}{24}$

Matt will need $53\dfrac{11}{24}$ yards of fence.

b. $60 = \dfrac{60 \cdot 24}{24} = \dfrac{1440}{24}$

$53\dfrac{11}{24} = \dfrac{1283}{24}$

$60 - 53\dfrac{11}{24} = \dfrac{1440}{24} - \dfrac{1283}{24}$

$\qquad\qquad = \dfrac{1440 - 1283}{24}$

$\qquad\qquad = \dfrac{157}{24} \text{ or } 6\dfrac{13}{24}$

Matt will have $6\dfrac{13}{24}$ yards of fence left over.

105. $\dfrac{1}{4} + \dfrac{1}{4} + 1 = \dfrac{1}{4} + \dfrac{1}{4} + \dfrac{4}{4} = \dfrac{6}{4} = \dfrac{3}{2} \text{ or } 1\dfrac{1}{2}$

The total thickness is $1\dfrac{1}{2}$ inches.

106. $4\dfrac{1}{2} = \dfrac{8+1}{2} = \dfrac{9}{2} = \dfrac{9}{2} \cdot \dfrac{6}{6} = \dfrac{54}{12}$

$1\dfrac{1}{6} = \dfrac{6+1}{6} = \dfrac{7}{6} = \dfrac{7}{6} \cdot \dfrac{2}{2} = \dfrac{14}{12}$

$1\dfrac{3}{4} = \dfrac{4+3}{4} = \dfrac{7}{4} = \dfrac{7}{4} \cdot \dfrac{3}{3} = \dfrac{21}{12}$

$4\dfrac{1}{2} + 1\dfrac{1}{6} + 1\dfrac{3}{4} = \dfrac{54}{12} + \dfrac{14}{12} + \dfrac{21}{12} = \dfrac{89}{12} = 7\dfrac{5}{12}$

The total weight is $7\dfrac{5}{12}$ tons.

107. $4\dfrac{2}{3} = \dfrac{12+2}{3} = \dfrac{14}{3}$

$28 \div \dfrac{14}{3} = \dfrac{28}{1} \cdot \dfrac{3}{14} = \dfrac{2}{1} \cdot \dfrac{3}{2} = \dfrac{6}{1} = 6$

There will be 6 whole strips of wood.

108. $4\dfrac{1}{2} = \dfrac{9}{2} = \dfrac{9}{2} \cdot \dfrac{12}{12} = \dfrac{108}{24}$

$2\dfrac{1}{3} = \dfrac{7}{3} = \dfrac{7}{3} \cdot \dfrac{8}{8} = \dfrac{56}{24}$

$\dfrac{1}{8} = \dfrac{1}{8} \cdot \dfrac{3}{3} = \dfrac{3}{24}$

$4\dfrac{1}{2} + 2\dfrac{1}{3} + \dfrac{1}{8} = \dfrac{108}{24} + \dfrac{56}{24} + \dfrac{3}{24} = \dfrac{167}{24} \text{ or } 6\dfrac{23}{24}$

The length of the shaft of the bolt must be $6\dfrac{23}{24}$ inches

109. a. Total height of computer + monitor

$= 7\dfrac{1}{2}$ in. $+ 14\dfrac{3}{8}$ in.

$7\dfrac{1}{2} = \dfrac{15}{2} = \dfrac{15}{2} \cdot \dfrac{4}{4} = \dfrac{60}{8}$

$14\dfrac{3}{8} = \dfrac{112+3}{8} = \dfrac{115}{8}$

$7\dfrac{1}{2} + 14\dfrac{3}{8} = \dfrac{60}{8} + \dfrac{115}{8} = \dfrac{175}{8} \text{ or } 21\dfrac{7}{8}$

Total height of computer and monitor is $21\dfrac{7}{8}$ inches, so there is sufficient room.

b. $22\dfrac{1}{2} = \dfrac{44+1}{2} = \dfrac{45}{2} = \dfrac{45}{2} \cdot \dfrac{4}{4} = \dfrac{180}{8}$

$22\dfrac{1}{2} - 21\dfrac{7}{8} = \dfrac{180}{8} - \dfrac{175}{8} = \dfrac{5}{8}$

There will be $\dfrac{5}{8}$ inch of extra height.

c. $22\dfrac{1}{2} = \dfrac{44+1}{2} = \dfrac{45}{2} = \dfrac{45}{2} \cdot \dfrac{2}{2} = \dfrac{90}{4}$

$26\dfrac{1}{2} = \dfrac{52+1}{2} = \dfrac{53}{2} = \dfrac{53}{2} \cdot \dfrac{2}{2} = \dfrac{106}{4}$

$2\dfrac{1}{2} = \dfrac{4+1}{2} = \dfrac{5}{2} = \dfrac{5}{2} \cdot \dfrac{2}{2} = \dfrac{10}{4}$

$1\dfrac{1}{4} = \dfrac{4+1}{4} = \dfrac{5}{4}$

$22\dfrac{1}{2} + 26\dfrac{1}{2} + 2\dfrac{1}{2} + 1\dfrac{1}{4}$

$= \dfrac{90}{4} + \dfrac{106}{4} + \dfrac{10}{4} + \dfrac{5}{4}$

$= \dfrac{211}{4} \text{ or } 52\dfrac{3}{4}$

The height of the desk is $52\dfrac{3}{4}$ in.

110. $(5 \cdot 2) \div 30 = 10 \div 30 = \dfrac{\overset{1}{\cancel{10}}}{1} \cdot \dfrac{1}{\underset{3}{\cancel{30}}} = \dfrac{1 \cdot 1}{1 \cdot 3} = \dfrac{1}{3}$

Each person gets $\dfrac{1}{3}$ liter.

111. a. $\dfrac{*}{a} + \dfrac{?}{a} = \dfrac{*+?}{a}$

b. $\dfrac{\odot}{?} - \dfrac{\square}{?} = \dfrac{\odot - \square}{?}$

c. $\dfrac{\triangle}{\square} + \dfrac{4}{\square} = \dfrac{\triangle + 4}{\square}$

d. $\dfrac{x}{3} - \dfrac{2}{3} = \dfrac{x-2}{3}$

e. $\dfrac{12}{x} - \dfrac{4}{x} = \dfrac{12-4}{x} = \dfrac{8}{x}$

112. a. $\dfrac{\triangle}{a} \cdot \dfrac{\square}{b} = \dfrac{\triangle\square}{ab}$

b. $\dfrac{6}{3} \cdot \dfrac{\triangle}{\square} = \dfrac{2}{1} \cdot \dfrac{\triangle}{\square} = \dfrac{2 \cdot \triangle}{1 \cdot \square} = \dfrac{2\triangle}{\square}$

c. $\dfrac{x}{a} \cdot \dfrac{y}{b} = \dfrac{xy}{ab}$

d. $\dfrac{3}{8} \cdot \dfrac{4}{y} = \dfrac{3}{_28} \cdot \dfrac{\overset{1}{\cancel{4}}}{y} = \dfrac{3 \cdot 1}{2 \cdot y} = \dfrac{3}{2y}$

e. $\dfrac{3}{x} \cdot \dfrac{x}{y} = \dfrac{3}{_1\cancel{x}} \cdot \dfrac{\overset{1}{\cancel{x}}}{y} = \dfrac{3 \cdot 1}{1 \cdot y} = \dfrac{3}{y}$

113. number of pills

$= \dfrac{\left(\text{mg per day}\right)\left(\text{days per month}\right)\left(\text{no. of months}\right)}{\text{mg per pill}}$

$= \dfrac{(450)(30)(6)}{300}$

$= 270$

Dr. Muechler should prescribe 270 pills

114. a. Flakes, 2 cups; milk, 6 tbsp

b. Flakes, 2 cups; milk, $7\dfrac{1}{3}$ tbsp

c. Flakes, 2 cups; milk, $\dfrac{1}{2}$ cup or 8 tbsp

d. Flakes, 2 cups; milk, $8\dfrac{2}{3}$ tbsp

e. Flakes are same, milk is different; $\dfrac{1}{3}$ cup is not twice 2 tbsp.

115. Answers will vary.

116. $\dfrac{9+8+15+32+16}{5} = \dfrac{80}{5} = 16$

The mean is 16.

117. In order, the values are: 8, 9, 15, 16, 32. The median is 15.

118. Variables are letters used to represent numbers.

Exercise Set 1.4

1. A set is a collection of elements.

2. A set that contains no elements is called the empty set or null set.

3. Answers will vary. One possible answer is: An empty set is a set that contains no elements.

4. The symbols that represent the empty set are { } and $\varnothing$.

5. The set of whole numbers contains zero and all of the natural numbers. The set of natural numbers does not contain zero.

6. The set of natural numbers is also the set of counting numbers and the set of positive integers.

7. a. The natural number 7 is a whole number because it is a member of {0, 1, 2, 3, ...}.

b. The natural number 7 is a rational number because it can be written as the quotient of two integers, $\dfrac{7}{1}$.

c. All natural numbers are real numbers.

8. a. A rational number is any number that can be expressed as a quotient of two integers, denominator not 0.

b. Any integer can be expressed as a quotient of two integers by writing it with a denominator of 1. Therefore every integer is a rational number.

9. a. yes

b. no

c. no

d. yes

10. Answers will vary.

11. The integers are $\{\dots, -3, -2, -1, 0, 1, 2, 3, \dots\}$.

12. The counting numbers are $\{1, 2, 3, 4, \dots\}$

13. The whole numbers are $\{0, 1, 2, 3, \dots\}$.

14. The positive integers are $\{1, 2, 3, 4, \dots\}$.

15. The negative integers are $\{\dots, -3, -2, -1\}$.

16. The natural numbers are $\{1, 2, 3, 4, \dots\}$.

17. True; the whole numbers are $\{0, 1, 2, 3, \dots\}$.

18. True; the negative integers are $\{-1, -2, -3, \dots\}$.

19. True; any number that can be represented on a real number line is a real number.

20. False; the integers are $\{\dots, -2, -1, 0, 1, 2, \dots\}$.

21. False; the integers are $\{\dots, -2, -1, 0, 1, 2, \dots\}$.

22. False; the natural numbers are $\{1, 2, 3, \dots\}$.

23. False; $\sqrt{2}$ cannot be expressed as the quotient of two integers.

24. True; any number that can be represented on a real number line is a real number.

25. True; $-\dfrac{1}{5}$ is a quotient of two integers, $\dfrac{-1}{5}$.

26. True; $-2\dfrac{1}{3}$ can be expressed as a quotient of two integers, $\dfrac{-7}{3}$.

27. True; 0 can be expressed as a quotient of two integers, $\dfrac{0}{1}$.

28. True; 9.2 can be expressed as a quotient of two integers $\dfrac{46}{5}$.

29. False; $4\dfrac{5}{8}$ is rational since it can be expressed as a quotient of two integers.

30. True; positive numbers are greater than zero.

31. True; $-\sqrt{5}$ is irrational since it cannot be expressed exactly as a decimal number.

32. True; every counting number can be expressed as a quotient of two integers.

33. True, either $\square$ or $\{\ \}$ is used.

34. False; the positive integers are not negative.

35. False; irrational numbers are real but not rational.

36. True; any negative integer can be represented on a real number line and is therefore real.

37. True; any rational number can be represented on a real number line and is therefore real.

38. True; the counting numbers are $\{1, 2, 3, \dots\}$, the whole numbers are $\{0, 1, 2, \dots\}$.

39. True; irrational numbers are real numbers which are not rational.

40. False; all irrational numbers are also real numbers.

41. False; any negative irrational number is a counterexample.

42. True; this is the definition of a real number.

43. True; the symbol $\mathbb{R}$ represents the set of real numbers.

44. True; this is the definition of a negative number.

45. False; every number greater than zero is positive but not necessarily an integer.

46. False; irrational numbers are real and so can be represented on a number line.

47. True; the integers are
$$\left\{\underbrace{\dots, -2, -1}_{\text{negative integers}}, \underbrace{0}_{\text{zero}}, \underbrace{1, 2, \dots}_{\text{positive integers}}\right\}.$$

48. True; all are names for the set $\{1, 2, 3, \dots\}$.

49. a. 13 is a positive integer.
    b. -2 and 13 are rational numbers.
    c. -2 and 13 are real numbers.
    d. 13 is a whole number.

50. a. 0 is an integer.

b. 0 and $2\frac{1}{2}$ are rational numbers.

c. 0 and $2\frac{1}{2}$ are real numbers.

51. a. 3 and 77 are positive integers.

b. 0, 3, and 77 are whole numbers

c. 0, –2, 3, and 77 are integers.

d. $-\frac{5}{7}$, 0, – 2, 3, $6\frac{1}{4}$, 1.63, and 77 are rational numbers.

e. $\sqrt{7}$ and $-\sqrt{3}$ are irrational numbers.

f. $-\frac{5}{7}$, 0, – 2, 3, $6\frac{1}{4}$, $\sqrt{7}$, $-\sqrt{3}$, 1.63, and 77 are real numbers.

52. a. 7 and 9 are positive integers.

b. 7, 0, and 9 are whole numbers.

c. –6, 7, 0, and 9 are integers.

d. –6, 7, 12.4, $-\frac{9}{5}$, $-2\frac{1}{4}$, 0, 9, and 0.35 are rational numbers.

e. $\sqrt{3}$ and $\sqrt{7}$ are irrational numbers.

f. –6, 7, 12.4, $-\frac{9}{5}$, $-2\frac{1}{4}$, $\sqrt{3}$, 0, 9, $\sqrt{7}$, and 0.35 are real numbers.

For Exercises 53–64, answers will vary. One possible answer is given for each exercise.

53. 0, 1, 2

54. $\frac{1}{2}$, $-\frac{1}{2}$, 0.6

55. $-\sqrt{2}$, $-\sqrt{3}$, $-\sqrt{7}$

56. 1, $\frac{1}{2}$, $-\frac{3}{5}$

57. $-\frac{2}{3}$, $\frac{1}{2}$, 6.3

58. –5, 0, 4

59. –13, –5, –1

60. –1, –2, –3

61. $\sqrt{2}$, $\sqrt{3}$, $-\sqrt{5}$

62. 1.5, 3, $6\frac{1}{4}$

63. –7, 1, 5

64. $-\frac{1}{2}$, $-\frac{5}{8}$, $-\sqrt{5}$

65. {8, 9, 10, 11, ..., 94}
94 – 8 + 1 = 86 + 1 = 87
The set has 87 elements.

66. {–4, –3, –2, –1, 0, 1, ..., 64}
$64 - (-4) + 1 = 64 + 4 + 1 = 69$
The set has 69 elements.

67. a. $A = \{1, 3, 4, 5, 8\}$

b. $B = \{2, 5, 6, 7, 8\}$

c. A and $B = \{5, 8\}$

d. A or $B = \{1, 2, 3, 4, 5, 6, 7, 8\}$

68. a. $A = \{\square, P, ?, \square\}$

b. $B = \{\square, \square, L, W, R\}$

c. A and $B = \{\square\}$

d. A or $B = \{\square, P, ?, \square, \square, L, W, R\}$

69. a. Set B continues beyond 4.

b. Set A has 4 elements.

c. Set B has an infinite number of elements.

d. Set B is an infinite set.

70. a. There are an infinite number of decimal numbers between any 2 numbers.

b. There are an infinite number of decimal numbers between any 2 numbers.

71. a. There are an infinite number of fractions between any 2 numbers.

b. There are an infinite number of fractions between any 2 numbers.

72. a. $\cup: \{1, 2, 3, 4, 5, 6, 7, 8, 9\}$; $\cap: \{2, 3, 8\}$

b. $\cup: \{a, b, c, d, g, h, i, j, m, p\}$; $\cap \{b, c, d\}$

c. $\cup: \{$red, blue, green, yellow, pink, orange, purple$\}$; $\cap: \varnothing$

73. $5\frac{2}{5} = \frac{5 \cdot 5 + 2}{5} = \frac{25 + 2}{5} = \frac{27}{5}$

74. $\frac{16}{3} = 5\frac{1}{3}$ because $16 \div 3 = 5 \text{ R } 1$

75. $\frac{7}{8} - \frac{2}{3}$

$\frac{7}{8} = \frac{7}{8} \cdot \frac{3}{3} = \frac{21}{24}$

$\frac{2}{3} = \frac{2}{3} \cdot \frac{8}{8} = \frac{16}{24}$

$\frac{7}{8} - \frac{2}{3} = \frac{21}{24} - \frac{16}{24} = \frac{21 - 16}{24} = \frac{5}{24}$

76. $\frac{3}{5} \div 6\frac{3}{4}$

$6\frac{3}{4} = \frac{24 + 3}{4} = \frac{27}{4}$

$\frac{3}{5} \div 6\frac{3}{4} = \frac{3}{5} \div \frac{27}{4} = \frac{\cancel{3}^{1}}{5} \cdot \frac{4}{\cancel{27}_{9}} = \frac{1 \cdot 4}{5 \cdot 9} = \frac{4}{45}$

Exercise Set 1.5

1. a.
```
<-+--+--+--+--+--+--+--+--+--+--+--+--+->
 -6 -5 -4 -3 -2 -1  0  1  2  3  4  5  6
```

   b.
```
<-+--+--●--+--●--+--+--+--+--+--+--+--+->
 -6 -5 -4 -3 -2 -1  0  1  2  3  4  5  6
```

   c. −2 is greater than −4 because it is farther to the right on the number line.

   d. $-4 < -2$

   e. $-2 > -4$

2. The absolute value of a number is the distance between the number and 0 on a number line.

3. a. 4 is 4 units from 0 on a number line.

   b. −4 is 4 units from 0 on a number line.

   c. 0 is 0 units from 0 on a number line.

4. Yes; $|0| = 0$ and 0 is not a positive number.

5. Yes; for example, $5 > 3$ and $3 < 5$. Also, $-2 > -5$ and $-5 < -2$.

6. Yes; for example, if $a = -2$, $|-2| - |-2| = 2 - 2 = 0$.

7. No, $-4 < -3$ but $|-4| > |-3|$.

8. No, $-3 > -4$ but $|-3| < |-4|$.

9. No, $|-3| < |-4|$ but $-3 > -4$.

10. No, $|-4| > |-3|$ but $-4 < -3$.

11. $|7| = 7$

12. $|-6| = 6$

13. $|-15| = 15$

14. $|0| = 0$

15. $-|0| = 0$

16. $|54| = 54$

17. $-|-5| = -(5) = -5$

18. $-|92| = -(92) = -92$

19. $-|21| = -(21) = -21$

20. $-|-34| = -(34) = -34$

21. $6 > 2$; 6 is to the right of 2 on a number line.

22. $4 > -2$; 4 is to the right of −2 on a number line.

23. $-4 < 0$; −4 is to the left of 0 on a number line.

24. $-6 < -4$; −6 is to the left of −4 on a number line.

25. $\frac{1}{2} > -\frac{2}{3}$; $\frac{1}{2}$ is to the right of $-\frac{2}{3}$ on a number line.

26. $\frac{3}{5} < \frac{4}{5}$; $\frac{3}{5}$ is to the left of $\frac{4}{5}$ on a number line.

27. $0.7 < 0.8$; 0.7 is to the left of 0.8 on a number line.

28. $-0.2 > -0.4$; −0.2 is to the right of −0.4 on a number line.

29. $-\frac{1}{2} > -1$; $-\frac{1}{2}$ is to the right of −1 on a number line.

30. $-0.1 > -0.9$; -0.1 is to the right of -0.9 on a number line.

31. $-5 < 5$; -5 is to the left of 5 on a number line.

32. $-\dfrac{3}{4} > -1$; $-\dfrac{3}{4}$ is to the right of -1 on a number line.

33. $-2.1 < -2$; -2.1 is to the left of -2 on a number line.

34. $-1.83 < -1.82$; -1.83 is to the left of -1.82 on a number line.

35. $\dfrac{4}{5} > -\dfrac{4}{5}$; $\dfrac{4}{5}$ is to the right of $-\dfrac{4}{5}$ on a number line.

36. $-9 > -12$; -9 is to the right of -12 on a number line.

37. $-\dfrac{3}{8} < \dfrac{3}{8}$; $-\dfrac{3}{8}$ is to the left of $\dfrac{3}{8}$ on a number line.

38. $-4.09 > -5.3$; -4.09 is to the right of -5.3 on a number line.

39. $0.49 > 0.43$; 0.49 is to the right of 0.43 on a number line.

40. $-1.0 < -0.7$; -1.0 is to the left of -0.7 on a number line.

41. $-0.086 > -0.095$; -0.086 is to the right of -0.095 on a number line.

42. $\dfrac{1}{2} > -\dfrac{1}{2}$; $\dfrac{1}{2}$ is to the right of $-\dfrac{1}{2}$ on a number line.

43. $0.001 < 0.002$; 0.001 is to the left of 0.002 on a number line.

44. $-0.006 > -0.007$; -0.006 is to the right of -0.007 on a number line.

45. $\dfrac{5}{8} > 0.6$ because $\dfrac{5}{8} = 0.625$ and 0.625 is to the right of 0.6 on a number line.

46. $2.7 < \dfrac{10}{3}$ since $\dfrac{10}{3} = 3\dfrac{1}{3}$ and $3\dfrac{1}{3}$ is to the right of 2.7 on a number line.

47. $-\dfrac{4}{3} < -\dfrac{1}{3}$; $-\dfrac{4}{3}$ is to the left of $-\dfrac{1}{3}$ on a number line.

48. $\dfrac{9}{2} > \dfrac{7}{2}$; $\dfrac{9}{2}$ is to the right of $\dfrac{7}{2}$ on a number line.

49. $-0.8 < -\dfrac{3}{5}$; -0.8 is to the left of -0.6 on a number line.

50. $-0.7 < -0.2$; -0.7 is to the left of -0.2 on a number line.

51. $0.3 < \dfrac{1}{3}$; 0.3 is to the left of $.333...$ on a number line.

52. $\dfrac{9}{20} > .42$; $.45$ is to the right of $.42$ on a number line.

53. $-\dfrac{17}{30} > -\dfrac{16}{20}$; $-\dfrac{34}{60}$ is to the right of $-\dfrac{48}{60}$ on a number line.

54. $\dfrac{13}{15} < \dfrac{8}{9}$; $\dfrac{39}{45}$ is to the left of $\dfrac{40}{45}$ on a number line.

55. $-(-6) > -(-5)$; 6 is to the right of 5 on a number line.

56. $-\left(\dfrac{-12}{13}\right) > \dfrac{7}{8}$; $\dfrac{96}{104}$ is to the right of $\dfrac{91}{104}$ on a number line.

57. $5 > |-2|$ since $|-2| = 2$

58. $|-12| < |-13|$ since $|-12| = 12$ and $|-13| = 13$

59. $\dfrac{3}{4} < |-4|$ since $|-4| = 4$

60. $|-4| > -3$ since $|-4| = 4$

61. $|0| < |-4|$ since $|0| = 0$ and $|-4| = 4$

62. $|-2.1| > |-1.8|$ since $|-2.1| = 2.1$ and $|-1.8| = 1.8$.

63. $4 < \left|-\dfrac{9}{2}\right|$ since $\left|-\dfrac{9}{2}\right| = \dfrac{9}{2}$ or $4\dfrac{1}{2}$

64. $|-5| > -|-6|$ since $|-5| = 5$ and $-|-6| = -6$

65. $\left|-\dfrac{4}{5}\right| < \left|-\dfrac{5}{4}\right|$ since $\left|-\dfrac{4}{5}\right| = \dfrac{4}{5} = \dfrac{16}{20}$ and

$\left|-\dfrac{5}{4}\right| = \dfrac{5}{4} = \dfrac{25}{20}$

66. $\left|\dfrac{2}{5}\right| = |-0.40|$ since $\left|\dfrac{2}{5}\right| = \dfrac{2}{5} = 0.40$ and

$|-0.40| = 0.40$

67. $|-4.6| = \left|-\dfrac{23}{5}\right|$ since $|-4.6| = 4.6$ and

$\left|-\dfrac{23}{5}\right| = \dfrac{23}{5} = 4.6$

68. $\left|-\dfrac{8}{3}\right| < |-3.5|$ since $\left|-\dfrac{8}{3}\right| = \dfrac{8}{3} = 2\dfrac{2}{3}$ and

$|-3.5| = 3.5$

69. $\dfrac{2}{3} + \dfrac{2}{3} + \dfrac{2}{3} + \dfrac{2}{3} = 4 \cdot \dfrac{2}{3}$ since

$\dfrac{2}{3} + \dfrac{2}{3} + \dfrac{2}{3} + \dfrac{2}{3} = \dfrac{2+2+2+2}{3} = \dfrac{8}{3}$ and

$4 \cdot \dfrac{2}{3} = \dfrac{4}{1} \cdot \dfrac{2}{3} = \dfrac{8}{3}$

70. $\dfrac{3}{4} + \dfrac{3}{4} > \dfrac{3}{4} \cdot \dfrac{3}{4}$ since $\dfrac{3}{4} + \dfrac{3}{4} = \dfrac{3+3}{4} = \dfrac{6}{4} = 1\dfrac{1}{2}$ and

$\dfrac{3}{4} \cdot \dfrac{3}{4} = \dfrac{3 \cdot 3}{4 \cdot 4} = \dfrac{9}{16}$

71. $\dfrac{1}{2} \cdot \dfrac{1}{2} < \dfrac{1}{2} \div \dfrac{1}{2}$ since $\dfrac{1}{2} \cdot \dfrac{1}{2} = \dfrac{1 \cdot 1}{2 \cdot 2} = \dfrac{1}{4}$ and

$\dfrac{1}{2} \div \dfrac{1}{2} = \dfrac{1}{2} \cdot \dfrac{2}{1} = \dfrac{1}{1} \cdot \dfrac{1}{1} = 1$

72. $5 \div \dfrac{2}{3} > \dfrac{2}{3} \div 5$ since $5 \div \dfrac{2}{3} = \dfrac{5}{1} \cdot \dfrac{3}{2} = \dfrac{15}{2} = 7\dfrac{1}{2}$ and

$\dfrac{2}{3} \div 5 = \dfrac{2}{3} \cdot \dfrac{1}{5} = \dfrac{2}{15}$

73. $\dfrac{5}{8} - \dfrac{1}{2} < \dfrac{5}{8} \div \dfrac{1}{2}$ since $\dfrac{5}{8} - \dfrac{1}{2} = \dfrac{5}{8} - \dfrac{4}{8} = \dfrac{1}{8}$ and

$\dfrac{5}{8} \div \dfrac{1}{2} = \dfrac{5}{8} \cdot \dfrac{2}{1} = \dfrac{10}{8}$

74. $3\dfrac{1}{5} + \dfrac{1}{3} > 3\dfrac{1}{5} \cdot \dfrac{1}{3}$ since $3\dfrac{1}{5} + \dfrac{1}{3} = \dfrac{16}{5} + \dfrac{1}{3}$

$= \dfrac{16}{5} \cdot \dfrac{3}{3} + \dfrac{1}{3} \cdot \dfrac{5}{5}$

$= \dfrac{48}{15} + \dfrac{5}{15}$

$= \dfrac{53}{15}$

$= 3\dfrac{8}{15}$

and $3\dfrac{1}{5} \cdot \dfrac{1}{3} = \dfrac{16}{5} \cdot \dfrac{1}{3} = \dfrac{16}{9} = 1\dfrac{7}{9}$

75. $-|-1|, \dfrac{3}{7}, \dfrac{4}{9}, 0.46, |-5|$ because $-|-1| = -1$,

$\dfrac{3}{7} \approx 0.429, \dfrac{4}{9} = 0.444...$, and $|-5| = 5$.

76. $-1.74, -\dfrac{3}{4}, -|0.6|, -\dfrac{5}{9}, |-1.9|$ because

$-\dfrac{3}{4} = -0.75, -|0.6| = -0.6, -\dfrac{5}{9} = -0.555...$,

and $|-1.9| = 1.9$.

77. $\dfrac{5}{12}, 0.6, \dfrac{2}{3}, \dfrac{19}{25}, |-2.6|$ because $\dfrac{5}{12} = 0.41666...$,

$\dfrac{2}{3} = 0.666..., \dfrac{19}{25} = 0.76$, and $|-2.6| = 2.6$.

78. $-|-5|, \dfrac{7}{12}, \left|\dfrac{-12}{5}\right|, 2.7, |-9|$ because

$-|-5| = -5, \dfrac{7}{12} = 0.58333..., \left|\dfrac{-12}{5}\right| = 2.4$,

and $|-9| = 9$.

79. 4 and -4 since $|4| = |-4| = 4$

80. 100 and -100 since $|100| = |-100| = 100$

For Exercises 81-88, answers will vary. One possible answer is given for each exercise.

81. There are no real numbers that are less than 4 and greater than 6.

82. Three numbers greater than 4 and less than 6 are $4\frac{1}{2}$, 5, 5.5.

83. Three numbers less than –2 and greater than –6 are –3, –4, –5.

84. Three real numbers that are greater than –5 and greater than –9 are –4, 0, and 3.

85. Three numbers greater than –3 and greater than 3 are 4, 5, 6.

86. Three numbers that are less than –3 and less than 3 are –4, –5, and –6.

87. Three numbers greater than $|-2|$ and less than $|-6|$ are 3, 4, 5.

88. There are no real numbers that are greater than $|-3|$ and less than $|3|$.

89. **a.** Between does not include endpoints.

    b. Three real numbers between 4 and 6 are 4.1, 5, and $5\frac{1}{2}$.

    c. No, 4 is an endpoint.

    d. Yes, 5 is greater than 4 and less than 6.

    e. True

90. **a.** 1984

    b. 2000

    c. 1973-1983

91. **a.** dietary fiber and thiamin

    b. vitamin E, niacin, and riboflavin

92. The result of multiplying any positive number by a number between 0 and 1 is smaller than the original number. Thus, when you multiply a number between 0 and 1 by itself, the result is smaller than the original number.

93. The result of dividing a number by itself is 1. Thus, the result of dividing a number between 0 and 1 by itself is a number, 1, which is greater than the original number.

94. 3 and –3 since $|3| = |-3| = 3$

95. No, an absolute value of a number cannot be negative.

96. **a.** If $x \geq 0$, then $|x| = x$.

    b. If $x < 0$, then $|x| = -x$.

    c. $|x| = \begin{cases} x, & x \geq 0 \\ -x, & x < 0 \end{cases}$

97. **a-d.**

98. $2\frac{3}{5} + 3\frac{1}{3}$

$$2\frac{3}{5} = \frac{10+3}{5} = \frac{13}{5} \cdot \frac{3}{3} = \frac{39}{15}$$

$$3\frac{1}{3} = \frac{9+1}{3} = \frac{10}{3} \cdot \frac{5}{5} = \frac{50}{15}$$

$$2\frac{3}{5} + 3\frac{1}{3} = \frac{39}{15} + \frac{50}{15} = \frac{39+50}{15} = \frac{89}{15} = 5\frac{14}{15}$$

99. The set of integer numbers is $\{\ldots, -3, -2, -1, 0, 1, 2, 3, \ldots\}$.

100. The set of whole numbers is $\{0, 1, 2, 3, \ldots\}$.

101. **a.** 5 is a natural number.

    b. 5 and 0 are whole numbers.

    c. 5, –2, and 0 are integers.

    d. 5, –2, 0, $\frac{1}{3}$, $-\frac{5}{9}$, and 2.3 are rational numbers.

    e. $\sqrt{3}$ is an irrational number.

    f. 5, –2, 0, $\frac{1}{3}$, $\sqrt{3}$, $-\frac{5}{9}$, and 2.3 are real numbers.

Mid-Chapter Test: 1.1-1.5

1. At least two hours of study and homework for each hour of class time is generally recommended.

2. **a.** The mean is
$$\frac{78.83 + 96.57 + 62.23 + 88.79 + 101.75 + 55.62}{6}$$
$$= \frac{483.78}{6} = \$80.63.$$

   b. To find the median place the numbers in order: 55.62, 62.23, 78.83, 88.79, 96.57, 101.75. Since there are an even amount of numbers, take the two in the middle and take their mean.
$$\frac{78.83 + 88.79}{2} = \frac{167.62}{2} = \$83.81.$$

3. New balance = Old balance + Deposits – Purchases
$$= 652.70 + 230.75 - 3(19.62)$$
$$= 652.70 + 230.75 - 58.86$$
$$= 824.59$$
   Her new balance is \$824.59.

4. **a.** Rental cost from Natwora's
$$= 7.50(\text{each 15-minute increment})$$
$$= 7.5(16)$$
$$= 120$$

   Rental cost for Gurney's
$$= 18(\text{each 30-minute increment})$$
$$= 18(8)$$
$$= 144$$

   Natwora's is the better deal.

   b. $144 - 120 = 24$
   You will save \$24.

5. We must find out how many 1000 gallons was used. $\dfrac{33,700}{1000} = 33.7$
   Water Bill = 1.85(number of 1000 gallons used)
$$= 1.85(33.7)$$
$$\approx 62.345$$
   The water bill would be \$62.35.

6. $\dfrac{3}{7} \cdot \dfrac{7}{18} = \dfrac{\cancel{3}^1}{\cancel{7}_1} \cdot \dfrac{\cancel{7}^1}{\cancel{18}_6} = \dfrac{1 \cdot 1}{1 \cdot 6} = \dfrac{1}{6}$

7. $\dfrac{9}{16} \div \dfrac{12}{13} = \dfrac{9}{16} \cdot \dfrac{13}{\cancel{12}_4}^{3} = \dfrac{3 \cdot 13}{16 \cdot 4} = \dfrac{39}{64}$

8. $\dfrac{5}{8} + \dfrac{3}{5}$

   $\dfrac{5}{8} \cdot \dfrac{5}{5} = \dfrac{25}{40}$

   $\dfrac{3}{5} \cdot \dfrac{8}{8} = \dfrac{24}{40}$

   $\dfrac{5}{8} + \dfrac{3}{5} = \dfrac{25}{40} + \dfrac{24}{40} = \dfrac{25+24}{40} = \dfrac{49}{40} = 1\dfrac{9}{40}$

9. $6\dfrac{1}{4} - 3\dfrac{1}{5}$

   $6\dfrac{1}{4} = \dfrac{24+1}{4} = \dfrac{25}{4} \cdot \dfrac{5}{5} = \dfrac{125}{20}$

   $3\dfrac{1}{5} = \dfrac{15+1}{5} = \dfrac{16}{5} \cdot \dfrac{4}{4} = \dfrac{64}{20}$

   $6\dfrac{1}{4} - 3\dfrac{1}{5} = \dfrac{125}{20} - \dfrac{64}{20} = \dfrac{125-64}{20} = \dfrac{61}{20} = 3\dfrac{1}{20}$

10. $p = 2l + 2w$
$$= 2\left(14\dfrac{2}{3}\right) + 2\left(12\dfrac{1}{2}\right)$$
$$= 2\left(\dfrac{44}{3}\right) + 2\left(\dfrac{25}{2}\right)$$
$$= \dfrac{88}{3} + \dfrac{50}{2}$$
$$= \left(\dfrac{88}{3} \cdot \dfrac{2}{2}\right) + \left(\dfrac{50}{2} \cdot \dfrac{3}{3}\right)$$
$$= \dfrac{176}{6} + \dfrac{150}{6}$$
$$= \dfrac{326}{6} = 54\dfrac{2}{6} = 54\dfrac{1}{3}$$

    He will need $54\dfrac{1}{3}$ feet of fencing.

11. False

12. True

13. False

14. True

15. False

16. $-\left|-\dfrac{7}{10}\right| = -\dfrac{7}{10}$

17. –0.005 > –0.006 because –0.005 is to the right of –0.006 on the number line.

18. $\frac{7}{8} > \frac{5}{6}$ because $\frac{7}{8} = \frac{7}{8} \cdot \frac{3}{3} = \frac{21}{24}$ and $\frac{5}{6} = \frac{5}{6} \cdot \frac{4}{4} = \frac{20}{24}$.

19. $|-9| < |-12|$ because $|-9| = 9$ and $|-12| = 12$.

20. $\left| -\frac{3}{8} \right| = |-0.375|$ because $\left| -\frac{3}{8} \right| = \frac{3}{8} = 0.375$ and $|-0.375| = 0.375$.

Exercise Set 1.6

1. The 4 basic operations of arithmetic are addition, subtraction, multiplication, and division.

2. **a.** Opposites or additive inverses are two numbers that sum to zero.

    b. One example is 3 and –3.

3. **a.** No; $-\frac{2}{3} + \frac{3}{2}$ does not sum to 0.

    b. The opposite of $-\frac{2}{3}$ is $\frac{2}{3}$ because $-\frac{2}{3} + \frac{2}{3} = 0$.

4. The sum of a positive number and a negative number can be either positive or negative. The sum of a positive number and a negative number has the same sign as the number that has larger absolute value.

5. If we add two negative numbers, the sum is negative. When two numbers have the same sign, their sum also has the same sign.

6. **a.** The sum $-24,692 + 30,519$ will be positive because $|30,519|$ is greater than $|-24,692|$.

    b. The sum $24,692 + (-30,519)$ will be negative because $|-30,519|$ is greater than $|24,692|$.

    c. The sum $-24,692 + (-30,519)$ will be negative because both addends are negative.

7 – 8. Answers will vary.

9. **a.** He owed 162, a negative, and then paid a positive amount, 85, toward his debt. This would translate to $-162 + 85$.

    b. $-162 + 85$
    The numbers have different signs so find the difference between the absolute values.
    $|-162| - |85| = 162 - 85 = 77$
    $|-162|$ is greater so sum is negative.
    $-162 + 85 = -77$

    c. Since this is a negative amount, it is considered a debt.

10. **a.** She owed 163, a negative, and then charged a negative amount. This would translate to $-163 + (-56)$.

    b. $-163 + (-56)$
    The numbers have the same sign, so add the absolute values. $|-163| + |-56| = 219$. The numbers are negative, so their sum is negative. $-163 + (-56) = -219$

    c. Answers will vary.

11. Yes, it is correct.

12. Yes, it is correct.

13. The opposite of 9 is –9 since $9 + (-9) = 0$.

14. The opposite of –7 is 7 since $-7 + 7 = 0$.

15. The opposite of –28 is 28 since $-28 + 28 = 0$.

16. The opposite of 3 is –3 since $3 + (-3) = 0$.

17. The opposite of 0 is 0 since $0 + 0 = 0$.

18. The opposite of $-3\frac{1}{2}$ is $3\frac{1}{2}$ since $-3\frac{1}{2} + 3\frac{1}{2} = 0$.

19. The opposite of $\frac{5}{3}$ is $-\frac{5}{3}$ since $\frac{5}{3} + \left(-\frac{5}{3} \right) = 0$.

20. The opposite of $-\frac{1}{4}$ is $\frac{1}{4}$ since $-\frac{1}{4} + \frac{1}{4} = 0$.

21. The opposite of $2\frac{3}{5}$ is $-2\frac{3}{5}$ since $2\frac{3}{5} + \left(-2\frac{3}{5} \right) = 0$.

22. The opposite of –1 is 1 since –1 + 1 = 0.

23. The opposite of 3.72 is –3.72 since
    $3.72 + (-3.72) = 0.$

24. The opposite of –0.721 is 0.721 since
    $-0.721 + 0.721 = 0$.

25. Numbers have same sign, so add absolute values.
    $|5| + |6| = 5 + 6 = 11$
    Numbers are positive so sum is positive.
    $5 + 6 = 11$

26. Numbers have different signs, so take difference between larger and smaller absolute values. $|-8| - |2| = 8 - 2 = 6$.
    $|-8|$ is greater than $|2|$ so sum is negative.
    $-8 + 2 = -6$

27. Numbers have different signs so find difference between larger and smaller absolute values.
    $|4| - |-3| = 4 - 3 = 1$. $|4|$ is greater than $|-3|$ so the sum is positive.
    $4 + (-3) = 1$

28. Numbers have different signs, so take difference between larger and smaller absolute values
    $|-12| - |9| = 12 - 9 = 3$. $|-12|$ greater than $|9|$ so sum is negative. $9 + (-12) = -3$

29. Numbers have same sign, so add absolute values.
    $|-4| + |-2| = 4 + 2 = 6$.
    Numbers are negative, so sum is negative.
    $-4 + (-2) = -6$

30. Numbers have same sign, so add absolute values.
    $|-3| + |-5| = 3 + 5 = 8$. Numbers are negative, so sum is negative. $-3 + (-5) = -8$

31. Numbers have different signs, so find difference between absolute values.
    $|6| - |-6| = 6 - 6 = 0$
    $6 + (-6) = 0$

32. Numbers have different signs, so take difference between absolute values.
    $|-8| - |8| = 0$
    $-8 + 8 = 0$

33. Numbers have different signs, so find difference between absolute values.
    $|-4| - |4| = 4 - 4 = 0$
    $-4 + 4 = 0$

34. Numbers have different signs, so find difference between absolute values.
    $|-6| - |6| = 6 - 6 = 0$
    $-6 + 6 = 0$

35. Numbers have same sign, so add absolute values. $|-8| + |-2| = 8 + 2 = 10$. Numbers are negative, so sum is negative. $-8 + (-2) = -10$

36. Numbers have different signs, so take difference between larger and smaller absolute values.
    $|6| - |-5| = 6 - 5 = 1$. $|6|$ is greater than $|-5|$ so sum is positive. $6 + (-5) = 1$

37. Numbers have different signs, so take difference between larger and smaller absolute values.
    $|-7| - |3| = 7 - 3 = 4$. $|-7|$ is greater than $|3|$ so sum is negative. $-7 + 3 = -4$

38. Numbers have different signs, so take difference between larger and smaller absolute values. $|9| - |-6| = 9 - 6 = 3$. $|9|$ is greater than $|-6|$ so sum is positive.
    $-6 + 9 = 3$

39. Numbers have same sign, so add absolute values.
    $|-8| + |-5| = 8 + 5 = 13$
    Numbers are negative, so sum is negative.
    $-8 + (-5) = -13$

40. $0 + (-3) = -3$

41. $0 + 0 = 0$

42. $0 + (-0) = 0$

43. $-6 + 0 = -6$

44. Numbers have different signs, so take difference between larger and smaller absolute values.
    $|13| - |-9| = 13 - 9 = 4$. $|13|$ is greater than $|-9|$ so sum is positive. $-9 + 13 = 4$

45. Numbers have different signs, so find difference between larger and smaller absolute values. $|18| - |-9| = 18 - 9 = 9$. $|18|$ is greater than $|-9|$ so sum is positive. $18 + (-9) = 9$

46. Numbers have different signs, so take difference between absolute values.
$|-7| - |7| = 7 - 7 = 0$
$-7 + 7 = 0$

47. Numbers have same sign, so add absolute values. $|-33| + |-31| = 33 + 31 = 64$. Numbers are negative, so sum is negative. $-33 + (-31) = -64$

48. Numbers have same sign, so add absolute values. $|-27| + |-9| = 27 + 9 = 36$. Numbers are negative, so sum is negative. $-27 + (-9) = -36$

49. Numbers have same sign, so add absolute values. $|7| + |9| = 7 + 9 = 16$. Numbers are positive, so sum is positive. $7 + 9 = 16$

50. Numbers have same sign, so add absolute values. $|12| + |3| = 12 + 3 = 15$. Numbers are positive, so sum is positive. $12 + 3 = 15$

51. Numbers have same sign, so add absolute values. $|-8| + |-4| = 8 + 4 = 12$. Numbers are negative, so sum is negative. $-8 + (-4) = -12$

52. Numbers have same sign, so add absolute values. $|-25| + |-36| = 25 + 36 = 61$. Numbers are negative, so sum is negative. $-25 + (-36) = -61$

53. Numbers have different signs, so find difference between larger and smaller absolute values. $|6| - |-3| = 6 - 3 = 3$. $|6|$ is greater than $|-3|$ so sum is positive. $6 + (-3) = 3$

54. Numbers have different signs, so take difference between larger and smaller absolute values. $|52| - |-25| = 52 - 25 = 27$. $|52|$ is greater than $|-25|$ so sum is positive. $52 + (-25) = 27$

55. Numbers have different signs, so take difference between larger and smaller absolute values. $|-19| + |13| = 19 - 13 = 6$. $|-19|$ is greater than $|13|$ so sum is negative. $13 + (-19) = -6$

56. Numbers have different signs, so take difference between larger and smaller absolute values. $|-40| - |34| = 40 - 34 = 6$. $|-40|$ is greater than $|34|$ so sum is negative. $34 + (-40) = -6$

57. Numbers have different signs, so find difference between larger and smaller absolute values. $|-200| - |180| = 200 - 180 = 20$. $|-200|$ is greater than $|180|$ so sum is negative.
$180 + (-200) = -20$

58. Numbers have different signs, so find difference between larger and smaller absolute values. $|-452| - |312| = 452 - 312 = 140$. $|-452|$ is greater than $|312|$ so sum is negative.
$-452 + 312 = -140$

59. Numbers have same sign, so add absolute values. $|-11| + |-20| = 11 + 20 = 31$. Numbers are negative, so sum is negative. $-11 + (-20) = -31$

60. Numbers have same sign, so add absolute values. $|-33| + |-92| = 33 + 92 = 125$. Numbers are negative, so sum is negative. $-33 + (-92) = -125$

61. Numbers have different signs, so find difference between larger and smaller absolute values. $|-67| - |28| = 67 - 28 = 39$. $|-67|$ is greater than $|28|$ so sum is negative. $-67 + 28 = -39$

62. Numbers have different signs, so take difference between absolute values.
$|183| - |-183| = 183 - 183 = 0$
$183 + (-183) = 0$

63. Numbers have different signs, so find difference between larger and smaller absolute values. $|184| - |-93| = 184 - 93 = 91$. $|184|$ is greater than $|-93|$ so sum is positive. $184 + (-93) = 91$

64. Numbers have different signs, so take difference between larger and smaller absolute values. $|176| - |-19| = 176 - 19 = 157$. $|176|$ is greater than $|-19|$ so sum is positive. $-19 + 176 = 157$

65. Numbers have different signs, so find difference between larger and smaller absolute values. $|-90.4| - |80.5| = 90.4 - 80.5 = 9.9$. $|-90.4|$ is greater than $|80.5|$ so sum is negative.
$80.5 + (-90.4) = -9.9$

66. Numbers have same sign, so add absolute values. $|-24.6| + |-13.9| = 24.6 + 13.9 = 38.5$. Numbers are negative so sum is negative.
$-24.6 + (-13.9) = -38.5$

67. Numbers have same sign, so add absolute values. $|-124.7| + |-19.3| = 124.7 + 19.3 = 144.0$. Numbers are negative, so sum is negative.
$-124.7 + (-19.3) = -144.0$

68. The numbers have different signs, so find the difference between the larger and smaller absolute values. $|-110.9| - |106.3| = 110.9 - 106.3 = 4.6$.

Now, $|-110.9|$ is greater than $|106.3|$ so the sum is negative. $106.3 + (-110.9) = -4.6$

69. Numbers have same sign, so add absolute values. $|-123.56| + |-18.35| = 123.56 + 18.35 = 141.91$. Numbers are negative, so sum is negative.
$-123.56 + (-18.35) = -141.91$

70. Numbers have different signs, so take difference between larger and smaller absolute values. $|-72.79| - |33.47| = 72.79 - 33.47 = 39.32$.
$|-72.79|$ is greater than $|33.47|$ so sum is negative.
$-72.79 + 33.47 = -39.32$

71. Numbers have different signs, so take difference between larger and smaller absolute values. $|-99.36| - |45.71| = 99.36 - 45.71 = 53.65$.
$|-99.36|$ is greater than $|45.71|$ so sum is negative.
$-99.36 + 45.71 = -53.65$

72. Numbers have same sign, so add absolute values. $|-84.15| + |-29.98| = 84.15 + 29.98 = 114.13$. Numbers are negative, so sum is negative.
$-84.15 + (-29.98) = -114.13$

73. $\dfrac{3}{5} + \dfrac{1}{7} = \dfrac{21}{35} + \dfrac{5}{35} = \dfrac{21+5}{35} = \dfrac{26}{35}$

74. $\dfrac{5}{8} + \dfrac{3}{5} = \dfrac{25}{40} + \dfrac{24}{40} = \dfrac{25+24}{40} = \dfrac{49}{40}$ or $1\dfrac{9}{40}$

75. $\dfrac{5}{12} + \dfrac{6}{7} = \dfrac{35}{84} + \dfrac{72}{84} = \dfrac{35+72}{84} = \dfrac{107}{84}$ or $1\dfrac{23}{84}$

76. $\dfrac{2}{9} + \dfrac{3}{10} = \dfrac{20}{90} + \dfrac{27}{90} = \dfrac{20+27}{90} = \dfrac{47}{90}$

77. $-\dfrac{8}{11} + \dfrac{4}{5} = -\dfrac{40}{55} + \dfrac{44}{55}$
The numbers have different signs, so find the difference between the larger and smaller absolute values. $\left|\dfrac{44}{55}\right| - \left|-\dfrac{40}{55}\right| = \dfrac{44}{55} - \dfrac{40}{55} = \dfrac{4}{55}$.
Now, $\left|\dfrac{44}{55}\right|$ is greater than $\left|-\dfrac{40}{55}\right|$, so the sum is positive. $-\dfrac{8}{11} + \dfrac{4}{5} = -\dfrac{40}{55} + \dfrac{44}{55} = \dfrac{4}{55}$

78. Numbers have different signs, so find difference between larger and smaller absolute values.
$-\dfrac{4}{9} + \dfrac{5}{27} = \left|-\dfrac{12}{27}\right| - \left|\dfrac{5}{27}\right| = \dfrac{12}{27} - \dfrac{5}{27} = \dfrac{12-5}{27} = \dfrac{7}{27}$
$\left|-\dfrac{12}{27}\right|$ is greater than $\left|\dfrac{5}{27}\right|$ so sum is negative.
$-\dfrac{4}{9} + \dfrac{5}{27} = -\dfrac{7}{27}$

79. $-\dfrac{7}{10} + \dfrac{11}{90} = -\dfrac{63}{90} + \dfrac{11}{90}$
The numbers have different signs, so find the difference between the larger and smaller absolute values. $\left|-\dfrac{63}{90}\right| - \left|\dfrac{11}{90}\right| = \dfrac{63}{90} - \dfrac{11}{90} = \dfrac{52}{90} = \dfrac{26}{45}$. Now,
$\left|-\dfrac{63}{90}\right|$ is greater than $\left|\dfrac{11}{90}\right|$, so the sum is negative.
$-\dfrac{7}{10} + \dfrac{11}{90} = -\dfrac{63}{90} + \dfrac{11}{90} = -\dfrac{52}{90} = -\dfrac{26}{45}$

80. Numbers have different signs, so find difference between larger and smaller absolute values.
$\dfrac{8}{9} + \left(-\dfrac{1}{3}\right) = \left|\dfrac{8}{9}\right| - \left|-\dfrac{3}{9}\right| = \dfrac{8}{9} - \dfrac{3}{9} = \dfrac{8-3}{9} = \dfrac{5}{9}$
$\left|\dfrac{8}{9}\right|$ is greater than $\left|-\dfrac{3}{9}\right|$ so sum is positive.
$\dfrac{8}{9} + \left(-\dfrac{1}{3}\right) = \dfrac{5}{9}$

81. $-\dfrac{7}{30}+\left(-\dfrac{5}{6}\right)=-\dfrac{7}{30}+\left(-\dfrac{25}{30}\right)$

The numbers have the same signs, so add the absolute values.

$\left|-\dfrac{7}{30}\right|+\left|-\dfrac{25}{30}\right|=\dfrac{7}{30}+\dfrac{25}{30}=\dfrac{32}{30}=\dfrac{16}{15}$. The numbers

are negative, so the sum is negative.

$-\dfrac{7}{30}+\left(-\dfrac{5}{6}\right)=-\dfrac{7}{30}+\left(-\dfrac{25}{30}\right)=-\dfrac{32}{30}=-\dfrac{16}{15}$ or

$-1\dfrac{1}{15}$

82. Numbers have same sign, so add absolute values.

$-\dfrac{7}{9}+\left(-\dfrac{1}{5}\right)=\left|-\dfrac{35}{45}\right|+\left|-\dfrac{9}{45}\right|=\dfrac{35}{45}+\dfrac{9}{45}=$

$\dfrac{35+9}{44}=\dfrac{44}{45}$

Numbers are negative so sum is negative.

$-\dfrac{7}{9}+\left(-\dfrac{1}{5}\right)=-\dfrac{44}{45}$

83. $\dfrac{9}{25}+\left(-\dfrac{3}{50}\right)=\dfrac{18}{50}+\left(-\dfrac{3}{50}\right)$

The numbers have different signs, so find the difference between the larger and smaller absolute

values. $\left|\dfrac{18}{50}\right|-\left|-\dfrac{3}{50}\right|=\dfrac{18}{50}-\dfrac{3}{50}=\dfrac{15}{50}=\dfrac{3}{10}$. Now,

$\left|\dfrac{18}{50}\right|$ is greater than $\left|-\dfrac{3}{50}\right|$, so the sum is positive.

$\dfrac{9}{25}+\left(-\dfrac{3}{50}\right)=\dfrac{18}{50}+\left(-\dfrac{3}{50}\right)=\dfrac{15}{50}=\dfrac{3}{10}$

84. Numbers have same sign, so add absolute values.

$-\dfrac{1}{15}+\left(-\dfrac{5}{6}\right)=\left|-\dfrac{2}{30}\right|+\left|-\dfrac{25}{30}\right|=\dfrac{2}{30}+\dfrac{25}{30}=\dfrac{2+25}{30}=$

$\dfrac{27}{30}=\dfrac{9}{10}$

Numbers are negative so sum is negative.

$-\dfrac{1}{15}+\left(-\dfrac{5}{6}\right)=-\dfrac{9}{10}$

85. $-\dfrac{4}{5}+\left(-\dfrac{5}{75}\right)=-\dfrac{60}{75}+\left(-\dfrac{5}{75}\right)$

The numbers have the same signs, so add the absolute values.

$\left|-\dfrac{60}{75}\right|+\left|-\dfrac{5}{75}\right|=\dfrac{60}{75}+\dfrac{5}{75}=\dfrac{65}{75}=\dfrac{13}{15}$. The

numbers are negative, so the sum is negative.

$-\dfrac{4}{5}+\left(-\dfrac{5}{75}\right)=-\dfrac{60}{75}+\left(-\dfrac{5}{75}\right)=-\dfrac{65}{75}=-\dfrac{13}{15}$

86. $\dfrac{5}{36}+\left(-\dfrac{5}{24}\right)=\dfrac{10}{72}+\left(-\dfrac{15}{72}\right)$

The numbers have different signs, so find the difference between the larger and smaller

absolute values. $\left|-\dfrac{15}{72}\right|-\left|\dfrac{10}{72}\right|=\dfrac{15}{72}-\dfrac{10}{72}=\dfrac{5}{72}$.

Now, $\left|-\dfrac{15}{72}\right|$ is greater than $\left|\dfrac{10}{72}\right|$, so the sum is

negative. $\dfrac{5}{36}+\left(-\dfrac{5}{24}\right)=\dfrac{10}{72}+\left(-\dfrac{15}{72}\right)=-\dfrac{5}{72}$

87. Numbers have different signs, so find difference between larger and smaller absolute values.

$-\dfrac{9}{24}+\dfrac{5}{7}=-\dfrac{63}{168}+\dfrac{120}{168}=\left|\dfrac{120}{168}\right|-\left|-\dfrac{63}{168}\right|=$

$\dfrac{120}{168}-\dfrac{63}{168}=\dfrac{120-63}{168}=\dfrac{57}{168}=\dfrac{19}{56}$

$\left|\dfrac{120}{168}\right|$ is greater than $\left|-\dfrac{63}{168}\right|$ so sum is positive.

$-\dfrac{9}{24}+\dfrac{5}{7}=\dfrac{19}{56}$

88. Numbers have different signs, so find difference between larger and smaller absolute values.

$-\dfrac{9}{40}+\dfrac{4}{15}=-\dfrac{27}{120}+\dfrac{32}{120}=\left|\dfrac{32}{120}\right|-\left|-\dfrac{27}{120}\right|=$

$\dfrac{32}{120}-\dfrac{27}{120}=\dfrac{32-27}{120}=\dfrac{5}{120}=\dfrac{1}{24}$

$\left|\dfrac{32}{120}\right|$ is greater than $\left|-\dfrac{27}{120}\right|$ so sum is positive.

$-\dfrac{9}{40}+\dfrac{4}{15}=\dfrac{1}{24}$

89. $-\dfrac{5}{12}+\left(-\dfrac{3}{10}\right)=-\dfrac{25}{60}+\left(-\dfrac{18}{60}\right)$

The numbers have the same signs, so add the

absolute values. $\left|-\dfrac{25}{60}\right|+\left|-\dfrac{18}{60}\right|=\dfrac{25}{60}+\dfrac{18}{60}=\dfrac{43}{60}$.

The numbers are negative, so the sum is

negative. $-\dfrac{5}{12}+\left(-\dfrac{3}{10}\right)=-\dfrac{25}{60}+\left(-\dfrac{18}{60}\right)=-\dfrac{43}{60}$

90. Numbers have different signs, so find difference between larger and smaller absolute values.

$\dfrac{7}{16}+\left(-\dfrac{5}{24}\right)=\dfrac{21}{48}+\left(-\dfrac{10}{48}\right)=\left|\dfrac{21}{48}\right|-\left|-\dfrac{10}{48}\right|=$

$\dfrac{21}{48}-\dfrac{10}{48}=\dfrac{21-10}{48}=\dfrac{11}{48}$

$\left|\dfrac{21}{48}\right|$ is greater than $\left|-\dfrac{10}{48}\right|$ so sum is positive.

$\dfrac{7}{16}+\left(-\dfrac{5}{24}\right)=\dfrac{11}{48}$

91. $-\dfrac{13}{14}+\left(-\dfrac{7}{42}\right)=-\dfrac{39}{42}+\left(-\dfrac{7}{42}\right)$

The numbers have the same signs, so add the absolute values.

$\left|-\dfrac{39}{42}\right|+\left|-\dfrac{7}{42}\right|=\dfrac{39}{42}+\dfrac{7}{42}=\dfrac{46}{42}=\dfrac{23}{21}$. The

numbers are negative, so the sum is negative.

$-\dfrac{13}{14}+\left(-\dfrac{7}{42}\right)=-\dfrac{39}{42}+\left(-\dfrac{7}{42}\right)=-\dfrac{46}{42}=-\dfrac{23}{21}$ or

$-1\dfrac{2}{21}$

92. Numbers have same sign, so add absolute values.

$-\dfrac{11}{27}+\left(-\dfrac{7}{18}\right)=-\dfrac{22}{54}+\left(-\dfrac{21}{54}\right)=\left|-\dfrac{22}{54}\right|+\left|-\dfrac{21}{54}\right|=$

$\dfrac{22}{54}+\dfrac{21}{54}=\dfrac{22+21}{54}=\dfrac{43}{54}$

Numbers are negative so sum is negative.

$-\dfrac{11}{27}+\left(-\dfrac{7}{18}\right)=-\dfrac{43}{54}$

93. a. Positive; $|587|$ is greater than $|-197|$ so sum will be positive.

  b. $587+(-197)=390$

c. Yes; By part a) we expect a positive sum. The magnitude of the sum is the difference between the larger and smaller absolute values.

94. a. Negative; the sum of two negative numbers is always negative.

  b. $-140+(-629)=-769$

  c. Yes. The sum of 2 negative numbers should be (and is) a negative number with a larger absolute value.

95. a. Negative; the sum of 2 negative numbers is always negative.

  b. $-84+(-289)=-373$

  c. Yes. The sum of 2 negative numbers should be (and is) a negative number with a larger absolute value.

96. a. Negative; $|-647|$ is greater than $|352|$ so sum will be negative.

  b. $-647+352=-295$

  c. Yes; by part a) we expect a negative sum. Magnitude of sum is difference between the larger and smaller absolute values.

97. a. Negative; $|-947|$ is greater than $|495|$ so sum will be negative.

  b. $-947+495=-452$

  c. Yes; by part a) we expect a negative sum. Magnitude of the sum is the difference between the larger and smaller absolute values.

98. a. Sum will be 0, since numbers have opposite signs and equal absolute values.

  b. $762+(-762)=0$

  c. Yes; by part a) answer makes sense.

99. a. Negative; the sum of 2 negative numbers is always negative.

  b. $-496+(-804)=-1300$

  c. Yes. The sum of 2 negative numbers should be (and is) a negative number with a larger absolute value.

100. a. Positive; $|1090|$ is greater than $|-354|$ so sum will be positive.

b. $-354 + 1090 = 736$

c. Yes; by part a) we expect a positive sum. Magnitude of sum is difference between the larger and smaller absolute values.

101. a. Negative; $|-375|$ is greater than $|263|$ so sum will be negative.

b. $-375 + 263 = -112$

c. Yes; by part a) we expect a negative sum. The magnitude of the sum is the difference between the larger and smaller absolute values.

102. a. Positive; $|1127|$ is greater than $|-84|$ so sum will be positive.

b. $1127 + (-84) = 1043$

c. Yes; by part a) we expect a positive sum. Magnitude of sum is difference between larger and smaller absolute values.

103. a. Negative; the sum of 2 negative numbers is always negative.

b. $-1833 + (-2047) = -3880$

c. Yes. The sum of 2 negative numbers should be (and is) a negative number with a larger absolute value.

104. a. Positive; $|572|$ is greater than $|-426|$ so sum will be positive.

b. $-426 + 572 = 146$

c. Yes; by part a) we expect a positive sum. Magnitude of sum is difference between larger and smaller absolute values.

105. a. Positive; $|3124|$ is greater than $|-2013|$ so sum will be positive.

b. $3124 + (-2013) = 1111$

c. Yes; by part a) we expect a positive sum. Magnitude of sum is difference between larger and smaller absolute values.

106. a. Negative; the sum of two negative numbers is always negative.

b. $-9095 + (-647) = -9742$

c. Yes. The sum of 2 negative numbers should be (and is) a negative number with a larger absolute value.

107. a. Negative; the sum of 2 negative numbers is always negative.

b. $-1025 + (-1025) = -2050$

c. Yes. The sum of 2 negative numbers should be (and is) a negative number with a larger absolute value.

108. a. Positive; $|7513|$ is greater than $|-4361|$ so sum will be positive.

b. $7513 + (-4361) = 3152$

c. Yes; by part a) we expect a positive sum. Magnitude of sum is difference between larger and smaller absolute values.

109. True; the sum of two negative numbers is always negative.

110. True; if the negative number has the larger absolute value, the sum will be negative number.

111. True; the sum of two positive numbers is always positive.

112. False; the sum has the sign of the number with the larger absolute value.

113. False; the sum has the sign of the number with the larger absolute value.

114. True; by definition of opposites.

115. David's balance was $-\$94$. His new balance can be found by adding. $-94 + (-183) = -277$ David owes the bank \$277.

116. $-142 + 87$
$|142| - |87| = 142 - 87 = 55$
$|-142|$ is greater than $|87|$ so the sum is negative. $-142 + 87 = -55$
Mrs. Chu still owes \$55.

117. Total loss can be represented as $-18 + (-3)$. $|-18| + |-3| = 18 + 3 = 21$. The total loss in yardage is 21 yards.

118. $-56 + (-162) = -218$
Mrs. Jahn has overdrawn her account by \$218.

119. The depth of the well can be found by adding $-27 + (-34) = -61$. The well is 61 feet deep.

120. a. $11,250 + (-18,560) = -7310$

    The Frenches had a loss of \$7310 the first month.

    b. $17,980 + (-12,750) = 5230$

    The Frenches had a gain of \$5230 the second month.

    c. $19,420 + (-16,980) = 2440$

    The Frenches had a gain of \$2440 the third month.

121. The total height can be represented by 33,480 feet. The base can be represented by $-19,684$ feet. The height of the peak above sea level is $33,480 + (-19,684) = 13,796$ feet.

122. $-3000 + 37,400 = 34,400$
    The profit for the year was \$34,400.

123. a. -12 million
    The deficit is \$12 million.

    b. 1999: -20 million; 2000; 8 million; 2001; 17 million
    $-20 + 8 + 17 = 5$
    From 1999-2001, there was a surplus of \$5 million.

124. $-3.2 + 0 + 1.2 + 12.2 + (-2.6) = 7.6$
    The percent change was 7.6%.

125. $(-4) + (-6) + (-12) = (-10) + (-12) = -22$

126. $5 + (-7) + (-8) = (-2) + (-8) = -10$

127. $29 + (-46) + 37 = (-17) + 37 = 20$

128. $4 + (-5) + 6 + (-8) = (-1) + 6 + (-8)$
    $= 5 + (-8)$
    $= -3$

129. $(-12) + (-10) + 25 + (-3) = (-22) + 25 + (-3)$
    $= 3 + (-3)$
    $= 0$

130. $(-4) + (-2) + (-15) + (-27) = (-6) + (-15) + (-27)$
    $= (-21) + (-27)$
    $= -48$

131. $\dfrac{1}{2} + \left(-\dfrac{1}{3}\right) + \dfrac{1}{5} = \left(\dfrac{3}{6} - \dfrac{2}{6}\right) + \dfrac{1}{5}$
    $= \dfrac{1}{6} + \dfrac{1}{5}$
    $= \dfrac{5}{30} + \dfrac{6}{30}$
    $= \dfrac{11}{30}$

132. $-\dfrac{3}{8} + \left(-\dfrac{2}{9}\right) + \left(-\dfrac{1}{2}\right) = \left(-\dfrac{27}{72} - \dfrac{16}{72}\right) + \left(-\dfrac{1}{2}\right)$
    $= -\dfrac{43}{72} - \dfrac{1}{2}$
    $= -\dfrac{43}{72} - \dfrac{36}{72}$
    $= -\dfrac{79}{72}$ or $-1\dfrac{7}{72}$

133. $1 + 2 + 3 + \cdots + 10 = (1 + 10) + (2 + 9) + \cdots + (5 + 6)$
    $= 5(11)$
    $= 55$

134. $1 + 2 + 3 + \cdots + 20$
    $= (1 + 20) + (2 + 19) + \cdots + (10 + 11)$
    $= (10)(21)$
    $= 210$

135. $2\dfrac{3}{8} = \dfrac{16 + 3}{8} = \dfrac{19}{8}$

    $\left(\dfrac{4}{7}\right)\left(2\dfrac{3}{8}\right) = \dfrac{\cancel{4}^{1}}{7} \cdot \dfrac{19}{\cancel{8}_{2}} = \dfrac{1 \cdot 19}{7 \cdot 2}$
    $= \dfrac{19}{14}$ or $1\dfrac{5}{14}$

136. $3 = \dfrac{3}{1} \cdot \dfrac{16}{16} = \dfrac{48}{16}$

    $3 - \dfrac{5}{16} = \dfrac{48}{16} - \dfrac{5}{16} = \dfrac{48 - 5}{16} = \dfrac{43}{16}$ or $2\dfrac{11}{16}$

137. False, -0.25 is less than zero and not an integer.

138. $|-3| > 2$ since $|-3| = 3$

139. $8 < |-12|$ since $|-12| = 12$

Exercise Set 1.7

1. $2 - 7$

2. $-4 - (-6)$

3. $\copyright - ?$

4. $\square - *$

5. **a.** To subtract b from a, add the opposite of b to a.

   b. $5 + (-14)$

   c. $5 + (-14) = -9$

6. **a.** $a - (+b) = a - b$

   b. $3 - (+9) = 3 - 9$

   c. $3 - 9 = 3 + (-9) = -6$

7. **a.** $a - (-b) = a + b$

   b. $-4 - (-12) = -4 + 12$

   c. $-4 + 12 = 8$

8. Evaluate an expression with 3 or more numbers and no parentheses from left to right.

9. **a.** $3 - (-6) + (-5) = 3 + 6 - 5$

   b. $3 + 6 - 5 = 9 - 5 = 4$

10. **a.** Replace each set of two signs next to each other with a single sign.
    $-12 + (-5) - (-4) = -12 - 5 + 4$

    b. $-12 - 5 + 4 = -17 + 4 = -13$

11. Yes it is correct.

12. Yes it is correct.

13. $8 - (+2) = 8 + (-2) = 6$

14. $17 - (+8) = 17 + (-8) = 9$

15. $12 - 5 = 12 + (-5) = 7$

16. $9 - 4 = 9 + (-4) = 5$

17. $8 - 9 = 8 + (-9) = -1$

18. $-6 - 3 = -6 + (-3) = -9$

19. $9 - (-3) = 9 + 3 = 12$

20. $17 - (-5) = 17 + 5 = 22$

21. $-6 - 6 = -6 + (-6) = -12$

22. $-4 - (-3) = -4 + 3 = -1$

23. $0 - 7 = 0 + (-7) = -7$

24. $9 - (-9) = 9 + 9 = 18$

25. $8 - 8 = 8 + (-8) = 0$

26. $10 - 10 = 10 + (-10) = 0$

27. $-3 - 1 = -3 + (-1) = -4$

28. $-5.7 - (-3.1) = -5.7 + 3.1 = -2.6$

29. $-8 - (-5) = -8 + 5 = -3$

30. $4 - 9 = 4 + (-9) = -5$

31. $6 - (-3) = 6 + 3 = 9$

32. $6 - 10 = 6 + (-10) = -4$

33. $-9 - 11 = -9 + (-11) = -20$

34. $37 - 40 = 37 + (-40) = -3$

35. $0 - (-9.8) = 0 + 9.8 = 9.8$

36. $-6.3 - 4.7 = -6.3 + (-4.7) = -11.0$

37. $-4.8 - (-5.1) = -4.8 + 5.1 = 0.3$

38. $-4 - (-4) = -4 + 4 = 0$

39. $14 - 7 = 14 + (-7) = 7$

40. $9 - 9 = 9 + (-9) = 0$

41. $-8 - (-12) = -8 + 12 = 4$

42. $-6 - (-2) = -6 + 2 = -4$

43. $18 - (-4) = 18 + 4 = 22$

44. $-25 - 16 = -25 + (-16) = -41$

45. $-9 - 2 = -9 + (-2) = -11$

46. $-35 - (-8) = -35 + 8 = -27$

47. $-90.7 - 40.3 = -90.7 + (-40.3) = -131.0$

48. $-52.6 - 37.9 = -52.6 + (-37.9) = -90.5$

49. $-45 - 37 = -45 + (-37) = -82$

50. $-50 - (-40) = -40 + 40 = -10$

51. $70 - (-70) = 70 + 70 = 140$

52. $130 - (-90) = 130 + 90 = 220$

53. $42.3 - 49.7 = 42.3 + (-49.7) = -7.4$

54. $81.3 - 92.5 = 81.3 + (-92.5) = -11.2$

55. $-7.85 - (-3.92) = -7.85 + 3.92 = -3.93$

56. $-12.43 - (-9.57) = -12.43 + 9.57 = -2.86$

57. $4 - 15 = 4 + (-15) = -11$

58. $1 - 7 = 1 + (-7) = -6$

59. $21 - 21 = 21 + (-21) = 0$

60. $13 - 13 = 13 + (-13) = 0$

61. $-6.3 - (-12.4) = -6.3 + 12.4 = 6.1$

62. $-9.8 - 17.3 = -9.8 + (-17.3) = -27.1$

63. $10.3 - (-7.9) = 10.3 + 7.9 = 18.2$

64. $-23 - (-23) = -23 + 23 = 0$

65. $13 - 24 = 13 + (-24) = -11$

66. $-5.2 - (-11.7) = -5.2 + 11.7 = 6.5$

67. $-10.3 - 7.8 = -10.3 + (-7.8) = -18.1$

68. $3.4 - (-9.6) = 3.4 + 9.6 = 13.0$

69.
$$\frac{5}{9} - \frac{3}{8} = \frac{5}{9} + \left(-\frac{3}{8}\right)$$
$$= \frac{40}{72} + \left(-\frac{27}{72}\right)$$
$$= \frac{40 + (-27)}{72}$$
$$= \frac{13}{72}$$

70.
$$\frac{4}{5} - \frac{5}{6} = \frac{4}{5} + \left(-\frac{5}{6}\right)$$
$$= \frac{24}{30} + \left(-\frac{25}{30}\right)$$
$$= \frac{24 + (-25)}{30}$$
$$= -\frac{1}{30}$$

71.
$$\frac{8}{15} - \frac{7}{45} = \frac{8}{15} + \left(-\frac{7}{45}\right)$$
$$= \frac{24}{45} + \left(-\frac{7}{45}\right)$$
$$= \frac{24 + (-7)}{45}$$
$$= \frac{17}{45}$$

72.
$$\frac{5}{12} - \frac{7}{8} = \frac{5}{12} + \left(-\frac{7}{8}\right)$$
$$= \frac{10}{24} + \left(-\frac{21}{24}\right)$$
$$= \frac{10 + (-21)}{24}$$
$$= -\frac{11}{24}$$

73.
$$-\frac{7}{10} - \frac{5}{12} = -\frac{7}{10} + \left(-\frac{5}{12}\right)$$
$$= -\frac{42}{60} + \left(-\frac{25}{60}\right)$$
$$= \frac{-42 + (-25)}{60}$$
$$= -\frac{67}{60}$$

74. $-\dfrac{1}{4} - \dfrac{2}{3} = -\dfrac{1}{4} + \left(-\dfrac{2}{3}\right)$

$= -\dfrac{3}{12} + \left(-\dfrac{8}{12}\right)$

$= \dfrac{-3 + (-8)}{12}$

$= -\dfrac{11}{12}$

75. $-\dfrac{4}{15} - \dfrac{3}{20} = -\dfrac{4}{15} + \left(-\dfrac{3}{20}\right)$

$= -\dfrac{16}{60} + \left(-\dfrac{9}{60}\right)$

$= \dfrac{-16 + (-9)}{60}$

$= -\dfrac{25}{60} = -\dfrac{5}{12}$

76. $-\dfrac{5}{4} - \dfrac{7}{11} = -\dfrac{5}{4} + \left(-\dfrac{7}{11}\right)$

$= -\dfrac{55}{44} + \left(-\dfrac{28}{44}\right)$

$= \dfrac{-55 + (-28)}{44}$

$= -\dfrac{83}{44}$

77. $-\dfrac{7}{12} - \dfrac{5}{40} = -\dfrac{7}{12} + \left(-\dfrac{5}{40}\right)$

$= -\dfrac{70}{120} + \left(-\dfrac{15}{120}\right)$

$= \dfrac{-70 + (-15)}{120}$

$= -\dfrac{85}{120} = -\dfrac{17}{24}$

78. $-\dfrac{5}{6} - \dfrac{3}{32} = -\dfrac{5}{6} + \left(-\dfrac{3}{32}\right)$

$= -\dfrac{80}{96} + \left(-\dfrac{9}{96}\right)$

$= \dfrac{-80 + (-9)}{96}$

$= -\dfrac{89}{96}$

79. $\dfrac{3}{8} - \dfrac{6}{48} = \dfrac{3}{8} + \left(-\dfrac{6}{48}\right)$

$= \dfrac{18}{48} + \left(-\dfrac{6}{48}\right)$

$= \dfrac{18 + (-6)}{48}$

$= \dfrac{12}{48} = \dfrac{1}{4}$

80. $\dfrac{17}{18} - \dfrac{13}{20} = \dfrac{17}{18} + \left(-\dfrac{13}{20}\right)$

$= \dfrac{170}{180} + \left(-\dfrac{117}{180}\right)$

$= \dfrac{53}{180}$

81. $-\dfrac{4}{9} - \left(-\dfrac{3}{5}\right) = -\dfrac{4}{9} + \dfrac{3}{5}$

$= -\dfrac{20}{45} + \dfrac{27}{45}$

$= \dfrac{-20 + 27}{45}$

$= \dfrac{7}{45}$

82. $\dfrac{5}{20} - \left(-\dfrac{1}{8}\right) = \dfrac{5}{20} + \dfrac{1}{8}$

$= \dfrac{10}{40} + \dfrac{5}{40}$

$= \dfrac{10 + 15}{40}$

$= \dfrac{15}{40} = \dfrac{3}{8}$

83. $\dfrac{3}{16} - \left(-\dfrac{5}{8}\right) = \dfrac{3}{16} + \dfrac{5}{8}$

$= \dfrac{3}{16} + \dfrac{10}{16}$

$= \dfrac{3 + 10}{16}$

$= \dfrac{13}{16}$

84. $-\dfrac{5}{12}-\left(-\dfrac{3}{8}\right)=-\dfrac{5}{12}+\dfrac{3}{8}$

$\qquad\qquad\qquad = -\dfrac{10}{24}+\dfrac{9}{24}$

$\qquad\qquad\qquad = \dfrac{-10+9}{24}$

$\qquad\qquad\qquad = -\dfrac{1}{24}$

85. $\dfrac{4}{7}-\dfrac{7}{9}=\dfrac{4}{7}+\left(-\dfrac{7}{9}\right)$

$\qquad\qquad\quad = \dfrac{36}{63}+\left(-\dfrac{49}{63}\right)$

$\qquad\qquad\quad = \dfrac{36+(-49)}{63}$

$\qquad\qquad\quad = -\dfrac{13}{63}$

86. $\dfrac{5}{8}-\dfrac{7}{15}=\dfrac{5}{8}+\left(-\dfrac{7}{15}\right)$

$\qquad\qquad\quad = \dfrac{75}{120}+\left(-\dfrac{56}{120}\right)$

$\qquad\qquad\quad = \dfrac{75+(-56)}{120}$

$\qquad\qquad\quad = \dfrac{19}{120}$

87. $-\dfrac{5}{12}-\left(-\dfrac{3}{10}\right)=-\dfrac{5}{12}+\dfrac{3}{10}$

$\qquad\qquad\qquad = -\dfrac{25}{60}+\dfrac{18}{60}$

$\qquad\qquad\qquad = \dfrac{-25+18}{60}$

$\qquad\qquad\qquad = -\dfrac{7}{60}$

88. $-\dfrac{9}{10}-\left(-\dfrac{5}{16}\right)=-\dfrac{9}{10}+\dfrac{5}{16}$

$\qquad\qquad\qquad = -\dfrac{72}{80}+\dfrac{25}{80}$

$\qquad\qquad\qquad = \dfrac{-72+25}{80}$

$\qquad\qquad\qquad = -\dfrac{47}{80}$

89. **a.** Positive; $378-279=378+(-279)$
|378| is greater than |−279| so the sum will be positive.

   b. $378+(-279)=99$

   c. Yes; by part a) we expect a positive sum. The size of the sum is the difference between the absolute values of the 2 numbers.

90. **a.** Negative; $483-569=483+(-569)$
$|-569|$ is greater than $|483|$ so sum will be negative.

   b. $483+(-569)=-86$

   c. Yes; by part a) we expect a negative sum. Size of sum is difference between larger and smaller absolute values.

91. **a.** Negative; $-482-137=-482+(-137)$
The sum of 2 negative numbers is always negative.

   b. $-482+(-137)=-619$

   c. Yes. The sum of 2 negative numbers should be (and is) a negative number with a larger absolute value.

92. **a.** Positive; $178-(-377)=178+377$
The sum of 2 positive numbers is always positive.

   b. $178+377=555$

   c. Yes; by part a) we expect a positive answer. The size of the sum is the sum of the absolute values of the numbers.

93. **a.** Positive; $843-(-745)=843+745$.
The sum of 2 positive numbers is always positive.

   b. $843+745=1588$

   c. Yes; by part a) we expect a positive answer. The size of the sum is the sum of the absolute values of the numbers.

94. **a.** Positive; $864-(-762)=864+762$.
The sum of two positive numbers is always positive.

   b. $864+762=1626$

   c. Yes; by part a) we expect a positive answer. The size of the sum is the sum of the absolute values of the two numbers.

95. a. Positive; $-408 - (-604) = -408 + 604$.

$|604|$ is greater than $|-408|$ so the sum will be positive.

b. $-408 + 604 = 196$

c. Yes; by part a) we expect a positive answer. The size of the answer is the difference between the larger and smaller absolute values.

96. a. Negative; $-623 - 111 = -623 + (-111)$.

The sum of two negative numbers is always negative.

b. $-623 + (-111) = -734$

c. Yes. The sum of 2 negative numbers should be (and is) a negative number with a larger absolute value.

97. a. Negative; $-1024 - (-576) = -1024 + 576$.

$|-1024|$ is greater than $|576|$ so the sum will be negative.

b. $-1024 + 576 = -448$

c. Yes; by part a) we expect a negative answer. The size of the answer is the difference between the larger and the smaller absolute values.

98. a. Negative; $-104.7 - 27.6 = -104.7 + (-27.6)$. The sum of two negative numbers is always negative.

b. $-104.7 + (-27.6) = -132.3$

c. Yes. The sum of 2 negative numbers should be (and is) a negative number with a larger absolute value.

99. a. Positive; $165.7 - 49.6 = 165.7 + (-49.6)$.

$|165.7|$ is greater than $|-49.6|$ so the sum will be positive.

b. $165.7 + (-49.6) = 116.1$

c. Yes; by part a) we expect a negative answer. The size of the answer is the difference between the larger and the smaller absolute values.

100. a. Negative; $-40.2 - (-12.6) = -40.2 + 12.6$.

$|-40.2|$ is greater than $|12.6|$ so sum will be negative.

b. $-40.2 + 12.6 = -27.6$

c. Yes; by part a) we expect a negative answer. The size of the answer is the difference between the larger and smaller absolute values.

101. a. Negative; $295 - 364 = 295 + (-364)$.

Since $|-364|$ is greater than $|295|$ the answer will be negative.

b. $295 + (-364) = -69$

c. Yes; by part a) we expect a negative answer. The size of the answer is the difference between the larger and the smaller absolute values.

102. a. Negative; $-932 - (-433) = -932 + 433$.

$|-932|$ is greater than $|433|$ so the sum will be negative.

b. $-932 + 433 = -499$

c. Yes; by part a) we expect a negative answer. The size of the answer is the difference between the larger and smaller absolute values.

103. a. Negative; $-1023 - 647 = -1023 + (-647)$. The sum of two negative numbers is always negative.

b. $-1023 + (-647) = -1670$

c. Yes. The sum of 2 negative numbers should be (and is) a negative number with a larger absolute value.

104. a. Negative; $-4120 - 2432 = -4120 + (-2432)$. The sum of 2 negative numbers is always negative.

b. $-4120 + (-2432) = -6552$

c. Yes. The sum of 2 negative numbers should be (and is) a negative number with a larger absolute value.

105. a. Zero; $-7.62 - (-7.62) = -7.62 + 7.62$.

The sum of two opposite numbers is always zero.

b. $-7.62 + 7.62 = 0$

c. Yes; by part a) we expect zero.

106. a. Negative; $-103.2 - 36.7 = -103.2 + (-36.7)$. The sum of two negative numbers is always negative.

b. $-103.2 + (-36.7) = -139.9$

c. Yes; the sum of two negative numbers should be (and is) a larger negative number.

107. $7 + 5 - (+8) = 7 + 5 + (-8) = 12 + (-8) = 4$

108. $15 - (+9) - (+5) = 15 + (-9) + (-5) = 6 + (-5) = 1$

109. $-6 + (-6) + 6 = -12 + 6 = -6$

110. $9 - 4 + (-2) = 9 + (-4) + (-2) = 5 + (-2) = 3$

111. $-13 - (+5) + 3 = -13 + (-5) + 3 = -18 + 3 = -15$

112. $7 - (+4) - (-3) = 7 + (-4) + 3 = 3 + 3 = 6$

113. $-9 - (-3) + 4 = -9 + 3 + 4 = -6 + 4 = -2$

114. $15 + (-7) - (-3) = 15 + (-7) + 3 = 8 + 3 = 11$

115. $5 - (-9) + (-1) = 5 + 9 + (-1) = 14 + (-1) = 13$

116. $12 + (-5) - (-4) = 12 + (-5) + 4 = 7 + 4 = 11$

117.
$$17 + (-8) - (+14) = 17 + (-8) + (-14)$$
$$= 9 + (-14)$$
$$= -5$$

118. $-7 + 6 - 3 = -7 + 6 + (-3) = -1 + (-3) = -4$

119. $-36 - 5 + 9 = -36 + (-5) + 9 = -41 + 9 = -32$

120. $45 - 3 - 7 = 45 + (-3) + (-7) = 42 + (-7) = 35$

121. $-2 + 7 - 9 = -2 + 7 + (-9) = 5 + (-9) = -4$

122. $-2 - 7 - 13 = -2 + (-7) + (-13) = -9 + (-13) = -22$

123. $25 - 19 + 3 = 25 + (-19) + 3 = 6 + 3 = 9$

124. $-4 - 1 + 5 = -4 + (-1) + 5 = -5 + 5 = 0$

125.
$$-4 - 6 + 5 - 7 = (-4) + (-6) + 5 + (-7)$$
$$= -10 + 5 + (-7)$$
$$= -5 + (-7)$$
$$= -12$$

126.
$$-9 - 3 - (-4) + 5 = -9 + (-3) + 4 + 5$$
$$= -12 + 4 + 5$$
$$= -8 + 5$$
$$= -3$$

127.
$$17 + (-3) - 9 - (-7) = 17 + (-3) + (-9) + 7$$
$$= 14 + (-9) + 7$$
$$= 5 + 7$$
$$= 12$$

128.
$$32 + 5 - 7 - 12 = 32 + 5 + (-7) + (-12)$$
$$= 37 + (-7) + (-12)$$
$$= 30 + (-12)$$
$$= 18$$

129.
$$-9 + (-7) + (-5) - (-3) = -9 + (-7) + (-5) + 3$$
$$= -16 + (-5) + 3$$
$$= -21 + 3$$
$$= -18$$

130.
$$6 - 9 - (-3) + 12 = 6 + (-9) + 3 + 12$$
$$= -3 + 3 + 12$$
$$= 0 + 12$$
$$= 12$$

131. a. $300 - 343 = 300 + (-343) = -43$

They had 43 sweaters on back order.

b. $43 + 100 = 143$

They would need to order 143 sweaters.

132. $10,152 - (-184) = 10,152 + 184 = 10,336$

The difference is 10,366 feet.

133. $2\dfrac{1}{4}-\dfrac{3}{8}=2\dfrac{1}{4}+\left(-\dfrac{3}{8}\right)$

$\qquad =\dfrac{9}{4}+\left(-\dfrac{3}{8}\right)$

$\qquad =\dfrac{18}{8}+\left(-\dfrac{3}{8}\right)$

$\qquad =\dfrac{18+(-3)}{8}$

$\qquad =\dfrac{15}{8}=1\dfrac{7}{8}$

After the second day $1\dfrac{7}{8}$ inches of water remains.

134. $1605.7-(-267.4)=1605.7+267.4=1873.1$
The vertical distance the package traveled was 1873.1 feet.

135. $44-(-56)=44+56=100$

Thus the temperature dropped $100°F$.

136. a. $58.5+67.3=125.8$
In one hour they will be 125.8 miles apart.

    b. $67.3-58.5=67.3+(-58.5)=8.8$

    In one hour, they will be 8.8 miles apart.

137. a. $288+(-7)=281$
In 2006, his score was 281.

    b. $-5-(-2)=5+2=-3$
T. Clark had 3 less strokes than S. Cink.

138. $32\dfrac{1}{2}-2\dfrac{3}{4}=32\dfrac{1}{2}+\left(-2\dfrac{3}{4}\right)$

$\qquad =\dfrac{65}{2}+\left(-\dfrac{11}{4}\right)$

$\qquad =\dfrac{130}{4}+\left(-\dfrac{11}{4}\right)$

$\qquad =\dfrac{130+(-11)}{4}$

$\qquad =\dfrac{119}{4}=29\dfrac{3}{4}$

The new inseam will be $29\dfrac{3}{4}$ inches.

139. $1-2+3-4+5-6+7-8+9-10$

$\qquad =(1-2)+(3-4)+(5-6)+(7-8)+(9-10)$

$\qquad =(-1)+(-1)+(-1)+(-1)+(-1)$

$\qquad =-5$

140. $1-2+3-4+5-6+\cdots+99-100$

$\qquad =(1-2)+(3-4)+(5-6)+\cdots+(99-100)$

$\qquad =(-1)+(-1)+(-1)+\cdots+(-1)$

$\qquad =-50$

141. a. 8 units

    b. $-3-(-11)=-3+11=8$

142. $[50-(0.10\cdot50)]+0.10[50-(0.10\cdot50)]$

$\qquad =[50-5]+0.10[50-5]$

$\qquad =45+4.5$

$\qquad =49.50$

or

$[50+(0.10\cdot50)]-0.10[50+(0.10\cdot50)]$

$\qquad =[50+5]-0.10[50+5]$

$\qquad =55-5.5$

$\qquad =49.50$

The value is the same either way, $49.50.

143. a. $3+2+2+1+1=9$
The ball travels 9 feet vertically.

    b. $-3+2+(-2)+1+(-1)=-3$
The net distance is –3 feet.

144. The counting numbers are $\{1,2,3,\ldots\}$.

145. The set of rational numbers together with the set of irrational numbers forms the set of real numbers.

146. $|-3|>-5$ since $|-3|=3$

147. $-|-9|<-|-5|$ since $-|-9|=-9$ and $-|-5|=-5$

148. $\dfrac{5}{6}-\dfrac{7}{8}=\dfrac{5}{6}+\left(-\dfrac{7}{8}\right)$

$\qquad =\dfrac{20}{24}+\left(-\dfrac{21}{24}\right)$

$\qquad =\dfrac{20+(-21)}{24}$

$\qquad =-\dfrac{1}{24}$

Exercise Set 1.8

1. Like signs: product is positive. Unlike signs: product is negative.

2. Like signs: quotient is positive. Unlike signs: quotient is negative.

3. When multiplying 3 or more real numbers, the product is positive if there is an even number of negative numbers and the product is negative if there is an odd number.

4. The product of 0 and any real number is 0

5. a. When a is a nonzero real number, $\dfrac{0}{a} = 0$.

   b. When a is a nonzero real number, $\dfrac{a}{0}$ is undefined.

6. A fraction of the form $\dfrac{a}{-b}$ is generally written $-\dfrac{a}{b}$ or $\dfrac{-a}{b}$.

7. a. With $3 - 5$ you subtract, but with $3(-5)$ you multiply.

   b. $3 - 5 = 3 + (-5) = -2$
      $3(-5) = -15$

8. a. To find $-4 - 2$ you subtract, but to find $(-4)(-2)$, you multiply.

   b. $-4 - 2 = -4 + (-2) = -6$
      $(-4)(-2) = 8$

9. a. With $x - y$ you subtract, but with $x(-y)$ you multiply.

   b. $x - y = 5 - (-2) = 5 + 2 = 7$

   c. $x(-y) = 5\left[-(-2)\right] = 5 \cdot 2 = 10$

   d. $-x - y = -5 - (-2) = -5 + 2 = -3$

10. a. $xy = (-9)(7) = -63$

    b. $x(-y) = (-9)(-7) = 63$

    c. $x - y = -9 - 7 = -9 + (-7) = -16$

    d. $-x - y = -(-9) - 7 = 9 + (-7) = 2$

11. The product $(8)(4)(-5)$ is negative since there is an odd number (1) of negatives.

12. The product $(-9)(-12)(20)$ will be positive since there is an even number of negatives (2).

13. The product $(-102)(-16)(24)(19)$ is positive since there is an even number of negatives.

14. The product $(1054)(-92)(-16)(-37)$ will be negative since there is an odd number of negatives (3).

15. The product $(-40)(-16)(30)(50)(-13)$ is negative since there is an odd number (3) of negatives.

16. The product $(-1)(3)(-462)(-196)(-312)$ will be positive since there is an even number (4) of negatives.

17. Since the numbers have like signs, the product is positive. $(-5)(-4) = 20$

18. Since the numbers have unlike signs, the product is negative. $-4(2) = -8$

19. Since the number have unlike signs, the product is negative. $6(-3) = -18$

20. Since the numbers have unlike signs, the product is negative. $6(-2) = -12$

21. Since the numbers have like signs, the product is positive. $(-8)(-10) = 80$

22. Since the numbers have unlike signs, the product is negative. $(-3)(2) = -6$

23. Since the numbers have unlike signs, the product is negative. $-2.1(6) = -12.6$

24. Since the numbers have unlike signs, the product is negative. $-1(8.7) = -8.7$

25. Since the numbers have like signs, the product is positive. $6(7) = 42$

26. Since the numbers have like signs, the product is positive. $-9(-4) = 36$

27. Since the numbers have unlike signs, the product is negative. $9(-9) = -81$

28. Since the numbers have unlike signs, the product is negative. $(7)(-8) = -56$

29. Since the numbers have like signs, the product is positive. $(-5)(-6) = 30$

30. Zero multiplied by any real number equals zero. $0(-5) = 0$

31. Zero multiplied by any real number equals zero. $(-9)(0)(-6) = 0(-6) = 0$

32. Since there is one negative number (an odd number), the product will be negative.
$5(-4)(2) = (-20)(2) = -40$

33. Since there is one negative number (an odd number), the product will be negative.
$(21)(-1)(4) = (-21)(4) = -84$

34. Since there are two negative numbers (an even number), the product will be positive.
$2(8)(-1)(-3) = 16(-1)(-3) = -16(-3) = 48$

35. Since there are three negative numbers (an odd number), the product will be negative.
$-1(-3)(3)(-8) = 3(3)(-8) = 9(-8) = -72$

36. Since there are three negative numbers (an odd number), the product will be negative.
$$(2)(-4)(-5)(-1) = (-8)(-5)(-1)$$
$$= (40)(-1)$$
$$= -40$$

37. Since there are two negative numbers (an even number), the product will be positive.
$$(-4)(5)(-7)(1) = (-20)(-7)(1)$$
$$= (140)(1)$$
$$= 140$$

38. Since there is one negative number (an odd number), the product will be negative.
$$(-3)(2)(5)(3) = (-6)(5)(3) = (-30)(3) = -90$$

39. Zero multiplied by any real number equals zero. $(-1)(3)(0)(-7) = (-3)(0)(-7) = 0(-7) = 0$

40. Since there are two negative numbers (an even number), the product will be positive.
$$(-6)(6)(4)(-4) = (-36)(4)(-4)$$
$$= (-144)(-4)$$
$$= 576$$

41. $\left(\dfrac{-1}{2}\right)\left(\dfrac{3}{5}\right) = \dfrac{(-1)(3)}{2 \cdot 5} = \dfrac{-3}{10} = -\dfrac{3}{10}$

42. $\left(\dfrac{1}{3}\right)\left(\dfrac{-3}{5}\right) = \left(\dfrac{1}{\cancel{3}_1}\right)\left(\dfrac{-\cancel{3}^1}{5}\right) = \dfrac{(1)(-1)}{1 \cdot 5} = \dfrac{-1}{5} = -\dfrac{1}{5}$

43. $\left(\dfrac{-5}{9}\right)\left(\dfrac{-7}{15}\right) = \left(\dfrac{-\cancel{5}^1}{9}\right)\left(\dfrac{-7}{\cancel{15}_3}\right) = \dfrac{(-1)(-7)}{9 \cdot 3} = \dfrac{7}{27}$

44. $\left(\dfrac{4}{5}\right)\left(\dfrac{-3}{10}\right) = \left(\dfrac{^2\cancel{4}}{5}\right)\left(\dfrac{-3}{\cancel{10}_5}\right) = \dfrac{2(-3)}{5(5)} = -\dfrac{6}{25}$

45. $\left(\dfrac{6}{-3}\right)\left(\dfrac{4}{-2}\right) = (-2)(-2) = 4$

46. $\left(\dfrac{9}{-10}\right)\left(\dfrac{6}{-7}\right) = \left(\dfrac{9}{-\cancel{10}_5}\right)\left(\dfrac{\cancel{6}^3}{-7}\right)$
$$= \dfrac{(9)(3)}{(-5)(-7)}$$
$$= \dfrac{27}{35}$$

47. $\left(\dfrac{3}{4}\right)\left(\dfrac{-2}{15}\right) = \left(\dfrac{^1\cancel{3}}{_2\cancel{4}}\right)\left(\dfrac{-\cancel{2}^1}{\cancel{15}_5}\right)$
$$= \dfrac{(1)(-1)}{(2)(5)}$$
$$= \dfrac{-1}{10} = -\dfrac{1}{10}$$

48. $\left(\dfrac{9}{10}\right)\left(\dfrac{7}{-8}\right) = \dfrac{(9)(7)}{(10)(-8)} = \dfrac{63}{-80} = -\dfrac{63}{80}$

49. Since the numbers have like signs, the quotient is positive. $\dfrac{42}{6} = 7$

50. Since the numbers have like signs, the quotient is positive. $25 \div (5) = \dfrac{25}{5} = 5$

51. Since the numbers have like signs, the quotient is positive. $-16 \div (-4) = \dfrac{-16}{-4} = 4$

52. Since the numbers have unlike signs, the quotient is negative $\dfrac{-18}{9} = -2$

53. Since the numbers have like signs, the quotient is positive. $\dfrac{-36}{-9} = 4$

54. Since the numbers have unlike signs, the quotient is negative. $\dfrac{30}{-6} = -5$

55. Since the numbers have unlike signs, the quotient is negative. $\dfrac{36}{-2} = -18$

56. Since the numbers have like signs, the quotient is positive. $\dfrac{-15}{-1} = 15$

57. Since the numbers have like signs, the quotient is positive. $\dfrac{-19.8}{-2} = 9.9$

58. Since the numbers have like signs, the quotient is positive. $-15.6/(-3) = \dfrac{-15.6}{-3} = 5.2$

59. Since the numbers have unlike signs, the quotient is negative. $40/(-4) = \dfrac{40}{-4} = -10$

60. Since the numbers have unlike signs, the quotient is negative. $\dfrac{63}{-7} = -9$

61. Since the numbers have unlike signs, the quotient is negative. $\dfrac{-66}{11} = -6$

62. Since the numbers have like signs, the quotient is positive. $\dfrac{-25}{-5} = 5$

63. Since the numbers have unlike signs, the quotient is negative. $\dfrac{48}{-6} = -8$

64. Since the numbers have unlike signs, the quotient is negative. $\dfrac{-10}{10} = -1$

65. Since the numbers have like signs, the quotient is positive. $-64.8 \div (-4) = \dfrac{-64.8}{-4} = 16.2$

66. Since the numbers have like signs, the quotient is positive. $-86.4/(-2) = \dfrac{-86.4}{-2} = 43.2$

67. Zero divided by any nonzero number is zero. $\dfrac{0}{4} = 0$

68. Since the numbers have unlike signs, the quotient is negative. $\dfrac{26}{-13} = -2$

69. Since the numbers have unlike signs, the quotient is negative. $\dfrac{30.8}{-5.6} = -5.5$

70. Since the numbers have unlike signs, the quotient is negative. $\dfrac{-67.64}{7.6} = -8.9$

71. Since the numbers have like signs, the quotient is positive. $\dfrac{-30}{-5} = 6$

72. Since the numbers have like signs, the quotient is positive. $\dfrac{-36}{-6} = 6$

73. $\dfrac{3}{12} \div \left(\dfrac{-5}{8}\right) = \dfrac{3}{12} \cdot \left(\dfrac{8}{-5}\right)$
$= \dfrac{1}{\cancel{12}_{1}} \cdot \left(\dfrac{\cancel{8}^{2}}{-5}\right)$
$= \dfrac{1 \cdot 2}{1(-5)}$
$= \dfrac{2}{-5} = -\dfrac{2}{5}$

74. $4 \div \left(-\dfrac{6}{13}\right) = \dfrac{\cancel{4}^{2}}{1} \cdot \dfrac{-13}{\cancel{6}_{3}}$
$= \dfrac{(2)(-13)}{1(3)}$
$= \dfrac{-26}{3} = -\dfrac{26}{3}$ or $-8\dfrac{2}{3}$

75. $\dfrac{-5}{12} \div (-3) = \dfrac{-5}{12} \cdot \dfrac{1}{-3} = \dfrac{-5(1)}{12(-3)} = \dfrac{-5}{-36} = \dfrac{5}{36}$

76. $\dfrac{6}{15} \div \dfrac{7}{30} = \dfrac{6}{\cancel{15}_1} \cdot \dfrac{\cancel{30}^2}{7} = \dfrac{6}{1} \cdot \dfrac{2}{7} = \dfrac{6 \cdot 2}{1 \cdot 7} = \dfrac{12}{7}$ or $1\dfrac{5}{7}$

77. $\dfrac{-15}{21} \div \left(\dfrac{-15}{21}\right) = \dfrac{-\cancel{15}^1}{_1\cancel{21}} \cdot \dfrac{\cancel{21}^1}{-\cancel{15}_1}$

$= \dfrac{(-1)(1)}{(1)(-1)}$

$= \dfrac{-1}{-1}$

$= 1$

78. $\dfrac{-4}{9} \div \left(\dfrac{-6}{7}\right) = \dfrac{-\cancel{4}^2}{9} \cdot \dfrac{7}{-\cancel{6}_3}$

$= \dfrac{(-2)(7)}{(9)(-3)}$

$= \dfrac{-14}{-27} = \dfrac{14}{27}$

79. $-12 \div \dfrac{5}{12} = \dfrac{-12}{1} \cdot \dfrac{12}{5}$

$= \dfrac{(-12)(12)}{(1)(5)}$

$= \dfrac{-144}{5}$

$= -\dfrac{144}{5}$

80. $\dfrac{-16}{3} \div \left(\dfrac{5}{-9}\right) = \dfrac{-16}{_1\cancel{3}} \cdot \dfrac{-\cancel{9}^3}{5}$

$= \dfrac{(-16)(-3)}{(1)(5)}$

$= \dfrac{48}{5}$

81. Since the numbers have unlike signs, the product is negative. $-4(8) = -32$

82. Since the numbers have like signs, the quotient is positive. $\dfrac{-18}{-2} = 9$

83. Since the numbers have like signs, the quotient is positive. $\dfrac{-100}{-5} = 20$

84. Since the numbers have like signs, the quotient is positive. $-50 \div (-10) = \dfrac{-50}{-10} = 5$

85. Since the numbers have unlike signs, the product is negative. $-7(2) = -14$

86. Since the numbers have unlike signs, the product is negative. $6.4(-8) = -51.2$

87. Since the numbers have unlike signs, the quotient is negative. $27.9 \div (-3) = \dfrac{27.9}{-3} = -9.3$

88. Since the numbers have unlike signs, the quotient is negative. $\dfrac{130}{-10} = -13$

89. Since the numbers have unlike signs, the quotient is negative. $\dfrac{-100}{5} = -20$

90. Since there are three negative signs (an odd number), the product is negative.
$4(-2)(-1)(-5) = (-8)(-1)(-5) = (8)(-5) = -40$

91. Since the numbers have like signs, the quotient is positive. $\dfrac{-90}{-90} = 1$

92. Since there is one negative sign (an odd number) the product is negative.
$(6)(1)(-3)(4) = (6)(-3)(4) = (-18)(4) = -72$

93. Zero divided by any nonzero number is zero.
$0 \div 8.6 = \dfrac{0}{8.6} = 0$

94. Any nonzero number divided zero is undefined.
$\dfrac{-2.7}{0}$ is undefined.

95. Any nonzero number divided by zero is undefined. $\dfrac{5}{0}$ is undefined.

96. Zero divided by any nonzero number is zero.

$$\frac{0}{1} = 0$$

97. Zero divided by any nonzero number is zero.

$$0 \div (-7) = \frac{0}{-7} = 0$$

98. Any nonzero number divided by zero is undefined. $\frac{6}{0}$ is undefined.

99. Any nonzero number divided by zero is undefined. $\frac{8}{0}$ is undefined.

100. Zero divided by any nonzero number is zero.

$$\frac{0}{12} = 0$$

101. a. Since the numbers have unlike signs, the product will be negative.
   b. $92(-38) = -3496$
   c. Yes; as expected the product is negative.

102. a. Since the numbers have unlike signs, the quotient will be negative.
   b. $\dfrac{-168}{42} = -4$
   c. Yes; as expected the quotient is negative.

103. a. Since the numbers have unlike signs, the quotient will be negative.
   b. $-240/15 = \dfrac{-240}{15} = -16$
   c. Yes; as expected the quotient is negative.

104. a. Zero divided by any nonzero number is zero.
   b. $0/12 = \dfrac{0}{12} = 0$
   c. Yes; as expected, the quotient is zero.

105. a. Since the numbers have unlike signs, the quotient will be negative.
   b. $243 \div (-27) = \dfrac{243}{-27} = -9$
   c. Yes; as expected the quotient is negative.

106. a. Since the numbers have unlike signs, the product will be negative.
   b. $(323)(-115) = -37,145$
   c. Yes; as expected the product is negative.

107. a. Since the numbers have like signs, the product will be positive.
   b. $(-49)(-126) = 6174$
   c. Yes; as expected the product is positive.

108. a. The product will be zero; zero multiplied by any real number is zero.
   b. $(1530)(0) = 0$
   c. Yes; as expected the product is zero.

109. a. The quotient will be zero; zero divided by any nonzero number is zero.
   b. $\dfrac{0}{5335} = 0$
   c. Yes; as expected the answer is zero.

110. a. Since the numbers have like signs, the quotient will be positive.
   b. $-86.4 \div (-36) = \dfrac{-86.4}{-36} = 2.4$
   c. Yes; as expected the answer is positive.

111. a. Undefined; any nonzero number divided by 0 is undefined.
   b. $8.2 \div 0 = \dfrac{8.2}{0}$ is undefined.
   c. Yes; as expected the quotient is undefined.

112. a. The quotient will be zero; zero divided by any nonzero number is zero.
   b. $-37.74 \div 0 = \dfrac{-37.74}{0}$ is undefined
   c. Yes; as expected the quotient is undefined.

113. a. Since the numbers have like signs, the quotient will be positive.
   b. $8 \div 2.5 = \dfrac{8}{2.5} = 3.2$
   c. Yes; as expected the quotient is positive.

114. **a.** Since there are no negative numbers, the product will be positive.

   b. $(1.1)(9.72)(6.3) = 67.3596$

   c. Yes; as expected the product is positive.

115. **a.** Since there are two negative numbers (an even number), the product will be positive.

   b. $(-3.0)(4.2)(-18) = 226.8$

   c. Yes; as expected the product is positive.

116. **a.** Since the numbers have unlike signs, the quotient will be negative.

   b. $-288.86/1.43 = \dfrac{-288.86}{1.43} = -202$

   c. Yes; as expected the quotient is negative.

117. False; the product of two numbers with like signs is a positive number

118. True; the product of two numbers with unlike signs is a negative number.

119. False; the quotient of two numbers with unlike signs is a negative number.

120. True; the quotient of two numbers with like signs is a positive number.

121. True; the quotient of two numbers with like signs is a positive number.

123. True

122. False; zero divided by any nonzero number is zero.

124. False; six divided by 0 is undefined.

125. False; zero divided by 1 is zero.

126. True

127. True; any nonzero number divided by zero is undefined.

128. True: any nonzero number divided by zero is undefined.

129. $3(-15) = -45$
The total loss was 45 yards.

130. $3(-160) = -480$
Its new depth is 480 feet below sea level.

131. **a.** $\dfrac{1}{5}(520) = \dfrac{520}{5} = 104$
She paid back $104.

   b. $-520 + 104 = -416$
Her new balance is –$416.

132. $4(40) - 500 = 160 + (-500) = -340$
He will still owe $340.

133. Find out how much is left after giving the husbands each $50.
$775.40 - (4 \cdot 50) = 775.40 - 200 = 575.40$
Now take the remainder and divide it by 4.
$\dfrac{575.40}{4} = 143.85$
Each woman receives $143.85.

134. $\dfrac{1}{3}(-30) = \dfrac{-30}{3} = \dfrac{-10}{1} = -10$
The wind chill was –10°F on Tuesday.

135. **a.** $5(-4) = -20$
Josue lost 20 points.

   b. $100 - 20 = 80$
His test score is 80.

136. **a.** The result is 1 divided by the number in decimal form.

   b. The result is the original number.

   c. You should get an error message since $\dfrac{1}{0}$ is undefined.

   d. You get an error message.

137. **a.** $220 - 50 = 170$
$60\% \text{ of } 170 = 0.6(170) = 102$
$75\% \text{ of } 170 = 0.75(170) = 127.5$
Target heart rate is 102 to 128 beats per minute.

   b. Answers will vary.

138. $3^4 = 3 \cdot 3 \cdot 3 \cdot 3 = 81$

139. $(-5)^3 = (-5)(-5)(-5) = 25(-5) = -125$

140. $\left(\dfrac{2}{3}\right)^3 = \dfrac{2}{3} \cdot \dfrac{2}{3} \cdot \dfrac{2}{3} = \dfrac{2 \cdot 2 \cdot 2}{3 \cdot 3 \cdot 3} = \dfrac{8}{27}$

141. $1^{100} = 1$

142. $(-1)^{81} = -1$ since 81 is odd

143. The product $(-1)(-2)(-3)(-4)\cdots(-10)$ will be positive because there are an even number (10) of negative numbers.

144. The product will be negative since there are an odd number (17) of negatives.

145. The country will start with D. Most students will select Denmark. They will most likely select kangaroo which leads to orange.

146. $|-3.6| > |-2.7|$

147. $\begin{aligned}-\dfrac{7}{12}+\left(-\dfrac{1}{10}\right) &= -\dfrac{35}{60}+\left(-\dfrac{6}{60}\right)\\ &= \dfrac{-35+(-6)}{60}\\ &= -\dfrac{41}{60}\end{aligned}$

148. $-20-(-18) = -20+18 = -2$

149. $6-3-4-2 = 3-4-2 = -1-2 = -3$

150. $\begin{aligned}5-(-2)+3-7 &= 5+2+3-7\\ &= 7+3-7\\ &= 10-7\\ &= 3\end{aligned}$

Exercise Set 1.9

1. In the expression a^b, a is the base and b is the exponent.

2. **a.** 3^2 means 2 factors of 3.

   b. 5^4 means 4 factors of 5.

   c. x^n means n factors of x.

3. **a.** Every number has an understood exponent of 1.

   b. In $5x^3y^2z$, 5 has exponent of 1, x has an exponent of 3, y has an exponent of 2, and z has an exponent of 1.

4. **a.** $x+x+x+x+x = 5x$

   b. $x \cdot x \cdot x \cdot x \cdot x = x^5$

5. **a.** $y+y+y+y = 4y$

   b. $y \cdot y \cdot y \cdot y = y^4$

6. **a.** $-x^2$ means $-\left(x^2\right)$. If x is a non-zero real number, then x^2 is positive and $-x^2$ is negative.

   b. $(-x)^2$ means $(-x)(-x)$. The product is positive when $x > 0$ or $x < 0$ since the factors have the same sign.

7. The order of operations are parentheses, exponents, multiplication or division, then addition or subtraction.

8. An expression with only additions or subtractions or only multiplications and divisions is evaluated from left to right.

9. No; $4+5\times2 = 4+10 = 14$, on a scientific calculator.

10. Parentheses are used in an expression to either change the order of operations or to clarify the expression.

11. **a.** $15-10\div5 = 15-2 = 13$

   b. $(15-10)\div5 = 5\div5 = 1$

   c. The keystrokes in b) are used since the fraction bar is a grouping symbol.

12. **a.** $20\div5-3 = 4-3 = 1$

   b. $20\div(5-3) = 20\div2 = 10$

   c. The keystrokes in b) are used since the fraction bar is a grouping symbol.

13. **b.** $\begin{aligned}\left[10-(16\div4)\right]^2-6^3 &= \left[10-4\right]^2-6^3\\ &= 6^2-6^3\\ &= 36-216\\ &= -180\end{aligned}$

14. **b.** $\begin{aligned}\left[(8\cdot3)-4^2\right]^2-5 &= \left[24-16\right]^2-5\\ &= 8^2-5\\ &= 64-5\\ &= 59\end{aligned}$

15. b. When $x = 5$:
$$-4x^2 + 3x - 6 = -4(5)^2 + 3(5) - 6$$
$$= -4(25) + 3(5) - 6$$
$$= -100 + 15 - 6$$
$$= -85 - 6$$
$$= -91$$

16. b. When $x = -2$:
$$-5x^2 - 2x + 8 = -5(-2)^2 - 2(-2) + 8$$
$$= -5(4) - 2(-2) + 8$$
$$= -20 + 4 + 8$$
$$= -16 + 8$$
$$= -8$$

17. $5^2 = 5 \cdot 5 = 25$

18. $2^3 = 2 \cdot 2 \cdot 2 = 8$

19. $1^7 = 1 \cdot 1 \cdot 1 \cdot 1 \cdot 1 \cdot 1 \cdot 1 = 1$

20. $4^1 = 4$

21. $-8^2 = -(8)(8) = -64$

22. $7^3 = 7 \cdot 7 \cdot 7 = 343$

23. $(-3)^2 = (-3)(-3) = 9$

24. $-6^3 = -(6)(6)(6) = -216$

25. $(-1)^3 = (-1)(-1)(-1) = -1$

26. $2^5 = 2 \cdot 2 \cdot 2 \cdot 2 \cdot 2 = 32$

27. $-10^2 = -(10)(10) = -100$

28. $5^3 = 5 \cdot 5 \cdot 5 = 125$

29. $(-9)^2 = (-9)(-9) = 81$

30. $(-3)^3 = (-3)(-3)(-3) = -27$

31. $3^3 = 3 \cdot 3 \cdot 3 = 27$

32. $-7^2 = -(7)(7) = -49$

33. $(-4)^4 = (-4)(-4)(-4)(-4) = 256$

34. $-4^4 = -(4)(4)(4)(4) = -256$

35. $-2^4 = -(2)(2)(2)(2) = -16$

36. $3^2(4)^2 = (3)(3)(4)(4) = 144$

37. $\left(\dfrac{3}{4}\right)^2 = \dfrac{3}{4} \cdot \dfrac{3}{4} = \dfrac{9}{16}$

38. $\left(\dfrac{5}{8}\right)^3 = \dfrac{5}{8} \cdot \dfrac{5}{8} \cdot \dfrac{5}{8} = \dfrac{125}{512}$

39. $\left(-\dfrac{1}{2}\right)^5 = \left(-\dfrac{1}{2}\right)\left(-\dfrac{1}{2}\right)\left(-\dfrac{1}{2}\right)\left(-\dfrac{1}{2}\right)\left(-\dfrac{1}{2}\right)$
$$= -\dfrac{1}{32}$$

40. $\left(-\dfrac{2}{3}\right)^4 = \left(-\dfrac{2}{3}\right)\left(-\dfrac{2}{3}\right)\left(-\dfrac{2}{3}\right)\left(-\dfrac{2}{3}\right) = \dfrac{16}{81}$

41. $5^2 \cdot 3^2 = 5 \cdot 5 \cdot 3 \cdot 3 = 225$

42. $(-1)^4(2)^4 = (-1)(-1)(-1)(-1)(2)(2)(2)(2)$
$$= 16$$

43. $4^3 \cdot 3^2 = 4 \cdot 4 \cdot 4 \cdot 3 \cdot 3 = 576$

44. $(-2)^3(-1)^9 = (-2)(-2)(-2)(-1)(-1)(-1)$
$$(-1)(-1)(-1)(-1)(-1)(-1) = 8$$

45. a. Positive; a positive number raised to any power is positive.

    b. $7^3 = 343$

    c. Yes; as expected the answer is positive.

46. a. Positive; a positive number raised to any power is positive.

    b. $4^6 = 4096$

    c. Yes; as expected the answer is positive.

47. a. Positive; a positive number raised to any power is positive.

    b. $6^4 = 1296$

    c. Yes; as expected the answer is positive.

48. a. Negative; 2^5 is positive so $-\left(2^5\right)$ is negative.

b. $-2^5 = -32$

c. Yes; as expected the answer is negative.

49. a. Negative; a negative number raised to an odd power is negative.

b. $(-3)^5 = -243$

c. Yes; as expected the answer is negative.

50. a. Positive; a positive number raised to any power is positive.

b. $10^3 = 1000$

c. Yes; as expected the answer is positive.

51. a. Positive; a negative number raised to an even power is positive.

b. $(-5)^4 = 625$

c. Yes; as expected the answer is positive.

52. a. Positive; a positive number raised to any power is positive.

b. $(1.3)^3 = 2.197$

c. Yes; as expected the answer is positive.

53. a. Negative; the opposite of a positive number is negative..

b. $-(-9)^2 = -(-9)(-9) = -81$

c. Yes; as expected the answer is negative.

54. a. Negative; a negative number raised to an odd power is negative.

b. $(-3.3)^3 = -35.937$

c. Yes; as expected the answer is negative.

55. a. Negative; $\left(\dfrac{3}{8}\right)^2$ is positive therefore,

$-\left(\dfrac{3}{8}\right)^2$ is negative.

b. $-\left(\dfrac{3}{8}\right)^2 = -0.140625$

c. Yes; as expected the answer is negative.

56. a. Negative; a negative number raised to an odd power is negative.

b. $\left(-\dfrac{3}{4}\right)^3 = -0.421875$

c. Yes; as expected the answer is negative.

57. $3 + 2 \cdot 6 = 3 + 12 = 15$

58. $7 - 5^2 + 2 = 7 - 25 + 2 = -18 + 2 = -16$

59. $6 - 6 + 8 = 0 + 8 = 8$

60. $\left(8^2 \div 4\right) - (20 - 4) = (64 \div 4) - (20 - 4)$
$$= 16 - 16$$
$$= 0$$

61. $-7 + 2 \cdot 6^2 - 8 = -7 + 2 \cdot 36 - 8$
$$= -7 + 72 - 8$$
$$= 65 - 8$$
$$= 57$$

62. $6 + 2 \cdot 3^2 - 10 = 6 + 2 \cdot 9 - 10$
$$= 6 + 18 - 10$$
$$= 24 - 10$$
$$= 14$$

63. $-3^3 + 27 = -27 + 27 = 0$

64. $(-2)^3 + 8 \div 4 = -8 + 8 \div 4 = -8 + 2 = -6$

65. $(4 - 3) \cdot (5 - 1)^2 = (1) \cdot (4)^2 = 1 \cdot 16 = 16$

66. $-10 - 6 - 3 - 2 = -16 - 3 - 2 = -19 - 2 = -21$

67. $3 \cdot 7 + 4 \cdot 2 = 21 + 8 = 29$

68. $4^2 - 3 \cdot 4 - 6 = 16 - 3 \cdot 4 - 6$
$$= 16 - 12 - 6$$
$$= 4 - 6$$
$$= -2$$

69. $5 - 2(7 + 5) = 5 - 2(12) = 5 - 24 = -19$

70. $8 + 3(6 + 4) = 8 + 3(10) = 8 + 30 = 38$

71. $-32 - 5(7-10)^2 = -32 - 5(-3)^2$
$$= -32 - 5(9)$$
$$= -32 - 45$$
$$= -77$$

72. $-40 - 3(4-8)^2 = -40 - 3(-4)^2$
$$= -40 - 3(16)$$
$$= -40 - 48$$
$$= -88$$

73. $\dfrac{3}{4} + 2\left(\dfrac{1}{5}\right)^2 = \dfrac{3}{4} + 2\left(\dfrac{1}{25}\right)$
$$= \dfrac{3}{4} + \dfrac{2}{25}$$
$$= \dfrac{75}{100} + \dfrac{8}{100}$$
$$= \dfrac{83}{100}$$

74. $-\dfrac{2}{3} - 3\left(\dfrac{3}{4}\right)^2 = -\dfrac{2}{3} - 3\left(\dfrac{9}{16}\right)$
$$= -\dfrac{2}{3} - \dfrac{27}{16}$$
$$= -\dfrac{32}{48} - \dfrac{81}{48}$$
$$= -\dfrac{113}{48} \ \text{ or } \ -2\dfrac{17}{48}$$

75. $-4 + 3\left[-1 + \left(12 \div 2^2\right)\right] = -4 + 3\left[-1 + (12 \div 4)\right]$
$$= -4 + 3[-1+3]$$
$$= -4 + 3[2]$$
$$= -4 + 6$$
$$= 2$$

76. $-2 + 4\left[-3 + \left(48 \div 4^2\right)\right] = -2 + 4\left[-3 + (48 \div 16)\right]$
$$= -2 + 4[-3+3]$$
$$= -2 + 4[0]$$
$$= -2 + 0$$
$$= -2$$

77. $(6 \div 3)^3 + 4^2 \div 8 = (2)^3 + 4^2 \div 8$
$$= 8 + 16 \div 8$$
$$= 8 + 2$$
$$= 10$$

78. $4 + \left(4^2 - 13\right)^4 - 3 = 4 + (16-13)^4 - 3$
$$= 4 + 3^4 - 3$$
$$= 4 + 81 - 3$$
$$= 85 - 3$$
$$= 82$$

79. $-7 - 48 \div 6 \cdot 2^2 + 5 = -7 - 48 \div 6 \cdot 4 + 5$
$$= -7 - 8 \cdot 4 + 5$$
$$= -7 - 32 + 5$$
$$= -39 + 5$$
$$= -34$$

80. $-7 - 56 \div 7 \cdot 2^2 + 4 = -7 - 56 \div 7 \cdot 4 + 4$
$$= -7 - 8 \cdot 4 + 4$$
$$= -7 - 32 + 4$$
$$= -39 + 4$$
$$= -35$$

81. $(9 \div 3) + 4(7-2)^2 = (9 \div 3) + 4(5)^2$
$$= (9 \div 3) + 4(25)$$
$$= 3 + 100$$
$$= 103$$

82. $(12 \div 4) + 5(6-4)^2 = (12 \div 4) + 5(2)^2$
$$= (12 \div 4) + 5(4)$$
$$= 3 + 20$$
$$= 23$$

83. $[4 + ((5-2)^2 \div 3)^2]^2 = [4 + ((3)^2 \div 3)^2]^2$
$$= [4 + (9 \div 3)^2]^2$$
$$= [4 + (3)^2]^2$$
$$= [4 + 9]^2$$
$$= (13)^2$$
$$= 169$$

84. $(20 \div 5 \cdot 5 \div 5 - 5)^2 = (4 \cdot 5 \div 5 - 5)^2$
$= (20 \div 5 - 5)^2$
$= (4 - 5)^2$
$= (-1)^2$
$= 1$

85. $(-3)^2 + 8 \div 2 = 9 + 8 \div 2$
$= 9 + 4$
$= 13$

86. $-3^2 + 8 \div 2 = -9 + 8 \div 2$
$= -9 + 4$
$= -5$

87. $2[1.55 + 5(3.7)] - 3.35 = 2[1.55 + 18.5] - 3.35$
$= 2(20.05) - 3.35$
$= 40.1 - 3.35$
$= 36.75$

88. $(8.4 + 3.1)^2 - (3.64 - 1.2) = (11.5)^2 - (2.44)$
$= 132.25 - 2.44$
$= 129.81$

89. $\left(\frac{2}{5} + \frac{3}{8}\right) - \frac{3}{20} = \left(\frac{16}{40} + \frac{15}{40}\right) - \frac{3}{20}$
$= \frac{31}{40} - \frac{3}{20}$
$= \frac{31}{40} - \frac{6}{40}$
$= \frac{25}{40} = \frac{5}{8}$

90. $\left(\frac{5}{6} \cdot \frac{4}{5}\right) + \left(\frac{2}{3} \cdot \frac{5}{8}\right) = \left(\frac{1}{3} \cdot \frac{2}{1}\right) + \left(\frac{1}{3} \cdot \frac{5}{4}\right)$
$= \frac{2}{3} + \frac{5}{12}$
$= \frac{8}{12} + \frac{5}{12}$
$= \frac{13}{12}$ or $1\frac{1}{12}$

91. $\frac{3}{4} - 4 \cdot \frac{5}{40} = \frac{3}{4} - \frac{4}{1} \cdot \frac{5}{40} = \frac{3}{4} - \frac{1}{2} = \frac{3}{4} - \frac{2}{4} = \frac{1}{4}$

92. $\frac{1}{8} - \frac{1}{4} \cdot \frac{3}{2} + \frac{3}{5} = \frac{1}{8} - \frac{3}{8} + \frac{3}{5}$
$= -\frac{2}{8} + \frac{3}{5}$
$= -\frac{10}{40} + \frac{24}{40}$
$= \frac{14}{40} = \frac{7}{20}$

93. $\frac{4}{5} + \frac{3}{4} \div \frac{1}{2} - \frac{2}{3} = \frac{4}{5} + \frac{3}{4} \cdot \frac{2}{1} - \frac{2}{3}$
$= \frac{4}{5} + \frac{3}{2} - \frac{2}{3}$
$= \frac{24}{30} + \frac{45}{30} - \frac{20}{30}$
$= \frac{49}{30}$

94. $\frac{12 - (4-6)^2}{6 + 4^2 \div 2^2} = \frac{12 - (-2)^2}{6 + 4^2 \div 2^2}$
$= \frac{12 - 4}{6 + 16 \div 4}$
$= \frac{12 - 4}{6 + 4}$
$= \frac{8}{10} = \frac{4}{5}$

95. $\frac{-4 - [2(9 \div 3) - 5]}{6^2 - 3^2 \cdot 7} = \frac{-4 - [2(3) - 5]}{36 - 9 \cdot 7}$
$= \frac{-4 - [6 - 5]}{36 - 63}$
$= \frac{-4 - 1}{-27}$
$= \frac{-5}{-27} = \frac{5}{27}$

96. $\frac{[(7-3)^2 - 4]^2}{9 - 16 \div 8 - 4} = \frac{[4^2 - 4]^2}{9 - 16 \div 8 - 4}$
$= \frac{[16 - 4]^2}{9 - 2 - 4}$
$= \frac{(12)^2}{7 - 4}$
$= \frac{144}{3}$
$= 48$

97. $\dfrac{-[4-(6-12)^2]}{[(9\div3)+4]^2+2^2}=\dfrac{-[4-(-6)^2]}{(3+4)^2+4}$

$\qquad\qquad\qquad = \dfrac{-[4-36]}{7^2+4}$

$\qquad\qquad\qquad = \dfrac{-(-32)}{49+4}$

$\qquad\qquad\qquad = \dfrac{32}{53}$

98. $\dfrac{[5-(3-7)-2]^2}{2\left[(16\div2^2)-(8\cdot4)\right]}=\dfrac{[5-(-4)-2]^2}{2\left[(16\div4)-32\right]}$

$\qquad\qquad\qquad = \dfrac{[5+4-2]^2}{2[4-32]}$

$\qquad\qquad\qquad = \dfrac{(7)^2}{2(-28)}$

$\qquad\qquad\qquad = \dfrac{49}{-56}=-\dfrac{7}{8}$

99. $\left\{5-2\left[4-(6\div2)\right]^2\right\}^2=\left\{5-2[4-3]^2\right\}^2$

$\qquad\qquad\qquad = \left\{5-2(1)^2\right\}^2$

$\qquad\qquad\qquad = \left\{5-2(1)\right\}^2$

$\qquad\qquad\qquad = \left\{5-2\right\}^2$

$\qquad\qquad\qquad = (3)^2$

$\qquad\qquad\qquad = 9$

100. $\left\{-6-\left[3\left(16\div4^2\right)^2\right]\right\}^2=\left\{-6-\left[3(16\div16)^2\right]\right\}^2$

$\qquad\qquad\qquad = \left\{-6-\left[3(1)^2\right]\right\}^2$

$\qquad\qquad\qquad = \left\{-6-\left[3(1)\right]\right\}^2$

$\qquad\qquad\qquad = \left\{-6-3\right\}^2$

$\qquad\qquad\qquad = (-9)^2$

$\qquad\qquad\qquad = 81$

101. $-\left\{4-\left[-3-(2-5)\right]^2\right\}=-\left\{4-\left[-3-(-3)\right]^2\right\}$

$\qquad\qquad\qquad = -\left\{4-[-3+3]^2\right\}$

$\qquad\qquad\qquad = -\left\{4-[0]^2\right\}$

$\qquad\qquad\qquad = -\left\{4-0\right\}$

$\qquad\qquad\qquad = -(4)$

$\qquad\qquad\qquad = -4$

102. $3\left\{4\left[(3-4)^2-3\right]^3-1\right\}=3\left\{4\left[(-1)^2-3\right]^3-1\right\}$

$\qquad\qquad\qquad = 3\left\{4[1-3]^3-1\right\}$

$\qquad\qquad\qquad = 3\left\{4[-2]^3-1\right\}$

$\qquad\qquad\qquad = 3\left\{4(-8)-1\right\}$

$\qquad\qquad\qquad = 3\left\{-32-1\right\}$

$\qquad\qquad\qquad = 3(-33)$

$\qquad\qquad\qquad = -99$

103. $\left\{4-3\left[2-(9\div3)\right]^2\right\}^2=\left\{4-3[2-3]^2\right\}^2$

$\qquad\qquad\qquad = \left\{4-3[-1]^2\right\}^2$

$\qquad\qquad\qquad = \left\{4-3[1]\right\}^2$

$\qquad\qquad\qquad = \left\{4-3\right\}^2$

$\qquad\qquad\qquad = 1^2$

$\qquad\qquad\qquad = 1$

104. $2\left\{5\left[(4-6)^3-1\right]^2-3\right\}=2\left\{5\left[(-2)^3-1\right]^2-3\right\}$

$\qquad\qquad\qquad = 2\left\{5[-8-1]^2-3\right\}$

$\qquad\qquad\qquad = 2\left\{5[-9]^2-3\right\}$

$\qquad\qquad\qquad = 2\left\{5[81]-3\right\}$

$\qquad\qquad\qquad = 2\left\{405-3\right\}$

$\qquad\qquad\qquad = 2\left\{402\right\}$

$\qquad\qquad\qquad = 804$

105. Substitute 5 for x

a. $x^2=5^2=5\cdot5=25$

b. $-x^2=-5^2=-(5)(5)=-25$

c. $(-5)^2=(-5)^2=(-5)(-5)=25$

106. Substitute 8 for x

a. $x^2=8^2=8\cdot8=64$

b. $-x^2=-8^2=-(8)(8)=-64$

c. $(-x)^2=(-8)^2=(-8)(-8)=64$

107. Substitute -2 for x

   a. $x^2 = (-2)^2 = (-2)(-2) = 4$

   b. $-x^2 = -(-2)^2 = -(-2)(-2) = -(4) = -4$

   c. $(-x)^2 = 2^2 = 2 \cdot 2 = 4$

108. Substitute -5 for x

   a. $x^2 = (-5)^2 = (-5)(-5) = 25$

   b. $-x^2 = -(-5)^2 = -(-5)(-5) = -25$

   c. $(-x)^2 = 5^2 = 5 \cdot 5 = 25$

109. Substitute 6 for x

   a. $x^2 = 6^2 = 6 \cdot 6 = 36$

   b. $-x^2 = -6^2 = -(6 \cdot 6) = -36$

   c. $(-x)^2 = (-6)^2 = (-6)(-6) = 36$

110. Substitute 7 for x

   a. $x^2 = 7^2 = 7 \cdot 7 = 49$

   b. $-x^2 = -7^2 = -(7)(7) = -49$

   c. $(-x)^2 = (-7)^2 = (-7)(-7) = 49$

111. Substitute $-\dfrac{1}{3}$ for x.

   a. $x^2 = \left(-\dfrac{1}{3}\right)^2 = \left(-\dfrac{1}{3}\right)\left(-\dfrac{1}{3}\right) = \dfrac{1}{9}$

   b. $-x^2 = -\left(-\dfrac{1}{3}\right)^2 = -\left(-\dfrac{1}{3}\right)\left(-\dfrac{1}{3}\right) = -\dfrac{1}{9}$

   c. $(-x)^2 = \left(\dfrac{1}{3}\right)^2 = \left(\dfrac{1}{3}\right)\left(\dfrac{1}{3}\right) = \dfrac{1}{9}$

112. Substitute $\dfrac{3}{4}$ for x.

   a. $x^2 = \left(\dfrac{3}{4}\right)^2 = \left(\dfrac{3}{4}\right)\left(\dfrac{3}{4}\right) = \dfrac{9}{16}$

   b. $-x^2 = -\left(\dfrac{3}{4}\right)^2 = -\left(\dfrac{3}{4}\right)\left(\dfrac{3}{4}\right) = -\dfrac{9}{16}$

   c. $(-x)^2 = \left(-\dfrac{3}{4}\right)^2 = \left(-\dfrac{3}{4}\right)\left(-\dfrac{3}{4}\right) = \dfrac{9}{16}$

113. Substitute -2 for x in the expression.
$$x + 6 = -2 + 6 = 4$$

114. Substitute 3 for each x in the expression.
$$2x - 4x + 5 = 2(3) - 4(3) + 5$$
$$= 6 - 12 + 5$$
$$= -6 + 5$$
$$= -1$$

115. Substitute 6 for z in the expression.
$$-7z - 3 = -7(6) - 3 = -42 - 3 = -45$$

116. Substitute 5 for x in the expression.
$$3(x - 2) = 3(5 - 2) = 3(3) = 9$$

117. Substitute -3 for a in the expression.
$$a^2 - 6 = (-3)^2 - 6 = 9 - 6 = 3$$

118. Substitute 5 for b in the expression.
$$b^2 - 8 = (5)^2 - 8 = 25 - 8 = 17$$

119. Substitute 2 for each p in the expression.
$$3p^2 - 6p - 4 = 3(2)^2 - 6(2) - 4$$
$$= 3(4) - 12 - 4$$
$$= 12 - 12 - 4$$
$$= 0 - 4$$
$$= -4$$

120. Substitute 1 for each r in the expression.
$$2r^2 - 5r + 3 = 2(1)^2 - 5(1) + 3$$
$$= 2(1) - 5 + 3$$
$$= 2 - 5 + 3$$
$$= -3 + 3$$
$$= 0$$

121. Substitute -1 for each x in the expression.
$$-4x^2 - 2x + 1 = -4(-1)^2 - 2(-1) + 1$$
$$= -4(1) - 2(-1) + 1$$
$$= -4 + 2 + 1$$
$$= -2 + 1$$
$$= -1$$

122. Substitute -4 for t in the expression.
$$-t^2 - 4t + 5 = -(-4)^2 - 4(-4) + 5$$
$$= -16 + 16 + 5$$
$$= 0 + 5$$
$$= 5$$

123. Substitute $\dfrac{1}{2}$ for each x in the expression.

$$-x^2 - 2x + 5 = -(\dfrac{1}{2})^2 - 2(\dfrac{1}{2}) + 5$$
$$= -\dfrac{1}{4} - 1 + 5$$
$$= -\dfrac{1}{4} - \dfrac{4}{4} + \dfrac{20}{4}$$
$$= -\dfrac{5}{4} + \dfrac{20}{4}$$
$$= \dfrac{15}{4} \text{ or } 3\dfrac{3}{4}$$

124. Substitute $\dfrac{3}{4}$ for each x in the expression.

$$2x^2 - 4x - 10 = 2(\dfrac{3}{4})^2 - 4(\dfrac{3}{4}) - 10$$
$$= 2(\dfrac{9}{16}) - 3 - 10$$
$$= \dfrac{18}{16} - 3 - 10$$
$$= \dfrac{9}{8} - \dfrac{24}{8} - \dfrac{80}{8}$$
$$= -\dfrac{15}{8} - \dfrac{80}{8}$$
$$= -\dfrac{95}{8} \text{ or } -11\dfrac{7}{8}$$

125. Substitute 5 for each x in the expression.

$$4(3x+1)^2 - 6x = 4(3(5)+1)^2 - 6(5)$$
$$= 4(15+1)^2 - 30$$
$$= 4(16)^2 - 30$$
$$= 4(256) - 30$$
$$= 1024 - 30$$
$$= 994$$

126. Substitute –4 for each n in the expression.

$$3n^2(2n-1) + 5 = 3(-4)^2(2(-4)-1) + 5$$
$$= 3(-4)^2(-8-1) + 5$$
$$= 3(16)(-9) + 5$$
$$= (48)(-9) + 5$$
$$= -432 + 5$$
$$= -427$$

127. Substitute –2 for r and –3 for s in the expression.
$$r^2 - s^2 = (-2)^2 - (-3)^2 = 4 - 9 = -5$$

128. Substitute 5 for p and –3 for q in the expression.
$$p^2 - p^2 = (5)^2 - (-3)^2 = 25 - 9 = 16$$

129. Substitute 1 for x and –5 for y in the expression.
$$5(x-6y) + 3x - 7y = 5(1-6(-5)) + 3(1) - 7(-5)$$
$$= 5(1-(-30)) + 3 + 35$$
$$= 5(31) + 3 + 35$$
$$= 155 + 3 + 35$$
$$= 158 + 35$$
$$= 193$$

130. Substitute 2 for x and 4 for y in the expression.
$$4(x+y)^2 + 2(x+y) + 3$$
$$= 4(2+4)^2 + 2(2+4) + 3$$
$$= 4(6)^2 + 2(6) + 3$$
$$= 4(36) + 2(6) + 3$$
$$= 144 + 12 + 3$$
$$= 156 + 3$$
$$= 159$$

131. Substitute –1 for x and –2 for y in the expression.
$$3(x-4)^2 - (3y-4)^2 = 3(-1-4)^2 - [3(-2)-4]^2$$
$$= 3(-5)^2 - (-6-4)^2$$
$$= 3(-5)^2 - (-10)^2$$
$$= 3(25) - 100$$
$$= 75 - 100$$
$$= -25$$

132. Substitute 2 for x and –3 for y in the expression.
$$6x^2 + 3xy - y^2 = 6(2)^2 + 3(2)(-3) - (-3)^2$$
$$= 6(4) + 3(2)(-3) - 9$$
$$= 24 + (-18) - 9$$
$$= 6 - 9$$
$$= -3$$

133. $6 \cdot 3$ Multiply 6 by 3

$(6 \cdot 3) - 4$ Subtract 4 from the product

$[(6 \cdot 3) - 4] - 2$ Subtract 2 from the difference

Evaluate:

$$[(6 \cdot 3) - 4] - 2 = [18 - 4] - 2 = 14 - 2 = 12$$

134. $9 + 4$ Add 4 to 9

$(9 + 4) \div 2$ Divide by 2

$\left[(9 + 4) \div 2 \right] + 10$ Add 10 to the quotient

Evaluate:

$[(9 + 4) \div 2] + 10 = [13 \div 2] + 10$

$\qquad = \dfrac{13}{2} + 10$

$\qquad = \dfrac{13}{2} + \dfrac{20}{2}$

$\qquad = \dfrac{33}{2}$

135. $10 \cdot 4$ Multiply 10 by 4

$(10 \cdot 4) + 9$ Add 9 to the product

$\left[(10 \cdot 4) + 9 \right] - 6$ Subtract 6 from the sum

$\left\{ \left[(10 \cdot 4) + 9 \right] - 6 \right\} \div 7$ Divide the difference by 7

Evaluate:

$\left\{ \left[(10 \cdot 4) + 9 \right] - 6 \right\} \div 7 = \left\{ [40 + 9] - 6 \right\} \div 7$

$\qquad = \left\{ 49 - 6 \right\} \div 7$

$\qquad = 43 \div 7$

$\qquad = \dfrac{43}{7}$ or $6\dfrac{1}{7}$

136. $6 \cdot 3$ Multiply 6 by 3

$(6 \cdot 3) + 27$ Add 27

$\left[(6 \cdot 3) + 27 \right] \div 8$ Divide by 8

$10 \left\{ \left[(6 \cdot 3) + 27 \right] \div 8 \right\}$ Multiply quotient by 10

Evaluate:

$10 \left\{ \left[(6 \cdot 3) + 27 \right] \div 8 \right\} = 10 \left\{ [18 + 27] \div 8 \right\}$

$\qquad = 10[45 \div 8]$

$\qquad = 10 \left(\dfrac{45}{8} \right)$

$\qquad = \dfrac{10}{1} \cdot \dfrac{45}{8}$

$\qquad = \dfrac{5}{1} \cdot \dfrac{45}{4}$

$\qquad = \dfrac{225}{4}$ or $56\dfrac{1}{4}$

137. $\dfrac{4}{5} + \dfrac{3}{7}$ Add $\dfrac{4}{5}$ to $\dfrac{3}{7}$

$\left(\dfrac{4}{5} + \dfrac{3}{7} \right) \cdot \dfrac{2}{3}$ Multiply the sum by $\dfrac{2}{3}$

Evaluate:

$\left(\dfrac{4}{5} + \dfrac{3}{7} \right) \cdot \dfrac{2}{3} = \left(\dfrac{28}{35} + \dfrac{15}{35} \right) \cdot \dfrac{2}{3}$

$\qquad = \left(\dfrac{43}{35} \right) \cdot \left(\dfrac{2}{3} \right)$

$\qquad = \dfrac{86}{105}$

138. $\dfrac{3}{8} \cdot \dfrac{4}{5}$ Multiply $\dfrac{3}{8}$ by $\dfrac{4}{5}$

$\left(\dfrac{3}{8} \cdot \dfrac{4}{5} \right) + \dfrac{7}{120}$ Add $\dfrac{7}{120}$

$\left[\left(\dfrac{3}{8} \cdot \dfrac{4}{5} \right) + \dfrac{7}{120} \right] - \dfrac{1}{60}$ Subtract $\dfrac{1}{60}$ from the sum

Evaluate:

$\left[\left(\dfrac{3}{8} \cdot \dfrac{4}{5} \right) + \dfrac{7}{120} \right] - \dfrac{1}{60} = \left[\left(\dfrac{3}{2} \cdot \dfrac{1}{5} \right) + \dfrac{7}{120} \right] - \dfrac{1}{60}$

$\qquad = \left[\dfrac{3}{10} + \dfrac{7}{120} \right] - \dfrac{1}{60}$

$\qquad = \left[\dfrac{36}{120} + \dfrac{7}{120} \right] - \dfrac{1}{60}$

$\qquad = \dfrac{43}{120} - \dfrac{1}{60}$

$\qquad = \dfrac{43}{120} - \dfrac{2}{120}$

$\qquad = \dfrac{41}{120}$

139. $-\left(x^2 \right) = -x^2$ is true for all real numbers.

140. When $x = 0$ or 1, $x = x^2$.

141. When $t = 2.5$, $65t = 65(2.5) = 162.5$
The car travels 162.5 miles.

142. When $d = 19.99$, $0.08d = 0.08(19.99) \approx 1.60$.
The sales tax is $1.60.

143. When $t = 2$,

$$-16t^2 + 48t + 70 = -16(2)^2 + 48(2) + 70$$
$$= -16(4) + 48(2) + 70$$
$$= -64 + 96 + 70$$
$$= 32 + 70$$
$$= 102$$

After 2 seconds the height will be 102 feet.

144. When $d = 17,000$,

$$d + 0.08d = 17,000 + 0.08(17,000)$$
$$= 17,000 + 1360$$
$$= 18,360$$

The total cost is \$18,360.

145. **a.** $2 \div 5^2 = 2 \div 25 = 0.08$

b. $(2 \div 5)^2 = (0.4)^2 = 0.16$

146. Any real number except 0 raised to the zero power is 1.

147. When $R = 2$ and $T = 70$,

$$0.2R^2 + 0.003RT + 0.0001T^2$$
$$= 0.2(2)^2 + 0.003(2)(70) + 0.0001(70)^2$$
$$= 0.2(4) + 0.003(2)(70) + 0.0001(4900)$$
$$= 0.8 + 0.42 + 0.49$$
$$= 1.71$$

The growth is 1.71 inches.

148. $(14 + 6) \div 2 \times 4 = 40$

149. $12 - (4 - 6) + 10 = 24$

150. $24 \div 4 \div (2 + 2) = 1$

151. **a.** $2^2 \cdot 2^3 = 2 \cdot 2 \cdot 2 \cdot 2 \cdot 2 = 2^5$

b. $3^2 \cdot 3^3 = 3 \cdot 3 \cdot 3 \cdot 3 \cdot 3 = 3^5$

c. $2^3 \cdot 2^4 = 2 \cdot 2 \cdot 2 \cdot 2 \cdot 2 \cdot 2 \cdot 2 = 2^7$

d. $x^m \cdot x^n = x^{m+n}$

152. **a.** $\dfrac{2^3}{2^2} = \dfrac{\cancel{2} \cdot \cancel{2} \cdot 2}{\cancel{2} \cdot \cancel{2}} = 2^1 = 2$

b. $\dfrac{3^4}{3^2} = \dfrac{\cancel{3} \cdot \cancel{3} \cdot 3 \cdot 3}{\cancel{3} \cdot \cancel{3}} = 3^2$

c. $\dfrac{4^5}{4^3} = \dfrac{\cancel{4} \cdot \cancel{4} \cdot \cancel{4} \cdot 4 \cdot 4}{\cancel{4} \cdot \cancel{4} \cdot \cancel{4}} = 4^2$

d. $\dfrac{x^m}{x^n} = x^{m-n}$

153. **a.** $(2^3)^2 = 2^3 \cdot 2^3 = 2 \cdot 2 \cdot 2 \cdot 2 \cdot 2 \cdot 2 = 2^6$

b. $(3^3)^2 = 3^3 \cdot 3^3 = 3 \cdot 3 \cdot 3 \cdot 3 \cdot 3 \cdot 3 = 3^6$

c. $(4^2)^2 = 4^2 \cdot 4^2 = 4 \cdot 4 \cdot 4 \cdot 4 = 4^4$

d. $(x^m)^n = x^{mn}$

154. **a.** $(2x)^2 = (2x) \cdot (2x) = 2 \cdot 2 \cdot x \cdot x = 2^2 x^2$

b. $(3x)^2 = (3x) \cdot (3x) = 3 \cdot 3 \cdot x \cdot x = 3^2 x^2$

c. $(4x)^3 = (4x) \cdot (4x) \cdot (4x)$
$$= 4 \cdot 4 \cdot 4 \cdot x \cdot x \cdot x$$
$$= 4^3 x^3$$

d. $(ax)^m = a^m x^m$

155. **a.** There are 3 houses with 2 dogs.

b.

Dogs	Number of Houses
0	4
1	5
2	3
3	1
4	1

c. $4(1) + 3(1) + 2(3) + 1(5) + 0(4)$
$$= 4 + 3 + 6 + 5 + 0$$
$$= 7 + 6 + 5$$
$$= 13 + 5$$
$$= 18$$

There are 18 dogs in all.

d. Number of dogs = 18

$$\text{mean} = \frac{\text{number of dogs}}{\text{number of houses}} = \frac{18}{14} \approx 1.29$$

There is a mean of 1.29 dogs per house.

156. $3 = \dfrac{6}{2} = \dfrac{1}{2} + \dfrac{5}{2} = \dfrac{1}{2} + \dfrac{20}{8}$

$\text{Cost} = \$2.40 + 20(0.20) = \$2.40 + \$4.00 = \$6.40$

157. $-\dfrac{7}{12} + \dfrac{4}{9} = \dfrac{-21}{36} + \dfrac{16}{36} = \dfrac{-21+16}{36} = -\dfrac{5}{36}$

158. $\left(\dfrac{-5}{7}\right) \div \left(\dfrac{-3}{14}\right) = \left(\dfrac{-5}{\cancel{7}}\right)\left(\dfrac{\cancel{14}^{\,2}}{-3}\right)$

$\qquad = \dfrac{-5}{1} \cdot \dfrac{2}{-3}$

$\qquad = \dfrac{(-5)(2)}{(1)(-3)}$

$\qquad = \dfrac{10}{3}$ or $3\dfrac{1}{3}$

Exercise Set 1.10

1. The commutative property of addition states that the sum of two numbers is the same regardless of the order in which they are added. One possible example is $3+4 = 4+3$.

2. The commutative property of multiplication states that the product of two numbers is the same regardless of the order in which they are multiplied. One possible example is $5(6) = 6(5)$.

3. The associative property of addition states that the sum of 3 numbers is the same regardless of the way the numbers are grouped. One possible example is $(2+3)+4 = 2+(3+4)$.

4. The associative property of multiplication states that the product of 3 numbers is the same regardless of the way the numbers are grouped. One possible example is $(2 \cdot 3) \cdot 4 = 2 \cdot (3 \cdot 4)$.

5. **a.** In $x+(y+z)$ the sum of y and z is added to x whereas in $x(y+z)$, x is multiplied by the sum.
   b. When $x = 4$, $y = 5$, and $z = 6$,
   $x+(y+z) = 4+(5+6) = 4+11 = 15$.
   c. When $x = 4$, $y = 5$, and $z = 6$,
   $x(y+z) = 4(5+6) = 4(11) = 44$.

6. The distributive property states that the product of a number with a sum is the same as the sum of the products of the number with each number in the sum. One possible example is
   $2(3+4) = 2(3)+2(4)$.

7. The associative property involves changing parentheses with one operation whereas the distributive property involves distributing a multiplication over an addition.

8. **a.** $x+(y+z) = (x+y)+z$
   b. $x(y+z) = xy + xz$

9. 0

10. 1

11. **a.** -6 **b.** $\dfrac{1}{6}$

12. **a.** -5 **b.** $\dfrac{1}{5}$

13. **a.** 3   **b.** $-\dfrac{1}{3}$

14. **a.** 7   **b.** $-\dfrac{1}{7}$

15. **a.** $-x$ **b.** $\dfrac{1}{x}$

16. **a.** $-z$ **b.** $\dfrac{1}{z}$

17. **a.** -1.6 **b.** $\dfrac{1}{1.6}$ or 0.625

18. **a.** 0.125 **b.** $-\dfrac{1}{0.125}$ or -8

19. **a.** $-\dfrac{1}{5}$ **b.** 5

20. **a.** $-\dfrac{1}{8}$ **b.** 8

21. **a.** $\dfrac{5}{6}$ **b.** $-\dfrac{6}{5}$

22. **a.** $\dfrac{2}{9}$ **b.** $-\dfrac{9}{2}$

23. Distributive property

24. Commutative property of addition

25. Associative property of addition

26. Distributive property

27. Commutative property of multiplication

28. Inverse property for addition

29. Associative property of multiplication

30. Distributive property

31. Distributive property

32. Associative property of addition

33. Identity property for multiplication

34. Identity property for addition

35. Inverse property for multiplication

36. Commutative property of multiplication

37. $1+(-4)$

38. 0

39. $(-6\cdot4)\cdot2$

40. $(-5+6)+8$

41. $-2x-2y$

42. $4x+12$

43. $y\cdot x$

44. $-\frac{1}{3}b$

45. $3y+4x$

46. $(-9\cdot3)\cdot8$

47. $a+(b+3)$

48. $3(x+2)$

49. $3x+(4+6)$

50. $3(y+x)$

51. $(m+n)3$

52. $3(xy)$

53. $4x+4y+12$

54. $3x+3y+6$

55. 0

56. $2x$

57. $\frac{5}{2}n$

58. 1

59. Yes; the order does not affect the outcome so the process is commutative.

60. No; the order affects the outcome, so the process is not commutative.

61. Yes; the order does not affect the outcome so the process is commutative.

62. No; the order affects the outcome, so the process is not commutative.

63. No; the order affects the outcome, so the process is not commutative.

64. No; the order affects the outcome, so the process is not commutative.

65. Yes; the outcome is not affected by whether you do the first two items first or the last two first, so the process is associative.

66. Yes; the outcome is not affected by whether you do the first two items first or the last two first, so the process is associative.

67. No; the outcome is affected by whether you do the first two items first or the last two first, so the process is not associative.

68. No; the outcome is affected by whether you do the first two items first or the last two first, so the process is not associative.

69. No; the outcome is affected by whether you do the first two items first or the last two first, so the process is not associative.

70. Yes; the outcome is not affected by whether you do the first two items first or the last two first, so the process is associative.

71. In $(3+4)+x = x+(3+4)$ the $(3+4)$ is treated as one value.

72. In $(3+4) \cdot x = x \cdot (3+4)$, the $(3+4)$ is treated as one value.

73. This illustrates the commutative property of addition because the change is $3 + 5 = 5 + 3$.

74. This illustrates the commutative property of addition. The $(3 + 5)$ is treated as one value and x is the other value.

75. No; it illustrates the associative property of addition since the grouping is changed.

76. In $(3+4) \cdot (5+6) = (5+6) \cdot (3+4)$, the $(3+4)$ is treated as one value and the $(5+6)$ is treated as one value.

77. $2\dfrac{3}{5} + \dfrac{2}{3}$

$2\dfrac{3}{5} = \dfrac{13}{5} = \dfrac{3}{3} \cdot \dfrac{13}{5} = \dfrac{39}{15}$

$\dfrac{2}{3} = \dfrac{2}{3} \cdot \dfrac{5}{5} = \dfrac{10}{15}$

$2\dfrac{3}{5} + \dfrac{2}{3} = \dfrac{39}{15} + \dfrac{10}{15} = \dfrac{49}{15}$ or $3\dfrac{4}{15}$

78. $3\dfrac{5}{8} - 2\dfrac{3}{16}$

$3\dfrac{5}{8} = \dfrac{29}{8} = \dfrac{2}{2} \cdot \dfrac{29}{8} = \dfrac{58}{16}$

$2\dfrac{3}{16} = \dfrac{35}{16}$

$3\dfrac{5}{8} - 2\dfrac{3}{16} = \dfrac{58}{16} - \dfrac{35}{16} = \dfrac{23}{16}$ or $1\dfrac{7}{16}$

79. $102.7 + (-113.9) = -11.2$

80. $-\dfrac{7}{8}$

Chapter 1 Review Exercises

1. $13(12) - (32 + 29 + 36 + 31) = 156 - 128$
$$= 28$$
He had 28 doughnuts left over.

2. $1.05 \left[1.05 (500.00) \right] = 1.05 [525] = 551.25$
In 2 years the goods will cost $551.25.

3. a. $899.99(.0825) = 74.25$
The sales tax is $74.25.

   b. total cost = cost of laptop + sales tax
total cost $= 899.99 + 74.25$
$$= 974.24$$
The total cost of the laptop is $974.24.

4. $\left[30 + 12(25) \right] - 300 = [30 + 300] - 300$
$$= 330 - 300$$
$$= 30$$
She can save $30.

5. a. mean $= \dfrac{75 + 79 + 86 + 88 + 64}{5} = \dfrac{392}{5} = 78.4$
The mean grade is 78.4.

   b. 64, 75, 79, 86, 88
The middle number is 79. The median grade is 79.

6. a. mean $= \dfrac{21 + 3 + 17 + 10 + 9 + 6}{6} = \dfrac{66}{6} = 11$
The mean is 11.

   b. 3, 6, 9, 10, 17, 21
The middle numbers are 9 and 10. Their average is $\dfrac{9+10}{2} = \dfrac{19}{2} = 9.5$. The median is 9.5.

7. a. 30 minutes

   b. 27 minutes

8. a. $1.6(0.637) = 1.0192$
In 1967, 1.0192 million freshman applied to two or fewer colleges.

   b. $2.1(0.247) = 0.5187$
In 2003, 0.5187 million freshman applied to six or more colleges.

9. $\dfrac{3}{5}\cdot\dfrac{5}{6}=\dfrac{\cancel{3}^{1}}{5}\cdot\dfrac{\cancel{5}^{1}}{\cancel{6}_{2}}=\dfrac{1\cdot 1}{1\cdot 2}=\dfrac{1}{2}$

10. $3\dfrac{5}{7}+2\dfrac{1}{3}=\dfrac{26}{7}+\dfrac{7}{3}$

$\qquad=\dfrac{26}{7}\cdot\dfrac{3}{3}+\dfrac{7}{3}\cdot\dfrac{7}{7}$

$\qquad=\dfrac{78}{21}+\dfrac{49}{21}$

$\qquad=\dfrac{78+49}{21}$

$\qquad=\dfrac{127}{21}$ or $6\dfrac{1}{21}$

11. $\dfrac{5}{12}\div\dfrac{3}{5}=\dfrac{5}{12}\cdot\dfrac{5}{3}=\dfrac{5\cdot 5}{12\cdot 3}=\dfrac{25}{36}$

12. $\dfrac{5}{6}+\dfrac{1}{3}=\dfrac{5}{6}+\dfrac{1}{3}\cdot\dfrac{2}{2}=\dfrac{5}{6}+\dfrac{2}{6}=\dfrac{7}{6}$ or $1\dfrac{1}{6}$

13. $3\dfrac{1}{6}-1\dfrac{1}{4}=\dfrac{19}{6}-\dfrac{5}{4}$

$\qquad=\dfrac{19}{6}\cdot\dfrac{2}{2}-\dfrac{5}{4}\cdot\dfrac{3}{3}$

$\qquad=\dfrac{38}{12}-\dfrac{15}{12}$

$\qquad=\dfrac{38-15}{12}$

$\qquad=\dfrac{23}{12}$ or $1\dfrac{11}{12}$

14. $7\dfrac{3}{8}\div\dfrac{5}{12}=7\dfrac{3}{8}\cdot\dfrac{12}{5}$

$\qquad=\dfrac{59}{\cancel{8}_{2}}\cdot\dfrac{\cancel{12}^{3}}{5}$

$\qquad=\dfrac{59\cdot 3}{2\cdot 5}$

$\qquad=\dfrac{177}{10}$ or $17\dfrac{7}{10}$

15. The natural numbers are $\{1, 2, 3, \ldots\}$.

16. The whole numbers are $\{0, 1, 2, 3, \ldots\}$.

17. The integers are $\{\ldots, -3, -2, -1, 0, 1, 2, \ldots\}$.

18. The set of rational numbers is the set of all numbers which can be expressed as the quotient of two integers, denominator not zero.

19. a. 3 and 426 are positive integers.

b. 3, 0, and 426 are whole numbers.

c. 3, –5, –12, 0, and 426 are integers.

d. 3, –5, –12, 0, $\dfrac{1}{2}$, –0.62, 426, and $-3\dfrac{1}{4}$ are rational numbers.

e. $\sqrt{7}$ is an irrational number.

f. 3, –5, –12, 0, $\dfrac{1}{2}$, –0.62, $\sqrt{7}$, 426, and $-3\dfrac{1}{4}$ are real numbers.

20. a. 1 is a natural number.

b. 1 is a whole number.

c. –8 and –9 are negative numbers.

d. –8, –9, and 1 are integers.

e. –2.3, –8, –9, $1\dfrac{1}{2}$, 1, and $-\dfrac{3}{17}$ are rational numbers.

f. –2.3, –8, –9, $1\dfrac{1}{2}$, $\sqrt{2}$, $-\sqrt{2}$, 1, and $-\dfrac{3}{17}$ are real numbers.

21. $-7 < -5$; –7 is to the left of –5 on a number line.

22. $-2.6 > -3.6$; –2.6 is to the right of –3.6 on a number line.

23. $0.50 < 0.509$; 0.50 is to the left 0.509 on a number line.

24. $4.6 > 4.06$; 4.6 is to the right of 4.06 on a number line.

25. $-6.3 < -6.03$; –6.3 is to the left of –6.03 on a number line.

26. $5 > |-3|$ since $|-3|$ equals 3.

27. $\left|-\dfrac{9}{2}\right| = |-4.5|$ since $\left|-\dfrac{9}{2}\right| = |-4.5| = 4.5$.

28. $|-10| > |-7|$ since $|-10|$ equals 10 and $|-7|$ equals 7.

29. $-9 + (-5) = -14$

30. $-6 + 6 = 0$

31. $0 + (-3) = -3$

32. $-10 + 4 = -6$

33. $-8 - (-2) = -8 + 2 = -6$

34. $-2 - (-4) = -2 + 4 = 2$

35. $4 - (-4) = 4 + 4 = 8$

36. $12 - 12 = 12 + (-12) = 0$

37. $2 - 7 = 2 + (-7) = -5$

38. $7 - (-7) = 7 + 7 = 14$

39. $0 - (-4) = 0 + 4 = 4$

40. $-7 - 5 = -7 + (-5) = -12$

41. $\dfrac{4}{3} - \dfrac{3}{4} = \dfrac{16}{12} - \dfrac{9}{12} = \dfrac{16-9}{12} = \dfrac{7}{12}$

42. $\dfrac{1}{2} + \dfrac{3}{5} = \dfrac{5}{10} + \dfrac{6}{10} = \dfrac{5+6}{10} = \dfrac{11}{10}$

43. $\dfrac{5}{9} - \dfrac{3}{4} = \dfrac{20}{36} - \dfrac{27}{36} = \dfrac{20-27}{36} = -\dfrac{7}{36}$

44. $-\dfrac{5}{7} + \dfrac{3}{8} = -\dfrac{40}{56} + \dfrac{21}{56} = \dfrac{-40+21}{56} = -\dfrac{19}{56}$

45. $-\dfrac{5}{12} - \dfrac{5}{6} = -\dfrac{5}{12} - \dfrac{10}{12} = \dfrac{-5-10}{12} = -\dfrac{15}{12} = -\dfrac{5}{4}$

46. $-\dfrac{6}{7} + \dfrac{5}{12} = -\dfrac{72}{84} + \dfrac{35}{84} = \dfrac{-72+35}{84} = -\dfrac{37}{84}$

47. $\dfrac{2}{9} - \dfrac{3}{10} = \dfrac{20}{90} - \dfrac{27}{90} = \dfrac{20-27}{90} = -\dfrac{7}{90}$

48. $\dfrac{5}{12} - \left(-\dfrac{3}{5}\right) = \dfrac{25}{60} + \dfrac{36}{60} = \dfrac{25+36}{60} = \dfrac{61}{60}$ or $1\dfrac{1}{60}$

49. $9 - 4 + 3 = 5 + 3 = 8$

50. $-8 - 9 + 4 = -17 + 4 = -13$

51. $-5 - 4 - 3 = -9 - 3 = -12$

52. $-2 + (-3) - 2 = -5 - 2 = -7$

53. $7 - (+4) - (-3) = 7 - 4 + 3 = 3 + 3 = 6$

54. $6 - (-2) + 3 = 6 + 2 + 3 = 8 + 3 = 11$

55. Since the numbers have unlike signs, the product is negative; $7(-9) = -63$

56. Since the numbers have like signs, the product is positive; $(-8.2)(-3.1) = 25.42$

57. Since there are an odd number (3) of negatives the product is negative;
$(-4)(-5)(-6) = (20)(-6) = -120$

58. $\left(\dfrac{3}{5}\right)\left(\dfrac{-2}{7}\right) = \dfrac{3(-2)}{5 \cdot 7} = \dfrac{-6}{35} = -\dfrac{6}{35}$

59. $\left(\dfrac{10}{11}\right)\left(\dfrac{3}{-5}\right) = \dfrac{2}{11} \cdot \dfrac{3}{-1} = \dfrac{2 \cdot 3}{(11)(-1)} = \dfrac{6}{-11} = -\dfrac{6}{11}$

60. $\left(\dfrac{-5}{8}\right)\left(\dfrac{-3}{7}\right) = \dfrac{(-5)(-3)}{8 \cdot 7} = \dfrac{15}{56}$

61. Zero multiplied by any real number is zero.
$0 \cdot \dfrac{4}{9} = 0$

62. Since there are four negative numbers (an even number), the product is positive.
$(-4)(-6)(-2)(-3) = (24)(-2)(-3)$
$= (-48)(-3)$
$= 144$

63. Since the numbers have unlike signs, the quotient is negative; $15 \div (-3) = \dfrac{15}{-3} = -5$

64. Since the numbers have unlike signs, the quotient is negative.
$12 \div (-2) = \dfrac{12}{-2} = -6$

65. Since the numbers have unlike signs, the quotient is negative;
$-14.72 \div 4.6 = \dfrac{-14.72}{4.6} = -3.2$

66. Since the numbers have like signs, the quotient is positive: $-37.41 \div (-8.7) = 4.3$

67. Since the numbers have like signs, the quotient is positive: $-88 \div (-11) = 8$

68. $-4 \div \left(\dfrac{-4}{9}\right) = \dfrac{-4}{1} \cdot \dfrac{9}{-4} = \dfrac{-1}{1} \cdot \dfrac{9}{-1} = \dfrac{-9}{-1} = 9$

69. $\dfrac{28}{-3} \div \left(\dfrac{9}{-2}\right) = \left(\dfrac{28}{-3}\right)\left(\dfrac{-2}{9}\right) = \dfrac{-56}{-27} = \dfrac{56}{27}$

70. $\dfrac{14}{3} \div \left(\dfrac{-6}{5}\right) = \dfrac{\overset{7}{\cancel{14}}}{3} \cdot \left(\dfrac{5}{\underset{3}{\cancel{-6}}}\right)$

$\qquad = \dfrac{7(5)}{3(-3)}$

$\qquad = \dfrac{35}{-9} = -\dfrac{35}{9}$

71. Zero divided by any nonzero number is zero;
$0 \div 5 = \dfrac{0}{5} = 0$

72. Zero divided by any nonzero number is zero;
$0 \div (-6) = \dfrac{0}{-6} = 0$

73. Any real number divided by zero is undefined;
$-12 \div 0 = \dfrac{-12}{0}$ is undefined.

74. Any real number divided by zero is undefined;
$-4 \div 0 = \dfrac{-4}{0}$ is undefined.

75. Any real number divided by zero is undefined;
$\dfrac{8.3}{0}$ is undefined

76. Zero divided by any nonzero number is zero;
$\dfrac{0}{-9.8} = 0$

77. $-5(3-8) = -5(-5) = 25$

78. $2(4-8) = 2(-4) = -8$

79. $(3-6) + 4 = -3 + 4 = 1$

80. $(-4+3) - (2-6) = (-1) - (-4) = -1 + 4 = 3$

81. $[6 + 3(-2)] - 6 = [6 + (-6)] - 6 = 0 - 6 = -6$

82. $(-5-3)(4) = (-5 + (-3))(4) = (-8)(4) = -32$

83. $[12 + (-4)] + (6-8) = 8 + (-2) = 6$

84. $9[3 + (-4)] + 5 = 9(-1) + 5 = -9 + 5 = -4$

85. $-4(-3) + [4 \div (-2)] = (12) + (-2) = 10$

86. $(-3 \cdot 4) \div (-2 \cdot 6) = -12 \div (-12) = 1$

87. $(-3)(-4) + 6 - 3 = 12 + 6 - 3 = 18 - 3 = 15$

88. $[-2(3) + 6] - 4 = [-6 + 6] - 4 = 0 - 4 = -4$

89. $-6^2 = -(6)(6) = -36$

90. $(-6)^2 = (-6)(-6) = 36$

91. $2^4 = (2)(2)(2)(2) = 16$

92. $(-3)^3 = (-3)(-3)(-3) = -27$

93. $(-1)^9 = (-1)(-1)(-1)(-1)(-1)(-1)(-1)(-1)(-1)$
$\qquad = -1$

94. $(-2)^5 = (-2)(-2)(-2)(-2)(-2) = -32$

95. $\left(\dfrac{-4}{5}\right)^2 = \left(\dfrac{-4}{5}\right)\left(\dfrac{-4}{5}\right) = \dfrac{16}{25}$

96. $\left(\dfrac{2}{5}\right)^3 = \left(\dfrac{2}{5}\right)\left(\dfrac{2}{5}\right)\left(\dfrac{2}{5}\right) = \dfrac{8}{125}$

97. $5^3 \cdot (-2)^2 = (5)(5)(5)(-2)(-2) = 500$

98. $(-2)^4\left(\dfrac{1}{2}\right)^2 = (-2)(-2)(-2)(-2)\left(\dfrac{1}{2}\right)\left(\dfrac{1}{2}\right) = 4$

99. $\left(-\dfrac{2}{3}\right)^2 \cdot 3^3 = \left(-\dfrac{2}{3}\right)\left(-\dfrac{2}{3}\right)(3)(3)(3) = 12$

100. $(-4)^3 (-2)^2 = (-4)(-4)(-4)(-2)(-2) = -256$

101. $-5 + 3 \cdot 4 = -5 + 12 = 7$

102. $4 \cdot 6 + 4 \cdot 2 = 24 + 8 = 32$

103. $(3.7 - 4.1)^2 + 6.2 = (-0.4)^2 + 6.2$
$= 0.16 + 6.2$
$= 6.36$

104. $10 - 36 \div 4 \cdot 3 = 10 - 9 \cdot 3 = 10 - 27 = -17$

105. $6 - 3^2 \cdot 5 = 6 - 9 \cdot 5 = 6 - 45 = -39$

106. $[6.9 - (3 \cdot 5)] + 5.8 = [6.9 - 15] + 5.8$
$= -8.1 + 5.8$
$= -2.3$

107. $\dfrac{6^2 - 4 \cdot 3^2}{-[6 - (3 - 4)]} = \dfrac{36 - 4 \cdot 9}{-[6 - (-1)]}$
$= \dfrac{36 - 36}{-7}$
$= \dfrac{0}{-7} = 0$

108. $\dfrac{4 + 5^2 \div 5}{6 - (-3 + 2)} = \dfrac{4 + 25 \div 5}{6 - (-1)} = \dfrac{4 + 5}{7} = \dfrac{9}{7}$ or $1\dfrac{2}{7}$

109. $3[9 - (4^2 + 3)] \cdot 2 = 3[9 - (16 + 3)] \cdot 2$
$= 3[9 - 19] \cdot 2$
$= 3(-10) \cdot 2$
$= -30 \cdot 2$
$= -60$

110. $(-3^2 + 4^2) + (3^2 \div 3) = (-9 + 16) + (9 \div 3)$
$= (7) + (3)$
$= 10$

111. $2^3 \div 4 + 6 \cdot 3 = 8 \div 4 + 6 \cdot 3 = 2 + 18 = 20$

112. $(4 \div 2)^4 + 4^2 \div 2^2 = (2)^4 + 16 \div 4$
$= 16 + 16 \div 4$
$= 16 + 4$
$= 20$

113. $(8 - 2^2)^2 - 4 \cdot 3 + 10 = (8 - 4)^2 - 4 \cdot 3 + 10$
$= (4)^2 - 4 \cdot 3 + 10$
$= 16 - 4 \cdot 3 + 10$
$= 16 - 12 + 10$
$= 4 + 10$
$= 14$

114. $4^3 \div 4^2 - 5(2 - 7) \div 5 = 4^3 \div 4^2 - 5(-5) \div 5$
$= 64 \div 16 - 5(-5) \div 5$
$= 4 - (-25) \div 5$
$= 4 - (-5)$
$= 4 + 5$
$= 9$

115. $-\{-4[27 \div 3^2 - 2(4 - 2)]\}$
$= -\{-4[27 \div 3^2 - 2(2)]\}$
$= -\{-4[27 \div 9 - 2(2)]\}$
$= -\{-4[3 - 4]\}$
$= -\{-4[-1]\}$
$= -\{4\}$
$= -4$

116. $2\{4^3 - 6[4 - (2 - 4)] - 3\}$
$= 2\{4^3 - 6[4 - (-2)] - 3\}$
$= 2\{4^3 - 6[6] - 3\}$
$= 2\{64 - 6[6] - 3\}$
$= 2\{64 - 36 - 3\}$
$= 2\{28 - 3\}$
$= 2\{25\}$
$= 50$

117. Substitute 4 for x;
$3x - 7 = 3(4) - 7 = 12 - 7 = 5$

118. Substitute -5 for x;
$6 - 4x = 6 - 4(-5) = 6 - (-20) = 6 + 20 = 26$

119. Substitute 6 for x;
$$2x^2 - 5x + 3 = 2(6)^2 - 5(6) + 3$$
$$= 2(36) - 30 + 3$$
$$= 72 - 30 + 3$$
$$= 42 + 3$$
$$= 45$$

120. Substitute -1 for y;
$$5y^2 + 3y - 2 = 5(-1)^2 + 3(-1) - 2$$
$$= 5(1) - 3 - 2$$
$$= 5 - 3 - 2$$
$$= 2 - 2$$
$$= 0$$

121. Substitute -2 for x;
$$-x^2 + 2x - 3 = -(-2)^2 + 2(-2) - 3$$
$$= -4 + (-4) - 3$$
$$= -8 - 3$$
$$= -11$$

122. Substitute 2 for x;
$$-x^2 + 2x - 3 = -2^2 + 2(2) - 3$$
$$= -4 + 4 - 3$$
$$= 0 - 3$$
$$= -3$$

123. Substitute 1 for x;
$$-3x^2 - 5x + 5 = -3(1)^2 - 5(1) + 5$$
$$= -3(1) - 5 + 5$$
$$= -3 - 5 + 5$$
$$= -8 + 5$$
$$= -3$$

124. Substitute -3 for x and -2 for y;
$$-x^2 - 8x - 12y = -(-3)^2 - 8(-3) - 12(-2)$$
$$= -9 - (-24) + 24$$
$$= -9 + 24 + 24$$
$$= 15 + 24$$
$$= 39$$

125. a. $278 + (-493) = -215$

b. $|-493|$ is greater than $|278|$ so the sum should be (and is) negative.

126. a. $324 - (-29.6) = 324 + 29.6 = 353.6$

b. The sum of two positive numbers is always positive. As expected, the answer is positive.

127. a. $\dfrac{-17.28}{6} = -2.88$

b. Since the numbers have unlike signs, the quotient is negative, as expected.

128. a. $(-62)(-1.9) = 117.8$

b. Since the numbers have like signs, the product is positive, as expected.

129. a. $(-4)^8 = 65,536$

b. A negative number raised to an even power is positive. As expected, the answer is positive.

130. a. $-(4.2)^3 = -74.088$

b. Since $(4.2)^3$ is positive, $-(4.2)^3$ should be (and is) negative.

131. Associative property of addition

132. Distributive property

133. Commutative property of addition

134. Commutative property of multiplication

135. Distributive property

136. Associative property of addition

137. Identity property of multiplication

138. Inverse property of addition

Chapter 1 Practice Test

1. a. $2(1.30) + 4.75 + 3(1.10)$
$= 2.60 + 4.75 + 3.30$
$= 7.35 + 3.30$
$= 10.65$
The bill is $10.65 before tax.

b. $0.07(3.30) \approx 0.23$
The tax on the soda is $0.23.

c. $10.65 + 0.23 = 10.88$
The total bill is $10.88.

d. $50 - 10.88 = 39.12$
Her change will be \$39.12.

2. $\dfrac{1,600,000}{643,500} \approx 2.48$

The price was about 2.5 times greater in the twelfth year compared to the first year.

3. a. $13.0 - 5.1 = 7.9$
About 7.9 million listened to WRAB at this time.

b. During this specific time, half the time KFUN had more than 8.8 million listeners and half the time KFUN had less than 8.8 million listeners.

4. a. 42 is a natural number.

b. 42 and 0 are whole numbers.

c. $-6, 42, 0, -7,$ and -1 are integers.

d. $-6, 42, -3\dfrac{1}{2}, 0, 6.52, \dfrac{5}{9}, -7,$ and -1 are rational numbers.

e. $\sqrt{5}$ is an irrational number.

f. $-6, 42, -3\dfrac{1}{2}, 0, 6.52, \sqrt{5}, \dfrac{5}{9}, -7,$ and -1 are real numbers.

5. $-9.9 < -9.09$; -9.9 is to the left of -9.09 on a number line.

6. $|-3| > |-2|$ since $|-3| = 3$ and $|-2| = 2$.

7. $-7 + (-8) = -15$

8. $-6 - 5 = -6 + (-5) = -11$

9. $15 - 12 - 17 = 3 - 17 = -14$

10. $(-4 + 6) - 3(-2) = (2) - (-6) = 2 + 6 = 8$

11. $(-4)(-3)(2)(-1) = (12)(2)(-1)$
$= (24)(-1)$
$= -24$

12. $\left(\dfrac{-2}{9}\right) \div \left(\dfrac{-7}{8}\right) = \dfrac{-2}{9} \cdot \dfrac{8}{-7} = \dfrac{-16}{-63} = \dfrac{16}{63}$

13. $\left(-18 \cdot \dfrac{1}{2}\right) \div 3 = \left(\dfrac{-\overset{9}{\cancel{18}}}{1} \cdot \dfrac{1}{\underset{1}{\cancel{2}}}\right) \div 3$
$= \left(\dfrac{-9 \cdot 1}{1 \cdot 1}\right) \div 3$
$= -9 \div 3$
$= -3$

14. $-\dfrac{3}{8} - \dfrac{4}{7} = -\dfrac{21}{56} - \dfrac{32}{56}$
$= \dfrac{-21 - 32}{56}$
$= -\dfrac{53}{56}$

15. $-6(-2 - 3) \div 5 \cdot 2 = -6(-5) \div 5 \cdot 2$
$= 30 \div 5 \cdot 2$
$= 6 \cdot 2$
$= 12$

16. $\left(-\dfrac{2}{3}\right)^5 = \left(-\dfrac{2}{3}\right)\left(-\dfrac{2}{3}\right)\left(-\dfrac{2}{3}\right)\left(-\dfrac{2}{3}\right)\left(-\dfrac{2}{3}\right)$
$= -\dfrac{32}{243}$

17. $\left[6 + ((9-3)^2 \div 18)^2\right]^2 = \left[6 + ((6)^2 \div 18)^2\right]^2$
$= \left[6 + (36 \div 18)^2\right]^2$
$= \left[6 + (2)^2\right]^2$
$= \left[6 + 4\right]^2$
$= \left[10\right]^2$
$= 100$

18. Answers will vary. One possibility follows:
$-x^2$ means $(-x)^2$ and x^2 will always be positive for any nonzero value of x. Therefore, $-x^2$ will always be negative.

19. Substitute -3 for x;
$5x^2 - 8 = 5(-3)^2 - 8 = 5(9) - 8 = 45 - 8 = 37$

20. Substitute -2 for each x;
$$-x^2 - 6x + 3 = -(-2)^2 - 6(-2) + 3$$
$$= -4 - (-12) + 3$$
$$= -4 + 12 + 3$$
$$= 8 + 3$$
$$= 11$$

21. Substitute 3 for x and -2 for y;
$$6x - 3y^2 + 4 = 6(3) - 3(-2)^2 + 4$$
$$= 6(3) - 3(4) + 4$$
$$= 18 - 12 + 4$$
$$= 6 + 4$$
$$= 10$$

22. Substitute 1 for x and -2 for y;
$$-x^2 + xy + y^2 = -(1)^2 + (1)(-2) + (-2)^2$$
$$= -1 + (-2) + 4$$
$$= -3 + 4$$
$$= 1$$

23. Commutative property of addition

24. Distributive property

25. Associative property of addition

Chapter 2

Exercise Set 2.1

1. **a.** The terms of an expression are the parts that are added.

   b. The terms of $3x - 4y - 5$ are $3x$, $-4y$, and -5.

   c. The terms of $6xy + 3x - y - 9$ are $6xy$, $3x$, $-y$, and -9.

2. **a.** The numerical part of a term is the numerical coefficient or coefficient of the term.

   b. The coefficient of $4x$ is 4.

   c. Since $x = 1x$, the coefficient of x is 1.

   d. Since $-x = -1x$, the coefficient of $-x$ is -1.

   e. Since $\dfrac{3x}{5} = \dfrac{3}{5}x$, the coefficient of $\dfrac{3x}{5}$ is $\dfrac{3}{5}$.

   f. The numerical coefficient of $\dfrac{4}{7}(3t - 5)$ is $\dfrac{4}{7}$.

3. **a.** In $2x - 5$, the x is called the variable.

   b. In $2x - 5$, the -5 is called the constant.

   c. In $2x - 5$, the 2 is called the coefficient.

4. **a.** Like terms have the same variables with the same exponents

   b. No, $3x$ and $4y$ are not like terms because they have different variables.

   c. Yes, 7 and -2 are like terms.

   d. No, $5x^2$ and $2x$ are not like terms because the variables have different exponents.

   e. No, $4x$ and $-5xy$ are not like terms because they have different variables.

5. **a.** Yes, $5x$ and $-7x$ are like terms because they have the same variable with the same exponent.

   b. No, $7y$ and 2 are not like terms because the 2 does not have a y variable.

   c. Yes, $-3(t + 2)$ and $6(t + 2)$ are like terms because they have the same variable with the same exponent.

   d. Yes, $4pq$ and $-9pq$ are like terms because they have the same variables with the same exponents

6. **a.** The parentheses may be removed without having to change the expression within the parentheses.

   b. $+(x - 8) = x - 8$

7. **a.** The signs of all the terms inside the parentheses are changed when the parentheses are removed.

   b. $-(x - 8) = -x + 8$

8. **a.** The factors of an expression are the parts that are multiplied.

   b. In $3x$, 3 and x are factors because they are multiplied together.

   c. In $5xy$, 5, x and y are factors because they are multiplied together.

9. $6x + 3x = 9x$

10. $4x - 5x = -x$

11. There are no like terms.
    $3x + 6$

12. There are no like terms.
    $4x + 3y$

13. $y + 3 + 4y = y + 4y + 3 = 5y + 3$

14. $4x - 7x + 4 = -3x + 4$

15. $\dfrac{3}{4} - \dfrac{6}{11} = \dfrac{33}{44} - \dfrac{24}{44} = \dfrac{9}{44}$
    $\dfrac{3}{4}a - \dfrac{6}{11}a = \dfrac{9}{44}a$

16. $\dfrac{3}{4} - \dfrac{2}{7} = \dfrac{21}{28} - \dfrac{8}{28} = \dfrac{13}{28}$
    $\dfrac{3}{4}p - \dfrac{2}{7}p = \dfrac{13}{28}p$

17. $2 - 6x + 5 = -6x + 2 + 5 = -6x + 7$

18. $-7 - 4m - 6 = -4m - 7 - 6 = -4m - 13$

19. $-2w - 3w + 5 = -5w + 5$

20. $-8y - 4y - 7 = -12y - 7$

21. $-x + 2 - x - 2 = -x - x + 2 - 2 = -2x$

22. $8x - 2y - 1 - 3x = 8x - 3x - 2y - 1 = 5x - 2y - 1$

23. $3 + 6x - 3 - 6x = 6x - 6x + 3 - 3 = 0$

24. $y - 2y + 5 = -y + 5$

25. $5 + 2x - 4x + 6 = 2x - 4x + 5 + 6 = -2x + 11$

26. $5s - 3s - 2s = 2s - 2s = 0$

27. $4r - 6 - 6r - 2 = 4r - 6r - 6 - 2 = -2r - 8$

28. $-6t + 5 + 2t - 9 = -6t + 2t + 5 - 9 = -4t - 4$

29. $3x^2 - 9y^2 + 7x^2 - 5 - y^2 - 2$
$= 3x^2 + 7x^2 - 9y^2 - y^2 - 5 - 2$
$= 10y^2 - 10y^2 - 7$

30. $-4x^2 - 6y - 3x^2 + 6 - y - 1$
$= -4x^2 - 3x^2 - 6y - y + 6 - 1$
$= -7x^2 - 7y + 5$

31. $-2x + 4x - 3 = 2x - 3$

32. $4 - x + 4x - 8 = -x + 4x + 4 - 8 = 3x - 4$

33. $b + 4 + \dfrac{3}{5} = b + \dfrac{20}{5} + \dfrac{3}{5} = b + \dfrac{23}{5}$

34. $\dfrac{3}{4}x + 2 + x = \dfrac{3}{4}x + x + 2$
$= \dfrac{3}{4}x + \dfrac{4}{4}x + 2$
$= \dfrac{7}{4}x + 2$

35. $5.1n + 6.42 - 4.3n = 5.1n - 4.3n + 6.42$
$= 0.8n + 6.42$

36. $2x^2 + 3y^2 + 4x + 5y^2 = 2x^2 + 4x + 3y^2 + 5y^2$
$= 2x^2 + 4x + 8y^2$

37. There are no like terms.
$\dfrac{1}{2}a + 3b + 1$

38. $x + \dfrac{1}{2}y - \dfrac{3}{8}y = x + \dfrac{4}{8}y - \dfrac{3}{8}y = x + \dfrac{1}{8}y$

39. $13.4x + 1.2x + 8.3 = 14.6x + 8.3$

40. $-4x^2 - 3.1 - 5.2 = -4x^2 - 8.3$

41. $-x^2 + 2x^2 + y = x^2 + y$

42. $1 + x^2 + 6 - 3x^2 = x^2 - 3x^2 + 1 + 6 = -2x^2 + 7$

43. $2x - 7y - 5x + 2y = 2x - 5x - 7y + 2y = -3x - 5y$

44. $3x - 7 - 9 + 4x = 3x + 4x - 7 - 9 = 7x - 16$

45. $4 - 3n^2 + 9 - 2n = -3n^2 - 2n + 4 + 9$
$= -3n^2 - 2n + 13$

46. $9x + y - 2 - 4x = 9x - 4x + y - 2 = 5x + y - 2$

47. $-19.36 + 40.02x + 12.25 - 18.3x$
$= 40.02x - 18.3x - 19.36 + 12.25$
$= 21.72x - 7.11$

48. $52x - 52x - 63.5 - 63.5 = 0x - 127 = -127$

49. $\dfrac{3}{5}x - 3 - \dfrac{7}{4}x - 2 = \dfrac{3}{5}x - \dfrac{7}{4}x - 3 - 2$
$= \dfrac{12}{20}x - \dfrac{35}{20}x - 5$
$= -\dfrac{23}{20}x - 5$

50. $\dfrac{1}{2}y - 4 + \dfrac{3}{4}x - \dfrac{1}{5}y = \dfrac{3}{4}x + \dfrac{1}{2}y - \dfrac{1}{5}y - 4$
$= \dfrac{3}{4}x + \dfrac{5}{10}y - \dfrac{2}{10}y - 4$
$= \dfrac{3}{4}x + \dfrac{3}{10}y - 4$

51. There are no like terms.
$5w^3 + 2w^2 + w + 3$

52. $4p^2 - 3p^2 + 2p - 5p = p^2 - 3p$

53. $2z - 5z^3 - 2z^3 - z^2 = -5z^3 - 2z^3 - z^2 + 2z$
$= -7z^3 - z^2 + 2z$

54. $5ab - 3ab = 2ab$

55. There are no like terms.
$6x^2 - 6xy + 3y^2$

56. $x^2 - 3xy - 2xy + 6 = x^2 - 5xy + 6$

57. $4a^2 - 3ab + 6ab + b^2 = 4a^2 + 3ab + b^2$

58. $4b^2 - 8bc + 5bc + c^2 = 4b^2 - 3bc + c^2$

59. $5(x+2) = 5x + 5(2) = 5x + 10$

60. $2(-y+5) = 2(-y) + 2(5) = -2y + 10$

61. $5(x+4) = 5x + 5(4) = 5x + 20$

62. $-2(y+8) = -2y + (-2)(8)$
$= -2y + (-16)$
$= -2y - 16$

63. $3(x-6) = 3x + 3(-6) = 3x - 18$

64. $-2(x-4) = -2[x + (-4)]$
$= -2x + (-2)(-4)$
$= -2x + 8$

65. $-\dfrac{1}{2}(2x-4) = -\dfrac{1}{2}[2x + (-4)]$
$= -\dfrac{1}{2}(2x) + \left(-\dfrac{1}{2}\right)(-4)$
$= -x + 2$

66. $-4(x+6) = -4x + (-4)(6)$
$= -4x + (-24)$
$= -4x - 24$

67. $1(-4+x) = 1(-4) + 1(x) = -4 + x = x - 4$

68. $\dfrac{2}{3}(m-9) = \dfrac{2}{3}m - \dfrac{2}{3}(9) = \dfrac{2}{3}m - 6$

69. $\dfrac{4}{5}(s-5) = \dfrac{4}{5}s - \dfrac{4}{5}(5) = \dfrac{4}{5}s - 4$

70. $5(x-y+5) = 5x - 5y + 5(5) = 5x - 5y + 25$

71. $-0.3(3x+5) = -0.3(3x) + (-0.3)(5)$
$= -0.9x + (-1.5)$
$= -0.9x - 1.5$

72. $-(x-3) = -1[x + (-3)]$
$= -1(x) + (-1)(-3)$
$= -x + 3$

73. $-\dfrac{1}{3}(3r-12) = -\dfrac{1}{3}(3r) + \left(-\dfrac{1}{3}\right)(-12) = -r + 4$

74. $-2(x+y-z) = -2[x + y + (-z)]$
$= -2x + (-2y) + (-2)(-z)$
$= -2x - 2y + 2z$

75. $0.7(2x+0.5) = 0.7(2x) + 0.7(0.5) = 1.4x + 0.35$

76. $-(x+4y) = -1(x+4y)$
$= -1(x) + (-1)(4y)$
$= -x + (-4y)$
$= -x - 4y$

77. $-(-x+y) = -1(-x+y)$
$= -1(-x) + (-1)(y)$
$= x + (-y)$
$= x - y$

78. $(3x+4y-6) = 1[3x + 4y + (-6)]$
$= 1(3x) + 1(4y) + 1(-6)$
$= 3x + 4y + (-6)$
$= 3x + 4y - 6$

79. $-(2x+4y-8) = -1[2x + 4y + (-8)]$
$= -1(2x) + (-1)(4y) + (-1)(-8)$
$= -2x + (-4y) + 8$
$= -2x - 4y + 8$

80. $-3(2a+3b-7) = -3[(2a) + (3b) + (-7)]$
$= -3(2a) + (-3)(3b) + (-3)(-7)$
$= -6a - 9b + 21$

81. $1.1(3.1x - 5.2y + 2.8)$
$= 1.1[3.1x + (-5.2y) + 2.8]$
$= (1.1)(3.1x) + (1.1)(-5.2y) + (1.1)(2.8)$
$= 3.41x + (-5.72y) + 3.08$
$= 3.41x - 5.72y + 3.08$

82. $-4(-2m-3n+8) = -4[(-2m) + (-3n) + 8]$
$= -4(2m) + (-4)(-3n) + (-4)(8)$
$= 8m + 12n - 32$

83. $(2x-9y)5 = (2x)5 + (-9y)5 = 10x - 45y$

84. $(8b-1)7 = (8b)7 + (-1)7 = 56b - 7$

85. $(x+3y-9) = 1\left[x+3y+(-9)\right]$

$\qquad = 1(x)+1(3y)+(1)(-9)$

$\qquad = x+3y+(-9) = x+3y-9$

86. $(-p+2q-3) = 1\left[-p+2q+(-3)\right]$

$\qquad = 1(-p)+1(2q)+1(-3)$

$\qquad = -p+2q+(-3)$

$\qquad = -p+2q-3$

87. $-3(-x+2y+4) = -3(-x)+(-3)(2y)+(-3)(4)$

$\qquad = 3x+(-6y)+(-12)$

$\qquad = 3x-6y-12$

88. $2.3(1.6x+5.1y-4.1)$

$\qquad = 2.3[1.6x+5.1y+(-4.1)]$

$\qquad = 2.3(1.6x)+2.3(5.1y)+2.3(-4.1)$

$\qquad = 3.68x+11.73y+(-9.43)$

$\qquad = 3.68x+11.73y-9.43$

89. $5-(3x+4) = 5-3x-4$

$\qquad = -3x+5-4$

$\qquad = -3x+1$

90. $7-(2x-9) = 7-2x+9$

$\qquad = -2x+7+9$

$\qquad = -2x+16$

91. $-2(3-x)+7 = -6+2x+7$

$\qquad = 2x-6+7$

$\qquad = 2x+1$

92. $-(3x-3)+5 = -3x+3+5 = -3x+8$

93. $6x+2(4x+9) = 6x+8x+18 = 14x+18$

94. $3(x+y)+2y = 3x+3y+2y = 3x+5y$

95. $2(x-y)+2x+3 = 2x-2y+2x+3$

$\qquad = 2x+2x-2y+3$

$\qquad = 4x-2y+3$

96. $6+(x-5)+3x = 6+x-5+3x$

$\qquad = x+3x+6-5$

$\qquad = 4x+1$

97. $4(2c-3)-3(c-4) = 8c-12-3c+12$

$\qquad = 8c-3c-12+12$

$\qquad = 5c$

98. $4+(2y+2)+y = 4+2y+2+y$

$\qquad = 2y+y+4+2$

$\qquad = 3y+6$

99. $8x-(x-3) = 8x-x+3 = 7x+3$

100. $-(x-5)-3x+4 = -x+5-3x+4$

$\qquad = -x-3x+5+4$

$\qquad = -4x+9$

101. $-\left(\dfrac{3}{4}x-\dfrac{1}{3}\right)+2x = -\dfrac{3}{4}x+\dfrac{1}{3}+2x$

$\qquad = -\dfrac{3}{4}x+2x+\dfrac{1}{3}$

$\qquad = -\dfrac{3}{4}x+\dfrac{8}{4}x+\dfrac{1}{3}$

$\qquad = \dfrac{5}{4}x+\dfrac{1}{3}$

102. $-\left(\dfrac{7}{8}x-\dfrac{1}{2}\right)-3x = -\dfrac{7}{8}x+\dfrac{1}{2}-3x$

$\qquad = -\dfrac{7}{8}x-3x+\dfrac{1}{2}$

$\qquad = -\dfrac{7}{8}x-\dfrac{24}{8}+\dfrac{1}{2}$

$\qquad = -\dfrac{31}{8}x+\dfrac{1}{2}$

103. $\dfrac{2}{3}x+\dfrac{1}{2}(5x-4) = \dfrac{2}{3}x+\dfrac{5}{2}x-2$

$\qquad = \dfrac{4}{6}x+\dfrac{15}{6}x-2$

$\qquad = \dfrac{19}{6}x-2$

104 $\dfrac{4}{5}x+\dfrac{1}{7}(3x-1) = \dfrac{4}{5}x+\dfrac{3}{7}x-\dfrac{1}{7}$

$\qquad = \dfrac{28}{35}x+\dfrac{15}{35}x-\dfrac{1}{7}$

$\qquad = \dfrac{43}{35}x-\dfrac{1}{7}$

105. $-(3s+4)-(s+2) = -3s-4-s-2$
$$= -3s-s-4-2$$
$$= -4s-6$$

106. $6-2(x+3)+5x = 6-2x-6+5x$
$$= -2x+5x+6-6$$
$$= 3x$$

107. $4(x-1)+2(3-x)-4 = 4x-4(1)+2(3)-2x-4$
$$= 4x-4+6-2x-4$$
$$= 4x-2x-4+6-4$$
$$= 2x-2$$

108. $4(3b-2)-5(c-4)-6b$
$$= 4(3b)+4(-2)-5(c)-5(-4)-6b$$
$$= 12b-8-5c+20-6b$$
$$= 12b-6b-5c+20-8$$
$$= 6b-5c+12$$

109. $4(m+3)-4m-12 = 4m+4(3)-4m-12$
$$= 4m+12-4m-12$$
$$= 4m-4m+12-12$$
$$= 0$$

110. $-3(a+2b)+3(a+2b) = -3a-3(2b)+3a+3(2b)$
$$= -3a-6b+3a+6b$$
$$= -3a+3a-6b+6b$$
$$= 0$$

111. $0.4-(y+5)+0.6-2 = 0.4-y-5+0.6-2$
$$= -y+0.4-5+0.6-2$$
$$= -y-6$$

112. $4-(2-x)+3x = 4-2+x+3x$
$$= x+3x+4-2$$
$$= 4x+2$$

113. $4+(3x-4)-5 = 4+3x-4-5$
$$= 3x+4-4-5$$
$$= 3x-5$$

114. $2y-6(y-2)+3 = 2y-6y-6(-2)+3$
$$= 2y-6y+12+3$$
$$= -4y+15$$

115. $4(x+2)-3(x-4)-5 = 4x+4(2)-3x-3(-4)-5$
$$= 4x+8-3x+12-5$$
$$= 4x-3x+8+12-5$$
$$= x+15$$

116. $6-(a-5)-(2b+1) = 6-a+5-2b-1$
$$= -a-2b+6+5-1$$
$$= -a-2b+10$$

117. $-0.2(6-x)-4(y+0.4)$
$$= -0.2(6)-0.2(-x)-4y-4(0.4)$$
$$= -1.2+0.2x-4y-1.6$$
$$= 0.2x-4y-1.2-1.6$$
$$= 0.2x-4y-2.8$$

118. $-5(2y-8)-3(1+x)-7$
$$= -5(2y)-5(-8)-3(1)-3x-7$$
$$= -10y+40-3-3x-7$$
$$= -3x-10y+40-3-7$$
$$= -3x-10y+30$$

119. $-6x+7y-(3+x)+(x+3)$
$$= -6x+7y-3-x+x+3$$
$$= -6x-x+x+7y-3+3$$
$$= -6x+7y$$

120. $3(t-2)-2(t+4)-6 = 3t-6-2t-8-6$
$$= 3t-2t-6-8-6$$
$$= t-14-6$$
$$= t-20$$

121. $\frac{1}{2}(x+3)+\frac{1}{3}(3x+6) = \frac{1}{2}x+\frac{3}{2}+\frac{3}{3}x+\frac{6}{3}$
$$= \frac{1}{2}x+\frac{3}{2}+x+2$$
$$= \frac{1}{2}x+x+\frac{3}{2}+2$$
$$= \frac{1}{2}x+\frac{2}{2}x+\frac{3}{2}+\frac{4}{2}$$
$$= \frac{3}{2}x+\frac{7}{2}$$

122. $\frac{2}{3}(r-2)-\frac{1}{2}(r+4)=\frac{2}{3}r-\frac{4}{3}-\frac{1}{2}r-\frac{4}{2}$

$$=\frac{2}{3}r-\frac{1}{2}r-\frac{4}{3}-2$$

$$=\frac{4}{6}r-\frac{3}{6}r-\frac{4}{3}-\frac{6}{3}$$

$$=\frac{1}{6}r-\frac{10}{3}$$

123. $\square+\ominus+\ominus+\square+\ominus=2\square+3\ominus$

124. $\otimes+\copyright+\otimes+\copyright+\copyright+\copyright=2\otimes+4\copyright$

125. $x+y+\Delta+\Delta+x+y+y=x+x+y+y+y+\Delta+\Delta$

$$=2x+3y+2\Delta$$

126. $2+x+2+\ominus+\ominus+2+y$

$$=x+y+\ominus+\ominus+2+2+2$$

$$=x+y+2\ominus+6$$

127. $3\Delta+5\square-\Delta-3\square=3\Delta-\Delta+5\square-3\square=2\Delta+2\square$

128. $8\copyright-4\boxdot-2\boxdot-3\copyright=8\copyright-3\copyright-4\boxdot-2\boxdot$

$$=5\copyright-6\boxdot$$

129. $1\cdot18, 2\cdot9, 3\cdot6$

positive factors: 1, 2, 3, 6, 9, 18

130. $1\cdot24, 2\cdot12, 3\cdot8, 4\cdot6$

positive factors: 1, 2, 3, 4, 6, 8, 12, 24

131. $4x^2+5y^2+6(3x^2-5y^2)-4x+3$

$$=4x^2+5y^2+18x^2-30y^2-4x+3$$

$$=4x^2+18x^2-4x+5y^2-30y^2+3$$

$$=22x^2-25y^2-4x+3$$

132. $2x^2-4x+8x^2-3(x+2)-x^2-2$

$$=2x^2-4x+8x^2-3x-6-x^2-2$$

$$=2x^2+8x^2-x^2-4x-3x-6-2$$

$$=9x^2-7x-8$$

133. $2\big[3+4(x-5)\big]-\big[2-(x-3)\big]$

$$=2\big[3+4x-20\big]-\big[2-x+3\big]$$

$$=6+8x-40-2+x-3$$

$$=8x+x+6-40-2-3$$

$$=9x-39$$

134. $\frac{1}{4}\big[3-2(y+1)\big]-\frac{1}{3}\big[2-(y-6)\big]$

$$=\frac{1}{4}\big[3-2y-2\big]-\frac{1}{3}\big[2-y+6\big]$$

$$=\frac{1}{4}\big[1-2y\big]-\frac{1}{3}\big[8-y\big]$$

$$=\frac{1}{4}-\frac{2}{4}y-\frac{8}{3}+\frac{1}{3}y$$

$$=-\frac{2}{4}y+\frac{1}{3}y+\frac{1}{4}-\frac{8}{3}$$

$$=-\frac{3}{6}+\frac{2}{6}y+\frac{3}{12}-\frac{32}{12}$$

$$=-\frac{1}{6}y-\frac{29}{12}$$

135. $|-7|=7$

136. $-|-16|=-(16)=-16$

137. $-4-3-(-6)=-4-3+6=-7+6=-1$

138. Answers will vary. The answer should include that the order is parentheses, exponents, multiplication and division from left to right, and addition and subtraction from left to right.

139. Substitute -1 for each x in the expression.

$$-x^2+5x-6=-(-1)^2+5(-1)-6$$

$$=-1+(-5)-6$$

$$=-6-6$$

$$=-12$$

Exercise Set 2.2

1. An equation is a statement that shows two algebraic expressions are equal.

2. **a.** The solution to an equation is the number or numbers that make the equation a true statement.

   b. To solve an equation means to find the number or numbers that make the equation a true statement.

3. A solution to an equation may be checked by substituting the value in the equation and determining if it results in a true statement.

4. Answers will vary.

5. Equivalent equations are two or more equations with the same solution.

6. a. When we isolate the variable, we get the variable by itself on one side of the equation.

    b. Answers will vary.

7. Subtract 2 from both sides of the equation to isolate the variable.

8. Add 4 to both sides of the equation to isolate the variable.

9. One example is $x + 2 = 1$.

10. Subtraction is defined in terms of addition.

11. All 3 equations have $x = 1$ as their solution.

12. Add $\square$ to both sides of the equation in order to isolate the variable.

13. Substitute 2 for $x = 2$.
$$4x - 3 = 5$$
$$4(2) - 3 = 5$$
$$8 - 3 = 5$$
$$5 = 5 \quad \text{True}$$
Since we obtain true statement, 2 is a solution.

14. Substitute -6 for x, $x = -6$.
$$2x + 1 = x - 5$$
$$2(-6) + 1 = -6 - 5$$
$$-12 + 1 = -11$$
$$-11 = -11 \text{ True}$$
Since we obtain a true statement, -6 is a solution.

15. Substitute -3 for x, $x = -3$.
$$2x - 5 = 5(x + 2)$$
$$2(-3) - 5 = 5\left[(-3) + 2\right]$$
$$-6 - 5 = 5(-1)$$
$$-11 = -5 \text{ False}$$
Since we obtain a false statement, -3 is not a solution.

16. Substitute 1 for x, $x = 1$.
$$2(x - 3) = -3(x + 1)$$
$$2(1 - 3) = -3(1 + 1)$$
$$2(-2) = -3(2)$$
$$-4 = -6 \text{ False}$$
Since we obtain a false statement, 1 is not a solution.

17. Substitute -15 for p, $p = -15$.
$$2p - 5(p + 7) = 10$$
$$2(-15) - 5(-15 + 7) = 10$$
$$-30 - 5(-8) = 10$$
$$-30 + 40 = 10$$
$$10 = 10 \quad \text{True}$$
Since we obtain a true statement, -15 is a solution.

18. Substitute -2 for k, $k = -2$.
$$5k - 6(k - 1) = 8$$
$$5(-2) - 6(-2 - 1) = 8$$
$$-10 - 6(-3) = 8$$
$$-10 + 18 = 8$$
$$8 = 8 \quad \text{True}$$
Since we obtain a true statement, -2 is a solution.

19. Substitute 3.4 for x, $x = 3.4$.
$$3(x + 2) - 3(x - 1) = 9$$
$$3(3.4 + 2) - 3(3.4 - 1) = 9$$
$$3(5.4) - 3(2.4) = 9$$
$$16.2 - 7.2 = 9$$
$$9 = 9 \quad \text{True}$$
Since we obtain a true statement, 3.4 is a solution.

20. Substitute $\dfrac{3}{4}$ for x, $x = \dfrac{3}{4}$.
$$x + 5 = 5x + 2$$
$$\frac{3}{4} + 5 = 5\left(\frac{3}{4}\right) + 2$$
$$\frac{3}{4} + \frac{20}{4} = \frac{15}{4} + \frac{8}{4}$$
$$\frac{23}{4} = \frac{23}{4} \quad \text{True}$$

Since we obtain a true statement, $\dfrac{3}{4}$ is a solution.

21. Substitute $\frac{1}{2}$ for x, $x = \frac{1}{2}$.

$$4x - 4 = 2x - 2$$

$$4\left(\frac{1}{2}\right) - 4 = 2\left(\frac{1}{2}\right) - 2$$

$$2 - 4 = 1 - 2$$

$$-2 = -1 \text{ False}$$

Since we obtain a false statement, $\frac{1}{2}$ is not a solution.

22. Substitute $\frac{1}{3}$ for x, $x = \frac{1}{3}$.

$$7x + 3 = 2x + 5$$

$$7\left(\frac{1}{3}\right) + 3 = 2\left(\frac{1}{3}\right) + 5$$

$$\frac{7}{3} + \frac{12}{3} = \frac{2}{3} + \frac{15}{3}$$

$$\frac{19}{3} = \frac{17}{3} \text{ False}$$

Since we obtain a false statement, $\frac{1}{3}$ is not a solution.

23. Substitute $\frac{11}{2}$ for x, $x = \frac{11}{2}$.

$$3(x + 2) = 5(x - 1)$$

$$3\left(\frac{11}{2} + 2\right) = 5\left(\frac{11}{2} - 1\right)$$

$$3\left(\frac{15}{2}\right) = 5\left(\frac{9}{2}\right)$$

$$\frac{45}{2} = \frac{45}{2} \text{ True}$$

Since we obtain a true statement, $\frac{11}{2}$ is a solution.

24. Substitute 3 for h, $h = 3$.

$$-(h - 5) - (h - 6) = 3h - 4$$

$$-(3 - 5) - (3 - 6) = 3(3) - 4$$

$$-(-2) - (-3) = 9 - 4$$

$$2 + 3 = 5$$

$$5 = 5 \text{ True}$$

Since we obtain a true statement, 3 is a solution.

25. $x + 2 = 7$

$$x + 2 - 2 = 7 - 2$$

$$x + 0 = 5$$

$$x = 5$$

Check: $x + 2 = 7$

$$5 + 2 = 7$$

$$7 = 7 \text{ True}$$

26. $x - 4 = 13$

$$x - 4 + 4 = 13 + 4$$

$$x + 0 = 17$$

$$x = 17$$

Check: $x - 4 = 13$

$$17 - 4 = 13$$

$$13 = 13 \text{ True}$$

27. $-6 = x + 1$

$$-6 - 1 = x + 1 - 1$$

$$-7 = x + 0$$

$$-7 = x$$

Check: $-6 = x + 1$

$$-6 = -7 + 1$$

$$-6 = -6 \text{ True}$$

28. $-5 = x + 4$

$$-5 - 4 = x + 4 - 4$$

$$-9 = x + 0$$

$$-9 = x$$

Check: $-5 = x + 4$

$$-5 = -9 + 4$$

$$-5 = -5 \text{ True}$$

29. $x - 4 = -8$

$$x - 4 + 4 = -8 + 4$$

$$x + 0 = -4$$

$$x = -4$$

Check: $x - 4 = 8$

$$-4 - 4 = -8$$

$$-8 = -8 \text{ True}$$

30. $x - 16 = -12$

$$x - 16 + 16 = -12 + 16$$

$$x + 0 = 4$$

$$x = 4$$

Check: $x - 16 = -12$

$$4 - 16 = -12$$

$$-12 = -12 \text{ True}$$

31. $x + 9 = 52$

$x + 9 - 9 = 52 - 9$

$x + 0 = 43$

$x = 43$

Check: $x + 9 = 52$

$43 + 9 = 52$

$52 = 52$ True

32. $x + 8 = 17$

$x + 8 = 17$

$x + 8 - 8 = 17 - 8$

$x + 0 = 9$

$x = 9$

Check: $x + 8 = 17$

$9 + 8 = 17$

$17 = 17$ True

33. $-6 + w = 9$

$-6 + 6 + w = 9 + 6$

$0 + w = 15$

$w = 15$

Check: $-6 + w = 9$

$-6 + 15 = 9$

$9 = 9$ True

34. $3 = 7 + t$

$3 - 7 = 7 - 7 + t$

$-4 = 0 + t$

$-4 = t$

Check: $3 = 7 + t$

$3 = 7 + (-4)$

$3 = 3$ True

35. $27 = x + 16$

$27 - 16 = x + 16 - 16$

$11 = x + 0$

$11 = x$

Check: $27 = x + 16$

$27 = 11 + 16$

$27 = 27$ True

36. $50 = x - 25$

$50 + 25 = x - 25 + 25$

$75 = x + 0$

$75 = x$

Check: $50 = x - 25$

$50 = 75 - 25$

$50 = 50$ True

37. $-18 = x - 14$

$-18 + 14 = x - 14 + 14$

$-4 = x + 0$

$-4 = x$

Check: $-18 = x - 14$

$-18 = -4 - 14$

$-18 = -18$ True

38. $-4 = x - 3$

$-4 + 3 = x - 3 + 3$

$-1 = x + 0$

$-1 = x$

Check: $-4 = x - 3$

$-4 = -1 - 3$

$-4 = -4$ True

39. $9 + x = 4$

$9 - 9 + x = 4 - 9$

$0 + x = -5$

$x = -5$

Check: $9 + x = 4$

$9 + (-5) = 4$

$4 = 4$ True

40. $x + 29 = -29$

$x + 29 - 29 = -29 - 29$

$x + 0 = -58$

$x = -58$

Check: $x + 29 = -29$

$-58 + 29 = -29$

$-29 = -29$ True

41. $4 + x = -9$

$4 - 4 + x = -9 - 4$

$0 + x = -13$

$x = -13$

Check: $4 + x = -9$

$4 + (-13) = -9$

$-9 = -9$ True

42. $9 = x - 3$
$9 + 3 = x - 3 + 3$
$12 = x + 0$
$12 = x$
Check: $9 = x - 3$
$9 = 12 - 3$
$9 = 9$ True

43. $7 + r = -23$
$7 + r = -23$
$7 - 7 + r = -23 - 7$
$0 + r = -30$
$r = -30$
Check: $7 + r = -23$
$7 + (-30) = -23$
$-23 = -23$ True

44. $a - 5 = -9$
$a - 5 + 5 = -9 + 5$
$a + 0 = -4$
$a = -4$
Check: $a - 5 = -9$
$-4 - 5 = -9$
$-9 = -9$ True

45. $8 = 8 + v$
$8 - 8 = 8 - 8 + v$
$0 = 0 + v$
$0 = v$
Check: $8 = 8 + v$
$8 = 8 + 0$
$8 = 8$ True

46. $9 + x = 12$
$9 - 9 + x = 12 - 9$
$0 + x = 3$
$x = 3$
Check: $9 + x = 12$
$9 + 3 = 12$
$12 = 12$ True

47. $7 + x = -50$
$7 - 7 + x = -50 - 7$
$0 + x = -57$
$x = -57$
Check: $7 + x = -50$
$7 + (-57) = -50$
$-50 = -50$ True

48. $-17 = 8 + x$
$-17 - 8 = 8 - 8 + x$
$-25 = 0 + x$
$-25 = x$
Check: $-17 = 8 + x$
$-17 = 8 + (-25)$
$-17 = -17$ True

49. $12 = 16 + x$
$12 - 16 = 16 - 16 + x$
$-4 = 0 + x$
$-4 = x$
Check: $12 = 16 + x$
$12 = 16 + (-4)$
$12 = 12$ True

50. $62 = z - 15$
$62 + 15 = z - 15 + 15$
$77 = z + 0$
$77 = z$
Check: $62 = z - 15$
$62 = 77 - 15$
$62 = 62$ True

51. $15 + x = -5$
$15 - 15 + x = -5 - 15$
$0 + x = -20$
$x = -20$
Check: $15 + x = -5$
$15 + (-20) = -5$
$-5 = -5$ True

52. $-20 = 4 + x$
$-20 - 4 = 4 - 4 + x$
$-24 = 0 + x$
$-24 = x$
Check: $-20 = 4 + x$
$-20 = 4 + (-24)$
$-20 = -20$ True

53. $-15 + x = -15$
$-15 + 15 + x = -15 + 15$
$0 + x = 0$
$x = 0$
Check: $-15 + x = -15$
$-15 + 0 = -15$
$-15 = -15$ True

54. $8 = 8 + x$

$8 - 8 = 8 - 8 + x$

$0 = 0 + x$

$0 = x$

Check: $8 = 8 + x$

$8 = 8 + 0$

$8 = 8$ True

55. $5 = x - 12$

$5 + 12 = x - 12 + 12$

$17 = x + 0$

$17 = x$

Check: $5 = x - 12$

$5 = 17 - 12$

$5 = 5$ True

56. $-12 = 20 + c$

$-12 - 20 = 20 - 20 + c$

$-32 = 0 + c$

$-32 = c$

Check: $-12 = 20 + c$

$-12 = 20 + (-32)$

$-12 = -12$ True

57. $-50 = x - 24$

$-50 + 24 = x - 24 + 24$

$-26 = x + 0$

$-26 = x$

Check: $-50 = x - 24$

$-50 = -26 - 24$

$-50 = -50$ True

58. $-29 + x = -15$

$-29 + 29 + x = -15 + 29$

$0 + x = 14$

$x = 14$

Check: $-29 + x = -15$

$-29 + 14 = -15$

$-15 = -15$ True

59. $43 = 15 + p$

$43 - 15 = 15 - 15 + p$

$28 = 0 + p$

$28 = p$

Check: $43 = 15 + p$

$43 = 15 + 28$

$43 = 43$ True

60. $-25 = 74 + x$

$-25 - 74 = 74 - 74 + x$

$-99 = 0 + x$

$-99 = x$

Check: $-25 = 74 + x$

$-25 = 74 + (-99)$

$-25 = -25$ True

61. $40.2 + x = -5.9$

$40.2 - 40.2 + x = -5.9 - 40.2$

$0 + x = -46.1$

$x = -46.1$

Check: $40.2 + x = -5.9$

$40.2 + (-46.1) = -5.9$

$-5.9 = -5.9$ True

62. $-27.23 + x = 9.77$

$-27.23 + 27.23 + x = 9.77 + 27.23$

$0 + x = 37$

$x = 37$

Check: $-27.23 + x = 9.77$

$-27.23 + 37 = 9.77$

$9.77 = 9.77$ True

63. $-37 + x = 9.5$

$-37 + 37 + x = 9.5 + 37$

$0 + x = 46.5$

$x = 46.5$

Check: $-37 + x = 9.5$

$-37 + 46.5 = 9.5$

$9.5 = 9.5$ True

64. $7.2 + x = 7.2$

$7.2 - 7.2 + x = 7.2 - 7.2$

$0 + x = 0$

$x = 0$

Check: $7.2 + x = 7.2$

$7.2 + 0 = 7.2$

$7.2 = 7.2$ True

65. $x - 8.77 = -17$

$x - 8.77 + 8.77 = -17 + 8.77$

$x + 0 = -8.23$

$x = -8.23$

Check: $x - 8.77 = -17$

$-8.23 - 8.77 = -17$

$-17 = -17$ True

66. $6.1 + x = 10.2$
$6.1 - 6.1 + x = 10.2 - 6.1$
$0 + x = 4.1$
$x = 4.1$
Check: $6.1 + x = 10.2$
$6.1 + 4.1 = 10.2$
$10.2 = 10.2$ True

67. $9.32 = x + 3.75$
$9.32 - 3.75 = x + 3.75 - 3.75$
$5.57 = x + 0$
$5.57 = x$
Check: $9.32 = x + 3.75$
$9.32 = 5.57 + 3.75$
$9.32 = 9.32$ True

68. $-5.62 = y + 11.39$
$-5.62 - 11.39 = y + 11.39 - 11.39$
$-17.01 = y + 0$
$-17.01 = y$
Check: $-5.62 = y + 11.39$
$-5.62 = -17.01 + 11.39$
$-5.62 = -5.62$ True

69. No; there are no real numbers that can make $x + 1 = x + 2$.

70. Yes; infinite number; the equation $x + 4 = x + 4$ is true no matter what real number is substituted for x.

71. $x - \Delta = \square$
$x - \Delta + \Delta = \square + \Delta$
$x = \square + \Delta$

72. $\square + \copyright = \Delta$
$\square - \square + \copyright = \Delta - \square$
$\copyright = \Delta - \square$

73. $\copyright = \square + \Delta$
$\copyright - \Delta = \square + \Delta - \Delta$
$\copyright - \Delta = \square$

74. $\square = \Delta + \copyright$
$\square - \Delta = \Delta - \Delta + \copyright$
$\square - \Delta = \copyright$

75. a. yes **b.** yes **c.** yes **d.** yes
e. Since the left side of the equation is equal to the right side of the equation, $2x + 6 = 2x + 6$, the solution is all real numbers.

76. $-\dfrac{7}{15} + \dfrac{5}{6} = -\dfrac{14}{30} + \dfrac{25}{30} = \dfrac{-14 + 25}{30} = \dfrac{11}{30}$

77. $-\dfrac{11}{12} + \left(-\dfrac{3}{8}\right) = -\dfrac{22}{24} + \left(-\dfrac{9}{24}\right) = \dfrac{-22 + (-9)}{24} = -\dfrac{31}{24}$

78. $4x + 3(x - 2) - 5x - 7 = 4x + 3x - 6 - 5x - 7$
$= 4x + 3x - 5x - 6 - 7$
$= 2x - 13$

79. $-(2t + 4) + 3(4t - 5) - 3t = -2t - 4 + 12t - 15 - 3t$
$= -2t + 12t - 3t - 4 - 15$
$= 7t - 19$

Exercise Set 2.3

1. Answers will vary. Answer should include that both sides of an equation can be multiplied by the same nonzero number without changing the solution to the equation.

2. Division is defined in terms of multiplication.

3. a. $-x = a$
$-1x = a$
$(-1)(-1x) = (-1)a$
$1x = -a$
$x = -a$

b. $-x = 5$
$-1x = 5$
$(-1)(-1x) = (-1)5$
$1x = -5$
$x = -5$

c. $-x = -5$
$-1x = -5$
$(-1)(-1x) = (-1)(-5)$
$1x = 5$
$x = 5$

4. Divide both sides by –2 to isolate the variable.

5. Divide both sides by 3 to isolate the variable.

6. Multiply both sides by 3 because $3 \cdot \dfrac{x}{3} = x$.

7. Multiply both sides by 2 because $2 \cdot \dfrac{x}{2} = x$.

8. We divide by a to isolate the variable x.

9. $4x = 12$

$$\frac{4x}{4} = \frac{12}{4}$$

$$x = 3$$

Check: $4x = 12$

$$4(3) = 12$$

$$12 = 12 \quad \text{True}$$

10. $5x = 50$

$$\frac{5x}{5} = \frac{50}{5}$$

$$x = 10$$

Check: $5x = 50$

$$5(10) = 50$$

$$50 = 50 \quad \text{True}$$

11. $\dfrac{x}{3} = 7$

$$3\left(\frac{x}{3}\right) = 3(7)$$

$$x = 21$$

Check: $\dfrac{x}{3} = 7$

$$\frac{21}{3} = 7$$

$$7 = 7 \quad \text{True}$$

12. $\dfrac{y}{5} = 3$

$$5\left(\frac{y}{5}\right) = 5(3)$$

$$y = 15$$

Check: $\dfrac{y}{5} = 3$

$$\frac{15}{5} = 3$$

$$3 = 3 \quad \text{True}$$

13. $-4x = 12$

$$\frac{-4x}{-4} = \frac{12}{-4}$$

$$x = -3$$

Check: $-4x = 12$

$$-4(-3) = 12$$

$$12 = 12 \quad \text{True}$$

14. $8 = 16y$

$$\frac{8}{16} = \frac{16y}{16}$$

$$\frac{1}{2} = y$$

Check: $8 = 16y$

$$8 = 16\left(\frac{1}{2}\right)$$

$$8 = 8 \quad \text{True}$$

15. $\dfrac{x}{4} = -2$

$$4\left(\frac{x}{4}\right) = 4(-2)$$

$$x = 4(-2)$$

$$x = -8$$

Check: $\dfrac{x}{4} = -2$

$$\frac{-8}{4} = -2$$

$$-2 = -2 \quad \text{True}$$

16. $\dfrac{x}{3} = -3$

$$3\left(\frac{x}{3}\right) = 3(-3)$$

$$x = -9$$

Check: $\dfrac{x}{3} = -3$

$$\frac{-9}{3} = -3$$

$$-3 = -3 \quad \text{True}$$

17. $\dfrac{x}{5} = 1$

$5\left(\dfrac{x}{5}\right) = 5(1)$

$x = 5$

Check: $\dfrac{x}{5} = 1$

$\dfrac{5}{5} = 1$

$1 = 1$ True

18. $-7x = 49$

$\dfrac{-7x}{-7} = \dfrac{49}{-7}$

$x = -7$

Check: $\quad -7x = 49$

$-7(-7) = 49$

$49 = 49$ True

19. $-27n = 81$

$\dfrac{-27n}{-27} = \dfrac{81}{-27}$

$n = -3$

Check: $\quad -27n = 81$

$-27(-3) = 81$

$81 = 81$ True

20. $\dfrac{x}{8} = -3$

$8\left(\dfrac{x}{8}\right) = 8(-3)$

$x = -24$

Check: $\quad \dfrac{x}{8} = -3$

$\dfrac{-24}{8} = -3$

$-3 = -3$ True

21. $-7 = 3r$

$\dfrac{-7}{3} = \dfrac{3r}{3}$

$-\dfrac{7}{3} = r$

Check: $-7 = 3r$

$-7 = 3\left(-\dfrac{7}{3}\right)$

$-7 = -7$ True

22. $16 = -4y$

$\dfrac{16}{-4} = \dfrac{-4y}{-4}$

$-4 = y$

Check: $16 = -4y$

$16 = -4(-4)$

$16 = 16$ True

23. $-x = 13$

$-1x = 13$

$(-1)(-1x) = (-1)(13)$

$1x = -13$

$x = -13$

Check: $\quad -x = 13$

$-(-13) = 13$

$13 = 13$ True

24. $-x = 9$

$-1x = 9$

$(-1)(-1x) = (-1)(9)$

$1x = -9$

$x = -9$

Check: $\quad -x = 9$

$-(-9) = 9$

$9 = 9$ True

25. $-x = -8$

$-1x = -8$

$(-1)(-1x) = (-1)(-8)$

$1x = 8$

$x = 8$

Check: $-x = -8$

$-(8) = -8$

$-8 = -8$ True

26. $-x = -15$

$-1x = -15$

$(-1)(-1x) = (-1)(-15)$

$1x = 15$

$x = 15$

Check: $\quad -x = -15$

$-(15) = -15$

$-15 = -15$ True

27.
$$-\frac{w}{3} = -13$$
$$\frac{w}{-3} = -13$$
$$(-3)\left(\frac{w}{-3}\right) = (-3)(-13)$$
$$w = 39$$
Check: $-\dfrac{w}{3} = -13$
$$-\frac{39}{3} = -13$$
$$-13 = -13 \ \text{True}$$

28.
$$-4 = \frac{c}{7}$$
$$7(-4) = 7\left(\frac{c}{7}\right)$$
$$-28 = c$$
Check: $-4 = \dfrac{c}{7}$
$$-4 = \frac{-28}{7}$$
$$-4 = -4 \ \text{True}$$

29.
$$4 = -12x$$
$$\frac{4}{-12} = \frac{-12x}{-12}$$
$$-\frac{1}{3} = x$$
Check: $4 = -12x$
$$4 = -12\left(-\frac{1}{3}\right)$$
$$4 = 4 \ \text{True}$$

30.
$$12y = -15$$
$$\frac{12y}{12} = \frac{-15}{12}$$
$$y = -\frac{5}{4}$$
Check: $12y = -15$
$$12\left(-\frac{5}{4}\right) = -15$$
$$-15 = -15 \ \text{True}$$

31.
$$-\frac{x}{3} = -2$$
$$\frac{x}{-3} = -2$$
$$(-3)\left(\frac{x}{-3}\right) = (-3)(-2)$$
$$x = 6$$
Check: $-\dfrac{x}{3} = -2$
$$-\frac{6}{3} = -2$$
$$-2 = -2 \ \text{True}$$

32.
$$-\frac{a}{8} = -7$$
$$\frac{a}{-8} = -7$$
$$(-8)\left(\frac{a}{-8}\right) = (-8)(-7)$$
$$a = 56$$
Check: $-\dfrac{a}{8} = -7$
$$-\frac{56}{8} = -7$$
$$-7 = -7 \ \text{True}$$

33.
$$43t = 26$$
$$\frac{43t}{43} = \frac{26}{43}$$
$$t = \frac{26}{43}$$
Check: $\qquad 43t = 26$
$$43\left(\frac{26}{43}\right) = 26$$
$$26 = 26 \ \text{True}$$

34.
$$-24x = -18$$
$$\frac{-24x}{-24} = \frac{-18}{-24}$$
$$x = \frac{3}{4}$$
Check: $\qquad -24x = -18$
$$-24\left(\frac{3}{4}\right) = -18$$
$$-18 = -18 \ \text{True}$$

35. $-4.2x = -8.4$

$$\frac{-4.2x}{-4.2} = \frac{-8.4}{-4.2}$$

$$x = 2$$

Check: $-4.2x = -8.4$

$$-4.2(2) = -8.4$$

$$-8.4 = -8.4 \text{ True}$$

36. $-3.88 = 1.94y$

$$\frac{-3.88}{1.94} = \frac{1.94y}{1.94}$$

$$-2 = y$$

Check: $-3.88 = 1.94y$

$$-3.88 = 1.94(-2)$$

$$-3.88 = -3.88 \text{ True}$$

37. $3x = \frac{3}{5}$

$$\frac{1}{3} \cdot 3x = \frac{1}{3} \cdot \frac{3}{5}$$

$$x = \frac{1}{1} \cdot \frac{1}{5}$$

$$x = \frac{1 \cdot 1}{1 \cdot 5}$$

$$x = \frac{1}{5}$$

Check: $3x = \frac{3}{5}$

$$3\left(\frac{1}{5}\right) = \frac{3}{5}$$

$$\frac{3}{5} = \frac{3}{5} \text{ True}$$

38. $7x = -7$

$$\frac{7x}{7} = \frac{-7}{7}$$

$$x = -1$$

Check: $7x = -7$

$$7(-1) = -7$$

$$-7 = -7 \text{ True}$$

39. $5x = -\frac{3}{8}$

$$\frac{1}{5} \cdot 5x = \left(\frac{1}{5}\right) \cdot \left(-\frac{3}{8}\right)$$

$$x = \frac{1(-3)}{5(8)}$$

$$x = -\frac{3}{40}$$

Check: $5x = -\frac{3}{8}$

$$5\left(-\frac{3}{40}\right) = -\frac{3}{8}$$

$$-\frac{3}{8} = -\frac{3}{8} \text{ True}$$

40. $-2b = -\frac{4}{5}$

$$\left(-\frac{1}{2}\right)(-2b) = \left(-\frac{1}{2}\right)\left(-\frac{4}{5}\right)$$

$$b = \frac{-1}{1} \cdot \frac{-2}{5}$$

$$b = \frac{-1 \cdot -2}{1 \cdot 5}$$

$$b = \frac{2}{5}$$

Check: $-2b = -\frac{4}{5}$

$$-2\left(\frac{2}{5}\right) = -\frac{4}{5}$$

$$-\frac{4}{5} = -\frac{4}{5} \text{ True}$$

41. $15 = -\frac{x}{4}$

$$15 = \frac{x}{-4}$$

$$(-4)(15) = (-4) \cdot \left(\frac{x}{-4}\right)$$

$$-60 = x$$

Check: $15 = -\frac{x}{4}$

$$15 = -\frac{(-60)}{4}$$

$$15 = 15 \text{ True}$$

42.
$$\frac{c}{9} = 0$$
$$9 \cdot \frac{c}{9} = 9 \cdot 0$$
$$c = 0$$
Check: $\frac{c}{9} = 0$
$$\frac{0}{9} = 0$$
$$0 = 0 \quad \text{True}$$

43.
$$-\frac{b}{4} = -60$$
$$\frac{b}{-4} = -60$$
$$-4\left(\frac{b}{-4}\right) = (-4)(-60)$$
$$b = 240$$
Check: $-\frac{b}{4} = -60$
$$-\frac{240}{4} = -60$$
$$-60 = -60 \quad \text{True}$$

44.
$$-x = -\frac{5}{9}$$
$$-1x = -\frac{5}{9}$$
$$(-1)(-1x) = (-1)\left(-\frac{5}{9}\right)$$
$$1x = \frac{5}{9}$$
$$x = \frac{5}{9}$$
Check: $-x = -\frac{5}{9}$
$$-\frac{5}{9} = -\frac{5}{9} \quad \text{True}$$

45.
$$\frac{x}{5} = -7$$
$$5\left(\frac{x}{5}\right) = 5(-7)$$
$$x = -35$$
Check: $\frac{x}{5} = -7$
$$\frac{-35}{5} = -7$$
$$-7 = -7 \quad \text{True}$$

46.
$$-3r = 0$$
$$\frac{-3r}{-3} = \frac{0}{-3}$$
$$r = 0$$
Check: $-3r = 0$
$$-3(0) = 0$$
$$0 = 0 \quad \text{True}$$

47.
$$5 = \frac{x}{4}$$
$$4 \cdot 5 = 4\left(\frac{x}{4}\right)$$
$$20 = x$$
Check: $5 = \frac{x}{4}$
$$5 = \frac{20}{4}$$
$$5 = 5 \quad \text{True}$$

48.
$$-3 = \frac{x}{-5}$$
$$(-5)(-3) = (-5)\left(\frac{x}{-5}\right)$$
$$15 = x$$
Check: $-3 = \frac{x}{-5}$
$$-3 = \frac{15}{-5}$$
$$-3 = -3 \quad \text{True}$$

49.
$$\frac{3}{5}d = -30$$
$$\frac{5}{3} \cdot \frac{3}{5}d = \frac{5}{3}(-30)$$
$$d = -50$$
Check: $\frac{3}{5}d = -30$
$$\frac{3}{5}(-50) = -30$$
$$-30 = -30 \quad \text{True}$$

50. $\dfrac{2}{7}x = 7$

$\dfrac{7}{2} \cdot \dfrac{2}{7}x = \dfrac{7}{2} \cdot 7$

$x = \dfrac{49}{2}$

Check: $\dfrac{2}{7}x = 7$

$\dfrac{2}{7} \cdot \dfrac{49}{2} = 7$

$\dfrac{1}{1} \cdot \dfrac{7}{1} = 7$

$7 = 7$ True

51. $\dfrac{y}{-2} = 0$

$(-2)\left(\dfrac{y}{-2}\right) = (-2)(0)$

$y = 0$

Check: $\dfrac{y}{-2} = 0$

$\dfrac{0}{-2} = 0$

$0 = 0$ True

52. $-6x = \dfrac{5}{2}$

$\left(-\dfrac{1}{6}\right)(-6x) = -\dfrac{1}{6} \cdot \dfrac{5}{2}$

$x = -\dfrac{5}{12}$

Check: $-6x = \dfrac{5}{2}$

$-6\left(-\dfrac{5}{12}\right) = \dfrac{5}{2}$

$\dfrac{5}{2} = \dfrac{5}{2}$ True

53. $\dfrac{-7}{8}w = 0$

$\dfrac{8}{-7}\left(\dfrac{-7}{8}w\right) = \dfrac{8}{-7} \cdot 0$

$w = 0$

Check: $\dfrac{-7}{8}w = 0$

$\dfrac{-7}{8}(0) = 0$

$0 = 0$ True

54. $-x = \dfrac{5}{8}$

$-1x = \dfrac{5}{8}$

$(-1)(-1)x = (-1)\dfrac{5}{8}$

$x = -\dfrac{5}{8}$

Check: $-x = \dfrac{5}{8}$

$-\left(-\dfrac{5}{8}\right) = \dfrac{5}{8}$

$\dfrac{5}{8} = \dfrac{5}{8}$ True

55. $\dfrac{1}{5}x = 4.5$

$5\left(\dfrac{1}{5}x\right) = 5(4.5)$

$x = 22.5$

Check: $\dfrac{1}{5}x = 4.5$

$\dfrac{1}{5}(22.5) = 4.5$

$4.5 = 4.5$ True

56. $-\dfrac{1}{4}x = \dfrac{3}{4}$

$\left(-\dfrac{4}{1}\right)\left(-\dfrac{1}{4}x\right) = \left(-\dfrac{4}{1}\right)\left(\dfrac{3}{4}\right)$

$x = -3$

Check: $-\dfrac{1}{4}x = \dfrac{3}{4}$

$-\dfrac{1}{4}(-3) = \dfrac{3}{4}$

$\dfrac{3}{4} = \dfrac{3}{4}$ True

57.
$$-4 = -\frac{2}{3}z$$
$$\left(-\frac{3}{2}\right)(-4) = \left(-\frac{3}{2}\right)\left(-\frac{2}{3}\right)z$$
$$6 = z$$
Check: $-4 = -\frac{2}{3}z$
$$-4 = -\frac{2}{3} \cdot 6$$
$$-4 = -4 \text{ True}$$

58.
$$-9 = \frac{-5}{3}n$$
$$\left(\frac{3}{-5}\right)(-9) = \left(\frac{3}{-5}\right)\left(\frac{-5}{3}\right)n$$
$$\frac{27}{5} = n$$
Check: $-9 = \frac{-5}{3}n$
$$-9 = \frac{-5}{3} \cdot \frac{27}{5}$$
$$-9 = -9 \quad \text{True}$$

59. $-1.4x = 28.28$
$$\frac{-1.4x}{-1.4} = \frac{28.28}{-1.4}$$
$$x = -20.2$$
Check: $\quad -1.4x = 28.28$
$$-1.4(-20.2) = 28.28$$
$$28.28 = 28.28 \text{ True}$$

60. $-0.42x = -2.142$
$$\frac{-0.42x}{-0.42} = \frac{-2.142}{-0.42}$$
$$x = 5.1$$
Check: $\quad -0.42x = -2.142$
$$-0.42(5.1) = -2.142$$
$$-2.142 = 2.142 \text{ True}$$

61. $-8x = -56$
$$x = \frac{-56}{-8}$$
$$x = 7$$
Check: $-8x = -56$
$$-8(7) = -56$$
$$-56 = -56 \text{ True}$$

62. $-9x = -45$
$$x = \frac{-45}{-9}$$
$$x = 5$$
Check: $\quad -9x = -45$
$$-9(5) = -45$$
$$-45 = -45$$

63. $\frac{2}{3}x = 6$
$$x = \frac{3}{2} \cdot 6$$
$$x = 9$$
Check: $\quad \frac{2}{3}x = 6$
$$\frac{2}{3}(9) = 6$$
$$6 = 6 \text{ True}$$

64. $\frac{1}{3}x = 15$
$$x = 3(15)$$
$$x = 45$$
Check: $\quad \frac{1}{3}x = 15$
$$\frac{1}{3}(45) = 15$$
$$15 = 15 \text{ True}$$

65. a. In $5 + x = 10$, 5 is added to the variable, whereas in $5x = 10$, 5 is multiplied by the variable.

   b.
$$5 + x = 10$$
$$5 + x - 5 = 10 - 5$$
$$x = 5$$

   c.
$$5x = 10$$
$$\frac{5x}{5} = \frac{10}{5}$$
$$x = 2$$

66. a. In $3 + x = 6$, 3 is added to the variable, whereas in $3x = 6$, 3 is multiplied by the variable.

   b.
$$3 + x = 6$$
$$3 + x - 3 = 6 - 3$$
$$x = 3$$

c. $3x = 6$

$$\frac{3x}{3} = \frac{6}{3}$$

$$x = 2$$

67. Multiplying by $\frac{3}{2}$ is easier because the equation involves fractions.

$$\frac{2}{3}x = 4$$

$$\left(\frac{3}{2}\right)\left(\frac{2}{3}\right)x = \left(\frac{3}{2}\right)\left(\frac{4}{1}\right)$$

$$x = \frac{12}{2}$$

$$x = 6$$

68. Multiplying by $\frac{1}{4}$ is easier because the equation involves a fraction.

$$4x = \frac{3}{5}$$

$$\left(\frac{1}{4}\right)4x = \left(\frac{1}{4}\right)\frac{3}{5}$$

$$x = \frac{3}{20}$$

69. Multiplying by $\frac{7}{3}$ is easier because the equation involves fractions.

$$\frac{3}{7}x = \frac{4}{5}$$

$$\left(\frac{7}{3}\right)\frac{3}{7}x = \left(\frac{7}{3}\right)\frac{4}{5}$$

$$x = \frac{28}{15}$$

70. a. ☉

b. Divide both sides of the equation by □.

c. $☉ = \dfrac{\triangle}{\square}$

71. a. ⊡

b. Divide both sides of the equation by Δ.

c. $⊡ = \dfrac{☺}{\triangle}$

72. a. ☺

b. Multiply both sides of the equation by △.

c. $\# = \dfrac{☺}{\triangle}$

$$\triangle \cdot \# = \triangle \cdot \frac{☺}{\triangle}$$

$$\triangle\# = ☺$$

73. $-8 - (-4) = -8 + 4 = -4$

74. $(-3)(-2)(5)(-1) = 6(5)(-1) = 30(-1) = -30$

75.
$$\begin{aligned}
4^2 - 2^3 \cdot 6 \div 3 + 6 &= 16 - 8 \cdot 6 \div 3 + 6 \\
&= 16 - 48 \div 3 + 6 \\
&= 16 - 16 + 6 \\
&= 0 + 6 \\
&= 6
\end{aligned}$$

76. Associative property of addition

77.
$$\begin{aligned}
-48 &= x + 9 \\
-48 - 9 &= x + 9 - 9 \\
-57 &= x + 0 \\
-57 &= x
\end{aligned}$$

Exercise Set 2.4

1. No; the variable x is on both sides of the equal sign.

2. Yes; the variable x is on only one side of the equal sign.

3. $x = \dfrac{1}{3}$ because $1x = x$.

4. $x = -\dfrac{3}{5}$ because $1x = x$.

5. $x = -\dfrac{1}{2}$ because $-x = -1x$.

6. $x = -\dfrac{7}{8}$ because $-x = -1x$.

7. $x = \dfrac{4}{9}$ because $-x = -1x$.

8. $x = \dfrac{3}{5}$ because $-x = -1x$.

9. You evaluate an expression. An expression cannot be solved. It is not true or false for given values; instead, it has a numerical value.

10. You solve an equation. An equation that contains a variable is true for certain values of that variable. We solve an equation to find those values.

11. a. Answers will vary.

    b. Answers will vary.

12. Multiplying both sides of the equation by the LCD is the first step.

13. a. Use the distributive property.
       Subtract 8 from both sides of the equation.
       Divide both sides of the equation by 6.

    b. $2(3x+4) = -4$

       $6x + 8 = -4$

       $6x + 8 - 8 = -4 - 8$

       $6x = -12$

       $\dfrac{6x}{6} = -\dfrac{12}{6}$

       $x = -2$

14. a. Use the distributive property.
       Combine like terms.
       Add 6 to both sides of the equation.
       Divide both sides of the equation by 2.

    b. $4x - 2(x+3) = 4$

       $4x - 2x - 6 = 4$

       $2x - 6 = 4$

       $2x - 6 + 6 = 4 + 6$

       $2x = 10$

       $\dfrac{2x}{2} = \dfrac{10}{2}$

       $x = 5$

15. $5x - 6 = 19$

    $5x - 6 + 6 = 19 + 6$

    $5x = 25$

    $\dfrac{5x}{5} = \dfrac{25}{5}$

    $x = 5$

16. $2x - 4 = 8$

    $2x - 4 + 4 = 8 + 4$

    $2x = 12$

    $\dfrac{2x}{2} = \dfrac{12}{2}$

    $x = 6$

17. $-4w - 5 = 11$

    $-4w - 5 + 5 = 11 + 5$

    $-4w = 16$

    $\dfrac{-4w}{-4} = \dfrac{16}{-4}$

    $w = -4$

18. $-4x + 6 = 20$

    $-4x + 6 - 6 = 20 - 6$

    $-4x = 14$

    $\dfrac{-4x}{-4} = \dfrac{14}{-4}$

    $x = -\dfrac{7}{2}$

19. $3x + 6 = 12$

    $3x + 6 - 6 = 12 - 6$

    $3x = 6$

    $\dfrac{3x}{3} = \dfrac{6}{3}$

    $x = 2$

20. $6 - 3x = 18$

    $6 - 6 - 3x = 18 - 6$

    $-3x = 12$

    $\dfrac{-3x}{-3} = \dfrac{12}{-3}$

    $x = -4$

21. $5x - 2 = 10$

    $5x - 2 + 2 = 10 + 2$

    $5x = 12$

    $\dfrac{5x}{5} = \dfrac{12}{5}$

    $x = \dfrac{12}{5}$

22. $-2t + 9 = 21$
$-2t + 9 - 9 = 21 - 9$
$-2t = 12$
$\dfrac{-2t}{-2} = \dfrac{12}{-2}$
$t = -6$

23. $-5k - 4 = -19$
$-5k - 4 + 4 = -19 + 4$
$-5k = -15$
$\dfrac{-5k}{-5} = \dfrac{-15}{-5}$
$k = 3$

24. $-4x - 7 = -6$
$-4x - 7 + 7 = -6 + 7$
$-4x = 1$
$\dfrac{-4x}{-4} = \dfrac{1}{-4}$
$x = -\dfrac{1}{4}$

25. $12 - x = 9$
$12 - 12 - x = 9 - 12$
$-x = -3$
$(-1)(-x) = (-1)(-3)$
$x = 3$

26. $-3x - 3 = -12$
$-3x - 3 + 3 = -12 + 3$
$-3x = -9$
$\dfrac{-3x}{-3} = \dfrac{-9}{-3}$
$x = 3$

27. $8 + 3x = 19$
$8 - 8 + 3x = 19 - 8$
$3x = 11$
$\dfrac{3x}{3} = \dfrac{11}{3}$
$x = \dfrac{11}{3}$

28. $-2x + 7 = -10$
$-2x + 7 - 7 = -10 - 7$
$-2x = -17$
$\dfrac{-2x}{-2} = \dfrac{-17}{-2}$
$x = \dfrac{17}{2}$

29. $16x + 5 = -14$
$16x + 5 - 5 = -14 - 5$
$16x = -19$
$\dfrac{16x}{16} = \dfrac{-19}{16}$
$x = -\dfrac{19}{16}$

30. $19 = 25 + 4x$
$19 - 25 = 25 - 25 + 4x$
$-6 = 4x$
$\dfrac{-6}{4} = \dfrac{4x}{4}$
$-\dfrac{3}{2} = x$

31. $-4.2 = 3x + 25.8$
$-4.2 - 25.8 = 3x + 25.8 - 25.8$
$-30 = 3x$
$\dfrac{-30}{3} = \dfrac{3x}{3}$
$-10 = x$

32. $-24 + 16x = -24$
$-24 + 24 + 16x = -24 + 24$
$16x = 0$
$\dfrac{16x}{16} = \dfrac{0}{16}$
$x = 0$

33. $7r - 16 = -2$
$7r - 16 + 16 = -2 + 16$
$7r = 14$
$\dfrac{7r}{7} = \dfrac{14}{7}$
$r = 2$

34.
$$-2w + 4 = -8$$
$$-2w + 4 - 4 = -8 - 4$$
$$-2w = -12$$
$$\frac{-2w}{-2} = \frac{-12}{-2}$$
$$w = 6$$

35.
$$60 = -5s + 9$$
$$60 - 9 = -5s + 9 - 9$$
$$51 = -5s$$
$$\frac{51}{-5} = \frac{-5s}{-5}$$
$$-\frac{51}{5} = s$$

36.
$$15 = 7x + 1$$
$$15 - 1 = 7x + 1 - 1$$
$$14 = 7x$$
$$\frac{14}{7} = \frac{7x}{7}$$
$$2 = x$$

37.
$$14 = 5x + 8 - 3x$$
$$14 = 5x - 3x + 8$$
$$14 = 2x + 8$$
$$14 - 8 = 2x + 8 - 8$$
$$6 = 2x$$
$$\frac{6}{2} = \frac{2x}{2}$$
$$3 = x$$

38.
$$15 = 6x - 3 + 3x$$
$$15 = 6x + 3x - 3$$
$$15 = 9x - 3$$
$$15 + 3 = 9x - 3 + 3$$
$$18 = 9x$$
$$\frac{18}{9} = \frac{9x}{9}$$
$$2 = x$$

39.
$$2.3x - 9.34 = 6.3$$
$$2.3x - 9.34 + 9.34 = 6.3 + 9.34$$
$$2.3x = 15.64$$
$$\frac{2.3x}{2.3} = \frac{15.64}{2.3}$$
$$x = 6.8$$

40.
$$x + 0.05x = 21$$
$$1.05x = 21$$
$$\frac{1.05x}{1.05} = \frac{21}{1.05}$$
$$x = 20$$

41.
$$0.91y + 2.25 - 0.01y = 5.85$$
$$0.91y - 0.01y + 2.25 = 5.85$$
$$0.90y + 2.25 = 5.85$$
$$0.90y + 2.25 - 2.25 = 5.85 - 2.25$$
$$0.90y = 3.60$$
$$\frac{0.90y}{0.90} = \frac{3.60}{0.90}$$
$$y = 4$$

42.
$$0.15 = 0.05x - 1.35 - 0.20x$$
$$0.15 = 0.05x - 0.20x - 1.35$$
$$0.15 = -0.15x - 1.35$$
$$0.15 + 1.35 = -0.15x - 1.35 + 1.35$$
$$1.50 = -0.15x$$
$$\frac{1.50}{-0.15} = \frac{-0.15x}{-0.15}$$
$$-10 = x$$

43.
$$28.8 = x + 1.40x$$
$$28.8 = 2.40x$$
$$\frac{28.8}{2.40} = \frac{2.40x}{2.40}$$
$$12 = x$$

44.
$$8.40 = 2.45x - 1.05x$$
$$8.40 = 1.40x$$
$$\frac{8.40}{1.40} = \frac{1.40x}{1.40}$$
$$6 = x$$

45.
$$\frac{1}{7}(x + 6) = 4$$
$$7\left[\frac{1}{7}(x + 6)\right] = 7(4)$$
$$x + 6 = 28$$
$$x + 6 - 6 = 28 - 6$$
$$x = 22$$

46. $\dfrac{m-6}{5} = 2$

$$5\left(\dfrac{m-6}{5}\right) = 5(2)$$

$$m-6 = 10$$

$$m-6+6 = 10+6$$

$$m = 16$$

47. $\dfrac{d+3}{7} = 9$

$$7\left(\dfrac{d+3}{7}\right) = 7(9)$$

$$d+3 = 63$$

$$d+3-3 = 63-3$$

$$d = 60$$

48. $\dfrac{1}{5}(x+2) = -3$

$$5\left[\dfrac{1}{5}(x+2)\right] = 5(-3)$$

$$x+2 = -15$$

$$x+2-2 = -15-2$$

$$x = -17$$

49. $\dfrac{1}{3}(t-5) = -6$

$$3\left[\dfrac{1}{3}(t-5)\right] = 3(-6)$$

$$t-5 = -18$$

$$t-5+5 = -18+5$$

$$t = -13$$

50. $\dfrac{2}{3}(n-3) = 8$

$$\dfrac{3}{2}\left[\dfrac{2}{3}(n-3)\right] = \dfrac{3}{2}(8)$$

$$n-3 = 12$$

$$n-3+3 = 12+3$$

$$n = 15$$

51. $\dfrac{3}{4}(x-5) = -12$

$$\dfrac{4}{3}\left[\dfrac{3}{4}(x-5)\right] = \dfrac{4}{3}(-12)$$

$$x-5 = -16$$

$$x-5+5 = -16+5$$

$$x = -11$$

52. $\dfrac{1}{4} = \dfrac{z+1}{4}$

$$4\left(\dfrac{1}{4}\right) = 4\left(\dfrac{z+1}{4}\right)$$

$$1 = z+1$$

$$1-1 = z+1-1$$

$$0 = z$$

53. $\dfrac{x+4}{7} = \dfrac{3}{7}$

$$7\left(\dfrac{x+4}{7}\right) = 7\left(\dfrac{3}{7}\right)$$

$$x+4 = 3$$

$$x+4-4 = 3-4$$

$$x = -1$$

54. $\dfrac{4x+5}{6} = \dfrac{7}{2}$

$$6\left(\dfrac{4x+5}{6}\right) = 6\left(\dfrac{7}{2}\right)$$

$$4x+5 = 21$$

$$4x+5-5 = 21-5$$

$$4x = 16$$

$$\dfrac{4x}{4} = \dfrac{16}{4}$$

$$x = 4$$

55. $\dfrac{3}{4} = \dfrac{4m-5}{6}$

$$12\left(\dfrac{3}{4}\right) = 12\left(\dfrac{4m-5}{6}\right)$$

$$9 = 2(4m-5)$$

$$9 = 8m-10$$

$$9+10 = 8m-10+10$$

$$19 = 8m$$

$$\dfrac{19}{8} = \dfrac{8m}{8}$$

$$\dfrac{19}{8} = m$$

56. $\dfrac{5}{6} = \dfrac{5t-4}{2}$

$6\left(\dfrac{5}{6}\right) = 6\left(\dfrac{5t-4}{2}\right)$

$5 = 3(5t-4)$

$5 = 15t-12$

$5+12 = 15t-12+12$

$17 = 15t$

$\dfrac{17}{15} = \dfrac{15t}{15}$

$\dfrac{17}{15} = t$

57. $4(n+2) = 8$

$4n+8 = 8$

$4n+8-8 = 8-8$

$4n = 0$

$\dfrac{4n}{4} = \dfrac{0}{4}$

$n = 0$

58. $3(x-2) = 12$

$3x-6 = 12$

$3x-6+6 = 12+6$

$3x = 18$

$\dfrac{3x}{3} = \dfrac{18}{3}$

$x = 6$

59. $-2(x-3) = 26$

$-2x+6 = 26$

$-2x+6-6 = 26-6$

$-2x = 20$

$\dfrac{-2x}{-2} = \dfrac{20}{-2}$

$x = -10$

60. $5(3-x) = 15$

$15-5x = 15$

$15-15-5x = 15-15$

$-5x = 0$

$\dfrac{-5x}{-5} = \dfrac{0}{-5}$

$x = 0$

61. $-4 = -(x+5)$

$-4 = -x-5$

$-4+5 = -x-5+5$

$1 = -x$

$(-1)(1) = (-1)(-x)$

$-1 = x$

62. $-3(2-3x) = 9$

$-6+9x = 9$

$-6+6+9x = 9+6$

$9x = 15$

$\dfrac{9x}{9} = \dfrac{15}{9}$

$x = \dfrac{5}{3}$

63. $12 = 4(x-3)$

$12 = 4x-12$

$12+12 = 4x-12+12$

$24 = 4x$

$\dfrac{24}{4} = \dfrac{4x}{4}$

$6 = x$

64. $-2(x+8)-5 = 1$

$-2x-16-5 = 1$

$-2x-21 = 1$

$-2x-21+21 = 1+21$

$-2x = 22$

$\dfrac{-2x}{-2} = \dfrac{22}{-2}$

$x = -11$

65. $2x-3(x+5) = 6$

$2x-3x-15 = 6$

$-x-15 = 6$

$-x-15+15 = 6+15$

$-x = 21$

$x = -21$

66. $5(3x+1)-12x=-2$

$15x+5-12x=-2$

$15x-12x+5=-2$

$3x+5=-2$

$3x+5-5=-2-5$

$3x=-7$

$\dfrac{3x}{3}=\dfrac{-7}{3}$

$x=-\dfrac{7}{3}$

67. $-3r-4(r+2)=11$

$-3r-4r-8=11$

$-7r-8=11$

$-7r-8+8=11+8$

$-7r=19$

$\dfrac{-7r}{-7}=\dfrac{19}{-7}$

$r=-\dfrac{19}{7}$

68. $9=-2(a-3)$

$9=-2a+6$

$9-6=-2a+6-6$

$3=-2a$

$\dfrac{3}{-2}=\dfrac{-2a}{-2}$

$-\dfrac{3}{2}=a$

69. $x-3(2x+3)=11$

$x-6x-9=11$

$-5x-9=11$

$-5x-9+9=11+9$

$-5x=20$

$\dfrac{-5x}{-5}=\dfrac{20}{-5}$

$x=-4$

70. $3y-(y+5)=9$

$3y-y-5=9$

$2y-5=9$

$2y-5+5=9+5$

$2y=14$

$\dfrac{2y}{2}=\dfrac{14}{2}$

$y=7$

71. $5x+3x-4x-7=9$

$4x-7=9$

$4x-7+7=9+7$

$4x=16$

$\dfrac{4x}{4}=\dfrac{16}{4}$

$x=4$

72. $4(x+2)=13$

$4x+8=13$

$4x+8-8=13-8$

$4x=5$

$\dfrac{4x}{4}=\dfrac{5}{4}$

$x=\dfrac{5}{4}$

73. $0.7(x-3)=1.4$

$0.7x-2.1=1.4$

$0.7x-2.1+2.1=1.4+2.1$

$0.7x=3.5$

$\dfrac{0.7x}{0.7}=\dfrac{3.5}{0.7}$

$x=5$

74. $21+(c-9)=24$

$21+c-9=24$

$c+12=24$

$c+12-12=24-12$

$c=12$

75. $2.5(4q-3)=0.5$

$10q-7.5=0.5$

$10q-7.5+7.5=0.5+7.5$

$10q=8$

$\dfrac{10q}{10}=\dfrac{8}{10}$

$q=0.8$

76.
$$0.1(2.4x+5)=1.7$$
$$0.24x+0.5=1.7$$
$$0.24x+0.5-0.5=1.7-0.5$$
$$0.24x=1.2$$
$$\frac{0.24}{0.24}=\frac{1.2}{0.24}$$
$$x=5$$

77.
$$3-2(x+3)+2=1$$
$$3-2x-6+2=1$$
$$-2x+3-6+2=1$$
$$-2x-1=1$$
$$-2x-1+1=1+1$$
$$-2x=2$$
$$\frac{-2x}{-2}=\frac{2}{-2}$$
$$x=-1$$

78.
$$2(3x-4)-4x=12$$
$$6x-8-4x=12$$
$$6x-4x-8=12$$
$$2x-8=12$$
$$2x-8+8=12+8$$
$$2x=20$$
$$\frac{2x}{2}=\frac{20}{2}$$
$$x=10$$

79.
$$1+(x+3)+6x=6$$
$$1+x+3+6x=6$$
$$x+6x+1+3=6$$
$$7x+4=6$$
$$7x+4-4=6-4$$
$$7x=2$$
$$\frac{7x}{7}=\frac{2}{7}$$
$$x=\frac{2}{7}$$

80.
$$5x-2x+7x=-81$$
$$10x=-81$$
$$\frac{10x}{10}=\frac{-81}{10}$$
$$x=-8.1$$

81.
$$4.85-6.4x+1.11=22.6$$
$$-6.4x+4.85+1.11=22.6$$
$$-6.4x+5.96=22.6$$
$$-6.4x+5.96-5.96=22.6-5.96$$
$$-6.4x=16.64$$
$$\frac{-6.4x}{-6.4}=\frac{16.64}{-6.4}$$
$$x=-2.6$$

82.
$$5.76-4.24x-1.9x=27.864$$
$$5.76-6.14x=27.864$$
$$5.786-5.76-6.14x=27.864-5.76$$
$$-6.14x=22.104$$
$$\frac{-6.14x}{-6.14}=\frac{22.104}{-6.14}$$
$$x=-3.6$$

83.
$$7=8-5(m+3)$$
$$7=8-5m-15$$
$$7=-5m-7$$
$$7+7=-5m-7+7$$
$$14=-5m$$
$$\frac{14}{-5}=\frac{-5m}{-5}$$
$$-\frac{14}{5}=m$$

84.
$$4=\frac{3t+1}{7}$$
$$7(4)=7\left(\frac{3t+1}{7}\right)$$
$$28=3t+1$$
$$28-1=3t+1-1$$
$$27=3t$$
$$\frac{27}{3}=\frac{3t}{3}$$
$$9=t$$

85.
$$10 = \frac{2s+4}{5}$$
$$5(10) = 5\left(\frac{2s+4}{5}\right)$$
$$50 = 2s+4$$
$$50-4 = 2s+4-4$$
$$46 = 2s$$
$$\frac{46}{2} = \frac{2s}{2}$$
$$23 = s$$

86.
$$12 = \frac{4d-1}{3}$$
$$3(12) = 3\left(\frac{4d-1}{3}\right)$$
$$36 = 4d-1$$
$$36+1 = 4d-1+1$$
$$37 = 4d$$
$$\frac{37}{4} = \frac{4d}{4}$$
$$\frac{37}{4} = d$$

87.
$$x + \frac{2}{3} = \frac{3}{5}$$
$$15\left(x+\frac{2}{3}\right) = 15\left(\frac{3}{5}\right)$$
$$15x+10 = 9$$
$$15x+10-10 = 9-10$$
$$15x = -1$$
$$\frac{15x}{15} = \frac{-1}{15}$$
$$x = -\frac{1}{15}$$

88.
$$n - \frac{1}{4} = \frac{1}{2}$$
$$4\left(n-\frac{1}{4}\right) = 4\left(\frac{1}{2}\right)$$
$$4n-1 = 2$$
$$4n-1+1 = 2+1$$
$$4n = 3$$
$$\frac{4n}{4} = \frac{3}{4}$$
$$n = \frac{3}{4}$$

89.
$$\frac{r}{3} + 2r = 7$$
$$3\left(\frac{r}{3}+2r\right) = 3(7)$$
$$r+6r = 21$$
$$7r = 21$$
$$\frac{7r}{7} = \frac{21}{7}$$
$$r = 3$$

90.
$$\frac{x}{4} - 6x = 23$$
$$4\left(\frac{x}{4}-6x\right) = 4(23)$$
$$x-24x = 92$$
$$-23x = 92$$
$$\frac{-23x}{-23} = \frac{92}{-23}$$
$$x = -4$$

91.
$$\frac{3}{7} = \frac{3t}{4} + 1$$
$$28\left(\frac{3}{7}\right) = 28\left(\frac{3t}{4}+1\right)$$
$$12 = 21t+28$$
$$12-28 = 21t+28-28$$
$$-16 = 21t$$
$$\frac{-16}{21} = \frac{21t}{21}$$
$$-\frac{16}{21} = t$$

92.
$$\frac{5}{8} = \frac{5t}{6} + 2$$
$$24\left(\frac{5}{8}\right) = 24\left(\frac{5t}{6}+2\right)$$
$$15 = 20t+48$$
$$15-48 = 20t+48-48$$
$$-33 = 20t$$
$$\frac{-33}{20} = \frac{20t}{20}$$
$$-\frac{33}{20} = t$$

93.
$$\frac{1}{2}r + \frac{1}{5}r = 7$$
$$10\left(\frac{1}{2}r + \frac{1}{5}r\right) = 10(7)$$
$$5r + 2r = 70$$
$$7r = 70$$
$$\frac{7r}{7} = \frac{70}{7}$$
$$r = 10$$

94.
$$\frac{x}{3} - \frac{3x}{4} = \frac{1}{12}$$
$$12\left(\frac{x}{3} - \frac{3x}{4}\right) = 12\left(\frac{1}{12}\right)$$
$$4x - 9x = 1$$
$$-5x = 1$$
$$\frac{-5x}{-5} = \frac{1}{-5}$$
$$x = -\frac{1}{5}$$

95.
$$\frac{2}{8} + \frac{3}{4} = \frac{w}{5}$$
$$\frac{1}{4} + \frac{3}{4} = \frac{w}{5}$$
$$\frac{4}{4} = \frac{w}{5}$$
$$1 = \frac{w}{5}$$
$$5(1) = 5\left(\frac{w}{5}\right)$$
$$5 = w$$

96.
$$\frac{x}{4} - \frac{x}{6} = \frac{1}{4}$$
$$12\left(\frac{x}{4} - \frac{x}{6}\right) = 12\left(\frac{1}{4}\right)$$
$$3x - 2x = 3$$
$$x = 3$$

97.
$$\frac{1}{2}x + 4 = \frac{1}{6}$$
$$6\left(\frac{1}{2}x + 4\right) = 6\left(\frac{1}{6}\right)$$
$$3x + 24 = 1$$
$$3x + 24 - 24 = 1 - 24$$
$$3x = -23$$
$$\frac{3x}{3} = \frac{-23}{3}$$
$$x = -\frac{23}{3}$$

98.
$$\frac{4}{5} + n = \frac{1}{3}$$
$$15\left(\frac{4}{5} + n\right) = 15\left(\frac{1}{3}\right)$$
$$12 + 15n = 5$$
$$12 - 12 + 15n = 5 - 12$$
$$15n = -7$$
$$\frac{15n}{15} = \frac{-7}{15}$$
$$n = -\frac{7}{15}$$

99.
$$\frac{4}{5}s - \frac{3}{4}s = \frac{1}{10}$$
$$20\left(\frac{4}{5}s - \frac{3}{4}s\right) = 20\left(\frac{1}{10}\right)$$
$$16s - 15s = 2$$
$$s = 2$$

100.
$$\frac{1}{3}x - \frac{3}{4}x = \frac{1}{5}$$
$$60\left(\frac{1}{3}x - \frac{3}{4}x\right) = 60\left(\frac{1}{5}\right)$$
$$20x - 45x = 12$$
$$-25x = 12$$
$$\frac{-25x}{-25} = \frac{12}{-25}$$
$$x = -\frac{12}{25}$$

101.
$$\frac{4}{9} = \frac{1}{3}(n-7)$$
$$\frac{4}{9} = \frac{1}{3}n - \frac{7}{3}$$
$$9\left(\frac{4}{9}\right) = 9\left(\frac{1}{3}n - \frac{7}{3}\right)$$
$$4 = 3n - 21$$
$$4 + 21 = 3n - 21 + 21$$
$$25 = 3n$$
$$\frac{25}{3} = \frac{3n}{3}$$
$$\frac{25}{3} = n$$

102.
$$-\frac{3}{8} = \frac{1}{8} - \frac{2x}{7}$$
$$56\left(-\frac{3}{8}\right) = 56\left(\frac{1}{8} - \frac{2x}{7}\right)$$
$$-21 = 7 - 16x$$
$$-21 - 7 = 7 - 7 - 16x$$
$$-28 = -16x$$
$$\frac{-28}{-16} = \frac{-16x}{-16}$$
$$\frac{7}{4} = x$$

103.
$$-\frac{3}{5} = -\frac{1}{9} - \frac{3}{4}x$$
$$180\left(-\frac{3}{5}\right) = 180\left(-\frac{1}{9} - \frac{3}{4}x\right)$$
$$-108 = -20 - 135x$$
$$-108 + 20 = -20 + 20 - 135x$$
$$-88 = -135x$$
$$\frac{-88}{-135} = \frac{-135x}{-135}$$
$$\frac{88}{135} = x$$

104.
$$-\frac{3}{5} = -\frac{1}{6} - \frac{5}{4}m$$
$$60\left(-\frac{3}{5}\right) = 60\left(-\frac{1}{6} - \frac{5}{4}m\right)$$
$$-36 = -10 - 75m$$
$$-36 + 10 = -10 + 10 - 75m$$
$$-26 = -75m$$
$$\frac{-26}{-75} = \frac{-75m}{-75}$$
$$\frac{26}{75} = m$$

105. a. By subtracting first, you will not have to work with fractions.

b.
$$3x + 2 = 11$$
$$3x + 2 - 2 = 11 - 2$$
$$3x = 9$$
$$\frac{3x}{3} = \frac{9}{3}$$
$$x = 3$$

106. a. By adding first, you will not have to work with fractions.

b.
$$5x - 3 = 12$$
$$5x - 3 + 3 = 12 + 3$$
$$5x = 15$$
$$\frac{5x}{5} = \frac{15}{5}$$
$$x = 3$$

107.
$$3(x-2) - (x+5) - 2(3-2x) = 18$$
$$3x - 6 - x - 5 - 6 + 4x = 18$$
$$3x - x + 4x - 6 - 5 - 6 = 18$$
$$6x - 17 = 18$$
$$6x - 17 + 17 = 18 + 17$$
$$6x = 35$$
$$\frac{6x}{6} = \frac{35}{6}$$
$$x = \frac{35}{6}$$

108.
$$-6 = -(x-5)-3(5+2x)-4(2x-4)$$
$$-6 = -x+5-15-6x-8x+16$$
$$-6 = -x-6x-8x+5-15+16$$
$$-6 = -15x+6$$
$$-6-6 = -15x+6-6$$
$$-12 = -15x$$
$$\frac{-12}{-15} = \frac{-15x}{-15}$$
$$\frac{-12}{-15} = x$$
$$\frac{4}{5} = x \text{ or } x = \frac{4}{5}$$

109.
$$4[3-2(x+4)]-(x+3)=13$$
$$4(3-2x-8)-x-3=13$$
$$4(-2x-5)-x-3=13$$
$$-8x-20-x-3=13$$
$$-9x-23=13$$
$$-9x-23+23=13+23$$
$$-9x=36$$
$$\frac{-9x}{-9} = \frac{36}{-9}$$
$$x=-4$$

110.
$$\square\smiley - \nabla = @$$
$$\square\smiley - \nabla + \nabla = @ + \nabla$$
$$\square\smiley = @ + \nabla$$
$$\frac{\square\smiley}{\square} = \frac{@+\nabla}{\square}$$
$$\smiley = \frac{@+\nabla}{\square}$$

111. a. Let x = cost of one box of stationery
$$3x + 6 = 42$$

   b.
$$3x+6=42$$
$$3x+6-6=42-6$$
$$3x=36$$
$$x=12$$
A box of stationery costs $12.00.

112. a. Let x = cost of one roll of candy.
$$3x + 0.5 = 2.75$$

   b.
$$3x+0.5=2.75$$
$$3x+0.5-0.5=2.75-0.5$$
$$3x=2.25$$
$$x=0.75$$
A roll of candy costs $0.75.

113. False. $\sqrt{2}$ is a real number but is irrational.

114.
$$\left[5(2-6)+3(8\div4)^2\right]^2 = \left[5(-4)+3(2)^2\right]^2$$
$$= \left[5(-4)+3(4)\right]^2$$
$$= [-20+12]^2$$
$$= [-8]^2$$
$$= 64$$

115. To solve an equation, we need to isolate the variable on one side of the equation.

116. To solve the equation, we divide both sides of the equation by –4.

Mid-Chapter Test: 2.1-2.4

1.
$$5x-9y-12+4y-7x+6$$
$$= 5x-7x-9y+4y-12+6$$
$$= -2x-5y-6$$

2.
$$\frac{2}{5}x-8-\frac{3}{4}x+\frac{1}{2} = \frac{2}{5}x-\frac{3}{4}x-8+\frac{1}{2}$$
$$= \frac{8}{20}x-\frac{15}{20}x-\frac{16}{2}+\frac{1}{2}$$
$$= -\frac{7}{20}x-\frac{15}{2}$$

3. $-4(2a-3b+6)=-8a+12b-24$

4. $1.6(2.1x-3.4y-5.2)=3.36x-5.44y-8.32$

5.
$$5(t-3)-3(t+7)-2 = 5t-15-3t-21-2$$
$$= 5t-3t-15-21-2$$
$$= 2t-38$$

6. Substitute 2 for x in the following equation .

$$3(x-4)=-2(x+1)$$
$$3(2-4)=-2(2+1)$$
$$3(-2)=-2(3)$$
$$-6=-6 \text{ True}$$

Since we obtained a true statement, 2 is a solution.

7. Substitute $\frac{2}{5}$ for p in the following equation .

$$7p-3=2p-5$$
$$7\left(\frac{2}{5}\right)-3=2\left(\frac{2}{5}\right)-5$$
$$\frac{14}{5}-\frac{15}{5}=\frac{4}{5}-\frac{25}{5}$$
$$-\frac{9}{5}=-\frac{21}{5} \text{ False}$$

Since we obtained a false statement, $\frac{2}{5}$ is not a solution.

8. $x-5=-9$ Check: $x-5=-9$
$x-5+5=-9+5$ $-4-5=-9$
$x=-4$ $-9=-9 \text{ True}$

9. $12+x=-4$ Check: $12+x=-4$
$12-12+x=-4-12$ $12+(-16)=-4$
$x=-16$ $-4=-4$

10. $-16=7+y$ Check: $-16=7+y$
$-16-7=7-7+y$ $-16=7+(-23)$
$-23=y$ $-16=-16 \text{ True}$

11. Multiply both sides of the equation by 4.

12. $6=12y$ Check: $6=12y$
$\frac{6}{12}=\frac{12y}{12}$ $6=12\left(\frac{1}{2}\right)$
$\frac{1}{2}=y$ $6=6 \text{ True}$

13. $\frac{x}{8}=3$ Check: $\frac{x}{8}=3$
$8\left(\frac{x}{8}\right)=8(3)$ $\frac{24}{8}=3$
$x=24$ $3=3 \text{ True}$

14. $-\frac{x}{5}=-2$ Check: $-\frac{x}{5}=-2$
$\frac{x}{-5}=-2$ $-\frac{10}{5}=-2$
$-5\left(\frac{x}{-5}\right)=-5(-2)$ $-2=-2 \text{ True}$
$x=10$

15. $-x=\frac{3}{7}$ Check: $-x=\frac{3}{7}$
$-1x=\frac{3}{7}$ $-\left(-\frac{3}{7}\right)=\frac{3}{7}$
$-1(-1x)=-1\left(\frac{3}{7}\right)$ $\frac{3}{7}=\frac{3}{7}$
$x=-\frac{3}{7}$

16. $6x-3=12$
$6x=15$
$x=\frac{15}{6}$
$x=\frac{5}{2}$

17. $-4=-2w-7$
$3=-2w$
$-\frac{3}{2}=w$

18. $\frac{3}{4}=\frac{4n-1}{6}$
$12\left(\frac{3}{4}\right)=12\left(\frac{4n-1}{6}\right)$
$9=2(4n-1)$
$9=8n-2$
$11=8n$
$\frac{11}{8}=n$

19. $-5(x+4)-7=3$
$-5x-20-7=3$
$-5x-27=3$
$-5x=30$
$x=-6$

20. $8-9(y+4)+6=-2$

$8-9y-36+6=-2$

$-9y+8-36+6=-2$

$-9y-22=-2$

$-9y=20$

$y=-\dfrac{20}{9}$

Exercise Set 2.5

1. Answers will vary.

2. A conditional equation is an equation that is true only under specific conditions.

3. a. An identity is an equation that is true for infinitely many values of the variable.

   b. The solution is all real numbers.

4. An equation is an identity when the same expression appears on both sides of the equation.

5. The equation is an identity because both sides of the equation are identical.

6. a. A contradiction is an equation that is has no solution.

   b. There is no solution.

7. An equation has no solution if it simplifies to a false statement.

8. The equation $x+5=x+4$ simplifies to 5 = 4, a false statement. Thus, it is a contradiction.

9. a. Use the distributive property.
Combine like terms.
Subtract $5x$ from both sides of the equation.
Subtract 6 from both sides of the equation.
Divide both sides of the equation by 2.

   b. $4x+3(x+2)=5x-10$

$4x+3x+6=5x-10$

$7x+6=5x-10$

$2x+6=-10$

$2x=-16$

$x=-8$

10. a. Use the distributive property.
Subtract $4x$ from both sides of the equation.
Add 30 to both sides of the equation.
Divide both sides of the equation by 2.

   b. $4(x+3)=6(x-5)$

$4x+12=6x-30$

$12=2x-30$

$42=2x$

$21=x$

11. $3x=-2x+15$

$3x+2x=-2x+2x+15$

$5x=15$

$\dfrac{5x}{5}=\dfrac{15}{5}$

$x=3$

12. $x+4=2x-7$

$x-x+4=2x-x-7$

$4=x-7$

$4+7=x-7+7$

$11=x$

13. $-4x+10=6x$

$-4x+4x+10=6x+4x$

$10=10x$

$\dfrac{10}{10}=\dfrac{10x}{10}$

$1=x$

14. $3a=4a+8$

$3a-4a=4a-4a+8$

$-1a=8$

$\dfrac{-1a}{-1}=\dfrac{8}{-1}$

$a=-8$

15. $5x+3=6$

$5x+3-3=6-3$

$5x=3$

$\dfrac{5x}{5}=\dfrac{3}{5}$

$x=\dfrac{3}{5}$

16.
$$-6x = 2x + 16$$
$$-6x - 2x = 2x - 2x + 16$$
$$-8x = 16$$
$$\frac{-8x}{-8} = \frac{16}{-8}$$
$$x = -2$$

17.
$$21 - 6p = 3p - 2p$$
$$21 - 6p = p$$
$$21 - 6p + 6p = p + 6p$$
$$21 = 7p$$
$$\frac{21}{7} = \frac{7p}{7}$$
$$3 = p$$

18.
$$8 - 3x = 4x + 50$$
$$8 - 3x + 3x = 4x + 3x + 50$$
$$8 = 7x + 50$$
$$8 - 50 = 7x + 50 - 50$$
$$-42 = 7x$$
$$\frac{-42}{7} = \frac{7x}{7}$$
$$-6 = x$$

19.
$$2x - 4 = 3x - 6$$
$$2x - 2x - 4 = 3x - 2x - 6$$
$$-4 = x - 6$$
$$-4 + 6 = x - 6 + 6$$
$$2 = x$$

20.
$$5x + 7 = 3x + 5$$
$$5x - 3x + 7 = 3x - 3x + 5$$
$$2x + 7 = 5$$
$$2x + 7 - 7 = 5 - 7$$
$$2x = -2$$
$$\frac{2x}{2} = \frac{-2}{2}$$
$$x = -1$$

21.
$$6 - 2y = 9 - 8y + 6y$$
$$6 - 2y = 9 - 2y$$
$$6 - 2y + 2y = 9 - 2y + 2y$$
$$6 = 9 \qquad \text{False}$$
Since a false statement is obtained, there is no solution.

22.
$$-4 + 2y = 2y - 6 + y$$
$$-4 + 2y = 3y - 6$$
$$-4 + 2y - 2y = 3y - 2y - 6$$
$$-4 = y - 6$$
$$-4 + 6 = y - 6 + 6$$
$$2 = y$$

23.
$$124.8 - 9.4x = 4.8x + 32.5$$
$$124.8 - 9.4x + 9.4x = 4.8x + 9.4x + 32.5$$
$$124.8 = 14.2x + 32.5$$
$$124.8 - 32.5 = 14.2x + 32.5 - 32.5$$
$$92.3 = 14.2x$$
$$\frac{92.3}{14.2} = \frac{14.2x}{14.2}$$
$$6.5 = x$$

24.
$$9 - 0.5x = 4.5x + 8.5$$
$$9 - 0.5x + 0.5x = 4.5x + 0.5x + 8.5$$
$$9 = 5x + 8.5$$
$$9 - 8.5 = 5x + 8.5 - 8.5$$
$$0.5 = 5x$$
$$\frac{0.5}{5} = \frac{5x}{5}$$
$$\frac{0.5}{5} = x$$
$$0.1 = x$$

25.
$$0.62x - .065 = 9.75 - 2.63x$$
$$0.62x + 2.63x - 0.65 = 9.75 - 2.63x + 2.63x$$
$$3.25x - 0.65 = 9.75$$
$$3.25x - 0.65 + 0.65 = 9.75 + 0.65$$
$$3.25x = 10.4$$
$$\frac{3.25x}{3.25} = \frac{10.4}{3.25}$$
$$x = 3.2$$

26.
$$8.71 - 2.44x = 11.02 - 5.74x$$
$$8.71 - 2.44x + 5.74x = 11.02 - 5.74x + 5.74x$$
$$8.71 + 3.3x = 11.02$$
$$8.71 - 8.71 + 3.3x = 11.02 - 8.71$$
$$3.3x = 2.31$$
$$\frac{3.3x}{3.3} = \frac{2.31}{3.3}$$
$$x = 0.7$$

27.
$$5x + 3 = 2(x + 6)$$
$$5x + 3 = 2x + 12$$
$$5x - 2x + 3 = 2x - 2x + 12$$
$$3x + 3 = 12$$
$$3x + 3 - 3 = 12 - 3$$
$$3x = 9$$
$$\frac{3x}{3} = \frac{9}{3}$$
$$x = 3$$

28.
$$x - 14 = 3(x + 2)$$
$$x - 14 = 3x + 6$$
$$x - x - 14 = 3x - x + 6$$
$$-14 = 2x + 6$$
$$-14 - 6 = 2x + 6 - 6$$
$$-20 = 2x$$
$$\frac{-20}{2} = \frac{2x}{2}$$
$$-10 = x$$

29.
$$4y - 2 - 8y = 19 + 5y - 3$$
$$4y - 8y - 2 = 5y + 19 - 3$$
$$-4y - 2 = 5y + 16$$
$$-4y + 4y - 2 = 5y + 4y + 16$$
$$-2 = 9y - 16$$
$$-2 - 16 = 9y + 16 - 16$$
$$-18 = 9y$$
$$\frac{-18}{9} = \frac{9y}{9}$$
$$-2 = y$$

30.
$$3x - 5 + 9x = 2 + 4x + 9$$
$$3x + 9x - 5 = 4x + 2 + 9$$
$$12x - 5 = 4x + 11$$
$$12x - 4x - 5 = 4x - 4x + 11$$
$$8x - 5 = 11$$
$$8x - 5 + 5 = 11 + 5$$
$$8x = 16$$
$$\frac{8x}{8} = \frac{16}{8}$$
$$x = 2$$

31.
$$2(x - 2) = 4x - 6 - 2x$$
$$2x - 4 = 2x - 6$$
$$2x - 2x - 4 = 2x - 2x - 6$$
$$-4 = -6 \text{ False}$$
Since a false statement is obtained, there is no solution.

32.
$$4r = 10 - 2(r - 4)$$
$$4r = 10 - 2r + 8$$
$$4r = 18 - 2r$$
$$4r + 2r = 18 - 2r + 2r$$
$$6r = 18$$
$$\frac{6r}{6} = \frac{18}{6}$$
$$r = 3$$

33.
$$-(w + 2) = -6w + 32$$
$$-w - 2 = -6w + 32$$
$$-w + w - 2 = -6w + w + 32$$
$$-2 = -5w + 32$$
$$-2 - 32 = -5w + 32 - 32$$
$$-34 = -5w$$
$$\frac{-34}{-5} = \frac{-5w}{-5}$$
$$\frac{34}{5} = w$$

34.
$$7(-3m + 5) = 3(10 - 6m)$$
$$-21m + 35 = 30 - 18m$$
$$-21m + 21m + 35 = 30 - 18m + 21m$$
$$35 = 30 + 3m$$
$$35 - 30 = 30 - 30 + 3m$$
$$5 = 3m$$
$$\frac{5}{3} = \frac{3m}{3}$$
$$\frac{5}{3} = m$$

35.
$$-3(2t - 5) + 5 = 3t + 13$$
$$-6t + 15 + 5 = 3t + 13$$
$$-6t + 20 = 3t + 13$$
$$-6t + 6t + 20 = 3t + 6t + 13$$
$$20 = 9t + 13$$
$$20 - 13 = 9t + 13 - 13$$
$$7 = 9t$$
$$\frac{7}{9} = \frac{9t}{9}$$
$$\frac{7}{9} = t$$

36. $4(x-3)+2 = 2x+8$
$4x-12+2 = 2x+8$
$4x-10 = 2x+8$
$4x-2x-10 = 2x-2x+8$
$2x-10 = 8$
$2x-10+10 = 8+10$
$2x = 18$
$\dfrac{2x}{2} = \dfrac{18}{2}$
$x = 9$

37. $\dfrac{a}{5} = \dfrac{a-3}{2}$
$10\left(\dfrac{a}{5}\right) = 10\left(\dfrac{a-3}{2}\right)$
$2a = 5(a-3)$
$2a = 5a-15$
$2a-5a = 5a-5a-15$
$-3a = -15$
$\dfrac{-3a}{-3} = \dfrac{-15}{-3}$
$a = 5$

38. $\dfrac{b}{16} = \dfrac{b-6}{4}$
$16\left(\dfrac{b}{16}\right) = 16\left(\dfrac{b-6}{4}\right)$
$b = 4(b-6)$
$b = 4b-24$
$b-4b = 4b-4b-24$
$-3b = -24$
$\dfrac{-3b}{-3} = \dfrac{-24}{-3}$
$b = 8$

39. $\dfrac{n}{10} = 9-\dfrac{n}{5}$
$10\left(\dfrac{n}{10}\right) = 10\left(9-\dfrac{n}{5}\right)$
$n = 90-2n$
$n+2n = 90-2n+2n$
$3n = 90$
$\dfrac{3n}{3} = \dfrac{90}{3}$
$n = 30$

40. $6-\dfrac{x}{4} = \dfrac{x}{8}$
$8\left(6-\dfrac{x}{4}\right) = 8\left(\dfrac{x}{8}\right)$
$48-2x = x$
$48-2x+2x = x+2x$
$48 = 3x$
$\dfrac{48}{3} = \dfrac{3x}{3}$
$16 = x$

41. $\dfrac{5}{2}-\dfrac{x}{3} = 3x$
$6\left(\dfrac{5}{2}-\dfrac{x}{3}\right) = 6(3x)$
$15-2x = 18x$
$15-2x+2x = 18x+2x$
$15 = 20x$
$\dfrac{15}{20} = \dfrac{20x}{20}$
$\dfrac{15}{20} = x$
$\dfrac{3}{4} = x$

42. $\dfrac{x}{4}-3 = -2x$
$4\left(\dfrac{x}{4}-3\right) = 4(-2x)$
$x-12 = -8x$
$x-x-12 = -8x-x$
$-12 = -9x$
$\dfrac{-12}{-9} = \dfrac{-9x}{-9}$
$\dfrac{12}{9} = x$
$\dfrac{4}{3} = x$

43.
$$\frac{5}{8} + \frac{1}{4}a = \frac{1}{2}a$$
$$8\left(\frac{5}{8} + \frac{1}{4}a\right) = 8\left(\frac{1}{2}a\right)$$
$$5 + 2a = 4a$$
$$5 + 2a - 2a = 4a - 2a$$
$$5 = 2a$$
$$\frac{5}{2} = \frac{2a}{2}$$
$$\frac{5}{2} = a$$

44.
$$\frac{3}{4}x + \frac{1}{2} = \frac{1}{2}x$$
$$4\left(\frac{3}{4}x + \frac{1}{2}\right) = 4\left(\frac{1}{2}x\right)$$
$$3x + 2 = 2x$$
$$3x - 3x + 2 = 2x - 3x$$
$$2 = -1x$$
$$\frac{2}{-1} = \frac{-1x}{-1}$$
$$-2 = x$$

45.
$$0.1(x + 10) = 0.3x - 4$$
$$0.1x + 1 = 0.3x - 4$$
$$0.1x - 0.1x + 1 = 0.3x - 0.1 - 4$$
$$1 = 0.2x - 4$$
$$1 + 4 = 0.2x - 4 + 4$$
$$5 = 0.2x$$
$$\frac{5}{0.2} = \frac{0.2x}{0.2}$$
$$25 = x$$

46.
$$5(3.2x - 3) = 2(x - 4)$$
$$16x - 15 = 2x - 8$$
$$16x - 2x - 15 = 2x - 2x - 8$$
$$14x - 15 = -8$$
$$14x - 15 + 15 = -8 + 15$$
$$14x = 7$$
$$\frac{14x}{14} = \frac{7}{14}$$
$$x = \frac{1}{2}$$

47.
$$2(x + 4) = 4x + 3 - 2x + 5$$
$$2x + 8 = 4x + 3 - 2x + 5$$
$$2x + 8 = 2x + 8$$
Since the left side of the equation is identical to the right side, the equation is true for all values of x. Thus the solution is all real numbers.

48.
$$3(y - 1) + 9 = 8y + 6 - 5y$$
$$3y - 3 + 9 = 3y + 6$$
$$3y + 6 = 3y + 6$$
Since the left side of the equation is identical to the right side, the equation is true for all values of x. Thus the solution is all real numbers.

49.
$$5(3n + 3) = 2(5n - 4) + 6n$$
$$15n + 15 = 10n - 8 + 6n$$
$$15n + 15 = 16n - 8$$
$$15n - 15n + 15 = 16n - 15n - 8$$
$$15 = n - 8$$
$$15 + 8 = n - 8 + 8$$
$$23 = n$$

50.
$$-4(-3z - 5) = -(10z + 8) - 2z$$
$$12z + 20 = -10z - 8 - 2z$$
$$12z + 20 = -12z - 8$$
$$12z + 12z + 20 = -12z + 12z - 8$$
$$24z + 20 = -8$$
$$24z + 20 - 20 = -8 - 20$$
$$24z = -28$$
$$\frac{24z}{24} = \frac{-28}{24}$$
$$z = \frac{-28}{24} = -\frac{7}{6}$$

51.
$$-(3 - p) = -(2p + 3)$$
$$-3 + p = -2p - 3$$
$$-3 + p + 2p = -2p + 2p - 3$$
$$-3 + 3p = -3$$
$$-3 + 3 + 3p = -3 + 3$$
$$3p = 0$$
$$\frac{3p}{3} = \frac{0}{3}$$
$$p = 0$$

52. $12 - 2x - 3(x + 2) = 4x + 6 - x$

$12 - 2x - 3x - 6 = 4x + 6 - x$

$-5x + 6 = 3x + 6$

$-5x + 5x + 6 = 3x + 5x + 6$

$6 = 8x + 6$

$6 - 6 = 8x + 6 - 6$

$0 = 8x$

$\dfrac{0}{8} = \dfrac{8x}{8}$

$0 = x$

53. $-(x + 4) + 5 = 4x + 1 - 5x$

$-x - 4 + 5 = 4x + 1 - 5x$

$-x + 1 = -x + 1$

Since the left side of the equation is identical to the right side, the equation is true for all values of x. Thus the solution is all real numbers.

54. $18x + 3(4x - 9) = -6x + 81$

$18x + 12x - 27 = -6x + 81$

$30x - 27 = -6x + 81$

$30x + 6x - 27 = -6x + 6x + 81$

$36x - 27 = 81$

$36x - 27 + 27 = 81 + 27$

$36x = 108$

$\dfrac{36x}{36} = \dfrac{108}{36}$

$x = 3$

55. $35(2x - 1) = 7(x + 4) + 3x$

$70x - 35 = 7x + 28 + 3x$

$70x - 35 = 10x + 28$

$70x - 10x - 35 = 10x - 10x + 28$

$60x - 35 = 28$

$60x - 35 + 35 = 28 + 35$

$60x = 63$

$\dfrac{60x}{60} = \dfrac{63}{60}$

$x = \dfrac{21}{20}$

56. $10(x - 10) + 5 = 5(2x - 20)$

$10x - 100 + 5 = 10x - 100$

$10x - 95 = 10x - 100$

$10x - 10x - 95 = 10x - 10x - 100$

$-95 = -100 \quad \text{False}$

Since a false statement is obtained, there is no solution.

57. $0.4(x + 0.7) = 0.6(x - 4.2)$

$0.4x + 0.28 = 0.6x - 2.52$

$0.4x - 0.4x + 0.28 = 0.6x - 0.4x - 2.52$

$0.28 = 0.2x - 2.52$

$0.28 + 2.52 = 0.2x - 2.52 + 2.52$

$2.8 = 0.2x$

$\dfrac{2.8}{0.2} = \dfrac{0.2x}{0.2}$

$14 = x$

58. $0.5(6x - 8) = 1.4(x - 5) - 0.2$

$3x - 4 = 1.4x - 7 - 0.2$

$3x - 4 = 1.4x - 7.2$

$3x - 1.4x - 4 = 1.4x - 1.4x - 7.2$

$1.6x - 4 = -7.2$

$1.6x - 4 + 4 = -7.2 + 4$

$1.6x = -3.2$

$\dfrac{1.6x}{1.6} = \dfrac{-3.2}{1.6}$

$x = -2$

59. $\dfrac{3}{5}x - 2 = x + \dfrac{1}{3}$

$15\left(\dfrac{3}{5}x - 2\right) = 15\left(x + \dfrac{1}{3}\right)$

$9x - 30 = 15x + 5$

$9x - 9x - 30 = 15x - 9x + 5$

$-30 = 6x + 5$

$-30 - 5 = 6x + 5 - 5$

$-35 = 6x$

$\dfrac{-35}{6} = \dfrac{6x}{6}$

$-\dfrac{35}{6} = x$

60.

$$\frac{3}{5}x + 4 = \frac{1}{5}x + 5$$

$$5\left(\frac{3}{5}x + 4\right) = 5\left(\frac{1}{5}x + 5\right)$$

$$3x + 20 = x + 25$$

$$3x - x + 20 = x - x + 25$$

$$2x + 20 = 25$$

$$2x + 20 - 20 = 25 - 20$$

$$2x = 5$$

$$\frac{2x}{2} = \frac{5}{2}$$

$$x = \frac{5}{2}$$

61.

$$\frac{y}{5} + 2 = 3(y - 4)$$

$$\frac{y}{5} + 2 = 3y - 12$$

$$\frac{y}{5} + 2 - 2 = 3y - 12 - 2$$

$$\frac{y}{5} = 3y - 14$$

$$5\left(\frac{y}{5}\right) = 5(3y - 14)$$

$$y = 15y - 70$$

$$y - 15y = 15y - 15y - 70$$

$$-14y = -70$$

$$\frac{-14y}{-14} = \frac{-70}{-14}$$

$$y = 5$$

62.

$$2(x - 4) = \frac{x}{5} + 10$$

$$2x - 8 = \frac{x}{5} + 10$$

$$2x - 8 - 10 = \frac{x}{5} + 10 - 10$$

$$2x - 18 = \frac{x}{5}$$

$$5(2x - 18) = 5\left(\frac{x}{5}\right)$$

$$10x - 90 = x$$

$$10x - 10x - 90 = x - 10x$$

$$-90 = -9x$$

$$\frac{-90}{-9} = \frac{-9x}{-9}$$

$$10 = x$$

63.

$$12 - 3x + 7x = -2(-5x + 6)$$

$$12 + 4x = 10x - 12$$

$$12 + 4x - 4x = 10x - 4x - 12$$

$$12 = 6x - 12$$

$$12 + 12 = 6x - 12 + 12$$

$$24 = 6x$$

$$\frac{24}{6} = \frac{6x}{6}$$

$$4 = x$$

64.

$$-2x - 3 - x = -3(-2x + 7)$$

$$-3x - 3 = 6x - 21$$

$$-3x + 3x - 3 = 6x + 3x - 21$$

$$-3 = 9x - 21$$

$$-3 + 21 = 9x - 21 + 21$$

$$18 = 9x$$

$$\frac{18}{9} = \frac{9x}{9}$$

$$2 = x$$

65. $3(x-6)-4(3x+1) = x-22$

$$3x-18-12x-4 = x-22$$
$$-9x-22 = x-22$$
$$-9x+9x-22 = x+9x-22$$
$$-22 = 10x-22$$
$$-22+22 = 10x-22+22$$
$$0 = 10x$$
$$\frac{0}{10} = \frac{10x}{10}$$
$$0 = x$$

66. $-2(-3x+5)+6 = 4(x-2)$

$$6x-10+6 = 4x-8$$
$$6x-4 = 4x-8$$
$$6x-4x-4 = 4x-4x-8$$
$$2x-4 = -8$$
$$2x-4+4 = -8+4$$
$$2x = -4$$
$$\frac{2x}{2} = \frac{-4}{2}$$
$$x = -2$$

67. $5+2x = 6(x+1)-5(x-3)$

$$5+2x = 6x+6-5x+15$$
$$5+2x = x+21$$
$$5+2x-x = x-x+21$$
$$5+x = 21$$
$$5-5+x = 21-5$$
$$x = 16$$

68. $4-(6x+6) = -(-2x+10)$

$$4-6x-6 = 2x-10$$
$$-6x-2 = 2x-10$$
$$-6x+6x-2 = 2x+6x-10$$
$$-2 = 8x-10$$
$$-2+10 = 8x-10+10$$
$$8 = 8x$$
$$\frac{8}{8} = \frac{8x}{8}$$
$$1 = x$$

69. $7-(-y-5) = 2(y+3)-6(y+1)$

$$7+y+5 = 2y+6-6y-6$$
$$12+y = -4y$$
$$12+y-y = -4y-y$$
$$12 = -5y$$
$$\frac{12}{-5} = \frac{-5y}{-5}$$
$$-\frac{12}{5} = y$$

70. $12-6x+3(2x+3) = 2x+5$

$$12-6x+6x+9 = 2x+5$$
$$21 = 2x+5$$
$$21-5 = 2x+5-5$$
$$16 = 2x$$
$$\frac{16}{2} = \frac{2x}{2}$$
$$8 = x$$

71. $\frac{3}{5}(x-6) = \frac{2}{3}(3x-5)$

$$\frac{3}{5}x-\frac{18}{5} = 2x-\frac{10}{3}$$
$$15\left(\frac{3}{5}x-\frac{18}{5}\right) = 15\left(2x-\frac{10}{3}\right)$$
$$9x-54 = 30x-50$$
$$9x-9x-54 = 30x-9x-50$$
$$-54 = 21x-50$$
$$-54+50 = 21x-50+50$$
$$-4 = 21x$$
$$\frac{-4}{21} = \frac{21x}{21}$$
$$-\frac{4}{21} = x$$

72. $\frac{1}{2}(2d+4) = \frac{1}{3}(4d-4)$

$$d+2 = \frac{4d}{3}-\frac{4}{3}$$
$$3(d+2) = 3\left(\frac{4d}{3}-\frac{4}{3}\right)$$
$$3d+6 = 4d-4$$
$$3d-3d+6 = 4d-3d-4$$
$$6 = d-4$$
$$6+4 = d-4+4$$
$$10 = d$$

73.
$$\frac{3(2r-5)}{5} = \frac{3r-6}{4}$$
$$\frac{6r-15}{5} = \frac{3r-6}{4}$$
$$20\left(\frac{6r-15}{5}\right) = 20\left(\frac{3r-6}{4}\right)$$
$$4(6r-15) = 5(3r-6)$$
$$24r-60 = 15r-30$$
$$24r-15r-60 = 15r-15r-30$$
$$9r-60 = -30$$
$$9r-60+60 = -30+60$$
$$9r = 30$$
$$\frac{9r}{9} = \frac{30}{9}$$
$$r = \frac{30}{9} = \frac{10}{3}$$

74.
$$\frac{3(x-4)}{4} = \frac{5(2x-3)}{3}$$
$$\frac{3x-12}{4} = \frac{10x-15}{3}$$
$$12\left(\frac{3x-12}{4}\right) = 12\left(\frac{10x-15}{3}\right)$$
$$3(3x-12) = 4(10x-15)$$
$$9x-36 = 40x-60$$
$$9x-9x-36 = 40x-9x-60$$
$$-36 = 31x-60$$
$$-36+60 = 31x-60+60$$
$$24 = 31x$$
$$\frac{24}{31} = \frac{31x}{31}$$
$$\frac{24}{31} = x$$

75.
$$\frac{2}{7}(5x+4) = \frac{1}{2}(3x-4)+1$$
$$\frac{10x}{7}+\frac{8}{7} = \frac{3x}{2}-2+1$$
$$\frac{10x}{7}+\frac{8}{7} = \frac{3x}{2}-1$$
$$14\left(\frac{10x}{7}+\frac{8}{7}\right) = 14\left(\frac{3x}{2}-1\right)$$
$$20x+16 = 21x-14$$
$$20x-20x+16 = 21x-20x-14$$
$$16 = x-14$$
$$16+14 = x-14+14$$
$$30 = x$$

76.
$$\frac{5}{12}(x+2) = \frac{2}{3}(2x+1)+\frac{1}{6}$$
$$\frac{5x}{12}+\frac{10}{12} = \frac{4x}{3}+\frac{2}{3}+\frac{1}{6}$$
$$12\left(\frac{5x}{12}+\frac{10}{12}\right) = 12\left(\frac{4x}{3}+\frac{2}{3}+\frac{1}{6}\right)$$
$$5x+10 = 16x+8+2$$
$$5x+10 = 16x+10$$
$$5x-5x+10 = 16x-5x+10$$
$$10 = 11x+10$$
$$10-10 = 11x+10-10$$
$$0 = 11x$$
$$\frac{0}{11} = \frac{11x}{11}$$
$$0 = x$$

77.
$$\frac{a-5}{2} = \frac{3a}{4}+\frac{a-25}{6}$$
$$12\left(\frac{a-5}{2}\right) = 12\left(\frac{3a}{4}+\frac{a-25}{6}\right)$$
$$6(a-5) = 9a+2(a-25)$$
$$6a-30 = 9a+2a-50$$
$$6a-30 = 11a-50$$
$$6a-6a-30 = 11a-6a-50$$
$$-30 = 5a-50$$
$$-30+50 = 5a-50+50$$
$$20 = 5a$$
$$\frac{20}{5} = \frac{5a}{5}$$
$$4 = a$$

78.

$$\frac{a-7}{3} = \frac{a+5}{2} - \frac{7a-1}{6}$$

$$6\left(\frac{a-7}{3}\right) = 6\left(\frac{a+5}{2} - \frac{7a-1}{6}\right)$$

$$2(a-7) = 3(a+5) - (7a-1)$$

$$2a - 14 = 3a + 15 - 7a + 1$$

$$2a - 14 = -4a + 16$$

$$2a + 4a - 14 = -4a + 4a + 16$$

$$6a - 14 = 16$$

$$6a - 14 + 14 = 16 + 14$$

$$6a = 30$$

$$\frac{6a}{6} = \frac{30}{6}$$

$$a = 5$$

79. a. One example is $x + x + 1 = x + 2$.

   b. It has a single solution.

   c. Answers will vary. For equation given in part **a**):

$$x + x + 1 = x + 2$$
$$2x + 1 = x + 2$$
$$2x - x + 1 = x - x + 2$$
$$x + 1 = 2$$
$$x + 1 - 1 = 2 - 1$$
$$x = 1$$

80. a. One example is $x + 2 = x + x + 1$.

   b. It has a single solution.

   c. Answers will vary. For equation given in part **a**):

$$x + 2 = x + x + 1$$
$$x + 2 = 2x + 1$$
$$x - x + 2 = 2x - x + 1$$
$$2 = x + 1$$
$$2 - 1 = x + 1 - 1$$
$$1 = x$$

81. a. One example is $x + x + 1 = 2x + 1$.

   b. Both sides simplify to the same expression.

   c. The solution is all real numbers.

82. a. One example is $2x + 1 = x + x + 1$.

   b. Both sides simplify to the same expression.

   c. The solution is all real numbers.

83. a. One example is $x + x + 1 = 2x + 2$.

   b. It simplifies to a false statement.

   c. The solution is that there is no solution.

84. a. One example is $x + x + 2 = x + x + 2 + 1$

   b. It simplifies to a false statement.

   c. The solution is that there is no solution.

85.

$$5* - 1 = 4* + 5*$$
$$5* - 5* - 1 = 9* - 5*$$
$$-1 = 4*$$
$$\frac{-1}{4} = \frac{4*}{4}$$
$$-\frac{1}{4} = *$$

86.

$$2\Delta - 4 = 3\Delta + 5 - \Delta$$
$$2\Delta - 4 = 2\Delta + 5$$
$$2\Delta - 2\Delta - 4 = 2\Delta - 2\Delta + 5$$
$$-4 = 5 \text{ False}$$

No solution

87. $3☺ - 5 = 2☺ - 5 + ☺$

$$3☺ - 5 = 3☺ - 5$$

The left side of the equation is identical to the right side. The solution is all real numbers.

88. $-2(x+3) + 5x = 3(4-2x) - (x+2)$

$$-2x - 6 + 5x = 12 - 6x - x - 2$$
$$3x - 6 = -7x + 10$$
$$3x + 7x - 6 = -7x + 7x + 10$$
$$10x - 6 = 10$$
$$10x - 6 + 6 = 10 + 6$$
$$10x = 16$$
$$\frac{10x}{10} = \frac{16}{10}$$
$$x = \frac{8}{5}$$

89. $4 - \left[5 - 3(x+2)\right] = x - 3$

$\quad\quad 4 - (5 - 3x - 6) = x - 3$

$\quad\quad 4 - 5 + 3x + 6 = x - 3$

$\quad\quad\quad\quad\quad 3x + 5 = x - 3$

$\quad\quad 3x - x + 5 = x - x - 3$

$\quad\quad\quad\quad\quad 2x + 5 = -3$

$\quad\quad 2x + 5 - 5 = -3 - 5$

$\quad\quad\quad\quad\quad\quad 2x = -8$

$\quad\quad\quad\quad\quad \dfrac{2x}{2} = \dfrac{-8}{2}$

$\quad\quad\quad\quad\quad\quad\; x = -4$

90. a. Let x be the cost of one chocolate bar.
$2x = x + 6$

b. $\quad\quad 2x = x + 6$

$\quad\; 2x - x = x + 6$

$\quad\quad\quad\; x = 6$

A chocolate bar costs \$6.00.

91. a. $|4| = 4$

b. $|-7| = 7$

c. $|0| = 0$

92. $\left(\dfrac{2}{3}\right)^5 \approx 0.131687243$

93. Factors are expressions that are multiplied together; terms are expressions that are added together.

94. $2(x-3) + 4x - (4-x) = 2x - 6 + 4x - 4 + x$

$\quad\quad\quad\quad\quad\quad\quad\quad = 7x - 10$

95. $2(x-3) + 4x - (4-x) = 0$

$\quad\quad 2x - 6 + 4x - 4 + x = 0$

$\quad\quad\quad\quad\quad\quad 7x - 10 = 0$

$\quad\quad\quad 7x - 10 + 10 = 0 + 10$

$\quad\quad\quad\quad\quad\quad\quad 7x = 10$

$\quad\quad\quad\quad\quad\quad \dfrac{7x}{7} = \dfrac{10}{7}$

$\quad\quad\quad\quad\quad\quad\; x = \dfrac{10}{7}$

96. $(x+4) - (4x-3) = 16$

$\quad\quad x + 4 - 4x + 3 = 16$

$\quad\quad\quad\quad -3x + 7 = 16$

$\quad\; -3x + 7 - 7 = 16 - 7$

$\quad\quad\quad\quad\quad -3x = 9$

$\quad\quad\quad\quad\; \dfrac{-3x}{-3} = \dfrac{9}{-3}$

$\quad\quad\quad\quad\quad\quad\; x = -3$

Exercise Set 2.6

1. A formula is an equation used to express a relationship mathematically.

2. To evaluate a formula means to substitute values and perform the indicated operations.

3. The simple interest formula is:
$i = prt$ where i is interest, p is principle, r is the interest rate, and t is time.

4. A quadrilateral is a 4-sided figure.

5. $d = rt$; d represents distance, r represents rate and t represents time

6. The radius is one-half of the diameter.

7. No, π is an irrational number that is approximately equal to 3.14, but not exactly.

8. **a.** Perimeter is the sum of the lengths of the sides of the figure.

   b. Area is the total surface within the figure boundaries.

9. When you multiply a unit by the same unit, you get a square unit.

10. When you multiply the same unit three times, you get a cubic unit.

11. Substitute 60 for r and 4 for t.
$d = rt$
$d = 60(4) = 240$

12. Substitute 6 for s.
$P = 4s$
$P = 4(6) = 24$

13. Substitute 12 for l and 8 for w.

$A = lw$

$A = 12(8) = 96$

14. Substitute 7 for s.

$A = s^2$

$A = (7)^2 = 49$

15. Substitute 2000 for p, 0.06 for r, and 3 for t.

$i = prt$

$i = 2000(0.06)(3) = 360$

16. Substitute 12 for i.

$c = 2.54i$

$c = 2.54(12) = 30.48$

17. Substitute 8 for l and 5 for w.

$P = 2l + 2w$

$P = 2(8) + 2(5) = 16 + 10 = 26$

18. Substitute 60 for m.

$f = 1.47m$

$f = 1.47(60) = 88.2$

19. Substitute 5 for r.

$A = \pi r^2$

$A = \pi(5)^2 = 25\pi \approx 78.54$

20. Substitute 16 for m and 56 for n.

$A = \dfrac{m+n}{2}$

$A = \dfrac{16+56}{2} = \dfrac{72}{2} = 36$

21. Substitute 72 for a, 81 for b, and 93 for c.

$A = \dfrac{a+b+c}{3}$

$A = \dfrac{72+81+93}{3} = \dfrac{246}{3} = 82$

22. Substitute 2000 for p and 4 for i.

$p = i^2 r$

$2000 = (4)^2 r$

$2000 = 16r$

$\dfrac{2000}{16} = \dfrac{16r}{16}$

$125 = r$

23. Substitute 100 for x, 80 for m, and 10 for s.

$z = \dfrac{x-m}{s}$

$z = \dfrac{100-80}{10} = \dfrac{20}{10} = 2$

24. Substitute 30 for A and 10 for h.

$A = \dfrac{1}{2}bh$

$30 = \dfrac{1}{2}b(10)$

$30 = 5b$

$\dfrac{30}{5} = \dfrac{5b}{5}$

$6 = b$

25. Substitute 28 for P and 6 for w.

$P = 2l + 2w$

$28 = 2l + 2(6)$

$28 = 2l + 12$

$28 - 12 = 2l + 12 - 12$

$16 = 2l$

$\dfrac{16}{2} = \dfrac{2l}{2}$

$8 = l$

26. Substitute 1050 for A, 1 for t, and 1000 for P.

$A = P(1 + rt)$

$1050 = 1000\left[1 + r(1)\right]$

$1050 = 1000(1 + r)$

$\dfrac{1050}{1000} = \dfrac{1000(1+r)}{1000}$

$1.05 = 1 + r$

$1.05 - 1 = 1 - 1 + r$

$0.05 = r$

27. Substitute 678.24 for V, and 6 for r.

$V = \pi r^2 h$

$678.24 = \pi(6)^2 h$

$678.24 = 36\pi h$

$\dfrac{678.24}{36\pi} = \dfrac{36\pi h}{36\pi}$

$\dfrac{678.24}{36\pi} = h$

$6.00 \approx h$

28. Substitute 8 for r.

$$V = \frac{4}{3}\pi r^3$$

$$V = \frac{4}{3}\pi(8)^3 = \frac{4}{3}\pi(512) \approx 2144.66$$

29. Substitute 24 for B and 61 for h.

$$B = \frac{703w}{h^2}$$

$$24 = \frac{703w}{(61)^2}$$

$$24(61)^2 = \frac{703w}{61^2}(61)^2$$

$$89,304 = 703w$$

$$\frac{89,304}{703} = \frac{703w}{703}$$

$$127.03 \approx w$$

30. Substitute 160 for C and 0.12 for r.
$$S = C + rC$$
$$S = 160 + (0.12)(160) = 160 + 19.20 = 179.20$$

31. Substitute 8 for r.
$$A = \pi r^2$$
$$A = \pi(4)^2 = 16\pi \approx 50.27 \text{ft}^2$$

32. Substitute 6 for b and 4 for h.
$$A = \frac{1}{2}bh$$
$$A = \frac{1}{2}(6)(4) = (3)(4) = 12 \text{ in.}^2$$

33. Substitute 3 for h, 4 for b and 7 for d.
$$A = \frac{1}{2}h(b+d)$$
$$A = \frac{1}{2}(3)(4+7) = \frac{1}{2}(3)(11) = \frac{1}{2}(33) = 16.5 \text{ ft}^2$$

34. Substitute 4 for l, 3 for w, and 5 for h.
$$V = lwh$$
$$V = (4)(3)(5) = 60 \text{ ft}^3$$

35. Substitute 4 for r and 9 for h.
$$V = \pi r^2 h$$
$$V = \pi(4)^2(9) = \pi(16)(9) = 144\pi \approx 452.39 \text{ cm}^3$$

36. Substitute 4 for r and 8 for h.

$$V = \frac{1}{3}\pi r^2 h$$

$$V = \frac{1}{3}\pi(4)^2(8)$$

$$= \frac{1}{3}\pi(16)(8) = \frac{1}{3}\pi(128) \approx 134.04 \text{ m}^3$$

37. Substitute 50 for F.

$$C = \frac{5}{9}(F-32)$$

$$C = \frac{5}{9}(50-32) = \frac{5}{9}(18) = 10$$

The equivalent temperature is 10°C.

38. Substitute 86 for F.

$$C = \frac{5}{9}(F-32)$$

$$C = \frac{5}{9}(86-32) = \frac{5}{9}(54) = 30$$

The equivalent temperature is 30°C.

39. Substitute 25 for C.

$$F = \frac{9}{5}C + 32$$

$$F = \frac{9}{5}(25) + 32 = 45 + 32 = 77$$

The equivalent temperature is 77°F.

40. Substitute 10 for C.

$$F = \frac{9}{5}C + 32$$

$$F = \frac{9}{5}(10) + 32 = 18 + 32 = 50$$

The equivalent temperature is 50°F.

41. $P = \dfrac{KT}{V}$

$$P = \frac{(2)(20)}{1} = \frac{40}{1} = 40$$

42. $P = \dfrac{KT}{V}$

$$80 = \frac{K(100)}{5}$$

$$80 = 20K$$

$$\frac{80}{20} = \frac{20K}{20}$$

$$4 = K$$

43. $P = \dfrac{KT}{V}$

$3 = \dfrac{(0.5)(30)}{V}$

$3 = \dfrac{15}{V}$

$3V = 15$

$V = \dfrac{15}{3} = 5$

44. $P = \dfrac{KT}{V}$

$100 = \dfrac{2T}{6}$

$100 = \dfrac{T}{3}$

$3(100) = 3\left(\dfrac{T}{3}\right)$

$300 = T$

45. $A = lw$

$\dfrac{A}{l} = \dfrac{lw}{l}$

$\dfrac{A}{l} = w$

46. $P = 4s$

$\dfrac{P}{4} = \dfrac{4s}{4}$

$\dfrac{P}{4} = s$

47. $d = rt$

$\dfrac{d}{r} = \dfrac{rt}{r}$

$\dfrac{d}{r} = t$

48. $C = \pi d$

$\dfrac{C}{\pi} = \dfrac{\pi d}{\pi}$

$\dfrac{C}{\pi} = d$

49. $i = prt$

$\dfrac{i}{pr} = \dfrac{prt}{pr}$

$\dfrac{i}{pr} = t$

50. $V = lwh$

$\dfrac{V}{wh} = \dfrac{lwh}{wh}$

$\dfrac{V}{wh} = l$

51. $A = \dfrac{1}{2}bh$

$2A = 2\left(\dfrac{1}{2}bh\right)$

$2A = bh$

$\dfrac{2A}{h} = \dfrac{bh}{h}$

$\dfrac{2A}{h} = b$

52. $E = IR$

$\dfrac{E}{R} = \dfrac{IR}{R}$

$\dfrac{E}{R} = I$

53. $P = 2l + 2w$

$P - 2l = 2l - 2l + 2w$

$P - 2l = 2w$

$\dfrac{P - 2l}{2} = \dfrac{2w}{2}$

$\dfrac{P - 2l}{2} = w$

54. $PV = KT$

$\dfrac{PV}{K} = \dfrac{KT}{K}$

$\dfrac{PV}{K} = T$

55.
$$3 - 2r = n$$
$$3 - 3 - 2r = n - 3$$
$$-2r = n - 3$$
$$\frac{-2r}{-2} = \frac{n - 3}{-2}$$
$$r = \frac{n - 3}{-2} = \frac{3 - n}{2}$$

56.
$$4m + 5n = 25$$
$$4m - 4m + 5n = 25 - 4m$$
$$5n = 25 - 4m$$
$$\frac{5n}{5} = \frac{25 - 4m}{5}$$
$$n = \frac{25 - 4m}{5} = \frac{-4m + 25}{5}$$

57.
$$y = mx + b$$
$$y - mx = mx - mx + b$$
$$y - mx = b$$

58.
$$y = mx + b$$
$$y - b = mx + b - b$$
$$y - b = mx$$
$$\frac{y - b}{m} = \frac{mx}{m}$$
$$\frac{y - b}{m} = x$$

59.
$$d = a + b + c$$
$$d - a = a - a + b + c$$
$$d - a = b + c$$
$$d - a - c = b + c - c$$
$$d - a - c = b$$

60.
$$ax + by = c$$
$$ax - ax + by = -ax + c$$
$$by = -ax + c$$
$$\frac{by}{b} = \frac{-ax + c}{b}$$
$$y = \frac{-ax + c}{b}$$

61.
$$ax + by + c = 0$$
$$ax - ax + by + c = -ax$$
$$by + c = -ax$$
$$by + c - c = -ax - c$$
$$by = -ax - c$$
$$\frac{by}{b} = \frac{-ax - c}{b}$$
$$y = \frac{-ax - c}{b}$$

62.
$$V = \pi r^2 h$$
$$\frac{V}{\pi r^2} = \frac{\pi r^2 h}{\pi r^2}$$
$$\frac{V}{\pi r^2} = h$$

63.
$$V = \frac{1}{3}\pi r^2 h$$
$$3V = 3\left(\frac{1}{3}\pi r^2 h\right)$$
$$3V = \pi r^2 h$$
$$\frac{3V}{\pi r^2} = \frac{\pi r^2 h}{\pi r^2}$$
$$\frac{3V}{\pi r^2} = h$$

64.
$$A = \frac{m + 2d}{3}$$
$$3A = 3\left(\frac{m + 2d}{3}\right)$$
$$3A = m + 2d$$
$$3A - m = m - m + 2d$$
$$3A - m = 2d$$
$$\frac{3A - m}{2} = \frac{2d}{2}$$
$$\frac{3A - m}{2} = d$$

65.
$$A = \frac{m + d}{2}$$
$$2A = 2\left(\frac{m + d}{2}\right)$$
$$2A = m + d$$
$$2A - d = m + d - d$$
$$2A - d = m$$

66. $L = \dfrac{c+2d}{4}$

$4L = 4\left(\dfrac{c+2d}{4}\right)$

$4L = c+2d$

$4L - c = c - c + 2d$

$4L - c = 2d$

$\dfrac{4L-c}{2} = \dfrac{2d}{2}$

$\dfrac{4L-c}{2} = d$

67. $2x + y = 5$

$2x - 2x + y = -2x + 5$

$y = -2x + 5$

68. $6x + 2y = -12$

$6x - 6x + 2y = -6x - 12$

$2y = -6x - 12$

$\dfrac{2y}{2} = \dfrac{-6x-12}{2}$

$y = \dfrac{-6x}{2} + \dfrac{-12}{2}$

$y = -3x - 6$

69. $-3x + 3y = -15$

$-3x + 3x + 3y = 3x - 15$

$3y = 3x - 15$

$\dfrac{3y}{3} = \dfrac{3x-15}{3}$

$y = \dfrac{3x}{3} + \dfrac{-15}{3}$

$y = x - 5$

70. $-2y + 4x = -8$

$-2y + 4x - 4x = -4x - 8$

$-2y = -4x - 8$

$\dfrac{-2y}{-2} = \dfrac{-4x-8}{-2}$

$y = \dfrac{-4x}{-2} + \dfrac{-8}{-2}$

$y = 2x + 4$

71. $4x = 6y - 8$

$4x + 8 = 6y - 8 + 8$

$4x + 8 = 6y$

$\dfrac{4x+8}{6} = \dfrac{6y}{6}$

$\dfrac{4x}{6} + \dfrac{8}{6} = y$

$\dfrac{2}{3}x + \dfrac{4}{3} = y$

$y = \dfrac{2}{3}x + \dfrac{4}{3}$

72. $15 = 3y - x$

$x + 15 = 3y - x + x$

$x + 15 = 3y$

$\dfrac{x+15}{3} = \dfrac{3y}{3}$

$\dfrac{x}{3} + \dfrac{15}{3} = y$

$\dfrac{1}{3}x + 5 = y$

$y = \dfrac{1}{3}x + 5$

73. $5y = -10 + 3x$

$\dfrac{5y}{5} = \dfrac{-10+3x}{5}$

$y = \dfrac{-10}{5} + \dfrac{3x}{5}$

$y = -2 + \dfrac{3}{5}x$

$y = \dfrac{3}{5}x - 2$

74. $-2y = -3x - 18$

$\dfrac{-2y}{-2} = \dfrac{-3x-18}{-2}$

$y = \dfrac{-3x}{-2} + \dfrac{-18}{-2}$

$y = \dfrac{3}{2}x + 9$

75. $-6y = 15 - 3x$

$$\frac{-6y}{-6} = \frac{15 - 3x}{-6}$$

$$y = \frac{15}{-6} + \frac{-3x}{-6}$$

$$y = -\frac{5}{2} + \frac{1}{2}x$$

$$y = \frac{1}{2}x - \frac{5}{2}$$

76. $-12 = -2x - 3y$

$$2x - 12 = -2x + 2x - 3y$$

$$2x - 12 = -3y$$

$$\frac{2x - 12}{-3} = \frac{-3y}{-3}$$

$$\frac{2x}{-3} + \frac{-12}{-3} = y$$

$$-\frac{2}{3}x + 4 = y$$

$$y = -\frac{2}{3}x + 4$$

77. $-8 = -x - 2y$

$$x - 8 = x - x - 2y$$

$$x - 8 = -2y$$

$$\frac{x - 8}{-2} = \frac{-2y}{-2}$$

$$\frac{-x}{2} + \frac{-8}{-2} = y$$

$$-\frac{1}{2}x + 4 = y$$

$$y = -\frac{1}{2}x + 4$$

78. $4x + 3y = 20$

$$4x - 4x + 3y = -4x + 20$$

$$3y = -4x + 20$$

$$\frac{3y}{3} = \frac{-4x + 20}{3}$$

$$y = \frac{-4x}{3} + \frac{20}{3}$$

$$y = -\frac{4}{3}x + \frac{20}{3}$$

79. $y + 3 = -\frac{1}{3}(x - 4)$

$$y + 3 = -\frac{1}{3}x + \frac{4}{3}$$

$$y + 3 - 3 = -\frac{1}{3}x + \frac{4}{3} - 3$$

$$y = -\frac{1}{3}x + \frac{4}{3} - \frac{9}{3}$$

$$y = -\frac{1}{3}x - \frac{5}{3}$$

80. $y - 3 = \frac{2}{3}(x + 4)$

$$y - 3 = \frac{2}{3}x + \frac{8}{3}$$

$$y - 3 + 3 = \frac{2}{3}x + \frac{8}{3} + 3$$

$$y = \frac{2}{3}x + \frac{8}{3} + \frac{9}{3}$$

$$y = \frac{2}{3}x + \frac{17}{3}$$

81. $y - \frac{1}{5} = 2\left(x + \frac{1}{3}\right)$

$$y - \frac{1}{5} = 2x + \frac{2}{3}$$

$$y - \frac{1}{5} + \frac{1}{5} = 2x + \frac{2}{3} + \frac{1}{5}$$

$$y = 2x + \frac{10}{15} + \frac{3}{15}$$

$$y = 2x + \frac{13}{15}$$

82. $y + 5 = \frac{3}{4}\left(x + \frac{1}{2}\right)$

$$y + 5 = \frac{3}{4}x + \frac{3}{8}$$

$$y + 5 - 5 = \frac{3}{4}x + \frac{3}{8} - 5$$

$$y = \frac{3}{4}x + \frac{3}{8} - \frac{40}{8}$$

$$y = \frac{3}{4}x - \frac{37}{8}$$

83. $d = rt$

$$d = (2r)\left(\frac{1}{2}t\right)$$

$$d = 2 \cdot \frac{1}{2}rt$$

$$d = rt$$

The distance remains the same.

84. $i = prt$

$$i = (2p)(2r)\left(\frac{1}{2}t\right)$$

$$i = 2 \cdot 2 \cdot \frac{1}{2}prt$$

$$i = 2prt$$

The interest doubles.

85. $A = s^2$

$$A = (2s)^2 = 4s^2$$

The area is 4 times as large as the original area.

86. $V = s^3$

$$V = (2s)^3 = 8s^3$$

The volume is 8 times as large as the original volume.

87. Substitute $\frac{1}{2}s$ for r in the area formula.

$$A_{\text{circle}} = \pi r^2$$

$$= \pi\left(\frac{1}{2}s\right)^2$$

$$= \frac{1}{4}\pi s^2$$

$$= \frac{1}{4}(3.14)s^2$$

$$= 0.785s^2$$

$$A_{\text{square}} = s^2$$

The area of a square is larger because $1s^2 > 0.785s^2$.

88. If the diagonal of a square is s then the side of the square can be represented by $\frac{s}{\sqrt{2}}$.

$$A_{\text{square}} = s^2$$

$$= \left(\frac{s}{\sqrt{2}}\right)^2$$

$$= \frac{s^2}{2}$$

$$A_{\text{circle}} = \pi r^2$$

$$= \pi\left(\frac{1}{2}s\right)^2$$

$$= \frac{1}{4}\pi s^2$$

$$= \frac{1}{4}(3.14)s^2$$

$$= 0.785s^2$$

The area of the circle is larger because $0.785s^2 > 0.5s^2$.

89. $i = prt$

$$i = (6000)(0.08)(3) = 1440$$

He will pay $1440 interest.

90. $i = prt$

$$640 = (4000)(r)(2)$$

$$640 = 8000r$$

$$\frac{640}{8000} = \frac{8000r}{8000}$$

$$0.08 = r$$

Her brother paid an interest rate of 8%.

91. $i = prt$

$$450 = p(0.03)(3)$$

$$450 = 0.09p$$

$$\frac{450}{0.09} = \frac{0.09p}{0.09}$$

$$5000 = p$$

She placed $5000 in the savings account.

92. $i = prt$

$840 = (6000)(0.035)(t)$

$840 = 210t$

$\dfrac{840}{210} = \dfrac{210t}{210}$

$4 = t$

His money had been in the account for 4 years.

93. $d = rt$

$150 = r(3)$

$50 = r$

Her average speed was 50 mph.

94. $d = rt$

$d = (3.4)(2) = 6.8$

She walked 6.8 mi.

95. $d = rt$

$d = (763.2)(0.01) = 7.632$

The car traveled 7.632 mi.

96. $d = rt$

$660 = r(0.3)$

$2200 = r$

The plane's average speed was 2200 mph.

97. $A = lw$

$A = (8)(6) = 48$

The area of the screen is 48 sq. in.

98. $P = 2l + 2w$

$P = 2(34.9) + 2(19.6) = 69.8 + 39.2 = 109$

The perimeter of the screen is 109 in.

99. $A = \dfrac{1}{2}bh$

$A = \dfrac{1}{2}(36)(31) = 558$

The area is 558 sq. in.

100. $P = 2l + 2w$

$P = 2(100) + 2(60) = 200 + 120 = 320$

He needs 320 feet of fencing.

101. $C = 2\pi r$

$C = 2\pi(12) = 24\pi \approx 75.40$

The circumference of the pool is about 75.40 ft.

102. $A = \pi r^2$

$A = \pi(1.5)^2 = \pi(2.25) \approx 7.07$

The area of the tabletop is about 7.07 square feet.

103. Total area = Area of top triangle + area of bottom triangle

Total Area $= 0.5b_1\,h_1 + 0.5b_2\,h_2$

Total Area $= 0.5(2)(1) + 0.5(2)(2)$

Total Area $= 1 + 2 = 3$

The area of the kite is 3 square feet.

104. $V = lwh$

$V = (26)(19.5)(11) = 5577$

The volume of the suitcase is 5577 cu in.

105. $A = \dfrac{1}{2}h(b + d)$

$A = \dfrac{1}{2}(2)(4+3) = \dfrac{1}{2}(2)(7) = (1)7 = 7$

The area of the sign is 7 sq. ft.

106. $V = \pi r^2 h$

$V = \pi(4)^2(3) = \pi(16)(3) = 48\pi \approx 150.80$

The volume of water in the Jacuzzi is about 150.80 cu ft.

107. $C = 2\pi r$

$390 = 2\pi(r)$

$390 = 2\pi r$

$\dfrac{390}{2\pi} = \dfrac{2\pi r}{2\pi}$

$62.07 \approx r$

The radius of the roots is about 62.07 feet.

The diameter is twice the radius, so
$d = 2(62.07) = 124.14$
The diameter is about 124.1 ft.

108. $A = \dfrac{1}{2}h(b + d)$

$A = \dfrac{1}{2}(100)(80 + 200)$

$= \dfrac{1}{2}(100)(280)$

$= (50)(280)$

$= 14,000$

The seating area is 14,000 sq. ft.

109. The radius is half the diameter.

$$V = \frac{4}{3}\pi r^3$$

$$V = \frac{4}{3}\pi\left(\frac{9}{2}\right)^3$$

$$V \approx 381.7$$

The volume of the basketball is about 381.7 cu. in.

110. $V = \pi r^2 h$

The radius is $\frac{1}{2}$ the diameter or

$\frac{1}{2}(24) = 12 = 1$ foot.

$V = \pi(1)^2(4) = 4\pi \approx 12.57$

The volume of the drum is about 12.57 cu. ft.

111. a. $B = \dfrac{703w}{h^2}$

b. 5 feet 3 inches $= 5(12) + 3$

$$= 60 + 3$$

$$= 63 \text{ inches}$$

$$B = \frac{703(135)}{(63)^2} = \frac{94,905}{3969} \approx 23.91$$

112. $B = \dfrac{703(162)}{(67)^2} = \dfrac{113,886}{4489} \approx 25.37$

113. a. $V = lwh$

$$V = (3x)(x)(6x-1)$$

$$= 3x^2(6x-1)$$

$$= 18x^3 - 3x^2$$

b. $V = 18x^3 - 3x^2$

$V = 18(7)^3 - 3(7)^2 = 6174 - 147 = 6027$

Volume is 6027 cm^3.

c. $S = 2lw + 2lh + 2wh$

$$S = 2(3x)(x) + 2(3x)(6x-1) + 2(x)(6x-1)$$

$$= 6x^2 + 36x^2 - 6x + 12x^2 - 2x$$

$$= 54x^2 - 8x$$

d. $S = 54x^2 - 8x$

$S = 54(7)^2 - 8(7) = 2646 - 56 = 2590$

Surface area is 2590 cm^2.

114. a. B^2

b. A^2

c. $A^2 - B^2$

d. $A^2 C$

e. $V = lwh$

$V = (1.5)(1.5)(0.8) = 1.8 \text{ ft.}^3$

115. $-\dfrac{4}{15} + \dfrac{2}{5} = -\dfrac{4}{15} + \dfrac{6}{15} = \dfrac{2}{15}$

116. $-6 + 7 - 4 - 3 = 1 - 4 - 3 = -3 - 3 = -6$

117. $\left[4(12 \div 2^2 - 3)^2\right]^2 = \left[4(12 \div 4 - 3)^2\right]^2$

$$= \left[4(3-3)^2\right]^2$$

$$= \left[4(0)^2\right]^2$$

$$= [0]^2$$

$$= 0$$

118. $\dfrac{r}{2} + 2r = 20$

$$2\left(\frac{r}{2} + 2r\right) = 2(20)$$

$$r + 4r = 40$$

$$5r = 40$$

$$r = 8$$

Exercise Set 2.7

1. A ratio is a quotient of two quantities.

2. In the ratio $a:b$, a and b are called terms of the ratio.

3. The ratio of c to d can be written as c to d, $c:d$, and $\dfrac{c}{d}$.

4. A proportion is a statement of equality between two ratios.

5. To set up and solve a proportion, we need a given ratio and one of the two parts of a second ratio.

6. Similar figures have corresponding angles that are equal and corresponding sides that are in proportion.

7. Yes, similar figures have the same shape but not necessarily the same size.

8. No, similar figures have the same shape but not necessarily the same size.

9. Yes; the terms in each ratio are in the same order.

10. Yes; The terms in each ratio are in the same order.

11. No; The terms in each ratio are not in the same order.

12. No; The terms in each ratio are not in the same order.

13. $6:9 = 2:3$

14. Total grades $= 6 + 4 + 9 + 3 + 2 = 24$
Ratio of F's to total grades
$2:24 = 1:12$

15. $3:6 = 1:2$

16. Grades better than C $= 6 + 4 = 10$
Ratio of grades better than C to total grades $= 10:24 = 5:12$

17. Total grades $= 6 + 4 + 9 + 3 + 2 = 24$
Ratio of total grades to D's $= 24:3 = 8:1$

18. Grades better than C $= 6 + 4 = 10$
Grades less than C $= 3 + 2 = 5$
Ratio of grades better than C to grades less than C $= 10:5 = 2:1$

19. $7:4$

20. $50:60 = 5:6$

21. $5:15 = 1:3$

22. $18:24 = 3:4$

23. 3 hours $= 3 \times 60 = 180$ minutes
Ratio is $\dfrac{180}{30} = \dfrac{6}{1}$ or 6:1.

24. 4 yards is $4 \times 3 = 12$ feet
Ratio is $\dfrac{6}{12} = \dfrac{1}{2}$ or 1:2.

25. 12 nickels is $12 \cdot \left(\dfrac{1}{2}\right) = 6$ dimes
Ratio is 7:6.

26. 4 pounds is $4 \times 16 = 64$ ounces
Ratio is $\dfrac{26}{64} = \dfrac{13}{32}$ or 13:32.

27. Gear ratio $= \dfrac{\text{number of teeth on driving gear}}{\text{number of teeth on driven gear}}$
$= \dfrac{40}{5} = \dfrac{8}{1}$
Gear ratio is 8:1.

28. Gear ratio $= \dfrac{\text{number of teeth on driving gear}}{\text{number of teeth on driven gear}}$
$= \dfrac{30}{8} = \dfrac{15}{4}$
Thus the gear ratio is 15:4.
Dividing both parts of the ratio by 4, ratio can also be expressed as 3.75:1.

29. **a.** 50:23
    b. Since $50 \div 23 \approx 2.17$, $50:23 \approx 2.17:1$.

30. **a.** 39:63 or 13:21
    b. Since $39 \div 63 \approx 0.62$, $39:63 \approx 0.62:1$.

31. **a.** 5.15:3.35 or 1.03:0.67
    b. Since $5.15 \div 3.35 \approx 1.54$, $5.15:3.35 \approx 1.54:1$.

32. **a.** 299:249
    b. Since $299 \div 249 \approx 1.20$, $299:249 \approx 1.20:1$.

33. **a.** 19.2:2.2 or 9.6:1.1
    b. 6.7:3.1

34. **a.** 5.6:8.8 or 0.7:1.1
    b. 7.0:6.3 or 1.0:0.9

35. **a.** 40:32 or 5:4
    b. 15:11

36. **a.** 78:10 or 39:5
    b. 2:4 or 1:2

37. $\dfrac{x}{3} = \dfrac{20}{5}$

$x \cdot 5 = 3 \cdot 20$

$5x = 60$

$\dfrac{5x}{5} = \dfrac{60}{5}$

$x = 12$

38. $\dfrac{x}{8} = \dfrac{24}{48}$

$x \cdot 48 = 8 \cdot 24$

$48x = 192$

$\dfrac{48x}{48} = \dfrac{192}{48}$

$x = 4$

39. $\dfrac{5}{3} = \dfrac{75}{a}$

$5 \cdot a = 3 \cdot 75$

$5a = 225$

$\dfrac{5a}{5} = \dfrac{225}{5}$

$a = 45$

40. $\dfrac{x}{3} = \dfrac{90}{30}$

$x \cdot 30 = 3 \cdot 90$

$30x = 270$

$\dfrac{30x}{30} = \dfrac{270}{30}$

$x = 9$

41. $\dfrac{-7}{3} = \dfrac{21}{p}$

$-7 \cdot p = 3 \cdot 21$

$-7p = 63$

$\dfrac{-7p}{-7} = \dfrac{63}{-7}$

$p = -9$

42. $\dfrac{-12}{13} = \dfrac{36}{x}$

$-12 \cdot x = 13 \cdot 36$

$-12x = 468$

$\dfrac{-12x}{-12} = \dfrac{468}{-12}$

$x = -39$

43. $\dfrac{15}{45} = \dfrac{x}{-6}$

$15 \cdot -6 = 45 \cdot x$

$-90 = 45x$

$\dfrac{-90}{45} = \dfrac{45x}{45}$

$-2 = x$

44. $\dfrac{y}{6} = \dfrac{7}{42}$

$42 \cdot y = 6 \cdot 7$

$42y = 42$

$\dfrac{42y}{42} = \dfrac{42}{42}$

$y = 1$

45. $\dfrac{3}{z} = \dfrac{-1.5}{27}$

$3 \cdot 27 = z \cdot -1.5$

$81 = -1.5z$

$\dfrac{81}{-1.5} = \dfrac{-1.5z}{-1.5}$

$-54 = z$

46. $\dfrac{3}{12} = \dfrac{-1.4}{z}$

$3 \cdot z = 12 \cdot -1.4$

$3z = -16.8$

$\dfrac{3z}{3} = \dfrac{-16.8}{3}$

$z = -5.6$

47. $\dfrac{9}{12} = \dfrac{x}{8}$

$9 \cdot 8 = 12 \cdot x$

$72 = 12x$

$\dfrac{72}{12} = \dfrac{12x}{12}$

$6 = x$

48. $\dfrac{2}{20} = \dfrac{x}{200}$

$2 \cdot 200 = 20 \cdot x$

$400 = 20x$

$\dfrac{400}{20} = \dfrac{20x}{20}$

$20 = x$

49. $\dfrac{3}{12} = \dfrac{8}{x}$

$3x = 12 \cdot 8$

$3x = 96$

$\dfrac{3x}{3} = \dfrac{96}{3}$

$x = 32$

Thus the side is 32 inches in length.

50. $\dfrac{2}{1.8} = \dfrac{0.8}{x}$

$2x = (1.8)(0.8)$

$2x = 1.44$

$\dfrac{2x}{2} = \dfrac{1.44}{2}$

$x = 0.72$

Thus the side is 0.72 feet in length.

51. $\dfrac{4}{7} = \dfrac{9}{x}$

$4x = 7 \cdot 9$

$4x = 63$

$\dfrac{4x}{4} = \dfrac{63}{4}$

$x = 15.75$

Thus the side is 15.75 inches in length.

52. $\dfrac{5}{7} = \dfrac{8}{x}$

$5x = 7 \cdot 8$

$5x = 56$

$\dfrac{5x}{5} = \dfrac{56}{5}$

$x = 11.2$

Thus the side is 11.2 feet in length.

53. $\dfrac{16}{12} = \dfrac{26}{x}$

$16x = (12)(26)$

$16x = 312$

$\dfrac{16x}{16} = \dfrac{312}{16}$

$x = 19.5$

Thus the side is 19.5 inches in length.

54. $\dfrac{20}{8} = \dfrac{14}{x}$

$20x = (8)(14)$

$20x = 112$

$\dfrac{20x}{20} = \dfrac{112}{20}$

$x = 5.6$

Thus the side is 5.6 inches in length.

55. Let x = number of loads one bottle can do.

$\dfrac{4 \text{ fl ounces}}{1 \text{ load}} = \dfrac{100 \text{ fl ounces}}{x \text{ loads}}$

$\dfrac{4}{1} = \dfrac{100}{x}$

$4x = 100$

$x = 25$

One bottle can do 25 loads.

56. Let x = amount of time it takes to lay cable in hours.

$\dfrac{42 \text{ feet}}{1 \text{ hour}} = \dfrac{252 \text{ feet}}{x \text{ hours}}$

$\dfrac{42}{1} = \dfrac{252}{x}$

$42x = 1 \cdot 252$

$42x = 252$

$x = 6$

It will take them 6 hours.

57. Let x = number of miles that can be driven with a full tank.

$\dfrac{19 \text{ miles}}{1 \text{ gallon}} = \dfrac{x}{14.2 \text{ gallons}}$

$\dfrac{19}{1} = \dfrac{x}{14.2}$

$x = (19)(14.2)$

$x = 269.8$

It can travel 269.8 miles on a full tank.

58. Let x = number of shares that can be purchased.

$\dfrac{2 \text{ shares}}{\$38.25} = \dfrac{x \text{ shares}}{\$344.25}$

$\dfrac{2}{38.25} = \dfrac{x}{344.25}$

$2(344.25) = 38.25 \cdot x$

$688.5 = 38.25x$

$18 = x$

18 shares can be purchased.

59. Let x = length of model in feet.

$$\frac{1 \text{ foot model}}{20 \text{ foot train}} = \frac{x \text{ foot model}}{30 \text{ foot train}}$$

$$\frac{1}{20} = \frac{x}{30}$$

$$20x = 30$$

$$x = 1.5$$

The model should be 1.5 feet long.

60. Let x = tax owed by the Estevez's.

$$\frac{\$1000 \text{ assessed value}}{\$9.475 \text{ tax}} = \frac{\$145,000 \text{ assessed value}}{x \text{ dollars tax}}$$

$$\frac{1000}{9.475} = \frac{145,000}{x}$$

$$1000x = (9.475)(145,000)$$

$$1000x = 1,373,875$$

$$x = 1373.88$$

Thus the Estevez's will owe \$1373.88 in tax.

61. Let x = number of teaspoons needed for sprayer.

$$\frac{3 \text{ teaspoons}}{1 \text{ gallon water}} = \frac{x \text{ teaspoons}}{8 \text{ gallons water}}$$

$$\frac{3}{1} = \frac{x}{8}$$

$$3 \cdot 8 = 1 \cdot x$$

$$24 = x$$

Thus 24 teaspoons are needed for the sprayer.

62. Let x = number of pounds of fertilizer needed.

$$\frac{5000 \text{ square feet}}{40 \text{ pounds fertilizer}} = \frac{26,000 \text{ square feet}}{x \text{ pounds fertilizer}}$$

$$\frac{5000}{40} = \frac{26,000}{x}$$

$$5000x = (40)(26,000)$$

$$5000x = 1,040,000$$

$$x = 208$$

Thus 208 pounds of fertilizer are needed for 26,000 square feet.

63. Let x = length of beak of blue heron in inches.

$$\frac{3.5 \text{ inches in photo}}{3.75 \text{ feet}} = \frac{0.4 \text{ inches in photo}}{x \text{ feet}}$$

$$\frac{3.5}{3.75} = \frac{0.4}{x}$$

$$3.5x = 3.75 \cdot 0.4$$

$$3.5x = 1.5$$

$$x \approx 0.43$$

It's beak is about 0.43 feet long.

64. Let x = length on a map in inches.

$$\frac{0.5 \text{ inches}}{22 \text{ miles}} = \frac{x \text{ inches}}{55 \text{ miles}}$$

$$\frac{0.5}{22} = \frac{x}{55}$$

$$0.5 \cdot 55 = 22 \cdot x$$

$$27.5 = 22x$$

$$1.25 = x$$

The length on the map will be 1.25 inches.

65. Let x = number of cups needed.

$$\frac{1\frac{1}{2} \text{ cups}}{6 \text{ servings}} = \frac{x \text{ cups}}{15 \text{ servings}}$$

$$\frac{\frac{3}{2}}{6} = \frac{x}{15}$$

$$6x = 15 \cdot \frac{3}{2}$$

$$6x = 22.5$$

$$x = 3.75$$

3.75 cups of onions are needed.

66. Let x = time in hours it will take Karen to read the entire novel.

$$\frac{72 \text{ pages}}{1.3 \text{ hours}} = \frac{656 \text{ pages}}{x \text{ hours}}$$

$$\frac{72}{1.3} = \frac{656}{x}$$

$$72 \cdot x = 0.3 \cdot 656$$

$$72x = 852.8$$

$$x \approx 11.84$$

It will take her about 11.84 hours.

67. Let x = length of the model bull in feet.

$$\frac{2.95 \text{ feet metal bull}}{1 \text{ feet real bull}} = \frac{28 \text{ feet metal bull}}{x \text{ feet real bull}}$$

$$\frac{2.95}{1} = \frac{28}{x}$$

$$2.95 \cdot x = 1 \cdot 28$$

$$2.95x = 28$$

$$x \approx 9.49$$

The model bull is about 9.49 feet long.

68. Let x = time, in minutes, it will take to remove the water.

$$\frac{3 \text{ inches}}{30 \text{ minutes}} = \frac{12 \text{ inches}}{x \text{ minutes}}$$

$$\frac{3}{30} = \frac{12}{x}$$

$$3x = 30 \cdot 12$$

$$3x = 360$$

$$x = \frac{360}{3} = 120$$

It will take 120 minutes or 2 hours.

69. Let x = number of milliliters to be given.

$$\frac{1 \text{ milliliter}}{400 \text{ micrograms}} = \frac{x \text{ milliliter}}{220 \text{ micrograms}}$$

$$\frac{1}{400} = \frac{x}{220}$$

$$1 \cdot 220 = 400 \cdot x$$

$$220 = 400x$$

$$\frac{220}{400} = x$$

$$0.55 = x$$

Thus 0.55 milliliter should be given.

70. Let x = number of grams of meprobanate to be given.

$$\frac{1 \text{ sq m body surface}}{0.7 \text{ grams}} = \frac{0.6 \text{ sq m body surface}}{x \text{ grams}}$$

$$\frac{1}{0.7} = \frac{0.6}{x}$$

$$x = (0.6)(0.7)$$

$$x = 0.42$$

Thus 0.42 g meprobamate should be given.

71. Let x = number of minutes to read entire book.

$$\frac{40 \text{ pages}}{30 \text{ minutes}} = \frac{760 \text{ pages}}{x \text{ minutes}}$$

$$\frac{40}{30} = \frac{760}{x}$$

$$40x = (30)(760)$$

$$40x = 22,800$$

$$x = \frac{22,800}{40} = 570$$

Thus it will take her 570 minutes or 9 hours 30 minutes to read the entire book.

72. Let x = time, in minutes, it takes Jason to swim 30 laps.

$$\frac{3 \text{ laps}}{2.3 \text{ minutes}} = \frac{30 \text{ laps}}{x \text{ minutes}}$$

$$\frac{3}{2.3} = \frac{30}{x}$$

$$3 \cdot x = 2.3 \cdot 30$$

$$3x = 69$$

$$x = 23$$

It will take him 23 minutes.

73. Let x = number of children born with Prader-Willi Syndrome.

$$\frac{12,000 \text{ births}}{1 \text{ baby with syndrome}} = \frac{4,063,000 \text{ births}}{x \text{ babies with syndrome}}$$

$$\frac{12,000}{1} = \frac{4,063,000}{x}$$

$$12,000x = 4,063,000$$

$$x = \frac{4,063,000}{12,000} \approx 339$$

Thus, about 339 children were born with Prader-Willi Syndrome.

74. Let x = time it takes her to complete the scrapbook.

$$\frac{4 \text{ pages}}{20.5 \text{ minutes}} = \frac{36 \text{ pages}}{x \text{ minutes}}$$

$$\frac{4}{20.5} = \frac{36}{x}$$

$$4 \cdot x = 20.5 \cdot 36$$

$$4x = 738$$

$$x = \frac{738}{4} = 184.5$$

It will take her 184.5 minutes or 3 hr. 4 min. 30 sec. to complete the scrapbook.

75.

$$\frac{12 \text{ inches}}{1 \text{ foot}} = \frac{78 \text{ inches}}{x \text{ feet}}$$

$$\frac{12}{1} = \frac{78}{x}$$

$$12x = 78$$

$$x = \frac{78}{12} = 6.5$$

Thus 78 inches equals 6.5 feet.

76. $\dfrac{1 \text{ mile}}{5280 \text{ feet}} = \dfrac{x \text{ miles}}{22{,}704 \text{ feet}}$

$\dfrac{1}{5280} = \dfrac{x}{22{,}704}$

$22{,}704 = 5280x$

$\dfrac{22{,}704}{5280} = x$

$4.3 = x$

Thus 22,704 feet equals 4.3 miles.

77. $\dfrac{9 \text{ square feet}}{1 \text{ square yard}} = \dfrac{26.1 \text{ square feet}}{x \text{ square yards}}$

$\dfrac{9}{1} = \dfrac{26.1}{x}$

$9x = 26.1$

$x = \dfrac{26.1}{9} = 2.9$

Thus 26.1 square feet equals 2.9 square yards.

78. $\dfrac{1 \text{ pound}}{16 \text{ ounces}} = \dfrac{x \text{ pounds}}{146.4 \text{ ounces}}$

$\dfrac{1}{16} = \dfrac{x}{146.4}$

$146.4 = 16x$

$\dfrac{146.4}{16} = x$

$9.15 = x$

Thus 146.4 ounces equals 9.15 pounds.

79. $\dfrac{2.54 \text{ cm}}{1 \text{ inch}} = \dfrac{50.8 \text{ cm}}{x \text{ inches}}$

$\dfrac{2.54}{1} = \dfrac{50.8}{x}$

$2.54x = 50.8$

$x = \dfrac{50.8}{2.54} = 20$

Thus the length of the newborn is 20 inches.

80. $\dfrac{1 \text{ mile}}{1.6 \text{ kilometers}} = \dfrac{520 \text{ miles}}{x \text{ kilometers}}$

$\dfrac{1}{1.6} = \dfrac{520}{x}$

$x = (1.6)(520)$

$x = 832$

Thus the distance from San Diego to San Francisco is 832 kilometers.

81. Let x = number of home runs needed to break Bonds' record

$\dfrac{73 \text{ home runs}}{162 \text{ games}} = \dfrac{x}{50 \text{ games}}$

$\dfrac{73}{162} = \dfrac{x}{50}$

$162 \cdot x = 73 \cdot 50$

$162x = 3650$

$x = \dfrac{3650}{162} \approx 22.53$

A player would need to hit 23 home runs.

82. Let x = number of pounds of topsoil needed

$\dfrac{40 \text{ pounds top soil}}{12 \text{ square feet}} = \dfrac{x \text{ pounds topsoil}}{350 \text{ square feet}}$

$\dfrac{40}{12} = \dfrac{x}{350}$

$12 \cdot x = 40 \cdot 350$

$12x = 14000$

$x = \dfrac{14000}{12} \approx 1166.67$

The amount of topsoil needed is 1166.67 pounds.

83. Let x = amount of interest Jim would earn after 500 days.

$\dfrac{\$110.52 \text{ interest}}{180 \text{ days}} = \dfrac{\$x \text{ interest}}{500 \text{ days}}$

$\dfrac{110.52}{180} = \dfrac{x}{500}$

$180x = 55{,}260$

$x = \dfrac{55{,}260}{180} = 307$

He would earn \$307 in interest.

84. Let x = cost in dollars per grain of gold.

$\dfrac{480 \text{ grains}}{408 \text{ dollars}} = \dfrac{1 \text{ grain}}{x \text{ dollars}}$

$\dfrac{480}{408} = \dfrac{1}{x}$

$480x = 408$

$x = \dfrac{408}{480} = 0.85$

Thus the cost per grain is \$0.85.

85. Let x = the number of pesos she would receive in return for U.S. dollars.

$$\frac{\$1.00 \text{ U.S.}}{10.567 \text{ pesos}} = \frac{\$200 \text{ U.S.}}{x \text{ pesos}}$$

$$\frac{1}{10.567} = \frac{200}{x}$$

$$x = 2113.4$$

She will receive 2113.4 pesos.

86. Let x = amount of U.S. dollars received.

$$\frac{\$13.50 \text{ Canadian}}{\$10 \text{ U.S.}} = \frac{600 \text{ Canadian}}{x \text{ U.S. dollars}}$$

$$\frac{13.50}{10} = \frac{600}{x}$$

$$13.50x = 6000$$

$$x = \frac{6000}{13.5} \approx 444.44$$

He will receive \$444.44 more.

87. The ratio of Mrs. Ruff's low density to high density cholesterol is $\frac{127}{60}$. If we divide 127 by 60 we obtain approximately 2.12. Thus Mrs. Ruff's ratio is approximately equivalent to 2.12:1. Therefore, her ratio is less than the desired 4:1 ratio.

88. a. Decreased; if the numerator remains the same and the denominator increases, the ratio decreases because you are dividing by a greater number.

  b. Yes; Mike's ratio is 220:40 = 4.4:1.

89. In $\frac{a}{b} = \frac{c}{d}$, if b and d remain the same while a increases, then c increases because $ad = bc$. If a increases ad increases, so bc must increase by increasing c.

90. In $\frac{a}{b} = \frac{c}{d}$, if a and c remain the same while d decreases, then b decreases because $ad = bc$. If d decreases ad decreases so bc must decrease by decreasing b.

91. Let x = number of miles remaining on the life of each tire.
Inches remaining on the life of each tire:
$$0.31 - 0.06 = 0.25$$

$$\frac{0.03 \text{ inches}}{5000 \text{ miles}} = \frac{0.25 \text{ miles}}{x \text{ miles}}$$

$$\frac{0.03}{5000} = \frac{0.25}{x}$$

$$0.03x = 5000 \cdot 0.25$$

$$0.03x = 1250$$

$$x = \frac{1250}{0.03}$$

$$x \approx 41,667$$

The tires will last about 41,667 more miles.

92. Let x represent the amount of the ingredient that should be used.

flour:
$$\frac{12}{8} = \frac{\frac{1}{2}}{x}$$

$$12x = \left(\frac{1}{2}\right)8$$

$$12x = 4$$

$$x = \frac{1}{3}$$

$\frac{1}{3}$ cup of flour should be used.

nutmeg:
$$\frac{12}{8} = \frac{1}{x}$$

$$12x = 8$$

$$x = \frac{2}{3}$$

$\frac{2}{3}$ teaspoon of nutmeg should be used.

cinnamon:
$$\frac{12}{8} = \frac{1}{x}$$

$$12x = 8$$

$$x = \frac{2}{3}$$

$\frac{2}{3}$ teaspoon of cinnamon should be used.

salt: $\dfrac{12}{8} = \dfrac{\frac{1}{4}}{x}$

$12x = \left(\dfrac{1}{4}\right)8$

$12x = 2$

$x = \dfrac{1}{6}$

$\dfrac{1}{6}$ teaspoon of salt should be used.

butter: $\dfrac{12}{8} = \dfrac{2}{x}$

$12x = 82$

$12x = 16$

$x = \dfrac{4}{3}$ or $1\dfrac{1}{3}$

$\dfrac{4}{3}$ or $1\dfrac{1}{3}$ tablespoons of butter should be used.

sugar: $\dfrac{12}{8} = \dfrac{\frac{3}{2}}{x}$

$12x = 8\left(\dfrac{3}{2}\right)$

$12x = 12$

$x = 1$

1 cup of sugar should be used.

93. Let x = number of cubic centimeters of fluid needed.

$\dfrac{1}{40} = \dfrac{x}{25}$

$40x = 25$

$x = \dfrac{25}{40}$

$x = 0.625$

0.625 cubic centimeters of fluid should be drawn up into a syringe.

94 – 95. Answers will vary.

96. Commutative property of addition

97. Associative property of multiplication

98. Distributive property

99. $3(4x - 3) = 6(2x + 1) - 15$

$12x - 9 = 12x + 6 - 15$

$12x - 9 = 12x - 9$

$12x - 12x - 9 = 12x - 12x - 9$

$-9 = -9$ True

Since a true statement is obtained, the solution is all real numbers.

100. $y = mx + b$

$y - b = mx + b - b$

$y - b = mx$

$\dfrac{y - b}{x} = \dfrac{mx}{x}$

$\dfrac{y - b}{x} = m$

Chapter 2 Review Exercises

1. $3(x + 4) = 3x + 3(4)$
   $= 3x + 12$

2. $5(x - 2) = 5\left[x + (-2)\right]$
   $= 5x + 5(-2)$
   $= 5x + (-10)$
   $= 5x - 10$

3. $-2(x + 4) = -2x + (-2)(4)$
   $= -2x + (-8)$
   $= -2x - 8$

4. $-(x + 2) = -1(x + 2)$
   $= (-1)(x) + (-1)(2)$
   $= -x + (-2)$
   $= -x - 2$

5. $-(m + 3) = -1(m + 3)$
   $= (-1)(m) + (-1)(3)$
   $= -m - 3$

6. $-4(4 - x) = -4\left[4 + (-x)\right]$
   $= (-4)(4) + (-4)(-x)$
   $= -16 + 4x$

7. $5(5-p) = 5[5+(-p)]$
    $= 5(5)+5(-p)$
    $= 25+(-5p)$
    $= 25-5p$

8. $6(4x-5) = 6(4x)-6(5)$
    $= 24x-30$

9. $-5(5x-5) = -5[5x+(-5)]$
    $= -5(5x)+(-5)(-5)$
    $= -25x+25$

10. $4(-x+3) = 4(-x)+4(3)$
    $= -4x+12$

11. $\frac{1}{2}(2x+4) = \left(\frac{1}{2}\right)(2x)+\left(\frac{1}{2}\right)(4)$
    $= x+2$

12. $-\frac{1}{3}(3+6y) = \left(-\frac{1}{3}\right)(3)+\left(-\frac{1}{3}\right)(6y)$
    $= -1+(-2y)$
    $= -1-2y$

13. $-(x+2y-z) = -1[x+2y+(-z)]$
    $= -1(x)+(-1)(2y)+(-1)(-z)$
    $= -x+(-2y)+z$
    $= -x-2y+z$

14. $-3(2a-5b+7) = -3[2a+(-5b)+7]$
    $= -3(2a)+(-3)(-5b)+(-3)(7)$
    $= -6a+15b+(-21)$
    $= -6a+15b-21$

15. $7x-3x = 4x$

16. $5-3y+3 = -3y+5+3 = -3y+8$

17. $1+3x+2x = 1+5x = 5x+1$

18. $-2x-x+3y = -3x+3y$

19. $4m+2n+4m+6n = 4m+4m+2n+6n$
    $= 8m+8n$

20. There are no like terms.
    $9x+3y+2$ cannot be further simplified.

21. $6x-2x+3y+6 = 4x+3y+6$

22. $x+8x-9x+3 = 9x-9x+3 = 3$

23. $-4x^2-8x^2+3 = -12x^2+3$

24. $-2(3a^2-4)+6a^2-8 = -6a^2+8+6a^2-8$
    $= -6a^2+6a^2+8-8$
    $= 0$

25. $2x+3(x+4)-5 = 2x+3x+12-5 = 5x+7$

26. $-4+2(3-2b)-b = -4+6-4b-b$
    $= 2-5b$
    $= -5b+2$

27. $6-(-7x+6)-7x = 6+7x-6-7x$
    $= 7x-7x+6-6$
    $= 0$

28. $2(2x+5)-10-4 = 4x+10-10-4$
    $= 4x-4$

29. $-6(4-3x)-18+4x = -24+18x-18+4x$
    $= 18x+4x-24-18$
    $= 22x-42$

30. $4y-3(x+y)+6x^2 = 4y-3x-3y+6x^2$
    $= 6x^2-3x+4y-3y$
    $= 6x^2-3x+y$

31. $\frac{1}{4}d+2-\frac{3}{5}d+5 = \frac{1}{4}d-\frac{3}{5}d+2+5$
    $= \frac{5}{20}d-\frac{12}{20}d+7$
    $= -\frac{7}{20}d+7$

32. $3-(x-y)+(x-y) = 3-x+y+x-y$
    $= -x+x+y-y+3$
    $= 3$

33. $\dfrac{5}{6}x - \dfrac{1}{3}(2x-6) = \dfrac{5}{6}x - \dfrac{2}{3}x + 2$

$\qquad\qquad\qquad\quad\ = \dfrac{5}{6}x - \dfrac{4}{6}x + 2$

$\qquad\qquad\qquad\quad\ = \dfrac{1}{6}x + 2$

34. $\dfrac{2}{3} - \dfrac{1}{4}n - \dfrac{1}{3}(n+2) = \dfrac{2}{3} - \dfrac{1}{4}n - \dfrac{1}{3}n - \dfrac{2}{3}$

$\qquad\qquad\qquad\qquad\quad\ = -\dfrac{1}{4}n - \dfrac{1}{3}n + \dfrac{2}{3} - \dfrac{2}{3}$

$\qquad\qquad\qquad\qquad\quad\ = -\dfrac{3}{12}n - \dfrac{4}{12}n + 0$

$\qquad\qquad\qquad\qquad\quad\ = -\dfrac{7}{12}n$

35. $-3x = -3$

$\quad\ \dfrac{-3x}{-3} = \dfrac{-3}{-3}$

$\qquad\ \ x = 1$

36. $x + 6 = -7$

$\ x + 6 - 6 = -7 - 6$

$\qquad\quad\ x = -13$

37. $x - 4 = 7$

$\ x - 4 + 4 = 7 + 4$

$\qquad\quad\ x = 11$

38. $\dfrac{x}{3} = -9$

$\quad 3\left(\dfrac{x}{3}\right) = 3(-9)$

$\qquad\quad\ x = -27$

39. $5x + 1 = 12$

$\ 5x + 1 - 1 = 12 - 1$

$\qquad\quad 5x = 11$

$\qquad\quad \dfrac{5x}{5} = \dfrac{11}{5}$

$\qquad\qquad x = \dfrac{11}{5}$

40. $14 = 3 + 2x$

$\ 14 - 3 = 3 - 3 + 2x$

$\qquad 11 = 2x$

$\qquad \dfrac{11}{2} = \dfrac{2x}{2}$

$\qquad \dfrac{11}{2} = x$

41. $4c + 3 = -21$

$\ 4c + 3 - 3 = -21 - 3$

$\qquad\quad 4c = -24$

$\qquad\quad \dfrac{4c}{4} = \dfrac{-24}{4}$

$\qquad\qquad c = -6$

42. $9 - 2a = 15$

$\ 9 - 9 - 2a = 15 - 9$

$\qquad\quad -2a = 6$

$\qquad\quad \dfrac{-2a}{-2} = \dfrac{6}{-2}$

$\qquad\qquad a = -3$

43. $-x = -12$

$\qquad -1x = -12$

$\ (-1)(-1x) = (-1)(-12)$

$\qquad\quad 1x = 12$

$\qquad\qquad x = 12$

44. $3(x-2) = 6$

$\qquad 3x - 6 = 6$

$\ 3x - 6 + 6 = 6 + 6$

$\qquad\quad 3x = 12$

$\qquad\quad \dfrac{3x}{3} = \dfrac{12}{3}$

$\qquad\qquad x = 4$

45. $-12 = 3(2x - 8)$

$\qquad -12 = 6x - 24$

$\ -12 + 24 = 6x - 24 + 24$

$\qquad\quad 12 = 6x$

$\qquad\quad \dfrac{12}{6} = \dfrac{6x}{6}$

$\qquad\qquad 2 = x$

46.
$$4(6+2x)=0$$
$$24+8x=0$$
$$24-24+8x=0-24$$
$$8x=-24$$
$$\frac{8x}{8}=\frac{-24}{8}$$
$$x=-3$$

47.
$$-6n+2n+6=0$$
$$-4n+6=0$$
$$-4n+6-6=0-6$$
$$-4n=-6$$
$$\frac{-4n}{-4}=\frac{-6}{-4}$$
$$n=\frac{6}{4}=\frac{3}{2}$$

48.
$$-3=3w-(4w+6)$$
$$-3=3w-4w-6$$
$$-3=-1w-6$$
$$-3+6=-1w-6+6$$
$$3=-1w$$
$$\frac{3}{-1}=\frac{-1w}{-1}$$
$$-3=w$$

49.
$$6-(2n+3)-4n=6$$
$$6-2n-3-4n=6$$
$$6-3-2n-4n=6$$
$$3-6n=6$$
$$3-3-6n=6-3$$
$$-6n=3$$
$$\frac{-6n}{-6}=\frac{3}{-6}$$
$$n=-\frac{3}{6}=-\frac{1}{2}$$

50.
$$4x+6-7x+9=18$$
$$-3x+15=18$$
$$-3x+15-15=18-15$$
$$-3x=3$$
$$\frac{-3x}{-3}=\frac{3}{-3}$$
$$x=-1$$

51.
$$5+3(x-1)=3(x+1)-1$$
$$5+3x-3=3x+3-1$$
$$3x+2=3x+2$$
$$3x-3x+2=3x-3x+2$$
$$2=2 \text{ True}$$
The solution is all real numbers.

52.
$$8.4r-6.3=6.3+2.1r$$
$$8.4r-2.1r-6.3=6.3+2.1r-2.1r$$
$$6.3r-6.3=6.3$$
$$6.3r-6.3+6.3=6.3+6.3$$
$$6.3r=12.6$$
$$\frac{6.3r}{6.3}=\frac{12.6}{6.3}$$
$$r=2$$

53.
$$19.6-21.3t=80.1-9.2t$$
$$19.6-21.3t+21.3t=80.1-9.2t+21.3t$$
$$19.6=80.1+12.1t$$
$$19.6-80.1=80.1-80.1+12.1t$$
$$-60.5=12.1t$$
$$\frac{-60.5}{12.1}=\frac{12.1t}{12.1}$$
$$-5=t$$

54.
$$0.35(c-5)=0.45(c+4)$$
$$0.35c-1.75=0.45c+1.8$$
$$0.35c-0.35c-1.75=0.45c-0.35c+1.8$$
$$-1.75=0.10c+1.8$$
$$-1.75-1.8=0.10c+1.8-1.8$$
$$-3.55=0.10c$$
$$\frac{-3.55}{0.10}=\frac{0.10c}{0.10}$$
$$-35.5=c$$

55.
$$0.2(x+6)=-0.3(2x-1)$$
$$0.2x+1.2=-0.6x+0.3$$
$$0.2x+0.6x+1.2=-0.6x+0.6x+0.3$$
$$0.8x+1.2=0.3$$
$$0.8x+1.2-1.2=0.3-1.2$$
$$0.8x=-0.9$$
$$\frac{0.8x}{0.8}=\frac{-0.9}{0.8}$$
$$x=-1.125$$

56.
$$-2.3(x-8) = 3.7(x+4)$$
$$-2.3x + 18.4 = 3.7x + 14.8$$
$$-2.3x + 2.3x + 18.4 = 3.7x + 2.3x + 14.8$$
$$18.4 = 6.0x + 14.8$$
$$18.4 - 14.8 = 6.0x + 14.8 - 14.8$$
$$3.6 = 6.0x$$
$$\frac{3.6}{6.0} = \frac{6.0x}{6.0}$$
$$0.6 = x$$

57.
$$\frac{p}{3} + 2 = \frac{1}{4}$$
$$12\left(\frac{p}{3} + 2\right) = 12\left(\frac{1}{4}\right)$$
$$4p + 24 = 3$$
$$4p + 24 - 24 = 3 - 24$$
$$4p = -21$$
$$\frac{4p}{4} = \frac{-21}{4}$$
$$p = -\frac{21}{4}$$

58.
$$\frac{d}{6} + \frac{1}{7} = 2$$
$$42\left(\frac{d}{6} + \frac{1}{7}\right) = 42(2)$$
$$7d + 6 = 84$$
$$7d + 6 - 6 = 84 - 6$$
$$7d = 78$$
$$\frac{7d}{7} = \frac{78}{7}$$
$$d = \frac{78}{7}$$

59.
$$\frac{3}{5}(r-6) = 3r$$
$$\frac{3}{5}r - \frac{18}{5} = 3r$$
$$5\left(\frac{3}{5}r - \frac{18}{5}\right) = 5(3r)$$
$$3r - 18 = 15r$$
$$3r - 3r - 18 = 15r - 3r$$
$$-18 = 12r$$
$$\frac{-18}{12} = \frac{12r}{12}$$
$$-\frac{18}{12} = r$$
$$-\frac{3}{2} = r$$

60.
$$\frac{2}{3}w = \frac{1}{7}(w-2)$$
$$\frac{2}{3}w = \frac{1}{7}w - \frac{2}{7}$$
$$21\left(\frac{2}{3}w\right) = 21\left(\frac{1}{7}w - \frac{2}{7}\right)$$
$$14w = 3w - 6$$
$$14w - 3w = 3w - 3w - 6$$
$$11w = -6$$
$$\frac{11w}{11} = \frac{-6}{11}$$
$$w = -\frac{6}{11}$$

61.
$$8x - 5 = -4x + 19$$
$$8x + 4x - 5 = -4x + 4x + 19$$
$$12x - 5 = 19$$
$$12x - 5 + 5 = 19 + 5$$
$$12x = 24$$
$$\frac{12x}{12} = \frac{24}{12}$$
$$x = 2$$

62.
$$-(w+2) = 2(3w-6)$$
$$-w-2 = 6w-12$$
$$-w-2+12 = 6w-12+12$$
$$-w+10 = 6w$$
$$-w+w+10 = 6w+w$$
$$10 = 7w$$
$$\frac{10}{7} = \frac{7w}{7}$$
$$\frac{10}{7} = w$$

63.
$$2x+6 = 3x+9-3$$
$$2x+6 = 3x+6$$
$$2x-2x+6 = 3x-2x+6$$
$$6 = x+6$$
$$6-6 = x+6-6$$
$$0 = x$$

64.
$$-5a+3 = 2a+10$$
$$-5a+3-10 = 2a+10-10$$
$$-5a-7 = 2a$$
$$-5a+5a-7 = 2a+5a$$
$$-7 = 7a$$
$$\frac{-7}{7} = \frac{7a}{7}$$
$$-1 = a$$

65.
$$5p-2 = -2(-3p+6)$$
$$5p-2 = 6p-12$$
$$5p-5p-2 = 6p-5p-12$$
$$-2 = p-12$$
$$-2+12 = p-12+12$$
$$10 = p$$

66.
$$3x-12x = 24-9x$$
$$-9x = 24-9x$$
$$-9x+9x = 24-9x+9x$$
$$0 = 24 \quad \text{False}$$
Since a false statement is obtained, there is no solution.

67.
$$4(2x-3)+4 = 8x-8$$
$$8x-12+4 = 8x-8$$
$$8x-8 = 8x-8$$
Since the equation is true for all values of x, the solution is all real numbers.

68.
$$4-c-2(4-3c) = 3(c-4)$$
$$4-c-8+6c = 3c-12$$
$$5c-4 = 3c-12$$
$$5c-3c-4 = 3c-3c-12$$
$$2c-4 = -12$$
$$2c-4+4 = -12+4$$
$$2c = -8$$
$$\frac{2c}{2} = \frac{-8}{2}$$
$$c = -4$$

69.
$$2(x+7) = 6x+9-4x$$
$$2x+14 = 6x+9-4x$$
$$2x+14 = 2x+9$$
$$2x-2x+14 = 2x-2x+9$$
$$14 = 9 \quad \text{False}$$
Since a false statement is obtained, there is no solution.

70.
$$-5(3-4x) = -6+20x-9$$
$$-15+20x = -6+20x-9$$
$$-15+20x = -15+20x$$
The statement is true for all values of x, thus the solution is all real numbers.

71.
$$4(x-3)-(x+5) = 0$$
$$4x-12-x-5 = 0$$
$$3x-17 = 0$$
$$3x-17+17 = 0+17$$
$$3x = 17$$
$$\frac{3x}{3} = \frac{17}{3}$$
$$x = \frac{17}{3}$$

72.
$$-2(4-x) = 6(x+2)+3x$$
$$-8+2x = 6x+12+3x$$
$$-8+2x = 9x+12$$
$$-8-12+2x = 9x+12-12$$
$$-20+2x = 9x$$
$$-20+2x-2x = 9x-2x$$
$$-20 = 7x$$
$$\frac{-20}{7} = \frac{7x}{7}$$
$$-\frac{20}{7} = x$$

73.
$$\frac{x+3}{2} = \frac{x}{2}$$
$$2(x+3) = 2x$$
$$2x+6 = 2x$$
$$2x-2x+6 = 2x-2x$$
$$6 = 0 \quad \text{False}$$
Since a false statement is obtained, there is no solution.

74.
$$\frac{x}{6} = \frac{x-4}{2}$$
$$2 \cdot x = 6(x-4)$$
$$2x = 6x-24$$
$$2x-6x = 6x-6x-24$$
$$-4x = -24$$
$$\frac{-4x}{-4} = \frac{-24}{-4}$$
$$x = 6$$

75.
$$\frac{1}{5}(3s+4) = \frac{1}{3}(2s-8)$$
$$\frac{3}{5}s+\frac{4}{5} = \frac{2}{3}s-\frac{8}{3}$$
$$15\left(\frac{3}{5}s+\frac{4}{5}\right) = 15\left(\frac{2}{3}s-\frac{8}{3}\right)$$
$$9s+12 = 10s-40$$
$$9s-9s+12 = 10s-9s-40$$
$$12 = s-40$$
$$12+40 = s-40+40$$
$$52 = s$$

76.
$$\frac{2(2t-4)}{5} = \frac{3t+6}{4}-\frac{3}{2}$$
$$\frac{4t-8}{5} = \frac{3t+6}{4}-\frac{3}{2}$$
$$20\left(\frac{4t-8}{5}\right) = 20\left(\frac{3t+6}{4}-\frac{3}{2}\right)$$
$$4(4t-8) = 5(3t+6)-30$$
$$16t-32 = 15t+30-30$$
$$16t-32 = 15t+0$$
$$16t-16t-32 = 15t-16t$$
$$-32 = -1t$$
$$\frac{-32}{-1} = \frac{-1t}{-1}$$
$$32 = t$$

77.
$$\frac{2}{5}(2-x) = \frac{1}{6}(-2x+2)$$
$$\frac{4}{5}-\frac{2}{5}x = -\frac{2}{6}x+\frac{2}{6}$$
$$\frac{4}{5}-\frac{2}{5}x = -\frac{1}{3}x+\frac{1}{3}$$
$$15\left(\frac{4}{5}-\frac{2}{5}x\right) = 15\left(-\frac{1}{3}x+\frac{1}{3}\right)$$
$$12-6x = -5x+5$$
$$12-6x+6x = -5x+6x+5$$
$$12 = x+5$$
$$12-5 = x+5-5$$
$$7 = x$$

78.
$$\frac{x}{4}+\frac{x}{6} = \frac{1}{2}(x+3)$$
$$\frac{x}{4}+\frac{x}{6} = \frac{x}{2}+\frac{3}{2}$$
$$12\left(\frac{x}{4}+\frac{x}{6}\right) = 12\left(\frac{x}{2}+\frac{3}{2}\right)$$
$$3x+2x = 6x+18$$
$$5x = 6x+18$$
$$5x-6x = 6x-6x+18$$
$$-1x = 18$$
$$\frac{-1x}{-1} = \frac{18}{-1}$$
$$x = -18$$

79. Substitute 7 for y, 2 for x, and 1 for b. Then solve for m.

$$y = mx + b$$
$$7 = m(2) + 1$$
$$7 = 2m + 1$$
$$7 - 1 = 2m + 1 - 1$$
$$6 = 2m$$
$$\frac{6}{2} = \frac{2m}{2}$$
$$3 = m$$

80. Substitute 12 for h, 3 for b, and 5 for d. Then solve for A.

$$A = \frac{1}{2}h(b + d)$$
$$A = \frac{1}{2}(12)(3 + 5) = \frac{1}{2}(12)(8) = 48$$

81. $A = \frac{1}{2}bh$

$$A = \frac{1}{2}(8)(3) = 12 \text{ cm}^2$$

82. $V = \frac{4}{3}\pi r^3$

$$V = \frac{4}{3}\pi(2)^3 = \frac{4}{3}\pi(8) = \frac{32}{3}\pi \approx 33.51 \text{ in.}^3$$

83.
$$P = 2l + 2w$$
$$P - 2w = 2l + 2w - 2w$$
$$P - 2w = 2l$$
$$\frac{P - 2w}{2} = \frac{2l}{2}$$
$$\frac{P - 2w}{2} = l$$

84. $y - y_1 = m(x - x_1)$

$$\frac{y - y_1}{x - x_1} = \frac{m(x - x_1)}{(x - x_1)}$$
$$\frac{y - y_1}{x - x_1} = m$$

85.
$$-x + 3y = 2$$
$$-x + x + 3y = 2 + x$$
$$3y = x + 2$$
$$\frac{3y}{3} = \frac{x + 2}{3}$$
$$y = \frac{x}{3} + \frac{2}{3}$$
$$y = \frac{1}{3}x + \frac{2}{3}$$

86. $d = rt$

$$d = (61.7)(5) = 308.5$$

He traveled 308.5 miles.

87. $A = lw$

$$A = (20)(12) = 240$$

The area of the flower garden is 240 sq. ft.

88. $V = \pi r^2 h$

$$V = \pi(2)^2(2) = 8\pi \approx 25.13$$

The volume of the tuna fish can is about 25.13 sq. in.

89. $12 : 20 = 3 : 5$

90. $80 \text{ ounces} = \frac{80}{16} = 5$ pounds

The ratio of 80 ounces to 12 pounds is thus 5:12.

91. 4 minutes = 240 seconds

The ratio of 4 minutes to 40 seconds is $\frac{240}{40} = \frac{6}{1}$.

The ratio is 6:1.

92. $\frac{x}{4} = \frac{8}{16}$

$$16 \cdot x = 8 \cdot 4$$
$$16x = 32$$
$$x = \frac{32}{16} = 2$$

93. $\frac{5}{20} = \frac{x}{80}$

$$20 \cdot x = 80 \cdot 5$$
$$20x = 400$$
$$x = \frac{400}{20} = 20$$

94. $\dfrac{3}{x} = \dfrac{15}{45}$

$3 \cdot 45 = 15 \cdot x$

$135 = 15x$

$\dfrac{135}{15} = x$

$9 = x$

95. $\dfrac{20}{45} = \dfrac{15}{x}$

$20 \cdot x = 15 \cdot 45$

$20x = 675$

$x = \dfrac{675}{20} = \dfrac{135}{4}$

96. $\dfrac{6}{5} = \dfrac{-12}{x}$

$6 \cdot x = -12 \cdot 5$

$6x = -60$

$x = \dfrac{-60}{6} = -10$

97. $\dfrac{b}{6} = \dfrac{8}{-3}$

$-3 \cdot b = 6 \cdot 8$

$-3b = 48$

$x = \dfrac{48}{-3} = -16$

98. $\dfrac{-7}{9} = \dfrac{-12}{y}$

$-7 \cdot y = -12 \cdot 9$

$-7y = -108$

$y = \dfrac{-108}{-7}$

$y = \dfrac{108}{7}$

99. $\dfrac{x}{-15} = \dfrac{30}{-5}$

$-5 \cdot x = -15 \cdot 30$

$-5x = -450$

$x = \dfrac{-450}{-5} = 90$

100. $\dfrac{6}{8} = \dfrac{30}{x}$

$6 \cdot x = 8 \cdot 30$

$6x = 240$

$x = \dfrac{240}{6} = 40$

Therefore the length of the side is 40 in.

101. $\dfrac{7}{3.5} = \dfrac{2}{x}$

$7 \cdot x = 2 \cdot 3.5$

$7x = 7$

$x = \dfrac{7}{7} = 1$

Therefore the length of the side is 1 ft.

102. Let t = the time it will take in hours to make the boat trip.

$\dfrac{40 \text{ miles}}{1.8 \text{ hours}} = \dfrac{140 \text{ miles}}{t \text{ hours}}$

$\dfrac{40}{1.8} = \dfrac{140}{t}$

$40 \cdot t = 1.8 \cdot 140$

$40t = 252$

$\dfrac{40t}{40} = \dfrac{252}{40}$

$t = 6.3$

It will take the boat 6.3 hours to travel 140 miles.

103. Let x = number of dishes he can wash in 21 minutes.

$\dfrac{12 \text{ dishes}}{3.5 \text{ minutes}} = \dfrac{x \text{ dishes}}{21 \text{ minutes}}$

$\dfrac{12}{3.5} = \dfrac{x}{21}$

$12 \cdot 21 = 3.5 \cdot x$

$252 = 3.5x$

$\dfrac{252}{3.5} = \dfrac{3.5x}{3.5}$

$72 = x$

He can wash 72 dishes in 21 minutes.

104. Let x = number of pages that can be copied in 22 minutes.

$$\frac{1 \text{ minutes}}{20 \text{ pages}} = \frac{22 \text{ minutes}}{x \text{ pages}}$$

$$\frac{1}{20} = \frac{22}{x}$$

$$1 \cdot x = 22 \cdot 20$$

$$x = 440$$

440 pages can be copied in 22 minutes.

105. Let x = number of inches representing 380 miles.

$$\frac{60 \text{ miles}}{1 \text{ inch}} = \frac{380 \text{ miles}}{x \text{ inches}}$$

$$\frac{60}{1} = \frac{380}{x}$$

$$60 \cdot x = 380 \cdot 1$$

$$60x = 380$$

$$x = \frac{380}{60} = 6\frac{1}{3}$$

$6\frac{1}{3}$ inches on the map represent 380 miles.

106. Let x = size of actual car in feet

$$\frac{1 \text{ inch}}{1.5 \text{ feet}} = \frac{10.5 \text{ inches}}{x \text{ feet}}$$

$$\frac{1}{1.5} = \frac{10.5}{x}$$

$$1 \cdot x = 1.5 \cdot 10.5$$

$$x = 15.75$$

The size of the actual car is 15.75 ft.

107. Let x = the value of 1 peso in terms of U.S. dollars.

$$\frac{\$1 \text{ U.S.}}{9.165 \text{ pesos}} = \frac{x \text{ dollars}}{1 \text{ peso}}$$

$$\frac{1}{9.165} = \frac{x}{1}$$

$$9.165 \cdot x = 1 \cdot 1$$

$$9.165x = 1$$

$$x = \frac{1}{9.165} \approx 0.109$$

1 peso equals about $0.109.

108. Let x = number of bottles the machine can fill and cap in 2 minutes.

$$2 \text{ minutes} = 120 \text{ seconds}$$

$$\frac{50 \text{ seconds}}{80 \text{ bottles}} = \frac{120 \text{ seconds}}{x \text{ bottles}}$$

$$\frac{50}{80} = \frac{120}{x}$$

$$50 \cdot x = 80 \cdot 120$$

$$50x = 9600$$

$$x = \frac{9600}{50} = 192$$

The machine can fill and cap 192 bottles in 2 minutes.

Chapter 2 Practice Test

1. $-3(4-2x) = -3[4+(-2x)]$
$$= -3(4)+(-3)(-2x)$$
$$= -12+6x \text{ or } 6x-12$$

2. $-(x+3y-4) = -[x+3y+(-4)]$
$$= -1[x+3y+(-4)]$$
$$= (-1)(x)+(-1)(3y)+(-1)(-4)$$
$$= -x+(-3y)+4$$
$$= -x-3y+4$$

3. $5x-8x+4 = -3x+4$

4. $4+2x-3x+6 = 2x-3x+4+6 = -x+10$

5. $-y-x-4x-6 = -x-4x-y-6 = -5x-y-6$

6. $a-2b+6a-6b-3 = a+6a-2b-6b-3$
$$= 7a-8b-3$$

7. $2x^2+3+2(3x-2) = 2x^2+3+6x-4$
$$= 2x^2+6x+3-4$$
$$= 2x^2+6x-1$$

8. $2.4x-3.9 = 3.3$
$$2.4x-3.9+3.9 = 3.3+3.9$$
$$2.4x = 7.2$$
$$\frac{2.4x}{2.4} = \frac{7.2}{2.4}$$
$$x = 3$$

9. $\frac{5}{6}(x-2) = x-3$

$\frac{5}{6}x - \frac{10}{6} = x - 3$

$6\left(\frac{5}{6}x - \frac{10}{6}\right) = 6(x-3)$

$5x - 10 = 6x - 18$

$5x - 5x - 10 = 6x - 5x - 18$

$-10 = x - 18$

$-10 + 18 = x - 18 + 18$

$8 = x$

10. $2x - 3(-2x+4) = -13 + x$

$2x + 6x - 12 = -13 + x$

$8x - 12 = -13 + x$

$8x - 12 + 12 = -13 + 12 + x$

$8x = -1 + x$

$8x - x = -1 + x - x$

$7x = -1$

$\frac{7x}{7} = \frac{-1}{7}$

$x = -\frac{1}{7}$

11. $3x - 4 - x = 2(x+5)$

$3x - 4 - x = 2x + 10$

$2x - 4 = 2x + 10$

$2x - 2x - 4 = 2x - 2x + 10$

$-4 = 10 \quad \text{False}$

Since a false statement is obtained, there is no solution.

12. $-3(2x+3) = -2(3x+1) - 7$

$-6x - 9 = -6x - 2 - 7$

$-6x - 9 = -6x - 9$

Since the equation is true for all values of x, the solution is all real numbers.

13. $ax + by + c = 0$

$ax + by - by + c = 0 - by$

$ax + c = -by$

$ax + c - c = -by - c$

$ax = -by - c$

$\frac{ax}{a} = \frac{-by-c}{a}$

$x = \frac{-by-c}{a}$

14. $-6x + 5y = -2$

$-6x + 6x + 5y = -2 + 6x$

$5y = 6x - 2$

$\frac{5y}{5} = \frac{6x-2}{5}$

$y = \frac{6x}{5} - \frac{2}{5}$

$y = \frac{6}{5}x - \frac{2}{5}$

15. $\frac{1}{7}(2x-5) = \frac{3}{8}x - \frac{5}{7}$

$\frac{2}{7}x - \frac{5}{7} = \frac{3}{8}x - \frac{5}{7}$

$56\left(\frac{2}{7}x - \frac{5}{7}\right) = 56\left(\frac{3}{8}x - \frac{5}{7}\right)$

$16x - 40 = 21x - 40$

$16x - 16x - 40 = 21x - 16x - 40$

$-40 = 5x - 40$

$-40 + 40 = 5x - 40 + 40$

$0 = 5x$

$\frac{0}{5} = \frac{5x}{5}$

$0 = x$

16. $\frac{9}{x} = \frac{3}{-15}$

$9(-15) = 3x$

$-135 = 3x$

$\frac{-135}{3} = x$

$-45 = x$

17. a. An equation that has exactly one solution is a conditional equation.

b. An equation that has no solution is a contradiction.

c. An equation that has all real numbers as its solution is an identity.

18. $\dfrac{3}{4} = \dfrac{8}{x}$

$3x = 4 \cdot 8$

$3x = 32$

$x = \dfrac{32}{3}$

The length of side x is $\dfrac{32}{3}$ feet or $10\dfrac{2}{3}$ feet.

19. Let r = the simple interest rate.

$i = prt$

$80 = 2000 \cdot r \cdot 1$

$80 = 2000r$

$\dfrac{80}{2000} = \dfrac{2000r}{2000}$

$0.04 = r$

The interest rate was 4%.

20. Let C= the circumference of the pie.

$C = 2\pi r$

$C = 2\pi(4.5) = 9\pi \approx 28.27$

The circumference of the pie is 28.27 in.

21. Let x = number of minutes it will take.

$\dfrac{25 \text{ miles}}{35 \text{ minutes}} = \dfrac{125 \text{ miles}}{x \text{ minutes}}$

$\dfrac{25}{35} = \dfrac{125}{x}$

$25x = 35 \cdot 125$

$25x = 4375$

$x = \dfrac{4375}{25} = 175$

It would take 175 minutes or 2 hours 55 minutes.

Chapter 2 Cumulative Review Test

1. $\dfrac{52}{15} \cdot \dfrac{10}{13} = \dfrac{\overset{4}{\cancel{52}}}{\underset{3}{\cancel{15}}} \cdot \dfrac{\overset{2}{\cancel{10}}}{\cancel{13}_1} = \dfrac{4 \cdot 2}{3 \cdot 1} = \dfrac{8}{3}$

2. $\dfrac{5}{24} \div \dfrac{2}{9} = \dfrac{5}{24} \cdot \dfrac{9}{2} = \dfrac{5}{8} \cdot \dfrac{3}{2} = \dfrac{5 \cdot 3}{8 \cdot 2} = \dfrac{15}{16}$

3. $|-2| > 1$ since $|-2| = 2$ and $2 > 1$.

4. $-5 - (-4) + 12 - 8 = -5 + 4 + 12 - 8$
$= -1 + 12 - 8$
$= 11 - 8$
$= 3$

5. $-7 - (-6) = -7 + 6 = -1$

6. $20 - 6 \div 3 \cdot 2 = 20 - 2 \cdot 2 = 20 - 4 = 16$

7. $3[6 - (4 - 3^2)] - 30 = 3[6 - (4 - 9)] - 30$
$= 3[6 - (-5)] - 30$
$= 3[6 + 5] - 30$
$= 3(11) - 30$
$= 33 - 30$
$= 3$

8. Substitute -2 for each x.
$-2x^2 - 6x + 8 = -2(-2)^2 - 6(-2) + 8$
$= -2(4) - (-12) + 8$
$= -8 + 12 + 8$
$= 4 + 8$
$= 12$

9. Distributive property

10. $8x + 2y + 4x - y = 8x + 4x + 2y - y$
$= 12x + y$

11. $9 - \dfrac{2}{3}x + 16 + \dfrac{3}{4}x = \dfrac{3}{4}x - \dfrac{2}{3}x + 9 + 16$
$= \dfrac{9}{12}x - \dfrac{8}{12}x + 25$
$= \dfrac{1}{12}x + 25$

12. $3x^2 + 5 + 4(2x - 7) = 3x^2 + 5 + 8x - 28$
$$= 3x^2 + 8x - 23$$

13.
$$7x + 3 = -4$$
$$7x + 3 - 3 = -4 - 3$$
$$7x = -7$$
$$\frac{7x}{7} = \frac{-7}{7}$$
$$x = -1$$

14.
$$\frac{1}{4}x = -11$$
$$4\left(\frac{1}{4}x\right) = 4(-11)$$
$$x = -44$$

15.
$$4(x - 2) = 5(x - 1) + 3x + 2$$
$$4x - 8 = 5x - 5 + 3x + 2$$
$$4x - 8 = 5x + 3x - 5 + 2$$
$$4x - 8 = 8x - 3$$
$$4x - 4x - 8 = 8x - 4x - 3$$
$$-8 = 4x - 3$$
$$-8 + 3 = 4x - 3 + 3$$
$$-5 = 4x$$
$$\frac{-5}{4} = \frac{4x}{4}$$
$$-\frac{5}{4} = x$$

16.
$$\frac{3}{4}n - \frac{1}{5} = \frac{2}{3}n$$
$$60\left(\frac{3}{4}n - \frac{1}{5}\right) = 60\left(\frac{2}{3}n\right)$$
$$45n - 12 = 40n$$
$$45n - 45n - 12 = 40n - 45n$$
$$-12 = -5n$$
$$\frac{-12}{-5} = \frac{-5n}{-5}$$
$$\frac{12}{5} = n$$

17.
$$A = \frac{a + b + c}{3}$$
$$3 \cdot A = 3 \cdot \left(\frac{a + b + c}{3}\right)$$
$$3A = a + b + c$$
$$3A - a = a - a + b + c$$
$$3A - a = b + c$$
$$3A - a - c = b + c - c$$
$$3A - a - c = b$$

18.
$$\frac{40}{30} = \frac{3}{x}$$
$$40 \cdot x = 30 \cdot 3$$
$$40x = 90$$
$$\frac{40x}{40} = \frac{90}{40}$$
$$x = \frac{90}{40} = \frac{9}{4} \text{ or } 2.25$$

19. Let A = the area of the trampoline.
$$A = \pi r^2$$
$$A = \pi(11)^2 = 122\pi \approx 380.13$$
The area of the trampoline is 380.13 sq. ft.

20. Let x = amount he earns after 8 hours.
$$\frac{2 \text{ hours}}{\$10.50} = \frac{8 \text{ hours}}{x \text{ dollars}}$$
$$\frac{2}{10.5} = \frac{8}{x}$$
$$2x = (10.5)(8)$$
$$2x = 84$$
$$x = \frac{84}{2} = 42$$
He earns \$42 after 8 hours.

Chapter 3

Exercise Set 3.1

1. Added to, more than, increased by, and sum indicate the operation of addition.

2. Subtracted from, less than, decreased by, and difference between indicate the operation of subtraction.

3. Multiplied by, product of, twice, and three times indicate the operation of multiplication.

4. Divided by, quotient of, one-half, and one-third indicate the operation of division.

5. The cost is increased by 25% of the cost, so the expression needs to be $c + 0.25c$.

6. The cost is decreased by 10% of the cost, so the expression needs to be $c - 0.10c$.

7. $25 - x$

8. $42 - y$

9. Answers will vary. Some possible answers are *is, was, will be, yields, gives*.

10. Juan's age is expressed in terms of Paul's age. Explanations will vary.

11. $h + 4$

12. $w + 20$

13. $a - 5$

14. $t - 3$

15. $5h$

16. $7l$

17. $2d$

18. $3r$

19. $\frac{1}{2}a$

20. $\frac{1}{3}w$

21. $r - 5$

22. $p - 9$

23. $8 - m$

24. $4 - n$

25. $2w + 8$

26. $3h + 6$

27. $5a - 4$

28. $\frac{1}{2}d + 1$

29. $\frac{1}{3}w - 7$

30. $\frac{1}{5}h + 2$

31. x = Sonya's height

32. x = the width of the rectangle

33. x = the length of Jones Beach

34. x = Natasha's speed

35. x = the number of medals Finland won

36. x = the distance to Tennessee

37. x = the cost of the Chevy

38. x = the number of votes that Tawnya received

39. x = Teri's grade

40. x = Nick's salary

41. x = the amount that Kristen receives or x = the amount Yvonne receives

42. x = the number of red marbles or x = the number of blue marbles

43. x = Don's weight or x = Angela's weight

44. x = the number of clients that Oliver has or x = the number of clients that Dalane has

45. If c = the cost of the chair, then $3c$ = the cost of the table.

46. If a = the area of Alfredo's house, then $a + 810$ = the area of Joan's house.

47. If a = the area of the kitchen, then $2a + 20$ = the area of the living room.

48. Let a = the amount of money in Carmen's savings account, then $4a - 250$ = the amount of money in Darla's savings account.

49. If w = the width of the rectangle, then $5w - 2$ = the length of the rectangle.

50. If x = the amount of money Evita receives, then $600 - x$ = amount that Brian receives.
If x = the amount of money Brian receives, then $600 - x$ = amount that Evita receives.

51. If w = the number of medals won by Sweden, then $38 - w$ = the number of medals won by Brazil.
If w = the number of medals won by Brazil, then $38 - w$ = the number of medals won by Sweden.

52. If n = the number of children's tickets sold, then $n + 220$ = the number of adult tickets sold.

53. If g = George's age, then $\frac{1}{2}g + 2$ = Mike's age.

54. If f = the number of copies of *Flycatcher* sold, then $5f - 4$ = the number of copies of *Golden Angels* sold.

55. If m = the number of miles Jan walked, then $6.4 - m$ = the number of miles Edward walked.
If m = the number of miles Edward walked, then $6.4 - m$ = the number of miles Jan walked.

56. If m = the number of miles Cheng drove, then $540 - m$ = the number of miles Elsie drove.
If m = the number of miles Elsie drove, then $540 - m$ = the number of miles Cheng drove.

57. $n + 8$

58. $p + 60$

59. $\frac{1}{2}x$ or $\frac{x}{2}$

60. $\frac{1}{3}c$ or $\frac{c}{3}$

61. $2a - 1$

62. $2c - 280$

63. $2t - 30$

64. $2p - 2.3$

65. $1.2p + 20$

66. $4000 + 300n$

67. $80{,}000 - m$

68. $83 - m$

69. $2r - 673$

70. $2b + 3.2$

71. $10x$

72. $16w$

73. $100d$

74. $600 - a$

75. $45 + 0.40x$

76. $60x + 48$

77. $s + 0.20s$

78. $s + 0.15s$

79. $e - 0.12e$

80. $c - 0.25c$

81. $c + 0.07c$

82. $r - 0.439r$

83. $m - 0.313m$

84. $p + 0.041p$

85. If f = Frieda's weight, then $(f + 15)$ = Jennifer's weight. The sum of their weights is $f + (f + 15)$.

86. If k = the length of the keel-billed toucan, then $(k + 3)$ = the length of the chestnut-mandibled toucan. The sum of their lengths is $k + (k + 3)$.

87. If l = Luis' height, then $(2l - 1)$ is Armando's height. The difference in their heights is $(2l - 1) - l$.

88. If p = the profit in 2006, then $(p - 100)$ = the profit in 2005. The difference in profit is $p - (p - 100)$.

89. If n = the larger number, then $(3n - 40)$ = the smaller number. Their difference is $n - (3n - 40)$.

90. If l = the larger number, then $(2l - 16)$ = the smaller number. Their difference is $l - (2l - 16)$.

91. If w = the younger child's weight, then $(2w - 3)$ = the weight of the older child. The sum of their weights is $w + (2w - 3)$.

92. If a = the assessed value of Olga's house, then $2a + 200$ = the assessed value of Glen's house. The sum of their assessed values is $a + (2a + 200)$.

93. If r = the area of Rhode Island, then $(479r + 462)$ = the area of Alaska. The sum of their areas is $r + (479r + 462)$.

94. If s = number of bear sightings in 2005, then $(2s - 6)$ = the number of sightings in 2006. Their difference is $(2s - 6) - s$.

95. If n = the cost of the bank stock, then $(n + 0.06n)$ = the price of Apple stock.
Their sum is $n + (n + 0.06n)$.

96. If c = the cost of the 2005 Corvette, then $(c + 0.012c)$ = the cost of the 2006 Corvette.
Their sum is $c + (c + 0.012c)$.

97. If a = the assets of the bank in 2005, then $(a - 0.023a)$ = the assets of the bank in 2006.
Their difference in assets is $a - (a - 0.023a)$.

98. If s = the number of pieces of spam that Laura received in 2005, then $(s - 0.12s)$ = the number of pieces of spam that she received in 2006.
Their difference is $s - (s - 0.12s)$.

99. Let x = one number, then $4x$ = second number.
First number + second number = 20
$x + 4x = 20$

100. Let x = Denise's age.
Then Marie's age = $x + 6$.
Denise's age + Marie's age = 48
$x + (x + 6) = 48$

101. Let x = smaller integer, then $x + 1$ = larger consecutive integer.
Smaller + larger = 41
$x + (x + 1) = 41$

102. Let x = smaller consecutive even integer.
Then $x + 2$ = larger consecutive even integer.
Smaller · larger = 74
$x(x + 2) = 74$

103. Let x = the number.
Twice the number decreased by 8 is 12.
$2x - 8 = 12$

104. Let x = smaller integer.
Then $x + 1$ = larger consecutive integer.
Smaller + twice the larger = 29
$x + 2(x + 1) = 29$

105. Let x = the number.
One-fifth of the sum of the number and 10 is 150.
$\frac{1}{5}(x + 10) = 150$

106. Let x = the number.
One-third of the sum of a number and 12 is 5.
$\frac{1}{3}(x + 12) = 5$

107. Let x = smaller consecutive even integer.
Then $x + 2$ = larger consecutive even integer.
smaller + twice larger = 22
$x + 2(x + 2) = 22$

108. Let x = smaller consecutive even integer.
Then $x + 2$ = larger consecutive odd integer.
Three times smaller + larger = 14
$3x + (x + 2) = 14$

109. $12.50h = 150$

110. $20t = 120$

111. $2.99x = 17.94$

112. $5.99p = 65.89$

113. $25q = 175$

114. $60m = 480$

115. Let a = Julie's age.
Then Darla's age = $2a + 1$
Julie's age + Darla's age = 52
$a + (2a + 1) = 52$

116. Let s = the number of horses Selina owns.
Then $(5s - 3)$ = the number of horses Marc owns. Their difference is equal to 5.
$(5s - 3) - s = 5$

117. Let s = the number of cards Saul owns.
Then $(2s + 300)$ = the number of cards Jakob owns.
Their difference is equal to 420.
$(2s + 300) - s = 420$

118. Let f = the distance Jennifer jogs.
Then $5f$ = the distance David jogs.
Their sum is equal to 8.
$f + 5f = 8$

119. Let s = the distance traveled by the Southern Pacific train.
Then $(2s - 4)$ = the distance traveled by the Amtrak train.
Their sum is equal to 890.
$s + (2s - 4) = 890$

120. Let b = the number of boys on a wagon ride.
Then $(2b - 6)$ = the number of girls on a wagon ride.
$b + (2b - 6) = 18$

121. Let m = the number of miles Malik walked.
Then $(3m - 2)$ = the number of miles Donna walked.
Their sum is equal to 12.6
$m + (3m - 2) = 12.6$

122. Let r = the distance Lilia ran.
Then $(2r - 4)$ = the distance she rollerbladed.
The total distance traveled was 15 miles.
$r + (2r - 4) = 15$

123. Let c = the cost of the car.
The new price is $89,600 after a 2.3% increase.
$c + 0.023c = 89,600$

124. Let d = Dan's 2005 income.
He received a 4.6% increase and now earns $56,900.
$d + 0.046d = 56,900$

125. Let p = the population of the town.
The town decreased by 1.9% to 12,087.
$p - 0.019p = 12,087$

126. Let c = the original cost of the VCR.
It was reduced in price by 10% to $208.
$c - 0.10c = 208$

127. Let c = the cost of the car.
When 7% sales tax was added the car increased in price to $32,600.
$c + 0.07c = 32,600$

128. Let c = the original cost of the sports coat.
The coat was reduced in price by 25% to $195.
$c - 0.25c = 195$

129. Let c = the cost of the meal.
When the 15% tip was added the price increased to $42.50.
$c + 0.15c = 42.50$

130. Let s = distance between the tracks in a standard gauge railroad.
The narrow gauge railway is 64% of the distance between the tracks in the standard gauge railroad.
$s - 0.64s = 1.67$

131. a. 1 minute = 60 seconds
1 hour = 60 minutes = 3600 seconds
1 day = 24 hours
$= 1440$ minutes
$= 86,400$ seconds
$86,400d + 3600h + 60m + s$

b. $86,400d + 3600h + 60m + s$
$= 86,400(4) + 3600(6) + 60(15) + 25$
$= 368,125$ seconds

132. Let t = the length of a shower in minutes.
$30 = 6t$

133. Let s = amount of weekly sales.
$200 + 0.05s = 100 + 0.08s$

134. $3\left[(4-16)\div 2\right] + 5^2 - 3$
$= 3\left[(-12)\div 2\right] + 25 - 3$
$= 3(-6) + 25 - 3$
$= -18 + 25 - 3$
$= 7 - 3$
$= 4$

135. Substitute 40 for P and 5 for w.
$P = 2l + 2w$
$40 = 2l + 2(5)$
$40 = 2l + 10$
$30 = 2l$
$15 = l$

136. $3x - 2y = 6$
$3x - 3x - 2y = -3x + 6$
$-2y = -3x + 6$
$\dfrac{-2y}{-2} = \dfrac{-3x+6}{-2}$
$y = \dfrac{3x-6}{2}$
$y = \dfrac{3}{2}x - 3$

137. $\dfrac{3.6}{x} = \dfrac{10}{7}$
$3.6 \cdot 7 = 10 \cdot x$
$25.2 = 10x$
$\dfrac{25.2}{10} = \dfrac{10x}{10}$
$2.52 = x$

138. First, to express the ratio, we need both quantites to be in the same units. Since there are 16 ounces in 1 pound, we can convert 4 pounds to 64 ounces. The ratio is $26:64$ or $13:32$ in lowest terms.

Exercise Set 3.2

1. Answers will vary.

2. Answers will vary.

3. Let n = a number
$$4n - 3 = 17$$
$$4n = 20$$
$$n = 5$$
The number is 5.

4. Let n = a number
$$6n - 5 = 13$$
$$6n = 18$$
$$n = 3$$
The number is 3.

5. Let x = smaller integer, then
$x + 1$ = next consecutive integer.
Smaller number + larger number = 87.
$$x + (x + 1) = 87$$
$$2x + 1 = 87$$
$$2x = 86$$
$$x = 43$$
Smaller number = 43
Larger number = $x + 1 = 43 + 1 = 44$

6. Let x = smaller integer, then
$x + 1$ = next consecutive integer.
Smaller number + larger number = 113.
$$x + (x + 1) = 113$$
$$2x + 1 = 113$$
$$2x = 112$$
$$x = 56$$
Smaller number = 56
Larger number = $x + 1 = 56 + 1 = 57$

7. Let x = smaller odd integer, then
$x + 2$ = next consecutive odd integer.
Sum of integers = 96.
$$x + (x + 2) = 96$$
$$2x + 2 = 96$$
$$2x = 94$$
$$x = 47$$
Smaller integer = 47
Larger integer = $47 + 2 = 49$

8. Let x = smaller even integer, then
$x + 2$ = next consecutive even integer.
Sum of integers = 146.
$$x + (x + 2) = 146$$
$$2x + 2 = 146$$
$$2x = 144$$
$$x = 72$$
Smaller integer = 72
Larger integer = $72 + 2 = 74$

9. Let x = one number.
Then $2x + 3$ = second number.
First number + second number = 27
$$x + (2x + 3) = 27$$
$$3x + 3 = 27$$
$$3x = 24$$
$$x = 8$$
First number = 8
Second number = $2x + 3 = 2(8) + 3 = 19$

10. Let x = one number.
Then $3x - 5$ = second number.
First number + second number = 43
$$x + (3x - 5) = 43$$
$$4x - 5 = 43$$
$$4x = 48$$
$$x = 12$$
First number = 12
Second number = $3x - 5 = 3(12) - 5 = 31$

11. Let x = the smaller number.
Then the larger number = $5x - 4$.
Larger number − smaller number = 4
$$(5x - 4) - x = 4$$
$$5x - 4 - x = 4$$
$$4x - 4 = 4$$
$$4x = 8$$
$$x = 2$$
The smaller number is 2 and the larger number is $5(2) - 4 = 6$.

12. Let x = one number.
Then the other number = $3x - 2$.
Larger number + smaller number = 26
$$x + (3x - 2) = 26$$
$$x + 3x - 2 = 26$$
$$4x - 2 = 26$$
$$4x = 28$$
$$x = 7$$
One number is 7 and the other number is $3(7) - 2 = 19$.

13. Let x = smaller integer, then
larger integer = $2x - 8$.
Larger integer – Smaller integer = 17
$(2x-8)-x=17$
$$2x-8-x=17$$
$$x-8=17$$
$$x=25$$
Smaller number = 25
Larger number $= 2x-8 = 2(25)-8 = 42$

14. Let x = the smaller page number
Then $x + 1$ = larger page number
Smaller integer + Larger integer = 145
$x+(x+1)=145$
$$2x+1=145$$
$$2x=144$$
$$x=72$$
Smaller page number = 72
Larger page number $= x+1 = 72+1 = 73$

15. Let x = the number of baseball cards given to Richey, then $3x$ = number of baseball cards given to Erin.
Number of cards given to Richey + Number of cards given to Erin = 260
$x + 3x = 260$
$$4x = 260$$
$$4x = 260$$
$$x = 65$$
Grandma gave 65 baseball cards to Richey.

16. Let x = the number of pairs of cross-country skis sold, then $6x$ = number of pairs of downhill skis sold.
Number of downhill skis sold – Number of cross-country skis sold = 1800
$6x - x = 1800$
$$5x = 1800$$
$$x = 360$$
The number of cross-country skis sold were 360 pairs.

17. Let x = the number of hours it takes to build a horse, then $(2x + 1.4)$ = the number of hours it takes to attach the gloves to the horse.
Time to build horse + Time to attach gloves to horse = 32.6
$x + (2x + 1.4) = 32.6$
$$3x + 1.4 = 32.6$$
$$3x = 31.2$$
$$x = 10.4$$
$2x + 1.4 = 2(10.4) + 1.4 = 22.2$
It took him 22.2 hours to attach the gloves to the horse.

18. Let x = the number of weeks, then $8x$ = the increase in production in the number of candles over x weeks.
Current production + Increased production over x weeks = Future production
$60 + 8x = 132$
$$8x = 72$$
$$x = 9$$
In 9 weeks, they will make 132 candles per week.

19. Let x = the number of weeks, then $6x$ = the amount she wishes to add to her collection over x weeks.
Amount started with in collection + Amount added each week to the collection over x weeks = Total number in collection
$422 + 6x = 500$
$$6x = 78$$
$$x = 13$$
It will take her about 13 weeks to get 500 frogs in her collection.

20. Let x = the time in years, then $1200x$ = the increase in population over x years.
Current population + Increase in population over x years = Future population
$6500 + 1200x = 20,600$
$$1200x = 14,100$$
$$x = 11.75$$
In 11.75 years, the population will reach 20,600.

21. Let x = the number of years, then $250x$ = the number of employees retiring after x years.
Current amount of employees – Employees retiring after x years = Future total employees
$4600 - 250x = 2200$
$$-250x = -2400$$
$$x = 9.6$$
In 9.6 years the total employment will be 2200.

22. Let x = the number of weeks, then $120x$ = the number of computers shipped after x weeks.
Current supply of computers – Number of computers shipped over x weeks = Future inventory
$3600 - 120x = 2000$
$$-120x = -1600$$
$$x \approx 13.3$$
It will take about 13.3 weeks for the computer inventory to drop to 2000.

23. Let x = the average number of tornados in December, then $(11x - 16)$ = the average number of tornados in June.

Number of tornados in June – Number of tornados in December = 204

$$\left(11x - 16\right) - x = 204$$
$$11x - 16 - x = 204$$
$$10x - 16 = 204$$
$$10x = 220$$
$$x = 22$$

There was an average of 22 tornados in December and $11(22) - 16 = 226$ in June.

24. Let x = amount of time spent reading, then $(5x + 16)$ = the amount of time spent watching television. Amount of time spent reading + Amount of time spent watching television = 274

$$x + \left(5x + 16\right) = 274$$
$$x + 5x + 16 = 274$$
$$6x + 16 = 274$$
$$6x = 258$$
$$x = 43$$

43 minutes are spent reading and $5(43) + 16 = 231$ minutes are spent watching television.

25. Let x = the average hourly wage paid to housekeepers in New Orleans, then $(2x + 1.46)$ = the average hourly wage paid to housekeepers in New York City.

Wage of housekeepers in New York – Wage of housekeepers in New Orleans = 8.10

$$\left(2x + 1.46\right) - x = 8.10$$
$$2x + 1.46 - x = 8.10$$
$$x + 1.46 = 8.10$$
$$x = 6.64$$

The average hourly wages paid to a housekeeper in New York City is $2(6.64) + 1.46 = \$14.74$.

26. Let x = sales in millions of Mariah Carey's album, then $(2x - 0.94)$ = sales in millions of Usher's album.

Sales of Mariah's album + Sales of Usher's album = 13.97

$$x + \left(2x - 0.94\right) = 13.97$$
$$x + 2x - 0.94 = 13.97$$
$$3x - 0.94 = 13.97$$
$$3x = 14.91$$
$$x = 4.97$$

Mariah Carey sold 4.97 million albums and Usher sold 9 million albums.

27. Let x = the cost to produce a shirt in Northern China, then $(3x - 0.16)$ = the cost to produce a shirt in Mexico.

Cost to produce a shirt in Northern China + the cost to produce a shirt in Mexico = 3.28

$$x + \left(3x - 0.16\right) = 3.28$$
$$x + 3x - 0.16 = 3.28$$
$$4x - 0.16 = 3.28$$
$$4x = 3.44$$
$$x = 0.86$$

The cost to produce a shirt in Northern China is $0.86 and the cost to produce a shirt in Mexico is $3(0.86) + 0.16 = \$2.42$.

28. Let x = the demand per day in China for oil in million gallons, then $(3x + 1.6)$ = the demand per day in the U.S. for oil in million gallons.

Oil used in China + Oil used in the U.S, = 26.8

$$x + \left(3x + 1.6\right) = 26.8$$
$$x + 3x + 1.6 = 26.8$$
$$4x + 1.6 = 26.8$$
$$4x = 25.2$$
$$x = 6.3$$

The amount of oil used per day in the U.S. in 2004 was $3(6.3) + 1.6 = 20.5$ million gallons.

29. Let x = number of gallons of gasoline that Luis can purchase.

(Cost per gallon) (Price per gallon) = Total cost

$$3.20x = 48$$
$$x = 15$$

Luis can purchase 15 gallons of gasoline.

30. Let x = the number of miles, then $0.30x$ = the cost of driving over x miles.

Daily cost + Mileage cost = Total cost

$$50 + 0.30x = 92$$
$$0.30x = 42$$
$$x = 140$$

Carol can drive a maximum of 140 miles.

31. Let x the number of copies made, then $0.02x$ = the cost to make x number of copies.

Cost of machine + Cost of copies made = Total cost

$$2100 + 0.02x = 2462$$
$$0.02x = 362$$
$$x = 18,100$$

In one year, 18,100 copies were made.

32. Let x = the number of months, then $40x$ = the cost of membership over x months.
Membership fee + Cost of membership over x months = Total cost
$$300 + 40x = 700$$
$$40x = 400$$
$$x = 10$$
Carlos has been a member for 10 months.

33. Let x = the number of On Demand movies watched, then $3.95x$ = the cost to watch x On Demand movies.
Cost for Cable + Additional fee for On Demand movies = 96.38
$$72.68 + 3.95x = 96.38$$
$$3.95x = 23.70$$
$$x = 6$$
He watched 6 movies.

34. Let x = square feet of floors purchased, then $1.90x$ = the cost to install the floors.
Material cost + Labor cost = 5120
$$2840 + 1.90x = 5120$$
$$1.90x = 2280$$
$$x = 1200$$
Ruth purchased 1200 square feet for her floors.

35. Let x = number of miles driven, then $20 + 0.25x$ = American rental fee and $35 + 0.15x$ = SavMor rental fee.
American rental fee = SavMor rental fee
$$20 + 0.25x = 35 + 0.15x$$
$$20 + 0.10x = 35$$
$$0.10x = 15$$
$$x = 150$$
Driving 150 miles would result in both plans having the same total cost.

36. Let x = the time before the costs are the same.
Total cost for Kenmore = total cost for Neptune
Price of Kenmore + energy costs = Price of Neptune + energy costs
$$362 + 84x = 454 + 38x$$
$$362 + 46x = 454$$
$$46x = 92$$
$$x = 2$$
It will take 2 years before the total cost is the same for both machines.

37. Let x = number of years until the salaries are the same.
yearly salary = base salary + (yearly increase) · (number of years)
yearly salary at Data Tech. = yearly salary at Nuteck
$$40,000 + 2400x = 49,600 + 800x$$
$$40,000 + 1600x = 49,600$$
$$1600x = 9600$$
$$x = 6$$
It will take 6 years for the two salaries to be the same.

38. Let x = number of hours that must be played per month for cost of the two plans to be equal. Then cost of court time for Plan 1 = $8x$ and cost for Court time for Plan 2 = $16.25x$
Monthly fee + court time for Plan 1 = court time for Plan 2
$$20 + 8x = 16.25x$$
$$20 = 8.25x$$
$$\frac{20}{8.25} = x$$
$$2.42 \approx x$$
You would have to play 3 hours per month for Plan 1 to be advantageous.

39. Let x = the number of pages, then $0.06x$ = the cost of printing x pages on the HP and $0.08x$ = the cost of printing x pages on the Lexmark.

Cost of the HP printer + Cost of printing x pages on the HP = Cost of the Lexmark printer + Cost of printing x pages on the Lexmark
$$499 + 0.06x = 419 + 0.08x$$
$$499 = 419 + 0.02x$$
$$80 = 0.02x$$
$$4000 = x$$
For the two printers to have the same cost, 4000 pages would have to be printed.

40. Let x = the number of months, then $68.70x$ = the monthly charge for the satellite receiver and $74.80x$ = the monthly charge for cable.

Initial cost of the satellite receiver + Monthly charge = Monthly charge for cable
$$298.90 + 68.70x = 74.80x$$
$$298.90 = 6.10x$$
$$49 = x$$
It will take 49 months before the total cost of the two systems will be equal.

41. Let x = the number of envelopes used, then $0.39x$ = the mailing cost.
Printing cost + Mailing cost = Total cost
$600 + 0.39x = 1380$
$$0.39x = 780$$
$$x = 2000$$
There were 2000 newsletters mailed.

42. Let x = the number of labor hours, then $40x$ = Labor charge for A & E Pavers and $25x$ = labor cost for the Fairman Company.
Cost of cement paver work from A & E Pavers = Cost of cement paver work from Fairman Company
$1500 + 40x = 1800 + 25x$
$$1500 + 15x = 1800$$
$$15x = 300$$
$$x = 20$$
It will take 20 hours of labor for the same total cost to result with both companies.

43. Let x = the cost of the flight before tax, then $0.07x$ = the sales tax on the flight.
Cost of flight before tax + Sales tax on flight = Total cost
$x + 0.07x = 280$
$$1.07x = 280$$
$$x = 261.68$$
The cost of the flight before taxes was $261.68.

44. Let x = the cost of the car before taxes, then $0.075x$ = the sales tax on the car.
Cost of car before tax + Sales tax on car = Total cost
$x + 0.075x = 24,600$
$$1.075x = 24600$$
$$x = 22883.72$$
The cost of the car before tax was $22,883.72.

45. Let x = Zhen's present salary, then $x + 0.30x$ = Zhen's salary at his new job.
New salary = 30,200
$x + 0.30x = 30,200$
$$1.3x = 30,200$$
$$x = 23230.77$$
Zhen's present salary is $23,230.77.

46. Let x = the present size of headquarters in square feet, then $x + 0.20x$ = new size of headquarters in square feet.
New size of headquarters = 14,200 square feet
$x + 0.20x = 14,200$
$$1.2x = 14,200$$
$$x = 11,833.33$$
The present size of the headquarters is about 11,833.33 square feet.

47. Let x = the number of bushels of oysters harvested in 2001, then $x - 0.93x$ = the number of bushels of oysters harvested in 2004.
The number of bushels of oysters harvested in 2004 = 26,000
$x - 0.93x = 26,000$
$$0.07x = 26,000$$
$$x \approx 371,428.57$$
About 371 thousand bushels were harvested in 2001.

48. Let x = pre-retirement income, then $x - 0.15x$ = retirement income.
Retirement income = $42,000
$x - 0.15x = 42,000$
$$0.85x = 42,000$$
$$x = 49411.76$$
Their pre-retirement income is $49,411.76.

49. Let x = total amount collected at door; $3000 + 3\%$ of admission fees = total amount received.
$3000 + 0.03x = 3750$
$$0.03x = 750$$
$$x = \frac{7.50}{0.03} = 25,000$$
The total amount collected at the door was $25,000.

50. Let x = original price of hat.
Then discount = $0.20x$
Original price – discount = 25.99
$x - 0.20x = 25.99$
$$0.08x = 25.99$$
$$x = \frac{25.99}{0.80} \approx 32.49$$
The regular price of the hat is $32.49.

51. Let x = average salary before wage cut.
(average salary before cut) – (decrease in salary) = average salary after wage cut
$x - 0.02x = 38,600$
$$0.98x = 38,600$$
$$x \approx 39,387.76$$
The average salary before the wage cut was $39,387.76.

52. Let x = Dana's recent salary, then his salary increase = $0.05x$.
 Present salary + increase in salary
 = future salary
 $x + 0.05x = 46{,}400$
 $1.05x = 46{,}400$
 $x = 44{,}190.48$
 His present salary is \$44,190.48.

53. Let x = the average salary of a graduate with a Bachelor's degree, then $x - 0.246x$ = the average salary of a graduate with an Associate's degree. Average salary of a graduate with an Associate's degree = 37,600
 $x - 0.246x = 37{,}600$
 $0.754x = 37{,}600$
 $x \approx 49{,}867.374$
 The average salary of a graduate with a bachelor's degree is about \$49,867.

54. Let x = total sales in a week.
 Then $0.06x$ = commission.
 Salary + commission = 710
 $350 + 0.06x = 710$
 $0.06x = 360$
 $x = \dfrac{360}{0.06} = 6000$
 Her total sales in a week must be \$6000.

55. Let x = the amount of sales in dollars, then $600 + 0.02x$ = Plan 1 salary and $0.10x$ = Plan 2 salary.
 Plan 1 salary = Plan 2 salary
 $600 + 0.02x = 0.10x$
 $600 = 0.08x$
 $7500 = x$
 Sales of \$7,500 will result in the same salary from both plans.

56. Let x = the area of the original building, then $x + 0.42x$ = the area of the new building.
 Area of the new building = 56,000 square feet
 $x + 0.42x = 56{,}000$
 $1.42x = 56{,}000$
 $x \approx 39{,}436.62$
 The area of the new building is about 39,436.62 square feet.

57. Let x = the number of pages in the second edition, then $x - 0.04x$ = the number of pages in the third edition.
 Number of pages in the third edition = 480
 $x - 0.04x = 480$
 $0.96x = 480$
 $x = 500$
 There were 500 pages in the second edition.

58. Let x = customer assets in dollar, then $1000 + 0.01x$ = Plan 1 charges and $500 + 0.02x$ = Plan 2 charges.
 Plan 1 charges = Plan 2 charges
 $1000 + 0.01x = 500 + 0.02x$
 $1000 = 500 + 0.01x$
 $500 = 0.01x$
 $50{,}000 = x$
 Customer assets of \$50,000 would result in both plans having the same total cost.

59. Let x = the amount of sales in dollars, then $400 + 0.02x$ = Plan 1 salary and $250 + 0.16x$ = Plan 2 salary.
 Plan 1 salary = Plan 2 salary
 $400 + 0.02x = 250 + 0.16x$
 $400 = 250 + 0.14x$
 $150 = 0.14x$
 $1071.43 = x$
 Sales of \$1071.43 will result in the same salary from both plans.

60. Let x = sales in dollars, then $500 + 0.03x$ = Plan 1 rental fee and $100 + 0.15x$ = Plan 2 rental fee.
 Plan 1 rental fee = Plan 2 rental fee
 $500 + 0.03x = 100 + 0.15x$
 $500 = 100 + 0.12x$
 $400 = 0.12x$
 $3333.33 = x$
 Sales of \$3333.33 would result in both plans having the same total cost.

61. Let x = maximum price of meal she can afford, then amount of tax = $0.07x$ and amount of tip = $0.15x$.
 Price of meal + tax + tip = 30
 $x + 0.07x + 0.15x = 30$
 $1.22x = 30$
 $x \approx 24.59$
 The maximum price she can afford for a meal is \$24.59.

62. Let x = regular membership fee, then amount of reduction = $0.10x$.

regular fee – reduction – 20 = new fee on a Monday

$$x - 0.10x - 20 = 250$$
$$x - 0.10x = 270$$
$$0.90x = 270$$
$$x = \frac{270}{0.90} = 300$$

Regular fee is $300.

63. Let x = the amount in dollars Phil's daughter receives, then x + 0.25x = amount in dollars Phil's wife receives.

Daughter's share + Wife's share = $140,000

$$x + (x + 0.25x) = 140,000$$
$$2x + 0.25x = 140,000$$
$$2,25x = 140,000$$
$$x = 62,222.22$$
$$x + 0.25x = 62,222.22 + (0.25)(62,222.22)$$
$$= 77,777.78$$

Phil's wife will receive $77,777.78.

64. Let x = the contribution made to United Way, then $x + 0.30x$ = the contribution to the American Red Cross.

UW contrib. + ARC contrib. = $200,000

$$x + (x + 0.30x) = 200,000$$
$$2x + 0.30x = 200,000$$
$$2.3x = 200,000$$
$$x = 86,956.52$$

The United Way received $86,956.52.

65. a.

$$\frac{74 + 88 + 76 + x}{4} = 80$$

b.

$$\frac{74 + 88 + 76 + x}{4} = 80$$
$$74 + 88 + 76 + x = 320$$
$$238 + x = 320$$
$$x = 82$$

Paul must receive an 82 on his fourth exam.

66. a. Yearly cost with 10% discount

$= 600 - 0.10(600) = \$540$. Let x = the number of years it will take for the costs to be equal.

Total cost with driver's ed = Total cost without driver's ed.

$$45 + 540x = 600x$$
$$45 = 60x$$
$$0.75 = x$$

It will take 0.75 years, or 9 months for the costs to be equal.

b. $25 - 18 = 7$ years. The cost with driver's ed is $45 + 540(7) = \$3825$. The cost without driver's ed is $600(7) = \$4200$. He will save $4200 - 3825 = \$375$.

67.
$$4\left[(4-6) \div 2\right] + 3^2 - 1$$
$$= 4\left[(-2) \div 2\right] + 9 - 1$$
$$= 4\left[-1\right] + 9 - 1$$
$$= -4 + 9 - 1$$
$$= 4$$

68. Commutative property of addition

69.
$$A = \frac{1}{2}bh$$
$$2A = 2\left(\frac{1}{2}bh\right)$$
$$2A = bh$$
$$\frac{2A}{b} = \frac{bh}{b}$$
$$\frac{2A}{b} = h$$

70.
$$\frac{4.5}{6} = \frac{9}{x}$$
$$4.5 \cdot x = 6 \cdot 9$$
$$4.5x = 54$$
$$x = 12$$

Mid-Chapter Test: 3.1-3.2

1. $6w$

2. $3h + 5$

3. $c + 0.20c$

4. Let m = number of miles driven, then $0.25m$ = total mileage cost. The total rental cost is $(40 + 0.25m)$.

5. $50n$

6. $25 - x$

7. $(c - 25)$ would be the cost of the item minus $25. The cost of an item at a 25% off sale would be $(c - 0.25c)$.

8. x = the length of the Poison Dart frog

9. If p = the distance Pedro traveled, then $(4p + 6)$ = the distance Mary traveled.

10. Let v = the value of a car in 2006, then
$(v - 0.18v)$ = the value of the car in 2005.
Car value in 2006 – Car value in 2005 =
$v - (v - 0.18v)$.

11. Let p = the original population of Cedar Oaks,
then $0.12p$ = the amount of increase in the
population.
Original population + the increase in population
= 38,619
$p + 0.12p = 38,619$

12. Let x = the smaller integer and $(x + 2)$ = the
larger consecutive odd integer.
Smaller integer + 3 times the larger is 26.
$x + 3(x + 2) = 26$

13. Let x = the smaller integer, then $(x + 1)$ = the
larger consecutive integer.
Smaller integer + Larger integer = 93
$$x + (x + 1) = 93$$
$$x + x + 1 = 93$$
$$2x + 1 = 93$$
$$2x = 92$$
$$x = 46$$
The smaller integer is 46 and the larger is
$(46 + 1) = 47$.

14. Let x = the smaller integer, then $(3x - 1)$ = the
larger integer.
Larger integer – Smaller integer = 7
$$(3x - 1) - x = 7$$
$$3x - 1 - x = 7$$
$$2x - 1 = 7$$
$$2x = 8$$
$$x = 4$$
The smaller number is 4 and the larger is
$3(4) - 1 = 11$.

15. Let x = the number of days of production, then
$20x$ = the increased production.
Original production + Increase = 600
$$240 + 20x = 600$$
$$20x = 360$$
$$x = 18$$
It will take 18 days for production to reach 600
boxes daily.

16. Let h = the number of hours tennis is played,
then $4h$ = the court cost at Dale's and $8h$ = the
court cost at Abel's.
Total cost at Dale's = Total cost at Abel's
$$90 + 4h = 30 + 8h$$
$$90 = 30 + 4h$$
$$60 = 4h$$
$$15 = h$$
Kristina would have to play 15 hours of tennis a
month for the total cost to be the same at both
clubs.

17. Let c = the cost of the television, then $0.07c$ =
the amount of sales tax.
Cost of the television + Sales tax = Total cost
$$c + 0.07c = 749$$
$$1.07c = 749$$
$$c = 700$$
The cost of the television before sales tax was
$700.

18. Let c = the number of clients that Betty has, then
$(2c + 12)$ = the number of clients that Anita has.
Clients of Betty + Clients of Anita = 600
$$c + (2c + 12) = 600$$
$$c + 2c + 12 = 600$$
$$3c + 12 = 600$$
$$3c = 588$$
$$c = 196$$
Betty has 196 clients and Anita has
$2(196) + 12 = 404$ clients.

19. Let m = the number of miles driven, then $0.18m$
= the mileage cost.
Truck cost + Mileage cost = Total cost
$$36 + 0.18m = 45.36$$
$$0.18m = 9.36$$
$$m = 52$$
There were 52 miles driven that day.

20. Let s = the amount of sales, then $0.08s$ = the
commission from Plan 1 and $0.06s$ = the
commission from Plan 2.
Total salary from Plan 1 = Total salary from Plan 2
$$200 + 0.08s = 300 + 0.06s$$
$$200 + 0.02s = 300$$
$$0.02s = 100$$
$$s = 5000$$
He must make $5,000 in sales per week for the two
plans to have the same total salary.

Exercise Set 3.3

1. $A = (2l) \cdot \left(\dfrac{w}{2}\right) = lw$

   The area remains the same

2. $A = (3s)^2 = 9s^2 = 9\left(s^2\right)$

   Area is nine times as great.

3. $V = 2l \cdot 2w \cdot 2h = 8(lwh)$

   The volume is eight times as great.

4. $C = 2\pi r = 2\pi(3r) = 6$

   The circumference is tripled.

5. $A = \pi r^2 = \pi(3r)^2 = \pi(9r^2) = 9\pi r^2$

   The area is nine times as great.

6. $V = \dfrac{4}{3}\pi(3r)^3 = \dfrac{4}{3}\pi\left(27r^3\right) = 27\left(\dfrac{4}{3}\pi r^3\right)$

   The volume is 27 times as great.

7. An isosceles triangle is a triangle with 2 equal sides.

8. A quadrilateral is a 4-sided figure.

9. The sum of the measures of the angles in a triangle is 180°.

10. The sum of the measures of the angles in a quadrilateral is 360°.

11. Let x = the measure of the two equal angles, then $x + 42$ = the measure of the third angle.
    Sum of the three angles = 180°
    $x + x + (x + 42) = 180$
    $\qquad 3x + 42 = 180$
    $\qquad\qquad 3x = 138$
    $\qquad\qquad\;\, x = 46$
    The two equal angles are each 46°. The third angle is $x + 42° = 46° + 42° = 88°$.

12. Let x = the length of each of the longer sides of the building, then $x - 50$ = the length of the shorter side of the building.
    Perimeter = 196 feet
    $x + x + (x - 50) = 196$
    $\qquad 3x - 50 = 196$
    $\qquad\qquad 3x = 246$
    $\qquad\qquad\;\, x = 82$
    The two longer sides are each 82 feet long and the short side is $x - 50 = 82 - 50 = 32$ feet long.

13. Let x = length of each side of the triangle, then $P = x + x + x = 3x$.
    Perimeter = 34.5
    $\qquad 3x = 34.5$
    $\qquad\;\, x = 11.5$
    The length of each side is 11.5 inches.

14. Let x = length of each side of the triangle, then $P = x + x + x = 3x$.
    Perimeter = 48.6 cm.
    $\qquad 3x = 48.6$
    $\qquad\;\, x = 16.2$
    The length of each side is 16.2 cm.

15. Let x = measure of angle B. Then
    $2x + 21$ = measure of angle A.
    Sum of the 2 angles = 90
    $x + (2x + 21) = 90$
    $\qquad 3x + 21 = 90$
    $\qquad\qquad 3x = 69$
    $\qquad\qquad\;\, x = 23$
    Measure of angle $A = 2(23) + 21 = 67°$

    Measure of angle $B = 23°$

16. Let x = measure of angle A, then
    $x - 14$ = measure of angle B.
    Sum of the 2 angles = 90°
    $x + (x - 14) = 90$
    $\qquad 2x - 14 = 90$
    $\qquad\qquad 2x = 104$
    $\qquad\qquad\;\, x = 52$
    Measure of angle $A = 52°$
    Measure of angle $B = x - 14 = 52 - 14 = 38°$.

17. Let x = measure of angle A, then
    $3x - 8$ = measure of angle B.
    Sum of the 2 angles = 180
    $x + (3x - 8) = 180$
    $\qquad 4x - 8 = 180$
    $\qquad\quad 4x = 188$
    $\qquad\quad\;\; x = \dfrac{188}{4} = 47$
    Measure of angle $A = 47°$
    Measure of angle $B = 3(47) - 8 = 141 - 8 = 133°$

18. Let x = measure of angle B. Then
$4x + 2$ = measure of angle A.
Sum of the 2 angles = 180º
$x + (4x + 2) = 180$
$5x + 2 = 180$
$5x = 178$
$x = 35.6$
Measure of angle B = 35.6º
Measure of angle A = 4(35.6) + 2 = 144.4º.

19. The two angles have equal measures.
$2x + 50 = 4x + 12$
$38 = 2x$
$19 = x$
$2x + 50 = 2(19) + 50 = 38 + 50 = 88$º
$4x + 12 = 4(19) + 12 = 76 + 12 = 88$º
Each angle measures 88º.

20. The two angles have equal measures.
$3x + 38 = 5x + 20$
$18 = 2x$
$9 = x$
$3x + 38 = 3(9) + 38 = 27 + 38 = 65$º
$5x + 20 = 5(9) + 20 = 45 + 20 = 65$º
Each angle measures 65º.

21. Let x = measure of smallest angle. Then second angle = $x + 10$ and third angle = $2x - 30$.
Sum of the 3 angles = 180
$x + (x + 10) + (2x - 30) = 180$
$4x - 20 = 180$
$4x = 200$
$x = 50$
The first angle is 50°.
The second angle is 50 + 10 = 60°.
The third angle is 2(50) – 30 = 70°.

22. Let x = measure of smallest angle. Then
$x + 20$ = measure of second angle and
$6x$ = measure of third angle.
Sum of the three angles = 180
$x + (x + 20) + 6x = 180$
$8x + 20 = 180$
$8x = 160$
$x = 20$
The three angles measure 20°, 20 + 20 = 40°
and 6(20) = 120°.

23. Let x = width of rectangle. Then $x + 6$ = length of rectangle.
$P = 2l + 2w$
$44 = 2(x + 6) + 2x$
$44 = 2x + 12 + 2x$
$44 = 4x + 12$
$32 = 4x$
$8 = x$
Width is 8 feet and length is 8 + 6 = 14 feet.

24. Let x = width of rectangle. Then $2x$ = length of rectangle.
$P = 2l + 2w$
$120 = 2(2x) + 2x$
$120 = 4x + 2x$
$120 = 6x$
$20 = x$
The width is 20 feet and the length is
2(20) = 40 feet.

25. Let x = width of tennis court.
Then $2x + 6$ = length of tennis court.
$P = 2l + 2w$
$228 = 2(2x + 6) + 2x$
$228 = 4x + 12 + 2x$
$228 = 6x + 12$
$216 = 6x$
$36 = x$
The width is 36 feet and the length is
$2(36) + 6 = 78$ feet.

26. Let x = width of patio.
Then $2x - 6$ = length of patio.
$P = 2l + 2w$
$96 = 2(2x - 6) + 2x$
$96 = 4x - 12 + 2x$
$96 = 6x - 12$
$108 = 6x$
$18 = x$
The width is 18 feet and the length is
2(18) – 6 = 30 feet.

27. Let x = measure of each smaller angle.
Then $3x - 20$ = measure of each larger angle.
(measure of the two smaller angles) + (measure of the two larger angles) = 360°

$$x + x + (3x - 20) + (3x - 20) = 360$$
$$8x - 40 = 360$$
$$8x = 400$$
$$x = 50$$

Each smaller angle is 50°. Each larger angle is $3(50) - 20 = 130°$.

28. Let x = measure of each smaller angle, then $2x - 27$ = measure of each larger angle.
(measure of the two smaller angles) + (measure of the two larger angles) = 360°

$$x + x + (2x - 27) + (2x - 27) = 360$$
$$6x - 54 = 360$$
$$6x = 414$$
$$x = 69$$

Each smaller angle is 69°.
Each larger angle is $2(69) - 27 = 111°$.

29. Let x = measure of each smaller angle, then $5x$ = measure of each larger angle.
(measure of the two smaller angles) + (measure of the two larger angles) = 360°

$$x + x + 5x + 5x = 360$$
$$12x = 360$$
$$x = 30$$

Each smaller angle is 30°.
Each larger angle is $5(30) = 150°$.

30. Let x = measure of each smaller angle, then $4x - 20$ = measure of each larger angle.
(measure of the two smaller angles) + (measure of the two larger angles) = 360°

$$x + x + (4x - 20) + (4x - 20) = 360$$
$$x + x + 4x - 20 + 4x - 20 = 360$$
$$10x - 40 = 360$$
$$10x = 400$$
$$x = 40$$

Each smaller angle is 40°.
Each larger angle is $4(40) - 20 = 140°$.

31. Let x = measure of the smallest angle.
Then $x + 10$ = measure of the second angle, $2x + 14$ = measure of third angle, and $x + 21$ = measure of fourth angle.
Sum of the four angles = 360°

$$x + (x + 10) + (2x + 14) + (x + 21) = 360$$
$$5x + 45 = 360$$
$$5x = 315$$
$$x = 63$$

Thus the angles are 63°, 63 + 10 = 73°
2(63) + 14 = 140° and 63 + 21 = 84°.

32. Let x = measure of the smallest angle.
Then $2x$ = measure of the second angle, $x + 20$ = measure of the third angle, and $2x - 20$ = measure of the fourth angle.
Sum of the four angles = 360°.

$$x + 2x + (x + 20) + (2x - 20) = 360$$
$$6x = 360$$
$$x = 60$$

Thus, the angles are 60°, 2(60) = 120°,
60 + 20 = 80°, and 2(60) − 20 = 100°.

33. Let x = width of bookcase shelf.
Then $x + 3$ = height of bookcase.
4 shelves + 2 sides = total lumber available.

$$4x + 2(x + 3) = 30$$
$$4x + 2x + 6 = 30$$
$$6x + 6 = 30$$
$$6x = 24$$
$$x = 4$$

The width of each shelf is 4 feet and the height is 4 + 3 = 7 feet.

34. Let x = length of a shelf.
Then $x + 2$ = height of bookcase.
4 shelves + 2 sides = total lumber available

$$4x + 2(x + 2) = 20$$
$$4x + 2x + 4 = 20$$
$$6x + 4 = 20$$
$$6x = 16$$
$$x = \frac{16}{6} = 2\frac{2}{3}$$

The width of the bookcase is $2\frac{2}{3}$ feet.

The height of the bookcase is $2\frac{2}{3} + 2 = 4\frac{2}{3}$ feet.

35. Let x = length of a shelf.
Then $2x$ = height of bookcase.
4 shelves + 2 sides = total lumber available
$$4x + 2(2x) = 20$$
$$4x + 4x = 20$$
$$8x = 20$$
$$x = \frac{20}{8} = 2.5$$
The width of the bookcase is 2.5 feet. The height of the bookcase is $2(2.5) = 5$ feet.

36. Let x = height of shelves.
Then $3x$ = length of shelves.
4 shelves + 3 sides = total lumber available
$$4(3x) + 3x = 45$$
$$12x + 3x = 45$$
$$15x = 45$$
$$x = 3$$
The height of the unit is 3 feet.
The length of the unit is 3(3) = 9 feet.

37. Let x = width of fenced in area.
Then $x + 5$ = length of fenced in area
Five "widths" + one "length" = total fencing
$$5x + (x + 5) = 71$$
$$6x + 5 = 71$$
$$6x = 66$$
$$x = 11$$
Width is 11 feet and length is 11 + 5 = 16 feet.

38. Let x = width of the garden. Then $x + 2$ = length of the garden. The total amount of border is 3 times the length + 2 times the width + 4.
$$3(x + 2) + 2x + 4 = 60$$
$$3x + 6 + 2x + 4 = 60$$
$$5x + 10 = 60$$
$$5x = 50$$
$$x = 10$$
The width is 10 feet and the length is 10 + 2 = 12 feet.

39. $ac + ad + bc + bd$

40. b. $a^2 + ab + ab + b^2 = a^2 + 2ab + b^2$

d. Let $b = 2a$
$$P = 4(a + b)$$
$$54 = 4(a + 2a)$$
$$54 = 4(3a)$$
$$54 = 12a$$
$$4.5 \text{ inches} = a$$
$$2(4.5) = 9 \text{ inches} = b$$

e. $A = (a + b)^2$
$$A = (4.5 + 9)^2$$
$$A = 13.5^2$$
$$A = 182.25 \text{ in.}^2$$

f. Area of the smaller square =
$a^2 = 4.5^2 = 20.25 \text{ in.}^2$
Area of each rectangle =
$ab = (4.5)(9) = 40.5 \text{ in.}^2$
Area of the larger square = $b^2 = 9^2 = 81 \text{ in.}^2$

g. Sum of the areas of the four pieces = 20.25 + 40.5 + 40.5 + 81 = 182.5 in.^{2}
This is the same as in part **e**. This is expected because the sum of the area of the parts equals the area of the whole.

41. $-\lvert -6 \rvert < \lvert -4 \rvert$ since $-\lvert -6 \rvert = -6$ and $\lvert -4 \rvert = 4$

42. $\lvert -3 \rvert > -\lvert 3 \rvert$ since $\lvert -3 \rvert = 3$ and $-\lvert 3 \rvert = -3$

43. $-8 - (-2) + (-4) = -8 + 2 + (-4)$
$$= -6 + (-4)$$
$$= -10$$

44. $-7y + x - 3(x - 2) + 2y$
$$= -7y + x - 3x + 6 + 2y$$
$$= x - 3x - 7y + 2y + 6$$
$$= -2x - 5y + 6$$

45.
$$6x + 3y = 9$$
$$6x - 6x + 3y = -6x + 9$$
$$3y = -6x + 9$$
$$\frac{3y}{3} = \frac{-6x + 9}{3}$$
$$y = \frac{-6x + 9}{3} \text{ or } y = -2x + 3$$

Exercise Set 3.4

1. Let t = time in hours it will take the ferries to be 6 miles apart.

Ferry	Rate	Time	Distance
Cat	34	t	$34t$
Bird	28	t	$28t$

$34t - 28t = 6$
$6t = 6$
$t = 1$
In 1 hour the two ferries will be 6 miles apart.

2. Let t = time that the two trains will be 5.9 miles apart.

Train	Rate	Time	Distance
Local	18.4	t	$18.4t$
Express	30.2	t	$30.2t$

$30.2t - 18.4t = 5.9$
$11.8t = 5.9$
$t = 0.5$
In 0.5 hours the two trains will be 5.9 miles apart.

3. Let r = Abe's rate of speed..

Person	Rate	Time	Distance
Jodi	8	2	16
Abe	r	2	$2r$

$16 - 2r = 4$
$-2r = -12$
$r = 6$
Abe was traveling at 6 mph.

4. Let r = Carl's rate of speed.

Person	Rate	Time	Distance
Betty	6	3	18
Carl	r	3	$3r$

$18 - 3r = 2.4$
$-3r = -15.6$
$r = 5.2$
Carl is traveling at 5.2 mph.

5. Let t be the time it takes for the planes to pass each other.

Plane	Rate	Time	Distance
Jet Blue	560	t	$560t$
SW	580	t	$580t$

$560t + 580t = 821$
$1140t = 821$
$t \approx 0.72$
It will take about 0.72 hours for the planes to pass each other.

6. Let t be the time it takes for the two girls to meet.

Person	Rate	Time	Distance
Barb	1.5	t	$1.5t$
Sandy	2.2	t	$2.2t$

$1.5t + 2.2t = 4780.4$
$3.7t = 4780.4$
$t = 1292$
It will take them 1292 seconds or about 21.53 minutes to meet.

7. Let t be the time it takes for Willie and Shanna to be 16.8 miles apart.

Person	Rate	Time	Distance
Willie	3	t	$3t$
Shanna	4	t	$4t$

$3t + 4t = 16.8$
$7t = 16.8$
$t = 2.4$
It will take 2.4 hours.

8. Let t be the time it takes for the jets to be 500 miles apart.

Jet	Rate	Time	Distance
First	1000	t	$1000t$
Second	1000	t	$1000t$

$1000t + 1000t = 500$
$2000t = 500$
$t = 0.25$
It will take 0.25 hour or 15 minutes.

9. Let r be the second rate of the machine.

Machine	Rate	Time	Distance
First	60	7.2	432
Second	r	6.8	$6.8r$

$$432 + 6.8r = 908$$
$$6.8r = 476$$
$$r = 70$$

The second speed the machine was set at was 70 miles per hour.

10. Let r be the rate of the second lift.

Train	Rate	Time	Distance
First	4	0.2	0.8
Second	r	0.3	0.4

$$0.3r = 0.4$$
$$r \approx 1.33$$

The speed of the second lift was about 1.33 miles per hour.

11. Let t be the time it takes for the waves to be 80 miles apart.

Wave	Rate	Time	Distance
p-wave	3.6	t	$3.6t$
s-wave	1.8	t	$1.8t$

$$3.6t - 1.8t = 80$$
$$1.8t = 80$$
$$t \approx 44.4$$

It will take approximately 44.4 seconds.

12. Let t be the time they have been walking.

Walker	Rate	Time	Distance
Sadie	220	t	$220t$
Jose	100	t	$100t$

$$220t - 100t = 600$$
$$120t = 600$$
$$t = 5$$

They have been walking for 5 minutes.

13. Let r be the speed of the cutter coming from the east (westbound). Then $r + 5$ is the speed of the cutter coming from the west (eastbound).

Cutter	Rate	Time	Distance
Eastbound	$r + 5$	3	$3(r + 5)$
Westbound	r	3	$3r$

$$3(r + 5) + 3r = 225$$
$$3r + 15 + 3r = 225$$
$$6r = 210$$
$$r = 35$$

The speed of the westbound cutter is 35 mph and the speed of the eastbound cutter is 40 mph.

14. Let r be the speed of Crew B.

Crew	Rate	Time	Distance
A	$r + 0.4$	0.5	$0.5(r + 0.4)$
B	r	0.5	$0.5r$

$$0.5(r + 0.4) + 0.5r = 2.56$$
$$0.5r + 0.2 + 0.5r = 2.56$$
$$1.0r + 0.2 = 2.56$$
$$r = 2.36$$

Crew B travels at 2.36 mph and Crew A travels at 2.36 + 0.4 = 2.76 mph.

15. Let t be amount of time Samia walked for before she turned around.

Trip	Rate	Time	Distance
In	4	t	$4t$
Out	3.2	$t + 0.5$	$3.2(t + 0.5)$

$$4t + 3.2(t + 0.5) = 6$$
$$4t + 3.2t + 1.6 = 6$$
$$7.2t = 4.4$$
$$t \approx 0.61$$

Samia walked 0.61 hours before she turned around.

16. Let t be the time it took Chuck to go back to Michigan, then $(t + 1)$ would be the time it took Chuck to travel to his grandchild's.

Trip	Rate	Time	Distance
To Texas	60	$t + \dfrac{1}{2}$	$60\left(t + \dfrac{1}{2}\right)$
To Michigan	70	t	$70t$

$$60\left(t + \frac{1}{2}\right) + 70t = 1343$$
$$60t + 30 + 70t = 1343$$
$$130t + 30 = 1343$$
$$130t = 1313$$
$$t \approx 10.1$$

It took Chuck $10.1 + 0.5 = 10.6$ hours to get to his grandchild's.

17. Let r be the rate of the slower crew. Then $r + 0.75$ is the rate of the faster crew.

Crew	Rate	Time	Distance
Slow	r	3.2	$3.2r$
Fast	$r + 0.75$	3.2	$3.2(r + 0.75)$

$$3.2r + 3.2\left(r + 0.75\right) = 12$$
$$3.2r + 3.2r + 2.4 = 12$$
$$6.4r = 9.6$$
$$r = 1.5$$

One crew works at a rate of 1.5 miles/day, and the other crew works at a rate of 2.25 miles/day.

18. Let r be the rate of Jane's group. Then $r + 0.5$ is the rate of Auturo's group.

Group	Rate	Time	Distance
Auturo's	$r + 0.5$	2	$2(r + 0.5)$
Jane's	r	2	$2r$

$$2\left(r + 0.5\right) + 2r = 7$$
$$2r + 1 + 2r = 7$$
$$4r = 6$$
$$r = 1.5$$

Jane's group walks at 1.5 miles per hour and Auturo's group walks at 2 miles per hour.

19. Let r be the rate of *Apollo*. Then $r + 4$ is the rate of *Pythagoras*.

Boat	Rate	Time	Distance
Apollo	r	0.7	$0.7r$
Pythagoras	$r + 4$	0.7	$0.7(r + 4)$

$$0.7r + 0.7\left(r + 4\right) = 9.8$$
$$0.7r + 0.7r + 2.8 = 9.8$$
$$1.4r = 7$$
$$r = 5$$

The speed of *Apollo* is 5 mph, and the speed of *Pythagoras* is 9 mph.

20. Let t be the time they run.

Person	Rate	Time	Distance
Phuong	4	t	$4t$
Dien	6	t	$6t$

$$4t + 6t = 11$$
$$10t = 11$$
$$t = 1.1$$

They ran for 1.1 hours.

21. Let t = time, in hours, Betty was traveling at 50 mph.

Speed	Rate	Time	Distance
Faster	70 mph	$t - 0.5$	$70(t - 0.5)$
Slower	50 mph	t	$50t$

$$50t - 70t + 35 = 5$$
$$-20t = -30$$
$$t = 1.5$$

Betty traveled for 1.5 hours at 50 mph.

22. Let r = speed of the second conveyor belt in ft/sec.

	Rate	Time	Distance
First Belt	$r - 0.6$	180	$180(r-0.6)$
Second Belt	r	160	$160r$

$$180(r-0.6)+160r=1116$$
$$180r-108+160r=1116$$
$$340r=1224$$
$$r=3.6$$

The second conveyor belt moves at 3.6 ft/sec.

23. a. Distance = rate × time = $(2.31)(1.04) \approx 2.4$ miles

b. Distance = rate × time = $(23.0)(4.87) \approx 112.0$ miles

c. Distance = rate × time = $(8.45)(3.1) \approx 26.2$ miles

d. $2.4 + 112.0 + 26.2 = 140.6$ miles

e. $1.04 + 4.87 + 3.10 = 9.01$ hours

24. a. Distance = rate × time = $(2.89)(0.83) \approx 2.40$ miles

b. Distance = rate × time = $(25.4)(4.40) \approx 112.0$ miles

c. Distance = rate × time = $(8.98)(2.92) \approx 26.20$ miles

d. $2.4 + 112.0 + 26.2 = 140.6$ miles

e. $0.83 + 4.40 + 2.92 = 8.15$ hours

25. Let x be the amount invested at 5%. Then $12,000 - x$ is the amount invested at 7%.

Principal	Rate	Time	Interest
x	5%	1	$0.05x$
$12,000 - x$	7%	1	$0.07(12,000-x)$

$$0.05x+0.07(12,000-x)=800$$
$$0.05x+840-0.07x=800$$
$$-0.02x=-40$$
$$x=2000$$

They invested \$2000 at 5% and \$10,000 at 7%.

26. Let x be the amount invested at 8%. Then $7000 - x$ is the amount invested at 5%.

Principal	Rate	Time	Interest
x	8%	1	$0.08x$
$7000 - x$	5%	1	$0.05(7000-x)$

$$0.08x+0.05(7000-x)=476$$
$$0.08x+350-0.05x=476$$
$$0.03x=126$$
$$x=4200$$

He invested \$4200 at 8% and \$2800 at 5%.

27. Let x be the amount invested at 6%. Then $6000 - x$ is the amount invested at 4%.

Principal	Rate	Time	Interest
x	6%	1	$0.06x$
$6000 - x$	4%	1	$0.04(6000-x)$

$$0.06x=0.04(6000-x)$$
$$0.06x=240-0.04x$$
$$0.10x=240$$
$$x=2400$$

She invested \$2400 at 6% and \$3600 at 4%.

28. Let x be the amount invested at 7%. Then $12,500 - x$ is the amount invested at 6%.

Principal	Rate	Time	Interest
x	7%	1	$0.07x$
$12,500 - x$	6%	1	$0.06(12,500-x)$

$$0.07x=0.06(12,500-x)$$
$$0.07x=750-0.06x$$
$$0.13x=750$$
$$x\approx5769.23$$

She invested \$5769.23 at 7% and \$6730.77 at 6%.

29. Let x be the amount invested at 4%. Then $10,000 - x$ is the amount invested at 5%.

Principal	Rate	Time	Interest
x	4%	1	$0.04x$
$10,000 - x$	5%	1	$0.05(10,000 - x)$

$$0.05\big(10,000 - x\big) - 0.04x = 320$$
$$500 - 0.05x - 0.04x = 320$$
$$-0.09x = -180$$
$$x = 2000$$

She invested $2000 at 4% and $8000 at 5%.

30. Let x be the amount invested at 5%. Then $20,000 - x$ is the amount invested at 7%.

Principal	Rate	Time	Interest
x	5%	1	$0.05x$
$20,000 - x$	7%	1	$0.07(20,000 - x)$

$$0.07\big(20,000 - x\big) - 0.05x = 440$$
$$1400 - 0.07x - 0.05x = 440$$
$$-0.12x = -960$$
$$x = 8000$$

She invested $8000 at 5% and $12,000 at 7%.

31. Let t be the time, in months, during which Patricia paid $17.10 per month. Then $12 - t$ is the time during which she paid $18.40 per month.

Rate	Time	Amount
17.10	t	$17.10t$
18.40	$12 - t$	$18.40(12 - t)$

$$17.10t + 18.40\big(12 - t\big) = 207.80$$
$$17.10t + 220.80 - 18.40t = 207.80$$
$$-1.30t = -13$$
$$t = 10$$

She paid $17.10 for the first 10 months of the year, and paid $18.40 for the remainder of the year. The rate increase took effect in November.

32. Let x be the number of months Violet paid $18.20. Then $12 - x$ is the number of months she paid $19.50.

Rate	Time	Amount
18.20	x	$18.20x$
19.50	$12 - x$	$19.50(12 - x)$

$$18.20x + 19.50\big(12 - x\big) = 230.10$$
$$18.20x + 234 - 19.50x = 230.10$$
$$-1.30x = -3.9$$
$$x = 3$$

The rate increased after three months, or in April.

33. Let x be the number of hours worked at Home Depot ($6.50 per hour). Then $18 - x$ is the number of hours worked at the veterinary clinic ($7.00 per hour).

Rate	Hours	Total
$6.50	x	$6.5x$
$7.00	$18 - x$	$7(18 - x)$

$$6.5x + 7\big(18 - x\big) = 122$$
$$6.5x + 126 - 7x = 122$$
$$-0.5x = -4$$
$$x = 8$$

Mihály worked 8 hours at Home Depot and 10 hours at the clinic.

34. Let x be the number of children who went to the Rock and Roll Hall of Fame. Then $1551 - x$ is the number of adults who attended.

	Price	Number	Total
Adults	20	$1551 - x$	$20(1551 - x)$
Children	11	x	$11x$

$$20\big(1551 - x\big) + 11x = 24,441$$
$$31,020 - 20x + 11x = 24,441$$
$$31,020 - 9x = 24,441$$
$$-9x = -6579$$
$$x = 731$$

There were 731 children at the Rock and Roll Hall of Fame.

35. Let x be the number of adults who went to the Baseball Hall of Fame. Then $2100 - x$ is the number of children who attended.

	Price	Number	Total
Adults	14.5	x	14.50x
Children	5.00	$2100 - x$	$5.00(2100 - x)$

$$14.5x + 5(2100 - x) = 21,900$$
$$14.5x + 10,500 - 5x = 21,900$$
$$9.5x = 11,400$$
$$x = 1200$$

There were 1200 adults at the Baseball Hall of Fame.

36. Let x be the number of adults who went to the evening show. Then $310 - x$ is the number of adults who attended the matinee.

Show	Price	Number	Total
Evening	7.50	x	7.5x
Matinee	4.75	$310 - x$	$4.75(310 - x)$

$$7.5x + 4.75(310 - x) = 2022.50$$
$$7.5x + 1472.5 - 4.75x = 2022.50$$
$$2.75x = 550$$
$$x = 200$$

So, there were 200 adults at the evening show and 110 at the matinee.

37. a. Let x be the number of shares of Nike. Then $5x$ is the number of shares of Kellogg.

Stock	Price	Shares	Total
Nike	78	x	78x
Kellogg	33	$5x$	$33(5x)$

$$78x + 33(5x) = 10,000$$
$$78x + 165x = 10,000$$
$$244x = 10,000$$
$$x \approx 40.98$$

Since only whole shares can be purchased, he will purchase 41 shares of Nike and 205 shares of Kellogg.

b. Mike spent $41(78) + 205(33) = \$9963$. He has $\$10,000 - \$9963 = \$37$ left over.

38. a. Let x be the number of shares of Mattel. Then $4x$ is the number of shares of Wal Mart.

Stock	Price	Shares	Total
Mattel	28	x	28x
Wal Mart	59	$4x$	$59(4x)$

$$28x + 59 \cdot 4x = 6000$$
$$28x + 236x = 6000$$
$$264x = 6000$$
$$x \approx 22.7$$

Since only whole shares can be purchased, she will purchase 22 shares of Mattel and 88 shares of Wal Mart.

b. Amy spent $28(22) + 88(59) = \$5808$. She has $\$6000 - \$5808 = \$192$ left over.

39. Let x be the number of pounds of almonds. Then $30 - x$ is the number of pounds of walnuts.

Nut	Cost	Pounds	Total
Almond	6.40	x	6.40x
Walnut	6.80	$30 - x$	$6.8(30 - x)$
Mixture	6.65	30	199.50

$$6.4x + 6.8(30 - x) = 199.50$$
$$6.4x + 204 - 6.8x = 199.50$$
$$-0.4x = -4.5$$
$$x = 11.25$$

So, 11.25 pounds of almonds should be mixed with 18.75 pounds of walnuts.

40. Let x be the amount of Family grass seed. Then $10 - x$ is the amount of Spot Filler grass seed.

Seed	Price	Amount	Total
Family	2.45	x	2.45x
Filler	2.10	$10 - x$	$2.10(10 - x)$
Mixture	2.20	10	22

$$2.45x + 2.10(10 - x) = 22$$
$$2.45x + 21 - 2.10x = 22$$
$$0.35x = 1$$
$$x \approx 2.86$$

2.86 pounds of Family grass seed and 7.14 pounds of Spot Filler grass seed should be mixed together.

41. Let x be the amount of topsoil in cubic yards.

Soil Type	Cost	Amount	Total
Strained	160	x	$160x$
Unstrained	120	$8 - x$	$120(8 - x)$
Mixture	150	8	$150(8)$

$$160x + 120(8 - x) = 150(8)$$
$$160x + 960 - 120x = 1200$$
$$40x + 960 = 1200$$
$$40x = 240$$
$$x = 6$$

He should mix 6 cubic yards of the strained with 2 cubic yards of the unstrained.

42. Let x be the cost per pound of the mixture.

Type	Cost	Pounds	Total
Sunflower Seeds	1.80	2.5	$1.80(2.5)$
Cracked Corn	1.40	1	$1.40(1)$
Mixture	x	3.5	$3.5x$

$$1.80(2.5) + 1.40(1) = 3.5x$$
$$4.50 + 1.40 = 3.5x$$
$$5.90 = 3.5x$$
$$1.69 \approx x$$

The mixture should sell for about $1.69 a pound.

43. Let x be the cost per pound of the mixture.

Type	Cost	Pounds	Total
Good & Plenty	2.49	3	$2.49(3)$
Sweet Treats	2.89	5	$2.89(5)$
Mixture	x	8	$8x$

$$2.49(3) + 2.89(5) = 8x$$
$$7.47 + 14.45 = 8x$$
$$21.92 = 8x$$
$$2.74 = x$$

The mixture should sell for $2.74 per pound.

44. Let x be the number of pounds of chocolate almond coffee beans. Then $6 - x$ is the number of pounds of hazelnut coffee beans.

Type	Cost	Pounds	Total
Chocolate	7.00	x	$7.00(x)$
Hazelnut	6.10	$6 - x$	$6.10(6 - x)$
Mixture	6.40	6	$6.40(6)$

$$7x + 6.10(6 - x) = 6.40(6)$$
$$7x + 36.60 - 6.10x = 38.40$$
$$0.90x = 1.80$$
$$x = 2$$

The mixture should have 2 pounds of chocolate almond coffee and 4 pounds of hazelnut coffee beans..

45. Let x be the percentage of alcohol in the mixture.

Percentage	Liters	Amount of Alcohol
12%	5	0.6
9%	2	0.18
x%	7	$\left(\frac{x}{100}\right) \cdot 7$

$$\left(\frac{x}{100}\right) \cdot 7 = 0.6 + 0.18$$
$$0.07x = 0.78$$
$$x \approx 11.1$$

The alcohol content of the mixture is about 11.1%.

46. Let x be the number of liters of the 60% solution. Then $0.5 - x$ is the number of liters of the 25% solution.

Solution	Strength	Liters	Amount
60%	0.60	x	$0.60x$
25%	0.25	$0.5 - x$	$0.25(0.5 - x)$
Mixture	0.40	0.5	0.20

$$0.60x + 0.25(0.5 - x) = 0.20$$
$$0.60x + 0.125 - 0.25x = 0.20$$
$$0.35x = 0.075$$
$$x \approx 0.21$$

So, mix 0.21 liters of the 60% solution with 0.29 liters of the 25% solution.

47. Let x be the amount of 12% sulfuric acid solution.

Solution	Strength	Liters	Amount
20%	0.20	1	0.20
12%	0.12	x	$0.12x$
Mixture	0.15	$x + 1$	$0.15(x + 1)$

$$0.20 + 0.12x = 0.15(x + 1)$$
$$0.20 + 0.12x = 0.15x + 0.15$$
$$-0.03x = -0.05$$
$$x = \frac{5}{3}$$

$1\frac{2}{3}$ liters of 12% sulfuric acid should be used.

48. Let x be the amount, in gallons, of the 5% pigment paint to be used. Then $x + 0.4$ is the amount of the mixture to be made.

Paint	Percentage	Gallons	Amount
2% pigment	2%	0.4	0.02(0.4)
5% pigment	5%	x	$0.05x$
Mixture	4%	$x + 0.4$	$0.04(x+0.4)$

$$0.02(0.4) + 0.05x = 0.04(x + 0.4)$$
$$0.008 + 0.05x = 0.04x + 0.016$$
$$0.01x = 0.008$$
$$x = 0.8$$

He should mix 0.8 gallons of the 5% yellow pigment paint.

49. Let x be the percentage of alcohol in the mixture.

Brand	Percentage	Ounces	Amount
Listerine	21.6%	6	$(0.216) \cdot 6$
Scope	15%	4	$(0.15) \cdot 4$
Mixture	$x\%$	10	$\left(\frac{x}{100}\right) \cdot 10$

$$(0.216) \cdot 6 + (0.15) \cdot 4 = \left(\frac{x}{100}\right) \cdot 10$$
$$1.296 + 0.6 = \frac{x}{10}$$
$$1.896 = \frac{x}{10}$$
$$18.96 = x$$

The mixture has an 18.96% alcohol content.

50. Let x be the amount of sodium hypochlorite when added to a quart of water.

Percent	Cups	Mixture
5.25%	1	0.0525
x	5	$5x$

$$0.0525 = 5x$$
$$0.0105 = x$$

The new mixture consists of 1.05% sodium hypochlorite.

51. Let x be the percent of orange juice in the new mixture.

Percent	Quarts	Orange Juice
12%	6	0.72
x	$6\frac{1}{2}$	$\frac{13}{2}x$

$$\frac{13}{2}x = 0.72$$
$$x \approx 0.111$$

The new mixture consists of about 11.1% orange juice.

52. Let x be the percent of malathion in the new mixture.

Percent	Ounces	Malathion
50%	1	0.50
x	129	$129x$

$$0.50 = 129x$$
$$0.0039 \approx x$$

The new mixture consists of about 0.39% malathion.

53. Let x be the percentage of pure juice before mixing.

Solution	Percentage	Amount of Solution	Amt. of Juice
Concentrate	x	12	$12\left(\frac{x}{100}\right)$
Mixture	10%	48	4.8

$$12\left(\frac{x}{100}\right) = 4.8$$
$$0.12x = 4.8$$
$$x = 40$$

40% of the concentrate is pure juice.

54. Let x be the number of gallons of 0% salt content.

Percentage of water without salt	Gallons	Amount
99.1%	50,000	0.991(50,000)
100%	x	$1x$
99.2%	$x + 50,000$	$0.992(x + 50,000)$

$$0.991(50,000) + 1x = 0.992(x + 50,000)$$
$$49,550 + 1x = 0.992x + 49,600$$
$$0.008x = 50$$
$$x = 6,250$$

To lower the salt concentration, 6,250 gallons of 0% salt content has to be added.

55. Let x be the amount of the Clorox to be added to a 6 cups of of water.

Product	Percentage	Cups	Amount
Clorox	5.25%	x	$(0.0525)x$
Shock Treatment	10.5%	$6 - x$	$0.105(6 - x)$
Mixture	7.2%	6	$0.072(6)$

$$0.0525x + 0.105(6 - x) = 0.072(6)$$
$$0.0525x + 0.63 - 0.105x = 0.432$$
$$-0.0525x = -0.198$$
$$x \approx 3.77$$

The mixture needs about 3.77 cups Clorox and $6 - 3.77 = 2.23$ cups of shock treatment.

56. Let x be the number of quarts of Prestone antifreeze added.

Brand	Percentage of antifreeze	Quarts	Amount
Prestone	12%	x	$0.12x$
Xeres	9%	$10 - x$	$0.09(10 - x)$
Mixture	10%	10	$0.10(10)$

$$0.12x + 0.09(10 - x) = 0.10(10)$$
$$0.12x + 0.9 - 0.09x = 1$$
$$0.03x + 0.9 = 1$$
$$0.03x = 0.1$$
$$x \approx 3.333$$

The mixture need to contain $3\frac{1}{3}$ qts of Prestone and $10 - 3\frac{1}{3} = 6\frac{2}{3}$ qts of Xeres.

57. Let x be the number of pints of 12% alcohol.

Type	Percentage	Pints	Amount
12% concen.	12%	x	$0.12x$
5% concen.	5%	15	$0.05(15)$
Mixture	8%	$x + 15$	$0.08(x + 15)$

$$0.12x + 0.05(15) = 0.08(x + 15)$$
$$0.12x + 0.75 = 0.08x + 1.2$$
$$0.04x + 0.75 = 1.2$$
$$0.04x = 0.45$$
$$x = 11.25$$

The mixture should consist of 11.25 pints of the 12% alcohol.

58. Let x be the percent of Nitrogen in the mixture.

Type	Percentage	Pints	Amount
All purpose	12%	2	$0.12(2)$
Quick Start	4%	3	$0.04(3)$
Mixture	$x\%$	5	$5x$

$$0.12(2) + 0.04(3) = 5x$$
$$0.24 + 0.12 = 5x$$
$$0.36 = 5x$$
$$0.072 = x$$

The mixture has 7.2% nitrogen.

59. The time it takes for the transport to make the trip is:

$$\text{Time} = \frac{\text{Distance}}{\text{Rate}} = \frac{1720}{370} \approx 4.65 \text{ hours}$$

The time it takes for the Hornets to make the trip is: $\text{Time} = \frac{\text{Distance}}{\text{Rate}} = \frac{1720}{900} \approx 1.91 \text{ hours}$

It takes the transport $4.65 - 1.91 = 2.74$ hours longer to make the trip. Since it needs to arrive 3 hours before the Hornets, it should leave about $2.74 + 3 = 5.74$ hours before them.

60. $r = \dfrac{d}{t}$

$$= \frac{\frac{3}{4} \text{ mile}}{62.41 \text{ sec.}} \cdot \frac{60 \text{ sec.}}{1 \text{ min.}} \cdot \frac{60 \text{ min.}}{1 \text{ hr.}}$$
$$= \frac{2700 \text{ mile}}{62.41 \text{ hr.}}$$
$$\approx 43.26 \text{ mph}$$

61. We must find the time it takes for the car to travel 100 feet.

$$d = rt$$
$$100 = 5.88t$$
$$17 = t$$

It takes the car 17 seconds to go 100 feet.
This will allow us to find out how fast the garage door needs to open.

$$d = rt$$
$$6 = r(17)$$
$$0.35 \approx r$$

It must open at 0.35 feet per second.

62. a. $2\dfrac{3}{4} \div 1\dfrac{5}{8} = \dfrac{11}{4} \div \dfrac{13}{8}$
$$= \frac{11}{4} \cdot \frac{8}{13}$$
$$= \frac{22}{13} \text{ or } 1\frac{9}{13}$$

b. $2\dfrac{3}{4} + 1\dfrac{5}{8} = \dfrac{11}{4} + \dfrac{13}{8}$
$$= \frac{22}{8} + \frac{13}{8}$$
$$= \frac{35}{8} \text{ or } 4\frac{3}{8}$$

63. $6(x - 3) = 4x - 18 + 2x$
$$6x - 18 = 6x - 18$$
All real numbers are solutions.

64. $\dfrac{6}{x} = \dfrac{72}{9}$
$$6 \cdot 9 = 72x$$
$$54 = 72x$$
$$x = \frac{54}{72} = \frac{3}{4} \text{ or } 0.75$$

65. Let x = the first integer. Then, $x+1$ is the next integer.

$$x+(x+1)=77$$
$$2x+1=77$$
$$2x=76$$
$$x=38$$

The two integers are 38 and 39.

Chapter 3 Review Exercises

1. $3n+7$

2. $1.2g$

3. $d-0.25d$

4. $16y$

5. $200-x$

6. Let d = Dino's age, then $7d+6$ = Mario's age.

7. Let c be the number of robberies in 2005, then $(c-0.12c)$ is the amount of robberies in 2006. The difference between the robberies is $c-(c-0.12c)$.

8. Let n be the larger number, then $(3n-24)$ is the smaller number. Their difference is 8. The equation is $n-(3n-24)=8$.

9. Let x = the smaller number.
Then $x+8$ = the larger number.
Smaller number + larger number = 74

$$x+(x+8)=74$$
$$2x+8=74$$
$$2x=66$$
$$x=33$$

The smaller number is 33 and the larger number is $33+8=41$.

10. Let x = smaller integer.
Then $x+1$ = next consecutive integer.
Smaller number + larger number = 237

$$x+(x+1)=237$$
$$2x+1=237$$
$$2x=236$$
$$x=118$$

The smaller number is 118 and the larger number is $118+1=119$.

11. Let x = the smaller integer.
Then $5x+3$ = the larger integer
Larger number − smaller number = 31

$$(5x+3)-x=31$$
$$4x+3=31$$
$$4x=28$$
$$x=7$$

The smaller number is 7 and the larger number is $5(7)+3=38$.

12. Let x = cost of car before tax.
Then $0.07x$ = amount of tax.
Cost of car before tax + tax on car
= cost of car after tax

$$x+0.07x=23,260$$
$$1.07x=23,260$$
$$x=\frac{23,260}{1.07}=21,738.32$$

The cost of the car before tax is $21,738.32.

13. Let x = the number of months, then $20x$ = the increase in production of bagels over x months.
Current production + Increase in production = Future production

$$520+20x=900$$
$$20x=380$$
$$x=19$$

It will take 19 months.

14. Let x = weekly dollar sales that would make total salaries from both companies the same.
The commission at present company = $0.03x$ and commission at new company = $0.08x$.
Salary + commission for present company
= salary + commission for new company

$$600+0.03x=500+0.08x$$
$$100+0.03x=0.08x$$
$$100=0.05x$$
$$2000=x$$

Irene's weekly sales would have to be $2000 for the total salaries from both companies to be the same.

15. Let x = original price of camcorder. Then $0.20x$ = reduction.
Original price −reduction = sale price

$$x-0.20x=495$$
$$0.8x=495$$
$$x=618.75$$

The original price of the camcorder was $618.75.

16. Let h = the number of hours for both landscapers to charge the same price.

Two Brothers Nursery = ABC Nursery

$$400 + 45h = 200 + 65h$$
$$400 = 200 + 20h$$
$$200 = 20h$$
$$10 = h$$

It would take 10 hours of labor before the costs from both landscapers would be the same.

17. Let x be the median cost of a house in 2003. Then $0.117x$ would be the amount of increase.

Median price in 2003 + Amount of increase = Median price in 2005

$$x + 0.117x = 191,000$$
$$1.117x = 191,000$$
$$x = 170,993.73$$

The median cost in 2003 was about \$171,000.

18. Let x be the average annual refund in 1980. Then $4x - 282$ is the average annual refund in 2004.

$$4x - 282 = 2454$$
$$4x = 2736$$
$$x = 684$$

The average annual refund in 1980 was \$684.

19. Let x = measure of the smallest angle. Then $x + 10$ = measure of second angle and $2x - 10$ = measure of third angle.

Sum of the three angles = $180°$

$$x + (x + 10) + (2x - 10) = 180$$
$$4x = 180$$
$$x = 45$$

The angles are $45°$, $45 + 10 = 55°$, and $2(45) - 10 = 80°$.

20. Let x = measure of the smallest angle. Then $x + 10$ = measure of second angle, $5x$ = measure of third angle, $4x + 20$ = measure of the fourth angle.

Sum of the four angles = $360°$

$$x + (x + 10) + 5x + (4x + 20) = 360$$
$$11x + 30 = 360$$
$$11x = 330$$
$$x = \frac{330}{11} = 30$$

The angles are $30°$, $30 + 10 = 40°$. $5(30) = 150°$, and $4(30) + 20 = 140°$.

21. Let w = width of garden. Then $w + 4$ = length of garden.

$$P = 2l + 2w$$
$$70 = 2(w + 4) + 2w$$
$$70 = 4w + 8$$
$$62 = 4w$$
$$15.5 = w$$

The width is 15.5 feet and the length is $15.5 + 4 = 19.5$ feet.

22. Let x = the width of the room. Then $x + 30$ = the length of the room. The amount of string used is the perimeter of the room plus the wall separating the two rooms.

$$P = 2l + 2w + w$$
$$P = 2l + 3w$$
$$310 = 2(x + 30) + 3x$$
$$310 = 2x + 60 + 3x$$
$$310 = 5x + 60$$
$$250 = 5x$$
$$50 = x$$

The width of the room is 50 feet and the length is $50 + 30 = 80$ feet.

23. Let a be the measure of each of the two smaller angles. Then each of the two larger angles is $3a$.

$$a + a + 3a + 3a = 360$$
$$8a = 360$$
$$a = 45$$

The angles measure $45°$, $45°$, and $3(45) = 135°$ and $135°$.

24. Let h be the height of the bookcase. Then $2h$ would be its length.

Amount of lumber for 4 shelves + Amount of lumber for the sides = 20

$$4(2h) + 2h = 20$$
$$8h + 2h = 20$$
$$10h = 20$$
$$h = 2$$

The height of the bookcase is 2 feet and the length is 4 feet.

25. Let t be the time it takes for the joggers to be 4 kilometers apart.

Jogger	Rate	Time	Distance
Harold	8	t	$8t$
Susan	6	t	$6t$

$$8t - 6t = 4$$
$$2t = 4$$
$$t = 2$$

It takes the joggers 2 hours to be 4 kilometers apart.

26. Let t be the amount of time it takes for the trains to be 440 miles apart.

Train	Rate	Time	Distance
First	50	t	$50t$
Second	60	t	$60t$

$$50t + 60t = 440$$
$$110t = 440$$
$$t = 4$$

After 4 hours, the two trains will be 440 miles apart.

27. Rate $= \dfrac{\text{Distance}}{\text{Time}} = \dfrac{200 \text{ feet}}{22.73 \text{ seconds}} \approx 8.8$ ft/sec

The cars travel at about 8.8 ft/sec.

28. Let x be the amount invested at 8%. Then $12{,}000 - x$ is the amount invested at $7\frac{1}{4}$%.

Principal	Rate	Time	Interest
x	8%	1	$0.08x$
$12{,}000 - x$	$7\frac{1}{4}$%	1	$0.0725(12{,}000 - x)$

$$0.08x + 0.0725\left(12{,}000 - x\right) = 900$$
$$0.08x + 870 - 0.0725x = 900$$
$$0.0075x = 30$$
$$x = 4000$$

Tatiana should invest $4000 at 8% and $8000 at $7\frac{1}{4}$%.

29. Let x be the amount invested at 3%. Then $4{,}000 - x$ is the amount invested at 3.5%.

Principal	Rate	Time	Interest
x	3%	1	$0.03x$
$4{,}000 - x$	3.5%	1	$0.035(4{,}000 - x)$

$$0.03x + 94.50 = 0.035(4{,}000 - x)$$
$$0.03x + 94.50 = 140 - .035x$$
$$0.065x = 45.5$$
$$x = 700$$

Aimee invested $700 in the 3% account and $3300 in the 3.5% account.

30. Let x be the number of gallons of pure punch. Then $2 - x$ is the number of liters of the 5% acid solution.

Punch Solution	Strength	Gallons	Amount
98%	0.98	2	0.98(2)
100%	1	x	$1x$
98.5%	0.985	$x + 2$	$0.985(x + 2)$

$$1.96 + x = 0.985(x + 2)$$
$$1.96 + x = 0.985x + 1.97$$
$$0.015x = 0.01$$
$$x \approx 0.67$$

Marcie should add about 0.67 gallons of pure punch.

31. Let x be the number of small wind chimes sold.

Type	Price	Number Sold	Amount
Small	$8	x	$8x$
Large	$20	$30 - x$	$20(30 - x)$

$$8x + 20(30 - x) = 492$$
$$8x + 600 - 20x = 492$$
$$-12x = -108$$
$$x = 9$$

He sold 9 small and 21 large wind chimes

32. Let x be the number of liters of the 10% solution.
Then $2 - x$ is the number of liters of the 5% acid solution.

Solution	Strength	Liters	Amount
10%	0.10	x	$0.10x$
5%	0.05	$2 - x$	$0.05(2 - x)$
Mixture	0.08	2	0.16

$$0.10x + 0.05(2 - x) = 0.16$$
$$0.10x + 0.10 - 0.05x = 0.16$$
$$0.05x = 0.06$$
$$x = 1.2$$

The chemist should mix 1.2 liters of 10% solution with 0.8 liters of 5% solution.

33. Let x = smaller odd integer. Then
$x + 2$ = next consecutive odd integer.
Smaller number + larger number = 208

$$x + (x + 2) = 208$$
$$2x + 2 = 208$$
$$2x = 206$$
$$x = 103$$

The smaller number is 103 and the larger number is $103 + 2 = 105$.

34. Let x = cost of television before tax. Then amount of tax = $0.06x$. Cost of television before tax + tax on television = cost of television after tax.

$$x + 0.06x = 477$$
$$1.06x = 477$$
$$x = \frac{477}{1.06} = 450$$

The cost of the television before tax is $450.

35. Let x = his dollar sales.
Then $0.05x$ = amount of commission.
Salary + commission = 900

$$300 + 0.05x = 900$$
$$0.05x = 600$$
$$x = \frac{600}{0.05} = 12,000$$

His sales last week were $12,000.

36. Let x = measure of the smallest angle. Then
$x + 8$ = measure of second angle and
$2x + 4$ = measure of third angle.
Sum of the three angles = 180°

$$x + (x + 8) + (2x + 4) = 180$$
$$4x + 12 = 180$$
$$4x = 168$$
$$x = 42$$

The angles are 42°, $42 + 8 = 50°$, and $2(42) + 4 = 88°$.

37. Let t = number of years. Then
$25t$ = increase in employees over t years
Present number of employees + increase in employees = future number of employees

$$427 + 25t = 627$$
$$25t = 200$$
$$t = \frac{200}{25} = 8$$

It will take 8 years before they reach 627 employees.

38. Let x = measure of each smaller angle. Then
$x + 40$ = measure of each larger angle
(measure of the two smaller angles)
+(measure of the two larger angles) = 360°

$$x + x + (x + 40) + (x + 40) = 360$$
$$4x + 80 = 360$$
$$4x = 280$$
$$x = 70$$

Each of the smaller angles is 70° and each of the two larger angles is $70 + 40 = 110°$.

39. Let x = number of copies that would result in both centers charging the same. Then charge for copies at Copy King = $0.04x$ and charge for copies at King Kopie = $0.03x$
Monthly fee + charge for copies at Copy King = monthly fee + charge for copies at King Kopie.

$$20 + 0.04x = 25 + 0.03x$$
$$0.04x = 5 + 0.03x$$
$$0.01x = 5$$
$$x = \frac{5}{0.01} = 500$$

500 copies would result in both centers charging the same.

40. Let r = Jim's swim rate.

Person	Rate	Time	Distance
Rita	1	0.5	0.5
Jim	r	0.5	$0.5r$

$$0.5 - 0.5r = 0.2$$
$$-0.5r = -0.3$$
$$r = 0.6$$

Jim swims at 0.6 mph.

41. Let x be the amount of $3.50 per pound ground beef. Then $80 - x$ is the amount of $4.10 per pound of ground beef.

Ground Beef	Price	Amount	Total
$3.50	3.50	x	$3.50x$
$4.10	4.10	$80 - x$	$4.10(80 - x)$
Mixture	3.65	80	292

$$3.50x + 4.10(80 - x) = 292$$
$$3.50x + 328 - 4.10x = 292$$
$$-0.60x = -36$$
$$x = 60$$

The butcher mixed 60 lbs of $3.50 per pound ground beef with 20 lbs of $4.10 per pound ground beef.

42. Let x = the rate the older brother travels. Then $x + 5$ = the rate the younger brother travels.

Brother	Rate	Time	Distance
Younger	$x + 5$	2	$2(x + 5)$
Older	x	2	$2x$

Younger brother's distance + older brother's distance = 230 miles.
$$2(x + 5) + 2x = 230$$
$$2x + 10 + 2x = 230$$
$$4x + 10 = 230$$
$$4x = 220$$
$$x = 55$$

The older brother travels at 55 miles per hour and the younger brother travels at $55 + 5 = 60$ miles per hour.

43. Let x = the number of liters of 30% solution.

Percent	Liters	Amount
30%	x	$0.30x$
12%	2	$(0.12)(2)$
15%	$x + 2$	$0.15(x + 2)$

$$0.30x + (0.12)(2) = 0.15(x + 2)$$
$$0.30x + 0.24 = 0.15x + 0.30$$
$$0.15x + 0.24 = 0.30$$
$$0.15x = 0.06$$
$$x = 0.4$$

0.4 liters of the 30% acid solution need to be added.

44. Let w be the width of the yard. Then $1.5w$ would be the width of the yard.
3 widths + 2 lengths = 96
$$3w + 2(1.5w) = 96$$
$$3w + 3w = 96$$
$$6w = 96$$
$$w = 16$$

The width of the yard is 16 ft. and the length is $1.5(16) = 24$ ft.

45. Let x be the number of liters of 8% solution.

Percent	Liters	Amount
3%	6	$0.03(6)$
8%	x	$0.08x$
4%	$6 + x$	$0.04(6 + x)$

$$0.03(6) + 0.08x = 0.04(6 + x)$$
$$0.18 + 0.08x = 0.24 + 0.04x$$
$$0.18 + 0.04x = 0.24$$
$$0.04x = 0.06$$
$$x = 1.5$$

There was 1.5 liters of the 8% solution used in the mixture.

Chapter 3 Practice Test

1. $500 - n$

2. $2w + 6000$

3. $60t$

4. $c + 0.06c$

5. If n = the number of packages of orange, then $7n - 105$ = number of packages of peppermint.

6. If x = the number of men, then $600 - x$ = the number of women.
   If x = the number of women, then $600 - x$ = the number of men.

7. If n = the smaller number, then $2n - 1$ is the larger number. The larger number minus the smaller number can be represented by $(2n - 1) - n$.

8. If n = the smaller bottle, then $n + 18$ is the larger bottle. The sum of the amounts can be represented by $n + (n + 18)$.

9. Let c = the cost of the peanuts, then $c + 0.84c$ is the cost of the deluxe can. Their difference is $(c + 0.84c) - c$.

10. Let x = smaller integer.
    Then $2x - 10$ = larger integer.
    Smaller number + larger number = 158
    $x + (2x - 10) = 158$
    $$3x - 10 = 158$$
    $$3x = 168$$
    $$x = 56$$
    The smaller number is 56 and the larger number is $2(56) - 10 = 102$

11. Let x = smallest integer.
    Then $x + 2$ is the consecutive odd integer.
    Sum of the two integers = 33
    $x + 4(x + 2) = 33$
    $$x + 4x + 8 = 33$$
    $$5x + 8 = 33$$
    $$5x = 25$$
    $$x = 5$$
    The integers are 5 and $5 + 2 = 7$

12. Let x = one number.
    Then $5x - 12$ is the other number.
    Sum of the two numbers = 42
    $$x + (5x - 12) = 42$$
    $$x + 5x - 12 = 42$$
    $$6x - 12 = 42$$
    $$6x = 54$$
    $$x = 9$$
    The integers are 9 and $5(9) - 12 = 33$.

13. Let c = the cost of the furniture before tax
    Tax amount = (cost) · (tax rate) = $0.06c$
    Total cost = cost before tax + tax amount
    $$2650 = c + 0.06c$$
    $$2640 = 1.06c$$
    $$\frac{2650}{1.06} = \frac{1.06c}{1.06}$$
    $$2500 = c$$
    The cost of the furniture before tax was $2500.

14. Let x = price of most expensive meal he can order. Then $0.15x$ = amount of the tip.
    $$x + 0.15x = 40$$
    $$1.15x = 40$$
    $$x = 34.78$$
    The price of the most expensive meal he can order is $34.78.

15. Let x = the amount of money Peter invested.
    Then $2x$ = the amount of money Julie invested.
    Then $2x$ = the amount of profit Julie receives.
    Peter's profit + Julie's profit = Total profit
    $x + 2x = 120,000$
    $$3x = 120,000$$
    $$x = 40,000$$
    Peter will receive $40,000 and Julie receives $2(\$40,000) = \$80,000$.

16. Let x = the number of times the plow is needed for the costs to be equal.
    Elizabeth's charge = $80 + 5x$
    Jon charge = $50 + 10x$
    The charges are equal when:
    $$80 + 5x = 50 + 10x$$
    $$30 + 5x = 10x$$
    $$30 = 5x$$
    $$6 = x$$
    The snow would need to be plowed 6 times for the costs to be the same.

17. Let x = number of pages to be printed for the total cost of both printers to be equal.
Then $0.01x$ = cost of printing x pages on the Delta printer,
and $0.03x$ = cost of printing x pages on the TexMar printer.
Delta = TexMar
$$499 + 0.01x = 350 + 0.03x$$
$$499 = 0.02x + 350$$
$$149 = 0.02x$$
$$7450 = x$$
It would take about 7450 pages to be printed for the costs to be the same.

18. Let x = length of smallest side.
Then $x + 15$ = length of second side and $2x$ = length of third side.
Sum of the three sides = perimeter
$$x + (x + 15) + 2x = 75$$
$$4x + 15 = 75$$
$$4x = 60$$
$$x = 15$$
The three sides are 15 inches,
$15 + 15 = 30$ inches, and $2(15) = 30$ inches.

19. Let w = width of flag
Then $2w - 4$ = length of flag.
$2l + 2w$ = perimeter
$$2(2w - 4) + 2w = 28$$
$$4w - 8 + 2w = 28$$
$$6w - 8 = 28$$
$$6w = 36$$
$$w = 6$$
The width is 6 feet and the length is 8 feet.

20. Let x = the measure of the two smaller angles, then $(2x + 3)$ = the measure of the two larger angles.
$$x + x + (2x + 3) + (2x + 3) = 360$$
$$x + x + 2x + 3 + 2x + 3 = 360$$
$$6x + 6 = 360$$
$$6x = 354$$
$$x = 59$$
The angles measure 59°, 59°, $2(59) + 3 = 121°$, 121°.

21. Let x = the rate Harlene digs.
Then $x + 0.2$ is the rate Ellis digs.

Name	Rate	Time	Distance
Harlene	x	84	$84x$
Ellis	$x + 0.2$	84	$84(x + 0.2)$

Distance Harlene digs + distance Ellis digs
= total length of trench
$$84x + 84(x + 0.2) = 67.2$$
$$84x + 84x + 16.8 = 67.2$$
$$168x = 50.4$$
$$x = 0.3$$
Harlene digs at 0.3 feet per minute and Ellis digs at $0.3 + 2 = 0.5$ feet per minute.

22. Let x = the rate Bonnie is running.

Name	Rate	Time	Distance
Alice	8	2	16
Bonnie	x	2	$2x$

$$16 - 2x = 4$$
$$-2x = -12$$
$$x = 6$$
Bonnie is running at 6 mph.

23. Let x be the number of pounds of Jelly Belly candy. Then $3 - x$ is the number of pounds of Kits candy.

Type	Cost	Pounds	Total
Jelly Belly	$2.20	x	$2.20(x)$
Kits	$2.75	$3 - x$	$2.75(3 - x)$
Mixture	$2.40	3	$2.40(3)$

$$2.20x + 2.75(3 - x) = 2.40(3)$$
$$2.2x + 8.25 - 2.75x = 7.2$$
$$-0.55x + 8.25 = 7.2$$
$$-0.55x = -1.05$$
$$x \approx 1.91$$
The mixture should contain about 1.91 pounds of Jelly Belly candy and about 1.09 pounds of Kits candy.

24. Let x = amount of 20% salt solution to be added.

Percent	Liters	Amount
20%	x	$0.20x$
40%	60	$(0.40)(60)$
35%	$x + 60$	$0.35(x + 60)$

$$0.20x + (0.40)(60) = 0.35(x + 60)$$
$$0.20x + 24 = 0.35x + 21$$
$$-0.15x + 24 = 21$$
$$-0.15x = -3$$
$$x = 20$$

20 liters of 20% solution must be added.

25. Let x = number of liters of 8% solution.

Percent	Liters	Amount
8%	x	$0.08x$
5%	$3 - x$	$0.05(3 - x)$
6%	3	$0.06(3)$

$$0.08x + 0.05(3 - x) = 0.06(3)$$
$$0.08x + 0.15 - 0.05x = 0.18$$
$$0.03x + 0.15 = 0.18$$
$$0.03x = 0.03$$
$$x = 1$$

There will be 1 liter of 8% solution and $3 - 1 = 2$ liters of 5% solution.

Chapter 3 Cumulative Review Test

1. 40% of $40,000 per year
$$(0.40)(40,000) = 16,000$$
Emily receives $16,000 in social security.

2. a. $38.7\% - 4.7\% = 34.0\%$

   b. 4.7% of 1.3 million
$$(0.047)(1.3) \approx 0.06 \text{ million or } 60,000$$

3. a. $\dfrac{5 + 6 + 8 + 12 + 5}{5} = 7.2$

   The mean level was 7.2 parts per million.

   b. Carbon dioxide levels in order: 5, 5, 6, 8, 12
The median is 6 parts per million.

4. $\dfrac{5}{12} \div \dfrac{3}{4} = \dfrac{5}{12} \cdot \dfrac{4}{3} = \dfrac{20}{36} = \dfrac{5}{9}$

5. $\dfrac{2}{3} - \dfrac{1}{8} = \dfrac{2 \cdot 8}{3 \cdot 8} - \dfrac{1 \cdot 3}{8 \cdot 3} = \dfrac{16}{24} - \dfrac{3}{24} = \dfrac{13}{24}$

$\dfrac{2}{3}$ inch is $\dfrac{13}{24}$ of an inch greater than $\dfrac{1}{8}$ inch.

6. a. $\{1, 2, 3, 4, \ldots\}$

   b. $\{0, 1, 2, 3, \ldots\}$

   c. A rational number is a quotient of two integers, denominator not 0.

7. a. $|-4| = 4$

   b. $|-5| = 5$ and $|-3| = 3$. Since $5 > 3$, $|-5| > |-3|$.

8. $2 - 6^2 \div 2 \cdot 2 = 2 - 36 \div 2 \cdot 2$
$$= 2 - 18 \cdot 2$$
$$= 2 - 36$$
$$= -34$$

9. $4(2x - 3) - 2(3x + 5) - 6$
$$= 8x - 12 - 6x - 10 - 6$$
$$= 2x - 28$$

10. $5x - 6 = x + 14$
$$5x - 6 - x = x - x + 14$$
$$4x - 6 = 14$$
$$4x - 6 + 6 = 14 + 6$$
$$4x = 20$$
$$\dfrac{4x}{4} = \dfrac{20}{4}$$
$$x = 5$$

11. $6r = 2(r + 3) - (r + 5)$
$$6r = 2r + 6 - r - 5$$
$$6r = r + 1$$
$$6r - r = r - r + 1$$
$$5r = 1$$
$$\dfrac{5r}{5} = \dfrac{1}{5}$$
$$r = \dfrac{1}{5}$$

12. $2(x+5) = 3(2x-4) - 4x$

$$2x + 10 = 6x - 12 - 4x$$
$$2x + 10 = 2x - 12$$
$$2x - 2x + 10 = 2x - 2x - 12$$
$$10 = -12 \text{ False}$$

The equation has no solution.

13. $\dfrac{4.8}{x} = -\dfrac{3}{5}$

$$5(4.8) = -3x$$
$$24 = -3x$$
$$-8 = x$$

14. Substitute 6 for r.

$$A = \pi r^2$$
$$A = \pi(6)^2 = 36\pi \approx 113.10$$

15. a. $4x + 8y = 16$

$$4x - 4x + 8y = 16 - 4x$$
$$8y = 16 - 4x$$
$$\frac{8y}{8} = \frac{16 - 4x}{8}$$
$$y = \frac{16}{8} - \frac{4x}{8}$$
$$y = 2 - \frac{1}{2}x$$
$$y = -\frac{1}{2}x + 2$$

b. Substitute –4 for x.

$$y = -\frac{1}{2}(-4) + 2 = 2 + 2 = 4$$

16. $P = 2l + 2w$

$$P - 2l = 2l + 2w - 2l$$
$$P - 2l = 2w$$
$$\frac{P - 2l}{2} = \frac{2w}{2}$$
$$\frac{P - 2l}{2} = w$$

17. $\dfrac{50 \text{ miles}}{2 \text{ gallons}} = \dfrac{225 \text{ miles}}{x \text{ gallons}}$

$$\frac{50}{2} = \frac{225}{x}$$
$$50x = 450$$
$$x = 9$$

It will need 9 gallons.

18. Let x = number of minutes for the two plans to have the same cost.
Cost for Plan A = $19.95 + 0.35x$
Cost for Plan B = $29.95 + 0.10x$
The costs will be equal when the cost for Plan A = cost for Plan B.

$$19.95 + 0.35x = 29.95 + 0.10x$$
$$0.35x = 10 + 0.10x$$
$$0.25x = 10$$
$$x = 40$$

Lori would need to talk 40 minutes in a month for the plans to have the same cost.

19. Let x = smaller number.
Then $2x + 11$ = larger number.
smaller number + larger number = 29

$$x + (2x + 11) = 29$$
$$3x + 11 = 29$$
$$3x = 18$$
$$x = 6$$

The smaller number is 6 and the larger number is $2(6) + 11 = 23$.

20. Let x = smallest angle. Then $x + 5$ = second angle, $x + 50$ = third angle, and $4x + 25$ = fourth angle. Sum of the angle measures = 360°

$$x + (x+5) + (x+50) + (4x+25) = 360$$
$$7x + 80 = 360$$
$$7x = 280$$
$$x = 40$$

The angle measures are 40°, $40 + 5 = 45°$, $40 + 50 = 90°$, and $4(40) + 25 = 185°$.

Chapter 4

Exercise Set 4.1

1. The *x*-coordinate is always listed first.

2. Another name for the Cartesian coordinate system is the rectangular coordinate system.

3. **a.** The horizontal axis is the *x*-axis.
   b. The vertical axis is the *y*-axis.

4. The origin is the point of intersection of the two axes.

5. Axis is singular, while axes is plural.

6. Place the point directly above the –2 on the *x*-axis and directly to the left of the 4 on the *y*-axis.

7. The graph of a linear equation is an illustration of the set of points whose coordinates satisfy the equation.

8. Arrowheads are added to show that the line extends indefinitely in both directions.

9. **a.** Two points are needed to graph a linear equation.
   b. It is a good idea to use three or more points when graphing a linear equation to catch errors.

10. The graph of a linear equation looks like a straight line.

11. $ax + by = c$

12. When points are collinear, they lie in a straight line.

13.

14. A linear equation in two variables has an infinite number of solutions.

15. II	16. II
17. IV	18. IV
19. I	20. I
21. III	22. I
23. III	24. I
25. II	26. IV

27. $A(3, 1)$; $B(-3, 0)$; $C(1, -3)$; $D(-2, -3)$; $E(0, 3)$; $F\left(\dfrac{3}{2}, -1\right)$

28. $A(8, 5)$; $B(4, 0)$; $C(6, -15)$; $D(-4, 20)$; $E(0, -20)$; $F(-6, -5)$; $G(-5, 10)$

29.   30.

31.   32.

33.

The points are collinear.

34.
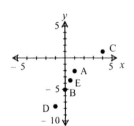

The points are not collinear since (4, 1) is not on the line.

35.

The points are not collinear since (–5, –3) is not on the line.

36.

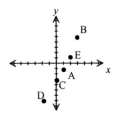

The points are not collinear since (3, 5) is not on the line.

37. a.

$y = x + 2$	$y = x + 2$
$4 = 2 + 2$	$0 = -2 + 2$
$4 = 4$ True	$0 = 0$ True
$y = x + 2$	$y = x + 2$
$5 = -1 + 2$	$2 = 0 + 2$
$5 = 1$ False	$2 = 2$ True

Point c) does not satisfy the equation.

b.

38. a.

$2x + y = -4$	$2x + y = -4$
$2(-2) + 0 = 4$	$2(2) + 3 = -4$
$-4 = -4$ True	$7 = -4$ False
$2x + y = -4$	$2x + y = -4$
$2(0) - 4 = -4$	$2(-1) - 2 = -4$
$-4 = -4$ True	$-4 = -4$ True

Point b) does not satisfy the equation.

b.

39. a.

$3x - 2y = 6$	$3x - 2y = 6$
$3(4) - 2(0) = 6$	$3(2) - 2(0) = 6$
$12 = 6$ False	$6 = 6$ True
$3x - 2y = 6$	$3x - 2y = 6$
$3\left(\dfrac{2}{3}\right) - 2(-2) = 6$	$3\left(\dfrac{4}{3}\right) - 2(-1) = 6$
$2 + 4 = 6$	$4 + 2 = 6$
$6 = 6$ True	$6 = 6$ True

Point a) does not satisfy the equation.

b.

40. a.

$4x - 3y = 0$	$4x - 3y = 0$
$4(3) - 3(4) = 0$	$4(-3) - 3(-4) = 0$
$12 - 12 = 0$	$-12 + 12 = 0$
$0 = 0$ True	$0 = 0$ True
$4x - 3y = 0$	$4x - 3y = 0$
$4(0) - 3(0) = 0$	$4(2) - 3(5) = 0$
$0 = 0$ True	$8 - 15 = 0$
	$-7 = 0$ False

Point d) does not satisfy the equation.

b.

41. a.

$\dfrac{1}{2}x + 4y = 4$	$\dfrac{1}{2}x + 4y = 4$
$\dfrac{1}{2}(-2) + 4(3) = 4$	$\dfrac{1}{2}(2) + 4\left(\dfrac{3}{4}\right) = 4$
$-1 + 12 = 4$	$1 + 3 = 4$
$11 = 4$ False	$4 = 4$ True
$\dfrac{1}{2}x + 4y = 4$	$\dfrac{1}{2}x + 4y = 4$
$\dfrac{1}{2}(0) + 4(1) = 4$	$\dfrac{1}{2}(-4) + 4\left(\dfrac{3}{2}\right) = 4$
$0 + 4 = 4$	$-2 + 6 = 4$
$4 = 4$ True	$4 = 4$ True

Point a) does not satisfy the equation.

b.

42. a. $\quad y = \dfrac{1}{2}x + 2 \qquad y = \dfrac{1}{2}x + 2$

$\quad 2 = \dfrac{1}{2}(0) + 2 \qquad 3 = \dfrac{1}{2}(-4) + 2$

$\quad 2 = 2 \text{ True} \qquad 3 = 0 \text{ False}$

$\quad y = \dfrac{1}{2}x + 2 \qquad y = \dfrac{1}{2}x + 2$

$\quad 1 = \dfrac{1}{2}(-2) + 2 \qquad 4 = \dfrac{1}{2}(4) + 2$

$\quad 1 = -1 + 2 \qquad 4 = 2 + 2$

$\quad 1 = 1 \text{ True} \qquad 4 = 4 \text{ True}$

Point b) does not satisfy the equation.

b.

$y = \dfrac{1}{2}x + 2$

43. $y = 3x - 4$

$y = 3(2) - 4$

$y = 6 - 4$

$y = 2$

44. $y = 3x - 4$

$y = 3(-1) - 4$

$y = -3 - 4$

$y = -7$

45. $y = 3x - 4$

$y = 3(0) - 4$

$y = 0 - 4$

$y = -4$

46. $y = 3x - 4$

$y = 3(3) - 4$

$y = 9 - 4$

$y = 5$

47. $\quad 2x + 3y = 12$

$\quad 2x + 3(2) = 12$

$\quad 2x + 6 = 12$

$\quad 2x = 6$

$\quad x = 3$

48. $\quad 2x + 3y = 12$

$\quad 2x + 3(4) = 12$

$\quad 2x + 12 = 12$

$\quad 2x = 0$

$\quad x = 0$

49. $\quad 2x + 3y = 12$

$\quad 2x + 3\left(\dfrac{11}{3}\right) = 12$

$\quad 2x + 11 = 12$

$\quad 2x = 1$

$\quad x = \dfrac{1}{2}$

50. $\quad 2x + 3y = 12$

$\quad 2x + 3\left(\dfrac{22}{3}\right) = 12$

$\quad 2x + 22 = 12$

$\quad 2x = -10$

$\quad x = -5$

51. The value of y is 0 when a straight line crosses the x-axis, because any point on the x-axis is neither above nor below the origin.

52. The value of x is 0 when a straight line crosses the y-axis, because any point on the y-axis is neither to the left nor to the right of the origin.

53. **a.** Latitude: 16°N   Longitude: 56°W
  b. Latitude: 29°N   Longitude: 90.5°W
  c. Latitude: 26°N   Longitude: 80.5°W
  d. Answers will vary.

54.

55.

56.

57. The general form of a linear equation in one variable is $ax + b = c$.

58. It is a linear equation that has only one solution.

59. $\qquad -2(-3x + 5) + 6 = 4(x - 2)$

$\quad -2(-3x) + (-2)(5) + 6 = 4(x) + 4(-2)$

$\qquad\qquad 6x - 10 + 6 = 4x - 8$

$\qquad\qquad\qquad 6x - 4 = 4x - 8$

$\qquad 6x - 4x - 4 = 4x - 4x - 8$

$\qquad\qquad\qquad 2x - 4 = -8$

$\qquad\qquad 2x - 4 + 4 = -8 + 4$

$\qquad\qquad\qquad\quad 2x = -4$

$\qquad\qquad\qquad \dfrac{2x}{2} = \dfrac{-4}{2}$

$\qquad\qquad\qquad\quad x = -2$

60. $C = 2\pi r$

$\quad = 2\pi(3)$

$\quad = 6\pi$

$\quad \approx 18.84 \text{ inches}$

$A = \pi r^2$

$\quad = \pi(3)^2$

$\quad = 9\pi$

$\quad \approx 28.27 \text{ in.}^2$

61.
$$2x - 5y = 6$$
$$2x - 2x - 5y = -2x + 6$$
$$-5y = -2x + 6$$
$$\frac{-5y}{-5} = \frac{-2x}{-5} + \frac{6}{-5}$$
$$y = \frac{2}{5}x - \frac{6}{5}$$

Exercise Set 4.2

1. To find the *x*-intercept, substitute 0 for *y* and find the corresponding value of *x*. To find the *y*-intercept, substitute 0 for *x* and find the corresponding value of *y*.

2. Two points are needed to graph a straight line, but three should be used to check for errors.

3. The graph of $y = b$ is a horizontal line.

4. The graph of $x = a$ is a vertical line.

5. You may not be able to read exact answers from a graph.

6. The salary depends on the sales because she gets paid a commission based on her sales.

7. Yes. The equation goes through the origin because the point (0, 0) satisfies the equation.

8. Answers will vary.

9.
$$3x + y = 9$$
$$3(3) + y = 9$$
$$9 + y = 9$$
$$y = 0$$

10.
$$3x + y = 9$$
$$3(-4) + y = 9$$
$$-12 + y = 9$$
$$y = 21$$

11.
$$3x + y = 9$$
$$3x + (-6) = 9$$
$$3x - 6 = 9$$
$$3x = 15$$
$$x = 5$$

12.
$$3x + y = 9$$
$$3x + (-9) = 9$$
$$3x - 9 = 9$$
$$3x = 18$$
$$x = 6$$

13.
$$3x + y = 9$$
$$3x + 0 = 9$$
$$3x = 9$$
$$x = 3$$

14.
$$3x + y = 9$$
$$3\left(\frac{3}{2}\right) + y = 9$$
$$\frac{9}{2} + y = 9$$
$$\frac{9}{2} + y = \frac{18}{2}$$
$$y = \frac{18}{2} - \frac{9}{2}$$
$$y = \frac{9}{2}$$

15.
$$3x - 2y = 8$$
$$3(4) - 2y = 8$$
$$12 - 2y = 8$$
$$-2y = -4$$
$$y = 2$$

16.
$$3x - 2y = 8$$
$$3(0) - 2y = 8$$
$$-2y = 8$$
$$y = -4$$

17.
$$3x - 2y = 8$$
$$3x - 2(0) = 8$$
$$3x = 8$$
$$x = \frac{8}{3}$$

18.
$$3x - 2y = 8$$
$$3x - 2\left(-\frac{5}{2}\right) = 8$$
$$3x + 5 = 8$$
$$3x = 3$$
$$x = 1$$

19.
$$3x - 2y = 8$$
$$3(-2) - 2y = 8$$
$$-6 - 2y = 8$$
$$-2y = 14$$
$$y = -7$$

20.
$$3x - 2y = 8$$
$$3x - 2(5) = 8$$
$$3x - 10 = 8$$
$$3x = 18$$
$$x = 6$$

21. $x = -3$ is a vertical line with *x*-intercept at $(-3, 0)$

22. $x = \frac{3}{2}$ is a vertical line with *x*-intercept at $\left(\frac{3}{2}, 0\right)$

23. An equation of the form $y = 4$ is a horizontal line with *y*-intercept at $(0, 4)$.

172

24. An equation of the form $y = -\dfrac{5}{3}$ is a horizontal

line with y-intercept at $\left(0, -\dfrac{5}{3}\right)$.

25. Let $x = 0$, $y = 3(0) - 1 = -1$, $(0, -1)$

Let $x = 1$, $y = 3(1) - 1 = 2$, $(1, 2)$

Let $x = 2$, $y = 3(2) - 1 = 5$, $(2, 5)$

26. Let $x = 0$, $y = -0 + 3 = 3$, $(0, 3)$

Let $x = 1$, $y = -1 + 3 = 2$, $(1, 2)$

Let $x = 2$, $y = -2 + 3 = 1$, $(2, 1)$

27. Let $x = 0$, $y = 4(0) - 2 = -2$, $(0, -2)$

Let $x = 1$, $y = 4(1) - 2 = 2$, $(1, 2)$

Let $x = 2$, $y = 4(2) - 2 = 6$, $(2, 6)$

28. Let $x = 0$, $y = 0 - 4 = -4$, $(0, -4)$

Let $x = 2$, $y = 2 - 4 = -2$, $(2, -2)$

Let $x = 4$, $y = 4 - 4 = 0$, $(4, 0)$

29. Let $x = 0$, then $0 + 2y = 6$

$2y = 6$

$y = 3 \rightarrow (0, 3)$

Let $x = 2$, then $2 + 2y = 6$

$2y = 4$

$y = 2 \rightarrow (2, 2)$

Let $x = 4$, then $4 + 2y = 6$

$2y = 2$

$y = 1 \rightarrow (4, 1)$

30. $-3x + 3y = 6$

$3y = 3x + 6$

$y = x + 2$

Let $x = -2$, $y = -2 + 2 = 0$, $(-2, 0)$

Let $x = 0$, $y = 0 + 2 = 2$, $(0, 2)$

Let $x = 1$, $y = 1 + 2 = 3$, $(1, 3)$

31. $3x - 2y = 4$

$-2y = -3x + 4$

$y = \dfrac{3}{2}x - 2$

Let $x = 0$, $y = \dfrac{3}{2}(0) - 2 = -2$, $(0, -2)$

Let $x = 2$, $y = \dfrac{3}{2}(2) - 2 = 1$, $(2, 1)$

Let $x = 4$, $y = \dfrac{3}{2}(4) - 2 = 4$, $(4, 4)$

173

32. $3x - 2y = 6$

$$-2y = -3x + 6$$

$$y = \frac{3}{2}x - 3$$

Let $x = 0$, $y = y = \frac{3}{2}(0) - 3 = -3$, $(0, -3)$

Let $x = 2$, $y = \frac{3}{2}(2) - 3 = 0$, $(2, 0)$

Let $x = 4$, $y = \frac{3}{2}(4) - 3 = 3$, $(4, 3)$

33. $4x + 3y = -9$

$$3y = -4x - 9$$

$$y = -\frac{4}{3}x - 3$$

Let $x = -3$, $y = -\frac{4}{3}(-3) - 3 = 1$, $(-3, 1)$

Let $x = 0$, $y = -\frac{4}{3}(0) - 3 = -3$, $(0, -3)$

Let $x = 3$, $y = -\frac{4}{3}(3) - 3 = -7$, $(3, -7)$

34. $6y - 12x = 18$

$$6y = 12x + 18$$

$$y = 2x + 3$$

Let $x = -1$, $y = 2(-1) + 3 = 1$, $(-1, 1)$

Let $x = 0$, $y = 2(0) + 3 = 3$, $(0, 3)$

Let $x = 1$, $y = 2(1) + 3 = 5$, $(1, 5)$

35. $6x + 5y = 30$

$$5y = -6x + 30$$

$$y = -\frac{6}{5}x + 6$$

Let $x = 0$, $y = -\frac{6}{5}(0) + 6 = 6$, $(0, 6)$

Let $x = 5$, $y = -\frac{6}{5}(5) + 6 = 0$, $(5, 0)$

Let $x = 10$, $y = -\frac{6}{5}(10) + 6 = -6$, $(10, -6)$

36. $2x + 3y = -6$

$$3y = -2x - 6$$

$$y = -\frac{2}{3}x - 2$$

Let $x = -3$, $y = -\frac{2}{3}(-3) - 2 = 0$, $(-3, 0)$

Let $x = 0$, $y = -\frac{2}{3}(0) - 2 = -2$, $(0, -2)$

Let $x = 3$, $y = -\frac{2}{3}(3) - 2 = -4$, $(3, -4)$

37. $-4x + 5y = 0$

$$5y = 4x$$

$$y = \frac{4}{5}x$$

Let $x = -5$, $y = \frac{4}{5}(-5) = -4$, $(-5, -4)$

Let $x = 0$, $y = \frac{4}{5}(0) = 0$, $(0, 0)$

Let $x = 5$, $y = \frac{4}{5}(5) = 4$, $(5, 4)$

38. $3x + 2y = 0$

$$2y = -3x$$

$$y = -\frac{3}{2}x$$

Let $x = -2$, $y = -\frac{3}{2}(-2) = 3$, $(-2, 3)$

Let $x = 0$, $y = -\frac{3}{2}(0) = 0$, $(0, 0)$

Let $x = 2$, $y = -\frac{3}{2}(2) = -3$, $(2, -3)$

39. Let $x = 0$, $y = -20(0) + 60 = 60$, $(0, 60)$

Let $x = 2$, $y = -20(2) + 60 = 20$, $(2, 20)$

Let $x = 4$, $y = -20(4) + 60 = -20$, $(4, -20)$

40. $2y - 100x = 50$

$$2y = 100x + 50$$

$$y = 50x + 25$$

Let $x = -1$, $y = 50(-1) + 25 = -25$, $(-1, -25)$

Let $x = 0$, $y = 50(0) + 25 = 25$, $(0, 25)$

Let $x = 1$, $y = 50(1) + 25 = 75$, $(1, 75)$

41. Let $x = -3$, $y = \frac{4}{3}(-3) = -4$, $(-3, -4)$

Let $x = 0$, $y = \frac{4}{3}(0) = 0$, $(0, 0)$

Let $x = 3$, $y = \frac{4}{3}(3) = 4$, $(3, 4)$

42. Let $x = -5$, $y = -\frac{3}{5}(-5) = 3$, $(-5, 3)$

Let $x = 0$, $y = -\frac{3}{5}(0) = 0$, $(0, 0)$

Let $x = 5$, $y = -\frac{3}{5}(5) = -3$, $(5, -3)$

43. Let $x = 0$, $y = \frac{1}{2}(0) + 4 = 4$, $(0, 4)$

Let $x = 2$, $y = \frac{1}{2}(2) + 4 = 5$, $(2, 5)$

Let $x = 4$, $y = \frac{1}{2}(4) + 4 = 6$, $(4, 6)$

44. Let $x = -5$, $y = -\frac{2}{5}(-5) + 2 = 4$, $(-5, 4)$

Let $x = 0$, $y = -\frac{2}{5}(0) + 2 = 2$, $(0, 2)$

Let $x = 5$, $y = -\frac{2}{5}(5) + 2 = 0$, $(5, 0)$

45. Let $x = 0$ Let $y = 0$

$y = 3x + 3$ $y = 3x + 3$

$y = 3(0) + 3$ $0 = 3x + 3$

$y = 3$ $-3x = 3$

         $x = -1$

46. Let $x = 0$ Let $y = 0$

$y = -3x + 6$ $y = -3x + 6$

$y = -3(0) + 6$ $0 = -3x + 6$

$y = 6$ $3x = 6$

         $x = 2$

47. Let $x = 0$ Let $y = 0$

$y = -4x + 2$ $y = -4x + 2$

$y = -4(0) + 2$ $0 = -4x + 2$

$y = 2$ $-2 = -4x$

         $x = \dfrac{1}{2}$

48. Let $x = 0$ Let $y = 0$

$y = -2x + 5$ $y = -2x + 5$

$y = -2(0) + 5$ $0 = -2x + 5$

$y = 5$ $2x = 5$

         $x = \dfrac{5}{2}$

49. Let $x = 0$ Let $y = 0$

$y = 4x + 16$ $y = 4x + 16$

$y = 4(0) + 16$ $0 = 4x + 16$

$y = 16$ $-4x = 16$

         $x = -4$

50. Let $x = 0$ Let $y = 0$

$y = -5x + 4$ $y = -5x + 4$

$y = -5(0) + 4$ $0 = -5x + 4$

$y = 4$ $-4 = -5x$

         $x = \dfrac{4}{5}$

51. $4y + 6x = 24$

     $4y = -6x + 24$

       $y = -\dfrac{3}{2}x + 6$

Let $x = 0$ Let $y = 0$

$y = -\dfrac{3}{2}(0) + 6$ $0 = -\dfrac{3}{2}x + 6$

$y = 6$ $\dfrac{3}{2}x = 6$

         $x = 4$

52. Let $x = 0$ | Let $y = 0$

$4x = 3y - 9$ $4x = 3y - 9$

$4(0) = 3y - 9$ $4x = 3(0) - 9$

$0 = 3y - 9$ $4x = -9$

$-3y = -9$ $x = -\dfrac{9}{4}$

$y = 3$

53. Let $x = 0$ | Let $y = 0$

$\dfrac{1}{2}x + 2y = 4$ $\dfrac{1}{2}x + 2y = 4$

$\dfrac{1}{2}(0) + 2y = 4$ $\dfrac{1}{2}x + 0 = 4$

$2y = 4$ $\dfrac{1}{2}x = 4$

$y = 2$ $x = 8$

54. Let $x = 0$ | Let $y = 0$

$x + \dfrac{1}{2}y = 2$ $x + \dfrac{1}{2}y = 2$

$0 + \dfrac{1}{2}y = 2$ $x + \dfrac{1}{2}(0) = 2$

$\dfrac{1}{2}y = 2$ $x + 0 = 2$

$y = 4$ $x = 2$

55. Let $x = 0$ | Let $y = 0$

$12x - 24y = 48$ $12x - 24y = 48$

$12(0) - 24y = 48$ $12x - 12(0) = 48$

$-24y = 48$ $12x = 48$

$y = -2$ $x = 4$

56. Let $x = 0$ | Let $y = 0$

$25x + 50y = 100$ $25x + 50y = 100$

$25(0) + 50y = 100$ $25x + 50(0) = 100$

$50y = 100$ $25x = 100$

$y = 2$ $x = 4$

57. Let $x = 0$ | Let $y = 0$

$8y = 6x - 12$ $8y = 6x - 12$

$8y = 6(0) - 12$ $8(0) = 6x - 12$

$8y = -12$ $0 = 6x - 12$

$y = -\dfrac{3}{2}$ $-6x = -12$

$x = 2$

58. Let $x = 0$ | Let $y = 0$

$6y = -4x + 12$ $6y = -4x + 12$

$6y = -4\big(0\big) + 12$ $6\big(0\big) = -4x + 12$

$6y = 12$ $4x = 12$

$y = 2$ $x = 3$

177

59. Let $x = 0$ Let $y = 0$

$y = 15x + 45$ $y = 15x + 45$

$y = 15(0) + 45$ $0 = 15x + 45$

$y = 45$ $-15x = 45$

         $x = -3$

60. Let $x = 0$ Let $y = 0$

$y = -10x + 30$ $y = -10x + 30$

$y = -10(0) + 30$ $0 = -10x + 30$

$y = 30$ $10x = 30$

         $x = 3$

61. Let $x = 0$ Let $y = 0$

$\dfrac{1}{3}x + \dfrac{1}{4}y = 12$ $\dfrac{1}{3}x + \dfrac{1}{4}y = 12$

$\dfrac{1}{3}(0) + \dfrac{1}{4}y = 12$ $\dfrac{1}{3}x + \dfrac{1}{4}(0) = 12$

$\dfrac{1}{4}y = 12$ $\dfrac{1}{3}x = 12$

$y = 48$ $x = 36$

62. Let $x = 0$ Let $y = 0$

$\dfrac{1}{4}x - \dfrac{2}{3}y = 60$ $\dfrac{1}{4}x - \dfrac{2}{3}y = 60$

$\dfrac{1}{4}(0) - \dfrac{2}{3}y = 60$ $\dfrac{1}{4}x - \dfrac{2}{3}(0) = 60$

$-\dfrac{2}{3}y = 60$ $\dfrac{1}{4}x = 60$

$y = -90$ $x = 240$

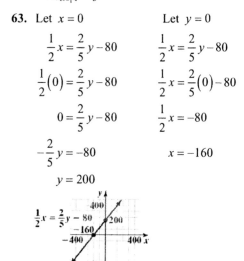

63. Let $x = 0$ Let $y = 0$

$\dfrac{1}{2}x = \dfrac{2}{5}y - 80$ $\dfrac{1}{2}x = \dfrac{2}{5}y - 80$

$\dfrac{1}{2}(0) = \dfrac{2}{5}y - 80$ $\dfrac{1}{2}x = \dfrac{2}{5}(0) - 80$

$0 = \dfrac{2}{5}y - 80$ $\dfrac{1}{2}x = -80$

$-\dfrac{2}{5}y = -80$ $x = -160$

$y = 200$

64. Let $x = 0$ Let $y = 0$

$\dfrac{2}{3}y = \dfrac{5}{4}x + 120$ $\dfrac{2}{3}y = \dfrac{5}{4}x + 120$

$\dfrac{2}{3}y = \dfrac{5}{4}(0) + 120$ $\dfrac{2}{3}(0) = \dfrac{5}{4}x + 120$

$\dfrac{2}{3}y = 120$ $0 = \dfrac{5}{4}x + 120$

$y = 180$ $-\dfrac{5}{4}x = 120$

         $x = -96$

65. $x = -2$

66. $x = \dfrac{5}{2}$

67. $y = 6$

68. $y = -\dfrac{9}{2}$

69.
$$ax + 3y = 10$$
$$a(2) + 3(0) = 10$$
$$2a + 0 = 10$$
$$2a = 10$$
$$a = 5$$

70.
$$ax + 7y = 6$$
$$a(3) + 7(0) = 6$$
$$3a + 0 = 6$$
$$3a = 6$$
$$a = 2$$

71.
$$3x + by = 14$$
$$3(0) + b(7) = 14$$
$$0 + 7b = 14$$
$$7b = 14$$
$$b = 2$$

72.
$$4x + by = 15$$
$$4(0) + b(-3) = 15$$
$$0 - 3b = 15$$
$$-3b = 15$$
$$b = -5$$

73. Yes. For each 15 minutes of time, the number of calories burned increases by 200 calories.

74. No. There is not an equal amount of change from one year to the next.

75. **a.** $C = 0.10n + 15$

b.

c. $19

d. 100 minutes

76. **a.** $d = 30t$

b.

c. 360 miles

d. 5 hours

77. **a.** $C = m + 40$

b.

c. $100

d. 30 miles

78. **a.** $I = (10,000)(0.05)t$

$I = 500t$

b.

c. $5000

d. 1 year

79. **a.**

b. $550

c. 800 videos

80. a. $C = 10h + 200$

b.

c. $700

d. 150 hours

81. Since each shaded area multiplied by the corresponding intercept must equal 6, the coefficients are 3 and 2 respectively.

82. Since the shaded area multiplied by the corresponding intercept equals 18, the coefficients are –6 and 3 respectively.

83. Since the first shaded area multiplied by the *x*-intercept must equal –12, the coefficient of *x* is 6. Since the opposite of the second shaded area multiplied by the *y*-intercept must equal –12, the coefficient of *y* is 4.

84. Since the first shaded area multiplied by the *x*-intercept must equal 30, the coefficient of *x* is –3. Since the opposite of the second shaded area multiplied by the *y*-intercept must equal 30, the coefficient of *y* is 2.

85. a.

b. (2, 3)

c.
$$y = 2x - 1 \qquad y = -x + 5$$
$$3 = 2(2) - 1 \qquad 3 = -2 + 5$$
$$3 = 3 \qquad 3 = 3$$

d. no

86.
Let $x = -3$	Let $x = 3$

$$y = x^2 - 4 \qquad y = x^2 - 4$$
$$y = (-3)^2 - 4 \quad y = 3^2 - 4$$
$$= 9 - 4 \qquad = 9 - 4$$
$$= 5 \qquad = 5$$
$$(-3, 5) \qquad (3, 5)$$

Let $x = -2$ Let $x = 2$
$$y = x^2 - 4 \qquad y = x^2 - 4$$
$$y = (-2)^2 - 4 \quad y = 2^2 - 4$$
$$= 4 - 4 \qquad = 4 - 4$$
$$= 0 \qquad = 0$$
$$(-2, 0) \qquad (2, 0)$$

Let $x = -1$ Let $x = 1$
$$y = x^2 - 4 \qquad y = x^2 - 4$$
$$y = (-1)^2 - 4 \quad = x^2 - 4$$
$$= 1 - 4 \qquad = 1 - 4$$
$$= -3 \qquad = -3$$
$$(-1, -3) \qquad (1, -3)$$

Let $x = 0$
$$y = x^2 - 4$$
$$y = 0^2 - 4$$
$$= 0 - 4$$
$$= -4$$
$$(0, -4)$$

87. a.-d.

e. They appear to be parallel.

f. The constant is the *y*-intercept.

88.
$$2\left[6 - (4 - 5)\right] \div 2 - 8^2 = 2\left[6 - (-1)\right] \div 2 - 64$$
$$= 2\left[7\right] \div 2 - 64$$
$$= 14 \div 2 - 64$$
$$= 7 - 64$$
$$= -57$$

89. $\dfrac{-3^2 \cdot 4 \div 2}{\sqrt{9}-2^2} = \dfrac{-9 \cdot 4 \div 2}{3-4}$

$\qquad = \dfrac{-36 \div 2}{-1}$

$\qquad = \dfrac{-18}{-1}$

$\qquad = 18$

90. $\dfrac{8 \text{ ounces}}{3 \text{ gallons}} = \dfrac{x \text{ ounces}}{2.5 \text{ gallons}}$

$\qquad \dfrac{8}{3} = \dfrac{x}{2.5}$

$\qquad 20 = 3x$

$\qquad 6.67 \approx x$

You should use 6.67 ounces of cleaner.

91. Let x = smaller integer. Then $3x + 1$ = larger integer.

$x + (3x+1) = 37$

$\qquad 4x + 1 = 37$

$\qquad 4x = 36$

$\qquad x = 9$

The smaller integer is 9.

The larger is $3(9)+1 = 27+1 = 28$.

Exercise Set 4.3

1. The slope of a line is the ratio of the vertical change to the horizontal change between any two points on the line.

2. To find the slope of a line, calculate the ratio of vertical to horizontal change between any two points.

3. A line with a positive slope rises from left to right.

4. A line with a negative slope falls from left to right.

5. Lines that rise from the left to right have a positive slope. Lines that fall from left to right have a negative slope.

6. The slope of a horizontal line is 0 since there is no vertical change.

7. No, since we cannot divide by 0, the slope is undefined.

8. m

9. Their slopes are the same.

10. Their slopes are negative reciprocals.

11. $m = \dfrac{5-1}{6-4}$

$\qquad = \dfrac{4}{2}$

$\qquad = 2$

12. $m = \dfrac{-4-(-2)}{7-9}$

$\qquad = \dfrac{-2}{-2}$

$\qquad = 1$

13. $m = \dfrac{-2-0}{4-8}$

$\qquad = \dfrac{-2}{-4}$

$\qquad = \dfrac{1}{2}$

14. $m = \dfrac{5-2}{6-(-4)}$

$\qquad = \dfrac{3}{10}$

15. $m = \dfrac{\frac{1}{2}-\frac{1}{2}}{-3-9}$

$\qquad = \dfrac{0}{-12} = 0$

16. $m = \dfrac{6-6}{-2-(-8)}$

$\qquad = \dfrac{0}{6} = 0$

17. $m = \dfrac{-3-(-6)}{8-5}$

$\qquad = \dfrac{3}{3} = 1$

18. $m = \dfrac{-6-3}{5-9}$

$\qquad = \dfrac{-9}{-4}$

$\qquad = \dfrac{9}{4}$

19. $m = \dfrac{2-4}{6-6}$

$\qquad = \dfrac{-2}{0}$

is undefined

20. $m = \dfrac{-1-8}{3-(-7)}$

$\qquad = \dfrac{-9}{10}$

$\qquad = -\dfrac{9}{10}$

21. $m = \dfrac{3-0}{-2-6}$

$\qquad = \dfrac{3}{-8}$

$\qquad = -\dfrac{3}{8}$

22. $m = \dfrac{-5-3}{-2-(-2)}$

$\qquad = \dfrac{-8}{0}$

is undefined

23. $m = \dfrac{2 - \dfrac{5}{2}}{\dfrac{3}{4} - 0} = \dfrac{-\dfrac{1}{2}}{\dfrac{3}{4}}$

    $= \dfrac{-1}{2} \cdot \dfrac{4}{-3}$

    $= \dfrac{-4}{-6}$

    $= \dfrac{2}{3}$

24. $m = \dfrac{-1 - 8}{\dfrac{1}{3} - (-1)} = \dfrac{-9}{\dfrac{4}{3}}$

    $= \dfrac{-9}{1} \cdot \dfrac{3}{4}$

    $= \dfrac{-27}{4}$

    $= -\dfrac{27}{4}$

25. $m = \dfrac{6}{3} = 2$

26. $m = \dfrac{3}{5}$

27. $m = \dfrac{-6}{3} = -2$

28. $m = \dfrac{-2}{5} = -\dfrac{2}{5}$

29. $m = \dfrac{4}{-7} = -\dfrac{4}{7}$

30. $m = \dfrac{4}{-3} = -\dfrac{4}{3}$

31. $m = \dfrac{7}{4}$

32. $m = \dfrac{3}{2}$

33. $m = \dfrac{0}{3} = 0$

34. $m = \dfrac{0}{8} = 0$

35. $m = \dfrac{-2}{3} = -\dfrac{2}{3}$

36. $m = \dfrac{-3}{4} = -\dfrac{3}{4}$

37. Vertical line, slope is undefined.

38. Vertical line, slope is undefined.

39.

40.

41.

42.

43.

44.

45.

46.

47.

48.

49. The lines are parallel because the slopes are the same.

50. The lines are neither parallel nor perpendicular.

51. The lines are perpendicular because the slopes are negative reciprocals.

52. The lines are parallel because the slopes are the same.

53. The lines are perpendicular because the slopes are negative reciprocals.

54. The lines are neither parallel nor perpendicular.

55. The lines are neither parallel nor perpendicular.

56. The lines are neither parallel nor perpendicular.

57. The lines are neither parallel nor perpendicular.

58. The lines are perpendicular because the slopes are negative reciprocals.

59. The lines are parallel because the slopes are the same.

60. The lines are neither parallel nor perpendicular.

61. The lines are parallel because the lines are both vertical.

62. The lines are perpendicular because if the slope is 0, the line is horizontal and if the slope is undefined the line is vertical.

63. The lines are perpendicular because if the slope is 0, the line is horizontal and if the slope is undefined the line is vertical.

64. The lines are neither parallel nor perpendicular.

65. Its slope would be 3.

66. Its slope would be –2.

67. Its slope would be $\dfrac{1}{4}$.

68. Its slope would be $-\dfrac{1}{5}$.

69. The first graph appears to pass through the points $(-1, 0)$ and $(0, 6)$. Its slope is $m = \dfrac{6-0}{0-(-1)} = \dfrac{6}{1} = 6$. The second graph appears to pass through the points $(-4, 0)$ and $(0, 6)$. Its slope is $m = \dfrac{6-0}{0-(-4)} = \dfrac{6}{4} = \dfrac{6}{4} = \dfrac{3}{2}$. The first graph has the greater slope.

70. The first graph appears to pass through the points $(0, -4)$ and $(1, 0)$. Its slope is $m = \dfrac{0-(-4)}{1-0} = \dfrac{4}{1} = 4$. The second graph appears to pass through the points $(0, -4)$ and $(1, 4)$. Its slope is $m = \dfrac{4-(-4)}{1-0} = \dfrac{8}{1} = 8$. The second graph has the greater slope.

71. a. $m = \dfrac{22-45}{1961-1957} = \dfrac{-23}{4} = -\dfrac{23}{4}$

b. $m = \dfrac{51-7}{1989-1985} = \dfrac{44}{4} = 11$

72. a. $m = \dfrac{410-280}{65-60} = \dfrac{130}{5} = 26$

b. $m = \dfrac{618-545}{80-75} = \dfrac{73}{5} = 14.6$

73. $m = \dfrac{-2-6}{4-2} = \dfrac{-8}{2} = -4$

Parallel lines have the same slope, so a line parallel to the given line would have a slope of -4.

74. $m = \dfrac{7-5}{4-(-2)} = \dfrac{2}{6} = \dfrac{1}{3}$

Parallel lines have the same slope, so a line parallel to the given line would have a slope of $\dfrac{1}{3}$.

75. $m = \dfrac{1-(-7)}{2-1} = \dfrac{1+7}{1} = 8$

Perpendicular lines have negative reciprocal slopes, so a line perpendicular to the given line would have a slope of $-\dfrac{1}{8}$.

76. $m = \dfrac{3-0}{-2-(-3)} = \dfrac{3}{1} = 3$

Perpendicular lines have negative reciprocal slopes, so a line perpendicular to the given line would have a slope of $-\dfrac{1}{3}$.

77. $m = \dfrac{-\dfrac{7}{2} - \left(-\dfrac{3}{8}\right)}{\dfrac{4}{9} - \dfrac{1}{2}}$

$= \dfrac{-\dfrac{28}{8} + \dfrac{3}{8}}{\dfrac{8}{18} - \dfrac{9}{18}} = \dfrac{-\dfrac{25}{8}}{-\dfrac{17}{18}}$

$= \left(-\dfrac{25}{\overset{}{\cancel{8}}_4}\right)\left(-\dfrac{\overset{9}{\cancel{18}}}{17}\right)$

$= \dfrac{(25)(9)}{(4)(17)} = \dfrac{225}{68}$

78. Answers will vary. One possible answer:

Writing the slope as $m = \dfrac{5}{-3}$ and starting at the given point, increase the y-coordinate by 5 and decrease the x-coordinate by 3.

$(6-3, -4+5) \Rightarrow (3, 1)$

Another point on the graph is $(3, 1)$.

79. a.

b. AC; $m = \dfrac{4-1}{5-0} = \dfrac{3}{5}$

CB; $m = \dfrac{4-2}{5-6} = \dfrac{2}{-1} = -2$

DB; $m = \dfrac{-1-2}{1-6} = \dfrac{-3}{-5} = \dfrac{3}{5}$

AD; $m = \dfrac{-1-1}{1-0} = \dfrac{-2}{1} = -2$

c. Yes; opposite sides are parallel.

80. a. ab; $m = \dfrac{1 - 0.5}{1850 - 1650}$

$= \dfrac{0.5}{200}$

$= 0.0025$ billion or 2,500,000

bc; $m = \dfrac{2 - 1}{1930 - 1850} = \dfrac{1}{80} = 0.0125$ billion

or 12,500,000

cd; $m = \dfrac{4 - 2}{1976 - 1930}$

$= \dfrac{2}{46}$

≈ 0.043478261 billion

or 43,478,261

de; $m = \dfrac{8 - 4}{2016 - 1976}$

$= \dfrac{4}{40}$

$= \dfrac{1}{10}$

$= 0.1$ billion

or 100,000,000

b. No; each segment has a different slope.

81. a. AB; $m = \dfrac{12 - 4}{2 - 0} = \dfrac{8}{2} = 4$

BC; $m = \dfrac{8 - 12}{4 - 2} = \dfrac{-4}{2} = -2$

CD; $m = \dfrac{16 - 8}{6 - 4} = \dfrac{8}{2} = 4$

b. $\dfrac{4 + (-2) + 4}{3} = \dfrac{6}{3} = 2$

c. $m = \dfrac{16 - 4}{6 - 0} = \dfrac{12}{6} = 2$

d. yes

e. Answers will vary.

82. a. Answers will vary.

b. The slope of a line has no particular units.

c. The slope of a hill is measured in degrees.

83. $4x^2 + 9x + \dfrac{x}{3} = 4(0)^2 + 9(0) + \dfrac{0}{3}$

$= 0 + 0 + 0$

$= 0$

84. a. $-x = -\dfrac{5}{2}$

$(-1)(-x) = (-1)\left(-\dfrac{5}{2}\right)$

$x = \dfrac{5}{2}$

b. $8x = 0$

$\dfrac{8x}{8} = \dfrac{0}{8}$

$x = 0$

85. $\dfrac{2}{3}x + \dfrac{1}{7}x = 4$

$21\left(\dfrac{2}{3}x + \dfrac{1}{7}x\right) = 21(4)$

$21\left(\dfrac{2}{3}x\right) + 21\left(\dfrac{1}{7}x\right) = 84$

$14x + 3x = 84$

$17x = 84$

$\dfrac{17x}{17} = \dfrac{84}{17}$

$x = \dfrac{84}{17}$

86. $d = a + b + c$

$d - a = a + b + c - a$

$d - a = b + c$

$d - a - b = b + c - b$

$d - a - b = c$

87. $5x - 3y = 30$

y-intercept	x-intercept
$x = 0$	$y = 0$
$5(0) - 3y = 30$	$5x - 3(0) = 30$
$-3y = 30$	$5x = 30$
$y = -10$	$x = 6$
$(0, -10)$	$(6, 0)$

Mid-Chapter Test: 4.1-4.3

1. IV

2.

3. a.
$$\frac{1}{3}x + y = -2$$
$$\frac{1}{3}(3) + (-3) = -2$$
$$1 - 3 = -2$$
$$-2 = -2 \text{ True}$$

b.
$$\frac{1}{3}x + y = -2$$
$$\frac{1}{3}(0) + (2) = -2$$
$$0 + 2 = -2$$
$$2 = -2 \text{ False}$$

c.
$$\frac{1}{3}x + y = -2$$
$$\frac{1}{3}(-6) + (0) = -2$$
$$-2 + 0 = -2$$
$$-2 = -2 \text{ True}$$

4.
$$y = 5x + 1$$
$$y = 5(-1) + 1$$
$$y = -5 + 1$$
$$y = -4$$

5.
$$3x - 4y = 1$$
$$3x - 4(2) = 1$$
$$3x - 8 = 1$$
$$3x = 9$$
$$x = 3$$

6. A graph of an equation in two variables is an illustration of a set of points whose coordinates satisfy the equation.

7.

8.

9. Let $x = -1$; $y = 3(-1) + 1 = -2$; $(-1, -2)$
Let $x = 0$; $y = 3(0) + 1 = 1$; $(0, 1)$
Let $x = 1$; $y = 3(1) + 1 = 4$; $(1, 4)$

10. Let $x = 2$; $y = -\frac{1}{2}(2) + 4 = 3$; $(2, 3)$
Let $x = 4$; $y = -\frac{1}{2}(4) + 4 = 2$; $(4, 2)$
Let $x = 6$; $y = -\frac{1}{2}(6) + 4 = 1$; $(6, 1)$

11.

y-intercept	x-intercept
Let $x = 0$	Let $y = 0$
$3(0) - 4y = 12$	$3x - 4(0) = 12$
$-4y = 12$	$3x = 12$
$y = -3$	$x = 4$

12.

y-intercept	x-intercept
Let $x = 0$	Let $y = 0$
$\frac{1}{2}(0) + \frac{1}{5}y = 10$	$\frac{1}{2}x + \frac{1}{5}(0) = 10$
$\frac{1}{5}y = 10$	$\frac{1}{2}x = 10$
$y = 50$	$x = 20$

13. $m = \dfrac{3-5}{6-(-1)} = -\dfrac{2}{7}$

14. $m = \dfrac{2-2}{7-4} = \dfrac{0}{3} = 0$

15. $m = \dfrac{5-0}{-3-(-3)} = \dfrac{5}{0}$

    is undefined

16.

17.

18. The lines are neither parallel nor perpendicular.

19. The lines are perpendicular because the slopes are negative reciprocals.

20. Use the points (0, 0) and (10, 100).

    The slope is $m = \dfrac{100-0}{10-0} = \dfrac{100}{10} = 10$.

Exercise Set 4.4

1. $y = mx + b$

2. Solve the equation for y.

3. $y = 3x - 5$

4. $y = -3x + 5$

5. Compare their slopes: If slopes are the same and their y-intercepts are different, the lines are parallel.

6. If the slopes and y-intercepts are the same, the lines are the same.

7. $y - y_1 = m(x - x_1)$

8. $m = 2$; (0, 0)

    $y - 0 = 2(x - 0)$

9. $m = 2$; y-intercept: (0, –6)

10. $m = -3$; y-intercept: (0, 17)

11. $m = \dfrac{4}{3}$; y-intercept: (0, –7)

12. $m = \dfrac{7}{5}$; y-intercept: (0, –5)

13. $m = 1$; y-intercept: (0, –3)

14. $m = -1$; y-intercept: (0, 5)

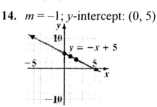

15. $m = 3$; y-intercept: (0, 2)

16. $3x + y = 4$

    $y = -3x + 4$

    $m = -3$; y-intercept: (0, 4)

17. $m = 2$; y-intercept: (0, 0)

18. $m = -4$; y-intercept: (0, 0)

19. $-2x + y = -3$

    $y = 2x - 3$

    $m = 2$; y-intercept: (0, –3)

20. $3x + 3y = 9$

$$3y = -3x + 9$$
$$y = -x + 3$$

$m = -1$; y-intercept: $(0, 3)$

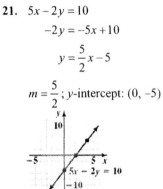

21. $5x - 2y = 10$

$$-2y = -5x + 10$$
$$y = \frac{5}{2}x - 5$$

$m = \frac{5}{2}$; y-intercept: $(0, -5)$

22. $-x + 2y = 8$

$$2y = x + 8$$
$$y = \frac{1}{2}x + 4$$

$m = \frac{1}{2}$; y-intercept: $(0, 4)$

23. $6x + 12y = 18$

$$12y = -6x + 18$$
$$y = -\frac{1}{2}x + \frac{3}{2}$$

$m = -\frac{1}{2}$; y-intercept: $\left(0, \frac{3}{2}\right)$

24. $16y = 8x + 32$

$$y = \frac{1}{2}x + 2$$

$m = \frac{1}{2}$; y-intercept: $(0, 2)$

25. $-6x + 2y - 8 = 0$

$$2y = 6x + 8$$
$$y = 3x + 4$$

$m = 3$; y-intercept: $(0, 4)$

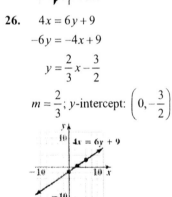

26. $4x = 6y + 9$

$$-6y = -4x + 9$$
$$y = \frac{2}{3}x - \frac{3}{2}$$

$m = \frac{2}{3}$; y-intercept: $\left(0, -\frac{3}{2}\right)$

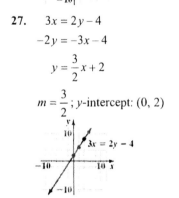

27. $3x = 2y - 4$

$$-2y = -3x - 4$$
$$y = \frac{3}{2}x + 2$$

$m = \frac{3}{2}$; y-intercept: $(0, 2)$

28. $20x = 80y + 40$

$-80y = -20x + 40$

$$y = \frac{1}{4}x - \frac{1}{2}$$

$m = \frac{1}{4}$; y-intercept: $\left(0, -\frac{1}{2}\right)$

29. $m = \frac{4}{4} = 1$, $b = -2$

$y = x - 2$

30. $m = \frac{2}{1} = 2$, $b = 0$

$y = 2x$

31. $m = \frac{-2}{6} = -\frac{1}{3}$, $b = 2$

$y = -\frac{1}{3}x + 2$

32. $m = \frac{-2}{4} = -\frac{1}{2}$, $b = -2$

$y = -\frac{1}{2}x - 2$

33. $m = \frac{-3}{1} = -3$, $b = -5$

$y = -3x - 5$

34. $m = \frac{-3}{1} = -3$, $b = 4$

$y = -3x + 4$

35. $m = \frac{10}{30} = \frac{1}{3}$, $b = 5$

$y = \frac{1}{3}x + 5$

36. $m = \frac{1}{8}$, $b = -\frac{5}{2}$

$y = \frac{1}{8}x - \frac{5}{2}$

37. Since the slopes of the lines are the same and y-intercepts are different, the lines are parallel.

38. $2x + 3y = 1 \qquad y = -\frac{2}{3}x + 3$

$3y = -2x + 1$

$$y = -\frac{2}{3}x + \frac{1}{3}$$

Since the slopes of the lines are the same and y-intercepts are different, the lines are parallel.

39. $4x + 2y = 7 \qquad 4x = 8y + 12$

$2y = -4x + 7 \qquad -8y = -4x + 12$

$y = -2x + \frac{7}{2} \qquad y = \frac{1}{2}x - \frac{3}{2}$

Since the slopes of the lines are opposite reciprocals, the lines are perpendicular.

40. $3x - 5y = 7 \qquad 5y + 3x = 4$

$-5y = -3x + 7 \qquad 5y = -3x + 4$

$y = \frac{3}{5}x - \frac{7}{5} \qquad y = -\frac{3}{5}x + \frac{4}{5}$

Since the slopes of the lines are not equal and are not opposite reciprocals, the lines are neither parallel nor perpendicular.

41. $3x + 5y = 9 \qquad 6x = -10y + 9$

$5y = -3x + 9 \qquad 10y = -6x + 9$

$y = -\frac{3}{5}x + \frac{9}{5} \qquad y = \frac{-6}{10}x + \frac{9}{10}$

$\qquad\qquad\qquad y = -\frac{3}{5}x + \frac{9}{10}$

Since the slopes of the lines are the same and y-intercepts are different, the lines are parallel.

42. $8x + 2y = 10 \qquad x - 7 = 4y$

$2y = -8x + 10 \qquad -4y = -x + 7$

$y = -4x + 5 \qquad y = \frac{1}{4}x - \frac{7}{4}$

Since the slopes of the lines are opposite reciprocals, the lines are perpendicular.

43. $y = \frac{1}{2}x - 2 \quad 2y = 6x + 9$

$$y = 3x + \frac{9}{2}$$

Since the slopes of the lines are not equal and are not opposite reciprocals, the lines are neither parallel nor perpendicular.

44. $3y - 4 = -5x$ $\qquad$ $y = -\dfrac{5}{3}x - 3$

$\qquad 3y = -5x + 4$

$\qquad y = -\dfrac{5}{3}x + \dfrac{4}{3}$

Since the slopes of the lines are the same and y-intercepts are different, the lines are parallel.

45. $5y = 2x + 9$ $\qquad$ $-10x = 4y + 11$

$\qquad y = \dfrac{2}{5}x + \dfrac{9}{5}$ $\qquad$ $-4y = 10x + 11$

$\qquad\qquad\qquad\qquad y = -\dfrac{5}{2} - \dfrac{11}{4}$

Since the slopes of the lines are opposite reciprocals, the lines are perpendicular.

46. $3x - 9y = 21$ $\qquad$ $-3x + 9y = 27$

$\qquad -9y = -3x + 21$ $\qquad$ $9y = 3x + 27$

$\qquad y = \dfrac{1}{3}x - \dfrac{7}{3}$ $\qquad$ $y = \dfrac{1}{3}x + 3$

Since the slopes of the lines are the same and y-intercepts are different, the lines are parallel.

47. $3x + 7y = 21$ $\qquad$ $7x + 3y = 21$

$\qquad 7y = -3x + 21$ $\qquad$ $3y = -7x + 21$

$\qquad y = -\dfrac{3}{7}x + 3$ $\qquad$ $y = -\dfrac{7}{3}x + 7$

Since the slopes of the lines are not equal and are not opposite reciprocals, the lines are neither parallel nor perpendicular.

48. $5x - 6y = 18$ $\qquad$ $-6x + 5y = 10$

$\qquad -6y = -5x + 18$ $\qquad$ $5y = 6x + 10$

$\qquad y = \dfrac{5}{6}x - 3$ $\qquad$ $y = \dfrac{6}{5}x + 2$

Since the slopes of the lines are not equal and are not opposite reciprocals, the lines are neither parallel nor perpendicular.

49. $y - 2 = 3(x - 0)$

$\qquad y = 3x + 2$

50. $y - 3 = 2(x - 4)$

$\qquad y - 3 = 2x - 8$

$\qquad y = 2x - 5$

51. $y - 5 = -3\left[x - (-4)\right]$

$\qquad y - 5 = -3(x + 4)$

$\qquad y - 5 = -3x - 12$

$\qquad y = -3x - 7$

52. $y - 0 = -3(x - 2)$

$\qquad y = -3x + 6$

53. $y - (-3) = \dfrac{1}{2}\left[x - (-1)\right]$

$\qquad y + 3 = \dfrac{1}{2}(x + 1)$

$\qquad y + 3 = \dfrac{1}{2}x + \dfrac{1}{2}$

$\qquad y = \dfrac{1}{2}x - \dfrac{5}{2}$

54. $y - (-5) = -\dfrac{2}{3}(x - 4)$

$\qquad y + 5 = -\dfrac{2}{3}x + \dfrac{8}{3}$

$\qquad y = -\dfrac{2}{3}x - \dfrac{7}{3}$

55. $y - 6 = \dfrac{2}{3}(x - 0)$

$\qquad y - 6 = \dfrac{2}{3}x$

$\qquad y = \dfrac{2}{3}x + 6$

56. $y - \left(-\dfrac{2}{5}\right) = \dfrac{1}{9}(x - 0)$

$\qquad y + \dfrac{2}{5} = \dfrac{1}{9}x$

$\qquad y = \dfrac{1}{9}x - \dfrac{2}{5}$

57. $m = \dfrac{4 - (-2)}{-2 - (-4)} = \dfrac{6}{2} = 3$

$\qquad y - (-2) = 3\left[x - (-4)\right]$

$\qquad y + 2 = 3(x + 4)$

$\qquad y + 2 = 3x + 12$

$\qquad y = 3x + 10$

58. $m = \dfrac{3 - 4}{6 - 7} = \dfrac{-1}{-1} = 1$

$\qquad y - 3 = 1(x - 6)$

$\qquad y - 3 = x - 6$

$\qquad y = x - 3$

59. $m = \dfrac{-12-9}{8-(-6)} = \dfrac{-21}{14} = -\dfrac{3}{2}$

$y - 9 = -\dfrac{3}{2}\big(x - (-6)\big)$

$y - 9 = -\dfrac{3}{2}(x + 6)$

$y - 9 = -\dfrac{3}{2}x - 9$

$y = -\dfrac{3}{2}x$

60. $m = \dfrac{5-0}{-3-3} = \dfrac{5}{-6} = -\dfrac{5}{6}$

$y - 0 = -\dfrac{5}{6}(x - 3)$

$y = -\dfrac{5}{6}x + \dfrac{5}{2}$

61. $m = \dfrac{-2-3}{0-10} = \dfrac{-5}{-10} = \dfrac{1}{2}$

$y - 3 = \dfrac{1}{2}(x - 10)$

$y - 3 = \dfrac{1}{2}x - 5$

$y = \dfrac{1}{2}x - 2$

62. $m = \dfrac{-3-(-2)}{5-(-6)} = \dfrac{-1}{11} = -\dfrac{1}{11}$

$y - (-2) = -\dfrac{1}{11}\big[x - (-6)\big]$

$y + 2 = -\dfrac{1}{11}(x + 6)$

$y + 2 = -\dfrac{1}{11}x - \dfrac{6}{11}$

$y = -\dfrac{1}{11}x - \dfrac{28}{11}$

63. $y - (-4.5) = 7.4(x - 0)$

$y + 4.5 = 7.4x$

$y = 7.4x - 4.5$

64. $y - \left(-\dfrac{3}{10}\right) = -\dfrac{7}{8}(x - 0)$

$y + \dfrac{3}{10} = -\dfrac{7}{8}x$

$y = -\dfrac{7}{8}x - \dfrac{3}{10}$

65. a. $y = 5x + 60$

b. $y = 5(30) + 60 = 150 + 60 = \$210$

66. a. $y = -10t - 300$

b. $y = -10(30) - 300$

$= -300 - 300$

$= -600$ feet

67. a. Use the slope-intercept form.

b. Use the point-slope form.

c. Use the point-slope form but first find the slope.

68. a. $20x - 30y = 50$

$-30y = -20x + 50$

$y = \dfrac{-20}{-30}x + \dfrac{50}{-30}$

$y = \dfrac{2}{3}x - \dfrac{5}{3}$

$-20x + 30y = 40$

$30y = 20x + 40$

$y = \dfrac{20}{30}x + \dfrac{40}{30}$

$y = \dfrac{2}{3}x + \dfrac{4}{3}$

Yes, they have the same slope.

b. Yes. They will be parallel because they have the same slope but different *y*-intercepts.

69. a. No. The equations will look different because different points are used.

b. $y - (-4) = 2\big[x - (-5)\big]$

$y + 4 = 2(x + 5)$

c. $y - 12 = 2(x - 3)$

d. $y + 4 = 2(x + 5)$

$y + 4 = 2x + 10$

$y = 2x + 6$

e. $y - 12 = 2(x - 3)$

$y - 12 = 2x - 6$

$y = 2x + 6$

f. Yes

70. a. No. The equations will look different because different points are used.

b. $y - 8 = -3 \left[x - (-1) \right]$
$y - 8 = -3(x+1)$

c. $y - (-1) = -3(x-2)$
$y + 1 = -3(x-2)$

d. $y - 8 = -3(x+1)$
$y - 8 = -3x - 3$
$y = -3x + 5$

e. $y + 1 = -3(x-2)$
$y + 1 = -3x + 6$
$y = -3x + 5$

f. Yes

71. a. Use the points (0, 0) and (200, 293) and substitute into the slope formula.
$m = \dfrac{293 - 0}{200 - 0} = \dfrac{293}{200} \approx 1.465$

b. Using the point-slope formula, the equation of the line is:
$y - y_1 = m(x - x_1)$
$f - 0 = 1.465(m - 0)$
$f = 1.465m$

c. $f = 1.465m$
$f = 1.465(142.7)$
$f \approx 209.06$
The speed was 209.06 feet per second.

d. It is about 150 feet per second.

e. It is about 55 miles per hour.

72. a. Using the slope formula for the points (30, 86) and (10, 50).
$m = \dfrac{50 - 86}{10 - 30} = \dfrac{-36}{-20} = \dfrac{-4 \cdot 9}{-4 \cdot 5} = \dfrac{9}{5}$

b. Using the point-slope formula, the equation of the line is:
$y - y_1 = m(x - x_1)$
$F - 50 = \dfrac{9}{5}(C - 10)$
$5(F - 50) = 5 \cdot \dfrac{9}{5}(C - 10)$
$5F - 250 = 9(C - 10)$
$5F - 250 = 9C - 90$
$5F = 9C + 160$
$F = \dfrac{9}{5}C + 32$

c. Substitute 20 for C into the equation arrived at in b.):
$F = \dfrac{9}{5}C + 32$
$F = \dfrac{9}{5}(20) + 32$
$F = 36 + 32$
$F = 68$
The temperature is 68°F.

d. It is about 38°C.

e. It is about −18°C.

73. First, find the slope of the line $2x + y = 6$.
$2x + y = 6$
$y = -2x + 6$
$m = -2$
Use $m = -2$ and $b = 5$ in the slope-intercept equation.
$y = -2x + 5$

74. Line with points (2, 0) and (0, 3):
$m = \dfrac{3 - 0}{0 - 2} = \dfrac{3}{-2} = -\dfrac{3}{2}$
Line with points (60, 30) and (20, 90):
$m = \dfrac{90 - 30}{20 - 60} = \dfrac{60}{-40} = -\dfrac{3}{2}$
$y - 30 = -\dfrac{3}{2}(x - 60)$
$y - 30 = -\dfrac{3}{2}x + 90$
$y = -\dfrac{3}{2}x + 120$

Yes; Since slopes are the same and the y-intercepts are different, they are parallel.

75. $3x - 4y = 6$

$$4y = 3x - 6$$

$$y = \frac{3}{4}x - \frac{3}{2}$$

$$m = \frac{3}{4}$$

$$y - (-1) = \frac{3}{4}\left[x - (-8)\right]$$

$$y + 1 = \frac{3}{4}(x + 8)$$

$$y + 1 = \frac{3}{4}x + 6$$

$$y = \frac{3}{4}x + 5$$

76. $y = x - 3$

77. a. $-3x + 2y = 4$

$$2y = 3x + 4$$

$$y = \frac{3}{2}x + 2$$

Let $x = -2$; $y = \frac{3}{2}(-2) + 2 = -1$

Let $x = 0$; $y = \frac{3}{2}(0) + 2 = 2$

Let $x = 2$; $y = \frac{3}{2}(2) + 2 = 5$

b. x-intercept:

$$-3x + 2(0) = 4$$

$$-3x = 4$$

$$x = -\frac{4}{3}$$

y-intercept:

$$-3(0) + 2y = 4$$

$$2y = 4$$

$$y = 2$$

The points $\left(-\frac{4}{3}, 0\right)$ and $(0, 2)$ are on the graph.

c. $m = \frac{3}{2}$; y-intercept = 2

The points $(0, 2)$ and $(0 + 2, 2 + 3) = (2, 5)$ are on the graph.

d.

78. $|-4| < |-9|$ because $4 < 9$.

79. True; the product of two numbers with like signs is a positive number.

80. True; the sum of two negative numbers is a negative number.

81. False; the sum has the sign of the number with the larger absolute value.

82. False; the quotient of two numbers with like signs is a positive number.

83. $4^3 = 4 \cdot 4 \cdot 4 = 16 \cdot 4 = 64$

84. $i = prt$

$$\frac{i}{pt} = \frac{prt}{pt}$$

$$\frac{i}{pt} = r$$

Chapter 4 Review Exercises

1.

2.

The points are not collinear.

3. a.
$$2x + 3y = 9$$
$$2(5) + 3\left(-\frac{1}{3}\right) = 9$$
$$10 - 1 = 9$$
$$9 = 9 \quad \text{True}$$

b.
$$2x + 3y = 9$$
$$2(3) + 3(1) = 9$$
$$9 = 9 \quad \text{True}$$

c.
$$2x + 3y = 9$$
$$2(-2) + 3(4) = 9$$
$$8 = 9 \quad \text{False}$$

d.
$$2x + 3y = 9$$
$$2(2) + 3\left(\frac{5}{3}\right) = 9$$
$$9 = 9 \quad \text{True}$$

4. a.
$$3x - 2y = 8$$
$$3(2) - 2y = 8$$
$$-2y = 2$$
$$y = -1$$

b.
$$3x - 2y = 8$$
$$3(0) - 2y = 8$$
$$-2y = 8$$
$$y = -4$$

c.
$$3x - 2y = 8$$
$$3x - 2(5) = 8$$
$$3x - 10 = 8$$
$$3x = 18$$
$$x = 6$$

d.
$$3x - 2y = 8$$
$$3x - 2(0) = 8$$
$$3x = 8$$
$$x = \frac{8}{3}$$

5. $y = 4$ is a horizontal line with y-intercept $= (0, 4)$.

6. $x = 2$ is a vertical line with x-intercept $= (2, 0)$.

7. Let $x = -1$, $y = 3(-1) = -3$, $(-1, -3)$
Let $x = 0$, $y = 3 \cdot 0 = 0$, $(0, 0)$
Let $x = 1$, $y = 3 \cdot 1 = 3$, $(1, 3)$

8. Let $x = 0$, $y = 2 \cdot 0 - 1 = -1$, $(0, -1)$
Let $x = 1$, $y = 2 \cdot 1 - 1 = 1$, $(1, 1)$
Let $x = 2$, $y = 2 \cdot 2 - 1 = 3$, $(2, 3)$

9. Let $x = 0$, $y = -2 \cdot 0 + 5 = 5$, $(0, 5)$
Let $x = 1$, $y = -2 \cdot 1 + 5 = 3$, $(1, 3)$
Let $x = 2$, $y = -2 \cdot 2 + 5 = 1$, $(2, 1)$

10. $2y + x = 8$
$$2y = -x + 8$$
$$y = -\frac{1}{2}x + 4$$

Let $x = 0$, $y = -\frac{1}{2}(0) + 4 = 4$, $(0, 4)$

Let $x = 2$, $y = -\frac{1}{2}(2) + 4 = 3$, $(2, 3)$

Let $x = 4$, $y = -\frac{1}{2}(4) + 4 = 2$, $(4, 2)$

11. Let $x = 0$ Let $y = 0$

$$-2x + 3y = 6 \quad\quad -2x + 3y = 6$$
$$-2 \cdot 0 + 3y = 6 \quad -2x + 3 \cdot 0 = 6$$
$$3y = 6 \quad\quad\quad -2x = 6$$
$$y = 2 \quad\quad\quad\quad x = -3$$

12. Let $x = 0$ Let $y = 0$

$$5x + 2y = -10 \quad\quad 5x + 2y = -10$$
$$5 \cdot 0 + 2y = -10 \quad 5x + 2 \cdot 0 = -10$$
$$2y = -10 \quad\quad\quad 5x = -10$$
$$y = -5 \quad\quad\quad\quad x = -2$$

13. Let $x = 0$ Let $y = 0$

$$5x + 10y = 20 \quad\quad 5x + 10y = 20$$
$$5 \cdot 0 + 10y = 20 \quad 5x + 10 \cdot 0 = 20$$
$$10y = 20 \quad\quad\quad 5x = 20$$
$$y = 2 \quad\quad\quad\quad x = 4$$

14. Let $x = 0$ Let $y = 0$

$$\frac{2}{3}x = \frac{1}{4}y + 20 \quad\quad \frac{2}{3}x = \frac{1}{4}y + 20$$
$$\frac{2}{3} \cdot 0 = \frac{1}{4}y + 20 \quad \frac{2}{3}x = \frac{1}{4} \cdot 0 + 20$$
$$0 = \frac{1}{4}y + 20 \quad\quad \frac{2}{3}x = 20$$
$$-\frac{1}{4}y = 20 \quad\quad\quad x = 30$$
$$y = -80$$

15. $m = \dfrac{5 - (-4)}{1 - 6}$

$= \dfrac{9}{-5}$

$= -\dfrac{9}{5}$

16. $m = \dfrac{-7 - (-6)}{8 - (-4)}$

$= \dfrac{-1}{12}$

$= -\dfrac{1}{12}$

17. $m = \dfrac{1 - (-3)}{-4 - (-2)}$

$= \dfrac{4}{-2}$

$= -2$

18. The slope of a horizontal line is 0.

19. The slope of a vertical line is undefined.

20. The slope of a straight line is the ratio of the vertical change to the horizontal change between any two points on the line.

21. $m = \dfrac{-2 - 4}{1 - (-2)} = \dfrac{-6}{3} = -2$

22. $m = \dfrac{2 - 0}{3 - (-5)} = \dfrac{2}{8} = \dfrac{1}{4}$

23. Neither. For the lines to be parallel the slopes have to be the same. For the lines to be perpendicular the slopes have to be opposite reciprocals.

24. Perpendicular, because the slopes are opposite reciprocals.

25. a. $m = \dfrac{415 - 201}{1996 - 1995} = \dfrac{214}{1} = 214$

     b. $m = \dfrac{415 - 268}{1996 - 1999} = \dfrac{147}{-3} = -49$

26. $6x + 7y = 21$

$$7y = -6x + 14$$
$$y = -\frac{6}{7}x + \frac{21}{7}$$
$$y = -\frac{6}{7}x + 3$$
$$m = -\frac{6}{7}, \ b = 3$$

The slope is $-\dfrac{6}{7}$; the y-intercept is $(0, 3)$.

27. $2x + 7 = 0$

$2x = -7$

$x = -\dfrac{7}{2}$

This is a vertical line, so the slope is undefined and there is no y-intercept.

28. $4y + 12 = 0$

$4y = -12$

$y = -3$

This is a horizontal line, so the slope is 0 and the y-intercept is $(0, -3)$.

29. $m = \dfrac{3}{1} = 3, b = -3$

$y = 3x - 3$

30. $m = \dfrac{-2}{4} = -\dfrac{1}{2}, b = 2$

$y = -\dfrac{1}{2}x + 2$

31. $y = 2x - 7 \quad 6y = 12x + 18$

$y = 2x + 3$

Since the slopes are the same and the y-intercepts are different, the lines are parallel.

32. $2x - 3y = 15 \qquad 3x + 2y = 12$

$-3y = -2x + 15 \qquad 2y = -3x + 12$

$y = \dfrac{2}{3}x - 5 \qquad y = -\dfrac{3}{2}x + 6$

Since the slopes are opposite reciprocals, the lines are perpendicular.

33. $y - 7 = 3(x - 2)$

$y - 7 = 3x - 6$

$y = 3x + 1$

34. $y - 2 = -\dfrac{2}{3}(x - 3)$

$y - 2 = -\dfrac{2}{3}x + 2$

$y = -\dfrac{2}{3}x + 4$

35. $y - 2 = 0(x - 6)$

$y - 2 = 0$

$y = 2$

36. Lines with undefined slopes are vertical and have the form $x = c$ where c is the value of x for any point on the line.

$x = 4$

37. $m = \dfrac{-3 - 4}{0 - (-2)} = \dfrac{-7}{2} = -\dfrac{7}{2}$

$y - (-3) = -\dfrac{7}{2}[x - 0]$

$y + 3 = -\dfrac{7}{2}x$

$y = -\dfrac{7}{2}x - 3$

38. $m = \dfrac{3 - (-2)}{-5 - (-5)} = \dfrac{5}{0}$ is undefined

Lines with undefined slopes are vertical and have the form $x = c$ where c is the value of x for any point on the line.

$x = -5$

Chapter 4 Practice Test

1. A graph is an illustration of the set of points that satisfy an equation.

2. a. IV **b.** II

3. a. $ax + by = c$

b. $y = mx + b$

c. $y - y_1 = m(x - x_1)$

4. a. $3y = 5x - 9$

$3(2) = 5(4) - 9$

$6 = 20 - 9$

$6 = 11 \qquad$ False

b. $3y = 5x - 9$

$3(0) = 5\left(\dfrac{9}{5}\right) - 9$

$0 = 9 - 9$

$0 = 0 \qquad$ True

c. $3y = 5x - 9$

$3(-10) = 5(-1) - 9$

$-30 = -5 - 9$

$-30 = -14 \qquad$ False

d.
$$3y = 5x - 9$$
$$3(-3) = 5(0) - 9$$
$$-9 = -9 \qquad \text{True}$$

$\left(\dfrac{9}{5}, 0\right)$ and $(0, -3)$ satisfy the equation.

5. $m = \dfrac{-3-5}{4-(-2)} = \dfrac{-8}{6} = -\dfrac{4}{3}$

6. $4x - 9y = 15$
$$-9y = -4x + 15$$
$$y = \dfrac{4}{9}x - \dfrac{5}{3}$$
$$m = \dfrac{4}{9}, \; b = -\dfrac{5}{3}$$

The slope is $\dfrac{4}{9}$; the *y*-intercept is $\left(0, -\dfrac{5}{3}\right)$.

7. $m = \dfrac{-1}{1} = -1$, $b = -1$
$$y = -x - 1$$

8. $x = -4$ is a vertical line with *x*-intercept $= (-4, 0)$.

9. $y = 2$ is a horizontal line with *y*-intercept $= (0, 2)$.

10. Let $x = 0$, $y = 3 \cdot 0 - 2 = -2$, $(0, -2)$
Let $x = 1$, $y = 3 \cdot 1 - 2 = 1$, $(1, 1)$
Let $x = 2$, $y = 3 \cdot 2 - 2 = 4$, $(2, 4)$

11. a. $3x - 6y = 12$
$$-6y = -3x + 12$$
$$y = \dfrac{1}{2}x - 2$$

b. Let $x = 0$, $y = \dfrac{1}{2}(0) - 2 = -2$, $(0, -2)$

Let $x = 2$, $y = \dfrac{1}{2}(2) - 2 = -1$, $(2, -1)$

Let $x = 4$, $y = \dfrac{1}{2}(4) - 2 = 0$, $(4, 0)$

12. $3x + 5y = 15$

Let $x = 0$	Let $y = 0$
$3(0) + 5y = 15$	$3x + 5(0) = 15$
$5y = 15$	$3x = 15$
$y = 3$	$x = 5$

13. $y - (-5) = 4(x - 2)$
$$y + 5 = 4x - 8$$
$$y = 4x - 13$$

14. $m = \dfrac{2 - (-1)}{-4 - 3} = \dfrac{3}{-7} = -\dfrac{3}{7}$

$$y - (-1) = -\dfrac{3}{7}(x - 3)$$
$$y + 1 = -\dfrac{3}{7}x + \dfrac{9}{7}$$
$$y = -\dfrac{3}{7}x + \dfrac{2}{7}$$

15. $2y = 3x - 6 \qquad y - \dfrac{3}{2}x = -5$

$\qquad y = \dfrac{3}{2}x - 3 \qquad\qquad y = \dfrac{3}{2}x - 5$

The lines are parallel since they have the same slope but different *y*-intercepts.

16. slope = 3, y-intercept is (0, –4).

17. $4x - 2y = 6$

$$-2y = -4x + 6$$
$$y = 2x - 3$$

Slope = 2, y intercept is (0, –3).

18. a.

    b. $450

Chapter 4 Cumulative Review Test

1. a. {1, 2, 3, ...}

    b. {0, 1, 2, 3, ...}

2. $4 - 9 - (-10) + 13 = 4 - 9 + 10 + 13$
$$= -5 + 10 + 13$$
$$= 5 + 13$$
$$= 18$$

3. $(8 \div 4)^3 + 9^2 \div 3 = 2^3 + 9^2 \div 3$
$$= 8 + 81 \div 3$$
$$= 8 + 27$$
$$= 35$$

4. $(10 \div 5 \cdot 5 + 5 - 5)^2 = (2 \cdot 5 + 5 - 5)^2$
$$= (10 + 5 - 5)^2$$
$$= (15 - 5)^2$$
$$= 10^2$$
$$= 100$$

5. a. distributive property

    b. commutative property of addition

6. $2x + 5 = 3(x - 5)$
$$2x + 5 = 3x - 15$$
$$-x + 5 = -15$$
$$-x = -20$$
$$x = 20$$

7. $3(x - 1) - (x + 4) = 2x - 7$
$$3x - 3 - x - 4 = 2x - 7$$
$$2x - 7 = 2x - 7$$
$$0 = 0$$

All real numbers are solutions

8. $\dfrac{2}{20} = \dfrac{x}{200}$
$$2(200) = 20x$$
$$400 = 20x$$
$$20 = x$$

9. $\dfrac{3 \text{ cans}}{\$1.50} = \dfrac{8 \text{ cans}}{x \text{ dollars}}$
$$\dfrac{3}{1.50} = \dfrac{8}{x}$$
$$3x = 12$$
$$x = \dfrac{12}{3} = 4$$

8 cans will cost $4.00.

10. $v = lwh$
$$\dfrac{v}{lh} = \dfrac{lwh}{lh}$$
$$\dfrac{v}{lh} = w$$

11. Let n = the number

$$11 + 2n = 19$$

$$11 - 11 + 2n = 19 - 11$$

$$2n = 8$$

$$\frac{2n}{2} = \frac{8}{2}$$

$$n = 4$$

The number is 4.

12. Let x = width of rectangle.

Then $2x + 3$ = length of rectangle.

$$P = 2l + 2w$$

$$36 = 2(2x + 3) + 2x$$

$$36 = 4x + 6 + 2x$$

$$36 = 6x + 6$$

$$30 = 6x$$

$$5 = x$$

The width is 5 feet and the length is

$2(5) + 3 = 13$ feet.

13. Let x = number of hours until the runners are 28 miles apart.

Runner	Rate	Time	Distance
First	6 mph	x	$6x$
Second	8 mph	x	$8x$

(Distance run by first runner) + (Distance run by second runner) = 28 miles

$$6x + 8x = 28$$

$$14x = 28$$

$$x = 2$$

It will take 2 hours.

14. Answers will vary. Some possible answers are $(0, 2)$, $(4, 0)$, $(2, 1)$.

15. Let $x = 0$, $y = f(0) = 3 \cdot 0 - 5 = -5$, $(0, -5)$

Let $x = 1$, $y = f(1) = 3 \cdot 1 - 5 = -2$, $(1, -2)$

Let $x = 2$, $y = f(2) = 3 \cdot 2 - 5 = 1$, $(2, 1)$

16. $6x - 3y = -12$

Let $x = 0$ Let $y = 0$

$6(0) - 3y = -12$ $6x - 3(0) = -12$

$\quad -3y = -12$ $\quad 6x = -12$

$\quad\quad y = 4$ $\quad\quad x = -2$

17. $m = \dfrac{-5 - (-6)}{6 - 5} = \dfrac{1}{1} = 1$

18. Since parallel lines have the same slope, the slope of the line will be -7.

19. Slope $= \dfrac{2}{3}$, y intercept is $(0, -3)$

20. $y - 2 = 3(x - 5)$

Chapter 5

Exercise Set 5.1

1. In the expression t^p, t is the base, p is the exponent.

2. a. $x^m \cdot x^n = x^{m+n}$

   b. Answers will vary. One possible answer is when multiplying terms with like bases, add the exponents.

3. a. $\dfrac{x^m}{x^n} = x^{m-n}$, $x \neq 0$

   b. Answers will vary. One possible answer is that to divide terms with like bases, subtract the exponents.

4. a. $x^0 = 1$, $x \neq 0$

   b. Answers will vary. One possible answer is that for any real number raised to the zero power, the result is 1.

5. a. $\left(x^m\right)^n = x^{m \cdot n}$

   b. Answers will vary. One possible answer is that to raise a power to a power, multiply the powers.

6. a. $\left(\dfrac{ax}{by}\right)^m = \dfrac{a^m x^m}{b^m y^m}$, $b \neq 0$, $y \neq 0$

   b. Answers will vary. One possible answer is that every factor within parentheses must be raised to the power outside the parentheses.

7. $a^2 b^5$

8. $p^3 q^4 r^6$

9. Answers will vary. See #2 and #5 above.

10. $x^0 \neq 1$ when $x = 0$.

11. $x^5 \cdot x^4 = x^{5+4} = x^9$

12. $x^6 \cdot x^1 = x^{6+1} = x^7$

13. $-z^4 \cdot z = -z^{4+1} = -z^5$

14. $x^7 \cdot x^2 = x^{7+2} = x^9$

15. $y^3 \cdot y^2 = y^{3+2} = y^5$

16. $4^2 \cdot 4^3 = 4^{2+3} = 4^5 = 1024$

17. $3^2 \cdot 3^3 = 3^{2+3} = 3^5 = 243$

18. $-x^3 \cdot x^4 = -x^{3+4} = -x^7$

19. $z^3 \cdot z^5 = z^{3+5} = z^8$

20. $2^4 \cdot 2^2 = 2^{4+2} = 2^6 = 64$

21. $\dfrac{6^2}{6} = \dfrac{6^2}{6^1} = 6^{2-1} = 6^1 = 6$

22. $\dfrac{x^4}{x^3} = x^{4-3} = x^1 = x$

23. $\dfrac{x^{10}}{x^3} = x^{10-3} = x^7$

24. $\dfrac{y^9}{y} = \dfrac{y^9}{y^1} = y^{9-1} = y^8$

25. $\dfrac{3^6}{3^2} = 3^{6-2} = 3^4 = 81$

26. $\dfrac{4^5}{4^3} = 4^{5-3} = 4^2 = 16$

27. $\dfrac{y^4}{y^6} = \dfrac{y^4}{y^4 \cdot y^2} = \dfrac{1}{1 \cdot y^2} = \dfrac{1}{y^2}$

28. $\dfrac{a^7}{a^9} = \dfrac{a^7}{a^7 \cdot a^2} = \dfrac{1}{1 \cdot a^2} = \dfrac{1}{a^2}$

29. $\dfrac{c^4}{c^4} = c^{4-4} = c^0 = 1$

30. $\dfrac{5^4}{5^4} = 5^{4-4} = 5^0 = 1$

31. $\dfrac{a^3}{a^9} = \dfrac{a^3}{a^3 \cdot a^6} = \dfrac{1}{1 \cdot a^6} = \dfrac{1}{a^6}$

32. $\dfrac{x^9}{x^{13}} = \dfrac{x^9}{x^9 \cdot x^4} = \dfrac{1}{1 \cdot x^4} = \dfrac{1}{x^4}$

33. $x^0 = 1$

34. $5^0 = 1$

35. $3x^0 = 3 \cdot 1 = 3$

36. $-7x^0 = -7 \cdot 1 = -7$

37. $4(5d)^0 = 4(5^0 d^0) = 4(1 \cdot 1) = 4 \cdot 1 = 4$

38. $-2(8x)^0 = -2(8^0 \cdot x^0) = -2(1 \cdot 1) = -2(1) = -2$

39. $-9(-4x)^0 = -9(-4)^0 \cdot x^0 = -9(1 \cdot 1) = -9(1) = -9$

40. $-(-x)^0 = -(1) = -1$

41. $6x^3 y^2 z^0 = 6x^3 y^2 (1) = 6x^3 y^2$

42. $-5xy^2 z^0 = -5xy^2 (1) = -5xy^2$

43. $-8r(st)^0 = -8rs^0 t^0 = -8r \cdot 1 \cdot 1 = -8r$

44. $-3\left(a^2 b^5 c^3\right)^0 = -3\left(a^{2 \cdot 0}\right)\left(b^{5 \cdot 0}\right)\left(c^{3 \cdot 0}\right)$
$\qquad = -3a^0 b^0 c^0$
$\qquad = -3 \cdot 1 \cdot 1 \cdot 1$
$\qquad = -3$

45. $\left(x^4\right)^2 = x^{4 \cdot 2} = x^8$

46. $\left(a^5\right)^3 = a^{5 \cdot 3} = a^{15}$

47. $\left(x^5\right)^5 = x^{5 \cdot 5} = x^{25}$

48. $\left(y^5\right)^2 = y^{5 \cdot 2} = y^{10}$

49. $\left(x^3\right)^1 = x^{3 \cdot 1} = x^3$

50. $\left(x^6\right)^2 = x^{6 \cdot 2} = x^{12}$

51. $\left(x^4\right)^3 = x^{4 \cdot 3} = x^{12}$

52. $\left(x^5\right)^4 = x^{5 \cdot 4} = x^{20}$

53. $\left(n^6\right)^3 = n^{6 \cdot 3} = n^{18}$

54. $(1.3x)^2 = (1.3)^2 x^2 = 1.69x^2$

55. $\left(-2w^2\right)^3 = (-2)^3 w^{2 \cdot 3} = -8w^6$

56. $(-3x)^2 = (-3)^2 x^2 = 9x^2$

57. $\left(-3x^3\right)^3 = (-3)^3 x^{3 \cdot 3} = -27x^9$

58. $(-xy)^4 = (-1)^4 x^4 y^4 = x^4 y^4$

59. $\left(4x^3 y^2\right)^3 = 4^3 \cdot x^{3 \cdot 3} y^{2 \cdot 3} = 64x^9 y^6$

60. $\left(3a^2 b^4\right)^3 = 3^3 \cdot a^{2 \cdot 3} b^{4 \cdot 3} = 27a^6 b^{12}$

61. $\left(\dfrac{x}{3}\right)^2 = \dfrac{x^2}{3^2} = \dfrac{x^2}{9}$

62. $\left(\dfrac{-2}{x}\right)^3 = \dfrac{(-2)^3}{x^3} = \dfrac{-8}{x^3} = -\dfrac{8}{x^3}$

63. $\left(\dfrac{y}{x}\right)^4 = \dfrac{y^4}{x^4}$

64. $\left(\dfrac{2}{y}\right)^4 = \dfrac{2^4}{y^4} = \dfrac{16}{y^4}$

65. $\left(\dfrac{-6}{x}\right)^3 = \dfrac{(-6)^3}{x^3} = \dfrac{-216}{x^3} = -\dfrac{216}{x^3}$

66. $\left(\dfrac{4m}{n}\right)^3 = \dfrac{4^3 m^3}{n^3} = \dfrac{64m^3}{n^3}$

67. $\left(\dfrac{2x}{y}\right)^3 = \dfrac{2^3 x^3}{y^3} = \dfrac{8x^3}{y^3}$

68. $\left(\dfrac{3s}{t^2}\right)^2 = \dfrac{3^2 \cdot s^2}{t^{2 \cdot 2}} = \dfrac{9s^2}{t^4}$

69. $\left(\dfrac{4p}{5}\right)^2 = \dfrac{4^2 p^2}{5^2} = \dfrac{16p^2}{25}$

70. $\left(\dfrac{2y^3}{x}\right)^4 = \dfrac{2^4 y^{3\cdot 4}}{x^4} = \dfrac{16y^{12}}{x^4}$

71. $\left(\dfrac{3x^4}{y}\right)^3 = \dfrac{3^3 x^{4\cdot 3}}{y^3} = \dfrac{27x^{12}}{y^3}$

72. $\left(\dfrac{-4x^2}{5}\right)^2 = \dfrac{(-4)^2 x^{2\cdot 2}}{5^2} = \dfrac{16x^4}{25}$

73. $\dfrac{a^8 b}{ab^4} = \dfrac{a\cdot a^7\cdot b}{a\cdot b\cdot b^3} = \dfrac{a^7}{b^3}$

74. $\dfrac{x^3 y^5}{x^7 y} = \dfrac{x^3\cdot y\cdot y^4}{x^3\cdot x^4\cdot y} = \dfrac{y^4}{x^4}$

75. $\dfrac{5x^{12} y^2}{10xy^9} = \dfrac{5\cdot x\cdot x^{11}\cdot y^2}{2\cdot 5\cdot x\cdot y^2\cdot y^7} = \dfrac{x^{11}}{2y^7}$

76. $\dfrac{10x^3 y^8}{2xy^{10}} = \dfrac{2\cdot 5\cdot x\cdot x^2\cdot y^8}{2\cdot x\cdot y^8\cdot y^2} = \dfrac{5x^2}{y^2}$

77. $\dfrac{30y^5 z^3}{5yz^6} = \dfrac{5\cdot 6\cdot y\cdot y^4\cdot z^3}{5\cdot y\cdot z^3\cdot z^3} = \dfrac{6y^4}{z^3}$

78. $\dfrac{3ab}{27a^3 b^4} = \dfrac{3\cdot a\cdot b}{3\cdot 9\cdot a\cdot a^2\cdot b\cdot b^3} = \dfrac{1}{9a^2 b^3}$

79. $\dfrac{35x^4 y^9}{15x^9 y^{12}} = \dfrac{5\cdot 7\cdot x^4\cdot y^9}{5\cdot 3\cdot x^4\cdot x^5\cdot y^9\cdot y^3} = \dfrac{7}{3x^5 y^3}$

80. $\dfrac{6m^3 n^9}{9m^7 n^{12}} = \dfrac{3\cdot 2\cdot m^3\cdot n^9}{3\cdot 3\cdot m^3\cdot m^4\cdot n^9\cdot n^3} = \dfrac{2}{3m^4 n^3}$

81. $\dfrac{-36xy^7 z}{12x^4 y^5 z} = -\dfrac{3\cdot 12\cdot x\cdot y^5\cdot y^2\cdot z}{12\cdot x\cdot x^3\cdot y^5\cdot z} = -\dfrac{3y^2}{x^3}$

82. $\dfrac{4x^4 y^7 z^3}{32x^5 y^4 z^9} = \dfrac{4\cdot x^4\cdot y^4\cdot y^3\cdot z^3}{4\cdot 8\cdot x^4\cdot x\cdot y^4\cdot z^3\cdot z^6} = \dfrac{y^3}{8xz^6}$

83. $-\dfrac{6x^2 y^7 z}{3x^5 y^9 z^6} = -\dfrac{2\cdot 3\cdot x^2\cdot y^7\cdot z}{3\cdot x^2\cdot x^3\cdot y^7\cdot y^2\cdot z\cdot z^5} = -\dfrac{2}{x^3 y^2 z^5}$

84. $-\dfrac{25x^4 y^{10}}{30x^3 y^7 z} = -\dfrac{5\cdot 5\cdot x^3\cdot x\cdot y^7\cdot y^3}{6\cdot 5\cdot x^3\cdot y^7\cdot z} = -\dfrac{5xy^3}{6z}$

85. $\left(\dfrac{10x^4}{5x^6}\right)^3 = \left(\dfrac{10}{5}\cdot\dfrac{x^4}{x^6}\right)^3 = \left(\dfrac{2}{x^2}\right)^3 = \dfrac{2^3}{x^{2\cdot 3}} = \dfrac{8}{x^6}$

86. $\left(\dfrac{4x^4}{8x^8}\right)^3 = \left(\dfrac{4}{8}\cdot\dfrac{x^4}{x^8}\right)^3 = \left(\dfrac{1}{2x^4}\right)^3 = \dfrac{1}{2^3 x^{4\cdot 3}} = \dfrac{1}{8x^{12}}$

87. $\left(\dfrac{6y^6}{2y^3}\right)^3 = \left(\dfrac{6}{2}\cdot\dfrac{y^6}{y^3}\right)^3 = (3y^3)^3 = 3^3 y^{3\cdot 3} = 27y^9$

88. $\left(\dfrac{4xy^5}{y}\right)^3 = \left(4x\cdot\dfrac{y^5}{y}\right)^3$

$= (4xy^4)^3$

$= 4^3 x^3 y^{4\cdot 3}$

$= 64x^3 y^{12}$

89. $\left(\dfrac{6a^2 b^4}{3a^2 b^9}\right)^0 = 1$

90. $\left(\dfrac{16y^6}{24y^{10}}\right)^3 = \left(\dfrac{16}{24}\cdot\dfrac{y^6}{y^{10}}\right)^3$

$= \left(\dfrac{2}{3y^4}\right)^3$

$= \dfrac{2^3}{3^3 y^{4\cdot 3}}$

$= \dfrac{8}{27y^{12}}$

91. $\left(\dfrac{x^4 y^3}{x^2 y^5}\right)^2 = \left(\dfrac{x^4}{x^2}\cdot\dfrac{y^3}{y^5}\right)^2 = \left(\dfrac{x^2}{y^2}\right)^2 = \dfrac{x^{2\cdot 2}}{y^{2\cdot 2}} = \dfrac{x^4}{y^4}$

92. $\left(\dfrac{2x^7 y^2}{4xy}\right)^3 = \left(\dfrac{2}{4}\cdot\dfrac{x^7}{x}\cdot\dfrac{y^2}{y}\right)^3$

$= \left(\dfrac{x^6 y}{2}\right)^3$

$= \dfrac{x^{6\cdot 3} y^3}{2^3}$

$= \dfrac{x^{18} y^3}{8}$

93. $\left(\dfrac{9y^2z^7}{18y^9z}\right)^4 = \left(\dfrac{9}{18}\cdot\dfrac{y^2}{y^9}\cdot\dfrac{z^7}{z}\right)^4$

$= \left(\dfrac{z^6}{2y^7}\right)^4$

$= \dfrac{z^{6\cdot4}}{2^4y^{7\cdot4}}$

$= \dfrac{z^{24}}{16y^{28}}$

94. $\left(\dfrac{y^7z^5}{y^8z^4}\right)^{10} = \left(\dfrac{y^7}{y^8}\cdot\dfrac{z^5}{z^4}\right)^{10} = \left(\dfrac{z}{y}\right)^{10} = \dfrac{z^{10}}{y^{10}}$

95. $\left(\dfrac{25s^4t}{5s^6t^4}\right)^3 = \left(\dfrac{25}{5}\cdot\dfrac{s^4}{s^6}\cdot\dfrac{t}{t^4}\right)^3$

$= \left(\dfrac{5}{s^2t^3}\right)^3$

$= \dfrac{5^3}{s^{2\cdot3}\cdot t^{3\cdot3}}$

$= \dfrac{125}{s^6t^9}$

96. $\left(-\dfrac{64xy^6}{32xy^9}\right)^4 = \left(-\dfrac{64}{32}\cdot\dfrac{x}{x}\cdot\dfrac{y^6}{y^9}\right)^4$

$= \left(\dfrac{-2}{y^3}\right)^4$

$= \dfrac{(-2)^4}{y^{3\cdot4}}$

$= \dfrac{16}{y^{12}}$

97. $\left(3xy^4\right)^2 = 3^2x^2y^{4\cdot2} = 9x^2y^8$

98. $\left(4ab^3\right)^3 = 4^3\cdot a^3\cdot b^{3\cdot3} = 64a^3b^9$

99. $\left(5ab^3\right)(b) = 5a\left(b^{3+1}\right) = 5ab^4$

100. $\left(6xy^5\right)\left(3x^2y^4\right) = (6\cdot3)\left(x^{1+2}\right)\left(y^{5+4}\right) = 18x^3y^9$

101. $(-2xy)(3xy) = (-2\cdot3)\left(x^{1+1}\right)\left(y^{1+1}\right) = -6x^2y^2$

102. $\left(-3x^4y^2\right)\left(5x^2y\right) = (-3\cdot5)\left(x^{4+2}\right)\left(y^{2+1}\right) = -15x^6y^3$

103. $\left(5x^2y\right)\left(3xy^5\right) = (5\cdot3)\left(x^{2+1}\right)\left(y^{1+5}\right) = 15x^3y^6$

104. $(-5xy)\left(-2xy^6\right) = (-5\cdot-2)\left(x^{1+1}\right)\left(y^{1+6}\right) = 10x^2y^7$

105. $\left(-3p^2q\right)^2\left(-p^2q\right) = \left[(-3)^2\,p^{2\cdot2}q^2\right]\left(-p^2q\right)$

$= \left(9p^4q^2\right)\left(-p^2q\right)$

$= \left[9(-1)\right]p^{4+2}q^{2+1}$

$= -9p^6q^3$

106. $\left(2c^3d^2\right)^2\left(3cd\right)^0 = (2^2c^{3\cdot2}d^{2\cdot2})(1) = 4c^6d^4$

107. $\left(7r^3s^2\right)^2\left(9r^3s^4\right)^0 = (7^2\cdot r^{3\cdot2}s^{2\cdot2})(1) = 49r^6s^4$

108. $\left(3x^2\right)^4\left(2xy^5\right) = \left(3^4x^{2\cdot4}\right)\left(2xy^5\right)$

$= \left(81x^8\right)\left(2xy^5\right)$

$= (81\cdot2)(x^{8+1})(y^5)$

$= 162x^9y^5$

109. $(-x)^2 = (-x)(-x) = x^2$

110. $\left(2xy^4\right)^3 = 2^3x^3y^{4\cdot3} = 8x^3y^{12}$

111. $\left(\dfrac{x^5y^5}{xy^5}\right)^3 = \left(\dfrac{x^5}{x}\cdot\dfrac{y^5}{y^5}\right)^3$

$= \left(x^4\cdot1\right)^3$

$= \left(x^4\right)^3$

$= x^{4\cdot3}$

$= x^{12}$

112. $\left(2x^2y^5\right)\left(3x^5y^4\right)^3 = \left(2x^2y^5\right)\left(3^3\cdot x^{5\cdot3}y^{4\cdot3}\right)$

$= \left(2x^2y^5\right)\left(27x^{15}y^{12}\right)$

$= (2\cdot27)\left(x^{2+15}\right)\left(y^{5+12}\right)$

$= 54x^{17}y^{17}$

113. $\left(2.5x^3\right)^2 = 2.5^2\cdot x^{3\cdot2} = 6.25x^6$

114. $\left(-3a^2b^3c^4\right)^3 = (-3)^3\cdot a^{2\cdot3}b^{3\cdot3}c^{4\cdot3} = -27a^6b^9c^{12}$

115. $\dfrac{x^9 y^3}{x^2 y^7} = \dfrac{x^9}{x^2} \cdot \dfrac{y^3}{y^7} = \dfrac{x^7}{y^4}$

116. $(xy^4)(xy^4)^3 = (xy^4)^4 = (x^{1\cdot 4} y^{4\cdot 4}) = x^4 y^{16}$

117. $\left(\dfrac{-m^4}{n^3}\right)^3 = \dfrac{(-1)^3 m^{4\cdot 3}}{n^{3\cdot 3}} = -\dfrac{m^{12}}{n^9}$

118. $\left(\dfrac{-12x}{16x^7 y^2}\right)^2 = \left(\dfrac{-12}{16} \cdot \dfrac{x}{x^7} \cdot \dfrac{1}{y^2}\right)^2$

$= \left(\dfrac{-3}{4x^6 y^2}\right)^2$

$= \dfrac{(-3)^2}{4^2 x^{6\cdot 2} y^{2\cdot 2}}$

$= \dfrac{9}{16x^{12} y^4}$

119. $(-6x^3 y^2)^3 = (-6)^3 x^{3\cdot 3} y^{2\cdot 3} = -216 x^9 y^6$

120. $(3x^6 y)^2 (4xy^8) = (3^2 x^{6\cdot 2} y^{2\cdot 1})(4xy^8)$

$= (9x^{12} y^2)(4xy^8)$

$= 9 \cdot 4 x^{12+1} y^{2+8}$

$= 36 x^{13} y^{10}$

121. $(-2x^4 y^2 z)^3 = (-2)^3 x^{4\cdot 3} y^{2\cdot 3} z^{1\cdot 3} = -8 x^{12} y^6 z^3$

122. $\left(\dfrac{z}{4}\right)^3 = \dfrac{z^3}{4^3} = \dfrac{z^3}{64}$

123. $(9r^4 s^5)^3 = 9^3 \cdot r^{4\cdot 3} \cdot s^{5\cdot 3} = 729 r^{12} s^{15}$

124. $(5x^4 z^{10})^2 (2x^2 z^8) = (5^2 x^{4\cdot 2} z^{10\cdot 2})(2x^2 z^8)$

$= (25x^8 z^{20})(2x^2 z^8)$

$= 25 \cdot 2 x^{8+2} z^{20+8}$

$= 50 x^{10} z^{28}$

125. $(4x^2 y)(3xy^2)^3 = (4x^2 y)(3^3 x^3 y^{2\cdot 3})$

$= (4x^2 y)(27 x^3 y^6)$

$= 4 \cdot 27 x^{2+3} y^{1+6}$

$= 108 x^5 y^7$

126. $\dfrac{x^2 y^6}{x^4 y} = \dfrac{x^2}{x^4} \cdot \dfrac{y^6}{y} = \dfrac{y^5}{x^2}$

127. $(7.3x^2 y^4)^2 = 7.3^2 x^{2\cdot 2} y^{4\cdot 2} = 53.29 x^4 y^8$

128. $\left(\dfrac{-3x^3}{4}\right)^3 = \dfrac{(-3)^3 x^{3\cdot 3}}{4^3} = -\dfrac{27x^9}{64}$

129. $(x^7 y^5)(xy^2)^4 = (x^7 y^5)(x^{1\cdot 4} y^{2\cdot 4})$

$= (x^7 y^5)(x^4 y^8)$

$= x^{7+4} y^{5+8}$

$= x^{11} y^{13}$

130. $(4c^3 d^2)(2c^5 d^3)^2 = (4c^3 d^2)(2^2 c^{5\cdot 2} d^{3\cdot 2})$

$= (4c^3 d^2)(4c^{10} d^6)$

$= 4 \cdot 4 c^{3+10} \cdot d^{2+6}$

$= 16 c^{13} d^8$

131. $\left(\dfrac{-x^4 z^7}{x^2 z^5}\right)^4 = \left(-1 \cdot \dfrac{x^4}{x^2} \cdot \dfrac{z^7}{z^5}\right)^4$

$= (-x^2 z^2)^4$

$= (-1)^4 x^{2\cdot 4} z^{2\cdot 4}$

$= x^8 z^8$

132. $(x^4 y^6)^3 (3x^2 y^5) = (x^{4\cdot 3} y^{6\cdot 3})(3x^2 y^5)$

$= (x^{12} y^{18})(3x^2 y^5)$

$= 3 x^{12+2} y^{18+5}$

$= 3 x^{14} y^{23}$

133. $\dfrac{a+b}{b}$ cannot be simplified.

134. $\dfrac{xy}{x} = y$

135. $\dfrac{y^2 + 3}{y}$ cannot be simplified.

136. $\dfrac{a+9}{3}$ cannot be simplified.

137. $\dfrac{6yz^4}{yz^2} = 6y^{1-1} \cdot z^{4-2} = 6z^2$

138. $\dfrac{x}{x+1}$ cannot be simplified.

139. $\dfrac{a^2+b^2}{a^2}$ cannot be simplified.

140. $\dfrac{x^4}{x^2 y} = \dfrac{x^2 \cdot x^2}{x^2 \cdot y} = \dfrac{x^2}{y}$

141. $a^3 b = 2^3 \cdot 5 = 8 \cdot 5 = 40$

142. $xy^2 = (-3)(-4)^2 = -3 \cdot 16 = -48$

143. $(xy)^0 = (-5 \cdot 3)^0 = (-15)^0 = 1$

144. $(xy)^0 = (2 \cdot 4)^0 = 8^0 = 1$

145. The sign will be positive because a negative number with an even number for an exponent will be positive. This is because $(-1)^m = 1$ when m is even.

146. The sign will be negative because a negative number with an odd number for an exponent will be negative. This is because $(-1)^m = -1$ when m is odd.

147. Area $= \text{Length} \cdot \text{Width} = 8x \cdot x = 8x^2$

148. Total Area $= (\text{Area Square 1}) + (\text{Area Square 2})$
$= (\text{Length} \cdot \text{Width}) +$
$(\text{Length} \cdot \text{Width})$
$= (y \cdot y) + (x \cdot x)$
$= y^2 + x^2$
$= x^2 + y^2$

149. Area $= (\text{Area of Top}) + (\text{Area of Middle})$
$+ (\text{Area of Bottom})$
$= (a \cdot b) + (a \cdot a) + (b \cdot b)$
$= ab + a^2 + b^2$

150. Area $= (\text{Area of Shape 1}) + (\text{Area of Shape 2})$
$= x \cdot 3x + x \cdot 2y + xy + xy$
$= 3x^2 + 2xy + 2xy$
$= 3x^2 + 4xy$

151. $(3yz^2)^2 \left(\dfrac{2y^3 z^5}{10y^6 z^4} \right)^0 (4y^2 z^3)^3$
$= (3^2 y^{1 \cdot 2} z^{2 \cdot 2}) \cdot 1 \cdot (4^3 y^{2 \cdot 3} z^{3 \cdot 3})$
$= (9y^2 z^4)(64y^6 z^9)$
$= 9 \cdot 64 y^{2+6} z^{4+9}$
$= 576 y^8 z^{13}$

152. $\left(\dfrac{3x^4 y^5}{6x^6 y^8} \right)^3 \left(\dfrac{9x^7 y^8}{3x^3 y^5} \right)^2$
$= \left(\dfrac{3}{6} \cdot \dfrac{x^4}{x^6} \cdot \dfrac{y^5}{y^8} \right)^3 \left(\dfrac{9}{3} \cdot \dfrac{x^7}{x^3} \cdot \dfrac{y^8}{y^5} \right)^2$
$= \left(\dfrac{1}{2x^2 y^3} \right)^3 \left(\dfrac{3x^4 y^3}{1} \right)^2$
$= \dfrac{1^3}{2^3 x^{2 \cdot 3} y^{3 \cdot 3}} \cdot \dfrac{3^2 x^{4 \cdot 2} y^{3 \cdot 2}}{1^2}$
$= \dfrac{9x^8 y^6}{8x^6 y^9}$
$= \dfrac{9x^2}{8y^3}$

153. a. $\dfrac{3^2}{3^3} = \dfrac{3 \cdot \cancel{3}}{3 \cdot 3 \cdot \cancel{3}} = \dfrac{3}{9} = \dfrac{1}{3}$

    b. $\dfrac{3^2}{3^3} = 3^{2-3} = 3^{-1}$

    c. $\dfrac{1}{3} = 3^{-1}$

    d. $\dfrac{2^3}{2^4} = \dfrac{2 \cdot \cancel{2} \cdot \cancel{2}}{2 \cdot 2 \cdot \cancel{2} \cdot \cancel{2}} = \dfrac{2}{4} = \dfrac{1}{2}$

    $\dfrac{2^3}{2^4} = 2^{3-4} = 2^{-1}$

    $\dfrac{1}{2} = 2^{-1}$

    e. $\dfrac{1}{x^m} = x^{-m}$

154. $3^4 \div 3^3 - (5-8) + 7 = 81 \div 27 - (-3) + 7$
$= 3 - (-3) + 7$
$= 6 + 7$
$= 13$

155. $-4(x-3)+5x-2 = -4x+12+5x-2$
$\qquad\qquad\qquad = -4x+5x+12-2$
$\qquad\qquad\qquad = x+10$

156. $2(x+4)-3 = 5x+4-3x+1$
$\qquad 2x+8-3 = 2x+5$
$\qquad\quad 2x+5 = 2x+5 \quad$ True
All real numbers are solutions to this equation.

157. a. $\qquad P = 2l+2w$
$\qquad 26 = 2(x+5)+2(x)$
$\qquad 26 = 2x+10+2x$
$\qquad 26 = 4x+10$
$\qquad 16 = 4x$
$\qquad\;\, 4 = x$
$\qquad x+5 = 4+5 = 9$
The sides are 4 and 9 inches long.

b. $\qquad P = 2l+2w$
$\qquad P-2l = 2l+2w-2l$
$\qquad P-2l = 2w$
$\qquad \dfrac{P-2l}{2} = w$

Exercise Set 5.2

1. When a variable or number is raised to a negative exponent, the expression may be written as 1 divided by the variable or number raised to that positive exponent.

2. No, it is not simplified because of the negative exponent.
$x^{-2} = \dfrac{1}{x^2}$

3. No, it is not simplified because of the negative exponent.
$x^5 y^{-3} = \dfrac{x^5}{y^3}$

4. The given simplification is not correct since
$a^6 b^{-2} = \dfrac{a^6}{b^2}$.

5. The given simplification is not correct since
$5^{-2} = \dfrac{1}{5^2} = \dfrac{1}{25}$.

6. a. Yes

b. No, it is not simplified because of the negative exponent.
$n^{-5} = \dfrac{1}{n^5}$

c. No, it is not simplified because of the negative exponent.
$\dfrac{a^{-4}}{2} = \dfrac{1}{2a^4}$

d. No, it is not simplified because of the negative exponent.
$\dfrac{x^{-4}}{x^4} = \dfrac{1}{x^4 \cdot x^4} = \dfrac{1}{x^8}$

7. a. The numerator has one term, $x^5 y^2$.

b. The factors of the numerator are x^5 and y^2.

8. a. The numerator has one term, $x^{-4} y^3$.

b. The factors of the numerator are x^{-4} and y^3.

9. The sign of the exponent changes when a factor is moved from the denominator to the numerator of a fraction.

10. The sign of the exponent changes when a factor is moved from the numerator to the denominator of a fraction.

11. $x^{-6} = \dfrac{1}{x^6}$

12. $y^{-5} = \dfrac{1}{y^5}$

13. $5^{-1} = \dfrac{1}{5}$

14. $7^{-2} = \dfrac{1}{7^2} = \dfrac{1}{49}$

15. $\dfrac{1}{x^{-3}} = x^3$

16. $\dfrac{1}{b^{-4}} = b^4$

17. $\dfrac{1}{a^{-1}} = a^1 = a$

18. $\dfrac{1}{y^{-4}} = y^4$

19. $\dfrac{1}{6^{-2}} = 6^2 = 36$

20. $\dfrac{1}{4^{-3}} = 4^3 = 64$

21. $\left(x^{-2}\right)^3 = x^{(-2)(3)} = x^{-6} = \dfrac{1}{x^6}$

22. $\left(m^{-5}\right)^{-2} = m^{(-5)(-2)} = m^{10}$

23. $\left(y^{-5}\right)^4 = y^{(-5)(4)} = y^{-20} = \dfrac{1}{y^{20}}$

24. $\left(a^5\right)^{-4} = a^{5(-4)} = a^{-20} = \dfrac{1}{a^{20}}$

25. $\left(x^4\right)^{-2} = x^{4(-2)} = x^{-8} = \dfrac{1}{x^8}$

26. $\left(x^{-9}\right)^{-2} = x^{(-9)(-2)} = x^{18}$

27. $\left(3^{-2}\right)^{-1} = 3^{(-2)(-1)} = 3^2 = 9$

28. $\left(2^{-3}\right)^2 = 2^{(-3)(2)} = 2^{-6} = \dfrac{1}{2^6} = \dfrac{1}{64}$

29. $y^4 \cdot y^{-2} = y^{4+(-2)} = y^2$

30. $x^{-3} \cdot x^1 = x^{-3+1} = x^{-2} = \dfrac{1}{x^2}$

31. $x^7 \cdot x^{-5} = x^{7+(-5)} = x^2$

32. $d^{-3} \cdot d^{-4} = d^{-3+(-4)} = d^{-7} = \dfrac{1}{d^7}$

33. $3^{-2} \cdot 3^4 = 3^{-2+4} = 3^2 = 9$

34. $6^{-3} \cdot 6^6 = 6^{-3+6} = 6^3 = 216$

35. $\dfrac{r^5}{r^6} = r^{5-6} = r^{-1} = \dfrac{1}{r}$

36. $\dfrac{x^2}{x^{-1}} = x^{2-(-1)} = x^3$

37. $\dfrac{p^0}{p^{-3}} = p^{0-(-3)} = p^3$

38. $\dfrac{x^{-2}}{x^5} = x^{-2-5} = x^{-7} = \dfrac{1}{x^7}$

39. $\dfrac{x^{-7}}{x^{-3}} = x^{-7-(-3)} = x^{-4} = \dfrac{1}{x^4}$

40. $\dfrac{z^{-11}}{z^{-12}} = z^{-11-(-12)} = z^1 = z$

41. $\dfrac{3^2}{3^{-1}} = 3^{2-(-1)} = 3^3 = 27$

42. $\dfrac{4^2}{4^{-1}} = 4^{2-(-1)} = 4^{2+1} = 4^3 = 64$

43. $5^{-3} = \dfrac{1}{5^3} = \dfrac{1}{125}$

44. $x^{-7} = \dfrac{1}{x^7}$

45. $\dfrac{1}{z^{-9}} = z^9$

46. $\dfrac{1}{3^{-3}} = 3^3 = 27$

47. $\left(p^{-4}\right)^{-6} = p^{-4(-6)} = p^{24}$

48. $\left(x^{-3}\right)^{-4} = x^{(-3)(-4)} = x^{12}$

49. $\left(y^{-2}\right)^{-3} = y^{(-2)(-3)} = y^6$

50. $z^9 \cdot z^{-12} = z^{9-12} = z^{-3} = \dfrac{1}{z^3}$

51. $x^3 \cdot x^{-7} = x^{3-7} = x^{-4} = \dfrac{1}{x^4}$

52. $x^{-3} \cdot x^{-5} = x^{-3-5} = x^{-8} = \dfrac{1}{x^8}$

53. $x^{-8} \cdot x^{-7} = x^{-8-7} = x^{-15} = \dfrac{1}{x^{15}}$

54. $8^{-3} \cdot 8^3 = 8^{-3+3} = 8^0 = 1$

55. $-4^{-2} = -\dfrac{1}{4^2} = -\dfrac{1}{16}$

56. $(-4)^{-2} = \dfrac{1}{(-4)^2} = \dfrac{1}{16}$

57. $-(-4)^{-2} = -\dfrac{1}{(-4)^2} = -\dfrac{1}{16}$

58. $-2^{-3} = -\dfrac{1}{2^3} = -\dfrac{1}{8}$

59. $(-2)^{-3} = \dfrac{1}{(-2)^3} = -\dfrac{1}{8}$

60. $-(-2)^{-3} = -\dfrac{1}{(-2)^3} = -\left(-\dfrac{1}{8}\right) = \dfrac{1}{8}$

61. $(-6)^{-2} = \dfrac{1}{(-6)^2} = \dfrac{1}{36}$

62. $-6^{-2} = -\dfrac{1}{6^2} = -\dfrac{1}{36}$

63. $\dfrac{x^{-5}}{x^5} = x^{-5-5} = x^{-10} = \dfrac{1}{x^{10}}$

64. $\dfrac{y^6}{y^{-8}} = y^{6-(-8)} = y^{14}$

65. $\dfrac{n^{-5}}{n^{-7}} = n^{-5-(-7)} = n^2$

66. $\dfrac{3^{-4}}{3} = 3^{-4-1} = 3^{-5} = \dfrac{1}{3^5} = \dfrac{1}{243}$

67. $\dfrac{9^{-3}}{9^{-3}} = 9^{-3-(-3)} = 9^0 = 1$

68. $\left(7q^5 r^2\right)^0 = 1$

69. $\left(2^{-1} + 3^{-1}\right)^0 = 1$

70. $\left(3^{-1} + 4^2\right)^0 = 1$

71. $\dfrac{2}{2^{-5}} = 2^{1-(-5)} = 2^6 = 64$

72. $\left(z^{-5}\right)^{-9} = z^{-5(-9)} = z^{45}$

73. $\left(x^{-4}\right)^{-2} = x^{(-4)(-2)} = x^8$

74. $\left(x^{-7}\right)^0 = 1$

75. $\left(x^0\right)^{-2} = (1)^{-2} = 1$

76. $\left(3^{-2}\right)^{-1} = 3^{(-2)(-1)} = 3^2 = 9$

77. $2^{-3} \cdot 2 = 2^{-3+1} = 2^{-2} = \dfrac{1}{2^2} = \dfrac{1}{4}$

78. $7^5 \cdot 7^{-3} = 7^{5-3} = 7^2 = 49$

79. $7^{-5} \cdot 7^3 = 7^{-5+3} = 7^{-2} = \dfrac{1}{7^2} = \dfrac{1}{49}$

80. $\dfrac{z^{-3}}{z^{-7}} = z^{-3-(-7)} = z^4$

81. $\dfrac{x^{-1}}{x^{-4}} = x^{-1-(-4)} = x^3$

82. $\dfrac{r^6}{r} = r^{6-1} = r^5$

83. $\left(4^2\right)^{-1} = 4^{2(-1)} = 4^{-2} = \dfrac{1}{4^2} = \dfrac{1}{16}$

84. $\left(2^{-2}\right)^{-2} = 2^{(-2)(-2)} = 2^4 = 16$

85. $\dfrac{5}{5^{-2}} = 5^{1-(-2)} = 5^3 = 125$

86. $\dfrac{x^6}{x^7} = x^{6-7} = x^{-1} = \dfrac{1}{x}$

87. $\dfrac{3^{-4}}{3^{-2}} = 3^{-4-(-2)} = 3^{-2} = \dfrac{1}{3^2} = \dfrac{1}{9}$

88. $x^{-10} \cdot x^8 = x^{-10+8} = x^{-2} = \dfrac{1}{x^2}$

89. $\dfrac{8^{-1}}{8^{-1}} = 8^{-1-(-1)} = 8^0 = 1$

90. $2x^{-1}y = 2 \cdot \dfrac{1}{x} \cdot y = \dfrac{2y}{x}$

91. $\left(-6x^2\right)^{-2} = (-6)^{-2} x^{2(-2)}$

$\qquad = (-6)^{-2} x^{-4} = \dfrac{1}{(-6)^2 x^4} = \dfrac{1}{36x^4}$

92. $\left(-3z^3\right)^{-2} = (-3)^{-2} z^{3(-2)}$

$\qquad = (-3)^{-2} z^{-6} = \dfrac{1}{(-3)^2 z^6} = \dfrac{1}{9z^6}$

93. $3x^{-2}y^2 = 3 \cdot \dfrac{1}{x^2} \cdot y^2 = \dfrac{3y^2}{x^2}$

94. $-5x^4 y^{-1} = -5 \cdot x^4 \cdot \dfrac{1}{y} = -\dfrac{5x^4}{y}$

95. $\left(\dfrac{1}{2}\right)^{-2} = \left(\dfrac{2}{1}\right)^2 = 2^2 = 4$

96. $\left(\dfrac{3}{5}\right)^{-2} = \left(\dfrac{5}{3}\right)^2 = \dfrac{5^2}{3^2} = \dfrac{25}{9}$

97. $\left(\dfrac{5}{4}\right)^{-3} = \left(\dfrac{4}{5}\right)^3 = \dfrac{4^3}{5^3} = \dfrac{64}{125}$

98. $\left(\dfrac{3}{5}\right)^{-3} = \left(\dfrac{5}{3}\right)^3 = \dfrac{5^3}{3^3} = \dfrac{125}{27}$

99. $\left(\dfrac{c^4}{d^2}\right)^{-2} = \left(\dfrac{d^2}{c^4}\right)^2 = \dfrac{d^{2\cdot 2}}{c^{4\cdot 2}} = \dfrac{d^4}{c^8}$

100. $\left(\dfrac{x^2}{y}\right)^{-2} = \left(\dfrac{y}{x^2}\right)^2 = \dfrac{y^2}{x^{2\cdot 2}} = \dfrac{y^2}{x^4}$

101. $-\left(\dfrac{r^4}{s}\right)^{-4} = -\left(\dfrac{s}{r^4}\right)^4 = -\dfrac{s^4}{r^{4\cdot 4}} = -\dfrac{s^4}{r^{16}}$

102. $-\left(\dfrac{m^3}{n^4}\right)^{-5} = -\left(\dfrac{n^4}{m^3}\right)^5 = -\dfrac{n^{4\cdot 5}}{m^{3\cdot 5}} = -\dfrac{n^{20}}{m^{15}}$

103. $-7a^{-3}b^{-4} = -7 \cdot \dfrac{1}{a^3} \cdot \dfrac{1}{b^4} = -\dfrac{7}{a^3 b^4}$

104. $\left(3x^2 y^3\right)^{-2} = 3^{-2} x^{2(-2)} y^{3(-2)}$

$\qquad = 3^{-2} x^{-4} y^{-6} = \dfrac{1}{3^2 x^4 y^6} = \dfrac{1}{9x^4 y^6}$

105. $\left(4x^5 y^{-3}\right)^{-3} = 4^{-3} x^{5(-3)} y^{(-3)(-3)}$

$\qquad = 4^{-3} x^{-15} y^9 = \dfrac{y^9}{4^3 x^{15}} = \dfrac{y^9}{64 x^{15}}$

106. $2w\left(3w^{-5}\right) = 2 \cdot 3 \cdot w \cdot w^{-5} = 6w^{-4} = \dfrac{6}{w^4}$

107. $\left(3z^{-4}\right)\left(6z^{-5}\right) = 3 \cdot 6 \cdot z^{-4} \cdot z^{-5} = 18z^{-9} = \dfrac{18}{z^9}$

108. $2x^5\left(3x^{-6}\right) = 2 \cdot 3 \cdot x^5 \cdot x^{-6} = 6x^{-1} = \dfrac{6}{x}$

109. $4x^4\left(-2x^{-4}\right) = 4 \cdot (-2) \cdot x^4 \cdot x^{-4} = -8x^0 = -8$

110. $9x^5\left(-3x^{-7}\right) = -9 \cdot 3 \cdot x^5 \cdot x^{-7} = -27x^{-2} = -\dfrac{27}{x^2}$

111. $\left(4x^2 y\right)\left(3x^3 y^{-1}\right) = 4 \cdot 3 \cdot x^2 \cdot x^3 \cdot y \cdot y^{-1} = 12x^5$

112. $\left(7a^{-6}b^{-1}\right)\left(a^9 b^0\right) = 7 \cdot a^{-6} \cdot a^9 \cdot b^{-1} \cdot b^0$

$\qquad = 7a^3 b^{-1}$

$\qquad = \dfrac{7a^3}{b}$

113. $\left(-5y^2\right)\left(4y^{-3}z^5\right) = -5 \cdot 4 \cdot y^2 \cdot y^{-3} \cdot z^5$

$\qquad = -20y^{-1}z^5$

$\qquad = -\dfrac{20z^5}{y}$

114. $\left(-3y^{-2}\right)\left(5x^{-1}y^3\right) = -3 \cdot 5 \cdot x^{-1} \cdot y^{-2} \cdot y^3$

$\qquad = -15x^{-1}y$

$\qquad = -\dfrac{15y}{x}$

115. $\dfrac{24d^{12}}{3d^8} = \dfrac{24}{3} \cdot d^{12-8} = 8d^4$

116. $\dfrac{8z^{-4}}{32z^{-2}} = \left(\dfrac{8}{32}\right)z^{-4-(-2)} = \left(\dfrac{1}{4}\right)z^{-2} = \dfrac{1}{4z^2}$

117. $\dfrac{36x^{-4}}{9x^{-2}} = \dfrac{36}{4} \cdot \dfrac{x^{-4}}{x^{-2}} = 4 \cdot \dfrac{1}{x^2} = \dfrac{4}{x^2}$

118. $\dfrac{18m^{-3}n^0}{6m^5n^9} = \dfrac{18}{6} \cdot \dfrac{m^{-3}}{m^5} \cdot \dfrac{n^0}{n^9} = 3 \cdot \dfrac{1}{m^8} \cdot \dfrac{1}{n^9} = \dfrac{3}{m^8n^9}$

119. $\dfrac{3x^4y^{-2}}{6y^3} = \dfrac{3}{6} \cdot x^4 \cdot \dfrac{y^{-2}}{y^3} = \dfrac{1}{2} \cdot x^4 \cdot \dfrac{1}{y^5} = \dfrac{x^4}{2y^5}$

120. $\dfrac{16x^{-7}y^{-2}}{4x^5y^2} = \dfrac{16}{4} \cdot \dfrac{x^{-7}}{x^5} \cdot \dfrac{y^{-2}}{y^2} = 4 \cdot \dfrac{1}{x^{12}} \cdot \dfrac{1}{y^4} = \dfrac{4}{x^{12}y^4}$

121. $\dfrac{32x^4y^{-2}}{4x^{-2}y^0} = \left(\dfrac{32}{4}\right)x^{4-(-2)}y^{-2-0} = 8x^6y^{-2} = \dfrac{8x^6}{y^2}$

122. $\dfrac{21x^{-3}z^2}{7xz^{-3}} = \left(\dfrac{21}{7}\right)x^{-3-1}z^{2-(-3)} = 3x^{-4}z^5 = \dfrac{3z^5}{x^4}$

123. $\left(\dfrac{5x^4y^{-7}}{z^3}\right)^{-2} = \left(\dfrac{z^3}{5x^4y^{-7}}\right)^2$

$\qquad = \dfrac{z^{3 \cdot 2}}{5^2 x^{4 \cdot 2}y^{-7 \cdot 2}} = \dfrac{z^6}{25x^8y^{-14}} = \dfrac{y^{14}z^6}{25x^8}$

124. $\left(\dfrac{b^4c^{-2}}{2d^{-3}}\right)^{-1} = \left(\dfrac{2d^{-3}}{b^4c^{-2}}\right)^1 = \dfrac{2d^{-3}}{b^4c^{-2}} = \dfrac{2c^2}{b^4d^3}$

125. $\left(\dfrac{2r^{-5}s^9}{t^{12}}\right)^{-4} = \left(\dfrac{t^{12}}{2r^{-5}s^9}\right)^4$

$\qquad = \dfrac{t^{12 \cdot 4}}{2^4 r^{-5 \cdot 4}s^{9 \cdot 4}}$

$\qquad = \dfrac{t^{48}}{16r^{-20}s^{36}}$

$\qquad = \dfrac{r^{20}t^{48}}{16s^{36}}$

126. $\left(\dfrac{5m^{-1}n^{-3}}{p^2}\right)^{-3} = \left(\dfrac{p^2}{5m^{-1}n^{-3}}\right)^3$

$\qquad = \dfrac{p^{2 \cdot 3}}{5^3 m^{-1 \cdot 3}n^{-3 \cdot 3}}$

$\qquad = \dfrac{p^6}{125m^{-3}n^{-9}}$

$\qquad = \dfrac{m^3n^9p^6}{125}$

127. $\left(\dfrac{x^3y^{-4}z}{y^{-2}}\right)^{-6} = \left(\dfrac{y^{-2}}{x^3y^{-4}z}\right)^6$

$\qquad = \dfrac{y^{-2 \cdot 6}}{x^{3 \cdot 6}y^{-4 \cdot 6}z^6}$

$\qquad = \dfrac{y^{-12}}{x^{18}y^{-24}z^6}$

$\qquad = \dfrac{y^{-12-(-24)}}{x^{18}z^6}$

$\qquad = \dfrac{y^{12}}{x^{18}z^6}$

128. $\left(\dfrac{3p^{-1}q^{-2}r^3}{p^2}\right)^3 = \dfrac{3^3 p^{-1 \cdot 3}q^{-2 \cdot 3}r^{3 \cdot 3}}{p^{2 \cdot 3}}$

$\qquad = \dfrac{27p^{-3}q^{-6}r^9}{p^6}$

$\qquad = 27p^{-3-6}q^{-6}r^9$

$\qquad = 27p^{-9}q^{-6}r^9$

$\qquad = \dfrac{27r^9}{p^9q^6}$

129.
$$\left(\frac{p^6 q^{-3}}{4 p^8}\right)^2 = \left(\frac{p^{6-8} q^{-3}}{4}\right)^2$$
$$= \left(\frac{p^{-2} q^{-3}}{4}\right)^2$$
$$= \frac{p^{-2 \cdot 2} q^{-3 \cdot 2}}{4^2}$$
$$= \frac{p^{-4} q^{-6}}{16}$$
$$= \frac{1}{16 p^4 q^6}$$

130.
$$\left(\frac{x^{12} y^5}{y^{-3} z}\right)^{-4} = \left(\frac{x^{12} y^{5-(-3)}}{z}\right)^{-4}$$
$$= \frac{x^{12 \cdot (-4)} y^{8 \cdot (-4)}}{z^{-4}}$$
$$= \frac{x^{-48} y^{-32}}{z^{-4}}$$
$$= \frac{z^4}{x^{48} y^{32}}$$

131.   **a.**   Yes, $p^{-1} q^{-1} = \frac{1}{p} \cdot \frac{1}{q} = \frac{1}{pq}$.

         b.   No, $p^{-1} + q^{-1} = \frac{1}{p} + \frac{1}{q} \neq \frac{1}{p+q}$.

132.   **a.**   Yes, $\frac{x^{-1} y^2}{z} = \frac{1}{x} \cdot \frac{y^2}{z} = \frac{y^2}{xz}$.

         b.   No, $\frac{x^{-1} + y^2}{z} = \frac{\frac{1}{x} + y^2}{z} \neq \frac{y^2}{x+z}$.

133. $4^2 + 4^{-2} = 16 + \frac{1}{4^2} = 16 + \frac{1}{16} = 16\frac{1}{16}$

134. $3^2 + 3^{-2} = 9 + \frac{1}{3^2} = 9 + \frac{1}{9} = 9\frac{1}{9}$

135. $5^3 + 5^{-3} = 125 + \frac{1}{5^3} = 125 + \frac{1}{125} = 125\frac{1}{125}$

136. $6^{-3} + 6^3 = \frac{1}{6^3} + 216 = \frac{1}{216} + 216 = 216\frac{1}{216}$

137. $5^0 - 3^{-1} = 1 - \frac{1}{3^1} = 1 - \frac{1}{3} = \frac{2}{3}$

138. $4^{-1} - 3^{-1} = \frac{1}{4^1} - \frac{1}{3^1} = \frac{1}{4} - \frac{1}{3} = \frac{3}{12} - \frac{4}{12} = -\frac{1}{12}$

139. $2^{-3} - 2^3 \cdot 2^{-3} = 2^{-3} - 2^{3-3} = \frac{1}{2^3} - 2^0 = \frac{1}{8} - 1 = -\frac{7}{8}$

140. $2 \cdot 4^{-1} + 4 \cdot 3^{-1} = 2\left(\frac{1}{4^1}\right) + 4\left(\frac{1}{3^1}\right)$
$$= 2\left(\frac{1}{4}\right) + 4\left(\frac{1}{3}\right)$$
$$= \frac{2}{4} + \frac{4}{3}$$
$$= \frac{6}{12} + \frac{16}{12}$$
$$= \frac{22}{12}$$
$$= \frac{11}{6}$$

141. $2 \cdot 4^{-1} - 4 \cdot 3^{-1} = 2 \cdot \frac{1}{4} - 4 \cdot \frac{1}{3}$
$$= \frac{2}{4} - \frac{4}{3}$$
$$= \frac{6}{12} - \frac{16}{12}$$
$$= -\frac{10}{12}$$
$$= -\frac{5}{6}$$

142. $2 \cdot 4^{-1} - 3^{-1} = 2 \cdot \frac{1}{4} - \frac{1}{3}$
$$= \frac{2 \cdot 1}{4} - \frac{1}{3}$$
$$= \frac{2}{4} - \frac{1}{3}$$
$$= \frac{6}{12} - \frac{4}{12}$$
$$= \frac{2}{12}$$
$$= \frac{1}{6}$$

143. $3 \cdot 5^0 - 5 \cdot 3^{-2} = 3 \cdot 1 - 5 \cdot \dfrac{1}{3^2}$

$$= 3 - 5 \cdot \dfrac{1}{9}$$

$$= 3 - \dfrac{5}{9}$$

$$= \dfrac{27}{9} - \dfrac{5}{9}$$

$$= \dfrac{22}{9}$$

144. $7 \cdot 2^{-3} - 2 \cdot 4^{-1} = 7 \cdot \dfrac{1}{2^3} - 2 \cdot \dfrac{1}{4}$

$$= 7 \cdot \dfrac{1}{8} - \dfrac{2}{4}$$

$$= \dfrac{7}{8} - \dfrac{2}{4}$$

$$= \dfrac{7}{8} - \dfrac{4}{8}$$

$$= \dfrac{3}{8}$$

145. The missing number is –2 since $3^{-2} = \dfrac{1}{3^2} = \dfrac{1}{9}$.

146. The missing number is –6 since $\dfrac{1}{2^{-6}} = 2^6 = 64$.

147. The missing number is –3 since $\dfrac{1}{6^{-3}} = 6^3 = 216$.

148. The missing number is –4 since $4^{-4} = \dfrac{1}{4^4} = \dfrac{1}{256}$.

149. The missing number is –2 since
$(x^{-2})^{-2} = x^{(-2)(-2)} = x^4$.

150. The missing number is –3 since
$(x^4)^{-3} = x^{4(-3)} = x^{-12} = \dfrac{1}{x^{12}}$ and
$(y^{-3})^{-3} = y^{(-3)(-3)} = y^9$.

151. The missing coefficient is 2 since $2^3 = 8$.
The missing exponent is –3 since
$(x^{-3})^3 = x^{(-3)(3)} = x^{-9} = \dfrac{1}{x^9}$.

152. a. $-a^{-1} = -x$

b. $\dfrac{1}{a^{-1}} = \dfrac{1}{x}$

153. The product rule is $(xy)^m = x^m y^m$, not
$(x+y)^m = x^m + y^m$.

154. a. $\left(\dfrac{3x^2 y^3}{x} \right)^{-2} = \left(3xy^3 \right)^{-2} = \dfrac{1}{\left(3xy^3 \right)^2} = \dfrac{1}{9x^2 y^6}$

b. $\left(\dfrac{3x^2 y^3}{x} \right)^{-2} = \left(\dfrac{3^{-2} x^{2 \cdot (-2)} y^{3 \cdot (-2)}}{x^{-2}} \right)$

$$= \left(\dfrac{3^{-2} x^{-4} y^{-6}}{x^{-2}} \right)$$

$$= 3^{-2} x^{-4 - (-2)} y^{-6}$$

$$= 3^{-2} x^{-2} y^{-6} = \dfrac{1}{9x^2 y^6}$$

c. $\left(\dfrac{3x^2 y^3}{x} \right)^{-2} = \left(\dfrac{x}{3x^2 y^3} \right)^2$

$$= \dfrac{x^2}{3^2 x^{2 \cdot 2} y^{3 \cdot 2}} = \dfrac{x^2}{9x^4 y^6} = \dfrac{1}{9x^2 y^6}$$

d. Answers will vary.

e. Answers will vary.

155. Let x = the number of miles.

$$\dfrac{104 \text{ miles}}{52 \text{ minutes}} = \dfrac{x}{93 \text{ minutes}}$$

$$\dfrac{104}{52} = \dfrac{x}{93}$$

$$52x = 9672$$

$$x = 186$$

It will travel 186 miles.

156. Let x = the first integer.
Then $x + 2$ = the second integer.

$$x + (x + 2) = 190$$

$$x + x + 2 = 190$$

$$2x + 2 = 190$$

$$2x = 188$$

$$x = 94$$

The numbers are 94 and $94 + 2 = 96$.

157. Let w = width of the shed.
Then $2w - 8$ = length of the shed.

$P = 2l + 2w$

$56 = 2(2w - 8) + 2w$

$56 = 4w - 16 + 2w$

$56 = 6w - 16$

$72 = 6w$

$12 = w$

The width is 12 ft and the length is $2(12) - 8 =$ 16 ft.

158. Let x = the amount invested at 3%.
Then $9000 - x$ = the amount invested at 4%.

Principal	Rat	Time	Interest
x	3%	1	$0.03x$
$9000 - x$	4%	1	$0.04(9000 - x)$

$0.03x - 0.04(9000 - x) = 32$

$0.03x - 360 + 0.04x = 32$

$0.07x - 360 = 32$

$0.07x = 392$

$x = 5600$

$5600 was invested at 3% and $9000 - 5600 =$ $3400 invested at 4%.

159. $(6xy^5)(3x^2 y^4) = 6 \cdot 3 \cdot x^1 \cdot x^2 \cdot y^5 \cdot y^4$

$\qquad = 18x^{1+2} y^{5+4}$

$\qquad = 18x^3 y^9$

Exercise Set 5.3

1. A number in scientific notation is written as a number greater than or equal to 1 and less than 10 that is multiplied by some power of 10.

2. a. Answers will vary.

  b. $315,200 = 3.152 \times 10^5$.

3. a. Answers will vary.

  b. $0.0000723 = 7.23 \times 10^{-5}$.

4. Move the decimal point 9 places to the left.

5. Move the decimal point 6 places to the right.

6. The exponent will be negative when the number is less than 1.

7. The exponent will be positive when the number is 10 or greater.

8. The exponent will be positive since $112,546 > 10$.

9. The exponent will be negative since $0.000937 < 1$.

10. $1,000,000 = 1 \times 10^6$

11. $0.000001 = 1 \times 10^{-6}$

12. a. No, in scientific notation, 82.39×10^4 is 8.239×10^5.

  b. No, in scientific notation, 0.083×10^{-5} is 8.3×10^{-7}.

13. $350,000 = 3.5 \times 10^5$

14. $3,610,000 = 3.61 \times 10^6$

15. $7950 = 7.95 \times 10^3$

16. $0.000089 = 8.9 \times 10^{-5}$

17. $0.053 = 5.3 \times 10^{-2}$

18. $19,000 = 1.9 \times 10^4$

19. $.000726 = 7.26 \times 10^{-4}$

20. $0.00000186 = 1.86 \times 10^{-6}$

21. $5,260,000,000 = 5.26 \times 10^9$

22. $0.0075 = 7.5 \times 10^{-3}$

23. $0.00000914 = 9.14 \times 10^{-6}$

24. $74,100 = 7.41 \times 10^4$

25. $220,300 = 2.203 \times 10^5$

26. $0.08 = 8 \times 10^{-2}$

27. $.005104 = 5.104 \times 10^{-3}$

28. $416,000 = 4.16 \times 10^5$

29. $4.3 \times 10^4 = 43,000$

30. $16.3 \times 10^{-4} = 0.00163$

31. $9.32 \times 10^{-6} = 0.00000932$

32. $6.15 \times 10^5 = 615,000$

33. $2.13 \times 10^{-5} = 0.0000213$

34. $7.26 \times 10^{-6} = .00000726$

35. $6.25 \times 10^5 = 625,000$

36. $4.6 \times 10^1 = 46$

37. $9.0 \times 10^6 = 9,000,000$

38. $6.475 \times 10^1 = 64.75$

39. $5.35 \times 10^2 = 535$

40. $3.14 \times 10^{-2} = 0.0314$

41. $7.73 \times 10^{-7} = 0.000000773$

42. $6.201 \times 10^{-4} = 0.0006201$

43. $1.0 \times 10^4 = 10,000$

44. $7.13 \times 10^{-4} = 0.000713$

45. 8 micrometers $= 8 \times 10^{-6} = 0.000008$ meters

46. 29 micrograms $= 29.0 \times 10^{-6} = 0.000029$ gram

47. 125 gigawatts $= 125 \times 10^9 = 125,000,000,000$ watts

48. 8.7 nanoseconds $= 8.7 \times 10^{-9} = 0.0000000087$ seconds

49. 15.3 km $= 15.3 \times 10^3 = 15,300$ meters

50. 80.2 megahertz $= 80.2 \times 10^6 = 80,200,000$ hertz

51. 48.2 mm $= 48.2 \times 10^{-3} = 0.0482$ meters

52. 3.12 mg $= 3.12 \times 10^{-3} = 0.00312$ gram

53. $(2.0 \times 10^2)(3.0 \times 10^5) = (2.0 \times 3.0)(10^2 \times 10^5)$
$$= 6.0 \times 10^7$$
$$= 60,000,000$$

54. $(2.0 \times 10^{-3})(3.0 \times 10^2) = (2.0 \times 3.0)(10^{-3} \times 10^2)$
$$= 6.0 \times 10^{-1}$$
$$= 0.6$$

55. $(2.7 \times 10^{-6})(9.0 \times 10^4) = (2.7 \times 9.0)(10^{-6} \times 10^4)$
$$= 24.3 \times 10^{-2}$$
$$= 0.243$$

56. $(1.3 \times 10^{-8})(1.74 \times 10^6) = (1.3 \times 1.74)(10^{-8} \times 10^6)$
$$= 2.262 \times 10^{-2}$$
$$= 0.02262$$

57. $(1.6 \times 10^{-2})(4.0 \times 10^{-3}) = (1.6 \times 4.0)(10^{-2} \times 10^{-3})$
$$= 6.4 \times 10^{-5}$$
$$= 0.000064$$

58. $(4.0 \times 10^5)(1.2 \times 10^{-4}) = (4.0 \times 1.2)(10^5 \times 10^{-4})$
$$= 4.8 \times 10^1$$
$$= 48$$

59. $\dfrac{3.9 \times 10^{-5}}{3.0 \times 10^{-2}} = \left(\dfrac{3.9}{3.0}\right)\left(\dfrac{10^{-5}}{10^{-2}}\right) = 1.3 \times 10^{-3} = 0.0013$

60. $\dfrac{6.0 \times 10^{-3}}{3.0 \times 10^1} = \left(\dfrac{6.0}{3.0}\right)\left(\dfrac{10^{-3}}{10^1}\right) = 2.0 \times 10^{-4} = 0.0002$

61. $\dfrac{7.5 \times 10^6}{3.0 \times 10^3} = \left(\dfrac{7.5}{3.0}\right)\left(\dfrac{10^6}{10^3}\right) = 2.5 \times 10^3 = 2500$

62. $\dfrac{1.4 \times 10^7}{4.0 \times 10^8} = \left(\dfrac{1.4}{4.0}\right)\left(\dfrac{10^7}{10^8}\right) = 0.35 \times 10^{-1} = 0.035$

63. $\dfrac{2.0 \times 10^4}{8.0 \times 10^{-2}} = \left(\dfrac{2.0}{8.0}\right)\left(\dfrac{10^4}{10^{-2}}\right) = 0.25 \times 10^6 = 250,000$

64. $\dfrac{1.6 \times 10^4}{8.0 \times 10^{-3}} = \left(\dfrac{1.6}{8.0}\right)\left(\dfrac{10^4}{10^{-3}}\right) = 0.2 \times 10^7 = 2,000,000$

65. $(700,000)(6,000,000) = (7 \times 10^5)(6 \times 10^6)$
$$= (7 \times 6)(10^5 \times 10^6)$$
$$= 42 \times 10^{11}$$
$$= 4.2 \times 10^{12}$$

66. $(0.003)(0.00015) = (3 \times 10^{-3})(1.5 \times 10^{-4})$
$$= (3 \times 1.5)(10^{-3} \times 10^{-4})$$
$$= 4.5 \times 10^{-7}$$

67. $(0.0004)(320) = (4 \times 10^{-4})(4.3 \times 10^2)$
$$= (4 \times 3.2)(10^{-4} \times 10^2)$$
$$= 12.8 \times 10^{-2}$$
$$= 1.28 \times 10^{-1}$$

68. $(67,000)(200,000) = (6.7 \times 10^4)(2.0 \times 10^5)$
$$= (6.7 \times 2.0)(10^4 \times 10^5)$$
$$= 13.4 \times 10^9$$
$$= 1.34 \times 10^{10}$$

69. $\dfrac{5,600,000}{8000} = \dfrac{5.6 \times 10^6}{8.0 \times 10^3}$
$$= \left(\dfrac{5.6}{8.0}\right)\left(\dfrac{10^6}{10^3}\right)$$
$$= 0.7 \times 10^3$$
$$= 7.0 \times 10^2$$

70. $\dfrac{0.00004}{200} = \dfrac{4.0 \times 10^{-5}}{2.0 \times 10^2} = \left(\dfrac{4.0}{2.0}\right)\left(\dfrac{10^{-5}}{10^2}\right) = 2.0 \times 10^{-7}$

71. $\dfrac{0.00035}{0.000002} = \dfrac{3.5 \times 10^{-4}}{2.0 \times 10^{-6}} = \left(\dfrac{3.5}{2.0}\right)\left(\dfrac{10^{-4}}{10^{-6}}\right) = 1.75 \times 10^2$

72. $\dfrac{150,000}{0.0005} = \dfrac{1.5 \times 10^5}{5.0 \times 10^{-4}}$
$$= \left(\dfrac{1.5}{5.0}\right)\left(\dfrac{10^5}{10^{-4}}\right)$$
$$= 0.3 \times 10^9$$
$$= 3.0 \times 10^8$$

73. $3.3 \times 10^{-4}, 5.3, 7.3 \times 10^2, 1.75 \times 10^6$

74. $8.3 \times 10^{-4}, 3.2 \times 10^{-1}, 4.6, 4.8 \times 10^5$

75. **a.** $(6.55 \times 10^9) - (2.99 \times 10^8)$
$$= (65.5 \times 10^8) - (2.99 \times 10^8)$$
$$= (65.5 - 2.99) \times 10^8$$
$$= 62.51 \times 10^8$$
$$\approx 6,251,000,000$$
The people that live outside the U.S. total about 6,251,000,000.

b. $\dfrac{6.55 \times 10^9}{2.99 \times 10^8} = \left(\dfrac{6.55}{2.99}\right)\left(\dfrac{10^9}{10^8}\right) \approx 2.19 \times 10 \approx 21.9$

The world is about 21.9 times greater than the U.S. population.

76. **a.** 18 billion $= 18,000,000,000 = 1.8 \times 10^{10}$

b. Distance to moon $= 2.38 \times 10^5$ miles
7 round trips is 14 one-way lengths.
$14(2.38 \times 10^5) = 33.32 \times 10^5 = 3.332 \times 10^6$
The length of the diapers placed end to end is 3.332×10^6 or 3,332,000 miles.

77. Minimum volume
$$= \left(\dfrac{100,000 \text{ ft}^3\text{sec}}{\text{sec}}\right)\left(\dfrac{60 \text{ sec}}{\text{min}}\right)\left(\dfrac{60 \text{ min}}{\text{hr}}\right)(24 \text{ hrs})$$
$$= (1.0 \times 10^5)(6.0 \times 10^1)(6.0 \times 10^1)(2.4 \times 10^1) \text{ ft}^3$$
$$= (1 \times 6 \times 6 \times 2.4)(10^5 \times 10^1 \times 10^1 \times 10^1) \text{ ft}^3$$
$$= 86.4 \times 10^8 \text{ ft}^3$$
$$= 8,640,000,000 \text{ ft}^3$$

78. **a.** $\$5,370,000 = \$5.37 \times 10^6$

b. $\dfrac{5.37 \times 10^6}{366} = \dfrac{5.37 \times 10^6}{3.66 \times 10^2}$
$$= \left(\dfrac{5.37}{3.66}\right)\left(\dfrac{10^6}{10^2}\right)$$
$$\approx 1.4672 \times 10^4$$
$$\approx 14,672$$
Tiger earned approximately \$14,672 daily in 2004.

79. $\left(2\times10^{-6}\right)\times\left(8\times10^{12}\right)=(2\times8)\left(10^{-6}\times10^{12}\right)$
$=16\times10^{6}$
$=1.6\times10^{7}$
It would take 1.6×10^{7} seconds.

80. a. 90% of 1.02×10^{9}
$90\%=0.9=9.0\times10^{-1}$
$\left(9\times10^{-1}\right)\left(1.02\times10^{9}\right)=(9\times1.02)\left(10^{-1}\times10^{9}\right)$
$=9.18\times10^{8}$
$\approx918,000,000$
Yang prints about 918,000,000 fortunes a year.

b. $\dfrac{9.18\times10^{8}}{365}=\dfrac{9.18\times10^{8}}{3.65\times10^{2}}$
$=\left(\dfrac{9.18}{3.65}\right)\left(\dfrac{10^{8}}{10^{2}}\right)$
$=2.515068\times10^{6}$
$\approx2,515,068$
Yang prints about 2,515,068 fortunes a day.

81. a. $\left(6.01\times10^{8}\right)-\left(4.33\times10^{8}\right)=(6.01-4.33)\times10^{8}$
$=1.68\times10^{8}$
Titanic grossed $\$1.68\times10^{8}$ more than *E.T.*

b. $\dfrac{6.01\times10^{8}}{4.33\times10^{8}}=\left(\dfrac{6.01}{4.33}\right)\left(\dfrac{10^{8}}{10^{8}}\right)\approx1.39(1)\approx1.39$
The gross ticket sales of *Titanic* was about 1.39 times greater than *E.T.*

82. a. $\left(5.5\times10^{4}\right)-\left(4.03\times10^{4}\right)=(5.5-4.03)\times10^{4}$
$=1.47\times10^{4}$
$\approx14,700$
There were about 14,700 more cases of melanoma in 2003 than 1997.

b. $\dfrac{5.5\times10^{4}}{4.03\times10^{4}}=\left(\dfrac{5.5}{4.03}\right)\left(\dfrac{10^{4}}{10^{4}}\right)\approx1.36(1)\approx1.36$
There were about 1.36 times greater cases in 2003 than 1997.

83. a. $\left(4.65\times10^{10}\right)-\left(9.9\times10^{9}\right)$
$=\left(46.5\times10^{9}\right)-\left(9.9\times10^{9}\right)$
$=(46.5-9.9)\times10^{9}$
$=36.6\times10^{9}$
$=36,600,000,000$
Bill Gates was $\$36,600,000,000$ richer than Pierre Omidyar.

b. $\dfrac{4.65\times10^{10}}{9.9\times10^{9}}=\left(\dfrac{4.65}{9.9}\right)\left(\dfrac{10^{10}}{10^{9}}\right)\approx0.47\times10\approx4.7$
Bill Gates was worth 4.7 times greater than Pierre Omidyar.

84. $\dfrac{9.3\times10^{7}}{1.86\times10^{5}}=\left(\dfrac{9.3}{1.86}\right)\left(\dfrac{10^{7}}{10^{5}}\right)=5\times10^{2}\approx500$
It takes 500 seconds or $500\div60\approx8.33$ minutes for light from the sun to reach Earth.

85. a. Earth: 5.794×10^{24} metric tons
Moon: 7.34×10^{19} metric tons
Jupiter: 1.899×10^{27} metric tons

b. $\dfrac{5.794\times10^{24}}{7.340\times10^{19}}=\left(\dfrac{5.794}{7.340}\right)\left(\dfrac{10^{24}}{10^{19}}\right)$
$\approx0.789\times10^{5}$
$\approx7.89\times10^{4}$

c. $\dfrac{1.899\times10^{27}}{5.794\times10^{24}}=\left(\dfrac{1.899}{5.794}\right)\left(\dfrac{10^{27}}{10^{24}}\right)$
$\approx0.328\times10^{3}$
$\approx3.28\times10^{2}$

86. 53% of 47,600
$0.53(47,600)=\left(5.3\times10^{-1}\right)\left(4.76\times10^{4}\right)$
$=(5.3\times4.76)\left(10^{-1}\times10^{4}\right)$
$=25.23\times10^{3}$
$=2.523\times10^{4}$
$\approx2.52\times10^{4}$
About 2.52×10^{4} of the missing persons were men.

87. 47% of 2,800,000,000

$$0.47(2,800,000,000) = (4.7 \times 10^{-1})(2.8 \times 10^9)$$
$$= (4.7 \times 2.8)(10^{-1} \times 10^9)$$
$$= 13.16 \times 10^8$$
$$= 1.316 \times 10^9$$

There was $\$1.316 \times 10^9$ revenue from digital products and services.

88. **a.** $418,000 = 4.18 \times 10^5$

b. $26,000 = 2.6 \times 10^4$

c. $(4.18 \times 10^5) - (2.6 \times 10^4)$
$$= (41.8 \times 10^4) - (2.6 \times 10^4)$$
$$= (41.8 - 2.6) \times 10^4$$
$$= 39.2 \times 10^4$$
$$= 3.92 \times 10^5$$

89. **a.** $55 - 59 : 200,000 = 2.0 \times 10^5$
$$20 - 24 : 48,000 = 4.8 \times 10^4$$

b. $(2.0 \times 10^5) + (4.8 \times 10^4)$
$$= (20 \times 10^4) + (4.8 \times 10^4)$$
$$= (20.0 + 4.8) \times 10^4$$
$$= 24.8 \times 10^4$$
$$= 2.48 \times 10^5$$

c. $(2.0 \times 10^5) - (4.8 \times 10^4)$
$$= (20 \times 10^4) - (4.8 \times 10^4)$$
$$= (20.0 - 4.8) \times 10^4$$
$$= 15.2 \times 10^4$$
$$= 1.52 \times 10^5$$

90. $\dfrac{49,000,000}{4} = \dfrac{4.9 \times 10^7}{4}$
$$= \left(\frac{4.9}{4}\right) \times 10^7$$
$$= 1.225 \times 10^7$$

They each earned $\$1.225 \times 10^7$.

91. $10^{-18} = 0.000000000000000001$

Thus, there are 17 zeros after the decimal.

92. **a.** In decimal form, 6.02×10^{23} would contain 24 digits.

b. $\dfrac{6.02 \times 10^{23}}{12} = \dfrac{6.02 \times 10^{23}}{1.2 \times 10^1}$
$$= \left(\frac{6.02}{1.2}\right)\left(\frac{10^{23}}{10^1}\right)$$
$$\approx 5.017 \times 10^{22}$$

93. Answers will vary.

94. 1 nanosecond $= 1 \times 10^{-9}$ second

1 millisecond $= 1 \times 10^{-3}$ second

$$\frac{1 \times 10^{-3}}{1 \times 10^{-9}} = 1 \times 10^{-3-(-9)} = 1 \times 10^6 = 1,000,000$$

A nanosecond is 1,000,000 times smaller than a millisecond.

95. $\dfrac{10^{-12}}{10^{-18}} = 10^{-12-(-18)} = 10^6 = 1,000,000$ times greater

96. Number of seconds in one year
$$= \frac{60 \text{ seconds}}{1 \text{ minute}} \cdot \frac{60 \text{ minutes}}{1 \text{ hour}} \cdot \frac{24 \text{ hours}}{1 \text{ day}} \cdot \frac{365 \text{ days}}{1 \text{ year}}$$
$$= \frac{3600 \text{ seconds}}{1 \text{ hour}} \cdot \frac{8760 \text{ hours}}{1 \text{ year}}$$
$$= \frac{3.6 \times 10^3 \text{ seconds}}{1 \text{ hour}} \cdot \frac{8.760 \times 10^3 \text{ hours}}{1 \text{ year}}$$
$$= \frac{31.536 \times 10^6 \text{ seconds}}{1 \text{ year}}$$
$$= \frac{3.1536 \times 10^7 \text{ seconds}}{1 \text{ year}}$$

Number of miles in a light year
$$\frac{1.86 \times 10^5 \text{ miles}}{1 \text{ second}} \cdot \frac{3.1536 \times 10^7 \text{ seconds}}{1 \text{ year}}$$
$$\approx \frac{5.87 \times 10^{12} \text{ miles}}{1 \text{ year}}$$

There are about 5.87×10^{12} miles in a light year.

97. a. $1,000,000 = 1.0 \times 10^6$

$1,000,000,000 = 1.0 \times 10^9$

$1,000,000,000,000 = 1.0 \times 10^{12}$

b. $\dfrac{1,000,000}{1000} = \dfrac{1.0 \times 10^6}{1.0 \times 10^3}$

$= 1.0\left(\dfrac{10^6}{10^3}\right)$

$= 1.0\left(10^3\right)$

$= 1000$ days

c. $\dfrac{1,000,000,000}{1000} = \dfrac{1.0 \times 10^9}{1.0 \times 10^3}$

$= 1.0\left(\dfrac{10^9}{10^3}\right)$

$= 1.0\left(10^6\right)$

$= 1,000,000$ days

d. $\dfrac{1,000,000,000,000}{1000} = \dfrac{1.0 \times 10^{12}}{1.0 \times 10^3}$

$= 1.0\left(\dfrac{10^{12}}{10^3}\right)$

$= 1.0\left(10^9\right)$

$= 1,000,000,000$ days

e. $\dfrac{1,000,000,000}{1,000,000} = \dfrac{1.0 \times 10^9}{1.0 \times 10^6}$

$= 1.0\left(\dfrac{10^9}{10^6}\right)$

$= 1.0 \times 10^3$

$= 1,000$

It is 1000 times greater.

98. $4x^2 + 3x + \dfrac{x}{2} = 4 \cdot 0^2 + 3 \cdot 0 + \dfrac{0}{2}$

$= 0 + 0 + 0$

$= 0$

99. a. If $-x = -\dfrac{3}{2}$, then $x = \dfrac{3}{2}$.

b. If $5x = 0$, then $x = 0$.

100. $2x - 3(x - 2) = x + 2$

$2x - 3x + 6 = x + 2$

$-x + 6 = x + 2$

$4 = 2x$

$2 = x$

101. $\left(\dfrac{-2x^5 y^7}{8x^8 y^3}\right)^3 = \left(\dfrac{-2}{8} \cdot \dfrac{x^5}{x^8} \cdot \dfrac{y^7}{y^3}\right)^3$

$= \left(\dfrac{-1}{4} \cdot \dfrac{1}{x^3} \cdot y^4\right)^3$

$= \left(-\dfrac{y^4}{4x^3}\right)^3$

$= \dfrac{(-1)^3 y^{4 \cdot 3}}{4^3 x^{3 \cdot 3}}$

$= -\dfrac{y^{12}}{64x^9}$

Mid-Chapter Test: 5.1-5.3

1. $y^{11} \cdot y^2 = y^{11+2} = y^{13}$

2. $\dfrac{x^{13}}{x^{10}} = x^{13-10} = x^3$

3. $\left(-3x^5 y^7\right)\left(-2xy^6\right) = (-3)(-2)x^{5+1}y^{7+6} = 6x^6 y^{13}$

4. $\dfrac{6a^{12}b^8}{9a^7 b^2} = \dfrac{6}{9}a^{12-7}b^{8-2} = \dfrac{2}{3}a^5 b^6 = \dfrac{2a^5 b^6}{3}$

5. $\left(-4x^2 y^4\right)^3 = (-4)^3 x^{2 \cdot 3} y^{4 \cdot 3} = -64x^6 y^{12}$

6. $\left(\dfrac{-5s^4 t^6}{10s^6 t^3}\right)^2 = \left(\dfrac{-5}{10}s^{4-6}t^{6-3}\right)^2$

$= \left(-\dfrac{1}{2}s^{-2}t^3\right)^2$

$= \left(-\dfrac{1}{2}\right)^2 s^{-2 \cdot 2}t^{3 \cdot 2}$

$= \dfrac{t^6}{4s^4}$

7. $\left(7x^9y^5\right)\left(-3xy^4\right)^2 = \left(7x^9y^5\right)\left[\left(-3\right)^2 x^2 y^{4\cdot 2}\right]$

$= \left(7x^9y^5\right)\left(9x^2y^8\right)$

$= \left(7\right)\left(9\right)x^{9+2}y^{5+8}$

$= 63x^{11}y^{13}$

8. $\dfrac{p^{-3}}{p^5} = p^{-3-5} = p^{-8} = \dfrac{1}{p^8}$

9. $x^{-4}\cdot x^{-6} = x^{-4+(-6)} = x^{-10} = \dfrac{1}{x^{10}}$

10. $\left(3^{-1}+5^2\right)^0 = 1$

11. $\left(\dfrac{3}{7}\right)^{-2} = \left(\dfrac{7}{3}\right)^2 = \dfrac{7^2}{3^2} = \dfrac{49}{9}$

12. $\left(8x^{-2}y^5\right)\left(4x^3y^{-6}\right) = \left(8\right)\left(4\right)x^{-2+3}y^{5-6}$

$= 32xy^{-1}$

$= \dfrac{32x}{y}$

13. $\dfrac{6m^{-4}n^{-7}}{2m^0n^{-1}} = \dfrac{6}{2}m^{-4-0}n^{-7-(-1)} = 3m^{-4}n^{-6} = \dfrac{3}{m^4 n^6}$

14. $\left(\dfrac{2x^{-3}y^{-4}}{x^3 yz^{-2}}\right)^{-2} = \left(2x^{-3-3}y^{-4-1}z^2\right)^{-2}$

$= \left(2x^{-6}y^{-5}z^2\right)^{-2}$

$= 2^{-2}x^{-6\cdot(-2)}y^{-5\cdot(-2)}z^{2\cdot(-2)}$

$= \dfrac{1}{4}x^{12}y^{10}z^{-4}$

$= \dfrac{x^{12}y^{10}}{4z^4}$

15. a. Answers will vary.

    b. Answers will vary.

16. 6.54×10^9

17. 0.0000327

18. $18.9\times 10^3 = 18,900$ meters

19. $\left(3.4\times 10^{-6}\right)\left(7.0\times 10^3\right) = \left(3.4\times 7.0\right)\left(10^{-6}\times 10^3\right)$

$= 23.8\times 10^{-6+3}$

$= 23.8\times 10^{-3}$

$= 0.0238$

20. $\dfrac{0.00006}{200} = \dfrac{6\times 10^{-5}}{2\times 10^2} = \dfrac{6}{2}\times 10^{-5-2} = 3\times 10^{-7}$

Exercise Set 5.4

1. A polynomial is an expression containing the sum of a finite number of terms of the form ax^n where a is a real number and n is a whole number.

2. No, it contains a fractional exponent.

3. No, it contains a negative exponent.

4. No, $\dfrac{2}{x}$ is $2x^{-1}$ contains a negative exponent.

5. a. A monomial is a one-termed polynomial.

    b. A binomial is a two-termed polynomial.

    c. A trinomial is a three-termed polynomial.

6. a. The exponent on the variable is the degree of the term.

    b. The degree of the polynomial is the same as the degree of the highest degree term in the polynomial.

7. Answers will vary.

8. Add the exponents on the variables.

9. b) and c). If you add the exponents on the variables, the sum is 4.

10. $\left(3x+2\right)-\left(4x-6\right) = 3x+2-4x+6$

11. Write with exponents on the variable decreasing from left to right.

12. Because the exponent on the variable in a constant term is 0.

13. To add polynomials, combine like terms.

14. a. Answers will vary.

  b. $4x^3 + 5x - 7$ will be rewritten as
  $4x^3 + 0x^2 + 5x - 7$

15. To subtract polynomials, use the distributive property to remove parentheses and then combine like terms.

16. a. Answers will vary.

  b. $\left(3x^2 - 4x + 5\right) - \left(x^2 + 7x - 4\right)$
  $= 3x^2 - 4x + 5 - x^2 - 7x + 4$

17. fifth

18. eleventh

19. eighth

20. fourth

21. third

22. seventh

23. tenth

24. thirteenth

25. ninth

26. twelfth

27. trinomial

28. binomial

29. monomial

30. not a polynomial

31. binomial

32. binomial

33. monomial

34. not a polynomial

35. not a polynomial

36. trinomial

37. polynomial

38. monomial

39. trinomial

40. not a polynomial

41. not a polynomial

42. polynomial

43. Already in descending order, 0 degree

44. $5x + 4$, first

45. $x^2 - 2x - 4$, second

46. Already in descending order, first

47. $3x^2 + x - 8$, second

48. $-3p^3 + 4$, third

49. Already in descending order, first

50. Already in descending order, second

51. Already in descending order, second

52. Already in descending order, 0 degree

53. $4x^3 - 3x^2 + x - 4$, third

54. $-x^3 + 3x + 1$, third

55. $-2x^4 + 3x^2 + 5x - 6$, fourth

56. $2r^4 - 5r^2 - 3r - 6$, fourth

57. $(9x - 2) + (x - 7) = 9x - 2 + x - 7$
$\qquad\qquad\qquad\quad = 9x + x - 2 - 7$
$\qquad\qquad\qquad\quad = 10x - 9$

58. $(5x - 6) + (2x - 3) = 5x - 6 + 2x - 3$
$\qquad\qquad\qquad\quad = 5x + 2x - 6 - 3$
$\qquad\qquad\qquad\quad = 7x - 9$

59. $(-3x + 8) + (2x + 3) = -3x + 8 + 2x + 3$
$\qquad\qquad\qquad\quad = -3x + 2x + 8 + 3$
$\qquad\qquad\qquad\quad = -x + 11$

60. $(-7x - 9) + (-2x + 9) = -7x - 9 - 2x + 9$
$\qquad\qquad\qquad\quad = -7x - 2x - 9 + 9$
$\qquad\qquad\qquad\quad = -9x$

61. $(t+7)+(-3t-8)=t+7-3t-8$
$$=t-3t+7-8$$
$$=-2t-1$$

62. $(4x-3)+(3x-3)=4x-3+3x-3$
$$=4x+3x-3-3$$
$$=7x-6$$

63. $(x^2+2.6x-3)+(4x+3.8)$
$$=x^2+2.6x-3+4x+3.8$$
$$=x^2+2.6x+4x-3+3.8$$
$$=x^2+6.6x+0.8$$

64. $(-4p^2-3p-2)+(-p^2-4)$
$$=-4p^2-3p-2-p^2-4$$
$$=-4p^2-p^2-3p-2-4$$
$$=-5p^2-3p-6$$

65. $(4m-3)+(5m^2-4m+7)$
$$=4m-3+5m^2-4m+7$$
$$=5m^2+4m-4m-3+7$$
$$=5m^2+4$$

66. $(-x^2-2x-4)+(4x^2+3)$
$$=-x^2-2x-4+4x^2+3$$
$$=4x^2-x^2-2x-4+3$$
$$=3x^2-2x-1$$

67. $(2x^2-3x+5)+(-x^2+6x-8)$
$$=2x^2-3x+5-x^2+6x-8$$
$$=2x^2-x^2+6x-3x+5-8$$
$$=x^2+3x-3$$

68. $(x^2-6x+7)+(-x^2+3x+5)$
$$=x^2-6x+7-x^2+3x+5$$
$$=x^2-x^2-6x+3x+7+5$$
$$=-3x+12$$

69. $(-x^2-4x+8)+\left(5x-2x^2+\dfrac{1}{2}\right)$
$$=-x^2-4x+8+5x-2x^2+\dfrac{1}{2}$$
$$=-x^2-2x^2-4x+5x+8+\dfrac{1}{2}$$
$$=-3x^2+x+\dfrac{17}{2}$$

70. $(8x^2+3x-5)+\left(x^2+\dfrac{1}{2}x+2\right)$
$$=8x^2+3x-5+x^2+\dfrac{1}{2}x+2$$
$$=8x^2+x^2+3x+\dfrac{1}{2}x+2-5$$
$$=9x^2+\dfrac{7}{2}x-3$$

71. $(5.2n^2-6n+1.7)+(3n^2+1.2n-2.3)$
$$=5.2n^2-6n+1.7+3n^2+1.2n-2.3$$
$$=5.2n^2+3n^2-6n+1.2n+1.7-2.3$$
$$=8.2n^2-4.8n-0.6$$

72. $(8x^2+4)+(-2.6x^2-5x-2.3)$
$$=8x^2+4-2.6x^2-5x-2.3$$
$$=8x^2-2.6x^2-5x+4-2.3$$
$$=5.4x^2-5x+1.7$$

73. $(-7x^3-3x^2+4)+(4x+5x^3-7)$
$$=-7x^3-3x^2+4+4x+5x^3-7$$
$$=-7x^3+5x^3-3x^2+4x+4-7$$
$$=-2x^3-3x^2+4x-3$$

74. $(6x^3-4x^2-7)+(3x^2+3x-3)$
$$=6x^3-4x^2-7+3x^2+3x-3$$
$$=6x^3+3x^2-4x^2+3x-7-3$$
$$=6x^3-x^2+3x-10$$

75. $(8x^2+2x-y)+(3x^2-9x+5)$
$$=8x^2+2x-y+3x^2-9x+5$$
$$=8x^2+3x^2+2x-9x-y+5$$
$$=11x^2-7x-y+5$$

76. $\left(-7a^2 + 3a - b\right) + \left(4a^2 - 2a - 8\right)$

$= -7a^2 + 3a - b + 4a^2 - 2a - 8$

$= -7a^2 + 4a^2 + 3a - 2a - b - 8$

$= -3a^2 + a - b - 8$

77. $\left(2x^2 y + 2x - 3\right) + \left(3x^2 y - 5x + 5\right)$

$= 2x^2 y + 2x - 3 + 3x^2 y - 5x + 5$

$= 2x^2 y + 3x^2 y + 2x - 5x - 3 + 5$

$= 5x^2 y - 3x + 2$

78. $\left(x^2 y + x - y\right) + \left(2x^2 y + 2x - 6y + 3\right)$

$= x^2 y + x - y + 2x^2 y + 2x - 6y + 3$

$= x^2 y + 2x^2 y + x + 2x - y - 6y + 3$

$= 3x^2 y + 3x - 7y + 3$

79. $\begin{array}{r} 8x - 7 \\ 3x + 4 \\ \hline 11x - 3 \end{array}$

80. $\begin{array}{r} -x + 5 \\ -4x - 5 \\ \hline -5x \end{array}$

81. $\begin{array}{r} 4y^2 - 2y + 4 \\ 3y^2 \quad\;\; + 1 \\ \hline 7y^2 - 2y + 5 \end{array}$

82. $\begin{array}{r} 6m^2 - 2m + 1 \\ -10m^2 \quad\;\; + 8 \\ \hline -4m^2 - 2m + 9 \end{array}$

83. $\begin{array}{r} -x^2 - 3x + 3 \\ 5x^2 + 5x - 7 \\ \hline 4x^2 + 2x - 4 \end{array}$

84. $\begin{array}{r} -2s^2 - s + 5 \\ 3s^2 - 6s \\ \hline s^2 - 7s + 5 \end{array}$

85. $\begin{array}{r} 2x^3 + 3x^2 + 6x \; - 9 \\ -4x^2 \quad\;\; + 7 \\ \hline 2x^3 - \; x^2 + 6x \; - 2 \end{array}$

86. $\begin{array}{r} -3x^3 \quad\quad + 3x + 9 \\ 2x^2 \quad\; - 4 \\ \hline -3x^3 + 2x^2 + 3x + 5 \end{array}$

87. $\begin{array}{r} 4n^3 - 5n^2 + n - 6 \\ -n^3 - 6n^2 - 2n + 8 \\ \hline 3n^3 - 11n^2 - n + 2 \end{array}$

88. $\begin{array}{r} 7x^3 \quad\quad + 5x - 6 \\ 3x^3 - 4x^2 - \; x + 8 \\ \hline 10x^3 - 4x^2 + 4x + 2 \end{array}$

89. $\left(4x - 4\right) - \left(2x + 2\right) = 4x - 4 - 2x - 2$

$= 4x - 2x - 4 - 2$

$= 2x - 6$

90. $\left(6x - 5\right) - \left(2x - 3\right) = 6x - 5 - 2x + 3$

$= 6x - 2x - 5 + 3$

$= 4x - 2$

91. $\left(-2x - 3\right) - \left(-5x - 7\right) = -2x - 3 + 5x + 7$

$= -2x + 5x - 3 + 7$

$= 3x + 4$

92. $\left(10x - 3\right) - \left(-2x + 7\right) = 10x - 3 + 2x - 7$

$= 10x + 2x - 3 - 7$

$= 12x - 10$

93. $\left(-r + 5\right) - \left(2r + 5\right) = -r + 5 - 2r - 5$

$= -r - 2r + 5 - 5$

$= -3r$

94. $\left(4x + 8\right) - \left(3x + 9\right) = 4x + 8 - 3x - 9$

$= 4x - 3x + 8 - 9$

$= x - 1$

95. $\left(-y^2 + 4y - 5.2\right) - \left(5y^2 + 2.1y + 7.5\right)$

$= -y^2 + 4y - 5.2 - 5y^2 - 2.1y - 7.5$

$= -y^2 - 5y^2 + 4y - 2.1y - 5.2 - 7.5$

$= -6y^2 + 1.9y - 12.7$

96. $\left(9x^2 + 7x - 5\right) - \left(3x^2 + 3.5\right)$

$= 9x^2 + 7x - 5 - 3x^2 - 3.5$

$= 9x^2 - 3x^2 + 7x - 5 - 3.5$

$= 6x^2 + 7x - 8.5$

97. $\left(5x^2 - x - 1\right) - \left(-3x^2 - 2x - 5\right)$

$= 5x^2 - x - 1 + 3x^2 + 2x + 5$

$= 5x^2 + 3x^2 - x + 2x - 1 + 5$

$= 8x^2 + x + 4$

98. $\left(-a^2 + 3a + 12\right) - \left(-4a^2 - 3\right)$

$= -a^2 + 4a^2 + 3a + 12 + 3$

$= 3a^2 + 3a + 15$

99. $\left(-4.1n^2 - 3n\right) - \left(2.3n^2 - 9n + 7.6\right)$

$= -4.1n^2 - 3n - 2.3n^2 + 9n - 7.6$

$= -4.1n^2 - 2.3n^2 - 3n + 9n - 7.6$

$= -6.4n^2 + 6n - 7.6$

100. $\left(7x - 0.6\right) - \left(-2x^2 + 4x - 8\right)$

$= 7x - 0.6 + 2x^2 - 4x + 8$

$= 2x^2 + 7x - 4x - 0.6 + 8$

$= 2x^2 + 3x + 7.4$

101. $\left(8x^3 - 2x^2 - 4x + 5\right) - \left(5x^2 + 8\right)$

$= 8x^3 - 2x^2 - 4x + 5 - 5x^2 - 8$

$= 8x^3 - 2x^2 - 5x^2 - 4x - 8 + 5$

$= 8x^3 - 7x^2 - 4x - 3$

102. $\left(9x^3 - \dfrac{1}{5}\right) - \left(x^2 + 5x\right) = 9x^3 - \dfrac{1}{5} - x^2 - 5x$

$= 9x^3 - x^2 - 5x - \dfrac{1}{5}$

103. $\left(2x^3 - 4x^2 + 5x - 7\right) - \left(3x + \dfrac{3}{5}x^2 - 5\right)$

$= 2x^3 - 4x^2 + 5x - 7 - 3x - \dfrac{3}{5}x^2 + 5$

$= 2x^3 - 4x^2 - \dfrac{3}{5}x^2 + 5x - 3x - 7 + 5$

$= 2x^3 - \dfrac{23}{5}x^2 + 2x - 2$

104. $\left(-3x^2 + 4x - 7\right) - \left(x^3 + 4x^2 - \dfrac{3}{4}x\right)$

$= -3x^2 + 4x - 7 - x^3 - 4x^2 + \dfrac{3}{4}x$

$= -x^3 - 3x^2 - 4x^2 + 4x + \dfrac{3}{4}x - 7$

$= -x^3 - 7x^2 + \dfrac{19}{4}x - 7$

105. $\left(8x + 2\right) - \left(7x + 4\right) = 8x + 2 - 7x - 4$

$= 8x - 7x + 2 - 4$

$= x - 2$

106. $\left(-3x - 9\right) - \left(-4x + 7\right) = -3x - 9 + 4x - 7$

$= -3x + 4x - 9 - 7$

$= x - 16$

107. $\left(2x^2 - 4x + 8\right) - \left(5x - 6\right)$

$= 2x^2 - 4x + 8 - 5x + 6$

$= 2x^2 - 4x - 5x + 8 + 6$

$= 2x^2 - 9x + 14$

108. $\left(-x^2 + 3x + 10\right) - \left(3x^2 - 5x - 3\right)$

$= -x^2 + 3x + 10 - 3x^2 + 5x + 3$

$= -x^2 - 3x^2 + 3x + 5x + 10 + 3$

$= -4x^2 + 8x + 13$

109. $\left(-5c^3 - 6c^2 + 7\right) - \left(-2c^2 + 7c - 7\right)$

$= -5c^3 - 6c^2 + 7 + 2c^2 - 7c + 7$

$= -5c^3 - 6c^2 + 2c^2 - 7c + 7 + 7$

$= -5c^3 - 4c^2 - 7c + 14$

110. $\left(3x^3 + 5x^2 + 9x - 7\right) - \left(4x^3 - 6x^2\right)$

$= 3x^3 + 5x^2 + 9x - 7 - 4x^3 + 6x^2$

$= 3x^3 - 4x^3 + 5x^2 + 6x^2 + 9x - 7$

$= -x^3 + 11x^2 + 9x - 7$

111.
$$
\begin{array}{rr}
6x + 5 \quad \text{or} & 6x + 5 \\
\underline{-(3x - 3)} & \underline{-3x + 3} \\
& 3x + 8
\end{array}
$$

112. $\quad 2x-5 \quad$ or $\quad 2x-5$

$\quad \underline{-(6x+8)} \qquad \underline{\;-6x+8}$

$\qquad\qquad\qquad\qquad -4x-13$

113. $\quad 5a^2-13a+19 \quad$ or $\quad 5a^2-13a+19$

$\quad \underline{-(2a^2+\;3a-\;9)} \qquad \underline{-2a^2-\;3a+\;9}$

$\qquad\qquad\qquad\qquad\qquad 3a^2-16a+28$

114. $\quad 8x^2+5x-9 \quad$ or $\quad 8x^2+5x-9$

$\quad \underline{-(4x^2-7x+3)} \qquad \underline{-4x^2+7x-3}$

$\qquad\qquad\qquad\qquad\quad 4x^2+12x-12$

115. $\quad 7x^2-3x-4 \quad$ or $\quad 7x^2-3x-4$

$\quad \underline{-(6x^2\qquad-1)} \qquad \underline{\;-6x^2+0x+1}$

$\qquad\qquad\qquad\qquad\quad x^2-3x-3$

116. $\quad 2n^3-6n+3 \quad$ or $\quad 2n^3-6n+3$

$\quad \underline{-(5n^3+7n-9)} \qquad \underline{-5n^3-7n+9}$

$\qquad\qquad\qquad\qquad\quad -3n^3-13n+12$

117. $\quad x^2+4 \quad$ or $\quad x^2+4$

$\quad \underline{-(5x^2+4)} \qquad \underline{-5x^2-4}$

$\qquad\qquad\qquad\quad -4x^2$

118. $\qquad m-6 \quad$ or $\qquad m-6$

$\quad \underline{-(-5m^2+6m)} \qquad \underline{\;5m^2-6m}$

$\qquad\qquad\qquad\qquad 5m^2-5m-6$

119. $\quad 4x^3-6x^2+7x-9 \quad$ or $\quad 4x^3-6x^2+7x-9$

$\quad \underline{-(x^2+6x-7)} \qquad \underline{\;-x^2-6x+7}$

$\qquad\qquad\qquad\qquad\qquad 4x^3-7x^2+x-2$

120. $\quad -5x^3+4x-12 \quad$ or $\quad -5x^3\qquad+4x-12$

$\quad \underline{-(2x^3+4x^2-9x)} \qquad \underline{-2x^3-4x^2+\;9x}$

$\qquad\qquad\qquad\qquad\qquad -7x^3-4x^2+13x-12$

121 – 124. Answers will vary.

125. Sometimes

126. Sometimes

127. Sometimes

128. Sometimes

129. Answers will vary; one example is: x^4-2x^3+x

130. Answers will vary; one example is: $x^6+x^3+x^2$

131. No, all three terms must have degree 4 or 1.

132. No, all three terms must have degree 5 or 0.

133. $a^2+2ab+b^2$

134. $3x^2+3xy$

135. $4x^2+3xy$

136. $x^2+xz+yz$

---

137. $\left(3x^2-6x+3\right)-\left(2x^2-x-6\right)-\left(x^2+7x-9\right)=3x^2-6x+3-2x^2+x+6-x^2-7x+9$

$\qquad\qquad\qquad\qquad\qquad\qquad\qquad = \left(3x^2-2x^2-x^2\right)+\left(-6x+x-7x\right)+\left(3+6+9\right)$

$\qquad\qquad\qquad\qquad\qquad\qquad\qquad = -12x+18$

138. $3x^2y-6xy-2xy+9xy^2-5xy+3x=3x^2y+\left(-6xy-2xy-5xy\right)+9xy^2+3x$

$\qquad\qquad\qquad\qquad\qquad\qquad\qquad\qquad = 3x^2y-13xy+9xy^2+3x$

139. $4\left(x^2+2x-3\right)-6\left(2-4x-x^2\right)-2x\left(x+2\right)=4x^2+8x-12-12+24x+6x^2-2x^2-4x$

$\qquad\qquad\qquad\qquad\qquad\qquad\qquad\qquad = \left(4x^2+6x^2-2x^2\right)+\left(8x+24x-4x\right)+\left(-12-12\right)$

$\qquad\qquad\qquad\qquad\qquad\qquad\qquad\qquad = 8x^2+28x-24$

140. Answers will vary.

141. $\dfrac{5}{9} = \dfrac{2.5}{x}$

$5x = 2.5(9)$

$5x = 22.5$

$x = 4.5$

142. $n - 5$

143. $3y = 9$

$y = 3$

This equation represents a horizontal line with y-intercept $(0, 3)$.

144. $y = -2x - 4$

This equation represents a line with y-intercept $(0, -4)$ and slope $m = \dfrac{-2}{1}$.

145. $\left(\dfrac{4x^3y^5}{12x^7y^4}\right)^3 = \left(\dfrac{x^{3-7}y^{5-4}}{3x^7}\right)^3$

$= \left(\dfrac{x^{-4}y^1}{3}\right)^3$

$= \left(\dfrac{y^1}{3x^4}\right)^3$

$= \dfrac{y^{1(3)}}{3^3 x^{4(3)}}$

$= \dfrac{y^3}{27x^{12}}$

146. $3.5 \times 10^{-2} = 0.035$

Exercise Set 5.5

1. To multiply two monomials, multiply their coefficients and use the product rule for exponents to determine the exponents on the variables.

2. The distributive property is used when multiplying a monomial by a polynomial.

3. First, Outer, Inner, Last

4. Every term multiplies every other term

5. Yes, FOIL is simply a way to remember the procedure.

6. Because the result, $a^2 - b^2$, is the difference of two squares.

7. $(a+b)^2 = a^2 + 2ab + b^2$

$(a-b)^2 = a^2 - 2ab + b^2$

8. Answers will vary.

9. No, $(x-2)^2 = x^2 - 4x + 4$

10. No, $(x+5)^2 = x^2 + 10x + 25$

11 – 13. Answers will vary.

14. Yes

15. $\left(3x^4\right)\left(-8x^2\right) = 3 \cdot (-8)x^{4+2} = -24x^6$

16. $\left(-7p^5\right)\left(-2p^3\right) = -7 \cdot (-2)p^{5+3} = 14p^8$

17. $5x^3y^5\left(4x^2y\right) = (5 \cdot 4)x^{3+2}y^{5+1} = 20x^5y^6$

18. $-5x^2y^4\left(2x^3y^2\right) = (-5 \cdot 2)x^{2+3}y^{4+2}$

$= (-10)x^5y^6$

$= -10x^5y^6$

19. $4xy^6\left(-7x^2y^9\right) = -28x^{1+2}y^{6+9} = -28x^3y^{15}$

20. $\left(4a^3b^7\right)\left(6a^2b\right) = 4 \cdot 6 \cdot a^{3+2} \cdot b^{7+1} = 24a^5b^8$

21. $9xy^6\left(6x^5y^8\right) = 9 \cdot 6x^{1+5}y^{6+8} = 54x^6y^{14}$

22. $\left(6m^3n^4\right)\left(3n^5\right)=6\cdot3\cdot m^3\cdot n^{4+5}=18m^3n^9$

23. $\left(6x^2y\right)\left(\dfrac{1}{2}x^4\right)=6\cdot\dfrac{1}{2}x^{2+4}y=3x^6y$

24. $\dfrac{3}{4}x\left(8x^2y^3\right)=\dfrac{3}{4}\cdot8x^{1+2}y^3=6x^3y^3$

25. $\left(3.3x^4\right)\left(1.8x^4y^3\right)=\left(3.3\cdot1.8\right)x^{4+4}y^3=5.94x^8y^3$

26. $\left(2.3x^5\right)\left(4.1x^2y^4\right)=\left(2.3\right)\left(4.1\right)x^{5+2}y^4=9.43x^7y^4$

27. $9\left(x-5\right)=\left(9\right)\left(x\right)+\left(9\right)\left(-5\right)=9x-45$

28. $4\left(x+3\right)=\left(4\right)\left(x\right)+4\left(3\right)=4x+12$

29. $-3x\left(2x-2\right)=\left(-3x\right)\left(2x\right)+\left(-3x\right)\left(-2\right)$
$=-6x^2+6x$

30. $-4p\left(-3p+6\right)=\left(-4p\right)\left(-3p\right)+\left(-4p\right)\left(6\right)$
$=12p^2-24p$

31. $-2\left(8y+5\right)=\left(-2\right)\left(8y\right)+\left(-2\right)\left(5\right)=-16y-10$

32. $2x\left(x^2+3x-1\right)=\left(2x\right)\left(x^2\right)+\left(2x\right)\left(3x\right)+\left(2x\right)\left(-1\right)$
$=2x^3+6x^2-2x$

33. $-2x\left(x^2-2x+5\right)$
$=\left(-2x\right)\left(x^2\right)+\left(-2x\right)\left(-2x\right)+\left(-2x\right)\left(5\right)$
$=-2x^3+4x^2-10x$

34. $-6c\left(-3c^2+5c-6\right)$
$=\left(-6c\right)\left(-3c^2\right)+\left(-6c\right)\left(5c\right)+\left(-6c\right)\left(-6\right)$
$=18c^3-30c^2+36c$

35. $5x\left(-4x^2+6x-4\right)$
$=\left(5x\right)\left(-4x^2\right)+\left(5x\right)\left(6x\right)+\left(5x\right)\left(-4\right)$
$=-20x^3+30x^2-20x$

36. $\left(3x^2+x-6\right)x=\left(3x^2\right)\left(x\right)+\left(x\right)\left(x\right)-\left(6\right)\left(x\right)$
$=3x^3+x^2-6x$

37. $0.5x^2\left(x^3-6x^2-1\right)$
$=\left(0.5x^2\right)\left(x^3\right)+\left(0.5x^2\right)\left(-6x^2\right)+\left(0.5x^2\right)\left(-1\right)$
$=0.5x^5-3x^4-0.5x^2$

38. $2.3b^2\left(2b^2-b+3\right)$
$=\left(2.3b^2\right)2b^2+\left(2.3b^2\right)\left(-b\right)+\left(2.3b^2\right)3$
$=4.6b^4-2.3b^3+6.9b^2$

39. $0.3x\left(2xy+5x-6y\right)$
$=\left(0.3x\right)\left(2xy\right)+\left(0.3x\right)\left(5x\right)+\left(0.3x\right)\left(-6y\right)$
$=0.6x^2y+1.5x^2-1.8xy$

40. $-\dfrac{1}{2}x^3\left(2x^2+4x-6y^2\right)$
$=\left(-\dfrac{1}{2}x^3\right)\left(2x^2\right)+\left(-\dfrac{1}{2}x^3\right)\left(4x\right)+\left(-\dfrac{1}{2}x^3\right)\left(-6y^2\right)$
$=-x^5-2x^4+3x^3y^2$

41. $\left(x^2-4y^3-3\right)y^4$
$=\left(x^2\right)\left(y^4\right)+\left(-4y^3\right)\left(y^4\right)+\left(-3\right)\left(y^4\right)$
$=x^2y^4-4y^7-3y^4$

42. $\dfrac{1}{4}y^4\left(y^2-12y+4x\right)$
$=\left(\dfrac{1}{4}y^4\right)\left(y^2\right)+\left(\dfrac{1}{4}y^4\right)\left(-12y\right)+\left(\dfrac{1}{4}y^4\right)\left(4x\right)$
$=\dfrac{1}{4}y^6-3y^5+xy^4$

43. $\left(5x-2\right)\left(x+4\right)$
$=\left(5x\right)\left(x\right)+\left(5x\right)\left(4\right)+\left(-2\right)\left(x\right)+\left(-2\right)\left(4\right)$
$=5x^2+20x-2x-8$
$=5x^2+18x-8$

44. $\left(2x-3\right)\left(x+5\right)$
$=\left(2x\right)\left(x\right)+\left(2x\right)\left(5\right)+\left(-3\right)\left(x\right)+\left(-3\right)\left(5\right)$
$=2x^2+10x-3x-15$
$=2x^2+7x-15$

45. $(2x+5)(3x-6)$

$=(2x)(3x)+(2x)(-6)+(5)(3x)+(5)(-6)$

$=6x^2-12x+15x-30$

$=6x^2+3x-30$

46. $(4a-1)(a+4)$

$=(4a)(a)+(4a)(4)+(-1)(a)+(-1)(4)$

$=4a^2+16a-a-4$

$=4a^2+15a-4$

47. $(2x-4)(2x+4)$

$=(2x)(2x)+(2x)(4)+(-4)(2x)+(-4)(4)$

$=4x^2+8x-8x-16$

$=4x^2-16$

48. $(4+5w)(3+w)$

$=(4)(3)+(4)(w)+(5w)(3)+(5w)(w)$

$=12+4w+15w+5w^2$

$=5w^2+19w+12$

49. $(8-5x)(6+x)$

$=(8)(6)+(8)(x)+(-5x)(6)+(-5x)(x)$

$=48+8x-30x-5x^2$

$=48-22x-5x^2$

$=-5x^2-22x+48$

50. $(-x+3)(2x+5)$

$=(-x)(2x)+(-x)(5)+(3)(2x)+(3)(5)$

$=-2x^2-5x+6x+15$

$=-2x^2+x+15$

51. $(6x-1)(-2x+5)$

$=(6x)(-2x)+(6x)(5)+(-1)(-2x)+(-1)(5)$

$=-12x^2+30x+2x-5$

$=-12x^2+32x-5$

52. $(7n-3)(2n+1)$

$=(7n)(2n)+(7n)(1)+(-3)(2n)+(-3)(1)$

$=14n^2+7n-6n-3$

$=14n^2+n-3$

53. $(x-2)(4x-2)$

$=(x)(4x)+(x)(-2)+(-2)(4x)+(-2)(-2)$

$=4x^2-2x-8x+4$

$=4x^2-10x+4$

54. $(2x+3)(x+5)$

$=(2x)(x)+(2x)(5)+(3)(x)+(3)(5)$

$=2x^2+10x+3x+15$

$=2x^2+13x+15$

55. $(3k-6)(4k-2)$

$=(3k)(4k)+(3k)(-2)+(-6)(4k)+(-6)(-2)$

$=12k^2-6k-24k+12$

$=12k^2-30k+12$

56. $(3d-5)(4d-1)$

$=(3d)(4d)+(3d)(-1)+(-5)(4d)+(-5)(-1)$

$=12d^2-3d-20d+5$

$=12d^2-23d+5$

57. $(x-2)(x+2)$

$=(x)(x)+(x)(2)+(-2)(x)+(-2)(2)$

$=x^2+2x-2x-4$

$=x^2-4$

58. $(3x-8)(2x+3)$

$=(3x)(2x)+(3x)(3)+(-8)(2x)+(-8)(3)$

$=6x^2+9x-16x-24$

$=6x^2-7x-24$

59. $(2x-3)(2x-3)$

$=(2x)(2x)+(2x)(-3)+(-3)(2x)+(-3)(-3)$

$=4x^2-6x-6x+9$

$=4x^2-12x+9$

60. $(7x+3)(2x+4)$

$=(7x)(2x)+(7x)(4)+(3)(2x)+(3)(4)$

$=14x^2+28x+6x+12$

$=14x^2+34x+12$

61. $(6z-4)(7-z)$

$= (6z)(7)+(6z)(-z)+(-4)(7)+(-4)(-z)$

$= 42z-6z^2-28+4z$

$= -6z^2+46z-28$

62. $(6-2m)(5m-3)$

$= 6(5m)+6(-3)+(-2m)(5m)+(-2m)(-3)$

$= 30m-18-10m^2+6m$

$= -10m^2+36m-18$

63. $(9-2x)(7-4x)$

$= (9)(7)+(9)(-4x)+(-2x)(7)+(-2x)(-4x)$

$= 63-36x-14x+8x^2$

$= 8x^2-50x+63$

64. $(2-5x)(7-2x)$

$= (2)(7)+(2)(-2x)+(-5x)(7)+(-5x)(-2x)$

$= 14-4x-35x+10x^2$

$= 10x^2-39x+14$

65. $(x+7)(y-3) = x(y)+(x)(-3)+7(y)+7(-3)$

$= xy-3x+7y-21$

66. $(z+2y)(4z-3)$

$= z(4z)+z(-3)+(2y)(4z)+(2y)(-3)$

$= 4z^2-3z+8yz-6y$

67. $(2x-3y)(3x+2y)$

$= (2x)(3x)+(2x)(2y)+(-3y)(3x)+(-3y)(2y)$

$= 6x^2+4xy-9xy-6y^2$

$= 6x^2-5xy-6y^2$

68. $(2x+3)(2y-5)$

$= (2x)(2y)+(2x)(-5)+3(2y)+3(-5)$

$= 4xy-10x+6y-15$

69. $(9x+y)(4-3x)$

$= (9x)(4)+(9x)(-3x)+y(4)+y(-3x)$

$= 36x-27x^2+4y-3xy$

$= -27x^2-3xy+36x+4y$

70. $(2x-0.1)(x+2.4)$

$= (2x)(x)+(2.4)(2x)-(0.1)(x)-(0.1)(2.4)$

$= 2x^2+4.8x-0.1x-0.24$

$= 2x^2+4.7x-0.24$

71. $(x+0.6)(x+0.3)$

$= x(x)+x(0.3)+(0.6)x+(0.6)(0.3)$

$= x^2+0.3x+0.6x+0.18$

$= x^2+0.9x+0.18$

72. $(3x-6)\left(x+\dfrac{1}{3}\right)$

$= 3x(x)+3x\left(\dfrac{1}{3}\right)+(-6)x+(-6)\left(\dfrac{1}{3}\right)$

$= 3x^2+x-6x-2$

$= 3x^2-5x-2$

73. $(x+4)\left(x-\dfrac{1}{2}\right)$

$= x(x)+x\left(-\dfrac{1}{2}\right)+4(x)+4\left(-\dfrac{1}{2}\right)$

$= x^2-\dfrac{1}{2}x+4x-2$

$= x^2+\dfrac{7}{2}x-2$

74. $(2y-4)\left(\dfrac{1}{2}x-1\right)$

$= (2y)\left(\dfrac{1}{2}x\right)+(2y)(-1)+(-4)\left(\dfrac{1}{2}x\right)+(-4)(-1)$

$= xy-2y-2x+4$

$= xy-2x-2y+4$

75. $(x+6)(x-6) = x^2-6^2 = x^2-36$

76. $(x+3)^2 = \left(x^2\right)+2(x)(3)+(3)^2 = x^2+6x+9$

77. $(3x-8)(3x+8) = (3x)^2-8^2 = 9x^2-64$

78. $(r-4)(r-4) = (r-4)^2$

$= r^2-2(r)(4)+(-4)^2$

$= r^2-8r+16$

79. $(x+y)^2 = (x)^2 + 2(x)(y) + (y)^2$
$= x^2 + 2xy + y^2$

80. $(2x-7)(2x+7) = (2x)^2 - (7)^2 = 4x^2 - 49$

81. $(x-0.2)^2 = (x)^2 - 2(x)(0.2) + (0.2)^2$
$= x^2 - 0.4x + 0.04$

82. $(a+3b)(a-3b) = a^2 - (3b)^2 = a^2 - 9b^2$

83. $(4x+5)(4x+5) = (4x)^2 + 2(4x)(5) + (5)^2$
$= 16x^2 + 40x + 25$

84. $(5x+4)(5x-4) = (5x)^2 - (4)^2 = 25x^2 - 16$

85. $(0.4x+y)^2 = (0.4x)^2 + 2(0.4x)(y) + (y)^2$
$= 0.16x^2 + 0.8xy + y^2$

86. $\left(x-\frac{1}{2}y\right)^2 = (x)^2 - 2(x)\left(\frac{1}{2}y\right) + \left(\frac{1}{2}y\right)^2$
$= x^2 - xy + \frac{1}{4}y^2$

87. $(4c-5d)(4c+5d) = (4c)^2 - (5d)^2 = 16c^2 - 25d^2$

88. $(4+3w)(4-3w) = 4^2 - (3w)^2 = 16 - 9w^2$

89. $(-2x+6)(-2x-6) = (-2x)^2 - 6^2 = 4x^2 - 36$

90. $(-3m+2n)(-3m-2n) = (-3m)^2 - (2n)^2$
$= 9m^2 - 4n^2$

91. $(7s-3t)^2 = (7s)^2 - 2(7s)(3t) + (3t)^2$
$= 49s^2 - 42st + 9t^2$

92. $(7a+2)^2 = (7a)^2 + 2(7a)(2) + 2^2$
$= 49a^2 + 28a + 4$

93. $(4m+3)(4m^2 - 5m + 6)$
$= 4m(4m^2 - 5m + 6) + 3(4m^2 - 5m + 6)$
$= 16m^3 - 20m^2 + 24m + 12m^2 - 15m + 18$
$= 16m^3 - 8m^2 + 9m + 18$

94. $(x+4)(3x^2 + 4x - 1)$
$= x(3x^2 + 4x - 1) + 4(3x^2 + 4x - 1)$
$= 3x^3 + 4x^2 - x + 12x^2 + 16x - 4$
$= 3x^3 + 16x^2 + 15x - 4$

95. $(3x+2)(4x^2 - x + 5)$
$= (3x)(4x^2 - x + 5) + 2(4x^2 - x + 5)$
$= 12x^3 - 3x^2 + 15x + 8x^2 - 2x + 10$
$= 12x^3 + 5x^2 + 13x + 10$

96. $(x-1)(3x^2 + 3x + 2)$
$= x(3x^2 + 3x + 2) - 1(3x^2 + 3x + 2)$
$= 3x^3 + 3x^2 + 2x - 3x^2 - 3x - 2$
$= 3x^3 - x - 2$

97. $(-2x^2 - 4x + 1)(7x - 3)$
$= -2x^2(7x-3) - 4x(7x-3) + 1(7x-3)$
$= -14x^3 + 6x^2 - 28x^2 + 12x + 7x - 3$
$= -14x^3 - 22x^2 + 19x - 3$

98. $(4x^2 + 9x - 2)(x - 2)$
$= 4x^2(x-2) + 9x(x-2) - 2(x-2)$
$= 4x^3 - 8x^2 + 9x^2 - 18x - 2x + 4$
$= 4x^3 + x^2 - 20x + 4$

99. $(a+b)(a^2 - ab + b^2)$
$= a(a^2 - ab + b^2) + b(a^2 - ab + b^2)$
$= a^3 - a^2b + ab^2 + a^2b - ab^2 + b^3$
$= a^3 + b^3$

100. $(a-b)(a^2 + ab + b^2)$
$= a(a^2 + ab + b^2) - b(a^2 + ab + b^2)$
$= a^3 + a^2b + ab^2 - a^2b - ab^2 - b^3$
$= a^3 - b^3$

101. $\left(3x^2 - 2x + 4\right)\left(2x^2 + 3x + 1\right)$

$= 3x^2\left(2x^2 + 3x + 1\right) - 2x\left(2x^2 + 3x + 1\right)$
$\quad + 4\left(2x^2 + 3x + 1\right)$

$= 6x^4 + 9x^3 + 3x^2 - 4x^3 - 6x^2 - 2x$
$\quad + 8x^2 + 12x + 4$

$= 6x^4 + 5x^3 + 5x^2 + 10x + 4$

102. $\left(x^2 - 2x + 3\right)\left(x^2 - 4\right)$

$= x^2\left(x^2 - 4\right) - 2x\left(x^2 - 4\right) + 3\left(x^2 - 4\right)$

$= x^4 - 4x^2 - 2x^3 + 8x + 3x^2 - 12$

$= x^4 - 2x^3 - x^2 + 8x - 12$

103. $\left(x^2 - x + 3\right)\left(x^2 - 2x\right)$

$= x^2\left(x^2 - 2x\right) - x\left(x^2 - 2x\right) + 3\left(x^2 - 2x\right)$

$= x^4 - 2x^3 - x^3 + 2x^2 + 3x^2 - 6x$

$= x^4 - 3x^3 + 5x^2 - 6x$

104. $\left(6x + 4\right)\left(2x^2 + 2x - 4\right)$

$= 6x\left(2x^2 + 2x - 4\right) + 4\left(2x^2 + 2x - 4\right)$

$= 12x^3 + 12x^2 - 24x + 8x^2 + 8x - 16$

$= 12x^3 + 20x^2 - 16x - 16$

105. $\left(2x^3 - 6x^2 + x - 3\right)\left(x^2 + 4x\right)$

$= 2x^3\left(x^2 + 4x\right) - 6x^2\left(x^2 + 4x\right) + x\left(x^2 + 4x\right)$
$\quad - 3\left(x^2 + 4x\right)$

$= 2x^5 + 8x^4 - 6x^4 - 24x^3 + x^3 + 4x^2 - 3x^2 - 12x$

$= 2x^5 + 2x^4 - 23x^3 + x^2 - 12x$

106. $\left(3y^3 + 4y^2 - y + 7\right)\left(y^2 - 5y\right)$

$= 3y^3\left(y^2 - 5y\right) + 4y^2\left(y^2 - 5y\right) - y\left(y^2 - 5y\right)$
$\quad + 7\left(y^2 - 5y\right)$

$= 3y^5 - 15y^4 + 4y^4 - 20y^3 - y^3 + 5y^2 + 7y^2 - 35y$

$= 3y^5 - 11y^4 - 21y^3 + 12y^2 - 35y$

107. $\left(b - 1\right)^3 = \left(b - 1\right)\left(b - 1\right)^2$

$= \left(b - 1\right)\left(b^2 - 2b + 1\right)$

$= b\left(b^2 - 2b + 1\right) - 1\left(b^2 - 2b + 1\right)$

$= b^3 - 2b^2 + b - b^2 + 2b - 1$

$= b^3 - 3b^2 + 3b - 1$

108. $\left(x + 2\right)^3 = \left(x + 2\right)\left(x + 2\right)^2$

$= \left(x + 2\right)\left(x^2 + 4x + 4\right)$

$= x\left(x^2 + 4x + 4\right) + 2\left(x^2 + 4x + 4\right)$

$= x^3 + 4x^2 + 4x + 2x^2 + 8x + 8$

$= x^3 + 6x^2 + 12x + 8$

109. $\left(3a - 5\right)^3$

$= \left(3a - 5\right)\left(3a - 5\right)^2$

$= \left(3a - 5\right)\left(9a^2 - 30a + 25\right)$

$= 3a\left(9a^2 - 30a + 25\right) - 5\left(9a^2 - 30a + 25\right)$

$= 27a^3 - 90a^2 + 75a - 45a^2 + 150a - 125$

$= 27a^3 - 135a^2 + 225a - 125$

110. $\left(2z + 3\right)^3$

$= \left(2z + 3\right)\left(2z + 3\right)^2$

$= \left(2z + 3\right)\left(4z^2 + 12z + 9\right)$

$= 2z\left(4z^2 + 12z + 9\right) + 3\left(4z^2 + 12z + 9\right)$

$= 8z^3 + 24z^2 + 18z + 12z^2 + 36z + 27$

$= 8z^3 + 36z^2 + 54z + 27$

111. Yes, it will always be a monomial.

112. No, it will always be a binomial.

113. No, it could have 2 or 4 terms.

114. Yes.

115. The missing exponents are 6, 3, and 1 since
$3x^2\left(2x^6 - 5x^3 + 3x^1\right)$

$= 3x^2\left(2x^6\right) - 3x^2\left(5x^3\right) + 3x^2\left(3x^1\right)$

$= 6x^8 - 15x^5 + 9x^3$

116. The missing exponents are 4, 2, and 1 since
$$4x^3(x^4 + 2x^2 - 5x^1)$$
$$= 4x^3(x^4) + 4x^3(2x^2) - 4x^3(5x^1)$$
$$= 4x^7 + 8x^5 - 20x^4$$

117. a. $A = (x+2)(2x+1)$
$$= x(2x) + x \cdot 1 + 2 \cdot 2x + 2 \cdot 1$$
$$= 2x^2 + x + 4x + 2$$
$$= 2x^2 + 5x + 2$$

    b. If $x = 4$, $A = 2 \cdot 4^2 + 5 \cdot 4 + 2 = 54$.
The area is 54 square feet.

    c. For the rectangle to be a square, all sides must have the same length. Thus,
$$x + 2 = 2x + 1.$$
$$x + 2 = 2x + 1$$
$$2 = x + 1$$
$$1 = x$$
The rectangle is a square when $x = 1$ foot.

118. a. $a + b$

    b. $a + b$

    c. Yes

    d. $(a+b)^2$

    e. Area of small square = $a \cdot a$
Area of larger square = $b \cdot b$
Area of each rectangle = $a \cdot b$
$$(a+b)^2 = a \cdot a + b \cdot b + 2(a \cdot b)$$
$$= a^2 + 2ab + b^2$$

    f. $(a+b)^2 = a^2 + 2ab + b^2$

119. a. Area of base $= (x+5)(3x+4)$
$$= 3x^2 + 4x + 15x + 20$$
$$= 3x^2 + 19x + 20$$

    b. Volume = height × Area
$$= (2x-2)(3x^2 + 19x + 20)$$
$$= 6x^3 + 38x^2 + 40x - 6x^2 - 38x - 40$$
$$= 6x^3 + 32x^2 + 2x - 40$$

    c. $6x^3 + 32x^2 + 2x - 40$
$$= 6(4)^3 + 32(4)^2 + 2 \cdot 4 - 40$$
$$= 6 \cdot 64 + 32 \cdot 16 + 8 - 40$$
$$= 384 + 512 - 32$$
$$= 864$$
The volume is 864 cubic feet.

    d. $(x+5)(3x+4)(2x-2)$
$$= (4+5)(3 \cdot 4 + 4)(2 \cdot 4 - 2)$$
$$= 9(12+4)(8-2)$$
$$= 9 \cdot 16 \cdot 6$$
$$= 864$$
The volume is 864 cubic feet.

    e. The volumes are the same.

120. $(2x^3 - 6x^2 + 5x - 3)(3x^3 - 6x + 4)$
$$= 2x^3(3x^3 - 6x + 4) - 6x^2(3x^3 - 6x + 4)$$
$$\quad + 5x(3x^3 - 6x + 4) - 3(3x^3 - 6x + 4)$$
$$= 2x^3(3x^3) + 2x^3(-6x) + 2x^3(4) - 6x^2(3x^3)$$
$$\quad - 6x^2(-6x) - 6x^2(4) + 5x(3x^3) + 5x(-6x) + 5x(4)$$
$$\quad - 3(3x^3) - 3(-6x) - 3(4)$$
$$= 6x^6 - 12x^4 + 8x^3 - 18x^5 + 36x^3 - 24x^2 + 15x^4$$
$$\quad - 30x^2 + 20x - 9x^3 + 18x - 12$$
$$= 6x^6 - 18x^5 + 3x^4 + 35x^3 - 54x^2 + 38x - 12$$

121. $\left(\dfrac{1}{2}x + \dfrac{2}{3}\right)\left(\dfrac{2}{3}x - \dfrac{2}{5}\right)$
$$= \left(\dfrac{1}{2}x\right)\left(\dfrac{2}{3}x\right) + \left(\dfrac{1}{2}x\right)\left(-\dfrac{2}{5}\right) + \left(\dfrac{2}{3}\right)\left(\dfrac{2}{3}x\right)$$
$$\quad + \left(\dfrac{2}{3}\right)\left(-\dfrac{2}{5}\right)$$
$$= \dfrac{1}{3}x^2 - \dfrac{1}{5}x + \dfrac{4}{9}x - \dfrac{4}{15}$$
$$= \dfrac{1}{3}x^2 - \dfrac{11}{45}x - \dfrac{4}{15}$$

122. a. Yes, one.

    b. $2x^2 + 7x + 3 = (2x+1)(x+3)$

    c. Answers will vary.

123. $3(x+7)-5=3x-17$

$\qquad 3x+21-5=3x-17$

$\qquad\quad 3x+16=3x-17$

$\qquad\qquad\quad 16=-17$ False

Since this is false, there is no solution.

124. Let x = measure of angle C

Then $x-16$ = measure of angle D.

$\qquad x+(x-16)=90$

$\qquad\quad 2x-16=90$

$\qquad\qquad 2x=106$

$\qquad\qquad\quad x=53$

Angle C measures $53°$ and angle D measures $53-16=37°$.

125. $\left(\dfrac{3xy^4}{6y^6}\right)^4=\left(\dfrac{3}{6}\cdot x\cdot\dfrac{y^4}{y^6}\right)^4$

$\qquad\qquad =\left(\dfrac{1}{2}\cdot x\cdot\dfrac{1}{y^2}\right)^4$

$\qquad\qquad =\left(\dfrac{x}{2y^2}\right)^4$

$\qquad\qquad =\dfrac{x^4}{2^4y^{2\cdot4}}$

$\qquad\qquad =\dfrac{x^4}{16y^8}$

126. a. $-6^3=-\left(6^3\right)=-216$

$\quad$ **b.** $6^{-3}=\dfrac{1}{6^3}=\dfrac{1}{216}$

127. $\left(-x^2-6x+5\right)-\left(4x^2-4x-9\right)$

$\qquad =-x^2-6x+5-4x^2+4x+9$

$\qquad =-x^2-4x^2-6x+4x+5+9$

$\qquad =-5x^2-2x+14$

Exercise Set 5.6

1. To divide a polynomial by a monomial, divide each term in the polynomial by the monomial.

2. (divisor)(quotient) + remainder = polynomial

3. $\dfrac{2x+8}{2}=\dfrac{2x}{2}+\dfrac{8}{2}=x+4$

4. $\dfrac{y+5}{y}=\dfrac{y}{y}+\dfrac{5}{y}=1+\dfrac{5}{y}$

5. Terms should be listed in descending order.

6. $\dfrac{x^3-14x+15}{x-3}=\dfrac{x^3+0x^2-14x+15}{x-3}$

7. $\dfrac{x^2-7}{x-2}=\dfrac{x^2+0x-7}{x-2}$

8. $(x-5)(x+2)+17=x^2-3x-10+17$

$\qquad\qquad\qquad\qquad\quad =x^2-3x+7$

9. $(x+5)(x-3)-2=x^2+2x-15-2$

$\qquad\qquad\qquad\qquad\quad =x^2+2x-17$

10. $(x+1)(x^2-x+3)-6$

$\quad =x(x^2-x+3)+1(x^2-x+3)-6$

$\quad =x^3-x^2+3x+x^2-x+3-6$

$\quad =x^3+2x-3$

11. $\dfrac{x^2-x-42}{x-7}=x+6$ or $\dfrac{x^2-x-42}{x+6}=x-7$

12. $\dfrac{3x^2+8x-3}{x+3}=3x-1$ or $\dfrac{3x^2+8x-3}{3x-1}=x+3$

13. $\dfrac{2x^2+5x+3}{2x+3}=x+1$ or $\dfrac{2x^2+5x+3}{x+1}=2x+3$

14. $\dfrac{2x^2-3x-5}{2x-5}=x+1$ or $\dfrac{2x^2-3x-5}{x+1}=2x-5$

15. $\dfrac{4x^2-9}{2x+3}=2x-3$ or $\dfrac{4x^2-9}{2x-3}=2x+3$

16. $\dfrac{3n^2-11n-20}{3n+4}=n-5$ or $\dfrac{3n^2-11n-20}{n-5}=3n+4$

17. $\dfrac{3x+6}{3}=\dfrac{3x}{3}+\dfrac{6}{3}=x+2$

18. $\dfrac{4x-6}{2} = \dfrac{4x}{2} - \dfrac{6}{2} = 2x - 3$

19. $\dfrac{4n+10}{2} = \dfrac{4n}{2} + \dfrac{10}{2} = 2n + 5$

20. $(-3x-8) \div 4 = \dfrac{-3x-8}{4} = -\dfrac{3x}{4} - \dfrac{8}{4} = -\dfrac{3}{4}x - 2$

21. $\dfrac{7x+6}{3} = \dfrac{7x}{3} + \dfrac{6}{3} = \dfrac{7}{3}x + 2$

22. $\dfrac{5x-10}{5} = \dfrac{5x}{5} - \dfrac{10}{5} = x - 2$

23. $\dfrac{-6x+4}{2} = \dfrac{-6x}{2} + \dfrac{4}{2} = -3x + 2$

24. $\dfrac{-5a+4}{-3} = \dfrac{-5}{-3}a + \dfrac{4}{-3} = \dfrac{5}{3}a - \dfrac{4}{3}$

25. $\dfrac{-9x-3}{-3} = \dfrac{-9x}{-3} + \dfrac{-3}{-3} = 3x + 1$

26. $\dfrac{8x-3}{-8} = \dfrac{(-1)(8x-3)}{(-1)(-8)}$

$\qquad = \dfrac{-8x+3}{8}$

$\qquad = \dfrac{-8x}{8} + \dfrac{3}{8}$

$\qquad = -x + \dfrac{3}{8}$

27. $\dfrac{2x+16}{4} = \dfrac{2x}{4} + \dfrac{16}{4} = \dfrac{1}{2}x + 4$

28. $\dfrac{2p-3}{2p} = \dfrac{2p}{2p} - \dfrac{3}{2p} = 1 - \dfrac{3}{2p}$

29. $\dfrac{4-10w}{-4} = \dfrac{(-1)(4-10w)}{(-1)(-4)}$

$\qquad = \dfrac{-4+10w}{4}$

$\qquad = -\dfrac{4}{4} + \dfrac{10w}{4}$

$\qquad = -1 + \dfrac{5}{2}w$

30. $\dfrac{6-5x}{-3x} = \dfrac{(-1)(6-5x)}{(-1)(-3x)}$

$\qquad = \dfrac{-6+5x}{3x}$

$\qquad = -\dfrac{6}{3x} + \dfrac{5x}{3x}$

$\qquad = -\dfrac{2}{x} + \dfrac{5}{3}$

31. $(4x^2 + 8x - 12) \div 4x^2 = \dfrac{4x^2 + 8x - 12}{4x^2}$

$\qquad = \dfrac{4x^2}{4x^2} + \dfrac{8x}{4x^2} + \dfrac{-12}{4x^2}$

$\qquad = 1 + \dfrac{2}{x} - \dfrac{3}{x^2}$

32. $\dfrac{12x^2 - 6x + 3}{3} = \dfrac{12x^2}{3} - \dfrac{6x}{3} + \dfrac{3}{3} = 4x^2 - 2x + 1$

33. $\dfrac{-4x^5 + 6x + 8}{2x^2} = \dfrac{-4x^5}{2x^2} + \dfrac{6x}{2x^2} + \dfrac{8}{2x^2}$

$\qquad = -2x^3 + \dfrac{3}{x} + \dfrac{4}{x^2}$

34. $\dfrac{6t^2 + 3t + 8}{2} = \dfrac{6t^2}{2} + \dfrac{3t}{2} + \dfrac{8}{2} = 3t^2 + \dfrac{3}{2}t + 4$

35. $(x^5 + 3x^4 - 3) \div x^3 = \dfrac{x^5 + 3x^4 - 3}{x^3}$

$\qquad = \dfrac{x^5}{x^3} + \dfrac{3x^4}{x^3} + \dfrac{-3}{x^3}$

$\qquad = x^2 + 3x - \dfrac{3}{x^3}$

36. $(6x^2 - 7x + 9) \div 3x = \dfrac{6x^2 - 7x + 9}{3x}$

$\qquad = \dfrac{6x^2}{3x} - \dfrac{7x}{3x} + \dfrac{9}{3x}$

$\qquad = 2x - \dfrac{7}{3} + \dfrac{3}{x}$

37. $\dfrac{6x^5 - 4x^4 + 12x^3 - 5x^2}{2x^3} = \dfrac{6x^5}{2x^3} - \dfrac{4x^4}{2x^3} + \dfrac{12x^3}{2x^3} - \dfrac{5x^2}{2x^3}$

$\qquad = 3x^2 - 2x + 6 - \dfrac{5}{2x}$

38. $\dfrac{9x^2 + 18x - 7}{-9} = \dfrac{(-1)(9x^2 + 18x - 7)}{(-1)(-9)}$

$\qquad = \dfrac{-9x^2 - 18x + 7}{9}$

$\qquad = \dfrac{-9x^2}{9} - \dfrac{18x}{9} + \dfrac{7}{9}$

$\qquad = -x^2 - 2x + \dfrac{7}{9}$

39. $\dfrac{8k^3 + 6k^2 - 8}{-4k} = \dfrac{(-1)\left(8k^3 + 6k^2 - 8\right)}{(-1)(-4k)}$

$\qquad = \dfrac{-8k^3 - 6k^2 + 8}{4k}$

$\qquad = \dfrac{-8k^3}{4k} - \dfrac{6k^2}{4k} + \dfrac{8}{4k}$

$\qquad = -2k^2 - \dfrac{3}{2}k + \dfrac{2}{k}$

40. $\dfrac{-12x^4 + 6x^2 - 15x + 4}{-3x}$

$= \dfrac{(-1)\left(-12x^4 + 6x^2 - 15x + 4\right)}{(-1)(-3x)}$

$= \dfrac{12x^4 - 6x^2 + 15x - 4}{3x}$

$= \dfrac{12x^4}{3x} - \dfrac{6x^2}{3x} + \dfrac{15x}{3x} - \dfrac{4}{3x}$

$= 4x^3 - 2x + 5 - \dfrac{4}{3x}$

41. $\dfrac{12x^5 + 3x^4 - 10x^2 - 9}{-3x^2}$

$= \dfrac{12x^5}{-3x^2} + \dfrac{3x^4}{-3x^2} - \dfrac{10x^2}{-3x^2} - \dfrac{9}{-3x^2}$

$= -4x^3 - x^2 + \dfrac{10}{3} + \dfrac{3}{x^2}$

42. $\dfrac{-15m^3 - 6m^2 + 15}{-5m^3} = \dfrac{(-1)\left(-15m^3 - 6m^2 + 15\right)}{(-1)\left(-5m^3\right)}$

$\qquad = \dfrac{15m^3 + 6m^2 - 15}{5m^3}$

$\qquad = \dfrac{15m^3}{5m^3} + \dfrac{6m^2}{5m^3} - \dfrac{15}{5m^3}$

$\qquad = 3 + \dfrac{6}{5m} - \dfrac{3}{m^3}$

43.
$$\begin{array}{r} x + 3 \\ x+1 \overline{\smash{\big)}\, x^2 + 4x + 3} \\ \underline{x^2 + x} \\ 3x + 3 \\ \underline{3x + 3} \\ 0 \end{array}$$

$\dfrac{x^2 + 4x + 3}{x + 1} = x + 3$

44.
$$\begin{array}{r} 2x - 7 \\ x+5 \overline{\smash{\big)}\, 2x^2 + 3x - 35} \\ \underline{2x^2 + 10x} \\ -7x - 35 \\ \underline{-7x - 35} \\ 0 \end{array}$$

$\left(2x^2 + 3x - 35\right) \div \left(x + 5\right) = 2x - 7$

45.
$$\begin{array}{r} 5y + 1 \\ y-7 \overline{\smash{\big)}\, 5y^2 - 34y - 7} \\ \underline{5y^2 - 35y} \\ y - 7 \\ \underline{y - 7} \\ 0 \end{array}$$

$\dfrac{5y^2 - 34y - 7}{y - 7} = 5y + 1$

46.
$$\begin{array}{r} 2p + 3 \\ p-5 \overline{\smash{\big)}\, 2p^2 - 7p - 15} \\ \underline{2p^2 - 10p} \\ 3p - 15 \\ \underline{3p - 15} \\ 0 \end{array}$$

$\dfrac{2p^2 - 7p - 15}{p - 5} = 2p + 3$

47.
$$\begin{array}{r} 2x + 4 \\ 3x+2 \overline{\smash{\big)}\, 6x^2 + 16x + 8} \\ \underline{6x^2 + 4x} \\ 12x + 8 \\ \underline{12x + 8} \\ 0 \end{array}$$

$\dfrac{6x^2 + 16x + 8}{3x + 2} = 2x + 4$

48.
$$r-1 \overline{\smash{)}3r^2 + 5r - 8}$$
$$\quad\quad 3r + 8$$
$$\quad\quad \underline{3r^2 - 3r}$$
$$\quad\quad\quad 8r - 8$$
$$\quad\quad\quad \underline{8r - 8}$$
$$\quad\quad\quad\quad 0$$

$$\frac{3r^2 + 5r - 8}{r - 1} = 3r + 8$$

49. $\dfrac{x^2 - 16}{-4 + x} = \dfrac{x^2 + 0x - 16}{x - 4}$

$$x-4 \overline{\smash{)}x^2 + 0x - 16}$$
$$\quad\quad x + 4$$
$$\quad\quad \underline{x^2 - 4x}$$
$$\quad\quad\quad 4x - 16$$
$$\quad\quad\quad \underline{4x - 16}$$
$$\quad\quad\quad\quad 0$$

$$\frac{x^2 - 16}{-4 + x} = x + 4$$

50.
$$3t+4 \overline{\smash{)}6t^2 - 7t - 20}$$
$$\quad\quad 2t - 5$$
$$\quad\quad \underline{6t^2 + 8t}$$
$$\quad\quad\quad -15t - 20$$
$$\quad\quad\quad \underline{-15t - 20}$$
$$\quad\quad\quad\quad 0$$

$$\frac{6t^2 - 7t - 20}{3t + 4} = 2t - 5$$

51.
$$2x-3 \overline{\smash{)}2x^2 + 7x - 18}$$
$$\quad\quad x + 5$$
$$\quad\quad \underline{2x^2 - 3x}$$
$$\quad\quad\quad 10x - 18$$
$$\quad\quad\quad \underline{10x - 15}$$
$$\quad\quad\quad\quad -3$$

$$(2x^2 + 7x - 18) \div (2x - 3) = x + 5 - \frac{3}{2x - 3}$$

52. $(4a^2 - 25) \div (2a - 5) = (4a^2 + 0a - 25) \div (2a - 5)$

$$2a-5 \overline{\smash{)}4a^2 + 0a - 25}$$
$$\quad\quad 2a + 5$$
$$\quad\quad \underline{4a^2 - 10a}$$
$$\quad\quad\quad 10a - 25$$
$$\quad\quad\quad \underline{10a - 25}$$
$$\quad\quad\quad\quad 0$$

$$\frac{4a^2 - 25}{2a - 5} = 2a + 5$$

53. $\dfrac{x^2 - 36}{x - 6} = \dfrac{x^2 + 0x - 36}{x - 6}$

$$x-6 \overline{\smash{)}x^2 + 0x - 36}$$
$$\quad\quad x + 6$$
$$\quad\quad \underline{x^2 - 6x}$$
$$\quad\quad\quad 6x - 36$$
$$\quad\quad\quad \underline{6x - 36}$$
$$\quad\quad\quad\quad 0$$

$$\frac{x^2 - 36}{x - 6} = x + 6$$

54. $\dfrac{9x^2 - 16}{3x - 4} = \dfrac{9x^2 + 0x - 16}{3x - 4}$

$$3x-4 \overline{\smash{)}9x^2 + 0x - 16}$$
$$\quad\quad 3x + 4$$
$$\quad\quad \underline{9x^2 - 12x}$$
$$\quad\quad\quad 12x - 16$$
$$\quad\quad\quad \underline{12x - 16}$$
$$\quad\quad\quad\quad 0$$

$$\frac{9x^2 - 16}{3x - 4} = 3x + 4$$

55. $\dfrac{-x+9x^3-16}{3x-4}=\dfrac{9x^3-x-16}{3x-4}$

$$3x-4\overline{)9x^3+0x^2-x-16} \quad \begin{array}{l} 3x^2+4x+5 \end{array}$$

$$\underline{9x^2-12x^2}$$
$$12x^2-x-16$$
$$\underline{12x^2-16x}$$
$$15x-16$$
$$\underline{15x-20}$$
$$4$$

$\dfrac{-x+9x^3-16}{3x-4}=3x^2+4x+5+\dfrac{4}{3x-4}$

56. $\dfrac{10x+3x^2+6}{x+2}=\dfrac{3x^2+10x+6}{x+2}$

$$x+2\overline{)3x^2+10x+6}\quad\begin{array}{l}3x+4\end{array}$$

$$\underline{3x^2+\ 6x}$$
$$4x+6$$
$$\underline{4x+8}$$
$$-2$$

$\dfrac{10x+3x^2+6}{x+2}=3x+4-\dfrac{2}{x+2}$

57. $\dfrac{6x+8x^2-12}{2x+3}=\dfrac{8x^2+6x-12}{2x+3}$

$$2x+3\overline{)8x^2+\ 6x-12}\quad\begin{array}{l}4x-\ 3\end{array}$$

$$\underline{8x^2+12x}$$
$$-6x-12$$
$$\underline{-6x\ -9}$$
$$-3$$

$\dfrac{6x+8x^2-12}{2x+3}=4x-3-\dfrac{3}{2x+3}$

58. $x+2\overline{)x^3+5x^2+2x-8}\quad\begin{array}{l}x^2+3x-4\end{array}$

$$\underline{x^3+2x^2}$$
$$3x^2+2x$$
$$\underline{3x^2+6x}$$
$$-4x-8$$
$$\underline{-4x-8}$$
$$0$$

$\dfrac{x^3+5x^2+2x-8}{x+2}=x^2+3x-4$

59. $x+4\overline{)7x^3+28x^2-5x-20}\quad\begin{array}{l}7x^2\qquad-5\end{array}$

$$\underline{7x^3+28x^2}$$
$$-5x-20$$
$$\underline{-5x-20}$$
$$0$$

$\dfrac{7x^3+28x^2-5x-20}{x+4}=7x^2-5$

60. $x-1\overline{)2x^3-3x^2-3x+6}\quad\begin{array}{l}2x^2-x-4\end{array}$

$$\underline{2x^3-2x^2}$$
$$-x^2-3x$$
$$\underline{-x^2+\ x}$$
$$-4x+6$$
$$\underline{-4x+4}$$
$$2$$

$\dfrac{2x^3-3x^2-3x+6}{x-1}=2x^2-x-4+\dfrac{2}{x-1}$

61. $\dfrac{2x^3-4x^2+12}{x-2}=\dfrac{2x^3-4x^2+0x+12}{x-2}$

$$x-2\overline{)2x^3-4x^2+0x+12}\quad\begin{array}{l}2x^2\end{array}$$

$$\underline{2x^3-4x^2}$$
$$0x+12$$

$\dfrac{2x^3-4x^2+12}{x-2}=2x^2+\dfrac{12}{x-2}$

62. $\dfrac{2x^3+6x-4}{x+4}=\dfrac{2x^3+0x^2+6x-4}{x+4}$

$$\begin{array}{r} 2x^2-8x+38 \\ x+4\overline{\smash{\big)}\,2x^3+0x^2+6x-\;4} \\ \underline{2x^3+8x^2} \\ -8x^2+6x \\ \underline{-8x^2-32x} \\ 38x-\;\;4 \\ \underline{38x+152} \\ -156 \end{array}$$

$\dfrac{2x^3+6x-4}{x+4}=2x^2-8x+38-\dfrac{156}{x+4}$

63. $\left(w^3-8\right)\div\left(w-3\right)=\left(w^3+0w^2+0w-8\right)\div\left(w-3\right)$

$$\begin{array}{r} w^2+3w+9 \\ w-3\overline{\smash{\big)}\,w^3+0w^2+0w-8} \\ \underline{w^3-3w^2} \\ 3w^2+0w \\ \underline{3w^2-9w} \\ 9w-\;8 \\ \underline{9w-27} \\ 19 \end{array}$$

$\left(w^3-8\right)\div\left(w-3\right)=w^2+3w+9+\dfrac{19}{w-3}$

64. $\dfrac{x^3+8}{x+2}=\dfrac{x^3+0x^2+0x+8}{x+2}$

$$\begin{array}{r} x^2-2x+4 \\ x+2\overline{\smash{\big)}\,x^3+0x^2+0x+8} \\ \underline{x^3+2x^2} \\ -2x^2+0x \\ \underline{-2x^2-4x} \\ 4x+8 \\ \underline{4x+8} \\ 0 \end{array}$$

$\dfrac{x^3+8}{x+2}=x^2-2x+4$

65. $\dfrac{x^3-27}{x-3}=\dfrac{x^3+0x^2+0x-27}{x-3}$

$$\begin{array}{r} x^2+3x+9 \\ x-3\overline{\smash{\big)}\,x^3+0x^2+0x-27} \\ \underline{x^3-3x^2} \\ 3x^2+0x \\ \underline{3x^2-9x} \\ 9x-27 \\ \underline{9x-27} \\ 0 \end{array}$$

$\dfrac{x^3-27}{x-3}=x^2+3x+9$

66. $\dfrac{x^3+64}{x+4}=\dfrac{x^3+0x^2+0x+64}{x+4}$

$$\begin{array}{r} x^2-4x+16 \\ x+4\overline{\smash{\big)}\,x^3+0x^2+0x+64} \\ \underline{x^3+4x^2} \\ -4x^2+0x \\ \underline{-4x^2-16x} \\ 16x+64 \\ \underline{16x+64} \\ 0 \end{array}$$

$\dfrac{x^3+64}{x+4}=x^2-4x+16$

67. $\dfrac{4x^3-5x}{2x-1}=\dfrac{4x^3+0x^2-5x+0}{2x-1}$

$$\begin{array}{r} 2x^2+x-2 \\ 2x-1\overline{\smash{\big)}\,4x^3+0x^2-5x+0} \\ \underline{4x^3-2x^2} \\ 2x^2-5x \\ \underline{2x^2-\;x} \\ -4x+0 \\ \underline{4x+2} \\ -2 \end{array}$$

$\dfrac{4x^3-5x}{2x-1}=2x^2+x-2-\dfrac{2}{2x-1}$

68. $\dfrac{9x^3 - x + 3}{3x - 2} = \dfrac{9x^3 + 0x^2 - x + 3}{3x - 2}$

$$
\begin{array}{r}
3x^2 + 2x + 1 \\
3x-2\overline{\smash{\big)}\,9x^3 + 0x^2 - x + 3} \\
\underline{9x^3 - 6x^2} \\
6x^2 - x \\
\underline{6x^2 - 4x} \\
3x + 3 \\
\underline{3x - 2} \\
5
\end{array}
$$

$\dfrac{9x^3 - x + 3}{3x - 2} = 3x^2 + 2x + 1 + \dfrac{5}{3x - 2}$

69.

$$
\begin{array}{r}
-m^2 - 7m - 5 \\
m-1\overline{\smash{\big)}\,-m^3 - 6m^2 + 2m - 3} \\
\underline{-m^3 + m^2} \\
-7m^2 + 2m \\
\underline{-7m^2 + 7m} \\
-5m - 3 \\
\underline{-5m + 5} \\
-8
\end{array}
$$

$\dfrac{-m^3 - 6m^2 + 2m - 3}{m - 1} = -m^2 - 7m - 5 - \dfrac{8}{m-1}$

70.

$$
\begin{array}{r}
-x^2 + 6x - 4 \\
x+3\overline{\smash{\big)}\,-x^3 + 3x^2 + 14x + 16} \\
\underline{-x^3 - 3x^2} \\
6x^2 + 14x \\
\underline{6x^2 + 18x} \\
-4x + 16 \\
\underline{-4x - 12} \\
28
\end{array}
$$

$\dfrac{-x^3 + 3x^2 + 14x + 16}{x + 3} = -x^2 + 6x - 4$

71. $\dfrac{4t^3 - t + 4}{t + 2} = \dfrac{4t^3 + 0t^2 - t + 4}{t + 2}$

$$
\begin{array}{r}
4t^2 - 8t + 15 \\
t+2\overline{\smash{\big)}\,4t^3 + 0t^2 - t + 4} \\
\underline{4t^3 + 8t^2} \\
-8t^2 - t \\
\underline{-8t^2 - 16t} \\
15t + 4 \\
\underline{15t + 30} \\
-26
\end{array}
$$

$\dfrac{4t^3 - t + 4}{t + 2} = 4t^2 - 8t + 15 - \dfrac{26}{t + 2}$

72. $\dfrac{9n^3 - 6n + 4}{3n - 3} = \dfrac{9n^3 + 0n^2 - 6n + 4}{3n - 3}$

$$
\begin{array}{r}
3n^2 + 3n + 1 \\
3n-3\overline{\smash{\big)}\,9n^3 + 0n^2 - 6n + 4} \\
\underline{9n^3 - 9n^2} \\
9n^2 - 6n \\
\underline{9n^2 - 9n} \\
3n + 4 \\
\underline{3n - 3} \\
7
\end{array}
$$

$\dfrac{9n^3 - 6n + 4}{3n - 3} = 3n^2 + 3n + 1 + \dfrac{7}{3n - 3}$

73. No, $\dfrac{2x + 1}{x^2} = \dfrac{2x}{x^2} + \dfrac{1}{x^2} = \dfrac{2}{x} + \dfrac{1}{x^2}$

74. No, $\dfrac{x^2 + 2x + 1}{x} = \dfrac{x^2}{x} + \dfrac{2x}{x} + \dfrac{1}{x} = x + 2 + \dfrac{1}{x}$

75. $(x + 4)(2x + 3) + 4 = 2x^2 + 3x + 8x + 12 + 4$
$= 2x^2 + 11x + 16$

76. $(2x - 3)(3x - 1) - 2 = 6x^2 - 2x - 9x + 3 - 2$
$= 6x^2 - 11x + 1$

77. Third Degree since $\dfrac{x^4}{x} = x^3$

78. First Degree since $\dfrac{x^2}{x} = x$

79. It has to be $4x$ since that is what must be multiplied with $4x^3$ in the quotient to get $16x^4$ in the dividend.

80. It has to be $3x^2$ since that is what must be multiplied with $3x^3$ in the quotient to get $9x^5$ in dividend.

81. When dividing by $2x^2$, each exponent will decrease by two. So, the shaded areas must be 5, 3, 2, 1, respectively.

82. Since the shaded areas minus 2 equal 5, 4, 2, and 0 respectively, the shaded areas are 7, 6, 4, and 2 respectively.

83. $\dfrac{3x^3 - 5}{3x - 2} = \dfrac{3x^3 + 0x^2 + 0x - 5}{3x - 2}$

$$
\begin{array}{r}
x^2 + \frac{2}{3}x + \frac{4}{9} \\
3x - 2 \overline{\smash{)}3x^3 + 0x^2 + 0x - 5} \\
\underline{3x^3 - 2x^2} \\
2x^2 + 0x \\
\underline{2x^2 - \frac{4}{3}x} \\
\frac{4}{3}x - 5 \\
\underline{\frac{4}{3}x - \frac{8}{9}} \\
-\frac{37}{9}
\end{array}
$$

$\dfrac{3x^3 - 5}{3x - 2} = x^2 + \dfrac{2}{3}x + \dfrac{4}{9} - \dfrac{37}{9(3x - 2)}$

84. $\dfrac{4x^3 - 4x + 6}{2x + 3} = \dfrac{4x^3 + 0x^2 - 4x + 6}{2x + 3}$

$$
\begin{array}{r}
2x^2 - 3x + \frac{5}{2} \\
2x + 3 \overline{\smash{)}4x^3 + 0x^2 - 4x + 6} \\
\underline{4x^3 + 6x^2} \\
-6x^2 - 4x \\
\underline{-6x^2 - 9x} \\
5x + 6 \\
\underline{5x + \frac{15}{2}} \\
-\frac{3}{2}
\end{array}
$$

$\dfrac{4x^3 - 4x + 6}{2x + 3} = 2x^2 - 3x + \dfrac{5}{2} - \dfrac{3}{2(2x + 3)}$

85.
$$
\begin{array}{r}
-3x + 3 \\
-x - 3 \overline{\smash{)}3x^2 + 6x - 10} \\
\underline{3x^2 + 9x} \\
-3x - 10 \\
\underline{-3x - 9} \\
-1
\end{array}
$$

$\dfrac{3x^2 + 6x - 10}{-x - 3} = -3x + 3 + \dfrac{1}{x + 3}$

86. $(x + 2)(x + 4) + 2 = x^2 + 6x + 8 + 2$
$$= x^2 + 6x + 10$$

87. $(x + 1)(x + 3) - 1 = x^2 + 4x + 3 - 1$
$$= x^2 + 4x + 2$$

88. **a.** 2 is a natural number.

   b. 2 and 0 are whole numbers.

   c. $2, -5, 0, \dfrac{2}{5}, -6.3,$ and $-\dfrac{23}{34}$ are rational numbers.

   d. $\sqrt{7}$ and $\sqrt{3}$ are irrational numbers.

   e. $2, -5, 0, \sqrt{7}, \dfrac{2}{5}, -6.3, \sqrt{3},$ and $-\dfrac{23}{34}$ are all real numbers.

89. **a.** $\dfrac{0}{1} = 0$

   b. $\dfrac{1}{0}$ is undefined

90. Evaluate expressions in parentheses first, then exponents, followed by multiplications and divisions from left to right, and finally additions and subtractions from left to right.

91. $2(x + 3) + 2x = x + 4$
$$2x + 6 + 2x = x + 4$$
$$4x + 6 = x + 4$$
$$4x = x - 2$$
$$3x = -2$$
$$x = -\dfrac{2}{3}$$

92. Let p = the purchase price of the sweater, then
$0.30p$ = the amount saved on the sweater.
$$p - 0.30p = 27.65$$
$$0.7p = 27.65$$
$$p = \frac{27.65}{0.7}$$
$$p = 39.5$$
The regular price of the sweater is $39.50.

93. $\dfrac{x^9}{x^{-4}} = x^{9-(-4)} = x^{9+4} = x^{13}$

Chapter 5 Review Exercises

1. $x^5 \cdot x^2 = x^{5+2} = x^7$

2. $x^2 \cdot x^4 = x^{2+4} = x^6$

3. $3^2 \cdot 3^3 = 3^{2+3} = 3^5 = 243$

4. $2^4 \cdot 2 = 2^{4+1} = 2^5 = 32$

5. $\dfrac{x^4}{x} = x^{4-1} = x^3$

6. $\dfrac{a^5}{a^5} = a^{5-5} = a^0 = 1$

7. $\dfrac{5^5}{5^3} = 5^{5-3} = 5^2 = 25$

8. $\dfrac{4^4}{4} = 4^{4-1} = 4^3 = 64$

9. $\dfrac{x^6}{x^8} = \dfrac{1}{x^{8-6}} = \dfrac{1}{x^2}$

10. $\dfrac{y^4}{y} = y^{4-1} = y^3$

11. $x^0 = 1$

12. $7y^0 = 7 \cdot 1 = 7$

13. $(-6z)^0 = 1$

14. $6^0 = 1$

15. $(5x)^2 = 5^2 x^2 = 25x^2$

16. $(3a)^3 = 3^3 a^3 = 27a^3$

17. $(-3x)^3 = (-3)^3 x^3 = -27x^3$

18. $(6s)^3 = 6^3 s^3 = 216s^3$

19. $(2x^2)^4 = 2^4 x^{2\cdot4} = 16x^8$

20. $(-x^4)^6 = (-1)^6 x^{4\cdot6} = x^{24}$

21. $(-p^8)^4 = (-1)^4 p^{8(4)} = p^{32}$

22. $\left(-\dfrac{2x^3}{y}\right)^2 = \dfrac{(-2)^2 x^{3(2)}}{y^2} = \dfrac{4x^6}{y^2}$

23. $\left(\dfrac{5y^2}{2b}\right)^2 = \dfrac{(-5)^2 y^{2(2)}}{2^2 b^2} = \dfrac{25y^4}{4b^2}$

24. $6x^2 \cdot 4x^3 = 6 \cdot 4 x^{2+3} = 24x^5$

25. $\dfrac{16x^2 y}{4xy^2} = \dfrac{16}{4} \cdot \dfrac{x^2}{x} \cdot \dfrac{y}{y^2} = 4x \cdot \dfrac{1}{y} = \dfrac{4x}{y}$

26. $2x(3xy^3)^3 = 2x(3^3 x^3 y^{3\cdot3})$
$= 2x(27x^3 y^9)$
$= 2 \cdot 27 x^{1+3} y^9$
$= 54x^4 y^9$

27. $\left(\dfrac{9x^2 y}{3xy}\right)^2 = \left(\dfrac{9}{3} \cdot \dfrac{x^2}{x} \cdot \dfrac{y}{y}\right)^2$
$= (3x)^2$
$= 3^2 x^2$
$= 9x^2$

28. $(2x^2 y)^3(3xy^4) = (2^3 x^{2\cdot3} y^3)(3xy^4)$
$= (8x^6 y^3)(3xy^4)$
$= 8 \cdot 3 x^{6+1} y^{3+4}$
$= 24x^7 y^7$

29. $4x^2y^3\left(2x^3y^4\right)^2 = 4x^2y^3\left(2^2x^{3(2)}y^{4(2)}\right)$

$\qquad = 4x^2y^3\left(4x^6y^8\right)$

$\qquad = 4\cdot4x^{2+6}y^{3+8}$

$\qquad = 16x^8y^{11}$

30. $3c^2(2c^4d^3) = 3\cdot2\cdot c^{2+4}\cdot d^3 = 6c^6d^3$

31. $\left(\dfrac{9a^3b^2}{3ab^7}\right)^3 = \left(\dfrac{9}{3}\cdot\dfrac{a^3}{a}\cdot\dfrac{b^2}{b^7}\right)^3$

$\qquad = \left(3a^{3-1}\cdot\dfrac{1}{b^5}\right)^3$

$\qquad = \left(\dfrac{3a^2}{b^5}\right)^3$

$\qquad = \dfrac{3^3a^{2\cdot3}}{b^{5\cdot3}}$

$\qquad = \dfrac{27a^6}{b^{15}}$

32. $\left(\dfrac{21x^4y^3}{7y^2}\right)^3 = \left(\dfrac{21}{7}\cdot x^4\cdot\dfrac{y^3}{y^2}\right)^3$

$\qquad = \left(3x^4y\right)^3$

$\qquad = 3^3x^{4\cdot3}y^3$

$\qquad = 27x^{12}y^3$

33. $b^{-9} = \dfrac{1}{b^9}$

34. $3^{-3} = \dfrac{1}{3^3} = \dfrac{1}{27}$

35. $5^{-2} = \dfrac{1}{5^2} = \dfrac{1}{25}$

36. $\dfrac{1}{z^{-2}} = z^2$

37. $\dfrac{1}{x^{-7}} = x^7$

38. $\dfrac{1}{4^{-2}} = 4^2 = 16$

39. $y^5\cdot y^{-8} = y^{5-8} = y^{-3} = \dfrac{1}{y^3}$

40. $x^{-2}\cdot x^{-3} = x^{-2-3} = x^{-5} = \dfrac{1}{x^5}$

41. $p^{-6}\cdot p^4 = p^{-6+4} = p^{-2} = \dfrac{1}{p^2}$

42. $a^{-2}\cdot a^{-3} = a^{-2+(-3)} = a^{-5} = \dfrac{1}{a^5}$

43. $\dfrac{m^5}{m^{-5}} = m^{5-(-5)} = m^{10}$

44. $\dfrac{x^5}{x^{-2}} = x^{5-(-2)} = x^7$

45. $\dfrac{x^{-3}}{x^3} = \dfrac{1}{x^{3+3}} = \dfrac{1}{x^6}$

46. $\left(3x^4\right)^{-2} = 3^{-2}x^{4(-2)} = 3^{-2}x^{-8} = \dfrac{1}{3^2x^8} = \dfrac{1}{9x^8}$

47. $\left(4x^{-3}y\right)^{-3} = 4^{-3}x^{(-3)(-3)}y^{-3}$

$\qquad = 4^{-3}x^9y^{-3}$

$\qquad = \dfrac{x^9}{4^3y^3}$

$\qquad = \dfrac{x^9}{64y^3}$

48. $\left(-2m^{-3}n\right)^2 = (-2)^2m^{-3(2)}n^{1\cdot2} = 4m^{-6}n^2 = \dfrac{4n^2}{m^6}$

49. $6y^{-2}\cdot2y^4 = 6\cdot2y^{-2+4} = 12y^2$

50. $\left(-5y^{-3}z\right)^3 = (-5)^3y^{(-3)(3)}z^3$

$\qquad = -125y^{-9}z^3$

$\qquad = -\dfrac{125z^3}{y^9}$

51. $\left(-4x^{-2}y^3\right)^{-2} = (-4)^{-2}x^{(-2)(-2)}y^{3(-2)}$

$\qquad = (-4)^{-2}x^4y^{-6}$

$\qquad = \dfrac{x^4}{(-4)^2y^6}$

$\qquad = \dfrac{x^4}{16y^6}$

52. $2x\left(3x^{-2}\right)=2\cdot 3x^{1-2}=6x^{-1}=\dfrac{6}{x}$

53. $\left(5x^{-2}y\right)\left(2x^{4}y\right)=5\cdot 2x^{-2+4}y^{1+1}=10x^{2}y^{2}$

54. $4y^{-2}\left(3x^{2}y\right)=4\cdot 3x^{2}y^{-2+1}=12x^{2}y^{-1}=\dfrac{12x^{2}}{y}$

55. $4x^{5}\left(6x^{-7}y^{2}\right)=4\cdot 6x^{5-7}y^{2}=24x^{-2}y^{2}=\dfrac{24y^{2}}{x^{2}}$

56. $\dfrac{6xy^{4}}{2xy^{-1}}=\dfrac{6}{2}\cdot\dfrac{x}{x}\cdot\dfrac{y^{4}}{y^{-1}}=3y^{5}$

57. $\dfrac{12x^{-2}y^{3}}{3xy^{2}}=\dfrac{12}{3}\cdot\dfrac{x^{-2}}{x}\cdot\dfrac{y^{3}}{y^{2}}=4\cdot\dfrac{1}{x^{3}}\cdot y=\dfrac{4y}{x^{3}}$

58. $\dfrac{49x^{2}y^{-3}}{7x^{-3}y}=\dfrac{49}{7}\cdot\dfrac{x^{2}}{x^{-3}}\cdot\dfrac{y^{-3}}{y}$

$\qquad =\left(\dfrac{49}{7}\right)x^{2-(-3)}y^{-3-1}$

$\qquad =7x^{5}y^{-4}$

$\qquad =\dfrac{7x^{5}}{y^{4}}$

59. $\dfrac{4x^{8}y^{-2}}{8x^{7}y^{3}}=\dfrac{4}{8}\cdot\dfrac{x^{8}}{x^{7}}\cdot\dfrac{y^{-2}}{y^{3}}=\dfrac{1}{2}\cdot x\cdot\dfrac{1}{y^{5}}=\dfrac{x}{2y^{5}}$

60. $\dfrac{36x^{4}y^{7}}{9x^{5}y^{-3}}=\dfrac{36}{9}\cdot\dfrac{x^{4}}{x^{5}}\cdot\dfrac{y^{7}}{y^{-3}}=4\cdot\dfrac{1}{x}\cdot y^{10}=\dfrac{4y^{10}}{x}$

61. $1,720,000=1.72\times 10^{6}$

62. $0.153=1.53\times 10^{-1}$

63. $0.00763=7.63\times 10^{-3}$

64. $47,000=4.7\times 10^{4}$

65. $5,760=5.76\times 10^{3}$

66. $0.000314=3.14\times 10^{-4}$

67. $7.5\times 10^{-3}=0.0075$

68. $6.52\times 10^{-4}=0.000652$

69. $8.9\times 10^{6}=8,900,000$

70. $5.12\times 10^{4}=51,200$

71. $3.14\times 10^{-5}=0.0000314$

72. $1.103\times 10^{7}=11,030,000$

73. 92 milliliters $=92\times 10^{-3}=0.092$ liters

74. 6 gigameters $=6\times 10^{9}=6,000,000,000$ meters

75. 12.8 micrograms $=12.8\times 10^{-6}$

$\qquad\qquad\qquad\quad =0.0000128$ grams

76. 19.2 kilograms $=19.2\times 10^{3}=19,200$ grams

77. $\left(2.5\times 10^{2}\right)\left(3.4\times 10^{-4}\right)=\left(2.5\times 3.4\right)\left(10^{2}\times 10^{-4}\right)$

$\qquad\qquad\qquad\qquad\qquad\quad =8.5\times 10^{-2}$

$\qquad\qquad\qquad\qquad\qquad\quad =0.085$

78. $\left(4.2\times 10^{-3}\right)\left(3.0\times 10^{5}\right)=\left(4.2\times 3\right)\left(10^{-3}\times 10^{5}\right)$

$\qquad\qquad\qquad\qquad\qquad\quad =12.6\times 10^{2}$

$\qquad\qquad\qquad\qquad\qquad\quad =1260$

79. $\left(3.5\times 10^{-2}\right)\left(7.0\times 10^{3}\right)=\left(3.5\times 7.0\right)\left(10^{-2}\times 10^{3}\right)$

$\qquad\qquad\qquad\qquad\qquad\quad =24.5\times 10^{1}$

$\qquad\qquad\qquad\qquad\qquad\quad =245$

80. $\dfrac{7.94\times 10^{6}}{2.0\times 10^{-2}}=\left(\dfrac{7.94}{2.0}\right)\left(\dfrac{10^{6}}{10^{-2}}\right)$

$\qquad\qquad\qquad =3.97\times 10^{8}$

$\qquad\qquad\qquad =397,000,000$

81. $\dfrac{1.5\times 10^{-2}}{5.0\times 10^{2}}=\left(\dfrac{1.5}{5}\right)\left(\dfrac{10^{-2}}{10^{2}}\right)=0.3\times 10^{-4}=0.00003$

82. $\dfrac{6.5\times 10^{4}}{2.0\times 10^{6}}=\left(\dfrac{6.5}{2.0}\right)\left(\dfrac{10^{4}}{10^{6}}\right)=3.25\times 10^{-2}=0.0325$

83. $\left(14,000\right)\left(260,000\right)=\left(1.4\times 10^{4}\right)\left(2.6\times 10^{5}\right)$

$\qquad\qquad\qquad\qquad\quad =\left(1.4\times 2.6\right)\left(10^{4}\times 10^{5}\right)$

$\qquad\qquad\qquad\qquad\quad =3.64\times 10^{9}$

84. $(0.00053)(40,000) = (5.3 \times 10^{-4})(4 \times 10^4)$

$$= (5.3 \times 4)(10^{-4} \times 10^4)$$

$$= 21.2 \times 10^0$$

$$= 2.12 \times 10^1$$

85. $(12,500)(400,000) = (1.25 \times 10^4)(4.0 \times 10^5)$

$$= (1.25 \times 4.0)(10^4 \times 10^5)$$

$$= 5.0 \times 10^9$$

86. $\dfrac{250}{500,000} = \dfrac{2.5 \times 10^2}{5.0 \times 10^5}$

$$= \left(\dfrac{2.5}{5.0}\right)\left(\dfrac{10^2}{10^5}\right)$$

$$= 0.5 \times 10^{-3}$$

$$= 5.0 \times 10^{-4}$$

87. $\dfrac{0.000068}{0.02} = \dfrac{6.8 \times 10^{-5}}{2 \times 10^{-2}} = \left(\dfrac{6.8}{2}\right)\left(\dfrac{10^{-5}}{10^{-2}}\right) = 3.4 \times 10^{-3}$

88. $\dfrac{850,000}{0.025} = \dfrac{8.5 \times 10^5}{2.5 \times 10^{-2}} = \left(\dfrac{8.50}{2.50}\right)\left(\dfrac{10^5}{10^{-2}}\right) = 3.4 \times 10^7$

89. $\dfrac{6.4 \times 10^6}{1.28 \times 10^2} = \left(\dfrac{6.4}{1.28}\right)\left(\dfrac{10^6}{10^2}\right) = 5 \times 10^4 = 50,000$

The milk tank holds 50,000 gallons.

90. a. $\$1,500,000,000,000$

b. $0.075(1.5 \times 10^{12}) = (7.5 \times 10^{-2})(1.5 \times 10^{12})$

$$= (7.5 \times 1.5)(10^{-2} \times 10^{12})$$

$$= 11.25 \times 10^{10}$$

$$= \$1.125 \times 10^{11}$$

91. Not a polynomial

92. monomial, zero degree

93. $x^2 + 3x - 4$, trinomial, second degree

94. $4x^2 - x - 3$, trinomial, second degree

95. Not a polynomial

96. $13x^3 - 4$, binomial, third degree

97. $-4x^2 + x$, binomial, second degree

98. Not a polynomial

99. $2x^3 + 4x^2 - 3x - 7$, polynomial, third degree

100. $(x + 8) + (4x - 11) = x + 8 + 4x - 11$

$$= x + 4x + 8 - 11$$

$$= 5x - 3$$

101. $(2d - 3) + (5d + 7) = 2d - 3 + 5d + 7$

$$= 2d + 5d - 3 + 7$$

$$= 7d + 4$$

102. $(-x - 10) + (-2x + 5) = -x - 10 - 2x + 5$

$$= -x - 2x - 10 + 5$$

$$= -3x - 5$$

103. $(-3x^2 + 9x + 5) + (-x^2 + 2x - 12)$

$$= -3x^2 + 9x + 5 - x^2 + 2x - 12$$

$$= -3x^2 - x^2 + 9x + 2x + 5 - 12$$

$$= -4x^2 + 11x - 7$$

104. $(-m^2 + 5m - 8) + (6m^2 - 5m - 2)$

$$= -m^2 + 6m^2 + 5m - 5m - 8 - 2$$

$$= 5m^2 - 10$$

105. $(6.2p - 4.3) + (1.9p + 7.1) = 6.2p + 1.9p - 4.3 + 7.1$

$$= 8.1p + 2.8$$

106. $(-6y - 7) - (-3y + 8) = -6y - 7 + 3y - 8$

$$= -6y + 3y - 7 - 8$$

$$= -3y - 15$$

107. $(4x^2 - 9x) - (3x + 15) = 4x^2 - 9x - 3x - 15$

$$= 4x^2 - 12x - 15$$

108. $(5a^2 - 6a - 9) - (2a^2 - a + 12)$

$$= 5a^2 - 6a - 9 - 2a^2 + a - 12$$

$$= 5a^2 - 2a^2 - 6a + a - 9 - 12$$

$$= 3a^2 - 5a - 21$$

109. $(x^2 + 7x - 3) - (x^2 + 3x - 5)$

$$= x^2 + 7x - 3 - x^2 - 3x + 5$$

$$= x^2 - x^2 + 7x - 3x - 3 + 5$$

$$= 4x + 2$$

110. $\left(-2x^2+8x-7\right)-\left(3x^2+12\right)$

$=-2x^2+8x-7-3x^2-12$

$=-2x^2-3x^2+8x-7-12$

$=-5x^2+8x-19$

111. $\dfrac{1}{7}x(21x+21)=\dfrac{1}{7}x(21x)+\dfrac{1}{7}x(21)$

$\qquad\qquad =\dfrac{21}{7}x^2+\dfrac{21}{7}x$

$\qquad\qquad =3x^2+3x$

112. $-3x(5x+4)=-3x\cdot 5x+(-3x)4$

$\qquad\qquad\quad =-15x^2-12x$

113. $3x\left(2x^2-4x+7\right)=3x\left(2x^2\right)+3x(-4x)+3x(7)$

$\qquad\qquad\qquad\qquad\quad =6x^3-12x^2+21x$

114. $-c\left(2c^2-3c+5\right)$

$=(-c)\left(2c^2\right)+(-c)(-3c)+(-c)(5)$

$=-2c^3+3c^2-5c$

115. $-7b\left(-4b^2-3b-5\right)$

$=(-7b)\left(-4b^2\right)+(-7b)(-3b)+(-7b)(-5)$

$=28b^3+21b^2+35b$

116. $(x+4)(x+5)=x\cdot x+x\cdot 5+4\cdot x+4\cdot 5$

$\qquad\qquad\qquad =x^2+5x+4x+20$

$\qquad\qquad\qquad =x^2+9x+20$

117. $(3x+6)(-4x+1)$

$=3x(-4x)+3x(1)+6(-4x)+6(1)$

$=-12x^2+3x-24x+6$

$=-12x^2-21x+6$

118. $(-5x+3)^2=(-5x)^2+2(-5x)(3)+(3)^2$

$\qquad\qquad\quad =25x^2-30x+9$

119. $(6-2x)(2+3x)$

$=6\cdot 2+6\cdot 3x+(-2x)(2)+(-2x)(3x)$

$=12+18x-4x-6x^2$

$=12+14x-6x^2$

$=-6x^2+14x+12$

120. $(r+5)(r-5)=(r)^2-(5)^2=r^2-25$

121. $(x-1)\left(3x^2+4x-6\right)$

$=x\left(3x^2+4x-6\right)-1\left(3x^2+4x-6\right)$

$=3x^3+4x^2-6x-3x^2-4x+6$

$=3x^3+x^2-10x+6$

122. $(3x+1)\left(x^2+2x+4\right)$

$=3x\left(x^2+2x+4\right)+1\left(x^2+2x+4\right)$

$=3x^3+6x^2+12x+x^2+2x+4$

$=3x^3+7x^2+14x+4$

123. $(-4x+2)\left(3x^2-x+7\right)$

$=-4x\left(3x^2-x+7\right)+2\left(3x^2-x+7\right)$

$=-12x^3+4x^2-28x+6x^2-2x+14$

$=-12x^3+10x^2-30x+14$

124. $\dfrac{2x+4}{2}=\dfrac{2x}{2}+\dfrac{4}{2}=x+2$

125. $\dfrac{12y+18}{3}=\dfrac{12y}{3}+\dfrac{18}{3}=4y+6$

126. $\dfrac{8x^2+4x}{x}=\dfrac{8x^2}{x}+\dfrac{4x}{x}=8x+4$

127. $\dfrac{6x^2+9x-4}{3}=\dfrac{6x^2}{3}+\dfrac{9x}{3}-\dfrac{4}{3}=2x^2+3x-\dfrac{4}{3}$

128. $\dfrac{6w^2-5w+3}{3w}=\dfrac{6w^2}{3w}-\dfrac{5w}{3w}+\dfrac{3}{3w}=2w-\dfrac{5}{3}+\dfrac{1}{w}$

129. $\dfrac{16x^6-8x^5-3x^3+1}{4x}=\dfrac{16x^6}{4x}-\dfrac{8x^5}{4x}-\dfrac{3x^3}{4x}+\dfrac{1}{4x}$

$\qquad\qquad\qquad\qquad\quad =4x^5-2x^4-\dfrac{3}{4}x^2+\dfrac{1}{4x}$

130. $\dfrac{8m-4}{-2}=\dfrac{8m+(-4)}{-2}=\dfrac{8m}{-2}+\dfrac{-4}{-2}=-4m+2$

131. $\dfrac{5x^3+10x+2}{2x^2}=\dfrac{5x^3}{2x^2}+\dfrac{10x}{2x^2}+\dfrac{2}{2x^2}=\dfrac{5}{2}x+\dfrac{5}{x}+\dfrac{1}{x^2}$

132. $\dfrac{5x^2-6x+15}{3x}=\dfrac{5x^2}{3x}-\dfrac{6x}{3x}+\dfrac{15}{3x}=\dfrac{5}{3}x-2+\dfrac{5}{x}$

133.

$$\begin{array}{r} x+4 \\ x-3{\overline{\smash{\big)}\,x^2+\ x-12}} \\ \underline{x^2-3x} \\ 4x-12 \\ \underline{4x-12} \\ 0 \end{array}$$

$$\frac{x^2+x-12}{x-3}=x+4$$

134.

$$\begin{array}{r} 5x-\ 2 \\ x+6{\overline{\smash{\big)}\,5x^2+28x-10}} \\ \underline{5x^2+30x} \\ -2x-10 \\ \underline{-2x-12} \\ 2 \end{array}$$

$$\frac{5x^2+28x-10}{x+6}=5x-2+\frac{2}{x+6}$$

135.

$$\begin{array}{r} n+3 \\ 6n+1{\overline{\smash{\big)}\,6n^2+19n+3}} \\ \underline{6n^2+\ n} \\ 18n+3 \\ \underline{18n+3} \\ 0 \end{array}$$

$$\frac{6n^2+19n+3}{6n+1}=n+3$$

136.

$$\begin{array}{r} 2x^2+3x-\ 4 \\ 2x+3{\overline{\smash{\big)}\,4x^3+12x^2+x-12}} \\ \underline{4x^3+\ 6x^2} \\ 6x^2+x \\ \underline{6x^2+9x} \\ -8x-12 \\ \underline{-8x-12} \\ 0 \end{array}$$

$$\frac{4x^3+12x^2+x-12}{2x+3}=2x^2+3x-4$$

137.

$$\begin{array}{r} 2x-3 \\ 2x-3{\overline{\smash{\big)}\,4x^2-12x+9}} \\ \underline{4x^2-\ 6x} \\ -6x+9 \\ \underline{-6x+9} \\ 0 \end{array}$$

$$\frac{4x^2-12x+9}{2x-3}=2x-3$$

Chapter 5 Practice Test

1. $5x^4\cdot3x^2=5\cdot3x^{4+2}=15x^6$

2. $\left(3xy^2\right)^3=3^3x^3y^{2(3)}=27x^3y^6$

3. $\dfrac{24p^7}{3p^2}=\dfrac{24}{3}p^{7-2}=8p^5$

4. $\left(\dfrac{3x^2y}{6xy^3}\right)^3=\left(\dfrac{3}{6}\cdot\dfrac{x^2}{x}\cdot\dfrac{y}{y^3}\right)^3$

$$=\left(\dfrac{1}{2}\cdot x\cdot\dfrac{1}{y^2}\right)^3$$

$$=\left(\dfrac{x}{2y^2}\right)^3$$

$$=\dfrac{x^3}{2^3y^{2\cdot3}}$$

$$=\dfrac{x^3}{8y^6}$$

5. $\left(2x^3y^{-2}\right)^{-2}=2^{-2}x^{3(-2)}y^{(-2)(-2)}$

$$=2^{-2}x^{-6}y^4$$

$$=\dfrac{y^4}{2^2x^6}$$

$$=\dfrac{y^4}{4x^6}$$

6. $\left(4x^0\right)\left(3x^2\right)^0=\left(4\cdot1\right)\cdot1=4$

7. $\dfrac{30x^6y^2}{45x^{-1}y}=\dfrac{30}{45}x^{6-(-1)}y^{2-1}=\dfrac{2}{3}x^7y=\dfrac{2x^7y}{3}$

8. $(285,000)(50,000)=\left(2.85\times10^5\right)\left(5.0\times10^4\right)$

$$=\left(2.85\times5.0\right)\left(10^5\times10^4\right)$$

$$=14.25\times10^9$$

$$=1.425\times10^{10}$$

9. $\dfrac{0.0008}{4000}=\dfrac{8.0\times10^{-4}}{4.0\times10^3}$

$$=\left(\dfrac{8.0}{4.0}\right)\left(\dfrac{10^{-4}}{10^3}\right)$$

$$=2.0\times10^{-7}$$

10. $4x$ is a monomial

11. $-8c + 5$, binomial

12. $x^{-2} + 4$, not a polynomial

13. $-5 + 6x^3 - 2x^2 + 5x = 6x^3 - 2x^2 + 5x - 5$, third degree

14. $(6x - 4) + (2x^2 - 5x - 3) = 6x - 4 + 2x^2 - 5x - 3$
$$= 2x^2 + 6x - 5x - 4 - 3$$
$$= 2x^2 + x - 7$$

15. $(y^2 - 7y + 3) - (4y^2 - 5y - 2)$
$$= y^2 - 7y + 3 - 4y^2 + 5y + 2$$
$$= y^2 - 4y^2 - 7y + 5y + 3 + 2$$
$$= -3y^2 - 2y + 5$$

16. $(4x^2 - 5) - (x^2 + x - 8) = 4x^2 - 5 - x^2 - x + 8$
$$= 4x^2 - x^2 - x - 5 + 8$$
$$= 3x^2 - x + 3$$

17. $-5d(-3d + 8) = -5d(-3d) - 5d(8)$
$$= 15d^2 - 40d$$

18. $(5x + 8)(3x - 4)$
$$= (5x)(3x) + (5x)(-4) + 8(3x) + 8(-4)$$
$$= 15x^2 - 20x + 24x - 32$$
$$= 15x^2 + 4x - 32$$

19. $(9 - 4c)(5 + 3c)$
$$= 9 \cdot 5 + 9(3c) + (-4c) \cdot 5 + (-4c)(3c)$$
$$= 45 + 27c - 20c - 12c^2$$
$$= -12c^2 + 7c + 45$$

20. $(3x - 5)(2x^2 + 4x - 5)$
$$= 3x(2x^2 + 4x - 5) - 5(2x^2 + 4x - 5)$$
$$= 3x \cdot 2x^2 + 3x \cdot 4x - 3x \cdot 5 - 5 \cdot 2x^2 - 5 \cdot 4x - 5(-5)$$
$$= 6x^3 + 12x^2 - 15x - 10x^2 - 20x + 25$$
$$= 6x^3 + 2x^2 - 35x + 25$$

21. $\dfrac{16x^2 + 8x - 4}{4} = \dfrac{16x^2}{4} + \dfrac{8x}{4} - \dfrac{4}{4}$
$$= 4x^2 + 2x - 1$$

22. $\dfrac{-12x^2 - 6x + 5}{-3x} = \dfrac{(-1)(-12x^2 - 6x + 5)}{(-1)(-3x)}$
$$= \dfrac{12x^2 + 6x - 5}{3x}$$
$$= \dfrac{12x^2}{3x} + \dfrac{6x}{3x} - \dfrac{5}{3x}$$
$$= 4x + 2 - \dfrac{5}{3x}$$

23.
$$
\begin{array}{r}
4x + 5 \\
2x - 3 \overline{)\,8x^2 - 2x - 15} \\
\underline{8x^2 - 12x} \\
10x - 15 \\
\underline{10x - 15} \\
0
\end{array}
$$
$$\dfrac{8x^2 - 2x - 15}{2x - 3} = 4x + 5$$

24.
$$
\begin{array}{r}
3x - 2 \\
4x + 5 \overline{)\,12x^2 + 7x - 12} \\
\underline{12x^2 + 15x} \\
-8x - 12 \\
\underline{-8x - 10} \\
-2
\end{array}
$$
$$\dfrac{12x^2 + 7x - 12}{4x + 5} = 3x - 2 - \dfrac{2}{4x + 5}$$

25. a. $5730 = 5.73 \times 10^3$

b. $\dfrac{4.46 \times 10^9}{5.73 \times 10^3} = \left(\dfrac{4.46}{5.73}\right)\left(\dfrac{10^9}{10^3}\right)$
$$\approx 0.778 \times 10^6$$
$$\approx 7.78 \times 10^5$$

Chapter 5: *Exponents and Polynomials*

Chapter 5 Cumulative Review Test

1. $12 + 8 \div 2^2 + 3 = 12 + 8 \div 4 + 3$
$$= 12 + 2 + 3$$
$$= 17$$

2. $7 - (2x - 3) + 2x - 8(1 - x)$
$$= 7 - 2x + 3 + 2x - 8 + 8x$$
$$= 7 + 3 - 8 - 2x + 2x + 8x$$
$$= 2 + 8x$$
$$= 8x + 2$$

3. $-4x^2 + x - 7 = -4(-2)^2 + (-2) - 7$
$$= -4(4) - 2 - 7$$
$$= -16 - 2 - 7$$
$$= -18 - 7$$
$$= -25$$

4. $\dfrac{5}{8} = \dfrac{5t}{6} + 2$
$$24\left(\dfrac{5}{8}\right) = 24\left(\dfrac{5t}{6} + 2\right)$$
$$15 = 20t + 48$$
$$15 - 48 = 20t + 48 - 48$$
$$-33 = 20t$$
$$\dfrac{-33}{20} = \dfrac{20t}{20}$$
$$-\dfrac{33}{20} = t$$

5. $3x + 5 = 4(x - 2)$
$$3x + 5 = 4x - 8$$
$$3x - 3x + 5 = 4x - 3x - 8$$
$$5 = x - 8$$
$$5 + 8 = x - 8 + 8$$
$$13 = x$$

6. $3(x + 2) + 3x - 5 = 4x + 1$
$$3x + 6 + 3x - 5 = 4x + 1$$
$$6x + 1 = 4x + 1$$
$$2x = 0$$
$$x = 0$$

7. $3x - 2 = y - 7$
$$y - 7 = 3x - 2$$
$$y = 3x - 2 + 7$$
$$y = 3x + 5$$

8. Let $(x_1, y_1) = (1, 3)$ and $(x_2, y_2) = (5, 1)$
$$m = \dfrac{y_2 - y_1}{x_2 - x_1} = \dfrac{1 - 3}{5 - 1} = \dfrac{-2}{4} = -\dfrac{1}{2}$$

9. Put each equation in slope intercept form.

$3x - 5y = 7$ $\qquad\qquad$ $5y + 3x = 2$
$-5y = -3x + 7$ $\qquad\qquad$ $5y = -3x + 2$
$y = \dfrac{-3x + 7}{-5}$ $\qquad\qquad$ $y = \dfrac{-3x + 2}{5}$
$y = \dfrac{3}{5}x - \dfrac{7}{5}$ $\qquad\qquad$ $y = -\dfrac{3}{5}x + \dfrac{2}{5}$

The slope of the first line is $\dfrac{3}{5}$ while the slope of the second lint is $-\dfrac{3}{5}$. Since the slopes are not equal, the two lines are not parallel.

10. $\left(\dfrac{5xy^{-3}}{x^{-2}y^5}\right)^2 = \left(5x^{1-(-2)}y^{-3-5}\right)^2$
$$= \left(5x^3 y^{-8}\right)^2$$
$$= 5^2 x^{3 \cdot 2} y^{-8 \cdot 2}$$
$$= \dfrac{25x^6}{y^{16}}$$

11. $-5x + 2 - 7x^2 = -7x^2 - 5x + 2$; second degree

12. $\left(x^2 + 4x - 3\right) + \left(2x^2 + 5x + 1\right)$
$$= x^2 + 4x - 3 + 2x^2 + 5x + 1$$
$$= x^2 + 2x^2 + 4x + 5x - 3 + 1$$
$$= 3x^2 + 9x - 2$$

13. $\left(6a^2 + 3a + 2\right) - \left(a^2 - 3a - 3\right)$
$$= 6a^2 + 3a + 2 - a^2 + 3a + 3$$
$$= 6a^2 - a^2 + 3a + 3a + 2 + 3$$
$$= 5a^2 + 6a + 5$$

14. $(5t-3)(2t-1) = 5t \cdot 2t + 5t \cdot (-1) - 3 \cdot 2t - 3 \cdot (-1)$

$\qquad = 10t^2 - 5t - 6t + 3$

$\qquad = 10t^2 - 11t + 3$

15. $(2x-1)(3x^2 - 5x + 2)$

$\qquad = 2x(3x^2 - 5x + 2) - 1(3x^2 - 5x + 2)$

$\qquad = 6x^3 - 10x^2 + 4x - 3x^2 + 5x - 2$

$\qquad = 6x^3 - 13x^2 + 9x - 2$

16. $\dfrac{10d^2 + 12d - 8}{4d} = \dfrac{10d^2}{4d} + \dfrac{12d}{4d} - \dfrac{8}{4d}$

$\qquad\qquad\qquad = \dfrac{5}{2}d + 3 - \dfrac{2}{d}$

17.
$$
\begin{array}{r}
2x+5 \\
3x-2\overline{)\,6x^2 + 11x - 10} \\
\underline{6x^2 - 4x} \\
15x - 10 \\
\underline{15x - 10} \\
0
\end{array}
$$

$\dfrac{6x^2 + 11x - 10}{3x - 2} = 2x + 5$

18. $\dfrac{x}{8} = \dfrac{1.25}{3}$

$3x = 8(1.25)$

$3x = 10$

$x = \dfrac{10}{3} \approx 3.33$

Eight cans of soup cost $3.33.

19. Let b = Bob's average speed.

Then $b + 7$ = Nick's average speed.

$d = r \cdot t$. Both Bob and Nick drove for 0.5 hour and the total distance they covered was 60 miles.

$0.5b + 0.5(b + 7) = 60$

$0.5b + 0.5b + 3.5 = 60$

$\qquad\quad b + 3.5 = 60$

$\qquad\qquad\quad b = 56.5$

Bob's average speed was 56.5 miles per hour, and Nick's average speed was 56.5 + 7 = 63.5 miles per hour.

20. Let x = the width of the rectangle.

Then $3x - 2$ = the length of the rectangle.

$P = 2l + 2w$

$28 = 2(3x - 2) + 2x$

$28 = 6x - 4 + 2x$

$28 = 8x - 4$

$32 = 8x$

$4 = x$

The width of the rectangle is 4 feet and the length is 3(4) – 2 = 10 feet.

Chapter 6

Exercise Set 6.1

1. To factor an expression means to write the expression as the product of factors.

2. A prime number is an integer greater than 1 that has exactly two factors, itself and 1.

3. A composite number is a positive integer, other than 1, that is not a prime number.

4. The number 1 is not a prime number. It is called unit.

5. The greatest common factor of two or more numbers is the greatest number that divides into all the numbers.

6. Answers will vary.

7. $1, 2, 4, x, 2x, 4x, x^2, 2x^2, 4x^2$ and the opposites of these factors.

8. A factoring problem may be checked by multiplying the factors.

9. $56 = 8 \cdot 7$
$\quad = 2 \cdot 4 \cdot 7$
$\quad = 2 \cdot 2 \cdot 2 \cdot 7$
$\quad = 2^3 \cdot 7$

10. $120 = 10 \cdot 12$
$\quad = 2 \cdot 5 \cdot 2 \cdot 6$
$\quad = 2 \cdot 5 \cdot 2 \cdot 2 \cdot 3$
$\quad = 2 \cdot 2 \cdot 2 \cdot 3 \cdot 5$
$\quad = 2^3 \cdot 3 \cdot 5$

11. $90 = 9 \cdot 10$
$\quad = 3 \cdot 3 \cdot 2 \cdot 5$
$\quad = 2 \cdot 3^2 \cdot 5$

12. $540 = 10 \cdot 54$
$\quad = 2 \cdot 5 \cdot 6 \cdot 9$
$\quad = 2 \cdot 5 \cdot 2 \cdot 3 \cdot 3 \cdot 3$
$\quad = 2 \cdot 2 \cdot 3 \cdot 3 \cdot 3 \cdot 5$
$\quad = 2^2 \cdot 3^3 \cdot 5$

13. $248 = 4 \cdot 62$
$\quad = 2 \cdot 2 \cdot 2 \cdot 31$
$\quad = 2^3 \cdot 31$

14. $144 = 12 \cdot 12$
$\quad = 2 \cdot 6 \cdot 2 \cdot 6$
$\quad = 2 \cdot 2 \cdot 3 \cdot 2 \cdot 2 \cdot 3$
$\quad = 2 \cdot 2 \cdot 2 \cdot 2 \cdot 3 \cdot 3$
$\quad = 2^4 \cdot 3^2$

15. $20 = 2^2 \cdot 5$, $24 = 2^3 \cdot 3$, so the greatest common factor is 2^2 or 4.

16. $45 = 3^2 \cdot 5$, $27 = 3^3$, so the greatest common factor is 3^2 or 9.

17. $70 = 2 \cdot 5 \cdot 7$, $98 = 2 \cdot 7^2$, so the greatest common factor is $2 \cdot 7$ or 14.

18. $120 = 2^3 \cdot 3 \cdot 5$, $96 = 2^5 \cdot 3$, so the greatest common factor is $2^3 \cdot 3$ or 24.

19. $80 = 2^4 \cdot 5$, $126 = 2 \cdot 3^2 \cdot 7$, so the greatest common factor is 2.

20. $88 = 2^3 \cdot 11$, $160 = 2^5 \cdot 5$, so the greatest common factor is 2^3 or 8.

21. The greatest common factor is x.

22. The greatest common factor is y^2.

23. The greatest common factor is $3x$.

24. The greatest common factor is $2p$.

25. The greatest common factor is a.

26. The greatest common factor is 1.

27. The greatest common factor is qr.

28. The greatest common factor is xy^2.

29. The greatest common factor is $x^3 y^5$.

30. The greatest common factor is 6.

31. The greatest common factor is 1.

32. The greatest common factor is $3s^2$.

33. The greatest common factor is $x^2 y^2$.

34. The greatest common factor is $4x^4 y^2$.

35. The greatest common factor is x.

36. The greatest common factor is $3p^2q^2$.

37. The greatest common factor is $x-4$.

38. The greatest common factor is $x-5$.

39. The greatest common factor is $2x-3$.

40. The greatest common factor is $9x-3$.

41. The greatest common factor is $3w+5$.

42. The greatest common factor is $b+3$.

43. The greatest common factor is $x-4$.

44. The greatest common factor is $3(x+2)$.

45. The greatest common factor is $x-1$.

46. The greatest common factor is $n+2$.

47. The greatest common factor is $x-9$.

48. The greatest common factor is $a-3$.

49. The greatest common factor is 4.
$$4x-8 = 4\cdot x - 4\cdot 2$$
$$= 4(x-2)$$

50. The greatest common factor is 2.
$$4x+2 = 2\cdot 2x + 2\cdot 1$$
$$= 2(2x+1)$$

51. The greatest common factor is 5.
$$15x-5 = 5\cdot 3x - 5\cdot 1$$
$$= 5(3x-1)$$

52. The greatest common factor is 3.
$$12x+15 = 3\cdot 4x + 3\cdot 5$$
$$= 3(4x+5)$$

53. The greatest common factor is 7.
$$7q+28 = 7\cdot q + 7\cdot 4$$
$$= 7(q+4)$$

54. The greatest common factor is t.
$$3t^2-10t = t\cdot 3t - t\cdot 10$$
$$= t(3t-10)$$

55. The greatest common factor is $3x$.
$$9x^2-12x = 3x\cdot 3x - 3x\cdot 4$$
$$= 3x(3x-4)$$

56. The greatest common factor is $6y$.
$$24y-6y^2 = 6y\cdot 4 - 6y\cdot y$$
$$= 6y(4-y)$$

57. The greatest common factor is x^4.
$$7x^5-9x^4 = x^4\cdot 7x - x^4\cdot 9$$
$$= x^4(7x-9)$$

58. The greatest common factor is $9x$.
$$9x+27x^3 = 9x\cdot 1 + 9x\cdot 3x^2$$
$$= 9x(1+3x^2)$$

59. The greatest common factor is $3x^2$.
$$3x^5-12x^2 = 3x^2\cdot x^3 - 3x^2\cdot 4$$
$$= 3x^2(x^3-4)$$

60. The greatest common factor is $2p$.
$$26p^2-8p = 2p\cdot 13p - 2p\cdot 4$$
$$= 2p(13p-4)$$

61. The greatest common factor is $12x^8$.
$$36x^{12}+24x^8 = 12x^8\cdot 3x^4 + 12x^8\cdot 2$$
$$= 12x^8(3x^4+2)$$

62. The greatest common factor is $15y^{10}$.
$$45y^{12}+30y^{10} = 15y^{10}\cdot 3y^2 + 15y^{10}\cdot 2$$
$$= 15y^{10}(3y^2+2)$$

63. The greatest common factor is $9y^3$.
$$27y^{15}-9y^3 = 9y^3\cdot 3y^{12} - 9y^3\cdot 1$$
$$= 9y^3(3y^{12}-1)$$

64. The greatest common factor is $5w^3$.
$$30w^5+25w^3 = 5w^3\cdot 6w^2 + 5w^3\cdot 5$$
$$= 5w^3(6w^2+5)$$

65. The greatest common factor is y.
$$y+6x^3y = y\cdot 1 + y\cdot 6x^3$$
$$= y(1+6x^3)$$

66. The greatest common factor is $2x$.
$$4x^2y-6x = 2x\cdot 2xy - 2x\cdot 3$$
$$= 2x(2xy-3)$$

67. The greatest common factor is a^2.

$$7a^4 + 3a^2 = a^2 \cdot 7a^2 + a^2 \cdot 3$$
$$= a^2 \left(7a^2 + 3 \right)$$

68. The greatest common factor is $3x^2 y$.

$$3x^2 y + 6x^2 y^2 = 3x^2 y \cdot 1 + 3x^2 y \cdot 2y$$
$$= 3x^2 y \left(1 + 2y \right)$$

69. The greatest common factor is $4xy$.

$$16xy^2 z + 4x^3 y = 4xy \cdot 4yz + 4xy \cdot x^2$$
$$= 4xy \left(4yz + x^2 \right)$$

70. The greatest common factor is $16mn^2$.

$$48m^4 n^2 - 16mn^2 = 16mn^2 \cdot 3m^3 - 16mn^2 \cdot 1$$
$$= 16mn^2 \left(3m^3 - 1 \right)$$

71. The greatest common factor is $4x^2 yz^3$.

$$80x^5 y^3 z^4 - 36x^2 yz^3$$
$$= 4x^2 yz^3 \cdot 20x^3 y^2 z - 4x^2 yz^3 \cdot 9$$
$$= 4x^2 yz^3 \left(20x^3 y^2 z - 9 \right)$$

72. The greatest common factor is $8y^4 z^2$.

$$56xy^5 z^{13} - 24y^4 z^2 = 8y^4 z^2 \cdot 7xyz^{11} - 8y^4 z^2 \cdot 3$$
$$= 8y^4 z^2 \left(7xyz^{11} - 3 \right)$$

73. The greatest common factor is $25x^2 yz$.

$$25x^2 yz^3 + 25x^3 yz = 25x^2 yz \cdot z^2 + 25x^2 yz \cdot x$$
$$= 25x^2 yz \left(z^2 + x \right)$$

74. The greatest common factor is $y^2 z^3$.

$$13y^5 z^3 - 11xy^2 z^5 = y^2 z^3 \cdot 13y^3 - y^2 z^3 \cdot 11xz^2$$
$$= y^2 z^3 \left(13y^3 - 11xz^2 \right)$$

75. The greatest common factor is $x^4 y^3 z^9$.

$$19x^4 y^{12} z^{13} - 8x^5 y^3 z^9$$
$$= x^4 y^3 z^9 \cdot 19y^9 z^4 - x^4 y^3 z^9 \cdot 8x$$
$$= x^4 y^3 z^9 \left(19y^9 z^4 - 8x \right)$$

76. The greatest common factor is $4r^4 s^4 t$.

$$16r^4 s^5 t^3 - 20r^5 s^4 t = 4r^4 s^4 t \cdot 4st^2 - 4r^4 s^4 t \cdot 5r$$
$$= 4r^4 s^4 t \left(4st^2 - 5r \right)$$

77. The greatest common factor is 4.

$$8c^2 - 4c - 32 = 4 \cdot 2c^2 - 4 \cdot c - 4 \cdot 8$$
$$= 4 \left(2c^2 - c - 8 \right)$$

78. The greatest common factor is x.

$$x^3 - 4x^2 - 3x = x \cdot x^2 - x \cdot 4x - x \cdot 3$$
$$= x \left(x^2 - 4x - 3 \right)$$

79. The greatest common factor is 3.

$$9x^2 + 18x + 3 = 3 \cdot 3x^2 + 3 \cdot 6x + 3 \cdot 1$$
$$= 3 \left(3x^2 + 6x + 1 \right)$$

80. The greatest common factor is 4.

$$4x^2 + 8x + 24 = 4 \cdot x^2 + 4 \cdot 2x + 4 \cdot 6$$
$$= 4 \left(x^2 + 2x + 6 \right)$$

81. The greatest common factor is $4x$.

$$4x^3 - 8x^2 + 12x = 4x \cdot x^2 - 4x \cdot 2x + 4x \cdot 3$$
$$= 4x \left(x^2 - 2x + 3 \right)$$

82. The greatest common factor is $4a$.

$$12a^3 - 16a^2 - 4a = 4a \cdot 3a^2 - 4a \cdot 4a - 4a \cdot 1$$
$$= 4a \left(3a^2 - 4a - 1 \right)$$

83. The greatest common factor is 8.

$$40b^2 - 48c + 24 = 8 \cdot 5b^2 - 8 \cdot 6c + 8 \cdot 3$$
$$= 8 \left(5b^2 - 6c + 3 \right)$$

84. The greatest common factor is x.

$$5x^3 - xy^2 + x = x \cdot 5x^2 - x \cdot y^2 + x \cdot 1$$
$$= x \left(5x^2 - y^2 + 1 \right)$$

85. The greatest common factor is 3.

$$15p^2 - 6p + 9 = 3 \cdot 5p^2 - 3 \cdot 2p + 3 \cdot 3$$
$$= 3 \left(5p^2 - 2p + 3 \right)$$

86. The greatest common factor is $9y$.

$$45y^3 - 63y^2 + 27y = 9y \cdot 5y^2 - 9y \cdot 7y + 9y \cdot 3$$
$$= 9y \left(5y^2 - 7y + 3 \right)$$

87. The greatest common factor is $3a$.

$$9a^4 - 6a^3 + 3ab = 3a \cdot 3a^3 - 3a \cdot 2a^2 + 3a \cdot b$$
$$= 3a \left(3a^3 - 2a^2 + b \right)$$

88. The greatest common factor is $5v$.
$$45v^4w^2 + 10v^2x - 20vw^5$$
$$= 5v \cdot 9v^3w^2 + 5v \cdot 2vx - 5v \cdot 4w^5$$
$$= 5v\left(9v^3w^2 + 2vx - 4w^5\right)$$

89. The greatest common factor is xy.
$$8x^2y + 12xy^2 + 5xy = xy \cdot 8x + xy \cdot 12y + xy \cdot 5$$
$$= xy(8x + 12y + 5)$$

90. The greatest common factor is 2.
$$52x^2y^2 + 16xy^3 + 26z$$
$$= 2 \cdot 26x^2y^2 + 2 \cdot 8xy^3 + 2 \cdot 13z$$
$$= 2\left(26x^2y^2 + 8xy^3 + 13z\right)$$

91. The greatest common factor is $x - 7$.
$$x(x-7) + 6(x-7) = (x-7)(x+6)$$

92. The greatest common factor is $3x - 4$.
$$9x(3x-4) - 4(3x-4) = (3x-4)(9x-4)$$

93. The greatest common factor is $a - 2$.
$$3b(a-2) - 4(a-2) = (a-2)(3b-4)$$

94. The greatest common factor is $7x + 1$.
$$3x(7x+1) - 2(7x+1) = (7x+1)(3x-2)$$

95. The greatest common factor is $2x + 1$.
$$4x(2x+1) + 1(2x+1) = (2x+1)(4x+1)$$

96. The greatest common factor is $5m - 1$.
$$4m(5m-1) - 3(5m-1) = (5m-1)(4m-3)$$

97. The greatest common factor is $2x + 1$.
$$5x(2x+1) + 2x + 1 = 5x(2x+1) + 1(2x+1)$$
$$= (2x+1)(5x+1)$$

98. The greatest common factor is $4x - 5$.
$$3x(4x-5) + 4x - 5$$
$$= 3x(4x-5) + 1(4x-5)$$
$$= (4x-5)(3x+1)$$

99. The greatest common factor is $6c + 7$.
$$3c(6c+7) - 2(6c+7) = (6c+7)(3c-2)$$

100. The greatest common factor is $t - 2$.
$$5t(t-2) - 3(t-2) = (t-2)(5t-3)$$

101. $12\nabla - 6\nabla^2 = 6\nabla \cdot 2 - 6\nabla \cdot \nabla$
$$= 6\nabla(2 - \nabla)$$

102. $3\star + 6 = 3 \cdot \star + 3 \cdot 2 = 3(\star + 2)$

103. $12\square^3 - 4\square^2 + 4\square$
$$= 4\square \cdot 3\square^2 - 4\square \cdot \square + 4\square \cdot 1$$
$$= 4\square\left(3\square^2 - \square + 1\right)$$

104. $\copyright + 11\triangle$ cannot be factored.

105. The greatest common factor is $2x^2(2x+7)$.
$$6x^5(2x+7) + 4x^3(2x+7) - 2x^2(2x+7)$$
$$= 2x^2(2x+7) \cdot 3x^3 + 2x^2(2x+7) \cdot 2x$$
$$\quad + 2x^2(2x+7) \cdot (-1)$$
$$= 2x^2(2x+7)\left(3x^3 + 2x - 1\right)$$

106. The greatest common factor is $2(x-3)$.
$$4x^2(x-3)^3 - 6x(x-3)^2 + 4(x-3)$$
$$= 2(x-3) \cdot 2x^2(x-3)^2 - 2(x-3) \cdot 3x(x-3)$$
$$\quad - 2(x-3) \cdot 2$$
$$= 2(x-3)\left[2x^2(x-3)^2 - 3x(x-3) + 2\right]$$

107. $x^2 + 2x + 3x + 6$
$$= x \cdot x + x \cdot 2 + 3 \cdot x + 3 \cdot 2$$
$$= x(x+2) + 3(x+2)$$
$$= (x+2)(x+3)$$

108. $2x - (x-5) + 4(3-x) = 2x - x + 5 + 12 - 4x$
$$= x - 4x + 17$$
$$= -3x + 17$$

109. $4 + 3(x-8) = x - 4(x+2)$
$$4 + 3x - 24 = x - 4x - 8$$
$$3x - 20 = -3x - 8$$
$$6x = 12$$
$$x = 2$$

110. $4x - 5y = 20$
$$-5y = -4x + 20$$
$$y = -\frac{-4x + 20}{-5}$$
$$y = \frac{4}{5}x - 4$$

111. $V = \dfrac{1}{3}\pi r^2 h$

$= \dfrac{1}{3}\pi(4)^2(12)$

$= \dfrac{1}{3}\pi(16)(12)$

$= 64\pi \text{ in.}^3 \text{ or } 201.06 \text{ in.}^3$

112. Let x = smaller number, then $2x - 1$ = the larger number.

$x + (2x - 1) = 41$

$x + 2x - 1 = 41$

$3x - 1 = 41$

$3x = 42$

$x = 14$

$2x - 1 = 2(14) - 1 = 28 - 1 = 27$

The numbers are 14 and 27.

113. $\left(\dfrac{3x^2 y^3}{2x^5 y^2}\right)^2 = \left(\dfrac{3y}{2x^3}\right)^2$

$= \dfrac{(3y)^2}{(2x^3)^2}$

$= \dfrac{3^2 y^2}{2^2 (x^3)^2}$

$= \dfrac{9y^2}{4x^6}$

Exercise Set 6.2

1. The first step in any factoring by grouping problem is to factor out a common factor, if one exists.

2. To check the solution to a factoring by grouping problem, multiply the factors to see if the product is the same as the original expression.

3. If you multiply $(x - 2y)(x - 3)$ using the FOIL method, you get the polynomial $x^2 - 3x - 2xy + 6y$

4. If you multiply $(x - 2)(x + 4)$ by the FOIL method, you get the polynomial $x^2 + 4x - 2x - 8$

5. The number that changes the sign of each term in an expression when factored from each term is -1.

6. Answers will vary.

7. $x^2 + 3x + 2x + 6 = x(x + 3) + 2(x + 3)$
$= (x + 3)(x + 2)$

8. $x^2 + 7x + 3x + 21 = x(x + 7) + 3(x + 7)$
$= (x + 7)(x + 3)$

9. $x^2 + 5x + 4x + 20 = x(x + 5) + 4(x + 5)$
$= (x + 5)(x + 4)$

10. $x^2 - x + 3x - 3 = x(x - 1) + 3(x - 1)$
$= (x - 1)(x + 3)$

11. $x^2 + 2x + 5x + 10 = x(x + 2) + 5(x + 2)$
$= (x + 2)(x + 5)$

12. $x^2 - 6x + 5x - 30 = x(x - 6) + 5(x - 6)$
$= (x - 6)(x + 5)$

13. $c^2 - 4c + 7c - 28 = c(c - 4) + 7(c - 4)$
$= (c - 4)(c + 7)$

14. $r^2 - 4r + 6r - 24 = r(r - 4) + 6(r - 4)$
$= (r - 4)(r + 6)$

15. $4x^2 - 6x + 6x - 9 = 2x(2x - 3) + 3(2x - 3)$
$= (2x - 3)(2x + 3)$

16. $4b^2 - 10b + 10b - 25$
$= 2b(2b - 5) + 5(2b - 5)$
$= (2b - 5)(2b + 5)$

17. $3x^2 + 9x + x + 3 = 3x(x + 3) + 1(x + 3)$
$= (x + 3)(3x + 1)$

18. $a^2 + a + 3a + 3 = a(a + 1) + 3(a + 1)$
$= (a + 1)(a + 3)$

19. $6x^2 + 3x - 2x - 1 = 3x(2x + 1) - 1(2x + 1)$
$= (2x + 1)(3x - 1)$

20. $5x^2 + 30x - 3x - 18 = 5x(x + 6) - 3(x + 6)$
$= (x + 6)(5x - 3)$

21. $8x^2 + 32x + x + 4 = 8x(x + 4) + 1(x + 4)$
$= (x + 4)(8x + 1)$

22. $9w^2 - 6w - 6w + 4$
$= 3w(3w - 2) - 2(3w - 2)$
$= (3w - 2)(3w - 2) = (3w - 2)^2$

23. $12t^2 - 8t - 3t + 2$
$= 4t(3t - 2) - 1(3t - 2)$
$= (3t - 2)(4t - 1)$

24. $12x^2 + 42x - 10x - 35$
$= 6x(2x + 7) - 5(2x + 7)$
$= (2x + 7)(6x - 5)$

25. $x^2 + 9x - x - 9 = x(x + 9) - 1(x + 9)$
$= (x + 9)(x - 1)$

26. $35x^2 - 40x + 21x - 24$
$= 5x(7x - 8) + 3(7x - 8)$
$= (7x - 8)(5x + 3)$

27. $6p^2 + 15p - 4p - 10$
$= 3p(2p + 5) - 2(2p + 5)$
$= (2p + 5)(3p - 2)$

28. $10c^2 + 25c - 6c - 15$
$= 5c(2c + 5) - 3(2c + 5)$
$= (2c + 5)(5c - 3)$

29. $x^2 + 2xy - 3xy - 6y^2$
$= x(x + 2y) - 3y(x + 2y)$
$= (x + 2y)(x - 3y)$

30. $x^2 - 3xy + 4xy - 12y^2$
$= x(x - 3y) + 4y(x - 3y)$
$= (x - 3y)(x + 4y)$

31. $3x^2 + 2xy - 9xy - 6y^2$
$= x(3x + 2y) - 3y(3x + 2y)$
$= (3x + 2y)(x - 3y)$

32. $3x^2 - 18xy + 4xy - 24y^2$
$= 3x(x - 6y) + 4y(x - 6y)$
$= (x - 6y)(3x + 4y)$

33. $10x^2 - 12xy - 25xy + 30y^2$
$= 2x(5x - 6y) - 5y(5x - 6y)$
$= (5x - 6y)(2x - 5y)$

34. $6a^2 - 3ab + 4ab - 2b^2$
$= 3a(2a - b) + 2b(2a - b)$
$= (2a - b)(3a + 2b)$

35. $x^2 - bx - ax + ab$
$= x(x - b) - a(x - b)$
$= (x - b)(x - a)$

36. $x^2 + bx + ax + ab$
$= x(x + b) + a(x + b)$
$= (x + b)(x + a)$

37. $xy + 9x - 5y - 45 = x(y + 9) - 5(y + 9)$
$= (y + 9)(x - 5)$

38. $x^2 - 2x + ax - 2a = x(x - 2) + a(x - 2)$
$= (x - 2)(x + a)$

39. $a^2 + 3a + ab + 3b = a(a + 3) + b(a + 3)$
$= (a + 3)(a + b)$

40. $3x^2 - 15x - 2xy + 10y = 3x(x - 5) - 2y(x - 5)$
$= (x - 5)(3x - 2y)$

41. $xy - x + 5y - 5 = x(y - 1) + 5(y - 1)$
$= (y - 1)(x + 5)$

42. $y^2 - yb + ya - ab = y(y - b) + a(y - b)$
$= (y - b)(y + a)$

43. $12 + 8y - 3x - 2xy = 4(3 + 2y) - x(3 + 2y)$
$= (3 + 2y)(4 - x)$

44. $7y - 49 - xy + 7x = 7(y - 7) - x(y - 7)$
$= (y - 7)(7 - x)$

45. $z^3 + 5z^2 + z + 5 = z^2(z + 5) + 1(z + 5)$
$= (z + 5)(z^2 + 1)$

46. $x^3 - 3x^2 + 2x - 6 = x^2(x-3) + 2(x-3)$

$\qquad\qquad\qquad = (x-3)(x^2+2)$

47. $x^3 - 5x^2 + 8x - 40 = x^2(x-5) + 8(x-5)$

$\qquad\qquad\qquad = (x-5)(x^2+8)$

48. $y^3 - 3y + 2y^2 - 6 = y^3 + 2y^2 - 3y - 6$

$\qquad\qquad\qquad = y^2(y+2) - 3(y+2)$

$\qquad\qquad\qquad = (y+2)(y^2-3)$

49. $2x^2 - 12x + 8x - 48$

$\qquad = 2 \cdot x^2 - 2 \cdot 6x + 2 \cdot 4x - 2 \cdot 24$

$\qquad = 2(x^2 - 6x + 4x - 24)$

$\qquad = 2[x(x-6) + 4(x-6)]$

$\qquad = 2(x-6)(x+4)$

50. $3x^2 - 3x - 3x + 3 = 3 \cdot x^2 - 3 \cdot x - 3 \cdot x + 3 \cdot 1$

$\qquad\qquad\qquad = 3(x^2 - x - x + 1)$

$\qquad\qquad\qquad = 3[x(x-1) - 1(x-1)]$

$\qquad\qquad\qquad = 3(x-1)(x-1)$

$\qquad\qquad\qquad = 3(x-1)^2$

51. $4x^2 + 8x + 8x + 16$

$\qquad = 4 \cdot x^2 + 4 \cdot 2x + 4 \cdot 2x + 4 \cdot 4$

$\qquad = 4(x^2 + 2x + 2x + 4)$

$\qquad = 4[x(x+2) + 2(x+2)]$

$\qquad = 4(x+2)(x+2)$

$\qquad = 4(x+2)^2$

52. $3z^4 - 3z^3 - 7z^3 + 7z^2$

$\qquad = z^2 \cdot 3z^2 - z^2 \cdot 3z - z^2 \cdot 7z + z^2 \cdot 7$

$\qquad = z^2(3z^2 - 3z - 7z + 7)$

$\qquad = z^2[3z(z-1) - 7(z-1)]$

$\qquad = z^2(z-1)(3z-7)$

53. $6x^3 + 9x^2 - 2x^2 - 3x$

$\qquad = x \cdot 6x^2 + x \cdot 9x - x \cdot 2x - x \cdot 3$

$\qquad = x(6x^2 + 9x - 2x - 3)$

$\qquad = x[3x(2x+3) - 1(2x+3)]$

$\qquad = x(2x+3)(3x-1)$

54. $9x^3 + 6x^2 - 45x^2 - 30x$

$\qquad = 3x \cdot 3x^2 + 3x \cdot 2x - 3x \cdot 15x - 3x \cdot 10$

$\qquad = 3x(3x^2 + 2x - 15x - 10)$

$\qquad = 3x[x(3x+2) - 5(3x+2)]$

$\qquad = 3x(x-5)(3x+2)$

55. $p^3 - 6p^2q + 2p^2q - 12pq^2$

$\qquad = p \cdot p^2 - p \cdot 6pq + p \cdot 2pq - p \cdot 12q^2$

$\qquad = p(p^2 - 6pq + 2pq - 12q^2)$

$\qquad = p[p(p-6q) + 2q(p-6q)]$

$\qquad = p(p-6q)(p+2q)$

56. $18x^2 + 27xy + 12xy + 18y^2$

$\qquad = 3 \cdot 6x^2 + 3 \cdot 9xy + 3 \cdot 4xy + 3 \cdot 6y^2$

$\qquad = 3(6x^2 + 9xy + 4xy + 6y^2)$

$\qquad = 3[3x(2x+3y) + 2y(2x+3y)]$

$\qquad = 3(2x+3y)(3x+2y)$

57. $5x + 3y + xy + 15 = xy + 5x + 3y + 15$

$\qquad\qquad\qquad = x(y+5) + 3(y+5)$

$\qquad\qquad\qquad = (y+5)(x+3)$

58. $5m + 2w + mw + 10$

$\qquad = mw + 2w + 5m + 10$

$\qquad = w(m+2) + 5(m+2)$

$\qquad = (m+2)(w+5)$

59. $6x + 5y + xy + 30 = 6x + xy + 5y + 30$

$\qquad\qquad\qquad = x(6+y) + 5(y+6)$

$\qquad\qquad\qquad = (x+5)(y+6)$

60. $ax - 10 - 5x + 2a = ax - 5x + 2a - 10$

$\qquad\qquad\qquad = x(a-5) + 2(a-5)$

$\qquad\qquad\qquad = (x+2)(a-5)$

61. $ax + by + ay + bx = ax + ay + bx + by$
$$= a(x+y) + b(x+y)$$
$$= (a+b)(x+y)$$

62. $ax - 21 - 3a + 7x = ax - 3a + 7x - 21$
$$= a(x-3) + 7(x-3)$$
$$= (a+7)(x-3)$$

63. $rs - 42 + 6s - 7r$
$$= rs - 7r + 6s - 42$$
$$= r(s-7) + 6(s-7)$$
$$= (s-7)(r+6)$$

64. $ca - 2b + 2a - cb = ca - cb + 2a - 2b$
$$= c(a-b) + 2(a-b)$$
$$= (c+2)(a-b)$$

65. $dc + 3c - ad - 3a = c(d+3) - a(d+3)$
$$= (d+3)(c-a)$$

66. $ac - bd - ad + bc = ac - ad + bc - bd$
$$= a(c-d) + b(c-d)$$
$$= (a+b)(c-d)$$

67. Not *any* arrangement of the terms of a polynomial is factorable by grouping. $xy + 2x + 5y + 10$ is factorable but $xy + 10 + 2x + 5y$ is not factorable in this arrangement.

68. $\otimes^2 + 3\otimes + 4\otimes + 12$
$$= \otimes(\otimes+3) + 4(\otimes+3)$$
$$= (\otimes+3)(\otimes+4)$$

69. $\odot^2 + 3\odot - 5\odot - 15 = \odot(\odot+3) - 5(\odot+3)$
$$= (\odot+3)(\odot-5)$$

70. $\triangle^2 + 2\triangle - \triangle + 6$
cannot be factored

71. a. $2x^2 - 11x + 15 = 2x^2 - 5x - 6x + 15$

   b. $2x^2 - 5x - 6x + 15 = x(2x-5) - 3(2x-5)$
$$= (x-3)(2x-5)$$

72. a. $3x^2 + 10x + 8 = 3x^2 + 4x + 6x + 8$

   b. $3x^2 + 4x + 6x + 8$
$$= x(3x+4) + 2(3x+4)$$
$$= (3x+4)(x+2)$$

73. a. $2x^2 - 11x + 15 = 2x^2 - 6x - 5x + 15$

   b. $2x^2 - 6x - 5x + 15$
$$= 2x(x-3) - 5(x-3)$$
$$= (x-3)(2x-5)$$

74. a. $3x^2 + 10x + 8 = 3x^2 + 6x + 4x + 8$

   b. $3x^2 + 6x + 4x + 8$
$$= 3x(x+2) + 4(x+2)$$
$$= (x+2)(3x+4)$$

75. a. $4x^2 - 17x - 15 = 4x^2 + 3x - 20x - 15$

   b. $4x^2 + 3x - 20x - 15 = x(4x+3) - 5(4x+3)$
$$= (x-5)(4x+3)$$

76. a. $4x^2 - 17x - 15 = 4x^2 - 20x + 3x - 15$

   b. $4x^2 - 20x + 3x - 15 = 4x(x-5) + 3(x-5)$
$$= (4x+3)(x-5)$$

77. $\star\odot + 3\star + 2\odot + 6 = \star(\odot+3) + 2(\odot+3)$
$$= (\odot+3)(\star+2)$$

78. $2\triangle^2 - 4\triangle\star - 8\triangle\star + 16\star^2$
$$= 2\cdot\triangle^2 - 2\cdot2\triangle\star - 2\cdot4\triangle\star + 2\cdot8\star^2$$
$$= 2(\triangle^2 - 2\triangle\star - 4\triangle\star + 8\star^2)$$
$$= 2[\triangle(\triangle - 2\star) - 4\star(\triangle - 2\star)]$$
$$= 2(\triangle - 2\star)(\triangle - 4\star)$$

79. $5 - 3(2x-7) = 4(x+5) - 6$
$$5 - 6x + 21 = 4x + 20 - 6$$
$$-6x + 26 = 4x + 14$$
$$12 = 10x$$
$$\frac{12}{10} = x$$
$$\frac{6}{5} = x$$

80. Let x = the number of pounds of jelly beans and $(50 - x)$ = the number of pounds of gumdrops.

Item	Price per pound	Quantity	Cost
Jellybeans	6.25	x	$6.25x$
Gumdrops	2.50	$50 - x$	$2.50(50 - x)$
Mixture	4.75	50	$4.75(50)$

$$6.25x + 2.50(50 - x) = 4.75(50)$$
$$6.25x + 125 - 2.50x = 237.5$$
$$3.75x + 125 = 237.5$$
$$3.75x = 112.5$$
$$x = 30$$

They should mix 30 pounds of jelly beans with 20 pounds of gumdrops.

81. $\dfrac{15x^3 - 6x^2 - 9x + 5}{3x} = \dfrac{15x^3}{3x} - \dfrac{6x^2}{3x} - \dfrac{9x}{3x} + \dfrac{5}{3x}$

$$= 5x^2 - 2x - 3 + \dfrac{5}{3x}$$

82.
$$\begin{array}{r} a - 4 \\ a + 4 \overline{\smash{)}\, a^2 \qquad\; -16} \\ \underline{a^2 + 4a} \\ -4a - 16 \\ \underline{-4a - 16} \\ 0 \end{array}$$

$$\dfrac{a^2 - 16}{a + 4} = a - 4$$

Exercise Set 6.3

1. Since 960 is positive, both signs will be the same. Since 92 is positive, both signs will be positive.

2. Since 4000 is positive, both signs will be the same. Since −500 is negative, both signs will be negative.

3. Since −1500 is negative, one sign will be positive, the other will be negative.

4. Since −7200 is negative, one sign will be positive, the other will be negative.

5. Since 8000 is positive, both signs will be the same. Since −240 is negative, both signs will be negative.

6. Since 600 is positive, both signs will be the same. Since 50 is positive, both signs will be positive

7. The trinomial $x^2 - 11x + 24$ is obtained by multiplying the factors using the FOIL method.

8. The trinomial $x^2 + 4xy - 12y^2$ is obtained by multiplying the factors using the FOIL method.

9. The trinomial $2x^2 - 8xy - 10y^2$ is obtained by multiplying all the factors and combining like terms.

10. The trinomial $5c^2 - 5d^2$ is obtained by multiplying all the factors and combining like terms.

11. The answer is not fully factored. A 2 can be factored from $(2x - 4)$.

12. The answer is not fully factored. A 3 can be factored from $(3x - 6)$.

13. A trinomial factoring problem can be checked by multiplying the factors to see if the product is the same as the original expression.

14. To determine the factors when factoring a trinomial of the form $x^2 + bx + c$. First, find two numbers whose product is c, and whose sum is b. The factors are (x + first number) and (x + second number).

15. $x^2 - 7x + 10 = (x - 5)(x - 2)$

16. $x^2 + 8x + 15 = (x + 5)(x + 3)$

17. $x^2 + 6x + 8 = (x + 4)(x + 2)$

18. $x^2 - 3x + 2 = (x - 2)(x - 1)$

19. $x^2 + 5x - 24 = (x + 8)(x - 3)$

20. $x^2 - x - 12 = (x - 4)(x + 3)$

21. $x^2 + 4x - 6$ is prime.

22. $y^2 - 6y + 8 = (y - 4)(y - 2)$

23. $y^2 - 13y + 12 = (y - 12)(y - 1)$

24. $x^2 + 3x - 54 = (x + 9)(x - 6)$

25. $a^2 - 2a - 8 = (a - 4)(a + 2)$

26. $p^2 + 3p - 10 = (p + 5)(p - 2)$

27. $r^2 - 2r - 15 = (r - 5)(r + 3)$

28. $x^2 - 6x + 8 = (x - 4)(x - 2)$

29. $b^2 - 11b + 18 = (b - 9)(b - 2)$

30. $x^2 + 11x - 30$ is prime.

31. $x^2 - 8x - 15$ is prime.

32. $x^2 - 8x + 7 = (x - 7)(x - 1)$

33. $q^2 + 4q - 45 = (q + 9)(q - 5)$

34. $x^2 + 10x + 25 = (x + 5)(x + 5)$
$$= (x + 5)^2$$

35. $x^2 - 7x - 30 = (x - 10)(x + 3)$

36. $b^2 - 9b - 36 = (b - 12)(b + 3)$

37. $x^2 + 4x + 4 = (x + 2)(x + 2)$
$$= (x + 2)^2$$

38. $x^2 - 4x + 4 = (x - 2)(x - 2)$
$$= (x - 2)^2$$

39. $s^2 - 8s + 16 = (s - 4)(s - 4)$
$$= (s - 4)^2$$

40. $u^2 + 2u + 1 = (u + 1)(u + 1)$
$$= (u + 1)^2$$

41. $p^2 - 12p + 36 = (p - 6)(p - 6)$
$$= (p - 6)^2$$

42. $x^2 - 10x - 25$ is prime.

43. $-18w + w^2 + 45$
$$= w^2 - 18w + 45$$
$$= (w - 15)(w - 3)$$

44. $-11x + x^2 + 10$
$$= x^2 - 11x + 10$$
$$= (x - 10)(x - 1)$$

45. $10x - 39 + x^2$
$$= x^2 + 10x - 39$$
$$= (x + 13)(x - 3)$$

46. $-3x + 8 + x^2 = x^2 - 3x + 8$ is prime.

47. $x^2 - x - 20 = (x - 5)(x + 4)$

48. $t^2 - 28t - 60 = (t - 30)(t + 2)$

49. $y^2 + 13y + 40 = (y + 5)(y + 8)$

50. $r^2 + 14r + 48 = (r + 6)(r + 8)$

51. $x^2 + 12x - 64 = (x + 16)(x - 4)$

52. $x^2 - 18x + 80 = (x - 8)(x - 10)$

53. $s^2 + 14s - 24$ is prime.

54. $x^2 - 13x + 36 = (x - 4)(x - 9)$

55. $x^2 - 20x + 64 = (x - 16)(x - 4)$

56. $x^2 + 19x + 48 = (x + 3)(x + 16)$

57. $a^2 - 20a + 99 = (a - 11)(a - 9)$

58. $x^2 + 5x - 24 = (x - 3)(x + 8)$

59. $x^2 + 2 + 3x = x^2 + 3x + 2$
$$= (x + 1)(x + 2)$$

60. $m^2 - 11 - 10m = m^2 - 10m - 11$
$$= (m - 11)(m + 1)$$

61. $7w - 18 + w^2 = w^2 + 7w - 18$
$$= (w + 9)(w - 2)$$

62. $30 + y^2 - 13y = y^2 - 13y + 30$
$$= (y - 10)(y - 3)$$

63. $x^2 - 8xy + 15y^2 = (x - 3y)(x - 5y)$

64. $x^2 - 2xy + y^2 = (x - y)(x - y)$
$\qquad\qquad = (x - y)^2$

65. $m^2 - 6mn + 9n^2 = (m - 3n)(m - 3n)$
$\qquad\qquad\quad = (m - 3n)^2$

66. $b^2 - 2bc - 3c^2 = (b - 3c)(b + c)$

67. $x^2 + 8xy + 12y^2 = (x + 6y)(x + 2y)$

68. $x^2 + 16xy - 17y^2 = (x + 17y)(x - y)$

69. $m^2 - 5mn - 24n^2 = (m - 8n)(m + 3n)$

70. $c^2 + 2cd - 24d^2 = (c - 4d)(c + 6d)$

71. $6x^2 - 30x + 24 = 6(x^2 - 5x + 4)$
$\qquad\qquad\quad = 6(x - 4)(x - 1)$

72. $2a^2 - 12a - 32 = 2(a^2 - 6a - 16)$
$\qquad\qquad\quad = 2(a - 8)(a + 2)$

73. $5x^2 + 20x + 15 = 5(x^2 + 4x + 3)$
$\qquad\qquad\quad = 5(x + 1)(x + 3)$

74. $4x^2 + 12x - 16 = 4(x^2 + 3x - 4)$
$\qquad\qquad\quad = 4(x + 4)(x - 1)$

75. $2x^2 - 18x + 40 = 2(x^2 - 9x + 20)$
$\qquad\qquad\quad = 2(x - 5)(x - 4)$

76. $3y^2 - 33y + 54 = 3(y^2 - 11y + 18)$
$\qquad\qquad\quad = 3(y - 2)(y - 9)$

77. $b^3 - 7b^2 + 10b = b(b^2 - 7b + 10)$
$\qquad\qquad\quad = b(b - 5)(b - 2)$

78. $c^3 + 8c^2 - 48c = c(c^2 + 8c - 48)$
$\qquad\qquad\quad = c(c + 12)(c - 4)$

79. $3z^3 - 21z^2 - 54z = 3z(z^2 - 7z - 18)$
$\qquad\qquad\quad = 3z(z - 9)(z + 2)$

80. $3x^3 - 36x^2 + 33x = 3x(x^2 - 12x + 11)$
$\qquad\qquad\quad = 3x(x - 11)(x - 1)$

81. $x^3 + 8x^2 + 16x = x(x^2 + 8x + 16)$
$\qquad\qquad\quad = x(x + 4)(x + 4)$
$\qquad\qquad\quad = x(x + 4)^2$

82. $2x^3y - 12x^2y + 10xy = 2xy(x^2 - 6x + 5)$
$\qquad\qquad\qquad = 2xy(x - 5)(x - 1)$

83. $7a^2 - 35ab + 42b^2 = 7(a^2 - 5ab + 6b^2)$
$\qquad\qquad\qquad = 7(a - 3b)(a - 2b)$

84. $3x^3 + 3x^2y - 18xy^2 = 3x(x^2 + xy - 6y^2)$
$\qquad\qquad\qquad = 3x(x + 3y)(x - 2y)$

85. $3r^3 + 6r^2t - 24rt^2 = 3r(r^2 + 2rt - 8t^2)$
$\qquad\qquad\qquad = 3r(r + 4t)(r - 2t)$

86. $r^2s + 7rs^2 + 12s^3 = s(r^2 + 7rs + 12s^2)$
$\qquad\qquad\qquad = s(r + 3s)(r + 4s)$

87. $x^4 - 4x^3 - 21x^2 = x^2(x^2 - 4x - 21)$
$\qquad\qquad\qquad = x^2(x - 7)(x + 3)$

88. $2z^5 + 14z^4 + 12z^3 = 2z^3(z^2 + 7z + 6)$
$\qquad\qquad\qquad = 2z^3(z + 6)(z + 1)$

89.

Sign of Coefficient of x-term	Sign of Constant of Trinomial	Signs of Constant Terms in the Binomial Factors
−	+	both negative
−	−	one positive and one negative
+	−	one positive and one negative
+	+	both positive

90. a. Since c is positive, both signs will be the same. Since b is negative, both signs will be negative.

b. Since c is positive, both signs will be the same. Since b is positive, both signs will be positive.

c. Since c is negative, one sign will be positive, the other will be negative.

d. Since c is negative, one sign will be positive and the other will be negative.

91. $x^2 - 12x + 32 = (x-8)(x-4)$

92. $x^2 + 5x + 4 = (x+1)(x+4)$

93. $x^2 - 2x - 35 = (x-7)(x+5)$

94. $x^2 + 5x - 14 = (x+7)(x-2)$

95. $x^2 + 0.6x + 0.08 = (x+0.4)(x+0.2)$

96. $x^2 - 0.5x - 0.06 = (x-0.6)(x+0.1)$

97. $x^2 + \dfrac{2}{5}x + \dfrac{1}{25} = \left(x+\dfrac{1}{5}\right)\left(x+\dfrac{1}{5}\right)$

$\qquad = \left(x+\dfrac{1}{5}\right)^2$

98. $x^2 - \dfrac{2}{7}x + \dfrac{1}{49} = \left(x-\dfrac{1}{7}\right)\left(x-\dfrac{1}{7}\right) = \left(x-\dfrac{1}{7}\right)^2$

99. $x^2 - 24x - 256 = (x+8)(x-32)$

100. $x^2 + 5x - 300 = (x+20)(x-15)$

101. $\quad 4(2x-4) = 5x+11$

$\qquad 8x-16 = 5x+11$

$\qquad 8x-5x-16 = 5x-5x+11$

$\qquad 3x-16 = 11$

$\qquad 3x-16+16 = 11+16$

$\qquad 3x = 27$

$\qquad x = 9$

102. Let x be the percent of acid in the mixture.

Solution	Strength	Liters	Amount
18%	0.18	4	0.72
26%	0.26	1	0.26
Mixture	$\dfrac{x}{100}$	5	$\dfrac{5x}{100}$

$$0.72 + 0.26 = \dfrac{5x}{100}$$

$$0.98 = \dfrac{x}{20}$$

$$19.6 = x$$

The mixture is a 19.6% acid solution.

103.

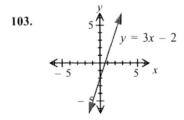

104. $\left(2x^2 + 5x - 6\right)(x - 2)$

$= 2x^2(x - 2) + 5x(x - 2) - 6(x - 2)$

$= 2x^3 - 4x^2 + 5x^2 - 10x - 6x + 12$

$= 2x^3 + x^2 - 16x + 12$

105.
$$
\begin{array}{r}
3x + 2 \\
x - 4 \overline{\smash{\big)}\ 3x^2 - 10x - 10} \\
\underline{3x^2 - 12x} \\
2x - 10 \\
\underline{2x - 8} \\
-2
\end{array}
$$

$\dfrac{3x^2 - 10x - 10}{x - 4} = 3x + 2 - \dfrac{2}{x - 4}$

106. $20x^2 + 8x - 15x - 6 = 4x(5x + 2) - 3(5x + 2)$

$= (5x + 2)(4x - 3)$

Exercise Set 6.4

1. Factoring trinomials is the reverse process of multiplying binomials.

2. When factoring a trinomial of the form $ax^2 + bx + c$, the product of the constants in the binomial factors must equal the constant, c, of the trinomial.

3. When factoring a trinomial of the form $ax^2 + bx + c$, the product of the first terms of the binomial factors must equal the first term of the trinomial, ax^2.

4. Answers will vary.

5. $2x^2 + 11x + 5 = (2x + 1)(x + 5)$

6. $2x^2 + 9x + 4 = (2x + 1)(x + 4)$

7. $3x^2 + 14x + 8 = (3x + 2)(x + 4)$

8. $7x^2 + 37x + 10 = (7x + 2)(x + 5)$

9. $5x^2 - 9x - 2 = (5x + 1)(x - 2)$

10. $3y^2 + 17y + 10 = (3y + 2)(y + 5)$

11. $3r^2 + 13r - 10 = (3r - 2)(r + 5)$

12. $3x^2 - 2x - 8 = (3x + 4)(x - 2)$

13. $4z^2 - 12z + 9 = (2z - 3)(2z - 3)$

$= (2z - 3)^2$

14. $4n^2 - 9n + 5 = (4n - 5)(n - 1)$

15. $6z^2 + z - 12 = (2z + 3)(3z - 4)$

16. $5m^2 - 17m + 6 = (5m - 2)(m - 3)$

17. $5a^2 - 12a + 6$ is prime.

18. $2x^2 - x - 6 = (2x + 3)(x - 2)$

19. $8x^2 + 19x + 6 = (8x + 3)(x + 2)$

20. $6y^2 - 11y + 4 = (3y - 4)(2y - 1)$

21. $3x^2 + 11x + 4$ is prime.

22. $3a^2 + 7a - 20 = (3a - 5)(a + 4)$

23. $5y^2 - 16y + 3 = (5y - 1)(y - 3)$

24. $5x^2 + 2x + 9$ is prime.

25. $7x^2 + 43x + 6 = (7x + 1)(x + 6)$

26. $7x^2 - 8x + 1 = (7x - 1)(x - 1)$

27. $4x^2 + 4x - 15 = (2x + 5)(2x - 3)$

28. $15x^2 - 19x + 6 = (5x - 3)(3x - 2)$

29. $49t^2 - 14t + 1 = (7t - 1)(7t - 1)$

$= (7t - 1)^2$

30. $16z^2 - 8z + 1 = (4z - 1)(4z - 1)$

$= (4z - 1)^2$

31. $5z^2 - 6z - 8 = (5z + 4)(z - 2)$

32. $3z^2 - 11z - 6$ is prime.

33. $4y^2 + 5y - 6 = (4y - 3)(y + 2)$

34. $5y^2 - 3y - 1$ is prime.

35. $10x^2 - 27x + 5 = (5x - 1)(2x - 5)$

36. $6a^2 + 7a - 10 = (6a - 5)(a + 2)$

37. $10d^2 - 7d - 12 = (5d + 4)(2d - 3)$

38. $6x^2 + 13x + 3$ is prime.

39. $8x^2 - 46x - 12 = 2 \cdot 4x^2 - 2 \cdot 23x - 2 \cdot 6$
$$= 2(4x^2 - 23x - 6)$$
$$= 2(4x + 1)(x - 6)$$

40. $12x^2 - 13x - 35 = (3x - 7)(4x + 5)$

41. $10t + 3 + 7t^2 = 7t^2 + 10t + 3$
$$= (7t + 3)(t + 1)$$

42. $n - 30 + n^2 = n^2 + n - 30$
$$= (n + 6)(n - 5)$$

43. $6x^2 + 16x + 10 = 2 \cdot 3x^2 + 2 \cdot 8x + 2 \cdot 5$
$$= 2(3x^2 + 8x + 5)$$
$$= 2(3x + 5)(x + 1)$$

44. $12z^2 + 32z + 20 = 4 \cdot 3z^2 + 4 \cdot 8z + 4 \cdot 5$
$$= 4(3z^2 + 8z + 5)$$
$$= 4(3z + 5)(z + 1)$$

45. $6x^3 - 5x^2 - 4x = x \cdot 6x^2 - x \cdot 5x - x \cdot 4$
$$= x(6x^2 - 5x - 4)$$
$$= x(2x + 1)(3x - 4)$$

46. $8x^3 + 8x^2 - 6x = 2x \cdot 4x^2 + 2x \cdot 4x - 2x \cdot 3$
$$= 2x(4x^2 + 4x - 3)$$
$$= 2x(2x - 1)(2x + 3)$$

47. $12x^3 + 28x^2 + 8x = 4x \cdot 3x^2 + 4x \cdot 7x + 4x \cdot 2$
$$= 4x(3x^2 + 7x + 2)$$
$$= 4x(3x + 1)(x + 2)$$

48. $18x^3 - 21x^2 - 9x = 3x \cdot 6x^2 - 3x \cdot 7x - 3x \cdot 3$
$$= 3x(6x^2 - 7x - 3)$$
$$= 3x(2x - 3)(3x + 1)$$

49. $4x^3 - 2x^2 - 12x = 2x \cdot 2x^2 - 2x \cdot x - 2x \cdot 6$
$$= 2x(2x^2 - x - 6)$$
$$= 2x(2x + 3)(x - 2)$$

50. $300x^2 - 400x - 400$
$$= 100 \cdot 3x^2 - 100 \cdot 4x - 100 \cdot 4$
$$= 100(3x^2 - 4x - 4)$$
$$= 100(3x + 2)(x - 2)$$

51. $48c^2 + 8c - 16 = 8 \cdot 6c^2 + 8 \cdot c - 8 \cdot 2$
$$= 8(6c^2 + 8c - 2)$$
$$= 8(2c - 1)(3c + 2)$$

52. $28x^2 - 28x + 7 = 7 \cdot 4x^2 - 7 \cdot 4x + 7 \cdot 1$
$$= 7(4x^2 - 4x + 1)$$
$$= 7(2x - 1)(2x - 1)$$
$$= 7(2x - 1)^2$$

53. $4p - 12 + 8p^2 = 8p^2 + 4p - 12$
$$= 4 \cdot 2p^2 + 4 \cdot p - 4 \cdot 3$
$$= 4(2p^2 + p - 3)$$
$$= 4(2p + 3)(p - 1)$$

54. $72 + 3r^2 - 30r = 3r^2 - 30r + 72$
$$= 3 \cdot r^2 - 3 \cdot 10r + 3 \cdot 24$
$$= 3(r^2 - 10r + 24)$$
$$= 3(r - 4)(r - 6)$$

55. $8c^2 + 41cd + 5d^2 = (8c + d)(c + 5d)$

56. $8x^2 - 8xy - 6y^2 = 2 \cdot 4x^2 - 2 \cdot 4xy - 2 \cdot 3y^2$
$$= 2(4x^2 - 4xy - 3y^2)$$
$$= 2(2x + y)(2x - 3y)$$

57. $15x^2 - xy - 6y^2 = (5x + 3y)(3x - 2y)$

58. $2x^2 - 7xy + 3y^2 = (2x - y)(x - 3y)$

59. $12x^2 + 10xy - 8y^2 = 2 \cdot 6x^2 + 2 \cdot 5xy - 2 \cdot 4y^2$
$$= 2(6x^2 + 5xy - 4y^2)$$
$$= 2(2x - y)(3x + 4y)$$

60. $12a^2 - 34ab + 24b^2 = 2 \cdot 6a^2 - 2 \cdot 17ab + 2 \cdot 12b^2$
$$= 2(6a^2 - 17ab + 12b^2)$$
$$= 2(3a - 4b)(2a - 3b)$$

61. $7p^2 + 13pq + 6q^2 = (7p + 6q)(p + q)$

62. $24x^2 - 92x + 80 = 4 \cdot 6x^2 - 4 \cdot 23x + 4 \cdot 20$
$$= 4(6x^2 - 23x + 20)$$
$$= 4(3x - 4)(2x - 5)$$

63. $6m^2 - mn - 2n^2 = (3m - 2n)(2m + n)$

64. $8m^2 + 4mn - 4n^2 = 4 \cdot 2m^2 + 4 \cdot mn - 4 \cdot n^2$
$$= 4(2m^2 + mn - n^2)$$
$$= 4(2m - n)(m + n)$$

65. $8x^3 + 10x^2 y + 3xy^2 = x \cdot 8x^2 + x \cdot 10xy + x \cdot 3y^2$
$$= x(8x^2 + 10xy + 3y^2)$$
$$= x(4x + 3y)(2x + y)$$

66. $8a^2 b + 10ab^2 + 3b^3 = b \cdot 8a^2 + b \cdot 10ab + b \cdot 3b^2$
$$= b(8a^2 + 10ab + 3b^2)$$
$$= b(4a + 3b)(2a + b)$$

67. $4x^4 + 8x^3 y + 3x^2 y^2$
$$= x^2 \cdot 4x^2 + x^2 \cdot 8xy + x^2 \cdot 3y^2$$
$$= x^2(4x^2 + 8xy + 3y^2)$$
$$= x^2(2x + y)(2x + 3y)$$

68. $26u^2 v + 6uv^2 + 24u^3$
$$= 2u \cdot 13uv + 2u \cdot 3v^2 + 2u \cdot 12u^2$$
$$= 2u(13uv + 3v^2 + 12u^2)$$
$$= 2u(12u^2 + 13uv + 3v^2)$$
$$= 2u(3u + v)(4u + 3v)$$

69. $3x^2 - 20x - 7$. This polynomial was obtained by multiplying the factors.

70. $24y^2 - 38y + 15$. This polynomial was obtained by multiplying the factors.

71. $10x^2 + 35x + 15$. This polynomial was obtained by multiplying the factors.

72. $6x^2 - 15x - 36$. This polynomial was obtained by multiplying the factors.

73. $3t^4 + 11t^3 - 4t^2$. This polynomial was obtained by multiplying the factors.

74. $30x^4 - 25x^3 - 105x^2$. This polynomial was obtained by multiplying the factors.

75. a. The second factor can be found by dividing the trinomial by the binomial.

b.
$$\begin{array}{r} 6x + 11 \\ 3x + 10 \overline{) 18x^2 + 93x + 110} \\ \underline{18x^2 + 60x} \\ 33x + 110 \\ \underline{33x + 110} \\ 0 \end{array}$$

The other factor is $6x + 11$.

76. The other factor is $5x + 13$. The product of the two first terms must equal $30x^2$, and the product of the constants must equal -247.

77. $18x^2 + 9x - 20 = (6x - 5)(3x + 4)$

78. $9p^2 - 104p + 55 = (9p - 5)(p - 11)$

79. $15x^2 - 124x + 160 = (5x - 8)(3x - 20)$

80. $16x^2 - 62x - 45 = (8x + 5)(2x - 9)$

81. $105a^2 - 220a - 160$
$$= 5 \cdot 21a^2 - 5 \cdot 44a - 5 \cdot 32$$
$$= 5(21a^2 - 44a - 32)$$
$$= 5(3a - 8)(7a + 4)$$

82. $72x^2 + 417x - 420$
$$= 3 \cdot 24x^2 + 3 \cdot 139x - 3 \cdot 140$$
$$= 3(24x^2 + 139x - 140)$$
$$= 3(8x - 7)(3x + 20)$$

83. The other factor is $2x + 45$. The product of the three first terms must equal $6x^3$, and the product of the constants must equal $2250x$.

84. The third factor is $x + 4$. The product of the three first terms must equal $2x^3$, and the product of the constants must equal -36.

85. $-x^2 - 4(y+3) + 2y^2$

$= -(-3)^2 - 4(-5+3) + 2(-5)^2$

$= -9 - 4(-2) + 2(25)$

$= -9 + 8 + 50$

$= 49$

86. $\dfrac{507.5}{3.56} \approx 142.56$

His average speed was about 142.56 miles per hour.

87. $36x^4 y^3 - 12xy^2 + 24x^5 y^6$

$= 12xy^2 \cdot 3x^3 y - 12xy^2 \cdot 1 + 12xy^2 \cdot 2x^4 y^4$

$= 12xy^2 \left(3x^3 y - 1 + 2x^4 y^4\right)$

88. $b^2 + 4b - 96 = (b+12)(b-8)$

Mid-Chapter Test: 6.1 – 6.4

1. Any factoring problem can be checked by multiplying the factors.

2. $18xy^2 : 2 \cdot 3^2 \cdot xy^2$

$27x^3 y^4 : 3^3 \cdot x^3 y^4$

$12x^2 y^3 : 2^2 \cdot 3 \cdot x^2 y^3$

GCF: $3 \cdot x \cdot y^2 = 3xy^2$

3. $4a^2 b^3 - 24a^3 b = 4a^2 b \cdot b^2 - 4a^2 b \cdot 6a$

$= 4a^2 b\left(b^2 - 6a\right)$

4. $5c(d-6) - 3(d-6) = (d-6)(5c-3)$

5. $7x(2x+9) + 2x + 9$

$= 7x(2x+9) + 1(2x+9)$

$= (2x+9)(7x+1)$

6. $x^2 + 4x + 7x + 28$

$= x(x+4) + 7(x+4)$

$= (x+4)(x+7)$

7. $x^2 + 5x - 3x - 15$

$= x(x+5) - 3(x+5)$

$= (x+5)(x-3)$

8. $6a^2 + 15ab - 2ab - 5b^2$

$= 3a(2a+5b) - b(2a+5b)$

$= (2a+5b)(3a-b)$

9. $5x^2 - 2xy - 45x + 18y$

$= x(5x-2y) - 9(5x-2y)$

$= (5x-2y)(x-9)$

10. $8x^3 + 4x^2 - 48x^2 - 24x$

$= 4x\left(2x^2 + x - 12x - 6\right)$

$= 4x\left[x(2x+1) - 6(2x+1)\right]$

$= 4x(2x+1)(x-6)$

11. $x^2 - 10x + 21 = (x-3)(x-7)$

12. $t^2 + 9t + 20 = (t+5)(t+4)$

13. $p^2 - 3p - 8$ is prime

14. $x^2 + 16x + 64 = (x+8)(x+8)$

$= (x+8)^2$

15. $m^2 - 4mn - 45n^2 = (m+5n)(m-9n)$

16. $3x^2 + 17x + 10 = (3x+2)(x+5)$

17. $4z^2 - 11z + 6 = (4z-3)(z-2)$

18. $3y^2 + 13y + 6$ is prime

19. $9x^2 - 6x + 1 = (3x-1)(3x-1)$

$= (3x-1)^2$

20. $6a^2 + 3ab - 3b^2 = 3\left(2a^2 + ab - b^2\right)$

$= 3(2a-b)(a+b)$

Exercise Set 6.5

1. a. $a^2 - b^2 = (a+b)(a-b)$

b. Answers will vary.

2. a. $a^3 - b^3 = (a-b)(a^2 + ab + b^2)$

b. Answers will vary.

3. a. $a^3 + b^3 = (a+b)(a^2 - ab + b^2)$

b. Answers will vary.

4. It is important to memorize the special factoring formulas to be able to use them whenever needed.

5. No, there is no special formula for factoring the sum of two squares.

6. Answers will vary.

7. $x^2 + 9$ is prime

8. $4y^2 + 1$ is prime

9. $3b^2 + 48 = 3(b^2 + 16)$

10. $16s^2 + 64t^2 = 16(s^2 + 4t^2)$

11. $16m^2 + 36n^2 = 4(4m^2 + 9n^2)$

12. $9y^2 + 16z^2$ is prime

13. $y^2 - 25 = y^2 - 5^2 = (y+5)(y-5)$

14. $x^2 - 4 = x^2 - 2^2$
$= (x+2)(x-2)$

15. $81 - z^2 = 9^2 - z^2$
$= (9+z)(9-z)$

16. $64 - z^2 = 8^2 - z^2$
$= (8+z)(8-z)$

17. $x^2 - 49 = x^2 - 7^2$
$= (x+7)(x-7)$

18. $c^2 - d^2 = (c+d)(c-d)$

19. $x^2 - y^2 = (x+y)(x-y)$

20. $16x^2 - 9 = (4x)^2 - 3^2$
$= (4x+3)(4x-3)$

21. $9y^2 - 25z^2 = (3y)^2 - (5z)^2$
$= (3y+5z)(3y-5z)$

22. $64z^2 - 9 = (8z)^2 - 3^2$
$= (8z+3)(8z-3)$

23. $64a^2 - 36b^2 = 4(16a^2 - 9b^2)$
$= 4[(4a)^2 - (3b)^2]$
$= 4(4a+3b)(4a-3b)$

24. $100x^2 - 81y^2 = (10x)^2 - (9y)^2$
$= (10x+9y)(10x-9y)$

25. $36 - 49x^2 = 6^2 - (7x)^2$
$= (6+7x)(6-7x)$

26. $100 - y^4 = 10^2 - (y^2)^2$
$= (10+y^2)(10-y^2)$

27. $z^4 - 81x^2 = (z^2)^2 - (9x)^2$
$= (z^2+9x)(z^2-9x)$

28. $9x^4 - 81y^2 = 9(x^4 - 9y^2)$
$= 9[(x^2)^2 - (3y)^2]$
$= 9(x^2+3y)(x^2-3y)$

29. $25x^4 - 49y^4 = (5x^2)^2 - (7y^2)^2$
$= (5x^2+7y^2)(5x^2-7y^2)$

30. $4x^4 - 25y^4 = (2x^2)^2 - (5y^2)^2$
$= (2x^2+5y^2)(2x^2-5y^2)$

31. $36m^4 - 49n^2 = (6m^2)^2 - (7n)^2$
$= (6m^2+7n)(6m^2-7n)$

32. $10x^2 - 160 = 10\left(x^2 - 16\right)$

$\qquad = 10\left(x^2 - 4^2\right)$

$\qquad = 10(x+4)(x-4)$

33. $2x^4 - 50y^2 = 2\left(x^4 - 25y^2\right)$

$\qquad = 2\left[\left(x^2\right)^2 - (5y)^2\right]$

$\qquad = 2\left(x^2 + 5y\right)\left(x^2 - 5y\right)$

34. $4x^3 - xy^2 = x\left(4x^2 - y^2\right)$

$\qquad = x\left[(2x)^2 - y^2\right]$

$\qquad = x(2x+y)(2x-y)$

35. $x^4 - 81 = \left(x^2\right)^2 - 9^2$

$\qquad = \left(x^2 + 9\right)\left(x^2 - 9\right)$

$\qquad = \left(x^2 + 9\right)\left(x^2 - 3^2\right)$

$\qquad = \left(x^2 + 9\right)(x+3)(x-3)$

36. $36x^4 - 4y^2 = 4\left(9x^4 - y^2\right)$

$\qquad = 4\left[\left(3x^2\right)^2 - y^2\right]$

$\qquad = 4\left(3x^2 + y\right)\left(3x^2 - y\right)$

37. $x^3 + y^3 = (x+y)\left(x^2 - xy + y^2\right)$

38. $a^3 - b^3 = (a-b)\left(a^2 + ab + b^2\right)$

39. $x^3 - y^3 = (x-y)\left(x^2 + xy + y^2\right)$

40. $a^3 + b^3 = (a+b)\left(a^2 - ab + b^2\right)$

41. $x^3 + 64 = x^3 + 4^3$

$\qquad = (x+4)\left(x^2 - 4x + 16\right)$

42. $x^3 - 8 = x^3 - 2^3$

$\qquad = (x-2)\left(x^2 + 2x + 4\right)$

43. $x^3 - 27 = x^3 - 3^3$

$\qquad = (x-3)\left(x^2 + 3x + 9\right)$

44. $a^3 + 27 = a^3 + 3^3$

$\qquad = (a+3)\left(a^2 - 3a + 9\right)$

45. $a^3 + 1 = a^3 + 1^3$

$\qquad = (a+1)\left(a^2 - a + 1\right)$

46. $t^3 - 1 = t^3 - 1^3$

$\qquad = (t-1)\left(t^2 + t + 1\right)$

47. $27x^3 - 1 = (3x)^3 - 1^3$

$\qquad = (3x-1)\left(9x^2 + 3x + 1\right)$

48. $64y^3 + 125 = (4y)^3 + 5^3$

$\qquad = (4y+5)\left(16y^2 - 20y + 25\right)$

49. $27a^3 - 125 = (3a)^3 - 5^3$

$\qquad = (3a-5)\left(9a^2 + 15a + 25\right)$

50. $125 + x^3 = 5^3 + x^3$

$\qquad = (5+x)\left(25 - 5x + x^2\right)$

51. $27 - 8y^3 = 3^3 - (2y)^3$

$\qquad = (3-2y)\left(9 + 6y + 4y^2\right)$

52. $8 + 27y^3 = 2^3 + (3y)^3$

$\qquad = (2+3y)\left(4 - 6y + 9y^2\right)$

53. $64m^3 + 27n^3 = (4m)^3 + (3n)^3$

$\qquad = (4m+3n)\left(16m^2 - 12mn + 9n^2\right)$

54. $64x^3 - 125y^3 = (4x)^3 - (5y)^3$

$\qquad = (4x-5y)\left(16x^2 + 20xy + 25y^2\right)$

55. $8a^3 - 27b^3 = (2a)^3 - (3b)^3$

$\qquad = (2a-3b)(4a^2 + 6ab + 9b^2)$

56. $27c^3 + 125d^3 = (3c)^3 + (5d)^3$

$\qquad = (3c+5d)(9c^2 - 15cd + 25d^2)$

57. $4x^2 - 24x + 36 = 4\left(x^2 - 6x + 9\right)$

$\qquad = 4(x-3)^2$

58. $3x^2 - 9x - 12 = 3(x^2 - 3x - 4)$
$\qquad = 3(x-4)(x+1)$

59. $50x^2 - 10x - 12 = 2(25x^2 - 5x - 6)$
$\qquad = 2(5x+2)(5x-3)$

60. $3x^2 - 48 = 3(x^2 - 16)$
$\qquad = 3(x^2 - 4^2)$
$\qquad = 3(x+4)(x-4)$

61. $2d^2 + 16d + 32 = 2(d^2 + 8d + 16)$
$\qquad = 2(d+4)^2$

62. $3x^2 + 9x + 12x + 36 = 3(x^2 + 3x + 4x + 12)$
$\qquad = 3[x(x+3) + 4(x+3)]$
$\qquad = 3(x+4)(x+3)$

63. $5x^2 - 10x - 15 = 5(x^2 - 2x - 3)$
$\qquad = 5(x-3)(x+1)$

64. $3xy - 6x + 9y - 18 = 3(xy - 2x + 3y - 6)$
$\qquad = 3[x(y-2) + 3(y-2)]$
$\qquad = 3(x+3)(y-2)$

65. $5x^2 - 20 = 5(x^2 - 4)$
$\qquad = 5(x^2 - 2^2)$
$\qquad = 5(x+2)(x-2)$

66. $x^2 y + 2xy - 6xy - 12y$
$\qquad = y(x^2 + 2x - 6x - 12)$
$\qquad = y[x(x+2) - 6(x+2)]$
$\qquad = y(x-6)(x+2)$

67. $2x^2 - 50 = 2(x^2 - 25)$
$\qquad = 2(x^2 - 5^2)$
$\qquad = 2(x+5)(x-5)$

68. $4a^2 y - 64y^3 = 4y(a^2 - 16y^2)$
$\qquad = 4y[a^2 - (4y)^2]$
$\qquad = 4y(a+4y)(a-4y)$

69. $2x^2 y - 18y = 2y(x^2 - 9)$
$\qquad = 2y(x^2 - 3^2)$
$\qquad = 2y(x+3)(x-3)$

70. $3x^3 - 147x = 3x(x^2 - 49)$
$\qquad = 3x(x^2 - 7^2)$
$\qquad = 3x(x+7)(x-7)$

71. $3x^3 y^2 + 3y^2 = 3y^2(x^3 + 1)$
$\qquad = 3y^2(x^3 + 1^3)$
$\qquad = 3y^2(x+1)(x^2 - x + 1)$

72. $x^4 - 125x = x(x^3 - 125)$
$\qquad = x(x^3 - 5^3)$
$\qquad = x(x-5)(x^2 + 5x + 25)$

73. $2x^3 - 16 = 2(x^3 - 8)$
$\qquad = 2(x^3 - 2^3)$
$\qquad = 2(x-2)(x^2 + 2x + 4)$

74. $x^3 - 27y^3 = x^3 - (3y)^3$
$\qquad = (x-3y)(x^2 + 3xy + 9y^2)$

75. $18x^2 - 50 = 2(9x^2 - 25)$
$\qquad = 2((3x)^2 - 5^2)$
$\qquad = 2(3x+5)(3x-5)$

76. $54a^3 - 16 = 2(27a^3 - 8)$
$\qquad = 2((3a)^3 - 2^3)$
$\qquad = 2(3a-2)(9a^2 + 6a + 4)$

77. $6t^2 r - 15tr + 21r = 3r(2t^2 - 5t + 7)$

78. $12n^2 + 4n - 16 = 4(3n^2 + n - 4)$
$\qquad = 4(3n+4)(n-1)$

79. $6x^2 - 4x + 24x - 16$

$= 2(3x^2 - 2x + 12x - 8)$

$= 2[x(3x-2) + 4(3x-2)]$

$= 2(3x-2)(x+4)$

80. $4ab^2 + 4ab - 24a = 4a(b^2 + b - 6)$

$= 4a(b+3)(b-2)$

81. $2rs^2 - 10rs - 48r = 2r(s^2 - 5s - 24)$

$= 2r(s+3)(s-8)$

82. $4x^4 - 26x^3 + 30x^2 = 2x^2(2x^2 - 13x + 15)$

$= 2x^2(2x-3)(x-5)$

83. $4x^2 + 5x - 6 = (x+2)(4x-3)$

84. $12a^2 + 36a + 27 = 3(4a^2 + 12a + 9)$

$= 3(2a+3)^2$

85. $25b^2 - 100 = 25(b^2 - 4)$

$= 25(b^2 - 2^2)$

$= 25(b+2)(b-2)$

86. $3b^2 - 75c^2 = 3(b^2 - 25c^2)$

$= 3[b^2 - (5c)^2]$

$= 3(b+5c)(b-5c)$

87. $a^5b^2 - 4a^3b^4 = a^3b^2(a^2 - 4b^2)$

$= a^3b^2[a^2 - (2b)^2]$

$= a^3b^2(a+2b)(a-2b)$

88. $12x^2 + 36x - 3x - 9 = 3(4x^2 + 12x - x - 3)$

$= 3[4x(x+3) - 1(x+3)]$

$= 3(x+3)(4x-1)$

89. $5x^4 + 10x^3 + 5x^2 = 5x^2(x^2 + 2x + 1)$

$= 5x^2(x+1)^2$

90. $3c^6 + 12c^4d^2 = 3c^4(c^2 + 4d^2)$

91. $x^3 + 25x = x(x^2 + 25)$

92. $8y^2 - 23y - 3 = (8y+1)(y-3)$

93. $y^4 - 16 = (y^2)^2 - 4^2$

$= (y^2 + 4)(y^2 - 4)$

$= (y^2 + 4)(y^2 - 2^2)$

$= (y^2 + 4)(y+2)(y-2)$

94. $36a^2 - 15ab - 6b^2 = 3(12a^2 - 5ab - 2b^2)$

$= 3(3a - 2b)(4a + b)$

95. $16m^3 + 250 = 2(8m^3 + 125)$

$= 2[(2m)^3 + 5^3]$

$= 2(2m+5)(4m^2 - 10m + 25)$

96. $2ab - 3b + 4a - 6 = b(2a-3) + 2(2a-3)$

$= (2a-3)(b+2)$

97. $ac + 2a + bc + 2b = a(c+2) + b(c+2)$

$= (a+b)(c+2)$

98. $x^3 - 100x = x(x^2 - 100)$

$= x(x^2 - 10^2)$

$= x(x+10)(x-10)$

99. $9 - 9y^4 = 9(1 - y^4)$

$= 9[1^2 - (y^2)^2]$

$= 9(1 + y^2)(1 - y^2)$

$= 9(1 + y^2)(1^2 - y^2)$

$= 9(1 + y^2)(1+y)(1-y)$

100. $a^2 + b^2$ cannot be factored using real numbers because the product of the two second terms is positive, so the two second terms must have the same sign and the product would have a middle term which has the same sign as the two second terms in the factors. Hence the middle term in the product could not be 0, as it is in $a^2 + b^2$.

101. You cannot divide both sides of the equation by $(a-b)$, because it equals 0.

102. $◆✻ + 2◆ + ☺✻ + 2☺$
$= ◆(✻ + 2) + ☺(✻ + 2)$
$= (✻ + 2)(◆ + ☺)$

103. $2◆^6 + 4◆^4 ✻^2$
$= 2◆^4 \left(◆^2 + 2✻^2 \right)$

104. $4◆^2 ✻ - 6◆ ✻ - 20✻◆ + 30✻$
$= 2✻ \left(2◆^2 - 3◆ - 10◆ + 15 \right)$
$= 2✻ \left[◆(2◆ - 3) - 5(2◆ - 3) \right]$
$= 2✻(2◆ - 3)(◆ - 5)$

105. $x^6 - 27y^9 = \left(x^2 \right)^3 - \left(3y^3 \right)^3$
$= \left(x^2 - 3y^3 \right)\left(x^4 + 3x^2 y^3 + 9y^6 \right)$

106. $x^6 + 1 = \left(x^2 \right)^3 + 1^3$
$= \left(x^2 + 1 \right)\left(x^4 - x^2 + 1 \right)$

107. $x^2 - 6x + 9 - 4y^2 = (x - 3)^2 - (2y)^2$
$= (x - 3 + 2y)(x - 3 - 2y)$

108. $x^6 - y^6$
$= \left(x^3 \right)^2 - \left(y^3 \right)^2$
$= \left(x^3 + y^3 \right)\left(x^3 - y^3 \right)$
$= \left[(x + y)\left(x^2 - xy + y^2 \right) \right]\left[(x - y)\left(x^2 + xy + y^2 \right) \right]$
$= (x + y)(x - y)\left(x^2 - xy + y^2 \right)\left(x^2 + xy + y^2 \right)$

109. $x^2 + 10x + 25 - y^2 + 4y - 4$
$= (x + 5)^2 - \left(y^2 - 4y + 4 \right)$
$= (x + 5)^2 - (y - 2)^2$
$= \left[(x + 5) + (y - 2) \right]\left[(x + 5) - (y - 2) \right]$
$= (x + y + 3)(x - y + 7)$

110. $7x - 2(x + 6) = 2x - 5$
$7x - 2x - 12 = 2x - 5$
$5x - 12 = 2x - 5$
$3x - 12 = -5$
$3x = 7$
$x = \dfrac{7}{3}$

111. Substitute 36 for A, 6 for b, and 12 for d.
$A = \dfrac{1}{2} h(b + d)$
$36 = \dfrac{1}{2} h(6 + 12)$
$36 = \dfrac{1}{2} h(18)$
$36 = 9h$
$4 = h$
The height is 4 inches.

112. $-9\left(a^3 b^2 c^6 \right)^0 = -9(1) = -9$

113. $\left(\dfrac{4x^4 y}{6xy^5} \right)^3 = \left(\dfrac{4}{6} \cdot \dfrac{x^4}{x} \cdot \dfrac{y}{y^5} \right)^3$
$= \left(\dfrac{2}{3} \cdot x^3 \cdot \dfrac{1}{y^4} \right)^3$
$= \left(\dfrac{2x^3}{3y^4} \right)^3$
$= \dfrac{2^3 x^{3 \cdot 3}}{3^3 y^{4 \cdot 3}}$
$= \dfrac{8x^9}{27y^{12}}$

114. $a^{-4} a^{-7} = a^{-4-7}$
$= a^{-11}$
$= \dfrac{1}{a^{11}}$

Exercise Set 6.6

1. Answers will vary.

2. A quadratic equation is an equation that contains a second-degree term, and no term of a higher degree.

3. The standard form of a quadratic equation is $ax^2 + bx + c = 0$, $a \neq 0$.

4. Answers will vary.

5. a. The zero-factor property may only be used when one side of the equation is equal to 0.

b. $(x+1)(x-2) = 4$
$x^2 - 2x + x - 2 = 4$
$x^2 - x - 6 = 0$
$(x-3)(x+2) = 0$
$x - 3 = 0$ or $x + 2 = 0$
$x = 3$ $x = -2$

6. You can eliminate the 3 by dividing both sides of the equation by 3 to get $(x-4)(x+5) = 0$. The 3 cannot equal zero.

7. $(x+6)(x-7) = 0$
$x + 6 = 0$ or $x - 7 = 0$
$x = -6$ $x = 7$

8. $-2x(x+9) = 0$
$-2x = 0$ or $x + 9 = 0$
$x = 0$ $x = -9$

9. $7x(x-8) = 0$
$x = 0$ or $x - 8 = 0$
$x = 8$

10. $(x+3)(x+5) = 0$
$x + 3 = 0$ or $x + 5 = 0$
$x = -3$ $x = -5$

11. $(3x+7)(2x-11) = 0$
$3x + 7 = 0$ or $2x - 11 = 0$
$3x = -7$ $2x = 11$
$x = -\dfrac{7}{3}$ $x = \dfrac{11}{2}$

12. $(3x-2)(x-5) = 0$
$3x - 2 = 0$ or $x - 5 = 0$
$3x = 2$ $x = 5$
$x = \dfrac{2}{3}$

13. $x^2 - 16 = 0$
$(x+4)(x-4) = 0$
$x + 4 = 0$ or $x - 4 = 0$
$x = -4$ $x = 4$

14. $x^2 - 9 = 0$
$(x+3)(x-3) = 0$
$x + 3 = 0$ or $x - 3 = 0$
$x = -3$ $x = 3$

15. $x^2 - 12x = 0$
$x(x-12) = 0$
$x = 0$ or $x - 12 = 0$
$x = 12$

16. $9x^2 + 27x = 0$
$9x(x+3) = 0$
$x = 0$ or $x + 3 = 0$
$x = -3$

17. $x^2 + 7x = 0$
$x(x+7) = 0$
$x = 0$ or $x + 7 = 0$
$x = -7$

18. $a^2 - 4a - 12 = 0$
$(a-6)(a+2) = 0$
$a - 6 = 0$ or $a + 2 = 0$
$a = 6$ $a = -2$

19. $x^2 - 8x + 16 = 0$
$(x-4)(x-4) = 0$
$x - 4 = 0$
$x = 4$

20. $x^2 + 12x + 36 = 0$

$(x+6)(x+6) = 0$

$x+6 = 0$

$x = -6$

21. $x^2 + 12x = -20$

$x^2 + 12x + 20 = 0$

$(x+10)(x+2) = 0$

$x+10 = 0 \quad$ or $\quad x+2 = 0$

$x = -10 \qquad\qquad x = -2$

22. $3y^2 - 4 = -4y$

$3y^2 + 4y - 4 = 0$

$(3y-2)(y+2) = 0$

$3y - 2 = 0 \quad$ or $\quad y + 2 = 0$

$3y = 2 \qquad\qquad y = -2$

$y = \dfrac{2}{3}$

23. $x^2 + 12x + 22 = 2$

$x^2 + 12x + 20 = 0$

$(x+2)(x+10) = 0$

$x+2 = 0 \quad$ or $\quad x+10 = 0$

$x = -2 \qquad\qquad x = -10$

24. $3x^2 = -21x - 18$

$3x^2 + 21x + 18 = 0$

$3(x^2 + 7x + 6) = 0$

$3(x+1)(x+6) = 0$

$x+1 = 0 \quad$ or $\quad x+6 = 0$

$x = -1 \qquad\qquad x = -6$

25. $2x^2 - 5x - 24 = -3x$

$2x^2 - 2x - 24 = 0$

$2(x^2 - x - 12) = 0$

$2(x-4)(x+3) = 0$

$x-4 = 0 \quad$ or $\quad x+3 = 0$

$x = 4 \qquad\qquad x = -3$

26. $x^2 = 4x + 21$

$x^2 - 4x - 21 = 0$

$(x-7)(x+3) = 0$

$x-7 = 0 \quad$ or $\quad x+3 = 0$

$x = 7 \qquad\qquad x = -3$

27. $23p - 24 = -p^2$

$p^2 + 23p - 24 = 0$

$(p+24)(p-1) = 0$

$p+24 = 0 \quad$ or $\quad p-1 = 0$

$p = -24 \qquad\qquad p = 1$

28. $3x^2 - 9x - 30 = 0$

$3(x^2 - 3x - 10) = 0$

$3(x-5)(x+3) = 0$

$x-5 = 0 \quad$ or $\quad x+2 = 0$

$x = 5 \qquad\qquad x = -2$

29. $33w + 90 = -3w^2$

$3w^2 + 33w + 90 = 0$

$3(w^2 + 11w + 30) = 0$

$3(w+5)(w+6) = 0$

$w+5 = 0 \quad$ or $\quad w+6 = 0$

$w = -5 \qquad\qquad w = -6$

30. $t^2 + 44 + 15t = 0$

$t^2 + 15t + 44 = 0$

$(t+4)(t+11) = 0$

$t+4 = 0 \quad$ or $\quad t+11 = 0$

$t = -4 \qquad\qquad t = -11$

31. $-2x - 15 = -x^2$

$x^2 - 2x - 15 = 0$

$(x-5)(x+3) = 0$

$x-5 = 0 \quad$ or $\quad x+3 = 0$

$x = 5 \qquad\qquad x = -3$

32. $-9x + 20 = -x^2$

$x^2 - 9x + 20 = 0$

$(x-4)(x-5) = 0$

$x - 4 = 0$ or $x - 5 = 0$

$x = 4$ $\qquad x = 5$

33. $-x^2 + 29x + 30 = 0$

$x^2 - 29x - 30 = 0$

$(x - 30)(x + 1) = 0$

$x - 30 = 0$ or $x + 1 = 0$

$x = 30$ $\qquad x = -1$

34. $12y - 11 = y^2$

$y^2 - 12y + 11 = 0$

$(y - 1)(y - 11) = 0$

$y - 1 = 0$ or $y - 11 = 0$

$y = 1$ $\qquad y = 11$

35. $-15 = 4m^2 + 17m$

$4m^2 + 17m + 15 = 0$

$(4m + 5)(m + 3) = 0$

$4m + 5 = 0$ or $m + 3 = 0$

$4m = -5$ $\qquad m = -3$

$m = -\dfrac{5}{4}$

36. $z^2 + 8z = -16$

$z^2 + 8z + 16 = 0$

$(z + 4)^2 = 0$

$z + 4 = 0$

$z = -4$

37. $9p^2 = -21p - 6$

$9p^2 + 21p + 6 = 0$

$3(3p^2 + 7p + 2) = 0$

$3(3p + 1)(p + 2) = 0$

$3p + 1 = 0$ or $p + 2 = 0$

$3p = -1$ $\qquad p = -2$

$p = -\dfrac{1}{3}$

38. $2x^2 - 5 = 3x$

$2x^2 - 3x - 5 = 0$

$(2x - 5)(x + 1) = 0$

$2x - 5 = 0$ or $x + 1 = 0$

$2x = 5$ $\qquad x = -1$

$x = \dfrac{5}{2}$

39. $3r^2 + 13r = 10$

$3r^2 + 13r - 10 = 0$

$(3r - 2)(r + 5) = 0$

$3r - 2 = 0$ or $r + 5 = 0$

$3r = 2$ $\qquad r = -5$

$r = \dfrac{2}{3}$

40. $3x^2 = 7x + 20$

$3x^2 - 7x - 20 = 0$

$(3x + 5)(x - 4) = 0$

$3x + 5 = 0$ or $x - 4 = 0$

$3x = -5$ $\qquad x = 4$

$x = -\dfrac{5}{3}$

41. $4x^2 + 4x - 48 = 0$

$4(x^2 + x - 12) = 0$

$4(x + 4)(x - 3) = 0$

$x + 4 = 0$ or $x - 3 = 0$

$x = -4$ $\qquad x = 3$

42. $6x^2 - 7x - 5 = 0$

$(3x - 5)(2x + 1) = 0$

$3x - 5 = 0$ or $2x + 1 = 0$

$3x = 5$ $\qquad 2x = -1$

$x = \dfrac{5}{3}$ $\qquad x = -\dfrac{1}{2}$

43.
$$8x^2 + 2x = 3$$
$$8x^2 + 2x - 3 = 0$$
$$(4x + 3)(2x - 1) = 0$$
$$4x + 3 = 0 \quad \text{or} \quad 2x - 1 = 0$$
$$4x = -3 \qquad 2x = 1$$
$$x = -\frac{3}{4} \qquad x = \frac{1}{2}$$

44.
$$2x^2 + 4x - 6 = 0$$
$$2(x^2 + 2x - 3) = 0$$
$$2(x + 3)(x - 1) = 0$$
$$x + 3 = 0 \quad \text{or} \quad x - 1 = 0$$
$$x = -3 \qquad x = 1$$

45.
$$c^2 = 64$$
$$c^2 - 64 = 0$$
$$c^2 - 8^2 = 0$$
$$(c + 8)(c - 8) = 0$$
$$c + 8 = 0 \quad \text{or} \quad c - 8 = 0$$
$$c = -8 \qquad c = 8$$

46.
$$2n^2 + 36 = -18n$$
$$2n^2 + 18n + 36 = 0$$
$$2(n^2 + 9n + 18) = 0$$
$$2(n + 6)(n + 3) = 0$$
$$n + 6 = 0 \quad \text{or} \quad n + 3 = 0$$
$$n = -6 \qquad n = -3$$

47.
$$2x^2 = 50x$$
$$2x^2 - 50x = 0$$
$$2x(x - 25) = 0$$
$$2x = 0 \quad \text{or} \quad x - 25 = 0$$
$$x = 0 \qquad x = 25$$

48.
$$4x^2 - 25 = 0$$
$$(2x)^2 - 5^2 = 0$$
$$(2x + 5)(2x - 5) = 0$$
$$2x + 5 = 0 \quad \text{or} \quad 2x - 5 = 0$$
$$2x = -5 \qquad 2x = 5$$
$$x = -\frac{5}{2} \qquad x = \frac{5}{2}$$

49.
$$x^2 = 100$$
$$x^2 - 100 = 0$$
$$x^2 - 10^2 = 0$$
$$(x + 10)(x - 10) = 0$$
$$x + 10 = 0 \quad \text{or} \quad x - 10 = 0$$
$$x = -10 \qquad x = 10$$

50.
$$3x^2 - 48 = 0$$
$$3(x^2 - 16) = 0$$
$$3(x^2 - 4^2) = 0$$
$$3(x + 4)(x - 4) = 0$$
$$x + 4 = 0 \quad \text{or} \quad x - 4 = 0$$
$$x = -4 \qquad x = 4$$

51.
$$(x - 2)(x - 1) = 12$$
$$x^2 - 3x + 2 = 12$$
$$x^2 - 3x - 10 = 0$$
$$(x + 2)(x - 5) = 0$$
$$x + 2 = 0 \quad \text{or} \quad x - 5 = 0$$
$$x = -2 \qquad x = 5$$

52.
$$(x + 2)(x + 5) = -2$$
$$x^2 + 7x + 10 = -2$$
$$x^2 + 7x + 12 = 0$$
$$(x + 4)(x + 3) = 0$$
$$x + 4 = 0 \quad \text{or} \quad x + 3 = 0$$
$$x = -4 \qquad x = -3$$

53.
$$(3x + 2)(x + 1) = 4$$
$$3x^2 + 5x + 2 = 4$$
$$3x^2 + 5x - 2 = 0$$
$$(3x - 1)(x + 2) = 0$$
$$3x - 1 = 0 \qquad x + 2 = 0$$
$$x = \frac{1}{3} \qquad x = -2$$

54. $(x-1)(2x-5) = 9$

$2x^2 - 7x + 5 = 9$

$2x^2 - 7x - 4 = 0$

$(2x+1)(x-4) = 0$

$2x + 1 = 0$ or $x - 4 = 0$

$x = -\dfrac{1}{2}$ $x = 4$

55. $2(a^2 + 9) = 15a$

$2a^2 + 18 = 15a$

$2a^2 - 15a + 18 = 0$

$(2a - 3)(a - 6) = 0$

$2a - 3 = 0$ or $a - 6 = 0$

$2a = 3$ $a = 6$

$a = \dfrac{3}{2}$

56. $x(x + 5) = 6$

$x^2 + 5x = 6$

$x^2 + 5x - 6 = 0$

$(x + 6)(x - 1) = 0$

$x + 6 = 0$ or $x - 1 = 0$

$x = -6$ $x = 1$

57. The solutions are 6 and –4, so the factors are $x - 6$ and $x + 4$.

$(x-6)(x+4) = x^2 - 2x - 24$

The equation is $x^2 - 2x - 24 = 0$.

58. The solutions are –3 and –5, so the factors are $x + 3$ and $x + 5$.

$(x+3)(x+5) = x^2 + 8x + 15$

The equation is $x^2 + 8x + 15 = 0$.

59. The solutions are 6 and 0, so the factors are $x - 0$ and $x - 6$.

$(x - 0)(x - 6) = x(x - 6)$

$\qquad\qquad = x^2 - 6x$

The equation is $x^2 - 6x = 0$.

60. The solutions are 0 and –9, so the factors are $x - 0$ and $x + 9$.

$(x - 0)(x + 9) = x(x + 9)$

$\qquad\qquad = x^2 + 9x$

The equation is $x^2 + 9x = 0$.

61. a. The solutions are

$x = \dfrac{1}{2}$ or $x = -\dfrac{1}{3}$

$2x = 1$ $3x = -1$

$2x - 1 = 0$ $3x + 1 = 0$

Thus the factors are:

$(2x - 1)$ and $(3x + 1)$.

b. The equation is $(2x - 1)(3x + 1)$

$= 6x^2 - x - 1 = 0$.

62. a. The solutions are

$x = \dfrac{2}{3}$ or $x = -\dfrac{3}{4}$

$3x = 2$ $4x = -3$

$3x - 2 = 0$ $4x + 3 = 0$

Thus the factors are:

$(3x - 2)$ and $(4x + 3)$.

b. The equation is

$(3x - 2)(4x + 3) = 12x^2 + x - 6 = 0$

63. $(2x - 3)(x - 4) = (x - 5)(x + 3) + 7$

$2x^2 - 11x + 12 = x^2 - 2x - 15 + 7$

$2x^2 - 11x + 12 = x^2 - 2x - 8$

$x^2 - 9x + 20 = 0$

$(x - 5)(x - 4) = 0$

$x - 5 = 0$ or $x - 4 = 0$

$x = 5$ $x = 4$

64. $(x - 3)(x - 2) = (x + 5)(2x - 3) + 21$

$x^2 - 5x + 6 = 2x^2 + 7x - 15 + 21$

$x^2 - 5x + 6 = 2x^2 + 7x + 6$

$0 = x^2 + 12x$

$0 = x(x + 12)$

$x = 0$ or $x + 12 = 0$

$x = -12$

65. $x(x - 3)(x + 2) = 0$

$x = 0$ or $x - 3 = 0$ or $x + 2 = 0$

$x = 3$ $x = -2$

66. $x^3 - 10x^2 + 24x = 0$

$x(x^2 - 10x + 24) = 0$

$x(x-6)(x-4) = 0$

$x = 0$ or $x - 6 = 0$ or $x - 4 = 0$

$x = 6$ $x = 4$

67. $\dfrac{3}{5} - \dfrac{2}{9} = \dfrac{27}{45} - \dfrac{10}{45} = \dfrac{27-10}{45} = \dfrac{17}{45}$

68. a. identity

    b. contradiction

69. Let x be the number of people admitted in 60 minutes.

$\dfrac{160 \text{ people}}{13 \text{ minutes}} = \dfrac{x}{60 \text{ minutes}}$

$13x = 160(60)$

$13x = 9600$

$x \approx 738$

About 738 people were admitted in 60 minutes.

70. $\left(\dfrac{3p^5 q^7}{p^9 q^8}\right)^2 = \left(3 \cdot p^{5-9} \cdot q^{7-8}\right)^2$

$= \left(3p^{-4} q^{-1}\right)^2$

$= \left(\dfrac{3}{p^4 q}\right)^2$

$= \dfrac{3^2}{p^{4 \cdot 2} q^{1 \cdot 2}} = \dfrac{9}{p^8 q^2}$

71. monomial

72. binomial

73. not a polynomial; can't have a variable in the denominator.

74. trinomial

Exercise Set 6.7

1. A right triangle is a triangle with a 90° angle.

2. a. The smaller sides are called legs.

   b. The largest side is called the hypotenuse.

3. The Pythagorean Theorem is $a^2 + b^2 = c^2$.

4. No it does not. The two shorter sides are represented by a and b.

5. $a^2 + b^2 = c^2$

$a^2 + 4^2 = 5^2$

$a^2 + 16 = 25$

$a^2 = 9$

$a = 3$

6. $a^2 + b^2 = c^2$

$8^2 + 15^2 = c^2$

$64 + 225 = c^2$

$289 = c^2$

$17 = c$

7. $a^2 + b^2 = c^2$

$12^2 + 5^2 = c^2$

$144 + 25 = c^2$

$169 = c^2$

$13 = c$

8. $a^2 + b^2 = c^2$

$a^2 + 24^2 = 26^2$

$a^2 + 576 = 676$

$a^2 = 100$

$a = 10$

9. $a^2 + b^2 = c^2$

$24^2 + b^2 = 30^2$

$576 + b^2 = 900$

$b^2 = 324$

$b = 18$

10. $a^2 + b^2 = c^2$

$12^2 + 16^2 = c^2$

$144 + 256 = c^2$

$400 = c^2$

$20 = c$

11. $a^2 + b^2 = c^2$

$15^2 + 36^2 = c^2$

$225 + 1296 = c^2$

$1521 = c^2$

$39 = c$

12. $a^2 + b^2 = c^2$

$a^2 + 20^2 = 25^2$

$a^2 + 400 = 625$

$a^2 = 225$

$a = 15$

13. Let x be the smaller of the two positive numbers. Then $x + 4$ is the other positive number.

$x(x+4) = 117$

$x^2 + 4x + 117 = 0$

$(x-9)(x+13) = 0$

$x - 9 = 0$ or $x + 13 = 0$

$x = 9$ $x = -13$

Since x must be positive, the two numbers are 9 and $9 + 4 = 13$.

14. Let x = first positive number. Then $5x$ is the second positive number.

$x(5x) = 245$

$5x^2 = 245$

$5x^2 - 245 = 0$

$5(x^2 - 49) = 0$

$5(x+7)(x-7) = 0$

$x + 7 = 0$ or $x - 7 = 0$

$x = -7$ $x = 7$

Since x must be positive, the numbers are 7 and $5(7) = 35$.

15. Let x = first positive number. Then $2x + 2$ is the other number.

$x(2x+2) = 84$

$2x^2 + 2x = 84$

$2x^2 + 2x - 84 = 0$

$2(x^2 + x - 42) = 0$

$2(x+7)(x-6) = 0$

$x + 7 = 0$ or $x - 6 = 0$

$x = -7$ $x = 6$

The numbers have to be positive. Thus the numbers are 6 and $2(6) + 2 = 14$.

16. Let x = first positive integer. Then $x + 1$ is the next consecutive integer.

$x(x+1) = 56$

$x^2 + x = 56$

$x^2 + x - 56 = 0$

$(x+8)(x-7) = 0$

$x + 8 = 0$ or $x - 7 = 0$

$x = -8$ $x = 7$

The numbers have to be positive. Thus the numbers are 7 and 8.

17. Let x be the first even integer. Then $x + 2$ is the next even integer.

$x(x+2) = 288$

$x^2 + 2x = 288$

$x^2 + 2x - 288 = 0$

$(x+18)(x-16) = 0$

$x + 18 = 0$ or $x - 16 = 0$

$x = -18$ $x = 16$

Since x must be positive, the numbers are 16 and 18.

18. Let x be the smaller of the two consecutive positive odd integers. Then $x + 2$ is the other integer.

$x(x+2) = 143$

$x^2 + 2x - 143 = 0$

$(x+13)(x-11) = 0$

$x + 13 = 0$ or $x - 11 = 0$

$x = -13$ $x = 11$

Since x must be positive, the two integers are 11 and $11 + 2 = 13$.

19. Let w = width. Then length = $4w$.

$A = lw$

$36 = (4w)(w)$

$36 = 4w^2$

$0 = 4w^2 - 36$

$0 = 4(w^2 - 9)$

$0 = 4(w+3)(w-3)$

$w + 3 = 0$ or $w - 3 = 0$

$w = -3$ $w = 3$

Since dimensions must be positive, the width is 3 feet and the length is $4(3) = 12$ feet.

20. Let l = length. Then width = $l - 3$.

$$lw = A$$
$$l(l-3) = 180$$
$$l^2 - 3l = 180$$
$$l^2 - 3l - 180 = 0$$
$$(l-15)(l+12) = 0$$
$$l - 15 = 0 \quad \text{or} \quad l + 12 = 0$$
$$l = 15 \qquad\qquad l = -12$$

Since dimensions must be positive, the length is 15 inches and the width is $15 - 3 = 12$ inches.

21. Let l = length of the garden and $\frac{2}{3}l$ = width of the garden.

$$lw = A$$
$$l\left(\frac{2}{3}l\right) = 150$$
$$2l^2 = 450$$
$$2l^2 - 450 = 0$$
$$2(l^2 - 225) = 0$$
$$2(l^2 - 15^2) = 0$$
$$2(l+15)(l-15) = 0$$
$$l + 15 = 0 \quad \text{or} \quad l - 15 = 0$$
$$l = -15 \qquad\qquad l = 15$$

Since dimensions must be positive, the length is 15 feet and the width is $\frac{2}{3}(15)$ = 10 feet.

22. a. Let h = height, $h + 7$ = length.

$$lh = A$$
$$(h+7)h = 120$$
$$h^2 + 7h - 120 = 0$$
$$(h+15)(h-8) = 0$$
$$h + 15 = 0 \quad \text{or} \quad h - 8 = 0$$
$$h = -15 \qquad\qquad h = 8$$

Since dimensions must be positive, the height is 8 feet and the length is $8 + 7 = 15$ feet.

b. 15 feet

c. The border will cost $4(15) = \$60$.

23. Let a = length of a side of the original square. Then $a + 5$ is the length of the new side.

$$(\text{side}) \cdot (\text{side}) = \text{Area}$$
$$(a+5)(a+5) = 81$$
$$a^2 + 10a + 25 = 81$$
$$a^2 + 10a - 56 = 0$$
$$(a+14)(a-4) = 0$$
$$a + 14 = 0 \quad \text{or} \quad a - 4 = 0$$
$$a = -14 \quad \text{or} \quad a = 4$$

Since length must be positive, the original square had sides of length 4 meters.

24. Let w = width. Then length = $w + 2$.

$$A = lw$$
$$35 = (w+2)(w)$$
$$35 = w^2 + 2w$$
$$0 = w^2 + 2w - 35$$
$$0 = (w+7)(w-5)$$
$$w = -7 \quad \text{or} \quad w = 5$$

Since dimensions must be positive, the width is 5 feet and the length is $w + 2 = 5 + 2 = 7$ feet.

25. $d = 16t^2$

$$256 = 16t^2$$
$$\frac{256}{16} = t^2$$
$$16 = t^2$$
$$0 = t^2 - 16$$
$$0 = (t+4)(t-4)$$
$$t + 4 = 0 \quad \text{or} \quad t - 4 = 0$$
$$t = -4 \qquad\qquad t = 4$$

Since time must be positive, it would take the egg 4 seconds to hit the ground.

26. $d = 16t^2$

$$400 = 16t^2$$
$$25 = t^2$$
$$5 = t$$

It would take 5 seconds for the rock to hit the sea.

27. $a^2 + b^2 = c^2$

$$7^2 + 24^2 = 25^2$$
$$49 + 576 = 625$$
$$625 = 625 \quad \text{True}$$

Since these values are true for the Pythagorean Theorem, a right triangle can exist.

28. $a^2 + b^2 = c^2$

$16^2 + 20^2 = 22^2$

$256 + 400 = 484$

$656 = 484$ False

Since these values are false for the Pythagorean Theorem, a right triangle cannot exist.

29. $a^2 + b^2 = c^2$

$9^2 + 40^2 = 41^2$

$81 + 1600 = 1681$

$1681 = 1681$ True

Since these values are true for the Pythagorean Theorem, a right triangle can exist.

30. $a^2 + b^2 = c^2$

$13^2 + 18^2 = 28^2$

$169 + 324 = 784$

$493 = 784$ False

Since these values are false for the Pythagorean Theorem, a right triangle cannot exist.

31. $a^2 + b^2 = c^2$

$30^2 + b^2 = 34^2$

$900 + b^2 = 1156$

$b^2 = 256$

$b = 16$ feet

32. $a^2 + b^2 = c^2$

$a^2 + 24^2 = 30^2$

$a^2 + 576 = 900$

$a^2 = 324$

$a = 18$ inches

33. $a^2 + b^2 = c^2$

$9^2 + 40^2 = c^2$

$81 + 1600 = c^2$

$1681 = c^2$

$41 = c$

$c = 41$ feet

34. $a^2 + b^2 = c^2$

$a^2 + 24^2 = 26^2$

$a^2 + 576 = 676$

$a^2 = 100$

$a = 10$ inches

35. Let x be the length of one leg of the triangle. Then $x + 2$ is the length of the other leg.

$a^2 + b^2 = c^2$

$x^2 + (x + 2)^2 = 10^2$

$x^2 + x^2 + 4x + 4 = 100$

$2x^2 + 4x + 4 = 100$

$2x^2 + 4x - 96 = 0$

$2(x^2 + 2x - 48) = 0$

$2(x + 8)(x - 6) = 0$

$x + 8 = 0$ or $x - 6 = 0$

$x = -8$ $x = 6$

Since length is positive, the lengths are 6 ft, 8ft and 10ft.

36. Let x be the length of one leg of the triangle. Then $2x + 2$ is the length of the other leg.

$a^2 + b^2 = c^2$

$x^2 + (2x + 2)^2 = 13^2$

$x^2 + 4x^2 + 8x + 4 = 169$

$5x^2 + 8x + 4 = 169$

$5x^2 + 8x - 165 = 0$

$(5x + 33)(x - 5) = 0$

$5x + 33 = 0$ or $x - 5 = 0$

$5x = -33$

$x = -\dfrac{33}{5}$ $x = 5$

Since length is positive, the lengths are 5 in., 12 in., and 13 in.

37. Let w = width of the frame, then $w + 3$ = the length of the frame. The diagonal is 15.

$a^2 + b^2 = c^2$

$(w + 3)^2 + w^2 = 15^2$

$w^2 + 6w + 9 + w^2 = 225$

$2w^2 + 6w + 9 = 225$

$2w^2 + 6w - 216 = 0$

$2(w^2 + 3w - 108) = 0$

$2(w + 12)(w - 9) = 0$

$w + 12 = 0$ or $w - 9 = 0$

$w = -12$ $w = 9$

The width is 9 in. and the length is $9 + 3 = 12$ in.

38. Let w = width of the computer, then $2w - 1$ = the length of the computer. The diagonal is 17.

$$a^2 + b^2 = c^2$$
$$(2w-1)^2 + w^2 = 17^2$$
$$4w^2 - 4w + 1 + w^2 = 289$$
$$5w^2 - 4w + 1 = 289$$
$$5w^2 - 4w - 288 = 0$$
$$(5w + 36)(w - 8) = 0$$
$$5w + 36 = 0 \quad \text{or} \quad w - 8 = 0$$
$$w = -\frac{36}{5} \qquad w = 8$$

The width is 8 in. and the length is $2(8) - 1 = 15$ in.

39. Let w be the width of the rectangle. Then $3w + 3$ is the length and $3w + 4$ is the length of the diagonal.

$$a^2 + b^2 = c^2$$
$$w^2 + (3w + 3)^2 = (3w + 4)^2$$
$$w^2 + 9w^2 + 18w + 9 = 9w^2 + 24w + 16$$
$$10w^2 + 18w + 9 = 9w^2 + 24w + 16$$
$$w^2 - 6w - 7 = 0$$
$$(w - 7)(w + 1) = 0$$
$$w - 7 = 0 \quad \text{or} \quad w + 1 = 0$$
$$w = 7 \qquad w = -1$$

Since length is positive, the dimensions of the garden are 7 ft for the width and $3w + 3 = 3(7) + 3 = 24$ ft for the length.

40. Let x be the length of the rope from the base of the tree to the anchor. Then $2x + 4$ is the height of the tree and $2x + 6$ is the length of the rope from the top of the tree to the anchor.

$$a^2 + b^2 = c^2$$
$$x^2 + (2x + 4)^2 = (2x + 6)^2$$
$$x^2 + 4x^2 + 16x + 16 = 4x^2 + 24x + 36$$
$$5x^2 + 16x + 16 = 4x^2 + 24x + 36$$
$$x^2 - 8x - 20 = 0$$
$$(x + 2)(x - 10) = 0$$
$$x + 2 = 0 \quad \text{or} \quad x - 10 = 0$$
$$x = -2 \qquad x = 10$$

Since length is positive, the height of the tree is $2x + 4 = 2(10) + 4 = 24$ feet.

41.
$$P = x^2 - 15x - 50$$
$$x^2 - 15x - 50 = 400$$
$$x^2 - 15 - 450 = 0$$
$$(x - 30)(x + 15) = 0$$
$$x - 30 = 0 \quad \text{or} \quad x + 15 = 0$$
$$x = 30 \qquad x = -15$$

Since x must be positive, she must sell 30 books for a profit of \$400.

42.
$$C = x^2 - 27x - 20$$
$$70 = x^2 - 27x - 20$$
$$0 = x^2 - 27x - 90$$
$$0 = (x + 3)(x - 30)$$
$$x + 3 = 0 \quad \text{or} \quad x - 30 = 0$$
$$x = -3 \qquad x = 30$$

Since the number of water sprinklers manufactured must be positive, 30 water sprinklers were manufactured at a cost of \$70.

43. a.
$$n^2 + n = 20$$
$$n^2 + n - 20 = 0$$
$$(n - 4)(n + 5) = 0$$
$$n - 4 = 0 \quad \text{or} \quad n + 5 = 0$$
$$n = 4 \qquad n = -5$$

Since n must be positive, $n = 4$.

b.
$$n^2 + n = 90$$
$$n^2 + n - 90 = 0$$
$$(n - 9)(n + 10) = 0$$
$$n - 9 = 0 \quad \text{or} \quad n + 10 = 0$$
$$n = 9 \qquad n = -10$$

Since n must be positive, $n = 9$.

44. a. $C = \dfrac{15(15-1)}{2} = \dfrac{15(14)}{2} = 15(7) = 105$

b. $55 = \dfrac{n(n-1)}{2}$

$110 = n(n-1)$

$110 = n^2 - n$

$0 = n^2 - n - 110$

$0 = (n-11)(n+10)$

$n - 11 = 0$ or $n + 10 = 0$

$n = 11$ $\quad\quad\quad$ $n = -10$

Since the number of lines must be positive, the switchboard has 11 lines.

45. Before area can be determined, the length of the rectangle must be found first. Let x be the length of the rectangle.

$a^2 + b^2 = c^2$

$x^2 + 18^2 = 30^2$

$x^2 + 324 = 900$

$x^2 = 576$

$x = 24$

Area of a rectangle can be found by multiplying the length and width.

$A = lw$

$= 24 \cdot 18$

$= 432$

The area of the rectangle is 432 square feet.

46. Before area can be determined, the length of the hypotenuse of the triangle must be found. Notice that the hypotenuse of the triangle is also the diameter of the circle.

$a^2 + b^2 = c^2$

$8^2 + 15^2 = c^2$

$64 + 225 = c^2$

$289 = c^2$

$17 = c$

Area of a circle can be found by squaring the radius and multiplying by pi.

$A = \pi r^2$

$= \pi(17 \div 2)^2$

$= \pi(8.5)^2$

$= \pi \cdot 72.25$

≈ 226.98

The area of the circle is about 227 square feet.

47. $x^3 - 4x^2 - 32x = 0$

$x(x^2 - 4x - 32) = 0$

$x(x-8)(x+4) = 0$

$x = 0$ or $x - 8 = 0$ or $x + 4 = 0$

$x = 8$ $\quad\quad\quad$ $x = -4$

48. $x^3 + 2x^2 - 15x = 0$

$x(x^2 + 2x - 15) = 0$

$x(x+5)(x-3) = 0$

$x = 0$ or $x + 5 = 0$ or $x - 3 = 0$

$x = -5$ $\quad\quad\quad$ $x = 3$

49. Solutions are –2, 0, and 3, so the factors are $x + 2$, x, and $x - 3$.

$x(x+2)(x-3) = x(x^2 - x - 6)$

$= x^3 - x^2 - 6x$

The equation is $x^3 - x^2 - 6x = 0$.

50. The numbers are the constants in the binomials that are factors of $x^2 - 2x - 63$.

$x^2 - 2x - 63 = (x-9)(x+7)$

The numbers are –9 and 7.

51. $x + y = 9$ and $x^2 + y^2 = 45$

$y = 9 - x$

$x^2 + (9-x)^2 = 45$

$x^2 + 81 - 18x + x^2 = 45$

$2x^2 - 18x + 81 - 45 = 0$

$2(x^2 - 9x + 18) = 0$

$2(x-3)(x-6) = 0$

$x - 3 = 0$ or $x - 6 = 0$

$x = 3$ $\quad\quad\quad$ $x = 6$

When $x = 3$, $y = 6$ and when $x = 6$, $y = 3$.

The numbers are 3 and 6.

52. Answers will vary.

53.
$$C = R$$
$$2x^2 - 20x + 600 = x^2 + 50x - 400$$
$$x^2 - 70x + 1000 = 0$$
$$(x - 50)(x - 20) = 0$$
$$x - 50 = 0 \quad \text{or} \quad x - 20 = 0$$
$$x = 50 \qquad x = 20$$

The manufacturer must produce 20 or 50 units to break even.

54. a. Substitute 3 for t.
$$h = -16t^2 + 128t$$
$$h = -16(3^2) + 128(3)$$
$$h = -16(9) + 384$$
$$h = -144 + 384$$
$$h = 240$$
After 3 seconds the height is 240 feet.

b. Let $h = 0$ and solve for t.
$$h = -16t^2 + 128t$$
$$0 = -16t^2 + 128t$$
$$0 = -16t(t - 8)$$

$$-16t = 0 \quad \text{or} \quad t - 8 = 0$$
$$t = 0 \qquad t = 8$$

It takes 8 sec. for the cannonball to hit the ground.

55. "Seven less than three times a number" is $3x - 7$.

56. $(3x + 2) - (x^2 - 4x + 6) = 3x + 2 - x^2 + 4x - 6$
$$= -x^2 + 3x + 4x + 2 - 6$$
$$= -x^2 + 7x - 4$$

57. $(3x^2 + 2x - 4)(2x - 1)$
$$= 3x^2(2x - 1) + 2x(2x - 1) - 4(2x - 1)$$
$$= 6x^3 - 3x^2 + 4x^2 - 2x - 8x + 4$$
$$= 6x^3 + x^2 - 10x + 4$$

58.
$$\begin{array}{r} 2x - 3 \\ 3x - 5 \overline{)\ 6x^2 - 19x + 15} \\ \underline{6x^2 - 10x} \\ -9x + 15 \\ \underline{-9x + 15} \\ 0 \end{array}$$

$$\frac{6x^2 - 19x + 15}{3x - 5} = 2x - 3$$

59. $\dfrac{6x^2 - 19x + 15}{3x - 5} = \dfrac{(3x - 5)(2x - 3)}{3x - 5}$
$$= 2x - 3$$

Chapter 6 Review Exercises

1. The greatest common factor is y^3.

2. The greatest common factor is $3p$.

3. The greatest common factor is $6c^2$.

4. The greatest common factor is $5x^2y^2$.

5. The greatest common factor is 1.

6. The greatest common factor is s.

7. The greatest common factor is $x - 3$.

8. The greatest common factor is $x + 5$.

9. $7x - 35 = 7(x - 5)$

10. $35x - 5 = 5(7x - 1)$

11. $24y^2 - 4y = 4y(6y - 1)$

12. $55p^3 - 20p^2 = 5p^2(11p - 4)$

13. $60a^2b - 36ab^2 = 12ab(5a - 3b)$

14. $9xy - 36x^3y^2 = 9xy(1 - 4x^2y)$

15. $20x^3y^2 + 8x^9y^3 - 16x^5y^2$
$$= 4x^3y^2(5 + 2x^6y - 4x^2)$$

16. $24x^2 - 13y^2 + 6xy$ is prime.

17. $14a^2b - 7b - a^3$ is prime.

18. $x(5x + 3) - 2(5x + 3) = (5x + 3)(x - 2)$

19. $3x(x-1)+4(x-1)=(x-1)(3x+4)$

20. $2x(4x-3)+4x-3=2x(4x-3)+1(4x-3)$
$$=(4x-3)(2x+1)$$

21. $x^2+6x+2x+12=x(x+6)+2(x+6)$
$$=(x+6)(x+2)$$

22. $x^2-5x+4x-20=x(x-5)+4(x-5)$
$$=(x-5)(x+4)$$

23. $y^2-6y-6y+36=y(y-6)-6(y-6)$
$$=(y-6)(y-6)$$
$$=(y-6)^2$$

24. $3xy+3x+2y+2=3x(y+1)+2(y+1)$
$$=(y+1)(3x+2)$$

25. $4a^2-4ab-a+b=4a(a-b)-1(a-b)$
$$=(a-b)(4a-1)$$

26. $2x^2+12x-x-6=2x(x+6)-1(x+6)$
$$=(x+6)(2x-1)$$

27. $x^2+3x-2xy-6y=x(x+3)-2y(x+3)$
$$=(x+3)(x-2y)$$

28. $5x^2-xy+20xy-4y^2$
$$=x(5x-y)+4y(5x-y)$$
$$=(5x-y)(x+4y)$$

29. $4x^2+12xy-5xy-15y^2$
$$=4x(x+3y)-5y(x+3y)$$
$$=(x+3y)(4x-5y)$$

30. $6a^2-10ab-3ab+5b^2$
$$=2a(3a-5b)-b(3a-5b)$$
$$=(3a-5b)(2a-b)$$

31. $pq-3q+4p-12=q(p-3)+4(p-3)$
$$=(p-3)(q+4)$$

32. $3x^2-9xy+2xy-6y^2=3x(x-3y)+2y(x-3y)$
$$=(x-3y)(3x+2y)$$

33. $7a^2+14ab-ab-2b^2=7a(a+2b)-b(a+2b)$
$$=(a+2b)(7a-b)$$

34. $8x^2-4x+6x-3=4x(2x-1)+3(2x-1)$
$$=(2x-1)(4x+3)$$

35. $x^2-x-6=(x+2)(x-3)$

36. $x^2+4x-15$ is prime.

37. $x^2+11x+18=(x+9)(x+2)$

38. $n^2+3n-40=(n+8)(n-5)$

39. $b^2+b-20=(b-4)(b+5)$

40. $x^2-15x+56=(x-8)(x-7)$

41. $c^2-10c-20$ is prime.

42. $y^2-10y-22$ is prime.

43. $x^3-17x^2+72x=x(x^2-17x+72)$
$$=x(x-9)(x-8)$$

44. $t^3-5t^2-36t=t(t^2-5t-36)$
$$=t(t-9)(t+4)$$

45. $x^2-2xy-15y^2=(x-5y)(x+3y)$

46. $4x^3+32x^2y+60xy^2=4x(x^2+8xy+15y^2)$
$$=4x(x+3y)(x+5y)$$

47. $2x^2-x-15=(2x+5)(x-3)$

48. $6x^2-29x-5=(6x+1)(x-5)$

49. $4x^2-9x+5=(4x-5)(x-1)$

50. $5m^2-14m+8=(5m-4)(m-2)$

51. $16y^2+8y-3=(4y+3)(4y-1)$

52. $5x^2-32x+12=(5x-2)(x-6)$

53. $2t^2+14t+9$ is prime.

54. $5x^2+37x-24=(5x-3)(x+8)$

55. $6s^2+13s+5=(2s+1)(3s+5)$

56. $6x^2 + 11x - 10 = (3x - 2)(2x + 5)$

57. $12x^2 + 2x - 4 = 2(6x^2 + x - 2)$
$$= 2(3x + 2)(2x - 1)$$

58. $25x^2 - 30x + 9 = (5x - 3)(5x - 3)$
$$= (5x - 3)^2$$

59. $9x^3 - 12x^2 + 4x = x(9x^2 - 12x + 4)$
$$= x(3x - 2)(3x - 2)$$
$$= x(3x - 2)^2$$

60. $18x^3 + 12x^2 - 16x = 2x(9x^2 + 6x - 8)$
$$= 2x(3x + 4)(3x - 2)$$

61. $4a^2 - 16ab + 15b^2 = (2a - 3b)(2a - 5b)$

62. $16a^2 - 22ab - 3b^2 = (8a + b)(2a - 3b)$

63. $x^2 - 100 = x^2 - 10^2$
$$= (x + 10)(x - 10)$$

64. $x^2 - 36 = x^2 - 6^2$
$$= (x + 6)(x - 6)$$

65. $3x^2 - 48 = 3(x^2 - 16)$
$$= 3(x^2 - 4^2)$$
$$= 3(x + 4)(x - 4)$$

66. $81x^2 - 9y^2 = 9(9x^2 - y^2)$
$$= 9\left[(3x)^2 - y^2\right]$$
$$= 9(3x + y)(3x - y)$$

67. $81 - a^2 = 9^2 - a^2$
$$= (9 + a)(9 - a)$$

68. $64 - x^2 = 8^2 - x^2$
$$= (8 + x)(8 - x)$$

69. $16x^4 - 49y^2 = (4x^2)^2 - (7y)^2$
$$= (4x^2 + 7y)(4x^2 - 7y)$$

70. $64x^6 - 49y^6 = (8x^3)^2 - (7y^3)^2$
$$= (8x^3 + 7y^3)(8x^3 - 7y^3)$$

71. $a^3 + b^3 = (a + b)(a^2 - ab + b^2)$

72. $x^3 - y^3 = (x - y)(x^2 + xy + y^2)$

73. $x^3 - 1 = (x - 1)(x^2 + x + 1)$

74. $x^3 + 8 = x^3 + 2^3$
$$= (x + 2)(x^2 - 2x + 4)$$

75. $a^3 + 27 = a^3 + 3^3$
$$= (a + 3)(a^2 - 3a + 9)$$

76. $b^3 - 64 = b^3 - 4^3$
$$= (b - 4)(b^2 + 4b + 16)$$

77. $125a^3 + b^3 = (5a)^3 + b^3$
$$= (5a + b)(25a^2 - 5ab + b^2)$$

78. $27 - 8y^3 = 3^3 - (2y)^3$
$$= (3 - 2y)(9 + 6y + 4y^2)$$

79. $3x^3 - 192y^3 = 3(x^3 - 64y^3)$
$$= 3\left[x^3 - (4y)^3\right]$$
$$= 3(x - 4y)(x^2 + 4xy + 16y^2)$$

80. $27x^4 - 75y^2 = 3(9x^4 - 25y^2)$
$$= 3\left[(3x^2)^2 - (5y)^2\right]$$
$$= 3(3x^2 + 5y)(3x^2 - 5y)$$

81. $x^2 - 14x + 48 = (x - 6)(x - 8)$

82. $3x^2 - 18x + 27 = 3(x^2 - 6x + 9)$
$$= 3(x - 3)^2$$

83. $5q^2 - 5 = 5(q^2 - 1)$
$$= 5(q^2 - 1^2)$$
$$= 5(q + 1)(q - 1)$$

84. $8x^2 + 16x - 24 = 8\left(x^2 + 2x - 3\right)$
$= 8(x+3)(x-1)$

85. $4y^2 - 36 = 4\left(y^2 - 9\right)$
$= 4\left(y^2 - 3^2\right)$
$= 4(y+3)(y-3)$

86. $x^2 - 6x - 27 = (x-9)(x+3)$

87. $9x^2 - 6x + 1 = (3x-1)(3x-1)$
$= (3x-1)^2$

88. $7x^2 + 25x - 12 = (7x-3)(x+4)$

89. $6b^3 - 6 = 6\left(b^3 - 1\right)$
$= 6\left(b^3 - 1^3\right)$
$= 6(b-1)\left(b^2 + b + 1\right)$

90. $x^3 y - 27y = y\left(x^3 - 27\right)$
$= y\left(x^3 - 3^3\right)$
$= y(x-3)\left(x^2 + 3x + 9\right)$

91. $a^2 b - 2ab - 15b = b\left(a^2 - 2a - 15\right)$
$= b(a+3)(a-5)$

92. $6x^3 + 30x^2 + 9x^2 + 45x$
$= 3x\left(2x^2 + 10x + 3x + 15\right)$
$= 3x\left[2x(x+5) + 3(x+5)\right]$
$= 3x(2x+3)(x+5)$

93. $x^2 - 4xy + 3y^2 = (x-3y)(x-y)$

94. $3m^2 + 2mn - 8n^2 = (3m-4n)(m+2n)$

95. $4x^2 + 12xy + 9y^2 = (2x+3y)(2x+3y)$
$= (2x+3y)^2$

96. $25a^2 - 49b^2 = (5a)^2 - (7b)^2$
$= (5a+7b)(5a-7b)$

97. $xy - 7x + 2y - 14 = x(y-7) + 2(y-7)$
$= (x+2)(y-7)$

98. $16y^5 - 25y^7 = y^5\left(16 - 25y^2\right)$
$= y^5\left[4^2 - (5y)^2\right]$
$= y^5(4+5y)(4-5y)$

99. $6x^2 + 5xy - 21y^2 = (2x-3y)(3x+7y)$

100. $4x^3 + 18x^2 y + 20xy^2 = 2x\left(2x^2 + 9xy + 10y^2\right)$
$= 2x(2x+5y)(x+2y)$

101. $16x^4 - 8x^3 - 3x^2 = x^2\left(16x^2 - 8x - 3\right)$
$= x^2(4x+1)(4x-3)$

102. $d^4 - 16 = \left(d^2\right)^2 - 4^2$
$= \left(d^2 + 4\right)\left(d^2 - 4\right)$
$= \left(d^2 + 4\right)(d+2)(d-2)$

103. $x(x+9) = 0$
$x = 0$ or $x + 9 = 0$
$x = -9$

104. $(a-2)(a+6) = 0$
$a - 2 = 0$ or $a + 6 = 0$
$a = 2$ $\qquad a = -6$

105. $(x+5)(4x-3) = 0$
$x + 5 = 0$ or $4x - 3 = 0$
$x = -5$ $\qquad 4x = 3$
$x = \dfrac{3}{4}$

106. $x^2 + 7x = 0$
$x(x+7) = 0$
$x = 0$ or $x + 7 = 0$
$x = -7$

107. $6x^2 + 30x = 0$
$6x(x+5) = 0$
$6x = 0$ or $x + 5 = 0$
$x = 0$ $\qquad x = -5$

108. $6x^2 + 18x = 0$

$6x(x+3) = 0$

$6x = 0$ or $x + 3 = 0$

$x = 0$ $x = -3$

109. $r^2 + 9r + 18 = 0$

$(r+3)(r+6) = 0$

$r + 3 = 0$ or $r + 6 = 0$

$r = -3$ $r = -6$

110. $x^2 - 3x = -2$

$x^2 - 3x + 2 = 0$

$(x-1)(x-2) = 0$

$x - 1 = 0$ or $x - 2 = 0$

$x = 1$ $x = 2$

111. $x^2 - 12 = -x$

$x^2 + x - 12 = 0$

$(x+4)(x-3) = 0$

$x + 4 = 0$ or $x - 3 = 0$

$x = -4$ $x = 3$

112. $15x + 12 = -3x^2$

$3x^2 + 15x + 12 = 0$

$3(x^2 + 5x + 4) = 0$

$3(x+1)(x+4) = 0$

$x + 1 = 0$ or $x + 4 = 0$

$x = -1$ $x = -4$

113. $x^2 - 6x + 8 = 0$

$(x-4)(x-2) = 0$

$x - 4 = 0$ or $x - 2 = 0$

$x = 4$ $x = 2$

114. $3p^2 + 6p = 45$

$3p^2 + 6p - 45 = 0$

$3(p^2 + 2p - 15) = 0$

$3(x-3)(x+5) = 0$

$x - 3 = 0$ or $x + 5 = 0$

$x = 3$ $x = -5$

115. $8x^2 - 3 = -10x$

$8x^2 + 10x - 3 = 0$

$(4x-1)(2x+3) = 0$

$4x - 1 = 0$ or $2x + 3 = 0$

$4x = 1$ $2x = -3$

$x = \dfrac{1}{4}$ $x = -\dfrac{3}{2}$

116. $3p^2 - 11p = 4$

$3p^2 - 11p - 4 = 0$

$(3p+1)(p-4) = 0$

$3p + 1 = 0$ or $p - 4 = 0$

$3p = -1$ $p = 4$

$p = -\dfrac{1}{3}$

117. $4x^2 - 16 = 0$

$4(x^2 - 4) = 0$

$4(x^2 - 2^2) = 0$

$4(x+2)(x-2) = 0$

$x + 2 = 0$ or $x - 2 = 0$

$x = -2$ $x = 2$

118. $49x^2 - 100 = 0$

$(7x)^2 - 10^2 = 0$

$(7x+10)(7x-10) = 0$

$7x + 10 = 0$ or $7x - 10 = 0$

$7x = -10$ $7x = 10$

$x = -\dfrac{10}{7}$ $x = \dfrac{10}{7}$

119. $8x^2 - 14x + 3 = 0$

$(2x-3)(4x-1) = 0$

$2x - 3 = 0$ or $4x - 1 = 0$

$2x = 3$ $4x = 1$

$x = \dfrac{3}{2}$ $x = \dfrac{1}{4}$

120.
$$-48x = -12x^2 - 45$$
$$12x^2 - 48x + 45 = 0$$
$$3(4x^2 - 16x + 15) = 0$$
$$3(2x - 3)(2x - 5) = 0$$
$$2x - 3 = 0 \quad \text{or} \quad 2x - 5 = 0$$
$$2x = 3 \qquad\qquad 2x = 5$$
$$x = \frac{3}{2} \qquad\qquad x = \frac{5}{2}$$

121. $a^2 + b^2 = c^2$

122. hypotenuse

123.
$$a^2 + b^2 = c^2$$
$$6^2 + 8^2 = c^2$$
$$36 + 64 = c^2$$
$$100 = c^2$$
$$10 \text{ ft} = c$$

124.
$$a^2 + b^2 = c^2$$
$$a^2 + 5^2 = 13^2$$
$$a^2 + 25 = 169$$
$$a^2 = 144$$
$$a = 12 \text{ m}$$

125. Let x be the smaller integer. The larger is $x + 2$.
$$x(x + 2) = 99$$
$$x^2 + 2x = 99$$
$$x^2 + 2x - 99 = 0$$
$$(x + 11)(x - 9) = 0$$
$$x + 11 = 0 \quad \text{or} \quad x - 9 = 0$$
$$x = -11 \qquad\qquad x = 9$$
The integers must be positive, so they are 9 and 11.

126. Let x be the smaller integer. Then the larger is $2x + 6$.
$$x(2x + 6) = 56$$
$$2x^2 + 6x = 56$$
$$2x^2 + 6x - 56 = 0$$
$$2(x^2 + 3x - 28) = 0$$
$$(x + 7)(x - 4) = 0$$
$$x + 7 = 0 \quad \text{or} \quad x - 4 = 0$$
$$x = -7 \qquad\qquad x = 4$$
The integers must be positive, so they are 4 and 14.

127. Let w be the width of the rectangle. Then the length is $w + 3$.
$$w(w + 3) = 180$$
$$w^2 + 3w = 180$$
$$w^2 + 3w - 180 = 0$$
$$(w + 15)(w - 12) = 0$$
$$w + 15 = 0 \quad \text{or} \quad w - 12 = 0$$
$$w = -15 \qquad\qquad w = 12$$
Since the width must be positive, it is 12 feet, and the length is 15 feet.

128. Let x be the length of one leg of the triangle. Then $x + 7$ is the length of the other leg and $x + 9$ is the length of the hypotenuse.
$$a^2 + b^2 = c^2$$
$$x^2 + (x + 7)^2 = (x + 9)^2$$
$$x^2 + x^2 + 14x + 49 = x^2 + 18x + 81$$
$$2x^2 + 14x + 49 = x^2 + 18x + 81$$
$$x^2 - 4x - 32 = 0$$
$$(x - 8)(x + 4) = 0$$
$$x - 8 = 0 \quad \text{or} \quad x + 4 = 0$$
$$x = 8 \qquad\qquad x = -4$$
Since lengths must be positive, the lengths of the three sides are 8 ft, 15 ft, and 17 ft.

129. Let x be the length of a side of the original square. Then $x - 4$ is the length of a side of the smaller square.
$$(x - 4)^2 = 25$$
$$x^2 - 8x + 16 = 25$$
$$x^2 - 8x + 16 - 25 = 0$$
$$x^2 - 8x - 9 = 0$$
$$(x - 9)(x + 1) = 0$$
$$x - 9 = 0 \quad \text{or} \quad x + 1 = 0$$
$$x = 9 \qquad\qquad x = -1$$
Since lengths must be positive, the length of a side of the original square is 9 inches.

130. Let w be the width of the table. Then the length is $w + 2$ and the diagonal is $w + 4$.

$$a^2 + b^2 = c^2$$

$$w^2 + (w+2)^2 = (w+4)^2$$

$$w^2 + w^2 + 4x + 4 = w^2 + 8x + 16$$

$$2w^2 + 4x + 4 = w^2 + 8x + 16$$

$$w^2 - 4w - 12 = 0$$

$$(w-6)(w+2) = 0$$

$$w - 6 = 0 \quad \text{or} \quad w + 2 = 0$$

$$w = 6 \qquad\qquad w = -2$$

Since lengths must be positive, the diagonal is $w + 4 = 6 + 4 = 10$ ft.

131. $d = 16t^2$

$$16 = 16t^2$$

$$1 = t^2$$

$$1 = t$$

It will take 1 second for the pear to hit the ground.

132. $C = x^2 - 79x + 20$

$$100 = x^2 - 79x + 20$$

$$0 = x^2 - 79x - 80$$

$$0 = (x - 80)(x + 1)$$

$$x - 80 = 0 \quad \text{or} \quad x + 1 = 0$$

$$x = 80 \qquad\qquad x = -1$$

Since only a positive number of dozens of brownies can be made, the association can make 80 dozen brownies.

Chapter 6 Practice Test

1. The greatest common factor is $3y^3$.

2. The greatest common factor is $8p^2q^2$.

3. $5x^2y^3 - 15x^5y^2 = 5x^2y^2\left(y - 3x^3\right)$

4. $8a^3b - 12a^2b^2 + 28a^2b = 4a^2b\left(2a - 3b + 7\right)$

5. $4x^2 - 20x + x - 5 = 4x(x - 5) + 1(x - 5)$
$$= (4x + 1)(x - 5)$$

6. $a^2 - 4ab - 5ab + 20b^2 = a(a - 4b) - 5b(a - 4b)$
$$= (a - 4b)(a - 5b)$$

7. $r^2 + 5r - 24 = (r + 8)(r - 3)$

8. $25a^2 - 5ab - 6b^2 = (5a - 3b)(5a + 2b)$

9. $4x^2 - 16x - 48 = 4\left(x^2 - 4x - 12\right)$
$$= 4(x + 2)(x - 6)$$

10. $2y^3 - y^2 - 3y = y\left(2y^2 - y - 3\right)$
$$= y(2y - 3)(y + 1)$$

11. $12x^2 - xy - 6y^2 = (3x + 2y)(4x - 3y)$

12. $x^2 - 9y^2 = x^2 - (3y)^2$
$$= (x + 3y)(x - 3y)$$

13. $x^3 - 64 = x^3 - 4^3$
$$= (x - 4)\left(x^2 + 4x + 16\right)$$

14. $(6x - 5)(x + 3) = 0$
$$6x - 5 = 0 \quad \text{or} \quad x + 3 = 0$$
$$6x = 5 \qquad\qquad x = -3$$
$$x = \frac{5}{6}$$

15. $x^2 - 6x = 0$
$$x(x - 6) = 0$$
$$x = 0 \quad \text{or} \quad x - 6 = 0$$
$$x = 6$$

16. $\qquad\qquad x^2 = 64$
$$x^2 - 64 = 0$$
$$x^2 - 8^2 = 0$$
$$(x + 8)(x - 8) = 0$$
$$x + 8 = 0 \quad \text{or} \quad x - 8 = 0$$
$$x = -8 \qquad\qquad x = 8$$

17. $x^2 + 18x + 81 = 0$
$$(x + 9)^2 = 0$$
$$x + 9 = 0$$
$$x = -9$$

18. $x^2 - 7x + 12 = 0$

$(x-3)(x-4) = 0$

$x - 3 = 0$ or $x - 4 = 0$

$\quad x = 3 \qquad\qquad x = 4$

19. $\qquad x^2 + 6 = -5x$

$\quad x^2 + 5x + 6 = 0$

$(x+2)(x+3) = 0$

$x - 2 = 0$ or $x + 3 = 0$

$\quad x = -2 \qquad\qquad x = -3$

20. Use Pythagorean Theorem.

$a^2 + b^2 = c^2$

$a^2 + 10^2 = 26^2$

$a^2 + 100 = 676$

$\qquad a^2 = 576$

$\qquad a = 24$ in.

21. Let x be the length of one leg. Then $2x - 2$ is the length of the other leg and $2x + 2$ is the length of the hypotenuse.

$x^2 + (2x-2)^2 = (2x+2)^2$

$x^2 + 4x^2 - 8x + 4 = 4x^2 + 8x + 4$

$5x^2 - 8x + 4 = 4x^2 + 8x + 4$

$x^2 - 16x = 0$

$x(x-16) = 0$

$x = 0$ or $x - 16 = 0$

$\qquad\qquad x = 16$

Since length has to be positive, the hypotenuse is $2x + 2 = 2(16) + 2 = 32 + 2 = 34$ ft.

22. Let x be the smaller of the two integers. Then $2x + 1$ is the larger.

$x(2x+1) = 36$

$2x^2 + x - 36 = 0$

$(x-4)(2x+9) = 0$

$x - 4 = 0$ or $2x + 9 = 0$

$\quad x = 4 \qquad\qquad 2x = -9$

$\qquad\qquad\qquad\quad x = -\dfrac{9}{2}$

Since x must be positive and an integer, the smaller integer is 4 and the larger is $2 \cdot 4 + 1 = 9$.

23. Let x be the smaller of the two consecutive even integers. Then $x + 2$ is the larger.

$x(x+2) = 168$

$x^2 + 2x - 168 = 0$

$(x+14)(x-12) = 0$

$x + 14 = 0$ or $x - 12 = 0$

$\quad x = -14 \qquad\qquad x = 12$

Since x must be positive, then the smaller integer is 12 and the larger is 14.

24. Let w be the width of the rectangle. Then the length is $w + 2$.

$w(w+2) = 24$

$w^2 + 2w = 24$

$w^2 + 2w - 24 = 0$

$(w+6)(w-4) = 0$

$w + 6 = 0$ or $w - 4 = 0$

$\quad w = -6 \qquad\qquad w = 4$

Since the width is positive, it is 4 meters, and the length is 6 meters.

25. $d = 16t^2$

$1600 = 16t^2$

$16t^2 - 1600 = 0$

$16(t^2 - 100) = 0$

$16(t^2 - 10^2) = 0$

$16(t+10)(t-10) = 0$

$t + 10 = 0$ or $t - 10 = 0$

$\quad t = -10 \qquad\qquad t = 10$

Since time must be positive, then it would take the object 10 seconds to fall 1600 feet to the ground.

Chapter 6 Cumulative Review Test

1. $4 - 5(2x + 4x^2 - 21)$

$= 4 - 5[2(-4) + 4(-4)^2 - 21]$

$= 4 - 5[-8 + 4(16) - 21]$

$= 4 - 5(-8 + 64 - 21)$

$= 4 - 5(35)$

$= 4 - 175$

$= -171$

2. $5x^2 - 3y + 7(2 + y^2 - 4x)$
$= 5(3)^2 - 3(-2) + 7[2 + (-2)^2 - 4(3)]$
$= 5(9) + 6 + 7(2 + 4 - 12)$
$= 45 + 6 + 7(-6)$
$= 51 - 42$
$= 9$

3. Let $x =$ the cost of the room before tax.
$x + (.15x) = 103.50$
$1.15x = 103.50$
$x = 90$
The motel room costs $90 before taxes.

4. a. 7 is a natural number

b. $-6, -0.2, \dfrac{3}{5}, 7, 0, -\dfrac{5}{9}$, and 1.34 are rational numbers.

c. $\sqrt{7}$ and $-\sqrt{2}$ are irrational numbers.

d. All of the numbers are real numbers.

5. $|-8|$ is greater than $-|8|$ since $|-8| = 8$ and $-|8| = -(8) = -8$.

6. $4x - 2 = 4(x - 7) + 2x$
$4x - 2 = 4x - 28 + 2x$
$4x - 2 = 6x - 28$
$26 = 2x$
$13 = x$

7. $\dfrac{5}{12} = \dfrac{8}{x}$
$5x = 8(12)$
$5x = 96$
$x = \dfrac{96}{5} = 19.2$

8. $\dfrac{1\ \text{gal}}{825\ \text{ft}^2} = \dfrac{x\ \text{gal}}{5775\ \text{ft}^2}$
$\dfrac{1}{825} = \dfrac{x}{5775}$
$\dfrac{5775}{825} = x$
$7 = x$
It will take 7 gallons of paint to cover the house.

9. $4x + 3y = 7$
$3y = -4x + 7$
$y = \dfrac{-4x + 7}{3}$
$y = -\dfrac{4}{3}x + \dfrac{7}{3}$

10. Let x be the amount of 10% acid solution needed.
$0.10x + 0.04(3) = 0.08(x + 3)$
$0.10x + 0.12 = 0.08x + 0.24$
$0.02x + 0.12 = 0.24$
$0.02x = 0.12$
$x = 6$
Six liters of the 10% solution is needed.

11. Let $t =$ the number of hours that Brooke has been skiing. Then Bob has been skiing for $\left(t + \dfrac{1}{4}\right)$ hours.

	rate	time	distance
Brooke	8 kph	t	$8t$
Bob	4 kph	$t + \dfrac{1}{4}$	$4\left(t + \dfrac{1}{4}\right)$

Brooke catches Bob when they have both gone the same distance.
$8t = 4\left(t + \dfrac{1}{4}\right)$
$8t = 4t + 1$
$4t = 1$
$t = \dfrac{1}{4}$

It will take Brooke $\dfrac{1}{4}$ hour to catch Bob.

12. $y = -\dfrac{3}{5}x + 1$

$m = -\dfrac{3}{5}$; y-intercept: $(0,1)$

Writing the slope as $m = \dfrac{-3}{5}$, we can use it and the y-intercept to obtain an additional point on the graph of the equation.

$(0+5, 1-3) \rightarrow (5,-2)$

The point $(5,-2)$ is also on the graph. Plot this point and the y-intercept, connect the points with a straight line and extend the line in both directions.

Note: If we had written the slope as $m = \dfrac{3}{-5}$, we would have plotted the point $(-5,4)$ with the y-intercept to obtain the graph.

13. The slope must be found first.

Let (3, 7) be (x_1, y_1) and (–2, 4) be (x_2, y_2).

$m = \dfrac{y_2 - y_1}{x_2 - x_1}$

$m = \dfrac{4-7}{-2-3} = \dfrac{-3}{-5} = \dfrac{3}{5}$

Now choose one of the points and the point-slope formula.

$y - y_1 = m(x - x_1)$

$y - 7 = \dfrac{3}{5}(x - 3)$

$y - 7 = \dfrac{3}{5}x - \dfrac{9}{5}$

$y - 7 + 7 = \dfrac{3}{5}x - \dfrac{9}{5} + 7$

$y = \dfrac{3}{5}x - \dfrac{9}{5} + \dfrac{35}{5}$

$y = \dfrac{3}{5}x + \dfrac{26}{5}$

14. $(2x^{-3})^{-2}(4x^{-3}y^2)^3 = 2^{-2}x^{-3(-2)}4^3x^{-3(3)}y^{2(3)}$

$= 2^{-2}x^6 4^3 x^{-9} y^6$

$= 2^{-2} \cdot 4^3 x^{-3} y^6$

$= \dfrac{4^3 y^6}{2^2 x^3} = \dfrac{64 y^6}{4x^3}$

$= \dfrac{16 y^6}{x^3}$

15. $(x^3 - x^2 + 6x - 5) - (4x^3 - 3x^2 + 7)$

$= x^3 - x^2 + 6x - 5 - 4x^3 + 3x^2 - 7$

$= x^3 - 4x^3 - x^2 + 3x^2 + 6x - 5 - 7$

$= -3x^3 + 2x^2 + 6x - 12$

16. $(3x - 2)(x^2 + 5x - 6)$

$= 3x(x^2) - 2(x^2) + 3x(5x) - 2(5x) + 3x(-6) - 2(-6)$

$= 3x^3 - 2x^2 + 15x^2 - 10x - 18x + 12$

$= 3x^3 + 13x^2 - 28x + 12$

17.

$$x+3 \overline{\smash{\big)}\,x^2 - 2x + 6}$$

$\quad\quad\quad x - 5$

$\quad\quad\;\; \underline{x^2 + 3x}$

$\quad\quad\quad\quad -5x + 6$

$\quad\quad\quad\quad \underline{-5x - 15}$

$\quad\quad\quad\quad\quad\quad 21$

$\dfrac{x^2 - 2x + 6}{x + 3} = x - 5 + \dfrac{21}{x + 3}$

18. $qr + 2q - 8r - 16 = q(r + 2) - 8(r + 2)$

$\quad\quad\quad\quad\quad\quad\quad\quad\quad = (r + 2)(q - 8)$

19. $5x^2 - 7x - 6 = (5x + 3)(x - 2)$

20. $7y^3 - 63y = 7y(y^2 - 9)$

$\quad\quad\quad\quad\quad = 7y(y^2 - 3^2)$

$\quad\quad\quad\quad\quad = 7y(y + 3)(y - 3)$

Chapter 7

Exercise Set 7.1

1. Answers will vary.

2. To determine the value or values of the variables that make a rational expression undefined, set the denominator equal to zero and then solve the resulting equation.

3. The value of the variable does not make the denominator equal to 0.

4. Answers will vary.

5. There is no factor common to both the numerator and denominator of $\dfrac{4+3x}{9}$.

6. There is no factor common to both the numerator and denominator of $\dfrac{5x+7y}{12xy}$.

7. The denominator cannot be 0.

8. The denominator cannot be 0.

9. $x - 2 = 0$
   $x \neq 2$

10. $(x+4)^2 = 0$
    $x \neq -4$

11. $\dfrac{x+8}{8-x} = \dfrac{x+8}{-(-8+x)} = -\dfrac{x+8}{x-8} \neq -1$

    No

12. $-\dfrac{3x+2}{-3x-2} = \dfrac{3x+2}{-(-3x-2)}$
    $\phantom{-\dfrac{3x+2}{-3x-2}} = \dfrac{3x+2}{3x+2}$
    $\phantom{-\dfrac{3x+2}{-3x-2}} = 1$

    Yes

13. The expression is defined for all real numbers except $x = 0$.

14. $r + 3 = 0$
    The expression is defined for all real numbers except $r = -3$.

15. $4n - 16 = 0$
    $4n = 16$
    $n = 4$
    The expression is defined for all real numbers except $n = 4$.

16. $2x - 3 = 0$
    The expression is defined for all real numbers except $x = \dfrac{3}{2}$.

17. $x^2 - 4 = 0$
    $(x-2)(x+2) = 0$
    $x - 2 = 0$ or $x + 2 = 0$
    $x = 2$ $x = -2$
    The expression is defined for all real numbers except $x = 2$, $x = -2$.

18. $x^2 + 4x - 5 = 0$
    $(x+5)(x-1) = 0$
    $x + 5 = 0$ or $x - 1 = 0$
    $x = -5$ $x = 1$
    The expression is defined for all real numbers except $x = -5$, $x = 1$.

19. $2x^2 - 9x + 9 = 0$
    $(2x-3)(x-3) = 0$
    $2x - 3 = 0$ or $x - 3 = 0$
    $x = \dfrac{3}{2}$ $x = 3$
    The expression is defined for all real numbers except $x = \dfrac{3}{2}$, $x = 3$.

20. $2x^2 - 13x + 15 = 0$
    $(2x-3)(x-5) = 0$
    $2x - 3 = 0$ or $x - 5 = 0$
    $x = \dfrac{3}{2}$ $x = 5$
    The expression is defined for all real numbers except $x = \dfrac{3}{2}$, $x = 5$.

21. All real numbers because $x^2 + 36 \neq 0$.

22. All real numbers because $9 + x^2 \neq 0$.

23.
$$4p^2 - 25 = 0$$
$$(2p+5)(2p-5) = 0$$
$$2p+5 = 0 \quad \text{or} \quad 2p-5 = 0$$
$$p = -\frac{5}{2} \qquad p = \frac{5}{2}$$
The expression is defined for all real numbers except $p = \pm\frac{5}{2}$.

24.
$$9r^2 - 16 = 0$$
$$(3r+4)(3r-4) = 0$$
$$3r+4 = 0 \quad \text{or} \quad 3r-4 = 0$$
$$r = -\frac{4}{3} \qquad r = \frac{4}{3}$$
The expression is defined for all real numbers except $r = \pm\frac{4}{3}$.

25.
$$\frac{8x^3 y}{24x^2 y^5} = \frac{8}{24} \cdot x^{3-2} \cdot y^{1-5}$$
$$= \frac{1}{3}xy^{-4}$$
$$= \frac{x}{3y^4}$$

26.
$$\frac{18x^3 y^2}{30x^4 y^5} = \frac{18}{30} \cdot x^{3-4} \cdot y^{2-5}$$
$$= \frac{3}{5}x^{-1}y^{-3}$$
$$= \frac{3}{5xy^3}$$

27.
$$\frac{\left(2a^4 b^5\right)^3}{2a^{12} b^{20}} = \frac{2^3 \cdot a^{4(3)} \cdot b^{5(3)}}{2a^{12} b^{20}}$$
$$= \frac{8a^{12} b^{15}}{2a^{12} b^{20}}$$
$$= 4a^{12-12} b^{15-20}$$
$$= 4a^0 b^{-5}$$
$$= \frac{4}{b^5}$$

28.
$$\frac{\left(5r^2 s^3\right)^2}{\left(3r^4 s\right)^3} = \frac{5^2 \cdot r^{2(2)} \cdot s^{3(2)}}{3^3 \cdot r^{4(3)} s^{1(3)}}$$
$$= \frac{25r^4 s^6}{27r^{12} s^3} = \frac{25}{27} \cdot r^{4-12} s^{6-3}$$
$$= \frac{25}{27} r^{-8} s^3$$
$$= \frac{25s^3}{27r^8}$$

29.
$$\frac{2x}{x+xy} = \frac{2x}{x(1+y)}$$
$$= \frac{2}{1+y}$$

30.
$$\frac{12x}{3x+9} = \frac{3(4x)}{3(x+3)}$$
$$= \frac{4x}{x+3}$$

31.
$$\frac{5x+15}{x+3} = \frac{5(x+3)}{x+3}$$
$$= 5$$

32.
$$\frac{3x^2 + 6x}{3x^2 + 9x} = \frac{3x(x+2)}{3x(x+3)}$$
$$= \frac{x+2}{x+3}$$

33.
$$\frac{x^3 + 6x^2 + 7x}{2x} = \frac{x\left(x^2 + 6x + 7\right)}{2x}$$
$$= \frac{x^2 + 6x + 7}{2}$$

34.
$$\frac{x^2 y^2 - 2xy + 5y}{y} = \frac{y\left(x^2 y - 2x + 5\right)}{y}$$
$$= x^2 y - 2x + 5$$

35.
$$\frac{r^2 - r - 2}{r-2} = \frac{(r-2)(r+1)}{(r-2)}$$
$$= r+1$$

36.
$$\frac{b-6}{b^2 - 8b + 12} = \frac{(b-6)}{(b-6)(b-2)}$$
$$= \frac{1}{b-2}$$

37. $\dfrac{x^2+2x}{x^2+4x+4} = \dfrac{x(x+2)}{(x+2)^2}$

$\qquad = \dfrac{x}{x+2}$

38. $\dfrac{x^2+3x-18}{4x-12} = \dfrac{(x-3)(x+6)}{4(x-3)}$

$\qquad = \dfrac{x+6}{4}$

39. $\dfrac{z^2-10z+25}{z^2-25} = \dfrac{(z-5)^2}{(z-5)(z+5)}$

$\qquad = \dfrac{z-5}{z+5}$

40. $\dfrac{k^2-6k+9}{k^2-9} = \dfrac{(k-3)(k-3)}{(k-3)(k+3)}$

$\qquad = \dfrac{k-3}{k+3}$

41. $\dfrac{x^2-2x-3}{x^2-x-6} = \dfrac{(x+1)(x-3)}{(x+2)(x-3)}$

$\qquad = \dfrac{x+1}{x+2}$

42. $\dfrac{4x^2-12x-40}{2x^2-16x+30} = \dfrac{4(x^2-3x-10)}{2(x^2-8x+15)}$

$\qquad = \dfrac{2(x-5)(x+2)}{(x-3)(x-5)}$

$\qquad = \dfrac{2x+4}{x-3}$

43. $\dfrac{4x-3}{3-4x} = \dfrac{4x-3}{-(4x-3)}$

$\qquad = -1$

44. $\dfrac{10a-6}{3-5a} = \dfrac{2(5a-3)}{-(5a-3)}$

$\qquad = -2$

45. $\dfrac{x^2-2x-8}{4-x} = \dfrac{(x-4)(x+2)}{-(x-4)}$

$\qquad = -(x+2)$

46. $\dfrac{7-s}{s^2-12s+35} = \dfrac{-(s-7)}{(s-7)(s-5)}$

$\qquad = -\dfrac{1}{s-5}$

47. $\dfrac{x^2+3x-18}{-2x^2+6x} = \dfrac{(x+6)(x-3)}{-2x(x-3)}$

$\qquad = -\dfrac{x+6}{2x}$

48. $\dfrac{3p^2-13p-10}{3p+2} = \dfrac{(3p+2)(p-5)}{(3p+2)} = p-5$

49. $\dfrac{2x^2+5x-3}{1-2x} = \dfrac{(2x-1)(x+3)}{-(2x-1)}$

$\qquad = -(x+3)$

50. $\dfrac{x^2-25}{x^2-2x-15} = \dfrac{(x+5)(x-5)}{(x+3)(x-5)}$

$\qquad = \dfrac{x+5}{x+3}$

51. $\dfrac{m-2}{4m^2-13m+10} = \dfrac{m-2}{(4m-5)(m-2)} = \dfrac{1}{4m-5}$

52. $\dfrac{2x^2-13x+21}{(x-3)^2} = \dfrac{(2x-7)(x-3)}{(x-3)^2}$

$\qquad = \dfrac{2x-7}{x-3}$

53. $\dfrac{x^2-25}{(x+5)^2} = \dfrac{(x-5)(x+5)}{(x+5)^2}$

$\qquad = \dfrac{x-5}{x+5}$

54. $\dfrac{16x^2+24x+9}{4x+3} = \dfrac{(4x+3)^2}{4x+3}$

$\qquad = 4x+3$

55. $\dfrac{6x^2-13x+6}{3x-2} = \dfrac{(3x-2)(2x-3)}{3x-2}$

$\qquad = 2x-3$

56. $\dfrac{6t^2+7t-5}{3t-5} = \dfrac{(2t+1)(3t-5)}{(3t-5)}$

$\qquad = 2t+1$

57. $\dfrac{x^2 - 3x + 4x - 12}{x+4} = \dfrac{x(x-3) + 4(x-3)}{x+4}$

$\qquad\qquad = \dfrac{(x+4)(x-3)}{(x+4)}$

$\qquad\qquad = x - 3$

58. $\dfrac{x^2 - 2x + 4x - 8}{2x^2 + 3x + 8x + 12} = \dfrac{x(x-2) + 4(x-2)}{x(2x+3) + 4(2x+3)}$

$\qquad\qquad = \dfrac{(x+4)(x-2)}{(2x+3)(x+4)}$

$\qquad\qquad = \dfrac{x-2}{2x+3}$

59. $\dfrac{2x^2 - 8x + 3x - 12}{2x^2 + 8x + 3x + 12} = \dfrac{2x(x-4) + 3(x-4)}{2x(x+4) + 3(x+4)}$

$\qquad\qquad = \dfrac{(x-4)(2x+3)}{(x+4)(2x+3)}$

$\qquad\qquad = \dfrac{x-4}{x+4}$

60. $\dfrac{x^3 - 125}{x^2 - 25} = \dfrac{(x-5)(x^2 + 5x + 25)}{(x+5)(x-5)}$

$\qquad\qquad = \dfrac{x^2 + 5x + 25}{x+5}$

61. $\dfrac{a^3 - 8}{a-2} = \dfrac{(a-2)(a^2 + 2a + 4)}{(a-2)}$

$\qquad\qquad = a^2 + 2a + 4$

62. $\dfrac{x^3 + 1}{x+1} = \dfrac{(x+1)(x^2 - x + 1)}{(x+1)}$

$\qquad\qquad = x^2 - x + 1$

63. $\dfrac{9s^2 - 16t^2}{3s - 4t} = \dfrac{(3s+4t)(3s-4t)}{3s-4t} = 3s + 4t$

64. $\dfrac{a+6b}{a^2 - 36b^2} = \dfrac{(a+6b)}{(a+6b)(a-6b)} = \dfrac{1}{a-6b}$

65. $\dfrac{6x + 9y}{2x^2 + xy - 3y^2} = \dfrac{3(2x+3y)}{(2x+3y)(x-y)} = \dfrac{3}{x-y}$

66. $\dfrac{3k^2 + 6kr - 9r^2}{k^2 + 5kr + 6r^2} = \dfrac{3\left(k^2 + 2kr - 3r^2\right)}{k^2 + 5kr + 6r^2}$

$\qquad\qquad = \dfrac{3(k+3r)(k-r)}{(k+3r)(k+2r)}$

$\qquad\qquad = \dfrac{3(k-r)}{k+2r}$

67. $\dfrac{3☺}{15} = \dfrac{3☺}{3 \cdot 5} = \dfrac{☺}{5}$

68. $\dfrac{☺}{☺ + 8☺^2} = \dfrac{☺}{☺(1 + 8☺)} = \dfrac{1}{1 + 8☺}$

69. $\dfrac{7\Delta}{14\Delta + 63} = \dfrac{7\Delta}{7(2\Delta + 9)} = \dfrac{\Delta}{2\Delta + 9}$

70. $\dfrac{\Delta^2 + 2\Delta}{\Delta^2 + 4\Delta + 4} = \dfrac{\Delta(\Delta + 2)}{(\Delta + 2)^2} = \dfrac{\Delta}{\Delta + 2}$

71. $\dfrac{3\Delta - 4}{4 - 3\Delta} = \dfrac{-(2 - 4\Delta)}{(2 - 4\Delta)} = -1$

72. $\dfrac{(\Delta - 3)^2}{\Delta^2 - 6\Delta + 9} = \dfrac{(\Delta - 3)^2}{(\Delta - 3)^2} = 1$

73. $x^2 - x - 6 = (x - 3)(x + 2)$

Denominator $= x + 2$

74. $2x^2 + 11x + 12 = (x + 4)(2x + 3)$

Denominator $= x + 4$

75. $(x + 4)(x + 5) = x^2 + 9x + 20$

Numerator $= x^2 + 9x + 20$

76. $(2x - 1)(x - 5) = 2x^2 - 11x + 5$

Numerator $= 2x^2 - 11x + 5$

77. a. $\dfrac{x-2}{x^2 - 2x + 3x - 6} = \dfrac{x-2}{x(x-2) + 3(x-2)}$

$\qquad\qquad = \dfrac{(x-2)}{(x+3)(x-2)}$

$\qquad x \neq -3, x \neq 2$

b. $\dfrac{(x-2)}{(x+3)(x-2)} = \dfrac{1}{x+3}$

78. a.
$$\frac{x-4}{2x^2-5x-8x+20}$$
$$=\frac{x-4}{x(2x-5)-4(2x-5)}$$
$$=\frac{x-4}{(x-4)(2x-5)}$$
$$x\neq 4, x\neq\frac{5}{2}$$

b.
$$\frac{x-4}{(x-4)(2x-5)}=\frac{1}{2x-5}$$

79. a.
$$\frac{x+5}{2x^3+7x^2-15x}=\frac{x+5}{x(2x^2+7x-15)}$$
$$=\frac{x+5}{x(2x-3)(x+5)}$$
$$x\neq 0, x\neq\frac{3}{2}, x\neq -5$$

b.
$$\frac{(x+5)}{x(2x-3)(x+5)}=\frac{1}{x(2x-3)}$$

80.
$$\frac{\frac{1}{6}x^5-\frac{2}{3}x^4}{x^4}=\frac{x^4\left(\frac{1}{6}x-\frac{2}{3}\right)}{x^4}$$
$$=\frac{1}{6}x-\frac{2}{3}$$

81.
$$\frac{\left(\frac{1}{5}x^5-\frac{2}{3}x^4\right)}{\left(\frac{1}{5}x^5-\frac{2}{3}x^4\right)}=1$$

82.
$$\frac{\frac{1}{5}x^5-\frac{2}{3}x^4}{\frac{2}{3}x^4-\frac{1}{5}x^5}=\frac{x^4\left(\frac{1}{5}x-\frac{2}{3}\right)}{(-1)x^4\left(-\frac{2}{3}+\frac{1}{5}x\right)}$$
$$=-1$$

83. a.
$$\frac{x^2-25}{x^3+2x^2-15x}=\frac{(x+5)(x-5)}{x(x^2+2x-15)}$$
$$=\frac{(x+5)(x-5)}{x(x+5)(x-3)}$$
Undefined at $x=0, x=3$, and $x=-5$.

b.
$$\frac{x^2-25}{x^3+2x^2-15x}=\frac{(x+5)(x-5)}{x(x^2+2x-15)}$$
$$=\frac{(x+5)(x-5)}{x(x+5)(x-3)}$$
$$=\frac{x-5}{x(x-3)}$$

c.
$$\frac{x^2-25}{x^3+2x^2-15x}=\frac{6^2-25}{6^3+2(6^2)-15(6)}$$
$$=\frac{36-25}{216+72-90}$$
$$=\frac{11}{198}$$
$$=\frac{1}{18}$$

d.
$$\frac{x-5}{x(x-3)}=\frac{6-5}{6(6-3)}=\frac{1}{18}$$

e.
$$\frac{x^2-25}{x^3+2x^2-15x}=\frac{(-2)^2-25}{(-2)^3+2(-2)^2-15(-2)}$$
$$=\frac{4-25}{-8+8+30}$$
$$=\frac{-21}{30}$$
$$=-\frac{7}{10}$$
$$\frac{x-5}{x(x-3)}=\frac{(-2)-5}{(-2)((-2)-3)}=\frac{-7}{(-2)(-5)}=-\frac{7}{10}$$

f. When a value that is defined is substituted in the original expression and in the simplified expression, the results are the same.

g. Since the expression is not defined for this value, −5 may not be substituted in the expression.

h. No, only for those values for which the expression is defined.

84.
$$z=\frac{x-y}{4}$$
$$4z=x-y$$
$$4z-x=-y$$
$$y=x-4z$$

85. Let x = measure of the smallest angle. Then the second angle = $x + 30$ and third angle = $3x + 10$.
angle 1 + angle 2 + angle 3 = $180°$
$$x + (x + 30) + (3x + 10) = 180$$
$$5x + 40 = 180$$
$$5x = 140$$
$$x = 28$$
$$x + 30 = 28 + 30 = 58$$
$$3x + 10 = 3(28) + 10 = 84 + 10 = 94 \ .$$
The three angles are $28°$, $58°$, and $94°$.

86. $\left(\dfrac{5x^2 y^2}{9x^4 y^3}\right)^2 = \left(\dfrac{5}{9x^2 y}\right)^2$
$$= \dfrac{25}{81x^4 y^2}$$

87. $3x^2 - 4x - 8 - \left(-5x^2 + 6x + 11\right)$
$$= 3x^2 - 4x - 8 + 5x^2 - 6x - 11$$
$$= 8x^2 - 10x - 19$$

88. $3a^2 - 6a - 72 = 3(a^2 - 2a - 24)$
$$= 3(a - 6)(a + 4)$$

89. $a^2 + b^2 = c^2$
$$5^2 + 12^2 = c^2$$
$$25 + 144 = c^2$$
$$169 = c^2$$
$$\sqrt{169} = \sqrt{c^2}$$
$$13 = c$$
The hypotenuse is 13 inches long.

Exercise Set 7.2

1. Answers will vary.

2. Answers will vary.

3. $\dfrac{x+3}{x-4} \cdot \dfrac{\boxed{}}{x+3} = x + 5$
Numerator must be $(x+5)(x-4) = x^2 + x - 20$

4. $\dfrac{x-5}{x+2} \cdot \dfrac{\boxed{}}{x-5} = 2x - 3$
Numerator must be $(x+2)(2x-3) = 2x^2 + x - 6$

5. $\dfrac{x-5}{x+5} \cdot \dfrac{x+5}{\boxed{}} = \dfrac{1}{x+7}$
Denominator must be
$$(x+7)(x-5) = x^2 + 2x - 35$$

6. $\dfrac{2x-1}{x-3} \cdot \dfrac{x-3}{\boxed{}} = \dfrac{1}{x-6}$
Denominator must be
$$(2x-1)(x-6) = 2x^2 - 13x + 6$$

7. $\left(\dfrac{2}{5}\right)\left(\dfrac{15}{19}\right) = \dfrac{2}{1\cancel{5}} \cdot \dfrac{\cancel{15}^{\,3}}{19} = \dfrac{2 \cdot 3}{1 \cdot 19} = \dfrac{6}{19}$

8. $\left(\dfrac{3}{8}\right)\left(-\dfrac{9}{33}\right) = \dfrac{\cancel{3}^{\,1}}{8} \cdot \dfrac{-9}{\cancel{33}_{11}} = \dfrac{1 \cdot (-9)}{8 \cdot 11} = -\dfrac{9}{88}$

9. $\left(\dfrac{6}{8}\right)\left(-\dfrac{10}{14}\right) = \dfrac{6}{8} \cdot \dfrac{-10}{14} = \dfrac{3}{4} \cdot \dfrac{-5}{7} = \dfrac{3 \cdot (-5)}{4 \cdot 7} = -\dfrac{15}{28}$

10. $\left(\dfrac{7}{9}\right)\left(\dfrac{81}{98}\right) = \dfrac{\cancel{7}^{\,1}}{1\cancel{9}} \cdot \dfrac{\cancel{81}^{\,9}}{\cancel{98}_{14}} = \dfrac{1 \cdot 9}{1 \cdot 14} = \dfrac{9}{14}$

11. $\left(-\dfrac{4}{11}\right)\left(-\dfrac{55}{64}\right) = \dfrac{-\cancel{4}^{\,1}}{1\cancel{11}} \cdot \dfrac{-\cancel{55}^{\,5}}{\cancel{64}_{16}} = \dfrac{-1 \cdot (-5)}{1 \cdot 16} = \dfrac{5}{16}$

12. $\left(-\dfrac{12}{13}\right)\left(-\dfrac{65}{42}\right) = \dfrac{-\cancel{12}^{\,2}}{1\cancel{13}} \cdot \dfrac{-\cancel{65}^{\,5}}{\cancel{42}_{7}} = \dfrac{-2 \cdot (-5)}{1 \cdot 7} = \dfrac{10}{7}$

13. $\dfrac{3}{7} \div \dfrac{5}{7} = \dfrac{3}{\cancel{7}} \cdot \dfrac{\cancel{7}}{5} = \dfrac{3}{5}$

14. $\dfrac{3}{8} \div \dfrac{15}{44} = \dfrac{\cancel{3}^{\,1}}{2\cancel{8}} \cdot \dfrac{\cancel{44}^{\,11}}{\cancel{15}_{5}} = \dfrac{1 \cdot 11}{2 \cdot 5} = \dfrac{11}{10}$

15. $-\dfrac{2}{9} \div \dfrac{32}{39} = \dfrac{-\cancel{2}^{\,1}}{3\cancel{9}} \cdot \dfrac{\cancel{39}^{\,13}}{\cancel{32}_{16}} = \dfrac{-1 \cdot 13}{3 \cdot 16} = -\dfrac{13}{48}$

16. $\left(-\dfrac{3}{4}\right) \div \left(-\dfrac{15}{16}\right) = \dfrac{-\cancel{3}^{\,1}}{1\cancel{4}} \cdot \dfrac{-\cancel{16}^{\,4}}{\cancel{15}_{5}} = \dfrac{-1 \cdot (-4)}{1 \cdot 5} = \dfrac{4}{5}$

17. $\dfrac{6x}{4y} \cdot \dfrac{y^2}{12} = \dfrac{6x}{4y} \cdot \dfrac{y^2}{6 \cdot 2}$
$$= \dfrac{xy}{8}$$

18. $\dfrac{15x^3y^2}{2z}\cdot\dfrac{z}{5xy^3}=\dfrac{15}{10}\cdot\dfrac{x^3}{x}\cdot\dfrac{y^2}{y^3}\cdot\dfrac{z}{z}$

$\qquad=\dfrac{3x^2}{2y}$

19. $\dfrac{14x^2}{y^4}\cdot\dfrac{5x^2}{y^2}=\dfrac{70x^4}{y^6}$

20. $\dfrac{7n^3}{16m}\cdot\dfrac{-4}{21m^2n^3}=\dfrac{7n^3}{4\cdot4m}\cdot\dfrac{-4}{3\cdot7m^2n^3}$

$\qquad=-\dfrac{1}{12m^3}$

21. $\dfrac{6x^5y^3}{5z^3}\cdot\dfrac{6x^4}{5yz^4}=\dfrac{36x^9y^2}{25z^7}$

22. $\dfrac{x^2-4}{x^2-16}\cdot\dfrac{x-4}{x-2}=\dfrac{(x+2)\cancel{(x-2)}\cancel{(x-4)}}{(x+4)\cancel{(x-4)}\cancel{(x-2)}}$

$\qquad=\dfrac{x+2}{x+4}$

23. $\dfrac{3x-2}{3x+2}\cdot\dfrac{x-1}{1-x}=\dfrac{3x-2}{3x+2}\cdot\dfrac{\cancel{(x-1)}}{-\cancel{(x-1)}}$

$\qquad=\dfrac{-3x+2}{3x+2}$

24. $\dfrac{m-5}{2m+5}\cdot\dfrac{8m}{-m+5}=\dfrac{\cancel{(m-5)}}{2m+5}\cdot\dfrac{8m}{-\cancel{(m-5)}}$

$\qquad=-\dfrac{8m}{2m+5}$

25. $\dfrac{x^2+7x+6}{x+6}\cdot\dfrac{1}{x+1}=\dfrac{\cancel{(x+6)}\cancel{(x+1)}}{\cancel{(x+6)}\cancel{(x+1)}}$

$\qquad=1$

26. $\dfrac{b^2+7b+12}{6b}\cdot\dfrac{b^2-4b}{b^2-b-12}$

$\qquad=\dfrac{(b+4)\cancel{(b+3)}}{6\cancel{b}}\cdot\dfrac{\cancel{b}\cancel{(b-4)}}{\cancel{(b-4)}\cancel{(b+3)}}$

$\qquad=\dfrac{b+4}{6}$

27. $\dfrac{a}{a^2-b^2}\cdot\dfrac{a+b}{a^2+ab}=\dfrac{\cancel{a}}{(a+b)(a-b)}\cdot\dfrac{\cancel{(a+b)}}{\cancel{a}\cancel{(a+b)}}$

$\qquad=\dfrac{1}{(a-b)(a+b)}$

$\qquad=\dfrac{1}{a^2-b^2}$

28. $\dfrac{t^2-36}{t^2+t-30}\cdot\dfrac{t-5}{4t}=\dfrac{(t-6)\cancel{(t+6)}}{\cancel{(t+6)}\cancel{(t-5)}}\cdot\dfrac{\cancel{(t-5)}}{4t}$

$\qquad=\dfrac{t-6}{4t}$

29. $\dfrac{6x^2-14x-12}{6x+4}\cdot\dfrac{2x+4}{2x^2-2x-12}$

$\qquad=\dfrac{2(3x^2-7x-6)}{2(3x+2)}\cdot\dfrac{2(x+2)}{2(x^2-x-6)}$

$\qquad=\dfrac{\cancel{2}(3x+2)(x-3)}{\cancel{2}(3x+2)}\cdot\dfrac{\cancel{2}(x+2)}{\cancel{2}(x-3)(x+2)}$

$\qquad=1$

30. $\dfrac{2x^2-9x+9}{8x-12}\cdot\dfrac{4x}{x^2-3x}$

$\qquad=\dfrac{(2x-3)(x-3)}{4(2x-3)}\cdot\dfrac{4x}{x(x-3)}$

$\qquad=1$

31. $\dfrac{3x^2-13x-10}{x^2-2x-15}\cdot\dfrac{x^2+x-2}{3x^2-x-2}$

$\qquad=\dfrac{(3x+2)\cancel{(x-5)}}{(x+3)\cancel{(x-5)}}\cdot\dfrac{(x+2)\cancel{(x-1)}}{(3x+2)\cancel{(x-1)}}$

$\qquad=\dfrac{x+2}{x+3}$

32. $\dfrac{2t^2-t-6}{2t^2-3t-2}\cdot\dfrac{2t^2-5t-3}{2t^2+11t+12}$

$\qquad=\dfrac{(2t+3)\cancel{(t-2)}}{\cancel{(2t+1)}\cancel{(t-2)}}\cdot\dfrac{\cancel{(2t+1)}(t-3)}{(2t+3)(t+4)}$

$\qquad=\dfrac{t-3}{t+4}$

33. $\dfrac{x+9}{x-3} \cdot \dfrac{x^3-27}{x^2+3x+9}$

$= \dfrac{(x+9)}{\cancel{(x-3)}} \cdot \dfrac{\cancel{(x-3)}\cancel{\left(x^2+3x+9\right)}}{\cancel{\left(x^2+3x+9\right)}}$

$= x+9$

34. $\dfrac{x^3+8}{x^2-x-6} \cdot \dfrac{x+5}{x^2-2x+4}$

$= \dfrac{\cancel{(x+2)}\cancel{\left(x^2-2x+4\right)}}{(x-3)\cancel{(x+2)}} \cdot \dfrac{x+5}{\cancel{\left(x^2-2x+4\right)}}$

$= \dfrac{x+5}{x-3}$

35. $\dfrac{12x^3}{y^2} \div \dfrac{3x}{y^3} = \dfrac{12x^3}{y^2} \cdot \dfrac{y^3}{3x}$

$= \dfrac{3 \cdot 4x^3}{y^2} \cdot \dfrac{y^3}{3x}$

$= 4x^2 y$

36. $\dfrac{9x^3}{5} \div \dfrac{1}{20y^2} = \dfrac{9x^3}{5} \cdot \dfrac{20y^2}{1}$

$= \dfrac{9x^3}{5} \cdot \dfrac{4 \cdot 5y^2}{1}$

$= 36x^3 y^2$

37. $\dfrac{15xy^2}{4z} \div \dfrac{5x^2 y^2}{12z^2} = \dfrac{3 \cdot 5xy^2}{4z} \cdot \dfrac{12z^2}{5x^2 y^2}$

$= \dfrac{3 \cdot 5xy^2}{4z} \cdot \dfrac{3 \cdot 4z^2}{5x^2 y^2}$

$= \dfrac{9z}{x}$

38. $\dfrac{36y}{5z^2} \div \dfrac{3xy}{2z} = \dfrac{3 \cdot 12y}{5z^2} \cdot \dfrac{2z}{3xy}$

$= \dfrac{24}{5xz}$

39. $\dfrac{11xy}{7ab^2} \div \dfrac{6xy}{7} = \dfrac{11xy}{7ab^2} \cdot \dfrac{7}{6xy}$

$= \dfrac{11}{6ab^2}$

40. $3xz \div \dfrac{6xy}{z} = 3xz \cdot \dfrac{z}{6xy}$

$= 3xz \cdot \dfrac{z}{2 \cdot 3xy}$

$= \dfrac{z^2}{2y}$

41. $\dfrac{12r+6}{r} \div \dfrac{2r+1}{r^3} = \dfrac{6\cancel{(2r+1)}}{\cancel{r}} \cdot \dfrac{\cancel{r} \cdot r^2}{\cancel{(2r+1)}}$

$= 6r^2$

42. $\dfrac{x-3}{10y^2} \div \dfrac{x^2-9}{5xy} = \dfrac{\cancel{(x-3)}}{2 \cdot \cancel{5} \cdot \cancel{y} \cdot y} \cdot \dfrac{\cancel{5}x\cancel{y}}{\cancel{(x-3)}(x+3)}$

$= \dfrac{x}{2y(x+3)}$

43. $\dfrac{x^2+11x+18}{x} \div \dfrac{x+2}{x} = \dfrac{(x+9)\cancel{(x+2)}}{\cancel{x}} \cdot \dfrac{\cancel{x}}{\cancel{(x+2)}}$

$= x+9$

44. $\dfrac{1}{x^2+7x-18} \div \dfrac{1}{x^2-17x+30}$

$= \dfrac{1}{x^2+7x-18} \cdot \dfrac{x^2-17x+30}{1}$

$= \dfrac{x^2-17x+30}{x^2+7x-18}$

$= \dfrac{(x-15)\cancel{(x-2)}}{(x+9)\cancel{(x-2)}}$

$= \dfrac{x-15}{x+9}$

45. $\dfrac{x^2-12x+32}{x^2-6x-16} \div \dfrac{x^2-x-12}{x^2-5x-24}$

$= \dfrac{x^2-12x+32}{x^2-6x-16} \cdot \dfrac{x^2-5x-24}{x^2-x-12}$

$= \dfrac{(x-8)\cancel{(x-4)}}{\cancel{(x-8)}(x+2)} \cdot \dfrac{\cancel{(x-8)}\cancel{(x+3)}}{\cancel{(x-4)}\cancel{(x+3)}}$

$= \dfrac{x-8}{x+2}$

46. $\dfrac{a-b}{9a+9b} \div \dfrac{a^2-b^2}{a^2+2a+7}$

$= \dfrac{(a-b)}{9(a+b)} \cdot \dfrac{a^2+2a+7}{(a-b)(a+b)}$

$= \dfrac{a^2+2a+7}{9(a+b)^2}$

47. $\dfrac{2x^2+9x+4}{x^2+7x+12} \div \dfrac{2x^2-x-1}{(x+3)^2}$

$= \dfrac{(2x+1)(x+4)}{(x+3)(x+4)} \cdot \dfrac{(x+3)(x+3)}{(2x+1)(x-1)}$

$= \dfrac{x+3}{x-1}$

48. $\dfrac{a^2-b^2}{9} \div \dfrac{3a-3b}{27x^2}$

$= \dfrac{(a-b)(a+b)}{9} \cdot \dfrac{9 \cdot 3x^2}{3(a-b)}$

$= (a+b)x^2$

$= ax^2 + bx^2$

49. $\dfrac{x^2-y^2}{x^2-2xy+y^2} \div \dfrac{x+y}{y-x}$

$= \dfrac{(x-y)(x+y)}{(x-y)(x-y)} \cdot \dfrac{-1(x-y)}{(x+y)}$

$= -1$

50. $\dfrac{9x^2-9y^2}{18x^2y^2} \div \dfrac{3x+3y}{12x^2y^5}$

$= \dfrac{9(x^2-y^2)}{18x^2y^2} \cdot \dfrac{12x^2y^5}{3(x+y)}$

$= \dfrac{9(x+y)(x-y)}{9 \cdot 2x^2y^2} \cdot \dfrac{3 \cdot 4 x^2 y^2 y^3}{3(x+y)}$

$= 2(x-y)y^3$

$= 2y^3(x-y)$

$= 2xy^3 - 2y^4$

51. $\dfrac{5x^2-4x-1}{5x^2+6x+1} \div \dfrac{x^2-5x+4}{x^2+2x+1}$

$= \dfrac{(5x+1)(x-1)}{(5x+1)(x+1)} \cdot \dfrac{(x+1)(x+1)}{(x-4)(x-1)}$

$= \dfrac{x+1}{x-4}$

52. $\dfrac{7n^2-15n+2}{n^2+n-6} \div \dfrac{n^2-3n-10}{n^2-2n-15}$

$= \dfrac{(7n-1)(n-2)}{(n+3)(n-2)} \cdot \dfrac{(n-5)(n+3)}{(n+2)(n-5)}$

$= \dfrac{7n-1}{n+2}$

53. $\dfrac{11z}{6y^2} \cdot \dfrac{24x^2y^4}{11z} = \dfrac{11z}{6y^2} \cdot \dfrac{6 \cdot 4 \cdot x^2 \cdot y^2 \cdot y^2}{11z}$

$= 4x^2y^2$

54. $\dfrac{5z^3}{7} \cdot \dfrac{9x^2}{15z} = \dfrac{3 \cdot 3 \cdot 3 x^2 z^2 z}{7 \cdot 3 \cdot 3 z} = \dfrac{3x^2z^2}{7}$

55. $\dfrac{63a^2b^3}{20c^3} \cdot \dfrac{4c^4}{9a^3b^5} = \dfrac{7 \cdot 9 \cdot 4 a^2 b^3 c^3 c}{5 \cdot 4 \cdot 9 a^2 a b^3 b^2 c^3} = \dfrac{7c}{5ab^2}$

56. $\dfrac{-2xw}{y^5} \div \dfrac{8x^2}{y^6} = \dfrac{-2xw}{y^5} \cdot \dfrac{y^6}{8x^2}$

$= \dfrac{-2xw}{y^5} \cdot \dfrac{y^5 y}{2 \cdot 4x x}$

$= -\dfrac{wy}{4x}$

57. $\dfrac{-xy}{a} \div \dfrac{-2ax}{6y} = \dfrac{-xy}{a} \cdot \dfrac{6y}{-2ax}$

$= \dfrac{xy}{a} \cdot \dfrac{2 \cdot 3y}{2ax}$

$= \dfrac{3y^2}{a^2}$

58. $\dfrac{27x}{8y^2} \div 3x^2y^2 = \dfrac{27x}{8y^2} \cdot \dfrac{1}{3x^2y^2}$

$= \dfrac{\cancel{3} \cdot 9\cancel{x}}{8y^2} \cdot \dfrac{1}{\cancel{3}\cancel{x}xy^2}$

$= \dfrac{9}{8xy^4}$

59. $\dfrac{64m^6}{21x^5y^7} \cdot \dfrac{14x^{12}y^5}{16m^5}$

$= \dfrac{\cancel{16} \cdot 4\cancel{m^5}m}{3 \cdot \cancel{7}\cancel{x^5}\cancel{y^5}y^2} \cdot \dfrac{2 \cdot \cancel{7}\cancel{x^5}x^7\cancel{y^5}}{\cancel{16}\cancel{m^5}}$

$= \dfrac{8mx^7}{3y^2}$

60. $\dfrac{-18x^2y}{11z^2} \cdot \dfrac{22z^3}{x^2y^5}$

$= \dfrac{-18\cancel{x^2}\cancel{y}}{\cancel{11}\cancel{z^2}} \cdot \dfrac{2 \cdot \cancel{11}\cancel{z^2}z}{\cancel{x^2}y^4\cancel{y}}$

$= -\dfrac{36z}{y^4}$

61. $\dfrac{(x+3)^2}{5x^2} \cdot \dfrac{10x}{x^2-9}$

$= \dfrac{(x+3)(x+3)}{\cancel{5}\cancel{x}x} \cdot \dfrac{\cancel{5} \cdot 2\cancel{x}}{(x+3)(x-3)}$

$= \dfrac{2(x+3)}{x(x-3)}$

62. $\dfrac{1}{4x-3} \cdot (24x-18) = \dfrac{1}{(4x-3)} \cdot \dfrac{6(4x-3)}{1}$

$= 6$

63. $\dfrac{1}{5x^2y^2} \div \dfrac{1}{35x^3y} = \dfrac{1}{\cancel{5}\cancel{x^2}\cancel{y}y} \cdot \dfrac{\cancel{5} \cdot 7\cancel{x^2}x\cancel{y}}{1}$

$= \dfrac{7x}{y}$

64. $\dfrac{x^2y^5}{3z} \div \dfrac{7z}{2x} = \dfrac{x^2y^5}{3z} \cdot \dfrac{2x}{7z}$

$= \dfrac{2x^3y^5}{21z^2}$

65. $\dfrac{(4m)^2}{8n^3} \div \dfrac{m^6n^8}{2} = \dfrac{16m^2}{8n^3} \cdot \dfrac{2}{m^6n^8}$

$= \dfrac{\cancel{8} \cdot 2\cancel{m^2}}{\cancel{8}n^3} \cdot \dfrac{2}{m^4\cancel{m^2}n^8}$

$= \dfrac{4}{m^4n^{11}}$

66. $\dfrac{11r^5s^2}{(r^2s^3)^3} \cdot \dfrac{6r^4}{4s} = \dfrac{11r^5s^2}{r^6s^9} \cdot \dfrac{6r^4}{4s}$

$= \dfrac{11}{\cancel{r}s^7} \cdot \dfrac{3\cancel{r}r^3}{2s}$

$= \dfrac{33r^3}{2s^8}$

67. $\dfrac{r^2+5r+6}{r^2+9r+18} \cdot \dfrac{r^2+4r-12}{r^2-5r+6}$

$= \dfrac{(r+2)(r+3)}{(r+6)(r+3)} \cdot \dfrac{(r+6)(r-2)}{(r-3)(r-2)}$

$= \dfrac{r+2}{r-3}$

68. $\dfrac{z^2-z-20}{z^2-3z-10} \cdot \dfrac{(z+2)^2}{(z+4)^2}$

$= \dfrac{(z-5)(z+4)}{(z-5)(z+2)} \cdot \dfrac{(z+2)(z+2)}{(z+4)(z+4)}$

$= \dfrac{z+2}{z+4}$

69. $\dfrac{x^2-12x+36}{x^2-8x+12} \div \dfrac{x^2-7x+12}{x^2-6x+8}$

$= \dfrac{x^2-12x+36}{x^2-8x+12} \cdot \dfrac{x^2-6x+8}{x^2-7x+12}$

$= \dfrac{(x-6)(x-6)}{(x-6)(x-2)} \cdot \dfrac{(x-4)(x-2)}{(x-4)(x-3)}$

$= \dfrac{x-6}{x-3}$

70. $\dfrac{p^2-5p+6}{p^2-10p+16} \div \dfrac{p^2+2p}{p^2-6p-16}$

$= \dfrac{p^2-5p+6}{p^2-10p+16} \cdot \dfrac{p^2-6p-16}{p^2+2p}$

$= \dfrac{(p-2)(p-3)}{(p-2)(p-8)} \cdot \dfrac{(p-8)(p+2)}{p(p+2)}$

$= \dfrac{p-3}{p}$

71. $\dfrac{2w^2+3w-35}{w^2-7w-8} \cdot \dfrac{w^2-5w-24}{w^2+8w+15}$

$= \dfrac{(2w-7)(w+5)}{(w-8)(w+1)} \cdot \dfrac{(w-8)(w+3)}{(w+5)(w+3)}$

$= \dfrac{2w-7}{w+1}$

72. $\dfrac{3z^2-4z-4}{z^2-4} \cdot \dfrac{2z^2+5z+2}{2z^2-3z-2}$

$= \dfrac{(3z+2)(z-2)}{(z+2)(z-2)} \cdot \dfrac{(2z+1)(z+2)}{(2z+1)(z-2)}$

$= \dfrac{3z+2}{z-2}$

73. $\dfrac{q^2-11q+30}{2q^2-7q-15} \div \dfrac{q^2-2q-24}{q^2-q-20}$

$= \dfrac{q^2-11q+30}{2q^2-7q-15} \cdot \dfrac{q^2-q-20}{q^2-2q-24}$

$= \dfrac{(q-6)(q-5)}{(2q+3)(q-5)} \cdot \dfrac{(q-5)(q+4)}{(q-6)(q+4)}$

$= \dfrac{q-5}{2q+3}$

74. $\dfrac{2x^2-19x+24}{x^2-12x+32} \div \dfrac{2x^2+x-6}{x^2+7x+10}$

$= \dfrac{2x^2-19x+24}{x^2-12x+32} \cdot \dfrac{x^2+7x+10}{2x^2+x-6}$

$= \dfrac{(2x-3)(x-8)}{(x-4)(x-8)} \cdot \dfrac{(x+5)(x+2)}{(2x-3)(x+2)}$

$= \dfrac{x+5}{x-4}$

75. $\dfrac{4n^2-9}{9n^2-1} \cdot \dfrac{3n^2-2n-1}{2n^2-5n+3}$

$= \dfrac{(2n+3)(2n-3)}{(3n+1)(3n-1)} \cdot \dfrac{(3n+1)(n-1)}{(2n-3)(n-1)}$

$= \dfrac{2n+3}{3n-1}$

76. $\dfrac{2z^2+9z+9}{4z^2-9} \div \dfrac{(z+3)^2}{(2z-3)^2}$

$= \dfrac{(2z+3)(z+3)}{(2z+3)(2z-3)} \cdot \dfrac{(2z-3)(2z-3)}{(z+3)(z+3)}$

$= \dfrac{2z-3}{z+3}$

77. $\dfrac{6\Delta^2}{13} \cdot \dfrac{13}{36\Delta^5} = \dfrac{6\Delta^2}{13} \cdot \dfrac{13}{6 \cdot 6\Delta^2 \Delta^3} = \dfrac{1}{6\Delta^3}$

78. $\dfrac{\Delta-7}{2\Delta+5} \cdot \dfrac{3\Delta}{-\Delta+7} = \dfrac{\Delta-7}{2\Delta+5} \cdot \dfrac{3\Delta}{-(\Delta-7)}$

$\qquad = \dfrac{3\Delta}{-(2\Delta+5)}$

$\qquad = -\dfrac{3\Delta}{2\Delta+5}$

79. $\dfrac{\Delta-\odot}{9\Delta-9\odot} \div \dfrac{\Delta^2-\odot^2}{\Delta^2+2\Delta\odot+\odot^2}$

$= \dfrac{\Delta-\odot}{9\Delta-9\odot} \cdot \dfrac{\Delta^2+2\Delta\odot+\odot^2}{\Delta^2-\odot^2}$

$= \dfrac{\Delta-\odot}{9(\Delta-\odot)} \cdot \dfrac{(\Delta+\odot)(\Delta+\odot)}{(\Delta+\odot)(\Delta-\odot)}$

$= \dfrac{\Delta+\odot}{9(\Delta-\odot)}$

80. $\dfrac{\Delta^2-\odot^2}{\Delta^2-2\Delta\odot+\odot^2} \div \dfrac{\Delta+\odot}{\odot-\Delta}$

$= \dfrac{\Delta^2-\odot^2}{\Delta^2-2\Delta\odot+\odot^2} \cdot \dfrac{\odot-\Delta}{\Delta+\odot}$

$= \dfrac{(\Delta+\odot)(\Delta-\odot)}{(\Delta-\odot)(\Delta-\odot)} \cdot \dfrac{-(-\odot+\Delta)}{\Delta+\odot}$

$= \dfrac{(\Delta+\odot)(\Delta-\odot)}{(\Delta-\odot)(\Delta-\odot)} \cdot \dfrac{-(\Delta-\odot)}{\Delta+\odot}$

$= -1$

81. $(x+2)(x+3) = x^2 + 3x + 2x + 6$

$= x^2 + 5x + 6$

Numerator is $x^2 + 5x + 6$.

82. $\dfrac{(x+5)(x-5)}{1} = x^2 - 25$

Denominator is $x^2 - 25$.

83. $(x-6)(x+2) = x^2 + 2x - 6x - 12$

$= x^2 - 4x - 12$

Numerator is $x^2 - 4x - 12$.

84. $(x^2 - 7x + 10) \div (x-2) = (x-5)(x-2) \cdot \dfrac{1}{(x-2)}$

$= x - 5$

Numerator is $x - 5$.

85. $(x^2 - 4)(x-1) \div (x+2) =$

$(x-2)(x+2)(x-1) \cdot \dfrac{1}{x+2} = x^2 - x - 2x + 2$

$= x^2 - 3x + 2$

Numerator is $x^2 - 3x + 2$.

86. $(x^2 + 9x + 20)(x-2) \div (x+4)$

$= (x+4)(x+5)(x-2) \cdot \dfrac{1}{x+4}$

$= x^2 - 2x + 5x - 10$

$= x^2 + 3x - 10$

Numerator is $x^2 + 3x - 10$.

87. $\left(\dfrac{x+2}{x^2-4x-12} \cdot \dfrac{x^2-9x+18}{x-2}\right) \div \dfrac{x^2+5x+6}{x^2-4} = \dfrac{x+2}{x^2-4x-12} \cdot \dfrac{x^2-9x+18}{x-2} \cdot \dfrac{x^2-4}{x^2+5x+6}$

$= \dfrac{\cancel{(x+2)}}{\cancel{(x-6)}\cancel{(x+2)}} \cdot \dfrac{(x-3)\cancel{(x-6)}}{\cancel{(x-2)}} \cdot \dfrac{\cancel{(x+2)}\cancel{(x-2)}}{\cancel{(x+2)}(x+3)}$

$= \dfrac{x-3}{x+3}$

88. $\left(\dfrac{x^2+4x+3}{x^2-6x-16}\right) \div \left(\dfrac{x^2+5x+6}{x^2-9x+8} \cdot \dfrac{x^2-1}{x^2+4x+4}\right) = \dfrac{x^2+4x+3^2}{x^2-6x-16} \cdot \dfrac{x^2-9x+8}{x^2+5x+6} \cdot \dfrac{x^2+4x+4}{x^2-1}$

$= \dfrac{\cancel{(x+1)}\cancel{(x+3)}}{\cancel{(x-8)}\cancel{(x+2)}} \cdot \dfrac{\cancel{(x-8)}\cancel{(x-1)}}{\cancel{(x+2)}\cancel{(x+3)}} \cdot \dfrac{\cancel{(x+2)}\cancel{(x+2)}}{\cancel{(x-1)}\cancel{(x+1)}}$

$= 1$

89. $\left(\dfrac{x^2-x-6}{2x^2-9x+9} \div \dfrac{x^2+x-12}{x^2+3x-4}\right) \cdot \dfrac{2x^2-5x+3}{x^2+x-2} = \dfrac{x^2-x-6}{2x^2-9x+9} \cdot \dfrac{x^2+3x-4}{x^2+x-12} \cdot \dfrac{2x^2-5x+3}{x^2+x-2}$

$= \dfrac{\cancel{(x-3)}\cancel{(x+2)}}{\cancel{(2x-3)}(x-3)} \cdot \dfrac{\cancel{(x+4)}(x-1)}{\cancel{(x+4)}\cancel{(x-3)}} \cdot \dfrac{\cancel{(2x-3)}\cancel{(x-1)}}{\cancel{(x+2)}\cancel{(x-1)}}$

$= \dfrac{x-1}{x-3}$

90. $\left(\dfrac{x^2+4x+3}{x^2-6x-16} \div \dfrac{x^2+5x+6}{x^2-9x+8}\right) \cdot \left(\dfrac{x^2-1}{x^2+4x+4}\right) = \dfrac{x^2+4x+3}{x^2-6x-16} \cdot \dfrac{x^2-9x+8}{x^2+5x+6} \cdot \dfrac{x^2-1}{x^2+4x+4}$

$= \dfrac{\cancel{(x+3)}(x+1)}{\cancel{(x-8)}(x+2)} \cdot \dfrac{\cancel{(x-8)}(x-1)}{(x+2)\cancel{(x+3)}} \cdot \dfrac{(x-1)(x+1)}{(x+2)^2}$

$= \dfrac{(x+1)^2(x-1)^2}{(x+2)^4}$

91. $\dfrac{(x-3)(x-2)}{(x+4)(x-5)} \cdot \dfrac{(x+4)(x-1)}{(x-3)(x-1)} = \dfrac{x-2}{x-5}$

The numerator is $(x-3)(x-2) = x^2 - 5x + 6$.

The denominator is $(x+4)(x-5) = x^2 - x - 20$.

92. $\dfrac{(x+3)(x-1)}{(x+2)(x-1)} \cdot \dfrac{(x+2)(x+4)}{(x+5)(x+4)} = \dfrac{x+3}{x+5}$

The first numerator is

$(x+3)(x-1) = x^2 + 2x - 3$.

The second denominator is

$(x+5)(x+4) = x^2 + 9x + 20$.

93. a. (2) and (3)

b. (1) $\left(\dfrac{x+2}{x-3}\right) \div \left(\dfrac{x^2-5x+6}{x-2} \cdot \dfrac{x+2}{x-3}\right)$

$= \left(\dfrac{x+2}{x-3}\right) \div \left(\dfrac{(x-3)(x-2)}{(x-2)} \cdot \dfrac{(x+2)}{(x-3)}\right)$

$= \dfrac{x+2}{x-3} \div (x+2)$

$= \dfrac{x+2}{x-3} \cdot \dfrac{1}{x+2} = \dfrac{1}{x-3}$

(2) $\left(\dfrac{x+2}{x-3} \div \dfrac{x^2-5x+6}{x-2}\right) \cdot \left(\dfrac{x+2}{x-3}\right)$

$= \left(\dfrac{x+2}{x-3} \cdot \dfrac{x-2}{x^2-5x+6}\right) \cdot \left(\dfrac{x+2}{x-3}\right)$

$= \left(\dfrac{x+2}{x-3} \cdot \dfrac{x-2}{(x-3)(x-2)}\right) \cdot \left(\dfrac{x+2}{x-3}\right)$

$= \dfrac{x+2}{(x-3)^2} \cdot \dfrac{x+2}{x-3}$

$= \dfrac{(x+2)^2}{(x-3)^3}$

(3)

$\left(\dfrac{x+2}{x-3}\right) \div \left(\dfrac{x^2-5x+6}{x-2}\right) \cdot \left(\dfrac{x+2}{x-3}\right)$

$= \dfrac{x+2}{x-3} \cdot \dfrac{x-2}{x^2-5x+6}$

$= \dfrac{x+2}{x-3} \cdot \dfrac{x-2}{(x-3)(x-2)} \cdot \dfrac{x+2}{x-3}$

$= \dfrac{x+2}{x-3} \cdot \dfrac{1}{x-3} \cdot \dfrac{x+2}{x-3}$

$= \dfrac{(x+2)^2}{(x-3)^3}$

94. Let $x =$ the time it takes the tug boat to reach the barge.

Then $x + 2 =$ the time it takes the tug boat to return to the dock.

	Rate	Time	Distance
Trip Out	15	x	$15(x)$
Return Trip	5	$x+2$	$5(x+2)$

Distance to barge = Distance back to dock

$15(x) = 5(x+2)$

$15x = 5x + 10$

$10x = 10$

$x = 1$

It took 1 hour for the tug boat to reach the barge.

95. $\left(4x^3 y^2 z^4\right)\left(3xy^3 z^7\right) = 4 \cdot 3 \cdot x^3 x y^2 y^3 z^4 z^7$

$= 12x^4 y^5 z^{11}$

96.

$$2x-1\overline{\smash{\big)}\,4x^3 + 0x^2 - 5x + 0}$$

with quotient $2x^2 + x - 2$

$\underline{4x^3 - 2x^2}$

$2x^2 - 5x$

$\underline{2x^2 - x}$

$-4x + 0$

$\underline{-4x + 2}$

-2

$\dfrac{4x^3 - 5x}{2x-1} = 2x^2 + x - 2 - \dfrac{2}{2x-1}$

97. $6x^2 - 18x - 60 = 6\left(x^2 - 3x - 10\right)$

$$= 6(x-5)(x+2)$$

98. $3x^2 - 9x - 30 = 0$

$$3\left(x^2 - 3x - 10\right) = 0$$

$$3(x-5)(x+2) = 0$$

$$x - 5 = 0 \quad \text{or} \quad x + 2 = 0$$

$$x = 5 \qquad\qquad x = -2$$

Exercise Set 7.3

1. Answers will vary.

2. Each term changes sign.

3. Answers will vary.

4. $\dfrac{1}{x} + \dfrac{1}{x+1}$

The only factor (other than 1) of the first denominator is x. The only factor (other than 1) of the second denominator is $x + 1$. The LCD is therefore $x(x+1)$.

5. $\dfrac{9}{x+6} - \dfrac{2}{x}$

The only factor (other than 1) of the first denominator is $x + 6$. The only factor (other than 1) of the second denominator is x. The LCD is therefore $x(x+6)$.

6. $\dfrac{10}{x-2} + \dfrac{3}{7}$

The only factor (other than 1) of the first denominator is $x - 2$. The only factor (other than 1) of the second denominator is 7. The LCD is therefore $7(x-2)$.

7. $\dfrac{2}{x+3} + \dfrac{1}{x} + \dfrac{1}{4}$

The only factor (other than 1) of the first denominator is $x + 3$. The only factor (other than 1) of the second denominator is x. The only factor (other than 1) of the third denominator is 4. The LCD is therefore $4x(x+3)$.

8. $\dfrac{6}{x-3} + \dfrac{1}{x} - \dfrac{1}{8}$

The only factor (other than 1) of the first denominator is $x - 3$. The only factor (other than 1) of the second denominator is x. The only factor (other than 1) of the third denominator is 8. The LCD is therefore $8x(x-3)$.

9. a. The negative sign in $-(2x - 9)$ was not distributed.

b. $\dfrac{4x-3}{5x+4} - \dfrac{2x-9}{5x+4} = \dfrac{4x-3-(2x-9)}{5x+4}$

$$= \dfrac{4x-3-2x+9}{5x+4}$$

$$\neq \dfrac{4x-3-2x-9}{5x+4}$$

10. a. The negative sign in $-(-3x - 7)$ was not distributed.

b. $\dfrac{5x}{2x-3} - \dfrac{-3x-7}{2x-3} = \dfrac{5x-(-3x-7)}{2x-3}$

$$= \dfrac{5x+3x+7}{2x-3}$$

$$\neq \dfrac{5x+3x-7}{2x-3}$$

11. a. The negative sign in $-\left(3x^2 - 4x + 5\right)$ was not distributed.

b. $\dfrac{8x-2}{x^2-4x+3} - \dfrac{3x^2-4x+5}{x^2-4x+3}$

$$= \dfrac{8x-2-\left(3x^2-4x+5\right)}{x^2-4x+3}$$

$$= \dfrac{8x-2-3x^2+4x-5}{x^2-4x+3}$$

$$\neq \dfrac{8x-2-3x^2-4x+5}{x^2-4x+3}$$

12. a. The negative sign in $-\left(-x^2+3x+6\right)$ was not distributed.

b.
$$\frac{2x+5}{x^2-6x}-\frac{-x^2+3x+6}{x^2-6x}$$
$$=\frac{2x+5-\left(-x^2+3x+6\right)}{x^2-6x}$$
$$=\frac{2x+5+x^2-3x-6}{x^2-6x}$$
$$\neq\frac{2x+5+x^2+3x+6}{x^2-6x}$$

13. $\dfrac{4}{7}+\dfrac{2}{7}=\dfrac{4+2}{7}=\dfrac{6}{7}$

14. $\dfrac{8}{5}-\dfrac{6}{5}=\dfrac{8-6}{5}=\dfrac{2}{5}$

15. $\dfrac{5r+2}{4}-\dfrac{3}{4}=\dfrac{5r+2-3}{4}=\dfrac{5r-1}{4}$

16. $\dfrac{3x+6}{2}-\dfrac{x}{2}=\dfrac{3x+6-x}{2}$
$$=\frac{2x+6}{2}$$
$$=\frac{2(x+3)}{2}$$
$$=x+3$$

17. $\dfrac{2}{x}+\dfrac{x+4}{x}=\dfrac{2+x+4}{x}$
$$=\frac{x+6}{x}$$

18. $\dfrac{3x+1}{x+1}+\dfrac{6x+8}{x+1}=\dfrac{3x+1+6x+8}{x+1}$
$$=\frac{9x+9}{x+1}$$
$$=\frac{9(x+1)}{x+1}$$
$$=9$$

19. $\dfrac{6}{n+1}+\dfrac{n+2}{n+1}=\dfrac{6+n+2}{n+1}$
$$=\frac{n+8}{n+1}$$

20. $\dfrac{7}{x-2}-\dfrac{x+4}{x-2}=\dfrac{7-(x+4)}{x-2}$
$$=\frac{7-x-4}{x-2}$$
$$=\frac{-x+3}{x-2}$$

21. $\dfrac{x}{x-3}+\dfrac{4x+9}{x-3}=\dfrac{x+4x+9}{x-3}=\dfrac{5x+9}{x-3}$

22. $\dfrac{4x-3}{x-7}-\dfrac{2x+8}{x-7}=\dfrac{4x-3-(2x+8)}{x-7}$
$$=\frac{4x-3-2x-8}{x-7}$$
$$=\frac{2x-11}{x-7}$$

23. $\dfrac{4t+7}{5t^2}-\dfrac{3t+4}{5t^2}=\dfrac{4t+7-(3t+4)}{5t^2}$
$$=\frac{4t+7-3t-4}{5t^2}$$
$$=\frac{t+3}{5t^2}$$

24. $\dfrac{3w+6}{w^2+2w+1}+\dfrac{-2w-5}{w^2+2w+1}=\dfrac{3w+6-2w-5}{w^2+2w+1}$
$$=\frac{w+1}{(w+1)^2}$$
$$=\frac{1}{w+1}$$

25. $\dfrac{5x+4}{x^2-x-12}+\dfrac{-4x-1}{x^2-x-12}=\dfrac{5x+4-4x-1}{x^2-x-12}$
$$=\frac{x+3}{(x+3)(x-4)}$$
$$=\frac{1}{x-4}$$

26. $\dfrac{-x-6}{x^2-16}+\dfrac{2(x+5)}{x^2-16}=\dfrac{-x-6+2x+10}{x^2-16}$
$$=\frac{x+4}{(x+4)(x-4)}$$
$$=\frac{1}{x-4}$$

27. $\dfrac{2m+5}{(m+4)(m-3)} - \dfrac{m+1}{(m+4)(m-3)}$

$= \dfrac{2m+5-(m+1)}{(m+4)(m-3)} = \dfrac{2m+5-m-1}{(m+4)(m-3)}$

$= \dfrac{m+4}{(m+4)(m-3)}$

$= \dfrac{1}{m-3}$

28. $\dfrac{x^2+3x}{(x+6)(x-3)} - \dfrac{x+15}{(x+6)(x-3)}$

$= \dfrac{x^2+3x-(x+15)}{(x+6)(x-3)} = \dfrac{x^2+3x-x-15}{(x+6)(x-3)}$

$= \dfrac{x^2+2x-15}{(x+6)(x-3)} = \dfrac{(x+5)(x-3)}{(x+6)(x-3)}$

$= \dfrac{x+5}{x+6}$

29. $\dfrac{2p-6}{p-5} - \dfrac{p+6}{p-5} = \dfrac{2p-6-(p+6)}{p-5}$

$= \dfrac{2p-6-p-6}{p-5}$

$= \dfrac{p-12}{p-5}$

30. $\dfrac{x^2-6}{3x} - \dfrac{x^2+4x-11}{3x} = \dfrac{x^2-6-\left(x^2+4x-11\right)}{3x}$

$= \dfrac{x^2-6-x^2-4x+11}{3x}$

$= \dfrac{-4x+5}{3x}$

31. $\dfrac{x^2+4x+1}{x+2} - \dfrac{5x+7}{x+2} = \dfrac{x^2+4x+1-(5x+7)}{x+2}$

$= \dfrac{x^2+4x+1-5x-7}{x+2}$

$= \dfrac{x^2-x-6}{x+2}$

$= \dfrac{(x-3)(x+2)}{x+2}$

$= x-3$

32. $\dfrac{-4x+2}{3x+6} + \dfrac{4(x-1)}{3x+6} = \dfrac{-4x+2+4(x-1)}{3x+6}$

$= \dfrac{-4x+2+4x-4}{3x+6}$

$= -\dfrac{2}{3x+6}$

33. $\dfrac{3x+13}{2x+10} - \dfrac{2(x+4)}{2x+10} = \dfrac{3x+13-2(x+4)}{2x+10}$

$= \dfrac{3x+13-2x-8}{2x+10}$

$= \dfrac{x+5}{2(x+5)}$

$= \dfrac{1}{2}$

34. $\dfrac{x^2}{x+4} - \dfrac{16}{x+4} = \dfrac{x^2-16}{x+4}$

$= \dfrac{(x+4)(x-4)}{x+4}$

$= x-4$

35. $\dfrac{b^2-2b-2}{b^2-b-6} + \dfrac{b-4}{b^2-b-6} = \dfrac{b^2-2b-2+b-4}{b^2-b-6}$

$= \dfrac{b^2-b-6}{b^2-b-6}$

$= 1$

36. $\dfrac{4x+17}{3-x} - \dfrac{3x+20}{3-x} = \dfrac{4x+17-3x-20}{3-x}$

$= \dfrac{x-3}{3-x}$

$= \dfrac{x-3}{-(x-3)}$

$= -1$

37. $\dfrac{t-3}{t+3} - \dfrac{-3t-15}{t+3} = \dfrac{t-3-(-3t-15)}{t+3}$

$= \dfrac{t-3+3t+15}{t+3}$

$= \dfrac{4t+12}{t+3}$

$= \dfrac{4(t+3)}{t+3}$

$= 4$

38. $\dfrac{x+8}{3x+2} - \dfrac{x+8}{3x+2} = \dfrac{x+8-(x+8)}{3x+2}$

$\qquad\qquad\qquad = \dfrac{0}{3x+2}$

$\qquad\qquad\qquad = 0$

39. $\dfrac{3x^2+15x}{x^3+2x^2-8x} + \dfrac{2x^2+5x}{x^3+2x^2-8x}$

$= \dfrac{3x^2+15x+2x^2+5x}{x^3+2x^2-8x}$

$= \dfrac{5x^2+20x}{x(x^2+2x-8)}$

$= \dfrac{5x(x+4)}{x(x-2)(x+4)}$

$= \dfrac{5}{x-2}$

40. $\dfrac{x^2-12}{x+5} - \dfrac{13}{x+5} = \dfrac{x^2-12-13}{x+5}$

$\qquad\qquad\qquad = \dfrac{x^2-25}{x+5}$

$\qquad\qquad\qquad = \dfrac{(x+5)(x-5)}{x+5}$

$\qquad\qquad\qquad = x-5$

41. $\dfrac{3x^2-9x}{4x^2-8x} + \dfrac{3x}{4x^2-8x} = \dfrac{3x^2-9x+3x}{4x^2-8x}$

$\qquad\qquad\qquad = \dfrac{3x^2-6x}{4x^2-8x}$

$\qquad\qquad\qquad = \dfrac{3x(x-2)}{4x(x-2)}$

$\qquad\qquad\qquad = \dfrac{3}{4}$

42. $\dfrac{x^3-10x^2+35x}{x(x-6)} - \dfrac{x^2+5x}{x(x-6)}$

$= \dfrac{x^3-10x^2+35x-(x^2+5x)}{x(x-6)}$

$= \dfrac{x^3-10x^2+35x-x^2-5x}{x(x-6)}$

$= \dfrac{x^3-11x^2+30x}{x(x-6)}$

$= \dfrac{x(x^2-11x+30)}{x(x-6)}$

$= \dfrac{x(x-6)(x-5)}{x(x-6)}$

$= x-5$

43. $\dfrac{3x^2-4x+6}{3x^2+7x+2} - \dfrac{10x+11}{3x^2+7x+2}$

$= \dfrac{3x^2-4x+6-(10x+11)}{3x^2+7x+2}$

$= \dfrac{3x^2-4x+6-10x-11}{3x^2+7x+2}$

$= \dfrac{3x^2-14x-5}{3x^2+7x+2}$

$= \dfrac{(3x+1)(x-5)}{(3x+1)(x+2)}$

$= \dfrac{x-5}{x+2}$

44. $\dfrac{x^2-2}{x^2+6x-7} - \dfrac{-4x+19}{x^2+6x-7}$

$= \dfrac{x^2-2-(-4x+19)}{x^2+6x-7}$

$= \dfrac{x^2-2+4x-19}{x^2+6x-7}$

$= \dfrac{x^2+4x-21}{x^2+6x-7}$

$= \dfrac{(x+7)(x-3)}{(x+7)(x-1)}$

$= \dfrac{x-3}{x-1}$

45. $\dfrac{x^2+3x-6}{x^2-5x+4}-\dfrac{-2x^2+4x-4}{x^2-5x+4}$

$=\dfrac{x^2+3x-6-(-2x^2+4x-4)}{x^2-5x+4}$

$=\dfrac{x^2+3x-6+2x^2-4x+4}{x^2-5x+4}$

$=\dfrac{3x^2-x-2}{x^2-5x+4}$

$=\dfrac{(3x+2)(x-1)}{(x-4)(x-1)}$

$=\dfrac{3x+2}{x-4}$

46. $\dfrac{4x^2+15}{9x^2-64}-\dfrac{x^2-x+39}{9x^2-64}$

$=\dfrac{4x^2+15-(x^2-x+39)}{9x^2-64}$

$=\dfrac{4x^2+15-x^2+x-39}{9x^2-64}$

$=\dfrac{3x^2+x-24}{9x^2-64}$

$=\dfrac{(3x-8)(x+3)}{(3x-8)(3x+8)}$

$=\dfrac{x+3}{3x+8}$

47. $\dfrac{5x^2+30x+8}{x^2-64}+\dfrac{x^2+19x}{x^2-64}$

$=\dfrac{5x^2+30x+8+x^2+19x}{x^2-64}$

$=\dfrac{6x^2+49x+8}{x^2-64}$

$=\dfrac{(6x+1)(x+8)}{(x-8)(x+8)}$

$=\dfrac{6x+1}{x-8}$

48. $\dfrac{20x^2+8x+1}{6x^2+x-2}-\dfrac{8x^2-9x-5}{6x^2+x-2}$

$=\dfrac{20x^2+8x+1-(8x^2-9x-5)}{6x^2+x-2}$

$=\dfrac{20x^2+8x+1-8x^2+9x+5}{6x^2+x-2}$

$=\dfrac{12x^2+17x+6}{6x^2+x-2}$

$=\dfrac{(4x+3)(3x+2)}{(2x-1)(3x+2)}$

$=\dfrac{4x+3}{2x-1}$

49. $\dfrac{x}{5}+\dfrac{x+4}{5}$

Least common denominator = 5

50. $\dfrac{2+r}{7}-\dfrac{12}{7}$

Least common denominator = 7

51. $\dfrac{3}{n}+\dfrac{1}{9n}$

Least common denominator = $9n$

52. $\dfrac{6}{x+1}-\dfrac{4}{7}$

Least common denominator $=7(x+1)$

53. $\dfrac{3}{5x}+\dfrac{7}{3}$

Least common denominator $=5x\cdot 3=15x$

54. $\dfrac{1}{8}+\dfrac{1}{z}$

Least common denominator = $8z$

55. $\dfrac{6}{p}+\dfrac{9}{p^3}$

Least common denominator = p^3

56. $\dfrac{2x}{x+3}+\dfrac{6}{x-9}$

Least common denominator = $(x+3)(x-9)$

57. $\dfrac{m+3}{3m-4}+m=\dfrac{m+3}{3m-4}+\dfrac{m}{1}$

Least common denominator = $3m-4$

58. $\dfrac{x+4}{2x}+\dfrac{8}{7x}$

Least common denominator $= 2x \cdot 7 = 14x$

59. $\dfrac{x}{6x}+\dfrac{4}{x^2}$

Least common denominator $= 6x^2$

60. $\dfrac{x}{5x^2}+\dfrac{9}{7x^3}$

Least common denominator $= 5 \cdot 7 \cdot x^3 = 35x^3$

61. $\dfrac{x+1}{12x^2 y}-\dfrac{7}{9x^3}=\dfrac{x+1}{3 \cdot 4x^2 y}-\dfrac{7}{3^2 x^3}$

Least common denominator
$= 4 \cdot 3^2 \cdot x^3 \cdot y = 36x^3 y$

62. $\dfrac{-3}{8x^2 y^2}+\dfrac{5}{12x^4 y^5}=\dfrac{-3}{4 \cdot 2x^2 y^2}+\dfrac{5}{4 \cdot 3x^4 y^5}$

Least common denominator
$= 2 \cdot 3 \cdot 4x^4 y^5 = 24x^4 y^5$

63. $\dfrac{4}{2r^4 s^5}-\dfrac{5}{9r^3 s^7}=\dfrac{4}{2r^4 s^5}-\dfrac{5}{3 \cdot 3r^3 s^7}$

Least common denominator
$= 2 \cdot 3 \cdot 3r^4 s^7 = 18r^4 s^7$

64. $\dfrac{5}{4w^5 z^4}+\dfrac{4}{9wz^2}=\dfrac{5}{2 \cdot 2w^5 z^4}+\dfrac{4}{3 \cdot 3wz^2}$

Least common denominator $=$
$2 \cdot 2 \cdot 3 \cdot 3w^5 z^4 = 36w^5 z^4$

65. $\dfrac{3}{m}-\dfrac{17m}{m+2}$

Least common denominator $= m(m+2)$

66. $\dfrac{x-3}{17}-\dfrac{6}{x-5}$

Least common denominator $= 17(x-5)$

67. $\dfrac{5x-2}{x^2+x}-\dfrac{13}{x}=\dfrac{5x-2}{x(x+1)}-\dfrac{13}{x}$

Least common denominator $= x(x+1)$

68. $\dfrac{3t}{t-5}+\dfrac{2}{5-t}=\dfrac{4t}{t-5}+\dfrac{(-1)2}{(-1)(5-t)}$

$=\dfrac{4t}{t-5}+\dfrac{-2}{t-5}$

Least common denominator $= t-5$ or $5-t$

69. $\dfrac{n}{4n-1}+\dfrac{n-8}{1-4n}=\dfrac{n}{4n-1}+\dfrac{(-1)(n-8)}{(-1)(1-4n)}$

$=\dfrac{n}{4n-1}+\dfrac{-n+8}{4n-1}$

Least common denominator $= 4n-1$ or $1-4n$

70. $\dfrac{3}{-2a+3b}-\dfrac{10}{2a-3b}=\dfrac{(-1)3}{(-1)(-2a+3b)}-\dfrac{10}{2a-3b}$

$=\dfrac{-3}{2a-3b}-\dfrac{10}{2a-3b}$

Least common denominator $= 2a-3b$ or $-2a+3b$

71. $\dfrac{3}{4k-5r}-\dfrac{10}{-4k+5r}$

$=\dfrac{3}{4k-5r}-\dfrac{(-1)10}{(-1)(-4k+5r)}$

$=\dfrac{3}{4k-5r}-\dfrac{-10}{4k-5r}$

Least common denominator $= 4k-5r$ or $-4k+5r$

72. $\dfrac{p}{4p^2+2p}-\dfrac{7}{2p+1}=\dfrac{p}{2p(2p+1)}-\dfrac{7}{2p+1}$

Least common denominator $= 2p(2p+1)$

73. $\dfrac{4}{2q^2+2q}-\dfrac{5}{9q}=\dfrac{4}{2q(q+1)}-\dfrac{5}{3 \cdot 3q}$

Least common denominator $= 2 \cdot 3 \cdot 3q(q+1)$
$= 18q(q+1)$

74. $\dfrac{10}{(x+4)(x+2)}-\dfrac{6+x}{x+2}$

Least common denominator $= (x+4)(x+2)$

75. $\dfrac{21}{24x^2 y}+\dfrac{x+4}{15xy^3}=\dfrac{21}{3 \cdot 8x^2 y}+\dfrac{x+4}{3 \cdot 5xy^3}$

Least common denominator
$= 8 \cdot 3 \cdot 5x^2 y^3 = 120x^2 y^3$

76. $\dfrac{p^2+4}{p^2-25}+\dfrac{9}{p-5}=\dfrac{p^2+4}{(p+5)(p-5)}+\dfrac{9}{p-5}$

Least common denominator $= (p+5)(p-5)$

77. $\dfrac{11}{3x+12}+\dfrac{3x+1}{2x+4}=\dfrac{11}{3(x+4)}+\dfrac{3x+1}{2(x+2)}$

Least common denominator
$=3\cdot2(x+4)(x+2)=6(x+4)(x+2)$

78. $6x^2+\dfrac{8x}{x-7}=\dfrac{6x^2}{1}+\dfrac{8x}{x-7}$

Least common denominator $= x-7$

79. $\dfrac{9x+4}{x+1}-\dfrac{2x-6}{x+8}$

Least common denominator $=(x+1)(x+8)$

80. $\dfrac{x+3}{x^2+11x+18}-\dfrac{x^2-11}{x^2-3x-10}$

$=\dfrac{x+3}{(x+9)(x+2)}-\dfrac{x^2-11}{(x-5)(x+2)}$

Least common denominator
$=(x+9)(x+2)(x-5)$

81. $\dfrac{x-2}{x^2-5x-24}+\dfrac{3}{x^2+11x+24}$

$=\dfrac{x-2}{(x-8)(x+3)}+\dfrac{3}{(x+8)(x+3)}$

Least common denominator
$=(x-8)(x+3)(x+8)$

82. $\dfrac{6n}{n^2-4}-\dfrac{n-3}{n^2-5n-14}$

$=\dfrac{6n}{(n+2)(n-2)}-\dfrac{n-3}{(n+2)(n-7)}$

Least common denominator
$=(n+2)(n-2)(n-7)$

83. $\dfrac{5}{(a-4)^2}-\dfrac{a+2}{a^2-7a+12}$

$=\dfrac{5}{(a-4)^2}-\dfrac{a+2}{(a-4)(a-3)}$

Least common denominator
$=(a-4)^2(a-3)$

84. $\dfrac{3x+5}{x^2-1}+\dfrac{x^2-18}{(x+1)^2}$

$=\dfrac{3x+5}{(x+1)(x-1)}+\dfrac{x^2-18}{(x+1)^2}$

Least common denominator $=(x-1)(x+1)^2$

85. $\dfrac{9x}{x^2+6x+5}-\dfrac{5x^2}{x^2+4x+3}$

$=\dfrac{9x}{(x+5)(x+1)}-\dfrac{5x^2}{(x+3)(x+1)}$

Least common denominator
$=(x+5)(x+1)(x+3)$

86. $\dfrac{6x+5}{x+2}+\dfrac{3x}{(x+2)^2}$

Least common denominator $=(x+2)^2$

87. $\dfrac{3x-5}{x^2-6x+9}+\dfrac{3}{x-3}$

$=\dfrac{3x+5}{(x-3)^2}+\dfrac{3}{x-3}$

Least common denominator $=(x-3)^2$

88. $\dfrac{2n+11}{(n+5)(n+2)}-\dfrac{3n-5}{(n-3)(n+5)}$

Least common denominator
$=(n+5)(n+2)(n-3)$

89. $\dfrac{8x^2}{x^2-7x+6}+x-9$

$=\dfrac{8x^2}{(x-6)(x-1)}+\dfrac{x-9}{1}$

Least common denominator $=(x-6)(x-1)$

90. $\dfrac{2x-1}{x^2-25}+x-10$

$=\dfrac{2x-1}{(x+5)(x-5)}+\dfrac{x-10}{1}$

Least common denominator $=(x+5)(x-5)$

91. $\dfrac{t-1}{3t^2+10t-8}-\dfrac{11}{3t^2+11t-4}$

$=\dfrac{t-1}{(3t-2)(t+4)}-\dfrac{11}{(3t-1)(t+4)}$

Least common denominator
$=(3t-2)(t+4)(3t-1)$

92. $\dfrac{-4x+9}{2x^2+5x+2}+\dfrac{x^2}{3x^2+4x-4}$

$=\dfrac{-4x+9}{(2x+1)(x+2)}+\dfrac{x^2}{(3x-2)(x+2)}$

Least common denominator
$=(2x+1)(x+2)(3x-2)$

93. $\dfrac{3x-1}{4x^2+4x+1}+\dfrac{x^2+x-9}{8x^2+10x+3}$

$=\dfrac{3x-1}{(2x+1)^2}+\dfrac{x^2+x-9}{(2x+1)(4x+3)}$

Least common denominator
$=(2x+1)^2(4x+3)$

94. $\dfrac{3x+7}{6x^2+11x-10}+\dfrac{x^2-8}{9x^2-12x+4}$

$=\dfrac{3x+7}{(3x-2)(2x+5)}+\dfrac{x^2-8}{(3x-2)^2}$

Least common denominator $=(3x-2)^2(2x+5)$

95. $\dfrac{1}{7}+\dfrac{2}{5}=\dfrac{5}{5}\cdot\dfrac{1}{7}+\dfrac{2}{5}\cdot\dfrac{7}{7}=\dfrac{5}{35}+\dfrac{14}{35}=\dfrac{19}{35}$

96. $\dfrac{3}{8}+\dfrac{1}{4}=\dfrac{3}{8}+\dfrac{1}{4}\cdot\dfrac{2}{2}=\dfrac{3}{8}+\dfrac{2}{8}=\dfrac{5}{8}$

97. $\dfrac{2}{9}+\dfrac{3}{4}=\dfrac{4}{4}\cdot\dfrac{2}{9}+\dfrac{3}{4}\cdot\dfrac{9}{9}=\dfrac{8}{36}+\dfrac{27}{36}=\dfrac{35}{36}$

98. $\dfrac{5}{6}-\dfrac{1}{3}=\dfrac{5}{6}-\dfrac{1}{3}\cdot\dfrac{2}{2}=\dfrac{5}{6}-\dfrac{2}{6}=\dfrac{3}{6}=\dfrac{1}{2}$

99. $\dfrac{5}{9}-\dfrac{1}{2}=\dfrac{2}{2}\cdot\dfrac{5}{9}-\dfrac{1}{2}\cdot\dfrac{9}{9}=\dfrac{10}{18}-\dfrac{9}{18}=\dfrac{1}{18}$

100. $\dfrac{6}{5}-\dfrac{3}{10}=\dfrac{2}{2}\cdot\dfrac{6}{5}-\dfrac{3}{10}=\dfrac{12}{10}-\dfrac{3}{10}=\dfrac{9}{10}$

101. $x^2-6x+3+\boxed{}=2x^2-5x-6$

$\boxed{}=2x^2-5x-6-(x^2-6x+3)$

$=2x^2-5x-6-x^2+6x-3$

$=x^2+x-9$

Sum of numerators must be $2x^2-5x-6$

102. $4x^2-6x-7-\boxed{}=2x^2+x-3$

$\boxed{}=4x^2-6x-7-(2x^2+x-3)$

$=4x^2-6x-7-2x^2-x+3$

$=2x^2-7x-4$

Difference of numerators must be $2x^2+x-3$

103. $-x^2-4x+3+\boxed{}=5x-7$

$\boxed{}=5x-7-(-x^2-4x+3)$

$=5x-7+x^2+4x-3$

$=x^2+9x-10$

Sum of numerator must be $5x-7$

104. $-3x^2-9-\boxed{}=x^2+3x$

$\boxed{}=-3x^2-9-(x^2+3x)$

$=-3x^2-9-x^2-3x$

$=-4x^2-3x-9$

Difference of numerators must be x^2+3x

105. $\dfrac{3}{☺}+\dfrac{4}{5☺}$

Least common denominator $=5☺$

106. $\dfrac{5}{8\Delta^2☺^2}+\dfrac{6}{5\Delta^4☺^5}$

Least common denominator
$=8\cdot5\Delta^4☺^5=40\Delta^4☺^5$

107. $\dfrac{8}{\Delta^2-9}-\dfrac{2}{\Delta+3}=\dfrac{8}{(\Delta+3)(\Delta-3)}-\dfrac{2}{\Delta+3}$

Least common denominator $=(\Delta+3)(\Delta-3)$

108. $\dfrac{6}{\Delta+3}-\dfrac{\Delta+5}{\Delta^2-4\Delta+3}=\dfrac{6}{\Delta+3}-\dfrac{\Delta+5}{(\Delta-3)(\Delta-1)}$

Least common denominator
$=(\Delta+3)(\Delta-3)(\Delta-1)$

109. $\dfrac{4x-1}{x^2-25}-\dfrac{3x^2-8}{x^2-25}+\dfrac{8x-7}{x^2-25}$

$=\dfrac{4x-1-\left(3x^2-8\right)+\left(8x-7\right)}{x^2-25}$

$=\dfrac{4x-1-3x^2+8+8x-7}{x^2-25}$

$=\dfrac{-3x^2+12x}{x^2-25}$

110. $\dfrac{x^2-8x+2}{x+7}+\dfrac{2x^2-5x}{x+7}-\dfrac{3x^2+7x+10}{x+7}$

$=\dfrac{x^2-8x+2+\left(2x^2-5x\right)-\left(3x^2+7x+10\right)}{x+7}$

$=\dfrac{x^2-8x+2+2x^2-5x-3x^2-7x-10}{x+7}$

$=\dfrac{-20x-8}{x+7}$

111. $\dfrac{7}{6x^5y^9}-\dfrac{9}{2x^3y}+\dfrac{6}{5x^{12}y^2}$

$=\dfrac{7}{2\cdot3x^5y^9}-\dfrac{9}{2x^3y}+\dfrac{6}{5x^{12}y^2}$

Least common denominator
$=2\cdot3\cdot5x^{12}y^9=30x^{12}y^9$

112. $\dfrac{2x}{x-3}-\dfrac{3}{x^2-9}+\dfrac{5}{x+3}$

$=\dfrac{2x}{x-3}-\dfrac{3}{(x+3)(x-3)}+\dfrac{5}{x+3}$

Least common denominator $=(x+3)(x-3)$

113. $\dfrac{3x}{x^2-x-12}+\dfrac{2}{x^2-6x+8}+\dfrac{3}{x^2+x-6}$

$=\dfrac{3x}{(x-4)(x+3)}+\dfrac{2}{(x-4)(x-2)}+\dfrac{3}{(x+3)(x-2)}$

Least common denominator
$=(x-4)(x+3)(x-2)$

114. $\dfrac{9}{x^2-4}-\dfrac{8}{3x^2+5x-2}+\dfrac{7}{3x^2-7x+2}$

$=\dfrac{9}{(x+2)(x-2)}-\dfrac{8}{(3x-1)(x+2)}+\dfrac{7}{(3x-1)(x-2)}$

Least common denominator $=$
$(x+2)(x-2)(3x-1)$

115. $4\dfrac{3}{5}-2\dfrac{5}{9}=\dfrac{23}{5}-\dfrac{23}{9}$

$=\dfrac{207}{45}-\dfrac{115}{45}$

$=\dfrac{92}{45}$

$=2\dfrac{2}{45}$

116. $6x+4=-(x+2)-3x+4$

$6x+4=-x-2-3x+4$

$6x+4=-4x+2$

$6x+4x=2-4$

$10x=-2$

$x=\dfrac{-2}{10}=-\dfrac{1}{5}$

117. $\dfrac{6}{128}=\dfrac{x}{48}$

$128x=6\cdot48$

$128x=288$

$x=\dfrac{288}{128}$

$x=\dfrac{9}{4}=2\dfrac{1}{4}$

You should use 2.25 ounces of concentrate.

118. Let $h=$ the number of hours played.
The cost under Plan 1 is $C=250+5h$ while the cost under Plan 2 is $C=600$.

Set the two costs equal
$250+5h=600$

$5h=350$

$h=70$

If Malcolm plays 70 hours in a year, the cost of the two plans is equal.

119. Use the two points given and find the slope between the two points. This is the slope of the line.

$m=\dfrac{y_2-y_1}{x_2-x_1}=\dfrac{5-(-2)}{4-(-3)}=\dfrac{7}{7}=1$

The slope of the line is 1.

120. $\dfrac{8.4\times10^8}{2.1\times10^{-3}}=4.0\times10^{8-(-3)}=4.0\times10^{11}$

121.
$$2x^2 - 3 = x$$
$$2x^2 - x - 3 = 0$$
$$(2x-3)(x+1) = 0$$
$$2x - 3 = 0 \quad \text{or} \quad x + 1 = 0$$
$$2x = 3 \qquad\qquad x = -1$$
$$x = \frac{3}{2}$$

Exercise Set 7.4

1. For each fraction, divide the LCD by the denominator.

2. The value does not change because you are, in effect, multiplying by 1.

3. a. Answers will vary.

   b.
   $$\frac{x}{x^2 - x - 6} + \frac{3}{x^2 - 4}$$
   $$= \frac{x}{(x-3)(x+2)} + \frac{3}{(x-2)(x+2)}$$
   $$= \frac{x(x-2)}{(x-3)(x+2)(x-2)} + \frac{3(x-3)}{(x-2)(x+2)(x-3)}$$
   $$= \frac{x^2 - 2x + 3x - 9}{(x-3)(x+2)(x-2)}$$
   $$= \frac{x^2 + x - 9}{(x-3)(x+2)(x-2)}$$

4. Multiply both the numerator and the denominator of one fraction by −1 to get a common denominator.
   One example is
   $$\frac{4}{x-7} + \frac{6x}{7-x} = \frac{4}{x-7} + \frac{-6x}{-(7-x)}$$
   $$= \frac{4}{x-7} + \frac{-6x}{x-7}$$
   $$= \frac{-6x+4}{x-7}$$

5. a.
   $$\frac{y}{4z} + \frac{5}{6z^2}$$
   $$4z = 2 \cdot 2 \cdot z$$
   $$6z^2 = 2 \cdot 3 \cdot z^2$$
   Least common denominator
   $$2 \cdot 2 \cdot 3 \cdot z^2 = 12z^2$$

   b.
   $$\frac{y}{4z} + \frac{5}{6z^2} = \frac{y}{4z} \cdot \frac{3z}{3z} + \frac{5}{6z^2} \cdot \frac{2}{2}$$
   $$= \frac{3yz}{12z^2} + \frac{10}{12z^2}$$
   $$= \frac{3yz + 10}{12z^2}$$

   c. Yes. After factoring out the common factors, the reduced form would be the same.

6. a. Yes
   b. No, because it is multiplication.
   c. Yes
   d. No, because it is division.

7.
   $$\frac{2}{x} + \frac{3}{y} = \frac{y}{y} \cdot \frac{2}{x} + \frac{3}{y} \cdot \frac{x}{x}$$
   $$= \frac{2y}{xy} + \frac{3x}{xy}$$
   $$= \frac{2y + 3x}{xy}$$

8.
   $$\frac{5}{x} - \frac{1}{y} = \frac{y}{y} \cdot \frac{5}{x} - \frac{1}{y} \cdot \frac{x}{x}$$
   $$= \frac{5y}{xy} - \frac{x}{xy}$$
   $$= \frac{5y - x}{xy}$$

9.
   $$\frac{5}{x^2} + \frac{1}{2x} = \frac{2}{2} \cdot \frac{5}{x^2} + \frac{1}{2x} \cdot \frac{x}{x}$$
   $$= \frac{10}{2x^2} + \frac{x}{2x^2}$$
   $$= \frac{x + 10}{2x^2}$$

10.
   $$7 - \frac{1}{x^2} = \frac{x^2}{x^2} \cdot \frac{7}{1} - \frac{1}{x^2}$$
   $$= \frac{7x^2}{x^2} - \frac{1}{x^2}$$
   $$= \frac{7x^2 - 1}{x^2}$$

11. $3 + \dfrac{8}{x} = \dfrac{x}{x} \cdot 3 + \dfrac{8}{x} = \dfrac{3x}{x} + \dfrac{8}{x} = \dfrac{3x+8}{x}$

12. $\dfrac{5}{6y} + \dfrac{3}{5y^2} = \dfrac{5y}{5y} \cdot \dfrac{5}{6y} + \dfrac{3}{5y^2} \cdot \dfrac{6}{6}$

$\qquad = \dfrac{25y}{30y^2} + \dfrac{18}{30y^2}$

$\qquad = \dfrac{25y+18}{30y^2}$

13. $\dfrac{2}{x^2} + \dfrac{3}{5x} = \dfrac{5}{5} \cdot \dfrac{2}{x^2} + \dfrac{3}{5x} \cdot \dfrac{x}{x}$

$\qquad = \dfrac{10}{5x^2} + \dfrac{3x}{5x^2}$

$\qquad = \dfrac{3x+10}{5x^2}$

14. $\dfrac{6}{x} - \dfrac{5}{x^2} = \dfrac{x}{x} \cdot \dfrac{6}{x} - \dfrac{5}{x^2} = \dfrac{6x}{x^2} - \dfrac{5}{x^2} = \dfrac{6x-5}{x^2}$

15. $\dfrac{9}{4x^2y} + \dfrac{3}{5xy^2} = \dfrac{5y}{5y} \cdot \dfrac{9}{4x^2y} + \dfrac{3}{5xy^2} \cdot \dfrac{4x}{4x}$

$\qquad = \dfrac{45y}{20x^2y^2} + \dfrac{12x}{20x^2y^2}$

$\qquad = \dfrac{45y+12x}{20x^2y^2}$

16. $\dfrac{7}{12x^4y} - \dfrac{1}{5x^2y^3} = \dfrac{5y^2}{5y^2} \cdot \dfrac{7}{12x^4y} - \dfrac{1}{5x^2y^3} \cdot \dfrac{12x^2}{12x^2}$

$\qquad = \dfrac{35y^2}{60x^4y^3} - \dfrac{12x^2}{60x^4y^3}$

$\qquad = \dfrac{35y^2 - 12x^2}{60x^4y^3}$

17. $4y + \dfrac{x}{y} = \dfrac{y}{y} \cdot \dfrac{4y}{1} + \dfrac{x}{y} = \dfrac{4y^2}{y} + \dfrac{x}{y} = \dfrac{4y^2+x}{y}$

18. $x + \dfrac{2x}{y} = \dfrac{y}{y} \cdot \dfrac{x}{1} + \dfrac{2x}{y} = \dfrac{xy}{y} + \dfrac{2x}{y} = \dfrac{xy+2x}{y}$

19. $\dfrac{3a-1}{2a} + \dfrac{2}{3a} = \dfrac{3}{3} \cdot \dfrac{3a-1}{2a} + \dfrac{2}{3a} \cdot \dfrac{2}{2}$

$\qquad = \dfrac{3(3a-1)}{3 \cdot 2a} + \dfrac{2 \cdot 2}{3a \cdot 2}$

$\qquad = \dfrac{9a-3}{6a} + \dfrac{4}{6a}$

$\qquad = \dfrac{9a-3+4}{6a}$

$\qquad = \dfrac{9a+1}{6a}$

20. $\dfrac{11}{n} + 5 = \dfrac{11}{n} + \dfrac{5}{1} \cdot \dfrac{n}{n} == \dfrac{11}{n} + \dfrac{5n}{n} = \dfrac{5n+11}{n}$

21. $\dfrac{6x}{y} + \dfrac{2y}{xy} = \dfrac{x}{x} \cdot \dfrac{6x}{y} + \dfrac{2y}{xy}$

$\qquad = \dfrac{6x^2}{xy} + \dfrac{2y}{xy}$

$\qquad = \dfrac{6x^2 + 2y}{xy}$

22. $\dfrac{4}{5p} - \dfrac{5}{2p^2} = \dfrac{2p}{2p} \cdot \dfrac{4}{5p} - \dfrac{5}{2p^2} \cdot \dfrac{5}{5}$

$\qquad = \dfrac{8p}{10p^2} - \dfrac{25}{10p^2}$

$\qquad = \dfrac{8p-25}{10p^2}$

23. $\dfrac{9}{b} - \dfrac{4}{5a^2} = \dfrac{5a^2}{5a^2} \cdot \dfrac{9}{b} - \dfrac{4}{5a^2} \cdot \dfrac{b}{b}$

$\qquad = \dfrac{45a^2}{5a^2b} - \dfrac{4b}{5a^2b}$

$\qquad = \dfrac{45a^2 - 4b}{5a^2b}$

24. $\dfrac{x-3}{x} - \dfrac{1}{6x} = \dfrac{6}{6} \cdot \dfrac{x-3}{x} - \dfrac{1}{6x}$

$\qquad = \dfrac{6(x-3)}{x} - \dfrac{1}{6x}$

$\qquad = \dfrac{6x-18}{6x} - \dfrac{1}{6x}$

$\qquad = \dfrac{6x-18-1}{6x}$

$\qquad = \dfrac{6x-19}{6x}$

25. $\dfrac{4}{x} + \dfrac{9}{x-3} = \dfrac{x-3}{x-3} \cdot \dfrac{4}{x} + \dfrac{9}{(x-3)} \cdot \dfrac{x}{x}$

$\qquad = \dfrac{4(x-3)}{x(x-3)} + \dfrac{9x}{x(x-3)}$

$\qquad = \dfrac{4x-12}{x(x-3)} + \dfrac{9x}{x(x-3)}$

$\qquad = \dfrac{4x-12+9x}{x(x-3)}$

$\qquad = \dfrac{13x-12}{x(x-3)}$

26. $10 - \dfrac{3}{x-3} = \dfrac{x-3}{x-3} \cdot \dfrac{10}{1} - \dfrac{3}{x-3}$

$= \dfrac{10(x-3)}{x-3} - \dfrac{3}{x-3}$

$= \dfrac{10x-30}{x-3} - \dfrac{3}{x-3}$

$= \dfrac{10x-30-3}{x-3}$

$= \dfrac{10x-33}{x-3}$

27. $\dfrac{9}{p+3} + \dfrac{2}{p} = \dfrac{p}{p} \cdot \dfrac{9}{p+3} + \dfrac{2}{p} \cdot \dfrac{p+3}{p+3}$

$= \dfrac{9p}{p(p+3)} + \dfrac{2(p+3)}{p(p+3)}$

$= \dfrac{9p}{p(p+3)} + \dfrac{2p+6}{p(p+3)}$

$= \dfrac{9p+2p+6}{p(p+3)}$

$= \dfrac{11p+6}{p(p+3)}$

28. $\dfrac{2a}{a+b} + \dfrac{a-b}{a} = \dfrac{a}{a} \cdot \dfrac{2a}{a+b} + \dfrac{a-b}{a} \cdot \dfrac{a+b}{a+b}$

$= \dfrac{a \cdot 2a}{a(a+b)} + \dfrac{(a-b)(a+b)}{a(a+b)}$

$= \dfrac{2a^2}{a(a+b)} + \dfrac{a^2-b^2}{a(a+b)}$

$= \dfrac{2a^2+a^2-b^2}{a(a+b)}$

$= \dfrac{3a^2-b^2}{a(a+b)}$

29. $\dfrac{5}{d+1} - \dfrac{d}{3d+5}$

$= \dfrac{3d+5}{3d+5} \cdot \dfrac{5}{d+1} - \dfrac{d}{3d+5} \cdot \dfrac{d+1}{d+1}$

$= \dfrac{5(3d+5)}{(3d+5)(d+1)} - \dfrac{d(d+1)}{(3d+5)(d+1)}$

$= \dfrac{15d+25}{(3d+5)(d+1)} - \dfrac{d^2+d}{(3d+5)(d+1)}$

$= \dfrac{15d+25-d^2-d}{(3d+5)(d+1)}$

$= \dfrac{-d^2+14d+25}{(3d+5)(d+1)}$

30. $\dfrac{2}{x-3} - \dfrac{5}{x-1} = \dfrac{x-1}{x-1} \cdot \dfrac{2}{x-3} - \dfrac{5}{x-1} \cdot \dfrac{x-3}{x-3}$

$= \dfrac{2(x-1)}{(x-1)(x-3)} - \dfrac{5(x-3)}{(x-1)(x-3)}$

$= \dfrac{2x-2-5x+15}{(x-1)(x-3)}$

$= \dfrac{-3x+13}{(x-1)(x-3)}$

31. $\dfrac{8}{p-3} + \dfrac{2}{3-p} = \dfrac{8}{p-3} + \dfrac{2}{3-p} \cdot \dfrac{-1}{-1}$

$= \dfrac{8}{p-3} + \dfrac{-2}{p-3}$

$= \dfrac{6}{p-3}$

32. $\dfrac{3}{n-5} - \dfrac{7}{5-n} = \dfrac{3}{n-5} - \dfrac{7}{5-n} \cdot \dfrac{-1}{-1}$

$= \dfrac{3}{n-5} - \dfrac{-7}{n-5}$

$= \dfrac{10}{n-5}$

33. $\dfrac{9}{x+7} - \dfrac{5}{-x-7} = \dfrac{9}{x+7} - \dfrac{5}{-x-7} \cdot \dfrac{-1}{-1}$

$= \dfrac{9}{x+7} - \dfrac{-5}{x+7}$

$= \dfrac{14}{x+7}$

34. $\dfrac{6}{7x-1}-\dfrac{3}{1-7x}=\dfrac{6}{7x-1}-\dfrac{3}{1-7x}\cdot\dfrac{-1}{-1}$

$\qquad\qquad=\dfrac{6}{7x-1}-\dfrac{-3}{7x-1}$

$\qquad\qquad=\dfrac{9}{7x-1}$

35. $\dfrac{8}{a-2}+\dfrac{a}{2a-4}=\dfrac{2}{2}\cdot\dfrac{8}{a-2}+\dfrac{a}{2(a-2)}$

$\qquad\qquad=\dfrac{16}{2(a-2)}+\dfrac{a}{2(a-2)}$

$\qquad\qquad=\dfrac{a+16}{2(a-2)}$

36. $\dfrac{4}{y-1}+\dfrac{3}{y+1}=\dfrac{y+1}{y+1}\cdot\dfrac{4}{y-1}+\dfrac{3}{y+1}\cdot\dfrac{y-1}{y-1}$

$\qquad\qquad=\dfrac{4(y+1)}{(y+1)(y-1)}+\dfrac{3(y-1)}{(y+1)(y-1)}$

$\qquad\qquad=\dfrac{4y+4+3y-3}{(y+1)(y-1)}$

$\qquad\qquad=\dfrac{7y+1}{(y+1)(y-1)}$

37. $\dfrac{x+5}{x-5}-\dfrac{x-5}{x+5}=\dfrac{x+5}{x+5}\cdot\dfrac{x+5}{x-5}-\dfrac{x-5}{x+5}\cdot\dfrac{x-5}{x-5}$

$\qquad\qquad=\dfrac{(x+5)^2}{(x+5)(x-5)}-\dfrac{(x-5)^2}{(x+5)(x-5)}$

$\qquad\qquad=\dfrac{x^2+10x+25-\left(x^2-10x+25\right)}{(x-5)(x+5)}$

$\qquad\qquad=\dfrac{x^2+10x+25-x^2+10x-25}{(x-5)(x+5)}$

$\qquad\qquad=\dfrac{20x}{(x-5)(x+5)}$

38. $\dfrac{x+7}{x+3}-\dfrac{x+3}{x+7}=\dfrac{x+7}{x+7}\cdot\dfrac{x+7}{x+3}-\dfrac{x+3}{x+7}\cdot\dfrac{x+3}{x+3}$

$\qquad\qquad=\dfrac{(x+7)^2}{(x+7)(x+3)}-\dfrac{(x+3)^2}{(x+7)(x+3)}$

$\qquad\qquad=\dfrac{x^2+14x+49-(x^2+6x+9)}{(x+7)(x+3)}$

$\qquad\qquad=\dfrac{x^2+14x+49-x^2-6x-9}{(x+7)(x+3)}$

$\qquad\qquad=\dfrac{8x+40}{(x+7)(x+3)}$

39. $\dfrac{5}{6n+3}-\dfrac{2}{n}=\dfrac{n}{n}\cdot\dfrac{5}{3(2n+1)}-\dfrac{2}{n}\cdot\dfrac{3(2n+1)}{3(2n+1)}$

$\qquad\qquad=\dfrac{5n}{3n(2n+1)}-\dfrac{6(2n+1)}{3n(2n+1)}$

$\qquad\qquad=\dfrac{5n}{3n(2n+1)}-\dfrac{12n+6}{3n(2n+1)}$

$\qquad\qquad=\dfrac{5n-12n-6}{3n(2n+1)}$

$\qquad\qquad=\dfrac{-7n-6}{3n(2n+1)}$

40. $\dfrac{x}{4x-4}-\dfrac{1}{3x}=\dfrac{3x}{3x}\cdot\dfrac{x}{4(x-1)}-\dfrac{1}{3x}\cdot\dfrac{4(x-1)}{4(x-1)}$

$\qquad\qquad=\dfrac{3x^2}{12x(x-1)}-\dfrac{4(x-1)}{12x(x-1)}$

$\qquad\qquad=\dfrac{3x^2-4x+4}{12x(x-1)}$

41. $\dfrac{3}{2w+10}+\dfrac{6}{w+2}$

$\qquad=\dfrac{w+2}{w+2}\cdot\dfrac{3}{2(w+5)}+\dfrac{6}{w+2}\cdot\dfrac{2(w+5)}{2(w+5)}$

$\qquad=\dfrac{3(w+2)}{2(w+2)(w+5)}+\dfrac{12(w+5)}{2(w+2)(w+5)}$

$\qquad=\dfrac{3w+6+12w+60}{2(w+2)(w+5)}$

$\qquad=\dfrac{15w+66}{2(w+2)(w+5)}$

42. $\dfrac{5k}{4k-8} - \dfrac{k}{k+2}$

$= \dfrac{k+2}{k+2} \cdot \dfrac{5k}{4(k-2)} - \dfrac{k}{k+2} \cdot \dfrac{4(k-2)}{4(k-2)}$

$= \dfrac{5k(k+2)}{4(k+2)(k-2)} - \dfrac{4k(k-2)}{4(k+2)(k-2)}$

$= \dfrac{5k^2 + 10k - 4k^2 + 8k}{4(k+2)(k-2)}$

$= \dfrac{k^2 + 18k}{4(k+2)(k-2)}$

43. $\dfrac{z}{z^2-16} + \dfrac{4}{z+4} = \dfrac{z}{(z+4)(z-4)} + \dfrac{4}{(z+4)} \cdot \dfrac{z-4}{z-4}$

$= \dfrac{z+4z-16}{(z+4)(z-4)}$

$= \dfrac{5z-16}{(z+4)(z-4)}$

44. $\dfrac{5}{(x+4)^2} + \dfrac{3}{x+4} = \dfrac{5}{(x+4)^2} + \dfrac{3}{x+4} \cdot \dfrac{x+4}{x+4}$

$= \dfrac{5}{(x+4)^2} + \dfrac{3(x+4)}{(x+4)^2}$

$= \dfrac{5+3x+12}{(x+4)^2}$

$= \dfrac{3x+17}{(x+4)^2}$

45. $\dfrac{x+2}{x^2-4} - \dfrac{2}{x+2} = \dfrac{x+2}{(x+2)(x-2)} - \dfrac{2}{x+2} \cdot \dfrac{x-2}{x-2}$

$= \dfrac{x+2}{(x+2)(x-2)} - \dfrac{2(x-2)}{(x+2)(x-2)}$

$= \dfrac{x+2-(2x-4)}{(x+2)(x-2)}$

$= \dfrac{x+2-2x+4}{(x+2)(x-2)}$

$= \dfrac{-x+6}{(x+2)(x-2)}$

46. $\dfrac{3}{(x-2)(x+3)} + \dfrac{5}{(x+2)(x+3)}$

$= \dfrac{x+2}{x+2} \cdot \dfrac{3}{(x-2)(x+3)} + \dfrac{5}{(x+2)(x+3)} \cdot \dfrac{x-2}{x-2}$

$= \dfrac{3(x+2)}{(x+2)(x-2)(x+3)} + \dfrac{5(x-2)}{(x+2)(x-2)(x+3)}$

$= \dfrac{3x+6+5x-10}{(x+2)(x-2)(x+3)}$

$= \dfrac{8x-4}{(x+2)(x-2)(x+3)}$

47. $\dfrac{3r+4}{r^2-10r+24} - \dfrac{2}{r-6}$

$= \dfrac{3r+4}{(r-6)(r-4)} - \dfrac{2}{r-6} \cdot \dfrac{r-4}{r-4}$

$= \dfrac{3r+4}{(r-6)(r-4)} - \dfrac{2(r-4)}{(r-6)(r-4)}$

$= \dfrac{3r+4-(2r-4)}{(r-6)(r-4)}$

$= \dfrac{3r+4-2r+8}{(r-6)(r-4)}$

$= \dfrac{r+12}{(r-6)(r-4)}$

48. $\dfrac{x+9}{x^2-3x-10} - \dfrac{2}{x-5}$

$= \dfrac{x+9}{(x-5)(x+2)} - \dfrac{2}{x-5} \cdot \dfrac{x+2}{x+2}$

$= \dfrac{x+9}{(x-5)(x+2)} - \dfrac{2(x+2)}{(x-5)(x+2)}$

$= \dfrac{x+9-(2x+4)}{(x-5)(x+2)}$

$= \dfrac{x+9-2x-4}{(x-5)(x+2)}$

$= \dfrac{-x+5}{(x-5)(x+2)}$

49. $\dfrac{x^2-3}{x^2+2x-8}-\dfrac{x-4}{x+4}$

$=\dfrac{x^2-3}{(x+4)(x-2)}-\dfrac{x-4}{x+4}\cdot\dfrac{x-2}{x-2}$

$=\dfrac{x^2-3}{(x+4)(x-2)}-\dfrac{(x-4)(x-2)}{(x+4)(x-2)}$

$=\dfrac{x^2-3-\left(x^2-6x+8\right)}{(x+4)(x-2)}$

$=\dfrac{x^2-3-x^2+6x-8}{(x+4)(x-2)}$

$=\dfrac{6x-11}{(x+4)(x-2)}$

50. $\dfrac{x+8}{x^2-4x+4}-\dfrac{x+1}{x-2}$

$=\dfrac{x+8}{(x-2)^2}-\dfrac{x+1}{x-2}\cdot\dfrac{x-2}{x-2}$

$=\dfrac{x+8}{(x-2)^2}-\dfrac{(x+1)(x-2)}{(x-2)^2}$

$=\dfrac{x+8-(x^2-x-2)}{(x-2)^2}$

$=\dfrac{x+8-x^2+x+2}{(x-2)^2}$

$=\dfrac{-x^2+2x+10}{(x-2)^2}$

51. $\dfrac{x-6}{x^2+10x+25}+\dfrac{x-3}{x+5}$

$=\dfrac{x-6}{(x+5)^2}+\dfrac{x-3}{x+5}\cdot\dfrac{x+5}{x+5}$

$=\dfrac{x-6}{(x+5)^2}+\dfrac{(x-3)(x+5)}{(x+5)^2}$

$=\dfrac{x-6+x^2+2x-15}{(x+5)^2}$

$=\dfrac{x^2+3x-21}{(x+5)^2}$

52. $\dfrac{x}{x^2-xy}-\dfrac{y}{xy-x^2}=\dfrac{x}{x(x-y)}-\dfrac{y}{x(y-x)}\cdot\dfrac{-1}{-1}$

$=\dfrac{x}{x(x-y)}-\dfrac{-y}{x(x-y)}$

$=\dfrac{x+y}{x(x-y)}$

53. $\dfrac{5}{a^2-9a+8}-\dfrac{6}{a^2-6a-16}$

$=\dfrac{a+2}{a+2}\cdot\dfrac{5}{(a-8)(a-1)}-\dfrac{6}{(a-8)(a+2)}\cdot\dfrac{a-1}{a-1}$

$=\dfrac{5(a+2)}{(a-8)(a-1)(a+2)}-\dfrac{6(a-1)}{(a-8)(a-1)(a+2)}$

$=\dfrac{5a+10-(6a-6)}{(a-8)(a-1)(a+2)}$

$=\dfrac{5a+10-6a+6}{(a-8)(a-1)(a+2)}$

$=\dfrac{-a+16}{(a-8)(a-1)(a+2)}$

54. $\dfrac{4}{a^2+2a-15}-\dfrac{1}{a^2-9}$

$=\dfrac{a+3}{a+3}\cdot\dfrac{4}{(a+5)(a-3)}-\dfrac{1}{(a+3)(a-3)}\cdot\dfrac{a+5}{a+5}$

$=\dfrac{4(a+3)}{(a+5)(a-3)(a+3)}-\dfrac{a+5}{(a+5)(a-3)(a+3)}$

$=\dfrac{4a+12-a-5}{(a+5)(a-3)(a+3)}$

$=\dfrac{3a+7}{(a+5)(a-3)(a+3)}$

55. $\dfrac{2}{x^2+6x+9}+\dfrac{7}{x^2+x-6}$

$=\dfrac{x-2}{x-2}\cdot\dfrac{2}{(x+3)(x+3)}+\dfrac{7}{(x+3)(x-2)}\cdot\dfrac{x+3}{x+3}$

$=\dfrac{2(x-2)}{(x+3)(x+3)(x-2)}+\dfrac{7(x+3)}{(x+3)(x+3)(x-2)}$

$=\dfrac{2x-4+7x+21}{(x+3)(x+3)(x-2)}$

$=\dfrac{9x+17}{(x+3)^2(x-2)}$

56. $\dfrac{x}{2x^2+7x-4}+\dfrac{4}{x^2-x-20}$

$=\dfrac{x-5}{x-5}\cdot\dfrac{x}{(2x-1)(x+4)}+\dfrac{4}{(x+4)(x-5)}\cdot\dfrac{2x-1}{2x-1}$

$=\dfrac{x(x-5)}{(2x-1)(x+4)(x-5)}+\dfrac{4(2x-1)}{(2x-1)(x+4)(x-5)}$

$=\dfrac{x^2-5x+8x-4}{(2x-1)(x+4)(x-5)}$

$=\dfrac{x^2+3x-4}{(2x-1)(x+4)(x-5)}$

57. $\dfrac{x}{2x^2+7x+3}-\dfrac{5}{3x^2+7x-6}$

$=\dfrac{3x-2}{3x-2}\cdot\dfrac{x}{(2x+1)(x+3)}-\dfrac{5}{(3x-2)(x+3)}\cdot\dfrac{2x+1}{2x+1}$

$=\dfrac{x(3x-2)}{(2x+1)(3x-2)(x+3)}-\dfrac{5(2x+1)}{(2x+1)(3x-2)(x+3)}$

$=\dfrac{3x^2-2x-(10x+5)}{(2x+1)(3x-2)(x+3)}$

$=\dfrac{3x^2-2x-10x-5}{(2x+1)(3x-2)(x+3)}$

$=\dfrac{3x^2-12x-5}{(2x+1)(3x-2)(x+3)}$

58. $\dfrac{x}{6x^2+7x+2}+\dfrac{5}{2x^2-3x-2}$

$=\dfrac{x-2}{x-2}\cdot\dfrac{x}{(3x+2)(2x+1)}+\dfrac{5}{(2x+1)(x-2)}\cdot\dfrac{3x+2}{3x+2}$

$=\dfrac{x(x-2)}{(3x+2)(2x+1)(x-2)}+\dfrac{5(3x+2)}{(3x+2)(2x+1)(x-2)}$

$=\dfrac{x^2-2x+15x+10}{(3x+2)(2x+1)(x-2)}$

$=\dfrac{x^2+13x+10}{(3x+2)(2x+1)(x-2)}$

59. $\dfrac{x}{4x^2+11x+6}-\dfrac{2}{8x^2+2x-3}$

$=\dfrac{2x-1}{2x-1}\cdot\dfrac{x}{(4x+3)(x+2)}-\dfrac{2}{(4x+3)(2x-1)}\cdot\dfrac{x+2}{x+2}$

$=\dfrac{x(2x-1)}{(4x+3)(x+2)(2x-1)}-\dfrac{2(x+2)}{(4x+3)(x+2)(2x-1)}$

$=\dfrac{2x^2-x-(2x+4)}{(4x+3)(x+2)(2x-1)}$

$=\dfrac{2x^2-x-2x-4}{(4x+3)(x+2)(2x-1)}$

$=\dfrac{2x^2-3x-4}{(4x+3)(x+2)(2x-1)}$

60. $\dfrac{x}{5x^2-9x-2}-\dfrac{1}{3x^2-7x+2}$

$=\dfrac{3x-1}{3x-1}\cdot\dfrac{x}{(5x+1)(x-2)}-\dfrac{1}{(3x-1)(x-2)}\cdot\dfrac{5x+1}{5x+1}$

$=\dfrac{x(3x-1)}{(5x+1)(x-2)(3x-1)}-\dfrac{1(5x+1)}{(5x+1)(x-2)(3x-1)}$

$=\dfrac{3x^2-x-(5x+1)}{(5x+1)(x-2)(3x-1)}$

$=\dfrac{3x^2-x-5x-1}{(5x+1)(x-2)(3x-1)}$

$=\dfrac{3x^2-6x-1}{(5x+1)(x-2)(3x-1)}$

61. $\dfrac{3w+12}{w^2+w-12}-\dfrac{2}{w-3}=\dfrac{3(w+4)}{(w-3)(w+4)}-\dfrac{2}{w-3}$

$=\dfrac{3\cancel{(w+4)}}{(w-3)\cancel{(w+4)}}-\dfrac{2}{w-3}$

$=\dfrac{3}{w-3}-\dfrac{2}{w-3}$

$=\dfrac{1}{w-3}$

62. $\dfrac{5x+10}{x^2-5x-14}-\dfrac{4}{x-7}=\dfrac{5(x+2)}{(x+2)(x-7)}-\dfrac{4}{x-7}$

$$=\dfrac{5(x+2)}{(x+2)(x-7)}-\dfrac{4}{x-7}$$

$$=\dfrac{5}{x-7}-\dfrac{4}{x-7}$$

$$=\dfrac{1}{x-7}$$

63. $\dfrac{4r}{2r^2-10r+12}+\dfrac{4}{r-2}$

$$=\dfrac{4r}{2(r^2-5r+6)}+\dfrac{4}{r-2}$$

$$=\dfrac{2\cdot 2r}{2(r-3)(r-2)}+\dfrac{4}{r-2}\cdot\dfrac{r-3}{r-3}$$

$$=\dfrac{2r}{(r-3)(r-2)}+\dfrac{4r-12}{(r-3)(r-2)}$$

$$=\dfrac{6r-12}{(r-3)(r-2)}$$

$$=\dfrac{6(r-2)}{(r-3)(r-2)}$$

$$=\dfrac{6}{(r-3)}$$

64. $\dfrac{6m}{3m^2-24m+48}-\dfrac{2}{m-4}$

$$=\dfrac{6m}{3(m^2-8m+16)}-\dfrac{2}{m-4}$$

$$=\dfrac{3\cdot 2m}{3(m-4)(m-4)}-\dfrac{2}{m-4}$$

$$=\dfrac{2m}{(m-4)(m-4)}-\dfrac{2}{m-4}\cdot\dfrac{m-4}{m-4}$$

$$=\dfrac{2m}{(m-4)(m-4)}-\dfrac{2m-8}{(m-4)(m-4)}$$

$$=\dfrac{2m-2m+8}{(m-4)(m-4)}$$

$$=\dfrac{8}{(m-4)^2}$$

65. $\dfrac{4}{x^2-4x}-\dfrac{x}{4x-16}$

$$=\dfrac{4}{x(x-4)}-\dfrac{x}{4(x-4)}$$

$$=\dfrac{4}{4}\cdot\dfrac{4}{x(x-4)}-\dfrac{x}{4(x-4)}\cdot\dfrac{x}{x}$$

$$=\dfrac{16}{4x(x-4)}-\dfrac{x^2}{4x(x-4)}$$

$$=\dfrac{16-x^2}{4x(x-4)}$$

$$=\dfrac{-1(x+4)(x-4)}{4x(x-4)}$$

$$=-\dfrac{x+4}{4x}$$

66. $\dfrac{6}{x^2-6x}-\dfrac{x}{6x-36}$

$$=\dfrac{6}{x(x-6)}-\dfrac{x}{6(x-6)}$$

$$=\dfrac{6}{6}\cdot\dfrac{6}{x(x-4)}-\dfrac{x}{6(x-6)}\cdot\dfrac{x}{x}$$

$$=\dfrac{36}{6x(x-4)}-\dfrac{x^2}{6x(x-4)}$$

$$=\dfrac{36-x^2}{6x(x-4)}$$

$$=\dfrac{-1(x+6)(x-6)}{6x(x-6)}$$

$$=-\dfrac{x+6}{6x}$$

67. $\dfrac{8}{x}+6$ is defined for all real numbers except $x=0$

68. $\dfrac{6}{x-1}-\dfrac{5}{x}$
$x-1=0$ when $x=1$
The expression is defined for all real numbers except $x=1$ and $x=0$.

69. $\dfrac{3}{x-4} + \dfrac{7}{x+6}$

$x - 4 = 0$ when $x = 4$ and $x + 6 = 0$ when $x = -6$
The expression is defined for all real
numbers except $x = 4$ and $x = -6$.

70. $\dfrac{4}{x^2-9} - \dfrac{9}{x+3} = \dfrac{4}{(x+3)(x-3)} - \dfrac{9}{x+3}$

$x + 3 = 0$ when $x = -3$ and $x - 3 = 0$ when $x = 3$
The expression is defined for all real numbers
except $x = -3$ and $x = 3$.

71. $\dfrac{3}{\Delta-2} - \dfrac{4}{2-\Delta} = \dfrac{3}{\Delta-2} + \dfrac{4}{\Delta-2}$

$\qquad = \dfrac{3+4}{\Delta-2}$

$\qquad = \dfrac{7}{\Delta-2}$

72. $\dfrac{\Delta}{2\Delta^2+7\Delta-4} + \dfrac{2}{\Delta^2-\Delta-20}$

$= \dfrac{\Delta}{(2\Delta-1)(\Delta+4)} + \dfrac{2}{(\Delta+4)(\Delta-5)}$

$= \dfrac{\Delta(\Delta-5)}{(2\Delta-1)(\Delta+4)(\Delta-5)} + \dfrac{2(2\Delta-1)}{(2\Delta-1)(\Delta+4)(\Delta-5)}$

$= \dfrac{\Delta^2-5\Delta+4\Delta-2}{(2\Delta-1)(\Delta+4)(\Delta-5)}$

$= \dfrac{\Delta^2-\Delta-2}{(2\Delta-1)(\Delta+4)(\Delta-5)}$

73. $\dfrac{5}{a+b} + \dfrac{4}{a}$

$a + b = 0$ when $a = -b$. The expression is defined
for all real numbers except $a = 0$ and $a = -b$.

74. $\dfrac{x+2}{x+5y} - \dfrac{y-3}{2x}$

$x + 5y = 0$ when $x = -5y$. The expression is
defined for all real numbers except $x = 0$ and
$x = -5y$.

75. $\dfrac{x}{x^2-9} + \dfrac{2x}{x+3} + \dfrac{2x^2-5x}{9-x^2}$

$= \dfrac{x}{x^2-9} + \dfrac{2x}{x+3} + \dfrac{2x^2-5x}{-1(x^2-9)}$

$= \dfrac{x}{(x+3)(x-3)} + \dfrac{2x}{(x+3)} \cdot \dfrac{x-3}{x-3} - \dfrac{2x^2-5x}{(x+3)(x-3)}$

$= \dfrac{x+2x^2-6x-(2x^2-5x)}{(x+3)(x-3)}$

$= \dfrac{x+2x^2-6x-2x^2+5x}{(x+3)(x-3)} = \dfrac{0}{(x+3)(x-3)}$

$= 0$

76. $\dfrac{8x+9}{x^2+x-6} + \dfrac{x}{x+3} - \dfrac{5}{x-2}$

$= \dfrac{8x+9}{(x+3)(x-2)} + \dfrac{x}{x+3} - \dfrac{5}{x-2}$

$= \dfrac{8x+9}{(x+3)(x-2)} + \dfrac{x}{x+3} \cdot \dfrac{x-2}{x-2} - \dfrac{5}{x-2} \cdot \dfrac{x+3}{x+3}$

$= \dfrac{8x+9+x^2-2x-(5x+15)}{(x+3)(x-2)}$

$= \dfrac{8x+9+x^2-2x-5x-15}{(x+3)(x-2)}$

$= \dfrac{x^2+x-6}{(x+3)(x-2)} = \dfrac{(x+3)\cancel{(x-2)}}{(x+3)\cancel{(x-2)}}$

$= 1$

77. $\dfrac{x+6}{4-x^2} - \dfrac{x+3}{x+2} + \dfrac{x-3}{2-x}$

$= \dfrac{x+6}{(2-x)(2+x)} - \dfrac{x+3}{x+2} + \dfrac{x-3}{2-x}$

$= \dfrac{x+6}{(2-x)(2+x)} - \dfrac{x+3}{x+2} \cdot \dfrac{2-x}{2-x} + \dfrac{x-3}{2-x} \cdot \dfrac{x+2}{x+2}$

$= \dfrac{x+6-(2x-x^2+6-3x)+(x^2-x-6)}{(2-x)(2+x)}$

$= \dfrac{x+6+x^2+x-6+x^2-x-6}{(2-x)(2+x)}$

$= \dfrac{2x^2+x-6}{(2-x)(2+x)} = \dfrac{(2x-3)\cancel{(x+2)}}{(2-x)\cancel{(2+x)}}$

$= \dfrac{2x-3}{2-x}$

78. $\dfrac{3x-1}{x+2}+\dfrac{x}{x-3}-\dfrac{4}{2x+3}=\dfrac{(3x-1)(x-3)(2x+3)}{(x+2)(x-3)(2x+3)}+\dfrac{x(x+2)(2x+3)}{(x+2)(x-3)(2x+3)}-\dfrac{4(x+2)(x-3)}{(x+2)(x-3)(2x+3)}$

$$=\dfrac{\left(6x^3-11x^2-24x+9\right)+\left(2x^3+7x^2+6x\right)-\left(4x^2-4x-24\right)}{(x+2)(x-3)(2x+3)}$$

$$=\dfrac{6x^3-11x^2-24x+9+2x^3+7x^2+6x-4x^2+4x+24}{(x+2)(x-3)(2x+3)}$$

$$=\dfrac{8x^3-8x^2-14x+33}{(x+2)(x-3)(2x+3)}$$

79. $\dfrac{2}{x^2-x-6}+\dfrac{3}{x^2-2x-3}+\dfrac{1}{x^2+3x+2}=\dfrac{2}{(x+2)(x-3)}+\dfrac{3}{(x-3)(x+1)}+\dfrac{1}{(x+2)(x+1)}$

$$=\dfrac{2(x+1)}{(x+2)(x-3)(x+1)}+\dfrac{3(x+2)}{(x+2)(x-3)(x+1)}+\dfrac{x-3}{(x+2)(x-3)(x+1)}$$

$$=\dfrac{2x+2+3x+6+x-3}{(x+2)(x-3)(x+1)}$$

$$=\dfrac{6x+5}{(x+2)(x-3)(x+1)}$$

80. $\dfrac{3x}{x^2-4}+\dfrac{4}{x^3+8}=\dfrac{3}{(x+2)(x-2)}+\dfrac{4}{(x+2)(x^2-2x+4)}$

$$=\dfrac{3x\left(x^2-2x+4\right)}{(x+2)(x-2)\left(x^2-2x+4\right)}+\dfrac{4(x-2)}{(x+2)(x-2)\left(x^2-2x+4\right)}$$

$$=\dfrac{3x^3-6x^2+12x+4x-8}{(x+2)(x-2)\left(x^2-2x+4\right)}$$

$$=\dfrac{3x^3-6x^2+16x-8}{(x+2)(x-2)\left(x^2-2x+4\right)}$$

81. a. $\dfrac{x+3y}{x^2+3xy+2y^2}+\dfrac{y-x}{2x^2+3xy+y^2}=\dfrac{x+3y}{(x+y)(x+2y)}+\dfrac{y-x}{(2x+y)(x+y)}$

The LCD is $(x+y)(x+2y)(2x+y)$.

b. $\dfrac{x+3y}{x^2+3xy+2y^2}+\dfrac{y-x}{2x^2+3xy+y^2}=\dfrac{x+3y}{(x+y)(x+2y)}+\dfrac{y-x}{(2x+y)(x+y)}$

$$=\dfrac{2x+y}{2x+y}\cdot\dfrac{x+3y}{(x+y)(x+2y)}+\dfrac{y-x}{(2x+y)(x+y)}\cdot\dfrac{x+2y}{x+2y}$$

$$=\dfrac{(2x+y)(x+3y)}{(2x+y)(x+y)(x+2y)}+\dfrac{(y-x)(x+2y)}{(2x+y)(x+y)(x+2y)}$$

c. $\dfrac{x+3y}{x^2+3xy+2y^2} + \dfrac{y-x}{2x^2+3xy+y^2} = \dfrac{x+3y}{(x+y)(x+2y)} + \dfrac{y-x}{(2x+y)(x+y)}$

$$= \frac{2x+y}{2x+y} \cdot \frac{x+3y}{(x+y)(x+2y)} + \frac{y-x}{(2x+y)(x+y)} \cdot \frac{x+2y}{x+2y}$$

$$= \frac{(2x+y)(x+3y)}{(2x+y)(x+y)(x+2y)} + \frac{(y-x)(x+2y)}{(2x+y)(x+y)(x+2y)}$$

$$= \frac{2x^2+7xy+3y^2+-xy+2y^2-x^2}{(2x+y)(x+y)(x+2y)}$$

$$= \frac{x^2+6xy+5y^2}{(2x+y)(x+y)(x+2y)}$$

$$= \frac{\cancel{(x+y)}(x+5y)}{(2x+y)\cancel{(x+y)}(x+2y)}$$

$$= \frac{x+5y}{(2x+y)(x+2y)}$$

d. $\dfrac{x+3y}{x^2+3xy+2y^2} = \dfrac{2+3(1)}{2^2+3(2)(1)+2(1)^2} = \dfrac{2+3}{4+6+2} = \dfrac{5}{12}$

e. $\dfrac{y-x}{2x^2+3xy+y^2} = \dfrac{1-2}{2(2)^2+3(2)(1)+1^2} = \dfrac{-1}{8+6+1} = -\dfrac{1}{15}$

f. $\dfrac{5}{12} + \left(-\dfrac{1}{15}\right) = \dfrac{5}{3\cdot4} - \dfrac{1}{3\cdot5} = \dfrac{5}{5}\cdot\dfrac{5}{3\cdot4} - \dfrac{1}{3\cdot5}\cdot\dfrac{4}{4} = \dfrac{25}{60} - \dfrac{4}{60} = \dfrac{21}{60} = \dfrac{7}{20}$

g. $\dfrac{(2x+y)(x+3y)}{(2x+y)(x+y)(x+2y)} + \dfrac{(y-x)(x+2y)}{(2x+y)(x+y)(x+2y)}$

$$= \frac{(2(2)+1)(2+3(1))}{(2(2)+1)(2+1)(2+2(1))} + \frac{(1-2)(2+2(1))}{(2(2)+1)(2+1)(2+2(1))}$$

$$= \frac{5\cdot5}{5\cdot3\cdot4} + \frac{-1\cdot4}{5\cdot3\cdot4}$$

$$= \frac{25}{60} + \frac{-4}{60}$$

$$= \frac{21}{60} = \frac{7}{20}$$

h. $\dfrac{x+5y}{(2x+y)(x+2y)} = \dfrac{2+5(1)}{(2(2)+1)(2+2(1))} = \dfrac{7}{5\cdot4} = \dfrac{7}{20}$

i. The simplified answer is equivalent to the unsimplified answer.

j. Yes.

82. Let $x =$ the number of hours it takes the train to travel 42 miles.

$$\frac{22 \text{ miles}}{0.8 \text{ hours}} = \frac{42 \text{ miles}}{x \text{ hours}}$$

$$22x = 0.8(42)$$

$$22x = 33.6$$

$$x \approx 1.53$$

It takes about 1.53 hours for the train to travel 42 miles.

83. $m = \dfrac{-2-6}{3-(-4)} = \dfrac{-8}{7} = -\dfrac{8}{7}$

84.
$$2x+3 \overline{\smash{\big)}\, 8x^2 + 6x - 15}$$
$$\begin{array}{r} 4x-3 \\ \underline{8x^2 + 12x} \\ -6x - 15 \\ \underline{-6x-\ 9} \\ -\ 6 \end{array}$$

$$(8x^2 + 6x - 15) \div (2x+3) = 4x - 3 - \frac{6}{2x+3}$$

85. $\dfrac{x^2 + xy - 6y^2}{x^2 - xy - 2y^2} \cdot \dfrac{y^2 - x^2}{x^2 + 2xy - 3y^2}$

$= \dfrac{(x+3y)(x-2y)}{(x+y)(x-2y)} \cdot \dfrac{-1(x-y)(x+y)}{(x+3y)(x-y)}$

$= -1$

Mid-Chapter Test: 7.1-7.4

1. $\dfrac{9}{3x-2}$

$3x - 2 = 0$ when $x = \dfrac{2}{3}$

The expression is defined for all real numbers except $x = \dfrac{2}{3}$.

2. $\dfrac{2x+1}{x^2 - 5x - 14}$

$x^2 - 5x - 14 = 0$

$(x-7)(x+2) = 0$

$x - 7 = 0$ or $x + 2 = 0$

$x = 7 \qquad\qquad x = -2$

The expression is defined for all real numbers except $x = 7, x = -2$.

3. $\dfrac{9x+18}{x+2} = \dfrac{9(x+2)}{(x+2)} = 9$

4. $\dfrac{2x^2 + 13x + 15}{3x^2 + 14x - 5} = \dfrac{(2x+3)(x+5)}{(3x-1)(x+5)} = \dfrac{2x+3}{3x-1}$

5. $\dfrac{25r^2 - 36t^2}{5r - 6t} = \dfrac{(5r+6t)(5r-6t)}{(5r-6t)} = 5r + 6t$

6. $\dfrac{15x^2}{2y} \cdot \dfrac{4y^4}{5x^5} = \dfrac{3 \cdot \cancel{5} \cdot \cancel{x}}{\cancel{2}\cancel{y}} \cdot \dfrac{2 \cdot \cancel{2} \cdot y^3 \cdot \cancel{y}}{\cancel{5} \cdot x^3 \cdot \cancel{x}} = \dfrac{6y^3}{x^3}$

7. $\dfrac{m-3}{m+4} \cdot \dfrac{m^2 + 8m + 16}{3-m}$

$= \dfrac{\cancel{m-3}}{\cancel{m+4}} \cdot \dfrac{(m+4)(m+4)}{-1(m-3)}$

$= -(m+4)$ or $-m - 4$

8. $\dfrac{x^3 + 27}{x^2 - 2x - 15} \cdot \dfrac{x^2 - 7x + 10}{x^2 - 3x + 9}$

$= \dfrac{(x+3)(x^2-3x+9)}{(x-5)(x+3)} \cdot \dfrac{(x-5)(x-2)}{(x^2-3x+9)}$

$= x - 2$

9. $\dfrac{5x-1}{x^2 + 11x + 10} \div \dfrac{10x-2}{x^2 + 17x + 70}$

$= \dfrac{5x-1}{x^2 + 11x + 10} \cdot \dfrac{x^2 + 17x + 70}{10x - 2}$

$= \dfrac{\cancel{5x-1}}{(x+10)(x+1)} \cdot \dfrac{(x+10)(x+7)}{2(5x-1)}$

$= \dfrac{x+7}{2(x+1)}$

10. $\dfrac{5x^2 + 7x + 2}{x^2 + 6x + 5} \div \dfrac{7x^2 - 39x - 18}{x^2 - x - 30}$

$= \dfrac{5x^2 + 7x + 2}{x^2 + 6x + 5} \cdot \dfrac{x^2 - x - 30}{7x^2 - 39x - 18}$

$= \dfrac{(5x+2)(x+1)}{(x+5)(x+1)} \cdot \dfrac{(x-6)(x+5)}{(7x+3)(x-6)}$

$= \dfrac{5x+2}{7x+3}$

Chapter 7: Rational Expressions and Equations

11. $\dfrac{x^2}{x+6} - \dfrac{36}{x+6} = \dfrac{x^2-36}{x+6}$

$\qquad = \dfrac{\cancel{(x+6)}(x-6)}{\cancel{(x+6)}}$

$\qquad = x-6$

12. $\dfrac{2x^2-2x}{2x+5} + \dfrac{x-15}{2x+5} = \dfrac{2x^2-2x+x-15}{2x+5}$

$\qquad = \dfrac{2x^2-x-15}{2x+5}$

$\qquad = \dfrac{\cancel{(2x+5)}(x-3)}{\cancel{(2x+5)}}$

$\qquad = x-3$

13. $\dfrac{3x^2-x}{4x^2-9x+2} - \dfrac{3x+4}{4x^2-9x+2} = \dfrac{3x^2-x-3x-4}{4x^2-9x+2}$

$\qquad = \dfrac{3x^2-4x-4}{4x^2-9x+2}$

$\qquad = \dfrac{(3x+2)\cancel{(x-2)}}{(4x-1)\cancel{(x-2)}}$

$\qquad = \dfrac{3x+2}{4x-1}$

14. $\dfrac{2m}{6m^2+3m} + \dfrac{m+7}{2m+1} = \dfrac{2m}{3m(2m+1)} + \dfrac{m+7}{2m+1}$

The LCD is $3m(2m+1)$.

15. $\dfrac{9x+8}{2x^2-5x-12} + \dfrac{2x+3}{x^2-9x+20}$

$\qquad = \dfrac{9x+8}{(2x+3)(x-4)} + \dfrac{2x+3}{(x-5)(x-4)}$

The LCD is $(2x+3)(x-4)(x-5)$.

16. $\dfrac{x+1}{2x} + \dfrac{4x-3}{5x} = \dfrac{5}{5}\cdot\dfrac{x+1}{2x} + \dfrac{4x-3}{5x}\cdot\dfrac{2}{2}$

$\qquad = \dfrac{5x+5}{10x} + \dfrac{8x-6}{10x}$

$\qquad = \dfrac{5x+5+8x-6}{10x}$

$\qquad = \dfrac{13x-1}{10x}$

17. $\dfrac{2a+5}{a+3} - \dfrac{3a+1}{a-4}$

$\qquad = \dfrac{a-4}{a-4}\cdot\dfrac{2a+5}{a+3} - \dfrac{3a+1}{a-4}\cdot\dfrac{a+3}{a+3}$

$\qquad = \dfrac{(a-4)(2a+5)}{(a-4)(a+3)} - \dfrac{(3a+1)(a+3)}{(a-4)(a+3)}$

$\qquad = \dfrac{2a^2-3a-20}{(a-4)(a+3)} - \dfrac{3a^2+10a+3}{(a-4)(a+3)}$

$\qquad = \dfrac{2a^2-3a-20-3a^2-10a-3}{(a-4)(a+3)}$

$\qquad = \dfrac{-a^2-13a-23}{(a-4)(a+3)} = \dfrac{-1(a^2+13a+23)}{a^2-a-12}$

$\qquad = -\dfrac{a^2+13a+23}{a^2-a-12}$

18. $\dfrac{x^2+5}{2x^2+13x+6} + \dfrac{3x-1}{2x+1}$

$\qquad = \dfrac{x^2+5}{(2x+1)(x+6)} + \dfrac{3x-1}{2x+1}$

$\qquad = \dfrac{x^2+5}{(2x+1)(x+6)} + \dfrac{3x-1}{2x+1}\cdot\dfrac{x+6}{x+6}$

$\qquad = \dfrac{x^2+5}{(2x+1)(x+6)} + \dfrac{3x^2+17x-6}{(2x+1)(x+6)}$

$\qquad = \dfrac{x^2+5+3x^2+17x-6}{(2x+1)(x+6)}$

$\qquad = \dfrac{4x^2+17x-1}{2x^2+13x+6}$

19. $\dfrac{x}{x^2+3x+2} - \dfrac{4}{x^2-x-6}$

$\qquad = \dfrac{x}{(x+2)(x+1)} - \dfrac{4}{(x-3)(x+2)}$

$\qquad = \dfrac{x-3}{x-3}\cdot\dfrac{x}{(x+2)(x+1)} - \dfrac{4}{(x-3)(x+2)}\cdot\dfrac{x+1}{x+1}$

$\qquad = \dfrac{x^2-3x}{(x-3)(x+2)(x+1)} - \dfrac{4x+4}{(x-3)(x+2)(x+1)}$

$\qquad = \dfrac{x^2-3x-4x-4}{(x-3)(x+2)(x+1)}$

$\qquad = \dfrac{x^2-7x-4}{(x-3)(x+2)(x+1)}$

324

20. To add these fractions a common denominator of $x(x+1)$ is needed.

$$\frac{7}{x+1}+\frac{8}{x}=\frac{x}{x}\cdot\frac{7}{x+1}+\frac{8}{x}\cdot\frac{x+1}{x+1}$$

$$=\frac{7x}{x(x+1)}+\frac{8x+8}{x(x+1)}$$

$$=\frac{7x+8x+8}{x(x+1)}$$

$$=\frac{15x+8}{x(x+1)}$$

Exercise Set 7.5

1. A complex fraction is a fraction whose numerator or denominator (or both) contains a fraction.

2. a. $\dfrac{5}{\dfrac{3}{x^2+5x+6}}$

Numerator, 5

Denominator, $\dfrac{3}{x^2+5x+6}$

b. $\dfrac{\dfrac{5}{3}}{x^2+5x+6}$

Numerator, $\dfrac{5}{3}$

Denominator, x^2+5x+6

3. a. $\dfrac{\dfrac{x+9}{4}}{\dfrac{7}{x^2+5x+6}}$

Numerator: $\dfrac{x+9}{4}$

Denominator: $\dfrac{7}{x^2+5x+6}$

b. $\dfrac{\dfrac{1}{2y}+x}{\dfrac{3}{y}+x^2}$

Numerator, $\dfrac{1}{2y}+x$

Denominator, $\dfrac{3}{y}+x^2$

4. a. Answers will vary.

b. $\dfrac{\dfrac{4}{x}-\dfrac{3}{y}}{x+\dfrac{1}{y}}$

Least common denominator $= xy$

$$\frac{\left(\dfrac{4}{x}-\dfrac{3}{y}\right)xy}{\left(x+\dfrac{1}{y}\right)xy}=\frac{4y-3x}{x^2y+x}$$

5. $\dfrac{4+\dfrac{2}{3}}{5+\dfrac{1}{3}}=\dfrac{\left(4+\dfrac{2}{3}\right)3}{\left(5+\dfrac{1}{3}\right)3}$

$$=\frac{12+2}{15+1}$$

$$=\frac{14}{16}$$

$$=\frac{7}{8}$$

6. $\dfrac{2+\dfrac{4}{5}}{1-\dfrac{9}{16}}=\dfrac{\left(2+\dfrac{4}{5}\right)80}{\left(1-\dfrac{9}{16}\right)80}=\dfrac{160+64}{80-45}$

$$=\frac{224}{35}$$

7. $\dfrac{2+\dfrac{3}{8}}{1+\dfrac{1}{3}}=\dfrac{\left(2+\dfrac{3}{8}\right)24}{\left(1+\dfrac{1}{3}\right)24}$

$$=\frac{48+9}{24+8}$$

$$=\frac{57}{32}$$

8. $\dfrac{\dfrac{1}{4}+\dfrac{5}{6}}{\dfrac{2}{3}+\dfrac{3}{5}}=\dfrac{\left(\dfrac{1}{4}+\dfrac{5}{6}\right)60}{\left(\dfrac{2}{3}+\dfrac{3}{5}\right)60}=\dfrac{15+50}{40+36}=\dfrac{65}{76}$

9. $\dfrac{\dfrac{2}{3}+\dfrac{1}{4}}{\dfrac{5}{6}-\dfrac{1}{3}}=\dfrac{\left(\dfrac{2}{3}+\dfrac{1}{4}\right)12}{\left(\dfrac{5}{6}-\dfrac{1}{3}\right)12}$

$$=\frac{8+3}{10-4}$$

$$=\frac{11}{6}$$

10. $\dfrac{\dfrac{5}{8}+\dfrac{1}{3}}{\dfrac{11}{12}-\dfrac{1}{6}}=\dfrac{\left(\dfrac{5}{8}+\dfrac{1}{3}\right)24}{\left(\dfrac{11}{12}-\dfrac{1}{6}\right)24}=\dfrac{15+8}{22-4}=\dfrac{23}{18}$

11. $\dfrac{\dfrac{xy^2}{7}}{\dfrac{3}{x^2}}=\dfrac{xy^2}{7}\cdot\dfrac{x^2}{3}=\dfrac{x^3y^2}{21}$

12. $\dfrac{\dfrac{11a}{b^3}}{\dfrac{b^2}{4}}=\dfrac{11a}{b^3}\cdot\dfrac{4}{b^2}=\dfrac{44a}{b^5}$

13. $\dfrac{\dfrac{6a^2b}{7}}{\dfrac{9ac^2}{b^2}}=\dfrac{6a^2b}{7}\cdot\dfrac{b^2}{9ac^2}$

$=\dfrac{6a^2b^3}{63ac^2}$

$=\dfrac{2ab^3}{21c^2}$

14. $\dfrac{\dfrac{18x^4}{5y^4z^5}}{\dfrac{9xy^2}{15z^5}}=\dfrac{18x^4}{5y^4z^5}\cdot\dfrac{15z^5}{9xy^2}$

$=\dfrac{{}^2\cancel{18}\cancel{x}^{\,x^3}}{{}_1\cancel{5}y^4\cancel{z}}\cdot\dfrac{\cancel{15}^3\cancel{z}}{\cancel{9}_1\cancel{x}y^2}$

$=\dfrac{6x^3}{y^6}$

15. $\dfrac{a-\dfrac{a}{b}}{\dfrac{3+a}{b}}=\dfrac{\left(a-\dfrac{a}{b}\right)b}{\left(\dfrac{3+a}{b}\right)b}=\dfrac{ab-a}{3+a}$

16. $\dfrac{a+\dfrac{2}{b}}{\dfrac{a}{b}}=\dfrac{\left(a+\dfrac{2}{b}\right)b}{\dfrac{a}{b}\cdot b}=\dfrac{ab+2}{a}$

17. $\dfrac{\dfrac{9}{x}+\dfrac{3}{x^2}}{3+\dfrac{1}{x}}=\dfrac{\left(\dfrac{9}{x}+\dfrac{3}{x^2}\right)x^2}{\left(3+\dfrac{1}{x}\right)x^2}$

$=\dfrac{9x+3}{3x^2+x}$

$=\dfrac{3(3x+1)}{x(3x+1)}$

$=\dfrac{3}{x}$

18. $\dfrac{\dfrac{4}{a}+\dfrac{1}{2a}}{a+\dfrac{a}{2}}=\dfrac{\left(\dfrac{4}{a}+\dfrac{1}{2a}\right)2a}{\left(a+\dfrac{a}{2}\right)2a}$

$=\dfrac{8+1}{2a^2+a^2}$

$=\dfrac{9}{3a^2}$

$=\dfrac{3}{a^2}$

19. $\dfrac{5-\dfrac{1}{x}}{4-\dfrac{1}{x}}=\dfrac{\left(5-\dfrac{1}{x}\right)x}{\left(4-\dfrac{1}{x}\right)x}=\dfrac{5x-1}{4x-1}$

20. $\dfrac{\dfrac{2x}{x-y}}{\dfrac{x^2}{y}}=\dfrac{2\cancel{x}}{x-y}\cdot\dfrac{y}{\cancel{x}^{\,x}}=\dfrac{2y}{x(x-y)}$

21. $\dfrac{\dfrac{m}{n}-\dfrac{n}{m}}{\dfrac{m+n}{n}}=\dfrac{\left(\dfrac{m}{n}-\dfrac{n}{m}\right)mn}{\left(\dfrac{m+n}{n}\right)mn}$

$=\dfrac{m^2-n^2}{m(m+n)}$

$=\dfrac{\cancel{(m+n)}(m-n)}{m\cancel{(m+n)}}$

$=\dfrac{m-n}{m}$

22. $\dfrac{5}{\dfrac{1}{x}+y}=\dfrac{(5)x}{\left(\dfrac{1}{x}+y\right)x}=\dfrac{5x}{1+xy}$

23. $\dfrac{\dfrac{a^2}{b}-b}{\dfrac{b^2}{a}-a}=\dfrac{\left(\dfrac{a^2}{b}-b\right)ab}{\left(\dfrac{b^2}{a}-a\right)ab}$

$=\dfrac{\left(a^2-b^2\right)a}{\left(b^2-a^2\right)b}$

$=\dfrac{a\left(a^2-b^2\right)}{-b\left(a^2-b^2\right)}$

$=-\dfrac{a}{b}$

24. $\dfrac{\dfrac{1}{x^2}-\dfrac{8}{x}}{3+\dfrac{1}{x^2}}=\dfrac{\left(\dfrac{1}{x^2}-\dfrac{8}{x}\right)x^2}{\left(3+\dfrac{1}{x^2}\right)x^2}=\dfrac{1-8x}{3x^2+1}$

25. $\dfrac{2-\dfrac{a}{b}}{\dfrac{a}{b}-2}=\dfrac{\left(2-\dfrac{a}{b}\right)b}{\left(\dfrac{a}{b}-2\right)b}$

$=\dfrac{2b-a}{a-2b}$

$=\dfrac{-1(-2b+a)}{a-2b}$

$=\dfrac{-1(a-2b)}{(a-2b)}$

$=-1$

26. $\dfrac{\dfrac{x}{y}-9}{-\dfrac{x}{y}+9}=\dfrac{\left(\dfrac{x}{y}-9\right)y}{\left(-\dfrac{x}{y}+9\right)y}$

$=\dfrac{x-9y}{-x+9y}$

$=\dfrac{-1(-x+9y)}{-x+9y}$

$=-1$

27. $\dfrac{\dfrac{4}{x^2}+\dfrac{4}{x}}{\dfrac{4}{x}+\dfrac{4}{x^2}}=\dfrac{\dfrac{4}{x^2}+\dfrac{4}{x}}{\dfrac{4}{x^2}+\dfrac{4}{x}}=1$

28. $\dfrac{\dfrac{a^2-b^2}{a}}{\dfrac{a+b}{a^4}}=\dfrac{a^2-b^2}{a}\cdot\dfrac{a^4}{a+b}$

$=\dfrac{(a+b)(a-b)}{a}\cdot\dfrac{a^4}{a+b}$

$=a^3(a-b)$

29. $\dfrac{\dfrac{1}{a}-\dfrac{1}{b}}{\dfrac{1}{ab}}=\dfrac{\left(\dfrac{1}{a}-\dfrac{1}{b}\right)ab}{\left(\dfrac{1}{ab}\right)ab}=\dfrac{b-a}{1}=b-a$

30. $\dfrac{\dfrac{1}{a}-\dfrac{1}{b}}{\dfrac{1}{a}+\dfrac{1}{b}}=\dfrac{\left(\dfrac{1}{a}-\dfrac{1}{b}\right)ab}{\left(\dfrac{1}{a}+\dfrac{1}{b}\right)ab}=\dfrac{b-a}{b+a}$

31. $\dfrac{\dfrac{a}{b}+\dfrac{1}{a}}{\dfrac{b}{a}+\dfrac{1}{a}}=\dfrac{\left(\dfrac{a}{b}+\dfrac{1}{a}\right)ab}{\left(\dfrac{b}{a}+\dfrac{1}{a}\right)ab}=\dfrac{a^2+b}{b^2+b}=\dfrac{a^2+b}{b(b+1)}$

32. $\dfrac{\dfrac{2}{a}+\dfrac{3}{b}}{\dfrac{1}{a}}=\dfrac{\left(\dfrac{2}{a}+\dfrac{3}{b}\right)ab}{\left(\dfrac{1}{a}\right)ab}=\dfrac{2b+3a}{b}$

33. $\dfrac{x}{\dfrac{1}{x}-\dfrac{1}{y}}=\dfrac{(x)xy}{\left(\dfrac{1}{x}-\dfrac{1}{y}\right)xy}=\dfrac{x^2y}{y-x}$

34. $\dfrac{\dfrac{1}{a}+\dfrac{1}{b}}{ab}=\dfrac{\left(\dfrac{1}{a}+\dfrac{1}{b}\right)ab}{(ab)ab}=\dfrac{b+a}{a^2b^2}$

35. $\dfrac{\dfrac{5}{a}+\dfrac{5}{a^2}}{\dfrac{5}{b}+\dfrac{5}{b^2}}=\dfrac{\left(\dfrac{5}{a}+\dfrac{5}{a^2}\right)a^2b^2}{\left(\dfrac{5}{b}+\dfrac{5}{b^2}\right)a^2b^2}$

$=\dfrac{5ab^2+5b^2}{5a^2b+5a^2}$

$=\dfrac{5b^2(a+1)}{5a^2(b+1)}$

$=\dfrac{ab^2+b^2}{a^2(b+1)}$

36. $\dfrac{\dfrac{x}{y}-\dfrac{2}{x}}{\dfrac{y}{x}+\dfrac{1}{y}}=\dfrac{\left(\dfrac{x}{y}-\dfrac{2}{x}\right)yx}{\left(\dfrac{y}{x}+\dfrac{1}{y}\right)yx}=\dfrac{x^2-2y}{y^2+x}=\dfrac{x^2-2y}{x+y^2}$

37. a. Answers will vary.

b. $\dfrac{5+\dfrac{3}{5}}{\dfrac{1}{8}-4}=\dfrac{\dfrac{25}{5}+\dfrac{3}{5}}{\dfrac{1}{8}-\dfrac{32}{8}}$

$=\dfrac{\dfrac{28}{5}}{-\dfrac{31}{8}}$

$=\dfrac{28}{5}\cdot\left(-\dfrac{8}{31}\right)$

$=-\dfrac{224}{155}$

c. $\dfrac{5+\dfrac{3}{5}}{\dfrac{1}{8}-4}=\dfrac{\left(5+\dfrac{3}{5}\right)40}{\left(\dfrac{1}{8}-4\right)40}=\dfrac{200+24}{5-160}=-\dfrac{224}{155}$

38. a. Answers will vary.

b. $\dfrac{\dfrac{x+y}{x^3}-\dfrac{1}{x}}{\dfrac{x-y}{x^5}+5}=\dfrac{\dfrac{x+y}{x^3}-\dfrac{x^2}{x^3}}{\dfrac{x-y}{x^5}+\dfrac{5x^5}{x^5}}$

$=\dfrac{\dfrac{x+y-x^2}{x^3}}{\dfrac{x-y+5x^5}{x^5}}$

$=\dfrac{x+y-x^2}{\cancel{x^3}}\cdot\dfrac{\cancel{x^5}^{\,x^2}}{x-y+5x^5}$

$=\dfrac{x^2(x+y-x^2)}{x-y+5x^5}$

$=\dfrac{x^3+x^2y-x^4}{x-y+5x^5}$

c. $\dfrac{\dfrac{x+y}{x^3}-\dfrac{1}{x}}{\dfrac{x-y}{x^5}+5}=\dfrac{\left(\dfrac{x+y}{x^3}-\dfrac{1}{x}\right)x^5}{\left(\dfrac{x-y}{x^5}+5\right)x^5}$

$=\dfrac{x^2(x+y)-x^4}{x-y+5x^5}$

$=\dfrac{x^3+x^2y-x^4}{x-y+5x^5}$

39. a. Answers will vary.

b. $\dfrac{\dfrac{x-y}{x+y}+\dfrac{6}{x+y}}{2-\dfrac{7}{x+y}}=\dfrac{\dfrac{x-y+6}{x+y}}{\dfrac{2(x+y)}{x+y}-\dfrac{7}{x+y}}$

$=\dfrac{\dfrac{x-y+6}{x+y}}{\dfrac{2x+2y-7}{x+y}}$

$=\dfrac{x-y+6}{\cancel{x+y}}\cdot\dfrac{\cancel{x+y}}{2x+2y-7}$

$=\dfrac{x-y+6}{2x+2y-7}$

c. $\dfrac{\dfrac{x-y}{x+y}+\dfrac{6}{x+y}}{2-\dfrac{7}{x+y}}=\dfrac{\dfrac{x-y+6}{x+y}}{2-\dfrac{7}{x+y}}$

$=\dfrac{\left(\dfrac{x-y+6}{x+y}\right)(x+y)}{\left(2-\dfrac{7}{x+y}\right)(x+y)}$

$=\dfrac{x-y+6}{2(x+y)-7}$

$=\dfrac{x-y+6}{2x+2y-7}$

40. a. Answers will vary.

b.
$$\frac{\dfrac{25}{x-y}+\dfrac{2}{x+y}}{\dfrac{5}{x-y}-\dfrac{3}{x+y}}$$

$$=\frac{\dfrac{25(x+y)}{(x-y)(x+y)}+\dfrac{2(x-y)}{(x-y)(x+y)}}{\dfrac{5(x+y)}{(x-y)(x+y)}-\dfrac{3(x-y)}{(x-y)(x+y)}}$$

$$=\frac{\dfrac{25x+25y+2x-2y}{(x-y)(x+y)}}{\dfrac{5x+5y-3x+3y}{(x-y)(x+y)}}$$

$$=\frac{\dfrac{27x+23y}{(x-y)(x+y)}}{\dfrac{2x+8y}{(x-y)(x+y)}}$$

$$=\frac{27x+23y}{\cancel{(x-y)}\,\cancel{(x+y)}}\cdot\frac{\cancel{(x-y)}\,\cancel{(x+y)}}{2x+8y}$$

$$=\frac{27x+23y}{2x+8y}$$

c.
$$\frac{\dfrac{25}{x-y}+\dfrac{2}{x+y}}{\dfrac{5}{x-y}-\dfrac{3}{x+y}}=\frac{\left(\dfrac{25}{x-y}+\dfrac{2}{x+y}\right)(x-y)(x+y)}{\left(\dfrac{5}{x-y}-\dfrac{3}{x+y}\right)(x-y)(x+y)}$$

$$=\frac{25(x+y)+2(x-y)}{5(x+y)-3(x-y)}$$

$$=\frac{25x+25y+2x-2y}{5x+5y-3x+3y}$$

$$=\frac{27x+23y}{2x+8y}$$

41. a.
$$\frac{\dfrac{5}{12x}}{\dfrac{8}{x^2}-\dfrac{4}{3x}}$$

b.
$$\frac{\dfrac{5}{12x}}{\dfrac{8}{x^2}-\dfrac{4}{3x}}=\frac{\dfrac{5}{12x}}{\dfrac{24-4x}{3x^2}}$$

$$=\frac{5}{12x}\cdot\frac{3x^2}{(24-4x)}$$

$$=\frac{5x}{4(24-4x)}$$

$$=\frac{5x}{96-16x}$$

42. a.
$$\frac{\dfrac{6}{x}-\dfrac{3}{2x}}{x+\dfrac{1}{x}}$$

b.
$$\frac{\dfrac{6}{x}-\dfrac{3}{2x}}{x+\dfrac{1}{x}}=\frac{\left(\dfrac{6}{x}-\dfrac{3}{2x}\right)(2x)}{\left(x+\dfrac{1}{x}\right)(2x)}$$

$$=\frac{12-3}{2x^2+2}$$

$$=\frac{9}{2x^2+2}$$

43.
$$\frac{x^{-1}+y^{-1}}{3}=\frac{\dfrac{1}{x}+\dfrac{1}{y}}{3}$$

$$=\frac{\left(\dfrac{1}{x}+\dfrac{1}{y}\right)xy}{3xy}$$

$$=\frac{y+x}{3xy}$$

44.
$$\frac{x^{-1}+y^{-1}}{y^{-1}}=\frac{\dfrac{1}{x}+\dfrac{1}{y}}{\dfrac{1}{y}}$$

$$=\frac{\left(\dfrac{1}{x}+\dfrac{1}{y}\right)xy}{\dfrac{1}{y}(xy)}$$

$$=\frac{y+x}{x}$$

45. $\dfrac{x^{-1}+y^{-1}}{x^{-1}y^{-1}}=\dfrac{\dfrac{1}{x}+\dfrac{1}{y}}{\dfrac{1}{xy}}$

$=\dfrac{\left(\dfrac{1}{x}+\dfrac{1}{y}\right)xy}{\left(\dfrac{1}{xy}\right)xy}$

$=\dfrac{y+x}{1}$

$=x+y$

46. $\dfrac{x^{-2}-y^{-2}}{y^{-1}-x^{-1}}=\dfrac{\dfrac{1}{x^2}-\dfrac{1}{y^2}}{\dfrac{1}{y}-\dfrac{1}{x}}$

$=\dfrac{\left(\dfrac{1}{x^2}-\dfrac{1}{y^2}\right)x^2y^2}{\left(\dfrac{1}{y}-\dfrac{1}{x}\right)x^2y^2}$

$=\dfrac{y^2-x^2}{x^2y-y^2x}$

$=\dfrac{(y-x)(y+x)}{-xy(y-x)}$

$=-\dfrac{x+y}{xy}$

47. a. $E=\dfrac{\dfrac{1}{2}\left(\dfrac{2}{3}\right)}{\dfrac{2}{3}+\dfrac{1}{2}}=\dfrac{\dfrac{2}{6}}{\dfrac{4+3}{6}}=\dfrac{2}{\cancel{6}}\cdot\dfrac{\cancel{6}}{7}=\dfrac{2}{7}$

b. $E=\dfrac{\dfrac{1}{2}\left(\dfrac{4}{5}\right)}{\dfrac{4}{5}+\dfrac{1}{2}}=\dfrac{\dfrac{4}{10}}{\dfrac{8+5}{10}}=\dfrac{4}{\cancel{10}}\cdot\dfrac{\cancel{10}}{13}=\dfrac{4}{13}$

48. $\dfrac{\dfrac{x}{y}+\dfrac{y}{x}+\dfrac{2}{x}}{\dfrac{x}{y}+y}=\dfrac{\left(\dfrac{x}{y}+\dfrac{y}{x}+\dfrac{2}{x}\right)xy}{\left(\dfrac{x}{y}+y\right)xy}=\dfrac{x^2+y^2+2y}{x^2+xy^2}$

49. $\dfrac{\dfrac{a+b-\dfrac{1}{b}}{a}}{\dfrac{a}{b^2}-\dfrac{b}{a}+\dfrac{3}{a^2}}=\dfrac{\dfrac{a^2+b^2a-b}{ba}}{\dfrac{a^3-ab^3+3b^2}{a^2b^2}}$

$=\dfrac{a^2+b^2a-b}{\cancel{ba}}\cdot\dfrac{\cancel{a}^{a}\,\cancel{b}^{b}}{a^3-ab^3+3b^2}$

$=\dfrac{(a^2+b^2a-b)ab}{a^3-ab^3+3b^2}$

$=\dfrac{a^3b+a^2b^3-ab^2}{a^3-ab^3+3b^2}$

50. $\dfrac{x}{4+\dfrac{x}{1+x}}=\dfrac{x(1+x)}{\left(4+\dfrac{x}{1+x}\right)(1+x)}$

$=\dfrac{x(1+x)}{4+4x+x}$

$=\dfrac{x^2+x}{5x+4}$

51. $2x-8(5-x)=9x-3(x+2)$

$2x-40+8x=9x-3x-6$

$10x-40=6x-6$

$4x=34$

$x=\dfrac{34}{4}=\dfrac{17}{2}$

52. A polynomial is an expression containing a finite number of terms of the form ax^n where a is a real number and n is a whole number.

53. $x^2-13x+40=(x-8)(x-5)$

54. $\dfrac{x}{3x^2+17x-6}-\dfrac{2}{x^2+3x-18}$

$=\dfrac{x}{(3x-1)(x+6)}-\dfrac{2}{(x+6)(x-3)}$

$=\dfrac{x}{(3x-1)(x+6)}\cdot\dfrac{x-3}{x-3}-\dfrac{2}{(x+6)(x-3)}\cdot\dfrac{3x-1}{3x-1}$

$=\dfrac{x^2-3x-(6x-2)}{(3x-1)(x+6)(x-3)}$

$=\dfrac{x^2-3x-6x+2}{(3x-1)(x+6)(x-3)}$

$=\dfrac{x^2-9x+2}{(3x-1)(x+6)(x-3)}$

Exercise Set 7.6

1. a. Answers will vary.

b. $\dfrac{1}{x-1} - \dfrac{1}{x+1} = \dfrac{3x}{x^2-1}$

$\dfrac{1}{x-1} - \dfrac{1}{x+1} = \dfrac{3x}{(x-1)(x+1)}$

Multiply both sides of the equation by the least common denominator, $(x-1)(x+1)$.

$$(x-1)(x+1)\left(\frac{1}{x-1} - \frac{1}{x+1}\right) = \left(\frac{3x}{(x-1)(x+1)}\right)(x-1)(x+1)$$

$$(x-1)(x+1)\left(\frac{1}{x-1}\right) - (x-1)(x+1)\left(\frac{1}{x+1}\right) = 3x$$

$$x+1-(x-1) = 3x$$

$$x+1-x+1 = 3x$$

$$2 = 3x$$

$$\frac{2}{3} = x$$

2. a. They will be the same because if you add

$\dfrac{2}{x+2}$ to both sides in the second equation, it will be the same as the first equation.

b. $\dfrac{3}{x-2} + \dfrac{2}{x+2} = \dfrac{4x}{x^2-4}$

Multiply both sides of the equation by the least common denominator, $(x-2)(x+2)$.

$$\frac{3}{x-2} + \frac{2}{x+2} = \frac{4x}{x^2-4}$$

$$\frac{3}{x-2} + \frac{2}{x+2} = \frac{4x}{(x-2)(x+2)}$$

$$(x-2)(x+2)\left[\frac{3}{x-2} + \frac{2}{x+2}\right] = (x-2)(x+2)\left[\frac{4x}{(x-2)(x+2)}\right]$$

$$3(x+2) + 2(x-2) = 4x$$

$$3x+6+2x-4 = 4x$$

$$5x+2 = 4x$$

$$x = -2$$

There is no solution because $x = -2$ is an extraneous solution.

3. a. The problem on the left is an expression to be simplified while the problem on the right is an equation to be solved.

b. Left: Write the fractions with the LCD, $12(x-1)$, then combine numerators.
Right: Multiply both sides of the equation by the LCD, $12(x-1)$, then solve.

c. Left: $\dfrac{x}{3} - \dfrac{x}{4} + \dfrac{1}{x-1} = \dfrac{x \cdot 4(x-1)}{3 \cdot 4(x-1)} - \dfrac{x \cdot 3(x-1)}{4 \cdot 3(x-1)} + \dfrac{1 \cdot 3 \cdot 4}{(x-1)3 \cdot 4}$

$$= \frac{4x(x-1) - 3x(x-1) + 12}{3 \cdot 4(x-1)}$$

$$= \frac{4x^2 - 4x - 3x^2 + 3x + 12}{12(x-1)}$$

$$= \frac{x^2 - x + 12}{12(x-1)}$$

Right:

$$\frac{x}{3} - \frac{x}{4} = \frac{1}{x-1}$$

$$12(x-1)\left(\frac{x}{3} - \frac{x}{4}\right) = \left(\frac{1}{x-1}\right)12(x-1)$$

$$12(x-1)\left(\frac{x}{3}\right) - 12(x-1)\left(\frac{x}{4}\right) = 12$$

$$4x(x-1) - 3x(x-1) = 12$$

$$4x^2 - 4x - 3x^2 + 3x = 12$$

$$x^2 - x - 12 = 0$$

$$(x-4)(x+3) = 0$$

$$x - 4 = 0 \quad \text{or} \quad x + 3 = 0$$

$$x = 4 \qquad\qquad x = -3$$

4. a. The problem on the right is an equation to be solved while the problem on the left is an expression to be simplified.

b. Left: Write the fractions with the LCD, $6(2x+7)$, then combine numerators.

Right: Multiply both sides of the equation by the LCD, $6(2x+7)$, then solve.

c. Left: $\dfrac{x}{2} - \dfrac{x}{3} + \dfrac{5}{2x+7} = \dfrac{x(3)(2x+7)}{6(2x+7)} - \dfrac{x(2)(2x+7)}{6(2x+7)} + \dfrac{5(2)(3)}{6(2x+7)}$

$$= \frac{6x^2 + 21x - 4x^2 - 14x + 30}{6(2x+7)}$$

$$= \frac{2x^2 + 7x + 30}{6(2x+7)}$$

Right:

$$\frac{x}{2} - \frac{x}{3} = \frac{5}{2x+7}$$

$$6(2x+7)\left(\frac{x}{2} - \frac{x}{3}\right) = \frac{5}{2x+7}\left[6(2x+7)\right]$$

$$3x(2x+7) - 2x(2x+7) = 5 \cdot 6$$

$$6x^2 + 21x - 4x^2 - 14x = 30$$

$$2x^2 + 7x - 30 = 0$$

$$(2x-5)(x+6) = 0$$

$$2x - 5 = 0 \quad \text{or} \quad x + 6 = 0$$

$$x = \frac{5}{2} \qquad\qquad x = -6$$

5. You must check for extraneous solutions when there is a variable in the denominator.

6. 0 cannot be a solution because it makes the denominator zero in the second term.

7. 2 cannot be a solution because it makes the denominator zero in the first term.

8. −5 cannot be a solution because it makes the denominator zero in the second term.

9. No, because there are no variables in the denominator.

10. Yes, because there are variables in the denominator.

11. Yes, because there is a variable in the denominator.

12. Yes, because there is a variable in the denominator.

13.
$$\frac{x}{3} - \frac{x}{4} = 1$$
$$12\left(\frac{x}{3} - \frac{x}{4}\right) = 12(1)$$
$$4x - 3x = 12$$
$$x = 12$$

14.
$$\frac{t}{5} - \frac{t}{6} = 2$$
$$30\left(\frac{t}{5} - \frac{t}{6}\right) = 30(2)$$
$$6t - 5t = 60$$
$$t = 60$$

15.
$$\frac{r}{6} = \frac{r}{4} + \frac{1}{3}$$
$$12\left(\frac{r}{6}\right) = 12\left(\frac{r}{4} + \frac{1}{3}\right)$$
$$2r = 3r + 4$$
$$-r = 4$$
$$r = -4$$

16.
$$\frac{n}{5} = \frac{n}{6} + \frac{2}{3}$$
$$30\left(\frac{n}{5}\right) = 30\left(\frac{n}{6} + \frac{2}{3}\right)$$
$$6n = 5n + 20$$
$$n = 20$$

17.
$$\frac{z}{2} + 6 = \frac{z}{5}$$
$$10\left(\frac{z}{2} + 6\right) = 10\left(\frac{z}{5}\right)$$
$$5z + 60 = 2z$$
$$3z = -60$$
$$z = -20$$

18.
$$\frac{3w}{5} - 6 = w$$
$$5\left(\frac{3w}{5} - 6\right) = 5w$$
$$3w - 30 = 5w$$
$$-2w = 30$$
$$w = -15$$

19.
$$\frac{z}{6} + \frac{2}{3} = \frac{z}{5} - \frac{1}{3}$$
$$30\left(\frac{z}{6} + \frac{2}{3}\right) = 30\left(\frac{z}{5} - \frac{1}{3}\right)$$
$$5z + 20 = 6z - 10$$
$$-z = -30$$
$$z = 30$$

20.
$$\frac{m-2}{6} = \frac{2}{3} + \frac{m}{12}$$
$$12\left(\frac{m-2}{6}\right) = 12\left(\frac{2}{3} + \frac{m}{12}\right)$$
$$2(m-2) = 8 + m$$
$$2m - 4 = 8 + m$$
$$m = 12$$

21.
$$d + 7 = \frac{3}{2}d + 5$$
$$2(d+7) = 2\left(\frac{3}{2}d + 5\right)$$
$$2d + 14 = 3d + 10$$
$$-d = -4$$
$$d = 4$$

22.
$$\frac{q}{5} + \frac{q}{2} = \frac{21}{10}$$
$$10\left(\frac{q}{5} + \frac{q}{2}\right) = 10\left(\frac{21}{10}\right)$$
$$2q + 5q = 21$$
$$7q = 21$$
$$q = 3$$

23.
$$3k + \frac{1}{6} = 4k - 4$$
$$6\left(3k + \frac{1}{6}\right) = 6(4k - 4)$$
$$18k + 1 = 24k - 24$$
$$-6k = -25$$
$$k = \frac{25}{6}$$

24.
$$\frac{p}{4} + \frac{1}{4} = \frac{p}{3} - \frac{1}{2}$$
$$12\left(\frac{p}{4} + \frac{1}{4}\right) = 12\left(\frac{p}{3} - \frac{1}{2}\right)$$
$$3p + 3 = 4p - 6$$
$$-p = -9$$
$$p = 9$$

25.
$$\frac{(n+6)}{3} = \frac{5(n-8)}{10}$$
$$10(n+6) = 3 \cdot 5(n-8)$$
$$10n + 60 = 15n - 120$$
$$180 = 5n$$
$$36 = n$$

26.
$$\frac{3(x-6)}{5} = \frac{4(x+2)}{8}$$
$$8 \cdot 3(x-6) = 5 \cdot 4(x+2)$$
$$24x - 144 = 20x + 40$$
$$4x = 184$$
$$x = 46$$

27.
$$\frac{x-5}{15} = \frac{3}{5} - \frac{x-4}{10}$$
$$30\left(\frac{x-5}{15}\right) = 30\left(\frac{3}{5} - \frac{x-4}{10}\right)$$
$$2(x-5) = 6(3) - 3(x-4)$$
$$2x - 10 = 18 - 3x + 12$$
$$2x - 10 = 30 - 3x$$
$$5x = 40$$
$$x = 8$$

28.
$$\frac{z+4}{6} = \frac{3}{2} - \frac{2z+2}{12}$$
$$12\left(\frac{z+4}{6}\right) = 12\left(\frac{3}{2} - \frac{2z+2}{12}\right)$$
$$2(z+4) = 6(3) - 1(2z+2)$$
$$2z + 8 = 18 - 2z - 2$$
$$2z + 8 = 16 - 2z$$
$$4z = 8$$
$$z = 2$$

29. $\dfrac{-p+1}{4}+\dfrac{13}{20}=\dfrac{p}{5}-\dfrac{p-1}{2}$

$20\left(\dfrac{-p+1}{4}+\dfrac{13}{20}\right)=20\left(\dfrac{p}{5}-\dfrac{p-1}{2}\right)$

$5(-p+1)+13=4p-10(p-1)$

$-5p+5+13=4p-10p+10$

$-5p+18=-6p+10$

$p=-8$

30. $\dfrac{1}{10}-\dfrac{n+1}{6}=\dfrac{1}{5}-\dfrac{n+10}{15}$

$30\left(\dfrac{1}{10}-\dfrac{n+1}{6}\right)=30\left(\dfrac{1}{5}-\dfrac{n+10}{15}\right)$

$3-5(n+1)=6-2(n+10)$

$3-5n-5=6-2n-20$

$-5n-2=-2n-14$

$-3n=-12$

$n=4$

31. $\dfrac{d-3}{4}+\dfrac{1}{15}=\dfrac{2d+1}{3}-\dfrac{34}{15}$

$60\left(\dfrac{d-3}{4}+\dfrac{1}{15}\right)=60\left(\dfrac{2d+1}{3}-\dfrac{34}{15}\right)$

$15(d-3)+4=20(2d+1)-4(34)$

$15d-45+4=40d+20-136$

$15d-41=40d-116$

$-25d=-75$

$d=3$

32. $\dfrac{t+4}{5}=\dfrac{5}{8}+\dfrac{t+7}{40}$

$40\left(\dfrac{t+4}{5}\right)=40\left(\dfrac{5}{8}+\dfrac{t+7}{40}\right)$

$8(t+4)=5(5)+(t+7)$

$8t+32=25+t+7$

$8t+32=32+t$

$7t=0$

$t=0$

33. $2+\dfrac{3}{x}=\dfrac{11}{4}$

$4x\left(2+\dfrac{3}{x}\right)=4x\left(\dfrac{11}{4}\right)$

$8x+12=44$

$8x=32$

$x=4$

Check: $2+\dfrac{3}{4}=\dfrac{11}{4}$

$\dfrac{8}{4}+\dfrac{3}{4}=\dfrac{11}{4}$

$\dfrac{11}{4}=\dfrac{11}{4}$ True

34. $3-\dfrac{1}{x}=\dfrac{14}{5}$

$5x\left(3-\dfrac{1}{x}\right)=5x\left(\dfrac{14}{5}\right)$

$15x-5=14x$

$x=5$

Check: $3-\dfrac{1}{5}=\dfrac{14}{5}$

$\dfrac{15}{5}-\dfrac{1}{5}=\dfrac{14}{5}$

$\dfrac{14}{5}=\dfrac{14}{5}$ True

35. $7-\dfrac{5}{x}=\dfrac{9}{2}$

$2x\left(7-\dfrac{5}{x}\right)=2x\left(\dfrac{9}{2}\right)$

$14x-10=9x$

$5x=10$

$x=2$

Check: $7-\dfrac{5}{2}=\dfrac{9}{2}$

$\dfrac{14}{2}-\dfrac{5}{2}=\dfrac{9}{2}$

$\dfrac{9}{2}=\dfrac{9}{2}$ True

36. $4+\dfrac{3}{z}=\dfrac{9}{2}$

$$2z\left(4+\dfrac{3}{z}\right)=2z\left(\dfrac{9}{2}\right)$$

$$8z+6=9z$$

$$-z=-6$$

$$z=6$$

Check: $4+\dfrac{3}{6}=\dfrac{9}{2}$

$$\dfrac{8}{2}+\dfrac{1}{2}=\dfrac{9}{2}$$

$$\dfrac{9}{2}=\dfrac{9}{2}\quad\text{True}$$

37. $\dfrac{4}{n}-\dfrac{3}{2n}=\dfrac{1}{2}$

$$2n\left(\dfrac{4}{n}-\dfrac{3}{2n}\right)=2n\left(\dfrac{1}{2}\right)$$

$$8-3=n$$

$$5=n$$

Check: $\dfrac{4}{5}-\dfrac{3}{10}=\dfrac{1}{2}$

$$\dfrac{8}{10}-\dfrac{3}{10}=\dfrac{1}{2}$$

$$\dfrac{5}{10}=\dfrac{1}{2}$$

$$\dfrac{1}{2}=\dfrac{1}{2}\quad\text{True}$$

38. $\dfrac{5}{3x}+\dfrac{2}{x}=1$

$$3x\left(\dfrac{5}{3x}+\dfrac{2}{x}\right)=3x(1)$$

$$5+6=3x$$

$$11=3x$$

$$\dfrac{11}{3}=x$$

Check: $\dfrac{5}{3\left(\frac{11}{3}\right)}+\dfrac{2}{\left(\frac{11}{3}\right)}=1$

$$\dfrac{5}{11}+\left(2\div\dfrac{11}{3}\right)=1$$

$$\dfrac{5}{11}+\left(2\cdot\dfrac{3}{11}\right)=1$$

$$\dfrac{5}{11}+\dfrac{6}{11}=1$$

$$\dfrac{11}{11}=1$$

$$1=1\quad\text{True}$$

39. $\dfrac{x-1}{x-5}=\dfrac{4}{x-5}$

$$(x-5)\left(\dfrac{x-1}{x-5}\right)=\left(\dfrac{4}{x-5}\right)(x-5)$$

$$x-1=4$$

$$x=5$$

Check: $\dfrac{x-1}{x-5}=\dfrac{4}{x-5}$

$$\dfrac{5-1}{5-5}=\dfrac{4}{5-5}$$

$$\dfrac{4}{0}=\dfrac{4}{0}$$

Since $\dfrac{4}{0}$ is not a real number, 5 is an extraneous solution. This equation has no solution.

40. $\dfrac{2x+3}{x+2}=\dfrac{3}{2}$

$$2(2x+3)=3(x+2)$$

$$4x+6=3x+6$$

$$x=0$$

Check: $\dfrac{2x+3}{x+2}=\dfrac{3}{2}$

$$\dfrac{2(0)+3}{0+2}=\dfrac{3}{2}$$

$$\dfrac{3}{2}=\dfrac{3}{2}\quad\text{True}$$

41. $\dfrac{5}{a+3}=\dfrac{4}{a+1}$

$5(a+1)=4(a+3)$

$5a+5=4a+12$

$a=7$

Check: $\dfrac{5}{a+3}=\dfrac{4}{a+1}$

$\dfrac{5}{7+3}=\dfrac{4}{7+1}$

$\dfrac{5}{10}=\dfrac{4}{8}$

$\dfrac{1}{2}=\dfrac{1}{2}$ True

42. $\dfrac{5}{x+2}=\dfrac{1}{x-4}$

$5(x-4)=1(x+2)$

$5x-20=x+2$

$4x=22$

$x=\dfrac{11}{2}$

Check: $\dfrac{5}{x+2}=\dfrac{1}{x-4}$

$\dfrac{5}{\frac{11}{2}+2}=\dfrac{1}{\frac{11}{2}-4}$

$\dfrac{5}{\frac{15}{2}}=\dfrac{1}{\frac{3}{2}}$

$5\left(\dfrac{2}{15}\right)=1\left(\dfrac{2}{3}\right)$

$\dfrac{2}{3}=\dfrac{2}{3}$ True

43. $\dfrac{y+3}{y-3}=\dfrac{6}{4}$

$4(y+3)=6(y-3)$

$4y+12=6y-18$

$30=2y$

$15=y$

Check: $\dfrac{y+3}{y-3}=\dfrac{6}{4}$

$\dfrac{15+3}{15-3}=\dfrac{6}{4}$

$\dfrac{18}{12}=\dfrac{6}{4}$

$\dfrac{3}{2}=\dfrac{3}{2}$ True

44. $\dfrac{x}{x+6}=\dfrac{2}{5}$

$5(x)=2(x+6)$

$5x=2x+12$

$3x=12$

$x=4$

Check: $\dfrac{x}{x+6}=\dfrac{2}{5}$

$\dfrac{4}{4+6}=\dfrac{2}{5}$

$\dfrac{4}{10}=\dfrac{2}{5}$

$\dfrac{2}{5}=\dfrac{2}{5}$ True

45. $\dfrac{2x-3}{x-4}=\dfrac{5}{x-4}$

$(x-4)\left(\dfrac{2x-3}{x-4}\right)=\left(\dfrac{5}{x-4}\right)(x-4)$

$2x-3=5$

$2x=8$

$x=4$

Check: $\dfrac{2x-3}{x-4}=\dfrac{5}{x-4}$

$\dfrac{2(4)-3}{4-4}=\dfrac{5}{4-4}$

$\dfrac{5}{0}=\dfrac{5}{0}$

Since $\dfrac{5}{0}$ is not a real number, 4 is an extraneous solution. This equation has no solution.

46. $\dfrac{3}{x} + 9 = \dfrac{3}{x}$

$x\left(\dfrac{3}{x} + 9\right) = \left(\dfrac{3}{x}\right)x$

$x\left(\dfrac{3}{x}\right) + x(9) = 3$

$3 + 9x = 3$

$9x = 0$

$x = 0$

Check: $\dfrac{3}{x} + 9 = \dfrac{3}{x}$

$\dfrac{3}{0} + 9 = \dfrac{3}{0}$

Since $\dfrac{3}{0}$ is not a real number, 0 is an extraneous solution. This equation has no solution.

47. $\dfrac{x^2}{x-3} = \dfrac{9}{x-3}$

$(x-3)\left(\dfrac{x^2}{x-3}\right) = (x-3)\left(\dfrac{9}{x-3}\right)$

$x^2 = 9$

$x^2 - 9 = 0$

$(x+3)(x-3) = 0$

$x + 3 = 0 \quad \text{or} \quad x - 3 = 0$

$x = -3 \qquad\qquad x = 3$

Check: $\quad x = -3 \qquad\qquad x = 3$

$\dfrac{(-3)^2}{-3-3} = \dfrac{9}{-3-3} \qquad \dfrac{(3)^2}{3-3} = \dfrac{9}{3-3}$

$\dfrac{9}{-6} = \dfrac{9}{-6}\,\text{True} \qquad \dfrac{9}{0} = \dfrac{9}{0}$

Since $\dfrac{9}{0}$ is not a real number, 3 is an extraneous solution. The solution is $x = -3$.

48. $\dfrac{x^2}{x+5} = \dfrac{25}{x+5}$

$(x+5)\left(\dfrac{x^2}{x+5}\right) = (x+5)\left(\dfrac{25}{x+5}\right)$

$x^2 = 25$

$x^2 - 25 = 0$

$(x+5)(x-5) = 0$

$x + 5 = 0 \quad \text{or} \quad x - 5 = 0$

$x = -5 \qquad\qquad x = 5$

$x = -5 \qquad\qquad x = 5$

Check: $\dfrac{(-5)^2}{-5+5} = \dfrac{25}{-5+5} \qquad \dfrac{(5)^2}{5+5} = \dfrac{25}{5+5}$

$\dfrac{25}{0} = \dfrac{25}{0} \qquad\qquad \dfrac{25}{10} = \dfrac{25}{10}\,$ True

Since $\dfrac{25}{0}$ is not a real number, -5 is an extraneous solution. The solution is $x = 5$.

49. $\dfrac{n-3}{n+2} = \dfrac{n+4}{n+10}$

$(n-3)(n+10) = (n+2)(n+4)$

$n^2 + 7n - 30 = n^2 + 6n + 8$

$n = 38$

Check: $\dfrac{38-3}{38+2} = \dfrac{38+4}{38+10}$

$\dfrac{35}{40} = \dfrac{42}{48}$

$\dfrac{7}{8} = \dfrac{7}{8}\,$ True

50. $\dfrac{x+5}{x+1} = \dfrac{x-6}{x-3}$

$(x+5)(x-3) = (x-6)(x+1)$

$x^2 + 2x - 15 = x^2 - 5x - 6$

$2x - 15 = -5x - 6$

$7x = 9$

$x = \dfrac{9}{7}$

Check: $\dfrac{x+5}{x+1} = \dfrac{x-6}{x-3}$

$\dfrac{\frac{9}{7}+5}{\frac{9}{7}+1} = \dfrac{\frac{9}{7}-6}{\frac{9}{7}-3}$

$\dfrac{\frac{44}{7}}{\frac{16}{7}} = \dfrac{-\frac{33}{7}}{-\frac{12}{7}}$

$\left(\dfrac{44}{7}\right)\left(\dfrac{7}{16}\right) = \left(-\dfrac{33}{7}\right)\left(-\dfrac{7}{12}\right)$

$\dfrac{44}{16} = \dfrac{33}{12}$

$\dfrac{11}{4} = \dfrac{11}{4}$ True

51. $\dfrac{1}{r} = \dfrac{3r}{8r+3}$

$1(8r+3) = 3r^2$

$0 = 3r^2 - 8r - 3$

$0 = (3r+1)(r-3)$

$3r+1=0$ or $r-3=0$

$3r=-1$ $r=3$

$r=-\dfrac{1}{3}$

Check: $\dfrac{1}{\frac{-1}{3}} = \dfrac{3\left(-\frac{1}{3}\right)}{8\left(\frac{-1}{3}\right)+3}$ $\dfrac{1}{3} = \dfrac{3(3)}{8(3)+3}$

$\dfrac{1}{\frac{-1}{3}} = \dfrac{-1}{\frac{-8}{3}+\frac{9}{3}}$ $\dfrac{1}{3} = \dfrac{9}{27}$

$-3 = \dfrac{-1}{\frac{1}{3}}$ $\dfrac{1}{3} = \dfrac{1}{3}$ True

$-3 = -3$ True

52. $\dfrac{1}{r} = \dfrac{2r}{r+15}$

$1(r+15) = 2r^2$

$0 = 2r^2 - r - 15$

$0 = (2r+5)(r-3)$

$2r+5=0$ or $r-3=0$

$2r=-5$ $r=3$

$r=-\dfrac{5}{2}$

Check: $\dfrac{1}{\frac{-5}{2}} = \dfrac{2\left(-\frac{5}{2}\right)}{\left(\frac{-5}{2}\right)+15}$ $\dfrac{1}{3} = \dfrac{2(3)}{3+15}$

$\dfrac{1}{\frac{-5}{2}} = \dfrac{-5}{\frac{-5}{2}+\frac{30}{2}}$ $\dfrac{1}{3} = \dfrac{6}{18}$

$-\dfrac{2}{5} = \dfrac{-5}{\frac{25}{2}}$ $\dfrac{1}{3} = \dfrac{1}{3}$ True

$-\dfrac{2}{5} = -5 \cdot \dfrac{2}{25}$

$-\dfrac{2}{5} = -\dfrac{2}{5}$ True

53. $\dfrac{k}{k+2} = \dfrac{3}{k-2}$

$k(k-2) = 3(k+2)$

$k^2 - 2k = 3k + 6$

$k^2 - 5k - 6 = 0$

$(k-6)(k+1) = 0$

$k-6=0$ or $k+1=0$

$k=6$ $k=-1$

Check: $\dfrac{6}{6+2} = \dfrac{3}{6-2}$ $\dfrac{-1}{-1+2} = \dfrac{3}{-1-2}$

$\dfrac{6}{8} = \dfrac{3}{4}$ $\dfrac{-1}{1} = \dfrac{3}{-3}$

$\dfrac{3}{4} = \dfrac{3}{4}$ True $-1=-1$ True

54.
$$\frac{3a-2}{2a+2}=\frac{3}{a-1}$$
$$(3a-2)(a-1)=(2a+2)(3)$$
$$3a^2-5a+2=6a+6$$
$$3a^2-11-4=0$$
$$(3a+1)(a-4)=0$$
$$3a+1=0 \quad \text{or} \quad a-4=0$$
$$3a=-1 \qquad a=4$$
$$a=-\frac{1}{3}$$

Check:
$$\frac{3\left(-\dfrac{1}{3}\right)-2}{2\left(-\dfrac{1}{3}\right)+2}=\frac{3}{-\dfrac{1}{3}-1}$$
$$\frac{-1-2}{-\dfrac{2}{3}+2}=\frac{3}{-\dfrac{1}{3}-\dfrac{3}{3}}$$
$$\frac{-3}{-\dfrac{2}{3}+\dfrac{6}{3}}=\frac{3}{-\dfrac{4}{3}}$$
$$\frac{-3}{\dfrac{4}{3}}=3\cdot-\frac{3}{4}$$
$$-3\cdot\frac{3}{4}=\frac{-9}{4}$$
$$-\frac{9}{4}=-\frac{9}{4} \quad \text{True}$$

$$\frac{3(4)-2}{2(4)+2}=\frac{3}{4-1}$$
$$\frac{12-2}{8+2}=\frac{3}{3}$$
$$\frac{10}{10}=1$$
$$1=1 \text{ True}$$

55.
$$\frac{4}{r}+r=\frac{20}{r}$$
$$r\left(\frac{4}{r}+r\right)=r\left(\frac{20}{r}\right)$$
$$4+r^2=20$$
$$r^2-16=0$$
$$(r+4)(r-4)=0$$
$$r+4=0 \quad \text{or} \quad r-4=0$$
$$r=-4 \qquad r=4$$

Check:
$$\frac{4}{4}+4=\frac{20}{4} \qquad\qquad \frac{4}{-4}-4=\frac{20}{-4}$$
$$\frac{4}{4}+\frac{16}{4}=\frac{20}{4} \qquad\qquad \frac{4}{-4}-\frac{16}{4}=\frac{20}{-4}$$
$$\frac{20}{4}=\frac{20}{4} \text{ True} \qquad -\frac{20}{4}=-\frac{20}{4} \text{ True}$$

56.
$$a+\frac{5}{a}=\frac{14}{a}$$
$$a\left(a+\frac{5}{a}\right)=a\left(\frac{14}{a}\right)$$
$$a^2+5=14$$
$$a^2-9=0$$
$$(a-3)(a+3)=0$$
$$a-3=0 \quad \text{or} \quad a+3=0$$
$$a=3 \qquad\qquad a=-3$$

Check $a=3$:
$$a+\frac{5}{a}=\frac{14}{a}$$
$$3+\frac{5}{3}=\frac{14}{3}$$
$$\frac{9}{3}+\frac{5}{3}=\frac{14}{3}$$
$$\frac{14}{3}=\frac{14}{3} \text{ True}$$

Check $a=-3$:
$$a+\frac{5}{a}=\frac{14}{a}$$
$$-3+\frac{5}{-3}=\frac{14}{-3}$$
$$\frac{-9}{3}-\frac{5}{3}=-\frac{14}{3}$$
$$-\frac{14}{3}=-\frac{14}{3} \text{ True}$$

57.
$$x + \frac{20}{x} = -9$$
$$x\left(x + \frac{20}{x}\right) = -9x$$
$$x^2 + 20 = -9x$$
$$x^2 + 9x + 20 = 0$$
$$(x+4)(x+5) = 0$$
$$x+4 = 0 \quad \text{or} \quad x+5 = 0$$
$$x = -4 \qquad\qquad x = -5$$

Check $x = -4$: $\quad x + \frac{20}{x} = -9$
$$-4 + \frac{20}{-4} = -9$$
$$-4 + (-5) = -9 \quad \text{True}$$

Check $x = -5$: $\quad x + \frac{20}{x} = -9$
$$-5 + \frac{20}{-5} = -9$$
$$5 + (-4) = -9 \quad \text{True}$$

58.
$$x - \frac{32}{x} = 4$$
$$x\left(x - \frac{32}{x}\right) = 4x$$
$$x^2 - 32 = 4x$$
$$x^2 - 4x - 32 = 0$$
$$(x-8)(x+4) = 0$$
$$x-8 = 0 \quad \text{or} \quad x+4 = 0$$
$$x = 8 \qquad\qquad x = -4$$

Check $x = 8$: $\quad x - \frac{32}{x} = 4$
$$8 - \frac{32}{8} = 4$$
$$8 - 4 = 4 \quad \text{True}$$

Check $x = -4$: $\quad x - \frac{32}{x} = 4$
$$-4 - \frac{32}{-4} = 4$$
$$-4 - (-8) = 4$$
$$-4 + 8 = 4$$
$$4 = 4 \quad \text{True}$$

59.
$$\frac{3y-2}{y+1} = 4 - \frac{y+2}{y-1}$$
$$(y+1)(y-1)\left(\frac{3y-2}{y+1}\right) = \left(4 - \frac{y+2}{y-1}\right)(y+1)(y-1)$$
$$(y-1)(3y-2) = 4(y+1)(y-1) - \left(\frac{y+2}{y-1}\right)(y+1)(y-1)$$
$$3y^2 - 5y + 2 = 4\left(y^2 - 1\right) - (y+2)(y+1)$$
$$3y^2 - 5y + 2 = 4y^2 - 4 - (y^2 + 3y + 2)$$
$$3y^2 - 5y + 2 = 3y^2 - 3y - 6$$
$$-5y + 2 = -3y - 6$$
$$8 = 2y$$
$$4 = y$$

Check: $\dfrac{3y-2}{y+1} = 4 - \dfrac{y+2}{y-1}$
$$\frac{3(4)-2}{4+1} = 4 - \frac{4+2}{4-1}$$
$$\frac{12-2}{5} = 4 - \frac{6}{3}$$
$$\frac{10}{5} = 4 - 2$$
$$2 = 2 \quad \text{True}$$

Chapter 7: Rational Expressions and Equations

60.

$$\frac{2b}{b+1} = 2 - \frac{5}{2b}$$

$$2b(b+1)\left(\frac{2b}{b+1}\right) = \left(2 - \frac{5}{2b}\right) \cdot 2b(b+1)$$

$$2b(2b) = 2 \cdot 2b(b+1) - \left(\frac{5}{2b}\right) \cdot 2b(b+1)$$

$$4b^2 = 4b(b+1) - 5(b+1)$$

$$4b^2 = 4b^2 + 4b - 5b - 5$$

$$0 = -b - 5$$

$$b = -5$$

Check $\dfrac{2b}{b+1} = 2 - \dfrac{5}{2b}$

$$\frac{2(-5)}{-5+1} = 2 - \frac{5}{2(-5)}$$

$$\frac{-10}{-4} = 2 - \frac{5}{-10}$$

$$\frac{5}{2} = 2 + \frac{1}{2}$$

$$\frac{5}{2} = \frac{5}{2} \quad \text{True}$$

61.

$$\frac{1}{x+3} + \frac{1}{x-3} = \frac{-5}{x^2-9}$$

$$\frac{1}{x+3} + \frac{1}{x-3} = \frac{-5}{(x-3)(x+3)}$$

$$(x-3)(x+3)\left[\frac{1}{x+3} + \frac{1}{x-3}\right] = \left[\frac{-5}{(x-3)(x+3)}\right](x-3)(x+3)$$

$$(x-3)(x+3)\left(\frac{1}{x+3}\right) + (x-3)(x+3)\left(\frac{1}{x-3}\right) = -5$$

$$x - 3 + x + 3 = -5$$

$$2x = -5$$

$$x = -\frac{5}{2}$$

Check: $\dfrac{1}{x+3} + \dfrac{1}{x-3} = \dfrac{-5}{x^2-9}$

$$\frac{1}{-\frac{5}{2}+3} + \frac{1}{-\frac{5}{2}-3} = \frac{-5}{\left(-\frac{5}{2}\right)^2-9}$$

$$\frac{1}{\frac{1}{2}} - \frac{1}{\left(-\frac{11}{2}\right)} = \frac{-5}{\frac{25}{4}-9}$$

$$2 - \frac{2}{11} = \frac{-5}{-\frac{11}{4}}$$

$$\frac{20}{11} = \frac{20}{11} \quad \text{True}$$

62.

$$\frac{t+2}{t-5} - \frac{3}{4} = \frac{6}{t-5}$$

$$4(t-5)\left[\frac{t+2}{t-5} - \frac{3}{4}\right] = 4(t-5)\left(\frac{6}{t-5}\right)$$

$$4(t+2) - 3(t-5) = 4(6)$$

$$4t + 8 - 3t + 15 = 24$$

$$t + 23 = 24$$

$$t = 1$$

Check: $\dfrac{t+2}{t-5} - \dfrac{3}{4} = \dfrac{6}{t-5}$

$$\frac{1+2}{1-5} - \frac{3}{4} = \frac{6}{1-5}$$

$$-\frac{3}{4} - \frac{3}{4} = \frac{6}{-4}$$

$$-\frac{6}{4} = -\frac{6}{4} \quad \text{True}$$

63.

$$\frac{x}{x-3}+\frac{3}{2}=\frac{3}{x-3}$$

$$2(x-3)\left(\frac{x}{x-3}+\frac{3}{2}\right)=2(x-3)\left(\frac{3}{x-3}\right)$$

$$2x+3(x-3)=2(3)$$

$$2x+3x-9=6$$

$$5x=15$$

$$x=3$$

Since $\dfrac{3}{0}$ is not a real number, 3 is an extraneous solution. This equation has no solution.

Check: $\dfrac{x}{x-3}+\dfrac{3}{2}=\dfrac{3}{x-3}$

$$\frac{3}{3-3}+\frac{3}{2}=\frac{3}{3-3}$$

$$\frac{3}{0}+\frac{3}{2}=\frac{3}{0}$$

64.

$$\frac{y}{2y+2}+\frac{2y-16}{4y+4}=\frac{y-3}{y+1}$$

$$\frac{y}{2(y+1)}+\frac{2y-16}{4(y+1)}=\frac{y-3}{y+1}$$

$$4(y+1)\left[\frac{y}{2(y+1)}+\frac{2y-16}{4(y+1)}\right]=\left[\frac{y-3}{y+1}\right]4(y+1)$$

$$4(y+1)\left[\frac{y}{2(y+1)}\right]+4(y+1)\left[\frac{2y-16}{4(y+1)}\right]=4(y-3)$$

$$2y+2y-16=4y-12$$

$$4y-16=4y-12$$

$$-16=-12\qquad\text{False}$$

Since this is a false statement, the equation has no solution.

65.

$$\frac{3}{x-5}-\frac{4}{x+5}=\frac{11}{x^2-25}$$

$$\frac{3}{x-5}-\frac{4}{x+5}=\frac{11}{(x-5)(x+5)}$$

$$(x-5)(x+5)\left[\frac{3}{x-5}-\frac{4}{x+5}\right]=\left[\frac{11}{(x-5)(x+5)}\right](x-5)(x+5)$$

$$(x-5)(x+5)\left(\frac{3}{x-5}\right)-(x-5)(x+5)\left(\frac{4}{x+5}\right)=11$$

$$3(x+5)-4(x-5)=11$$

$$3x+15-4x+20=11$$

$$-x+35=11$$

$$24=x$$

Check: $\dfrac{3}{x-5}-\dfrac{4}{x+5}=\dfrac{11}{x^2-25}$

$$\frac{3}{24-5}-\frac{4}{24+5}=\frac{11}{24^2-25}$$

$$\frac{3}{19}-\frac{4}{29}=\frac{11}{576-25}$$

$$\frac{87}{551}-\frac{76}{551}=\frac{11}{551}$$

$$\frac{11}{551}=\frac{11}{551}\qquad\text{True}$$

66.

$$\frac{n+1}{n+3}+\frac{n-3}{n-2}=\frac{2n^2-15}{n^2+n-6}$$

$$\frac{n+1}{n+3}+\frac{n-3}{n-2}=\frac{2n^2-15}{(n+3)(n-2)}$$

$$(n+3)(n-2)\left[\frac{n+1}{n+3}+\frac{n-3}{n-2}\right]=\left[\frac{2n^2-15}{(n+3)(n-2)}\right](n+3)(n-2)$$

$$(n+3)(n-2)\left(\frac{n+1}{n+3}\right)+(n+3)(n-2)\left(\frac{n-3}{n-2}\right)=2n^2-15$$

$$(n-2)(n+1)+(n+3)(n-3)=2n^2-15$$

$$n^2-n-2+n^2-9=2n^2-15$$

$$2n^2-n-11=2n^2-15$$

$$-n-11=-15$$

$$-n=-4$$

$$n=4$$

Check: $\dfrac{n+1}{n+3}+\dfrac{n-3}{n-2}=\dfrac{2n^2-15}{n^2+n-6}$

$$\frac{4+1}{4+3}+\frac{4-3}{4-2}=\frac{2(4)^2-15}{(4)^2+4-6}$$

$$\frac{5}{7}+\frac{1}{2}=\frac{32-15}{16+4-6}$$

$$\frac{17}{14}=\frac{17}{14} \text{ True}$$

67.

$$\frac{3x}{x^2-9}+\frac{1}{x-3}=\frac{3}{x+3}$$

$$\frac{3x}{(x-3)(x+3)}+\frac{1}{x-3}=\frac{3}{x+3}$$

$$(x-3)(x+3)\left[\frac{3x}{(x-3)(x+3)}+\frac{1}{x-3}\right]=\left[\frac{3}{x+3}\right](x-3)(x+3)$$

$$(x-3)(x+3)\left(\frac{3x}{(x-3)(x+3)}\right)+(x-3)(x+3)\left(\frac{1}{x-3}\right)=3(x-3)$$

$$3x+x+3=3x-9$$

$$4x+3=3x-9$$

$$x+3=-9$$

$$x=-12$$

Check: $\dfrac{3x}{x^2-9}+\dfrac{1}{x-3}=\dfrac{3}{x+3}$

$\dfrac{3(-12)}{(-12)^2-9}+\dfrac{1}{-12-3}=\dfrac{3}{-12+3}$

$\dfrac{-36}{144-9}+\dfrac{1}{-15}=\dfrac{3}{-9}$

$-\dfrac{36}{135}-\dfrac{1}{15}=-\dfrac{1}{3}$

$-\dfrac{4}{15}-\dfrac{1}{15}=-\dfrac{1}{3}$

$-\dfrac{5}{15}=-\dfrac{1}{3}$

$-\dfrac{1}{3}=-\dfrac{1}{3}$ True

68.

$$\dfrac{3}{x+3}+\dfrac{5}{x+4}=\dfrac{12x+7}{x^2+7x+12}$$

$$\dfrac{3}{x+3}+\dfrac{5}{x+4}=\dfrac{12x+7}{(x+3)(x+4)}$$

$$(x+3)(x+4)\left[\dfrac{3}{x+3}+\dfrac{5}{x+4}\right]=\left[\dfrac{12x+7}{(x+3)(x+4)}\right](x+3)(x+4)$$

$$(x+3)(x+4)\left(\dfrac{3}{x+3}\right)+(x+3)(x+4)\left(\dfrac{5}{x+4}\right)=12x+7$$

$$3(x+4)+5(x+3)=12x+7$$

$$3x+12+5x+15=12x+7$$

$$8x+27=12x+7$$

$$20=4x$$

$$5=x$$

Check: $\dfrac{3}{x+3}+\dfrac{5}{x+4}=\dfrac{12x+7}{x^2+7x+12}$

$\dfrac{3}{5+3}+\dfrac{5}{5+4}=\dfrac{12(5)+7}{(5)^2+7(5)+12}$

$\dfrac{3}{8}+\dfrac{5}{9}=\dfrac{60+7}{25+35+12}$

$\dfrac{27}{72}+\dfrac{40}{72}=\dfrac{67}{72}$

$\dfrac{67}{72}=\dfrac{67}{72}$ True

69.

$$\frac{1}{y-1}+\frac{1}{2}=\frac{2}{y^2-1}$$

$$\frac{1}{y-1}+\frac{1}{2}=\frac{2}{(y+1)(y-1)}$$

$$2(y+1)(y-1)\left[\frac{1}{y-1}+\frac{1}{2}\right]=2(y+1)(y-1)\left[\frac{2}{(y+1)(y-1)}\right]$$

$$2(y+1)(y-1)\left(\frac{1}{y-1}\right)+2(y+1)(y-1)\left(\frac{1}{2}\right)=2(2)$$

$$2(y+1)+(y+1)(y-1)=4$$

$$2y+2+y^2-1=4$$

$$y^2+2y-3=0$$

$$(y+3)(y-1)=0$$

$$y+3=0 \quad \text{or} \quad y-1=0$$

$$y=-3 \qquad\qquad y=1$$

Check: $y=-3$

$$\frac{1}{y-1}+\frac{1}{2}=\frac{2}{y^2-1}$$

$$\frac{1}{-3-1}+\frac{1}{2}=\frac{2}{(-3)^2-1}$$

$$\frac{1}{-4}+\frac{1}{2}=\frac{2}{8}$$

$$\frac{1}{4}=\frac{1}{4} \qquad \text{True}$$

Check: $y=1$

$$\frac{1}{y-1}+\frac{1}{2}=\frac{2}{y^2-1}$$

$$\frac{1}{1-1}+\frac{1}{2}=\frac{2}{1^2-1}$$

$$\frac{1}{0}+\frac{1}{2}=\frac{2}{0}$$

The solution to the equation is –3. Since $\frac{1}{0}$ and $\frac{2}{0}$ are not real numbers, 1 is an extraneous solution.

70.

$$\frac{2y}{y+2}=\frac{y}{y+3}-\frac{3}{y^2+5y+6}$$

$$\frac{2y}{y+2}=\frac{y}{y+3}-\frac{3}{(y+2)(y+3)}$$

$$(y+2)(y+3)\left(\frac{2y}{y+2}\right)=\left[\frac{y}{y+3}-\frac{3}{(y+2)(y+3)}\right](y+2)(y+3)$$

$$2y(y+3)=(y+2)(y+3)\left(\frac{y}{y+3}\right)-(y+2)(y+3)\left[\frac{3}{(y+2)(y+3)}\right]$$

$$2y^2+6y=y(y+2)-3$$

$$2y^2+6y=y^2+2y-3$$

$$y^2+4y+3=0$$

$$(y+1)(y+3)=0$$

$$y+1=0 \quad \text{or} \quad y+3=0$$

$$y=-1 \qquad\qquad y=-3$$

Check: $y = -1$

$$\frac{2y}{y+2} = \frac{y}{y+3} - \frac{3}{y^2 + 5y + 6}$$

$$\frac{2(-1)}{-1+2} = \frac{-1}{-1+3} - \frac{3}{(-1)^2 + 5(-1) + 6}$$

$$\frac{-2}{1} = \frac{-1}{2} - \frac{3}{1-5+6}$$

$$-2 = -\frac{1}{2} - \frac{3}{2}$$

$$-2 = -\frac{4}{2} \quad \text{True}$$

Check: $y = -3$

$$\frac{2y}{y+2} = \frac{y}{y+3} - \frac{3}{y^2 + 5y + 6}$$

$$\frac{2(-3)}{-3+2} = \frac{-3}{-3+3} - \frac{3}{(-3)^2 + 5(-3) + 6}$$

$$\frac{-6}{-1} = \frac{-3}{0} - \frac{3}{9-15+6}$$

Since $\frac{3}{0}$ is not a real number, -3 is an extraneous solution. The solution to the equation is -1.

71.

$$\frac{3t}{6t+6} + \frac{t}{2t+2} = \frac{2t-3}{t+1}$$

$$\frac{3t}{6(t+1)} + \frac{t}{2(t+1)} = \frac{2t-3}{t+1}$$

$$6(t+1)\left[\frac{3t}{6(t+1)} + \frac{t}{2(t+1)}\right] = 6(t+1)\left(\frac{2t-3}{t+1}\right)$$

$$3t + 3t = 6(2t-3)$$

$$6t = 12t - 18$$

$$-6t = -18$$

$$t = 3$$

Check:

$$\frac{3(3)}{6(3)+6} + \frac{3}{2(3)+2} = \frac{2(3)-3}{3+1}$$

$$\frac{9}{18+6} + \frac{3}{6+2} = \frac{6-3}{4}$$

$$\frac{9}{24} + \frac{3}{8} = \frac{3}{4}$$

$$\frac{3}{8} + \frac{3}{8} = \frac{3}{4}$$

$$\frac{6}{8} = \frac{3}{4}$$

$$\frac{3}{4} = \frac{3}{4} \quad \text{True}$$

72.

$$\frac{2}{x-2} - \frac{1}{x+1} = \frac{2}{x^2-x-2}$$

$$\frac{2}{x-2} - \frac{1}{x+1} = \frac{2}{(x-2)(x+1)}$$

$$(x-2)(x+1)\left[\frac{2}{x-2} - \frac{1}{x+1}\right] = \left[\frac{2}{(x-2)(x+1)}\right](x-2)(x+1)$$

$$(x-2)(x+1)\left(\frac{2}{x-2}\right) - (x-2)(x+1)\left(\frac{1}{x+1}\right) = 2$$

$$2(x+1) - (x-2) = 2$$

$$2x+2-x+2 = 2$$

$$x+4 = 2$$

$$x = -2$$

Check: $\dfrac{2}{x-2} - \dfrac{1}{x+1} = \dfrac{2}{x^2-x-2}$

$$\frac{2}{-2-2} - \frac{1}{(-2)+1} = \frac{2}{(-2)^2-(-2)-2}$$

$$\frac{2}{-4} - \frac{1}{-1} = \frac{2}{4+2-2}$$

$$-\frac{1}{2} + 1 = \frac{2}{4}$$

$$\frac{1}{2} = \frac{1}{2} \text{ True}$$

73. The solution is 5. Since $3 = x - 2$, $x = 5$.

74. The solution is 4.
Since $1 + x = 5$, $x = 4$.

75. The solution is 0.
Since $x + x = 0$, $x = 0$.

76. x can be any real number.
$$\frac{1}{4}x + \frac{3}{4}x = 1x = x$$

77. x can be any real number.
$x - 2 + x - 2 = 2x - 4$.

78. x can be any real number except 0.
$$\frac{3}{x} - \frac{1}{x} = \frac{3-1}{x} = \frac{2}{x} \text{ if } x \neq 0.$$

79. $\dfrac{1}{p} + \dfrac{1}{q} = \dfrac{1}{f}$

$$\frac{1}{30} + \frac{1}{q} = \frac{1}{10}$$

$$\frac{1}{q} = \frac{1}{10} - \frac{1}{30}$$

$$\frac{1}{q} = \frac{2}{30}$$

$$2q = 30$$

$$q = 15$$

The image will appear 15 cm from the mirror.

80. a. If you try to solve this equation using cross multiplication, a cubic equation would be obtained.

b.
$$\frac{x^2}{x-3} = \frac{9}{x-3}$$

$$(x-3)\left(\frac{x^2}{x-3}\right) = (x-3)\left(\frac{9}{x-3}\right)$$

$$x^2 = 9$$

$$x^2 - 9 = 0$$

$$(x+3)(x-3) = 0$$

$$x+3 = 0 \quad \text{or} \quad x-3 = 0$$

$$x = -3 \qquad x = 3$$

Since $\dfrac{9}{0}$ is not a real number, 3 is an extraneous solution. The solution to the equation is -3.

81.
$$\frac{x-4}{x^2-2x} = \frac{-4}{x^2-4}$$

$$\frac{x-4}{x(x-2)} = \frac{-4}{(x+2)(x-2)}$$

$$x(x+2)(x-2)\left(\frac{x-4}{x(x-2)}\right) = x(x+2)(x-2)\left(\frac{-4}{(x+2)(x-2)}\right)$$

$$(x+2)(x-4) = -4x$$

$$x^2 - 2x - 8 = -4x$$

$$x^2 + 2x - 8 = 0$$

$$(x+4)(x-2) = 0$$

$$x+4 = 0 \quad \text{or} \quad x-2 = 0$$

$$x = -4 \qquad x = 2$$

Since $\dfrac{-2}{0}$ and $\dfrac{-4}{0}$ are not a real numbers, 2 is an extraneous solution.

The solution to the equation is -4.

82. a.
$$\frac{1}{R_T} = \frac{1}{R_1} + \frac{1}{R_2}$$

$$\frac{1}{R_T} = \frac{1}{200} + \frac{1}{300}$$

$$R_T(200)(300)\left(\frac{1}{R_T}\right) = R_T(200)(300)\left(\frac{1}{200} + \frac{1}{300}\right)$$

$$60,000 = 300R_T + 200R_T$$

$$60,000 = 500R_T$$

$$120 = R_T$$

The total resistance is 120 ohms.

b. $\dfrac{1}{R_T} = \dfrac{1}{R} + \dfrac{1}{R} + \dfrac{1}{R}$

$\dfrac{1}{300} = \dfrac{3}{R}$

$R(1) = 3(300)$

$R = 900$

Each should be 900 ohms.

83. No, it is impossible for both sides of the equation to be equal.

84. a. You can solve the equation by cross-multiplying or use the LCD.

b. $\dfrac{x+3}{5} = \dfrac{x}{4}$

$20\left(\dfrac{x+3}{5}\right) = 20\left(\dfrac{x}{4}\right)$

$4(x+3) = 5x$

$4x + 12 = 5x$

$12 = x$

$\dfrac{x+3}{5} = \dfrac{x}{4}$

$4(x+3) = 5x$

$4x + 12 = 5x$

$12 = x$

Check: $\dfrac{x+3}{5} = \dfrac{x}{4}$

$\dfrac{12+3}{5} = \dfrac{12}{4}$

$3 = 3$ True

c. $\dfrac{5}{x+3} = \dfrac{4}{x}$

d. $\dfrac{5}{x+3} = \dfrac{4}{x}$

$5x = 4x + 12$

$x = 12$

Check: $\dfrac{5}{x+3} = \dfrac{4}{x}$

$\dfrac{5}{12+3} = \dfrac{4}{12}$

$\dfrac{1}{3} = \dfrac{1}{3}$ True

e. $\dfrac{1}{x} + \dfrac{1}{3} = \dfrac{2}{x}$

$3x\left(\dfrac{1}{x} + \dfrac{1}{3}\right) = 3x\left(\dfrac{2}{x}\right)$

$3 + x = 6$

$x = 3$

Check: $\dfrac{1}{x} + \dfrac{1}{3} = \dfrac{2}{x}$

$\dfrac{1}{3} + \dfrac{1}{3} = \dfrac{2}{3}$

$\dfrac{2}{3} = \dfrac{2}{3}$ True

f. $\dfrac{x}{1} + \dfrac{3}{1} = \dfrac{x}{2}$

g. $\dfrac{x}{1} + \dfrac{3}{1} = \dfrac{x}{2}$

$2\left(\dfrac{x}{1} + \dfrac{3}{1}\right) = 2\left(\dfrac{x}{2}\right)$

$2x + 6 = x$

$x = -6$

Check: $\dfrac{x}{1} + \dfrac{3}{1} = \dfrac{x}{2}$

$\dfrac{-6}{1} + \dfrac{3}{1} = \dfrac{-6}{2}$

$-6 + 3 = -3$

$-3 = -3$ True

h. The solution will be the same.

85. Let x be the number of minutes of internet access over 5 hours.

Plan 1: $7.95 + 0.15x$

Plan 2: 19.95

$7.95 + 0.15x = 19.95$

$0.15x = 12$

$x = 80$

80 minutes $= \dfrac{80}{60}$ hours $= 1\dfrac{1}{3}$ hours

Jake would have to use the internet more than

$5 + 1\dfrac{1}{3} = 6\dfrac{1}{3}$ hours.

86. $\dfrac{600 \text{ gallons}}{4 \text{ gallons/minute}} = 150$ minutes

87. Let x = measure of larger angle

$\dfrac{1}{2}x - 30$ = measure of smaller angle

$$x + \left(\dfrac{1}{2}x - 30\right) = 180$$

$$\dfrac{3}{2}x - 30 = 180$$

$$\dfrac{3}{2}x = 210$$

$$\dfrac{2}{3} \cdot \dfrac{3}{2}x = \dfrac{2}{3} \cdot 210$$

$$x = 140$$

The angles measure 40° and 140°.

88. $(3.4 \times 10^{-5})(2 \times 10^{13})$

$= (3.4 \cdot 2) \times (10^{-5} \cdot 10^{13})$

$= 6.8 \times 10^{-5+13}$

$= 6.8 \times 10^{8}$

89. A linear equation is an equation that can be written in the form $ax + b = c$ where a, b, and c are real numbers and $a \neq 0$. An example would be $5x + 8 = 19$. A quadratic equation has the form $ax^2 + bx + c = 0$ where a, b, and c are real numbers and $a \neq 0$. An example would be $4x^2 + 7x + 2 = 0$.

Exercise Set 7.7

1. Some examples are:

$A = \dfrac{1}{2}bh$, $A = \dfrac{1}{2}h(b_1 + b_2)$, $V = \dfrac{1}{3}\pi r^2 h$, and

$V = \dfrac{4}{3}\pi r^3$

2. a. $t = \dfrac{60}{r+10}$

   b. $t = \dfrac{60}{r-10}$

3. It represents 1 complete task.

4. Tracy, $\dfrac{1}{3}$; John, $\dfrac{1}{7}$

5. Let w = width, then $\dfrac{2}{3}w + 5$ = length

area = width · length

$$99 = w\left(\dfrac{2}{3}w + 5\right)$$

$$99 = \dfrac{2w^2}{3} + 5w$$

$$3(99) = 3\left(\dfrac{2w^2}{3} + 5w\right)$$

$$297 = 2w^2 + 15w$$

$$2w^2 + 15w - 297 = 0$$

$$2w^2 + 15w - 297 = 0$$

$$(2w + 33)(w - 9) = 0$$

$2w + 33 = 0$ or $w - 9 = 0$

$w = -\dfrac{33}{2}$ $w = 9$

Since the width cannot be negative, $w = 9$

$$l = \dfrac{2}{3}w + 5$$

$$l = \dfrac{2}{3}(9) + 5$$

$$l = 6 + 5 = 11$$

The length is 11 inches and the width is 9 inches.

6. Let l = length, then $\dfrac{2}{3}l$ = height and $w = 10$ in.

Volume = lwh

$$3840 = l(10)\left(\dfrac{2}{3}l\right)$$

$$3840 = \dfrac{20l^2}{3}$$

$$3(3840) = 3\left(\dfrac{20l^2}{3}\right)$$

$$11520 = 20l^2$$

$$576 = l^2$$

$$0 = l^2 - 576$$

$$0 = (l + 24)(l - 24)$$

$l + 24 = 0$ or $l - 24 = 0$

$l = -24$ $l = 24$

Since the length cannot be negative, $l = 24$.

height = $\dfrac{2}{3}l = \dfrac{2}{3}(24) = 16$

The length is 24 in., the width is 10 in. and the height is 16 in.

7. Let x = height, then $x + 5$ = base

$$\text{area} = \frac{1}{2} \cdot \text{height} \cdot \text{base}$$

$$42 = \frac{1}{2}x(x+5)$$

$$2(42) = 2\left[\frac{1}{2}x(x+5)\right]$$

$$84 = x(x+5)$$

$$84 = x^2 + 5x$$

$$0 = x^2 + 5x - 84$$

$$0 = (x-7)(x+12)$$

$$x - 7 = 0 \quad \text{or} \quad x + 12 = 0$$
$$x = 7 \qquad\qquad x = -12$$

Since the height cannot be negative, $x = 7$.
base $= x + 5 = 7 + 15 = 12$
The base is 12 cm and the height is 7 cm.

8. Let b = base, then $b - 5$ = height

$$A = \frac{1}{2}bh$$

$$558 = \frac{1}{2}b(b-5)$$

$$2(558) = 2\left[\frac{1}{2}b(b-5)\right]$$

$$1116 = b(b-5)$$

$$0 = b^2 - 5b - 1116$$

$$0 = (b-36)(b+31)$$

$$b - 36 = 0 \quad \text{or} \quad b + 31 = 0$$
$$b = 36 \quad \text{or} \qquad b = -31$$

Since a length cannot be negative, the base is 36 inches.

9. Let b = the base of the triangle, then $\left(\frac{1}{2}b - 1\right)$ is the height.

$$A = \frac{1}{2}bh$$

$$12 = \frac{1}{2}b\left(\frac{1}{2}b - 1\right)$$

$$12 = \frac{1}{4}b^2 - \frac{1}{2}b$$

$$4(12) = 4\left(\frac{1}{4}b^2 - \frac{1}{2}b\right)$$

$$48 = b^2 - 2b$$

$$0 = b^2 - 2b - 48$$

$$0 = (b-8)(b+6)$$

$$b - 8 = 0 \quad \text{or} \quad b + 6 = 0$$
$$b = 8 \quad \text{or} \qquad b = -6$$

Since a length cannot be negative, the base is 8 feet.

10. Let b = the sum of the two bases, then $h = \frac{1}{5}b$.

$$A = \frac{1}{2}h(\text{sum of two bases})$$

$$10 = \frac{1}{2}\left(\frac{1}{5}b\right)b$$

$$10 = \frac{1}{10}b^2$$

$$10(10) = 10\left(\frac{1}{10}b^2\right)$$

$$100 = b^2$$

$$0 = b^2 - 100$$

$$0 = (b+10)(b-10)$$

$$b + 10 = 0 \quad \text{or} \quad b - 10 = 0$$
$$b = -10 \quad \text{or} \qquad b = 10$$

Since a length cannot be negative, then the height is $\frac{1}{5}b = \frac{1}{5}(10) = 2$ feet.

11. Let one number be x, then the other number is $9x$.

$$\frac{1}{x} - \frac{1}{9x} = 1$$

$$9x\left(\frac{1}{x} - \frac{1}{9x}\right) = 9x(1)$$

$$9 - 1 = 9x$$

$$8 = 9x$$

$$\frac{8}{9} = x$$

The numbers are $\frac{8}{9}$ and $9\left(\frac{8}{9}\right) = 8$.

12. Let one number be y; then the other number is $3y$.

$$\frac{1}{3y} + \frac{1}{y} = \frac{4}{3}$$

$$\left(\frac{1}{3y} + \frac{1}{y}\right)3y = \left(\frac{4}{3}\right)3y$$

$$1 + 3 = 4y$$

$$4 = 4y$$

$$1 = y$$

The numbers are 1 and $3(1) = 3$.

13. Let x = amount by which the numerator was increased.

$$\frac{3+x}{4} = \frac{5}{2}$$

$$4\left(\frac{3+x}{4}\right) = \left(\frac{5}{2}\right)4$$

$$3 + x = 10$$

$$x = 7$$

The numerator was increased by 7.

14. Let x = amount by which the denominator was decreased.

$$\frac{8}{21-x} = \frac{1}{2}$$

$$8(2) = 1(21-x)$$

$$16 = 21 - x$$

$$-5 = -x$$

$$5 = x$$

The denominator was decreased by 5.

15. Let r = speed of Creole Queen paddle boat.

$$t = \frac{d}{r}$$

Time upstream = time downstream

$$\frac{6}{r-3} = \frac{12}{r+3}$$

$$6(r+3) = 12(r-3)$$

$$6r + 18 = 12r - 36$$

$$54 = 6r$$

$$9 = r$$

The boat's speed in still water is 9 mph.

16. Let c = current.

$$t = \frac{d}{r}$$

Time upstream = time downstream

$$\frac{5}{6-c} = \frac{10}{6+c}$$

$$5(6+c) = 10(6-c)$$

$$30 + 5c = 60 - 10c$$

$$15c = 30$$

$$c = 2$$

The current is 2 mph.

17. Let d = distance and $t = \frac{d}{r}$.

Time going + Time returning = $\frac{5}{2}$.

$$\frac{d}{12} + \frac{d}{12} = \frac{5}{2}$$

$$\frac{2d}{12} = \frac{5}{2}$$

$$4d = 60$$

$$d = 15$$

The trolley traveled 15 miles in one direction.

18. Let s be Jason's speed. Then $s + 30$ is Brandy's speed.

$$t = \frac{d}{r}$$

$$\frac{250}{s} = \frac{400}{s+30}$$

$$250(s+30) = 400s$$

$$250s + 7500 = 400s$$

$$7500 = 150s$$

$$50 = s$$

Jason is riding at 50 km/hr while Brandy's speed is 80 km/hr.

19. Let r be the speed of the propeller plane, then $4r$ is the speed of the jet.

$$\frac{d}{r} = t$$

time by jet + time by propeller plane = 6 hr

$$\frac{1600}{4r} + \frac{500}{r} = 6$$

$$\frac{400}{r} + \frac{300}{r} = 6$$

$$\frac{900}{r} = 6$$

$$r = \frac{900}{6} = 150$$

The speed of the propeller plane is 150 mph and the speed of the jet is 600 mph.

20. Let r = walking rate, then $2r$ = jogging rate.

$$t = \frac{d}{r}$$

time walking + time jogging = total time

$$\frac{2}{r} + \frac{2}{2r} = 1$$

$$4r\left(\frac{2}{r} + \frac{2}{2r}\right) = 4r(1)$$

$$8 + 4 = 4r$$

$$12 = 4r$$

$$3 = r$$

He walks at 3 mph and jogs at 6 mph.

21. Let d = distance from the dock to the no wake zone, then $36.6 - d$ = distance from the no wake zone to Paradise Island.

$$t = \frac{d}{r}$$

time traveled to no wake zone + time traveled from no wake zone = total time

$$\frac{d}{4} + \frac{36.6 - d}{28} = 1.7$$

$$28\left(\frac{d}{4} + \frac{36.6 - d}{28}\right) = 1.7(28)$$

$$7d + 36.6 - d = 47.6$$

$$6d = 11$$

$$d = \frac{11}{6} \approx 1.83$$

$$36.6 - d = 36.6 - 1.83 \approx 34.77$$

The dock is about 1.83 miles from the no wake zone and about 34.77 miles from the no wake zone to the island.

22. Let d = distance jogged, then $5 - d$ = distance walked.

$$t = \frac{d}{r}$$

Time walked + time jogged = 1.4 hr

$$\frac{d}{5} + \frac{5 - d}{3} = 1.4$$

$$15\left(\frac{d}{5} + \frac{5 - d}{3}\right) = 15(1.4)$$

$$3d + 5(5 - d) = 21$$

$$3d + 25 - 5d = 21$$

$$25 - 2d = 21$$

$$-2d = -4$$

$$d = 2$$

She jogs 2 miles and walks $5 - 2 = 3$ miles.

23. Let d = the distance flown with the wind, then $2900 - d$ = the time flown against the wind.

$$\text{time with wind } = \frac{d}{600}$$

$$\text{time against wind } = \frac{2900 - d}{550}$$

$$\frac{d}{600} + \frac{2900 - d}{550} = 5$$

$$3300\left(\frac{d}{600} + \frac{2900 - d}{550}\right) = 5(3300)$$

$$5.5d + 17,400 - 6d = 16,500$$

$$-0.5d = -900$$

$$d = 1800$$

$$\text{time with wind } = \frac{1800}{600} = 3$$

$$\text{time against wind } = \frac{2900 - 800}{550} = 2$$

It flew 3 hours at 600 mph and 2 hours at 550 mph.

24. Let d = distance traveled from Brussels to Amsterdam.

$$t = \frac{d}{r}$$

time for bullet train $= \dfrac{d}{240}$

time for old train $= \dfrac{d}{120}$

$$\frac{d}{240} = \frac{d}{120} - 0.88$$

$$240\left(\frac{d}{240}\right) = 240\left(\frac{d}{120} - 0.88\right)$$

$$d = 2d - 211.2$$

$$-d = -211.2$$

$$d = 211.2$$

The distance is 211.2 km.

25. time at 30 ft/s $= \dfrac{d}{30}$

time at 25 ft/s $= \dfrac{d}{25}$

$$\frac{d}{25} = \frac{d}{30} + 8$$

$$150\left(\frac{d}{25}\right) = \left(\frac{d}{30} + 8\right)150$$

$$6d = 5d + 1200$$

$$d = 1200$$

The boat traveled 1200 feet in one direction.

26. Let d = length of trail.

$$t = \frac{d}{r}$$

Alana's time $= \dfrac{d}{9}$

Tim's time $= \dfrac{d}{6}$

$$\frac{d}{6} = \frac{d}{9} + 0.25$$

$$54\left(\frac{d}{6}\right) = 54\left(\frac{d}{9} + 0.25\right)$$

$$9d = 6d + 13.5$$

$$3d = 13.5$$

$$d = 4.5$$

The trail is 4.5 miles long.

27. Felicia's rate $= \dfrac{1}{6}$

Reynaldo's rate $= \dfrac{1}{8}$

$$\frac{t}{6} + \frac{t}{8} = 1$$

$$48\left(\frac{t}{6} + \frac{t}{8}\right) = 48(1)$$

$$8t + 6t = 48$$

$$14t = 48$$

$$t = 3\frac{3}{7}$$

It will take them $3\dfrac{3}{7}$ hours.

28. First conveyor belt's rate $= \dfrac{1}{20}$

Second conveyor belt's rate $= \dfrac{1}{30}$

$$\frac{t}{20} + \frac{t}{30} = 1$$

$$60\left(\frac{t}{20} + \frac{t}{30}\right) = 60(1)$$

$$3t + 2t = 60$$

$$5t = 60$$

$$t = 12$$

It will take 12 minutes.

29. Gary's rate $= \dfrac{1}{6}$

Alex's rate $= \dfrac{1}{12}$

$$\frac{t}{6} + \frac{t}{12} = 1$$

$$12\left(\frac{t}{6} + \frac{t}{12}\right) = 12(1)$$

$$2t + t = 12$$

$$3t = 12$$

$$t = 4$$

It will take them 4 hours.

30. Becky's rate $= \dfrac{1}{30}$

Karen's rate $= \dfrac{1}{20}$

$$\frac{t}{30} + \frac{t}{20} = 1$$

$$60\left(\frac{t}{30} + \frac{t}{20}\right) = 60(1)$$

$$2t + 3t = 60$$

$$5t = 60$$

$$t = 12$$

It will take them 12 minutes.

31. Eric's rate $= \dfrac{1}{60}$

Jessup's rate $= \dfrac{1}{40}$

$$\frac{t}{60} + \frac{t}{40} = 1$$

$$120\left(\frac{t}{60} + \frac{t}{40}\right) = 120(1)$$

$$2t + 3t = 120$$

$$5t = 120$$

$$t = 24$$

It will take them 24 minutes.

32. Robert's rate $= \dfrac{1}{6.5}$

Andrea's rate $= \dfrac{1}{7}$

$$\frac{t}{6.5} + \frac{t}{7} = 1$$

$$45.5\left(\frac{t}{6.5} + \frac{t}{7}\right) = 45.5(1)$$

$$7t + 6.5t = 45.5$$

$$13.5t = 45.5$$

$$t \approx 3.37$$

It will take them about 3.37 hours.

33. input rate $= \dfrac{1}{40}$

output rate $= \dfrac{1}{60}$

$$\frac{t}{40} - \frac{t}{60} = 1$$

$$120\left(\frac{t}{40} - \frac{t}{60}\right) = 120(1)$$

$$3t - 2t = 120$$

$$t = 120$$

It will take 120 minutes or 2 hours for the tub to fill.

34. input rate $= \dfrac{1}{8}$

output rate $= \dfrac{1}{12}$

$$\frac{t}{8} - \frac{t}{12} = 1$$

$$24\left(\frac{t}{8} - \frac{t}{12}\right) = 24(1)$$

$$3t - 2t = 24$$

$$t = 24$$

It will take 24 hours.

35. Rate for first $= \dfrac{1}{40}$

Rate for second $= \dfrac{1}{t}$

In 24 minutes, the first computer completes $\dfrac{24}{40} = \dfrac{3}{5}$ of the checks and the second computer completes $\dfrac{24}{t}$.

$$\frac{3}{5} + \frac{24}{t} = 1$$

$$5t\left(\frac{3}{5} + \frac{24}{t}\right) = 5t(1)$$

$$3t + 120 = 5t$$

$$120 = 2t$$

$$60 = t$$

It would take the second computer 60 minutes or 1 hour.

36. Input rate for small hose $= \dfrac{1}{6}$

Input rate for larger hose $= \dfrac{1}{t}$

In 2 hours, the smaller hose does $\dfrac{2}{6}$ of the filling

and the larger hose does $\dfrac{2}{t}$.

$$\frac{2}{6} + \frac{2}{t} = 1$$

$$6t\left(\frac{2}{6} + \frac{2}{t}\right) = 6t \cdot 1$$

$$2t + 12 = 6t$$

$$12 = 4t$$

$$3 = t$$

It would take the larger hose 3 hours.

37. Rate for first backhoe $= \dfrac{1}{12}$

Rate for second backhoe $= \dfrac{1}{15}$

Work done by first $= \dfrac{1}{12} \cdot 5 = \dfrac{5}{12}$

Work done by second $= \dfrac{1}{15} \cdot t = \dfrac{t}{15}$

$$\frac{5}{12} + \frac{t}{15} = 1$$

$$60\left(\frac{5}{12} + \frac{t}{15}\right) = 1 \cdot 60$$

$$25 + 4t = 60$$

$$4t = 35$$

$$t = \frac{35}{4} = 8\frac{3}{4}$$

It takes the smaller backhoe $8\dfrac{3}{4}$ days to finish

the trench.

38. Let t = time Ian will drive.

Melissa's rate $= \dfrac{1}{8}$

Ian's rate $= \dfrac{1}{10}$

After 4 hours, Melissa has completed $\dfrac{4}{8}$ of the

trip.

$$\frac{4}{8} + \frac{t}{10} = 1$$

$$40\left(\frac{4}{8} + \frac{t}{10}\right) = 40(1)$$

$$20 + 4t = 40$$

$$4t = 20$$

$$t = 5$$

Ian will drive for 5 hours.

39. Ken's rate $= \dfrac{1}{4}$

Bettina's rate $= \dfrac{1}{6}$

$$\frac{t+3}{6} + \frac{t}{4} = 1$$

$$12\left(\frac{t+3}{6} + \frac{t}{4}\right) = 12 \cdot 1$$

$$2(t+3) + 3t = 12$$

$$2t + 6 + 3t = 12$$

$$5t = 6$$

$$t = \frac{6}{5}$$

It will take them $\dfrac{6}{5}$ hour or 1 hr, 12 min longer.

40. a. Oldest's rate $= \dfrac{1}{3}$

New baler # 1 rate $= \dfrac{1}{2}$

New baler # 2 rate $= \dfrac{1}{2}$

$$\frac{t}{3} + \frac{t}{2} + \frac{t}{2} = 1$$

$$6\left(\frac{t}{3} + \frac{t}{2} + \frac{t}{2}\right) = 6(1)$$

$$2t + 3t + 3t = 6$$

$$8t = 6$$

$$t = \frac{3}{4}$$

It would take the three balers $\dfrac{3}{4}$ hour for 1 acre.

b. $375\left(\dfrac{3}{4}\right) = 281.25$

It would take them $281\dfrac{1}{4}$ hours for 375 acres.

41. Rate of first skimmer $= \dfrac{1}{60}$

Rate of second skimmer $= \dfrac{1}{50}$

Rate of transfer $= \dfrac{1}{30}$

$$\frac{t}{60} + \frac{t}{50} - \frac{t}{30} = 1$$

$$300\left(\frac{t}{60} + \frac{t}{50} - \frac{t}{30}\right) = 300$$

$$5t + 6t - 10t = 300$$

$$t = 300$$

It will take 300 hours to fill the tank.

42. Rate of Bob $= \dfrac{1}{8}$

Rate of Mary $= \dfrac{1}{10}$

Rate of Gloria $= \dfrac{1}{12}$

$$120\left(\frac{t}{8} + \frac{t}{10} + \frac{t}{12}\right) = 120 \cdot 1$$

$$15t + 12t + 10t = 120$$

$$37t = 120$$

$$t = \frac{120}{37} \approx 3.24$$

It would take them about 3.24 hours.

43. Let x be the number.

$$\frac{3}{x} + 2x = 7$$

$$x\left(\frac{3}{x} + 2x\right) = 7x$$

$$3 + 2x^2 = 7x$$

$$2x^2 - 7x + 3 = 0$$

$$(2x - 1)(x - 3) = 0$$

$$2x - 1 = 0 \quad \text{or} \quad x - 3 = 0$$

$$x = \frac{1}{2} \qquad\qquad x = 3$$

The numbers are 3 or $\dfrac{1}{2}$.

44.
$$\frac{1}{x-5} = 2\left(\frac{1}{2x-10}\right)$$

$$\frac{1}{x-5} = \frac{2}{2x-10}$$

$$2(x-5) = 1(2x-10)$$

$$2x - 10 = 2x - 10 \quad \text{True}$$

All real numbers except 5.

45. Ed's rate $= \dfrac{1}{8}$

Samantha's rate $= \dfrac{1}{4}$

$$\frac{p}{4} - 1 = \frac{p}{8}$$

$$8\left(\frac{p}{4} - 1\right) = 8\left(\frac{p}{8}\right)$$

$$2p - 8 = p$$

$$p = 8$$

Each must pick 8 pints.

46. Old model's rate $= \dfrac{1}{60 \text{ minutes}}$

Newer's model $= \dfrac{1}{30 \text{ minutes}}$

$$\frac{t}{60} + \frac{t}{30} = 1$$

$$60\left(\frac{t}{60} + \frac{t}{30}\right) = 60(1)$$

$$t + 2t = 60$$

$$3t = 60$$

$$t = 20$$

It will take them or 20 minutes.

47.
$$\frac{1}{2}(x+3) - (2x+5) = \frac{1}{2}x + \frac{3}{2} - 2x - 5$$

$$= \frac{x}{2} - \frac{4x}{2} + \frac{3}{2} - \frac{10}{2}$$

$$= -\frac{3x}{2} - \frac{7}{2}$$

48.

49. $\dfrac{x^2-14x+48}{x^2-5x-24} \div \dfrac{2x^2-13x+6}{2x^2+5x-3} = \dfrac{x^2-14x+48}{x^2-5x-24} \cdot \dfrac{2x^2+5x-3}{2x^2-13x+6}$

$\qquad\qquad = \dfrac{(x-6)(x-8)}{(x+3)(x-8)} \cdot \dfrac{(2x-1)(x+3)}{(2x-1)(x-6)}$

$\qquad\qquad = 1$

50. $\dfrac{x}{6x^2-x-15} - \dfrac{5}{9x^2-12x-5} = \dfrac{x}{(2x+3)(3x-5)} - \dfrac{5}{(3x+1)(3x-5)}$

$\qquad\qquad = \dfrac{x(3x+1)}{(2x+3)(3x-5)(3x+1)} - \dfrac{5(2x+3)}{(2x+3)(3x-5)(3x+1)}$

$\qquad\qquad = \dfrac{3x^2+x-(10x+15)}{(2x+3)(3x-5)(3x+1)}$

$\qquad\qquad = \dfrac{3x^2+x-10x-15}{(2x+3)(3x-5)(3x+1)}$

$\qquad\qquad = \dfrac{3x^2-9x-15}{(2x+3)(3x-5)(3x+1)}$

Exercise Set 7.8

1. a. As one quantity increases, the other increases.

   b. Answers will vary.

   c. Answers will vary.

2. a. As one quantity increases, the other decreases.

   b. Answers will vary.

   c. Answers will vary.

3. One quantity varies as a product of two or more quantities.

4. One quantity varies as a combination of variables.

5. a. y decreases; as x increases, the denominator increases which makes the value of the whole fraction smaller.

   b. inverse variation; as one quantity increases, the other decreases.

6. a. z increases

   b. direct variation

7. Direct

8. Direct

9. Inverse

10. Direct

11. Direct

12. Direct

13. Direct

14. Direct

15. Direct

16. Inverse

17. Inverse

18. Direct

19. Direct

20. Direct

21. Inverse

22. Direct

23. Inverse

24. Direct

25. a. $x = ky$

b. Substitute 12 for y and 6 for k.
$x = 6(12)$
$x = 72$

26. a. $C = kZ^2$

b. Substitute $\frac{3}{4}$ for k and 9 for Z.

$C = \left(\frac{3}{4}\right)(9)^2 = \frac{3}{4}(81) = \frac{243}{4} = 60.75$

27. a. $y = kR$

b. Substitute 180 for R and 1.7 for k.
$y = 1.7(180)$
$y = 306$

28. a. $x = \frac{k}{y}$

b. Substitute 5 for k and 25 for y.

$x = \frac{5}{25} = \frac{1}{5} = 0.2$

29. a. $R = \frac{k}{W}$

b. Substitute 160 for W and 8 for k.

$R = \frac{8}{160}$

$R = \frac{1}{20} = 0.05$

30. a. $L = \frac{k}{P^2}$

b. Substitute 100 for k and 4 for P.

$L = \frac{100}{4^2} = \frac{100}{16} = \frac{25}{4} = 6.25$

31. a. $A = \frac{kB}{C}$

b. Substitute 12 for B, 4 for C, and 3 for k.

$A = \frac{3(12)}{4} = \frac{36}{4} = 9$

32. a. $A = \frac{kR_1 R_2}{L^2}$

b. Substitute 120 for R_1, 8 for R_2, 5 for L, and $\frac{3}{2}$ for k.

$A = \frac{\frac{3}{2}(120)(8)}{5^2} = \frac{1440}{25} = \frac{288}{5} = 57.6$

33. a. $x = ky$

b. To find k, substitute 12 for x and 3 for y.
$12 = k(3)$

$\frac{12}{3} = k$

$4 = k$
Thus, $x = 4y$.
Now substitute 5 for y.
$x = 4(5) = 20$

34. a. $Z = kW$

b. To find k, substitute 7 for Z and 28 for W.
$7 = k(28)$

$\frac{7}{28} = k$

$\frac{1}{4} = k$

Thus, $Z = \frac{1}{4}W$.
Now substitute 140 for W.

$Z = \frac{1}{4}(140) = 35$

35. a. $y = kR^2$

b. To find k, substitute 5 for y and 5 for R.
$5 = k(5)^2$
$5 = k(25)$

$\frac{5}{25} = k$

$\frac{1}{5} = k$

Thus $y = \frac{1}{5}R^2$.
Now substitute 10 for R.

$y = \frac{1}{5}(10)^2 = \frac{1}{5}(100) = 20$

36. a. $P = kQ^2$

b. To find k, substitute 32 for P and 4 for Q.
$32 = k(4)^2$
$32 = 16k$

$\frac{32}{16} = k$

$2 = k$
Thus, $P = 2Q^2$. Now substitute 7 for Q.

$P = 2(7)^2 = 2(49) = 98$

37. a. $S = \dfrac{k}{G}$

    b. To find k, substitute 12 for S and 0.4 for G.

$$12 = \frac{k}{0.4}$$
$$12(0.4) = k$$
$$4.8 = k$$

Thus $S = \dfrac{4.8}{G}$.

Now substitute 5 for G.

$$S = \frac{4.8}{5} = 0.96$$

38. a. $C = \dfrac{k}{J}$

    b. To find k, substitute 7 for C and 0.7 for J.

$$7 = \frac{k}{0.7}$$
$$7(0.7) = k$$
$$4.9 = k$$

Thus $C = \dfrac{4.9}{J}$.

Now substitute 12 for J.

$$C = \frac{4.9}{12} \approx 0.41$$

39. a. $x = \dfrac{k}{P^2}$

    b. To find k, substitute 5 for P and 4 for x.

$$4 = \frac{k}{5^2}$$
$$4 = \frac{k}{25}$$
$$100 = k$$

Thus $x = \dfrac{100}{P^2}$.

Now substitute 2 for P.

$$x = \frac{100}{(2)^2} = \frac{100}{4} = 25$$

40. a. $R = \dfrac{k}{T^2}$

    b. To find k, substitute 3 for R and 6 for T.

$$3 = \frac{k}{(6)^2}$$
$$3 = \frac{k}{36}$$
$$108 = k$$

Thus, $R = \dfrac{108}{T^2}$.

Now substitute 2 for T.

$$R = \frac{108}{(2)^2} = \frac{108}{4} = 27$$

41. a. $F = \dfrac{kM_1 M_2}{d}$

    b. To find k, substitute 5 for M_1, 10 for M_2, 0.2 for d, and 20 for F.

$$20 = \frac{k(5)(10)}{0.2}$$
$$20 = k(250)$$
$$k = \frac{20}{250} = 0.08$$

Thus $F = \dfrac{0.08 M_1 M_2}{d}$.

Now substitute 10 for M_1, 20 for M_2, and 0.4 for d.

$$F = \frac{0.08(10)(20)}{0.4} = \frac{16}{0.4} = 40$$

42. a. $F = \dfrac{k q_1 q_2}{d^2}$

    b. To find k, substitute 8 for F, 2 for q_1, 8 for q_2, and 4 for d.

$$8 = \frac{k(2)(8)}{4^2}$$
$$8 = \frac{16k}{16}$$
$$8 = k$$

Thus $F = \dfrac{8 q_1 q_2}{d^2}$.

Now substitute 28 for q_1, 12 for q_2, and 2 for d.

$$F = \frac{8(28)(12)}{2^2} = \frac{2688}{4} = 672$$

43. $a = kb$
$k(2b) = 2(kb) = 2a$
If b is doubled, a is doubled.

44. $a = kb^2$
$k(2b)^2 = 4kb = 4a$
If b is doubled, a is quadrupled.

45. $y = \dfrac{k}{x}$
$\dfrac{k}{2x} = \dfrac{1}{2}\left(\dfrac{k}{x}\right) = \dfrac{1}{2}y$
If x is doubled, y is halved.

46. $y = \dfrac{k}{a^2}$
$\dfrac{k}{(2a)^2} = \dfrac{k}{4a^2} = \dfrac{1}{4}\left(\dfrac{k}{a^2}\right) = \dfrac{1}{4}y$
If a is doubled, y is quartered.

47. $F = \dfrac{km_1m_2}{d^2}$
$\dfrac{k(2m_1)m_2}{d^2} = \dfrac{2km_1m_2}{d^2} = 2 \cdot \dfrac{km_1m_2}{d^2} = 2F$
If m_1 is doubled, F is doubled.

48. $F = \dfrac{km_1m_2}{d^2}$
$\dfrac{k(4m_1)m_2}{(2d)^2} = \dfrac{4km_1m_2}{4d^2} = \dfrac{4}{4} \cdot \dfrac{km_1m_2}{d^2} = F$
If m_1 is quadrupled and d is doubled, F is unchanged.

49. $F = \dfrac{km_1m_2}{d^2}$
$\dfrac{k(2m_1)\left(\dfrac{1}{2}m_2\right)}{d^2} = \dfrac{2 \cdot \dfrac{1}{2}km_1m_2}{d^2} = \dfrac{1 \cdot km_1m_2}{d^2} = F$
If m_1 is doubled and m_2 is halved, F is unchanged.

50. $F = \dfrac{km_1m_2}{d^2}$
$\dfrac{km_1m_2}{\left(\dfrac{1}{2}d\right)^2} = \dfrac{km_1m_2}{\dfrac{1}{4}d^2} =$
$\dfrac{1}{\dfrac{1}{4}} \cdot \dfrac{km_1m_2}{d^2} = 4 \cdot \dfrac{km_1m_2}{d^2} = 4F$
If d is halved, F is quadrupled.

51. $F = \dfrac{km_1m_2}{d^2}$
$\dfrac{k\left(\dfrac{1}{2}m_1\right)(4m_2)}{d^2} = \dfrac{\dfrac{1}{2} \cdot 4km_1m_2}{d^2} =$
$\dfrac{2 \cdot km_1m_2}{d^2} = 2 \cdot \dfrac{km_1m_2}{d^2} = 2F$
If m_1 is halved and m_2 is quadrupled, F is doubled.

52. $F = \dfrac{km_1m_2}{d^2}$
$\dfrac{k(2m_1)(4m_2)}{(4d)^2} = \dfrac{2 \cdot 4km_1m_2}{16d^2}$
$= \dfrac{8 \cdot km_1m_2}{16d^2} = \dfrac{1}{2} \cdot \dfrac{km_1m_2}{d^2} = \dfrac{1}{2}F$
If m_1 is doubled, m_2 is quadrupled, and d is quadrupled, then F is halved.

53. Notice that as x gets bigger, y gets smaller. This suggests that the variation is inverse rather than direct. Therefore use the equation $y = \dfrac{k}{x}$. To determine the value of k, choose one of the ordered pairs and substitute the values into the equation $y = \dfrac{k}{x}$ and solve for k. We'll use the ordered pair (5, 1).
$y = \dfrac{k}{x}$
$1 = \dfrac{k}{5} \Rightarrow k = 5$

54. Notice that as x gets bigger, y gets bigger as well. This suggests that the variation is direct rather than inverse. Therefore use the equation $y = kx$. To determine the value of k, choose one of the ordered pairs and substitute the values into the equation $y = kx$ and solve for k. We'll use the ordered pair $(6, 2)$.

$y = kx$

$2 = k \cdot 6 \Rightarrow k = \dfrac{2}{6} = \dfrac{1}{3}$

55. The equation is $p = kl$ To find k substitute 150 for l and 2542.50 for p.

$2542.50 = k(150)$

$k = \dfrac{2542.50}{150}$

$k = 16.95$

Thus $p = 16.95l$.
Now substitute 520 for l.

$p = 16.95(520)$

$p = 8814$

The profit would be $8814.

56. The equation is $p = ks$ To find k substitute 65 for s and 4056 for p.

$4056 = k(65)$

$k = \dfrac{4056}{65}$

$k = 62.4$

Thus $p = 62.4s$.
Now substitute 80 for s.

$p = 62.4(80)$

$p = 4992$

The profit would be $4992.

57. The equation is $d = kw$. To find k, substitute 2376 for d and 132 for w.

$2376 = k132$

$k = \dfrac{2376}{132}$

$k = 18$

Thus $d = 18w$. Now substitute 172 for w.

$d = 18(172)$

$d = 3096$

The recommended dosage for Nathan is 3096 mg.

58. The equation is $p = kd$. To find k substitute 275 for d and 2433.75 for p.

$2433.75 = k(275)$

$k = \dfrac{2433.75}{275}$

$k = 8.85$

Thus $p = 8.85d$.
Now substitute 400 for d.

$p = 8.85(400)$

$p = 3540$

He would get 3540 pesos.

59. The equation is $S = kF$. To find k, substitute 1.4 for S and 20 for F.

$1.4 = k(20)$

$\dfrac{1.4}{20} = k$

$0.07 = k$

Thus, $S = 0.07F$.
Now substitute 15 for F.

$S = 0.07(15) = 1.05$

The spring will stretch 1.05 inches.

60. The equation is $d = kt$. To find k, substitute 150 for d and 2.5 for t.

$150 = k(2.5)$

$k = \dfrac{150}{2.5}$

$k = 60$

Thus $d = 60t$.
Now substitute 4 for t.

$d = 60(4)$

$d = 240$

The car will travel 240 miles in 4 hours.

61. The equation is $V = \dfrac{k}{P}$. To find k, substitute 800

for V and 200 for P.

$$800 = \frac{k}{200}$$

$$800(200) = k$$

$$160,000 = k$$

Thus $V = \dfrac{160,000}{P}$.

Now substitute 25 for P.

$$V = \frac{160,000}{25} = 6400$$

The volume is 6400 cc.

62. The equation is $t = \dfrac{k}{n}$. To find k, substitute

8 for t and 5 for n.

$$8 = \frac{k}{5}$$

$$k = 8(5)$$

$$k = 40$$

Thus $t = \dfrac{40}{n}$.

Now substitute 4 for n.

$$t = \frac{40}{4}$$

$$t = 10$$

It will take 4 bricklayers 10 hours.

63. The equation is $t = \dfrac{k}{s}$. To find k, substitute 6 for

s and 2.6 for t.

$$2.6 = \frac{k}{6}$$

$$k = 6(2.6)$$

$$k = 15.6$$

Thus $t = \dfrac{15.6}{s}$.

Now substitute 5 for s.

$$t = \frac{15.6}{5}$$

$$t = 3.12$$

Jackie will take 3.12 hours.

64. The equation $t = \dfrac{k}{s}$. To find k, substitute 90 for s

and 0.459 for t.

$$0.459 = \frac{k}{90}$$

$$k = 90(0.459) = 41.31$$

Thus $t = \dfrac{41.31}{s}$. Now substitute 75 for s.

$$t = \frac{41.31}{75} = 0.5508$$

It takes 0.5508 seconds for the ball to reach the plate.

65. The equation is $I = \dfrac{k}{d^2}$. To find k, substitute 20

for I and 15 for d.

$$20 = \frac{k}{(15)^2}$$

$$20 = \frac{k}{225}$$

$$k = 20(225) = 4500$$

Thus $I = \dfrac{4500}{d^2}$.

Now substitute 10 for d.

$$I = \frac{4500}{(10)^2}$$

$$I = \frac{4500}{100}$$

$$I = 45$$

The intensity is 45 foot-candles.

66. The equation is $t = \dfrac{k}{s}$. To find k, substitute 122

for s and 0.21 for t.

$$0.21 = \frac{k}{122}$$

$$k = 0.21(122)$$

$$k = 25.62$$

Thus $t = \dfrac{25.62}{s}$.

Now substitute 80 for s.

$$t = \frac{25.62}{80} \approx 0.32$$

It takes about 0.32 seconds for the ball to hit the ground in the service box.

67. The equation is $d = ks^2$. To find k, substitute 40 for s and 60 for d.

$$d = ks^2$$
$$60 = k(40)^2$$
$$60 = 1600k$$
$$k = \frac{60}{1600} = 0.0375$$

Thus $d = 0.0375s^2$. Now substitute 56 for s.

$$d = 0.0375s^2$$
$$d = 0.0375(56)^2$$
$$d = 117.6$$

The stopping distance is 117.6 feet.

68. The equation is $d = kt^2$. To find k, substitute 0.5 for t and 4 for d.

$$d = kt^2$$
$$4 = k(0.5)^2$$
$$4 = 0.25k$$
$$k = \frac{4}{0.25} = 16$$

Thus $d = 16t^2$. Now substitute 3 for t.

$$d = 16(3)^2 = 144$$

The rock falls 144 feet in 3 seconds.

69. The equation is $V = kBh$. To find k, substitute 160 for V, 48 for B, and 10 for h.

$$160 = k(48)(10)$$
$$160 = 480k$$
$$\frac{160}{480} = k$$
$$\frac{1}{3} = k$$

Thus, $V = \frac{1}{3}Bh$. Now substitute 42 for B and 9 for h.

$$V = \frac{1}{3}(42)(9) = 14(9) = 126$$

The volume of the pyramid would be 126 m^3.

70. The equation is $P = krm$. To find k, substitute 50,000 for m and 0.07 for r and 332.5 for P.

$$332.5 = k(0.07)(50,000)$$
$$332.5 = 3500k$$
$$k = \frac{332.5}{3500} = 0.095$$

Thus $P = 0.095rm$.
Now substitute 66,000 for m and 0.07 for r.

$$P = 0.095(0.07)(66,000)$$
$$P = 438.9$$

The payment is \$438.90.

71. The equation is $R = \frac{kA}{P}$. To find k, substitute 400 for A, 2 for P, and 4600 for R.

$$4600 = \frac{k(400)}{2}$$
$$4600 = 200k$$
$$k = \frac{4600}{200} = 23$$

Thus $R = \frac{23A}{P}$. Now substitute 500 for A and 2.50 for P.

$$R = \frac{23(500)}{2.50}$$
$$R = \frac{11,500}{2.50}$$
$$R = 4600 \text{ DVDs}$$

They would still rent 4600 DVDs per week.

72. The equation is $R = \frac{kL}{A}$. To find k, substitute 0.2 for R, 200 for L, and 0.05 for A.

$$0.02 = \frac{k(200)}{0.05}$$
$$0.2 = k(4000)$$
$$\frac{0.2}{4000} = k$$
$$0.00005 = k$$

Thus $R = \frac{0.00005L}{A}$. Now substitute 5000 for L and 0.01 for A.

$$R = \frac{0.00005(5000)}{0.01}$$
$$R = \frac{0.25}{0.01}$$
$$R = 25$$

The resistance is 25 ohms.

73. The equation is $w = \dfrac{k}{d^2}$. To find k, substitute 140 for w and 4000 for d.

$$140 = \frac{k}{(4000)^2}$$

$$140 = \frac{k}{16,000,000}$$

$$140(16,000,000) = k$$

$$2,240,000,000 = k$$

Thus $w = \dfrac{2,240,000,000}{d^2}$. Now substitute 4100 for d.

$$w = \frac{2,240,000,000}{(4100)^2}$$

$$w = \frac{2,240,000,000}{16,810,000}$$

$$w \approx 133.25$$

The weight is about 133.25 pounds.

74. The equation is $W = kI^2R$. To find k, substitute 3 for W, 0.1 for I, and 100 for R.

$$3 = k(0.1)^2(100)$$

$$3 = k(0.01)(100)$$

$$3 = k(1)$$

$$3 = k$$

Thus $W = 3I^2R$. Now substitute 0.4 for I and 250 for R.

$$W = 3(0.4)^2(250)$$

$$W = 3(0.16)(250)$$

$$W = 120$$

The wattage is 120 watts.

75. The equation is $N = \dfrac{kp_1p_2}{d}$. To find k, substitute 100,000 for N, 300 for d, 60,000 for p_1, and 200,000 for p_2.

$$100,000 = \frac{k(60,000)(200,000)}{300}$$

$$100,000 = 40,000,000k$$

$$\frac{100,000}{40,000,000} = k$$

$$0.0025 = k$$

Thus $N = \dfrac{0.0025p_1p_2}{d}$.

Now substitute 450 for d, 125,000 for p_1, and 175,000 for p_2.

$$N = \frac{0.0025(125,000)(175,000)}{450}$$

$$N \approx 121,528$$

About 121,528 calls are made.

76. The equation is $W = \dfrac{kTA\sqrt{F}}{R}$

To find k, substitute 78 for T, 5.6 for R, 4 for F, 1000 for A, and 68 for W.

$$68 = \frac{k(78)(1000)\sqrt{4}}{5.6}$$

$$68 = \frac{156,000k}{5.6}$$

$$\frac{(68)(5.6)}{156,000} = k$$

$$0.002441 \approx k$$

Thus $W = \dfrac{0.002441TA\sqrt{E}}{R}$

Now, substitute 78 for T, 5.6 for R, 6 for E, and 1500 for A.

$$W = \frac{0.002441(78)(1500)\sqrt{6}}{5.6} \approx 124.92$$

The water bill is about \$124.92.

77. Let I be the intensity of the illumination and d be the distance the subject is from the flash.

The equation is $I = \dfrac{k}{d^2}$. To find k, substitute $\dfrac{1}{16}$ for I and 4 for d.

$$\frac{1}{16} = \frac{k}{4^2}$$

$$\frac{1}{16} = \frac{k}{16}$$

$$1 = k$$

Thus $I = \dfrac{1}{d^2}$.

Now, substitute 7 for d.

$$I = \frac{1}{7^2} = \frac{1}{49}$$

The illumination is $\dfrac{1}{49}$ of the light of the flash.

78. a. The equation is $F = \dfrac{km_1 m_2}{d^2}$.

b. If m_1 becomes $2m_1$, m_2 becomes $3m_2$ and d becomes $\dfrac{d}{2}$, then

$F = \dfrac{k(2m_1)(3m_2)}{\left(\dfrac{d}{2}\right)^2}$

$= \dfrac{6km_1 m_2}{\dfrac{d^2}{4}}$

$= 24\dfrac{km_1 m_2}{d^2}$

The new force is 24 times the original force.

79. a. The equation is $P = 14.7 + kx$

b. The find k, substitute 40.5 for P and 60 for x.

$40.5 = 14.7 + 60k$

$25.8 = 60k$

$\dfrac{25.8}{60} = k$

$0.43 = k$

c. The equation is $P = 14.7 + 0.43x$.
Substitute 160 for P.

$160 = 14.7 + 0.43x$

$145.3 = 0.43x$

$\dfrac{145.3}{0.43} = x$

$337.9 \approx x$

The submarine can go about 337.9 feet deep.

80.
$$\begin{array}{r} 2x-3 \\ 4x+9\overline{)8x^2+6x-21} \\ \underline{8x^2+18x} \\ -12x-21 \\ \underline{-12x-27} \\ 6 \end{array}$$

$\dfrac{8x^2+6x-21}{4x+9} = 2x-3+\dfrac{6}{4x+9}$

81. $y(z-2)+8(z-2)=(z-2)(y+8)$

82.
$3x^2-24=-6x$
$3x^2+6x-24=0$
$x^2+2x-8=0$
$(x+4)(x-2)=0$
$x+4=0 \quad$ or $\quad x-2=0$
$\quad x=-4 \qquad\qquad x=2$

83. $\dfrac{x+8}{x-3}\cdot\dfrac{x^3-27}{x^2+3x+9} = \dfrac{(x+8)(x-3)(x^2+3x+9)}{(x-3)(x^2+3x+9)}$

$= x+8$

Chapter 7 Review Exercises

1. $\dfrac{5}{2x-18}$
$2x-18=0$
$2(x-9)=0$
$x-9=0$
$x=9$
The expression is defined for all real numbers except $x=9$.

2. $\dfrac{2x+1}{x^2-8x+15}$
$x^2-8x+15=0$
$(x-3)(x-5)=0$
$x-3=0 \quad$ or $\quad x-5=0$
$\quad x=3 \qquad\qquad x=5$
The expression is defined for all real numbers except $x=3$, $x=5$.

3. $\dfrac{7x-1}{5x^2+4x-1}$
$5x^2+4x-1=0$
$(5x-1)(x+1)=0$
$5x-1=0 \quad$ or $\quad x+1=0$
$\quad x=\dfrac{1}{5} \qquad\qquad x=-1$
The expression is defined for all real numbers except $x=\dfrac{1}{5}$, $x=-1$.

4. $\dfrac{y}{xy-3y} = \dfrac{y}{y(x-3)} = \dfrac{1}{x-3}$

5. $\dfrac{x^3 + 5x^2 + 12x}{x} = \dfrac{x\left(x^2 + 5x + 12\right)}{x}$

$= x^2 + 5x + 12$

6. $\dfrac{9x^2 + 3xy}{3x} = \dfrac{\cancel{3x}\left(3x + y\right)}{\cancel{3x}} = 3x + y$

7. $\dfrac{x^2 + 2x - 8}{x - 2} = \dfrac{\cancel{(x-2)}(x+4)}{\cancel{x-2}} = x + 4$

8. $\dfrac{a^2 - 81}{a - 9} = \dfrac{\cancel{(a-9)}(a+9)}{\cancel{a-9}} = a + 9$

9. $\dfrac{-2x^2 + 7x + 4}{x - 4} = \dfrac{-1\left(2x^2 + 7x + 4\right)}{(x - 4)}$

$= \dfrac{-1(2x+1)\cancel{(x-4)}}{\cancel{(x-4)}}$

$= -(2x+1)$

10. $\dfrac{b^2 - 2b + 10}{b^2 - 3b - 10} = \dfrac{\cancel{(b-5)}(b-2)}{\cancel{(b-5)}(b+2)} = \dfrac{b-2}{b+2}$

11. $\dfrac{4x^2 - 11x - 3}{4x^2 - 7x - 2} = \dfrac{\cancel{(4x+1)}(x-3)}{\cancel{(4x+1)}(x-2)}$

$= \dfrac{x-3}{x-2}$

12. $\dfrac{2x^2 - 21x + 40}{4x^2 - 4x - 15} = \dfrac{(x-8)\cancel{(2x-5)}}{(2x+3)\cancel{(2x-5)}}$

$= \dfrac{x-8}{2x+3}$

13. $\dfrac{5a^2}{6b} \cdot \dfrac{2}{4a^2b} = \dfrac{5 \cdot 2}{6 \cdot 4} \cdot \dfrac{a^2}{a^2} \cdot \dfrac{1}{b \cdot b}$

$= \dfrac{10}{24b^2}$

$= \dfrac{5}{12b^2}$

14. $\dfrac{30x^2y^3}{3z} \cdot \dfrac{6z^3}{5xy^3} = \dfrac{15 \cdot 2 \cdot 6}{15}\left(\dfrac{x^2}{x}\right)\left(\dfrac{y^3}{y^3}\right)\left(\dfrac{z^3}{z}\right)$

$= 12xz^2$

15. $\dfrac{20a^3b^4}{7c^3} \cdot \dfrac{14c^7}{5a^5b} = \dfrac{20}{5} \cdot \dfrac{14}{7} \cdot \dfrac{a^3}{a^5} \cdot \dfrac{b^4}{b} \cdot \dfrac{c^7}{c^3}$

$= 8\dfrac{1}{a^2}b^3c^4$

$= \dfrac{8b^3c^4}{a^2}$

16. $\dfrac{1}{x-4} \cdot \dfrac{4-x}{9} = \dfrac{1}{\cancel{x-4}} \cdot \dfrac{-1\cancel{(x-4)}}{9}$

$= -\dfrac{1}{9}$

17. $\dfrac{-m+4}{15m} \cdot \dfrac{10m}{m-4} = \dfrac{-1\cancel{(m-4)}}{3 \cdot \cancel{5m}} \cdot \dfrac{2 \cdot \cancel{5m}}{\cancel{m-4}}$

$= \dfrac{-2}{3}$

18. $\dfrac{a-2}{a+3} \cdot \dfrac{a^2 + 4a + 3}{a^2 - a - 2} = \dfrac{\cancel{(a-2)}\cancel{(a+3)}\cancel{(a+1)}}{\cancel{(a+3)}\cancel{(a-2)}\cancel{(a+1)}}$

$= 1$

19. $\dfrac{9x^6}{y^2} \div \dfrac{x^4}{4y} = \dfrac{9x^6}{y^2} \cdot \dfrac{4y}{x^4} = \dfrac{36x^6y}{x^4y^2} = \dfrac{36x^2}{y}$

20. $\dfrac{5xy^2}{z} \div \dfrac{x^4y^2}{4z^2} = \dfrac{5xy^2}{z} \cdot \dfrac{4z^2}{x^4y^2} = \dfrac{20z}{x^3}$

21. $\dfrac{6a + 6b}{a^2} \div \dfrac{a^2 - b^2}{a^2} = \dfrac{6\cancel{(a+b)}}{\cancel{a^2}} \cdot \dfrac{\cancel{a^2}}{\cancel{(a+b)}(a-b)}$

$= \dfrac{6}{a-b}$

22. $\dfrac{1}{a^2 + 8a + 15} \div \dfrac{8}{a+5} = \dfrac{1}{\cancel{(a+5)}(a+3)} \cdot \dfrac{\cancel{a+5}}{8}$

$= \dfrac{1}{8(a+3)}$

23. $(t+8) \div \dfrac{t^2 + 5t - 24}{t-3} = \dfrac{\cancel{(t+8)}}{1} \cdot \dfrac{\cancel{t-3}}{\cancel{(t-3)}\cancel{(t+8)}}$

$= 1$

24. $\dfrac{x^2 + xy - 2y^2}{2y} \div \dfrac{x + 2y}{12y^2} = \dfrac{(x-y)\cancel{(x+2y)}}{2y} \cdot \dfrac{12y^2}{\cancel{x+2y}}$

$= 6y(x-y)$

25. $\dfrac{n}{n+5} - \dfrac{2}{n+5} = \dfrac{n-2}{n+5}$

26. $\dfrac{4x}{x+7} + \dfrac{28}{x+7} = \dfrac{4x+28}{x+7} = \dfrac{4\cancel{(x+7)}}{\cancel{x+7}} = 4$

27. $\dfrac{5x-4}{x+8} + \dfrac{44}{x+8} = \dfrac{5x-4+44}{x+8}$

$= \dfrac{5x+40}{x+8} = \dfrac{5\cancel{(x+8)}}{\cancel{x+8}}$

$= 5$

28. $\dfrac{7x-3}{x^2+7x-30} - \dfrac{3x+9}{x^2+7x-30} = \dfrac{7x-3-(3x+9)}{x^2+7x-30}$

$= \dfrac{7x-3-3x-9}{x^2+7x-30}$

$= \dfrac{4x-12}{x^2+7x-30}$

$= \dfrac{4\cancel{(x-3)}}{(x+10)\cancel{(x-3)}}$

$= \dfrac{4}{x+10}$

29. $\dfrac{5h^2+12h-1}{h+5} - \dfrac{h^2-5h+14}{h+5}$

$= \dfrac{5h^2+12h-1-\left(h^2-5h+14\right)}{h+5}$

$= \dfrac{5h^2+12h-1-h^2+5h-14}{h+5}$

$= \dfrac{4h^2+17h-15}{h+5}$

$\dfrac{(4h-3)\cancel{(h+5)}}{\cancel{h+5}}$

$= 4h-3$

30. $\dfrac{6x^2-4x}{2x-3} - \dfrac{-3x+12}{2x-3}$

$= \dfrac{6x^2+4x-(-3x+12)}{2x-3}$

$= \dfrac{6x^2-4x+3x-12}{2x-3}$

$= \dfrac{6x^2-x-12}{2x-3}$

$= \dfrac{(3x+4)\cancel{(2x-3)}}{\cancel{2x-3}}$

$= 3x+4$

31. $\dfrac{a}{8} + \dfrac{5a}{3}$

Least common denominator $= 2(2)(2)(3) = 24$

32. $\dfrac{10}{x+3} + \dfrac{2x}{x+3}$

Least common denominator $= x+3$

33. $\dfrac{10}{4xy^3} - \dfrac{11}{10x^2y}$

Least common denominator $= 20x^2y^3$

34. $\dfrac{6}{x-3} - \dfrac{2}{x}$

Least common denominator $= x(x-3)$

35. $\dfrac{8}{n+5} + \dfrac{2n-3}{n-4}$

Least common denominator $= (n+5)(n-4)$

36. $\dfrac{5x-12}{x^2+2x} - \dfrac{4}{x+2} = \dfrac{5x-12}{x(x+2)} - \dfrac{4}{x+2}$

Least common denominator $= x(x+2)$

37. $\dfrac{2r+1}{r-s} - \dfrac{6}{r^2-s^2} = \dfrac{2r+1}{r-s} - \dfrac{6}{(r+s)(r-s)}$

Least common denominator $= (r+s)(r-s)$

38. $\dfrac{3x^2}{x-9} + 10x^3 = \dfrac{4x^2}{x-9} + \dfrac{10x^3}{1}$

Least common denominator $= x-9$

39. $\dfrac{19x-5}{x^2+2x-35}+\dfrac{-10x+1}{x^2+9x+14}$

$=\dfrac{19x-5}{(x+7)(x-5)}+\dfrac{-10x+1}{(x+7)(x+2)}$

Least common denominator

$=(x+7)(x-5)(x+2)$

40. $\dfrac{5}{3y^2}+\dfrac{y}{2y}=\dfrac{5}{3y^2}+\dfrac{1}{2}$

$=\dfrac{5}{3y^2}\cdot\dfrac{2}{2}+\dfrac{1}{2}\cdot\dfrac{3y^2}{3y^2}$

$=\dfrac{10}{6y^2}+\dfrac{3y^2}{6y^2}$

$=\dfrac{10+3y^2}{6y^2}$

$=\dfrac{3y^2+10}{6y^2}$

41. $\dfrac{3x}{xy}+\dfrac{1}{4x}=\dfrac{3x}{xy}\cdot\dfrac{4}{4}+\dfrac{1}{4x}\cdot\dfrac{y}{y}$

$=\dfrac{12x}{4xy}+\dfrac{y}{4xy}$

$=\dfrac{12x+y}{4xy}$

42. $\dfrac{5x}{3xy}-\dfrac{6}{x^2}=\dfrac{5x}{3xy}\cdot\dfrac{x}{x}-\dfrac{6}{x^2}\cdot\dfrac{3y}{3y}$

$=\dfrac{5x^2}{3x^2y}-\dfrac{18y}{3x^2y}$

$=\dfrac{5x^2-18y}{3x^2y}$

43. $7-\dfrac{2}{x+2}=7\left(\dfrac{x+2}{x+2}\right)-\dfrac{2}{x+2}$

$=\dfrac{7x+14-2}{x+2}$

$=\dfrac{7x+12}{x+2}$

44. $\dfrac{x-y}{y}-\dfrac{x+y}{x}=\dfrac{x-y}{y}\cdot\dfrac{x}{x}-\dfrac{x+y}{x}\cdot\dfrac{y}{y}$

$=\dfrac{x(x-y)}{xy}-\dfrac{y(x+y)}{xy}$

$=\dfrac{x^2-xy-xy-y^2}{xy}$

$=\dfrac{x^2-2xy-y^2}{xy}$

45. $\dfrac{7}{x+4}+\dfrac{2}{x}=\dfrac{7}{x+4}\cdot\dfrac{x}{x}+\dfrac{2}{x}\cdot\dfrac{x+4}{x+4}$

$=\dfrac{7x}{x(x+4)}+\dfrac{2(x+4)}{x(x+4)}$

$=\dfrac{7x+2x+8}{x(x+4)}$

$=\dfrac{9x+8}{x(x+4)}$

46. $\dfrac{2}{3x}-\dfrac{3}{3x-6}=\dfrac{2}{3x}-\dfrac{3}{3(x-2)}$

$=\dfrac{2}{3x}\cdot\dfrac{x-2}{x-2}-\dfrac{3}{3(x-2)}\cdot\dfrac{x}{x}$

$=\dfrac{2(x-2)}{3x(x-2)}-\dfrac{3x}{3x(x-2)}$

$=\dfrac{2x-4-3x}{3x(x-2)}$

$=\dfrac{-x-4}{3x(x-2)}$

47. $\dfrac{1}{z+5}+\dfrac{9}{(z+5)^2}=\dfrac{1}{z+5}\cdot\dfrac{z+5}{z+5}+\dfrac{9}{(z+5)^2}$

$=\dfrac{1(z+5)}{(z+5)^2}+\dfrac{9}{(z+5)^2}$

$=\dfrac{z+5+9}{(z+5)^2}$

$=\dfrac{z+14}{(z+5)^2}$

48. $\dfrac{x+2}{x^2-x-6}+\dfrac{x-3}{x^2-8x+15}$

$=\dfrac{x+2}{(x-3)(x+2)}+\dfrac{x-3}{(x-3)(x-5)}$

$=\dfrac{1}{x-3}+\dfrac{1}{x-5}$

$=\dfrac{1}{x-3}\cdot\dfrac{x-5}{x-5}+\dfrac{1}{x-5}\cdot\dfrac{x-3}{x-3}$

$=\dfrac{x-5}{(x-3)(x-5)}+\dfrac{x-3}{(x-5)(x-3)}$

$=\dfrac{x-5+x-3}{(x-5)(x-3)}$

$=\dfrac{2x-8}{(x-5)(x-3)}$

49. $\dfrac{x+4}{x+6}-\dfrac{x-5}{x+2}=\dfrac{(x+4)(x+2)}{(x+6)(x+2)}-\dfrac{(x-5)(x+6)}{(x+2)(x+6)}$

$=\dfrac{x^2+6x+8-(x^2+x-30)}{(x+6)(x+2)}$

$=\dfrac{x^2+6x+8-x^2+x+30}{(x+6)(x+2)}$

$=\dfrac{5x+38}{(x+6)(x+2)}$

50. $2+\dfrac{x}{x-4}=\dfrac{2(x-4)}{x-4}+\dfrac{x}{x-4}$

$=\dfrac{2x-8+x}{x-4}$

$=\dfrac{3x-8}{x-4}$

51. $\dfrac{a+2}{b}\div\dfrac{a-2}{5b^2}=\dfrac{a+2}{b}\cdot\dfrac{5b^2}{a-2}$

$=\dfrac{5b(a+2)}{a-2}$

$=\dfrac{5ab+10b}{a-2}$

52. $\dfrac{x+5}{x^2-9}+\dfrac{2}{x+3}=\dfrac{x+5}{(x-3)(x+3)}+\dfrac{2}{x+3}$

$=\dfrac{x+5}{(x-3)(x+3)}+\dfrac{2(x-3)}{(x-3)(x+3)}$

$=\dfrac{x+5+2x-6}{(x-3)(x+3)}$

$=\dfrac{3x-1}{(x-3)(x+3)}$

53. $\dfrac{6p+12q}{p^2q}\cdot\dfrac{p^4}{p+2q}=\dfrac{6\cancel{(p+2q)}p^4}{\cancel{(p+2q)}p^2q}=\dfrac{6p^2}{q}$

54. $\dfrac{8}{(x+2)(x-3)}-\dfrac{6}{(x-2)(x+2)}$

$=\dfrac{8(x-2)}{(x+2)(x-3)(x-2)}-\dfrac{6(x-3)}{(x+2)(x-3)(x-2)}$

$=\dfrac{8(x-2)-6(x-3)}{(x+2)(x-3)(x-2)}$

$=\dfrac{8x-16-6x+18}{(x+2)(x-3)(x-2)}$

$=\dfrac{2x+2}{(x+2)(x-3)(x-2)}$

55. $\dfrac{x+7}{x^2+9x+14}-\dfrac{x-10}{x^2-49}$

$=\dfrac{x+7}{(x+7)(x+2)}-\dfrac{x-10}{(x+7)(x-7)}$

$=\dfrac{x+7}{(x+7)(x+2)}\cdot\dfrac{(x-7)}{(x-7)}-\dfrac{x-10}{(x+7)(x-7)}\cdot\dfrac{(x+2)}{(x+2)}$

$=\dfrac{x^2-49-\left(x^2-8x-20\right)}{(x+7)(x-7)(x+2)}$

$=\dfrac{8x-29}{(x+7)(x-7)(x+2)}$

56. $\dfrac{x-y}{x+y}\cdot\dfrac{xy+x^2}{x^2-y^2}=\dfrac{\cancel{x-y}}{x+y}\cdot\dfrac{x\cancel{(y+x)}}{\cancel{(x+y)}\cancel{(x-y)}}$

$=\dfrac{x}{x+y}$

57. $\dfrac{3x^2-27y^2}{30} \div \dfrac{(x-3y)^2}{6}$

$= \dfrac{3\left(x^2-9y^2\right)}{30} \cdot \dfrac{6}{(x-3y)^2}$

$= \dfrac{3\cancel{(x-3y)}(x+3y)}{\cancel{6}\cdot 5} \cdot \dfrac{\cancel{6}}{\cancel{(x-3y)}(x-3y)}$

$= \dfrac{3(x+3y)}{5(x-3y)}$

58. $\dfrac{a^2-11a+30}{a-6} \cdot \dfrac{a^2-8a+15}{a^2-10a+25}$

$= \dfrac{\cancel{(a-6)}\cancel{(a-5)}}{\cancel{a-6}} \cdot \dfrac{\cancel{(a-5)}(a-3)}{\cancel{(a-5)^2}}$

$= a-3$

59. $\dfrac{a}{a^2-1} - \dfrac{3}{3a^2-2a-5}$

$= \dfrac{a}{(a-1)(a+1)} - \dfrac{3}{(3a-5)(a+1)}$

$= \dfrac{a(3a-5)}{(a-1)(a+1)(3a-5)} - \dfrac{3(a-1)}{(a-1)(a+1)(3a-5)}$

$= \dfrac{a(3a-5)-3(a-1)}{(a-1)(a+1)(3a-5)}$

$= \dfrac{3a^2-5a-3a+3}{(a-1)(a+1)(3a-5)}$

$= \dfrac{3a^2-8a+3}{(a-1)(a+1)(3a-5)}$

60. $\dfrac{2x^2+6x-20}{x^2-2x} \div \dfrac{x^2+7x+10}{2x^2-8}$

$= \dfrac{2\left(x^2+3x-10\right)}{x(x-2)} \cdot \dfrac{2\left(x^2-4\right)}{(x+5)(x+2)}$

$= \dfrac{2(x+5)(x-2)}{x(x-2)} \cdot \dfrac{2(x+2)(x-2)}{(x+5)(x+2)}$

$= \dfrac{4(x-2)}{x}$

$= \dfrac{4x-8}{x}$

61. $\dfrac{5+\dfrac{2}{3}}{\dfrac{3}{4}} = \dfrac{12\left(5+\dfrac{2}{3}\right)}{12\left(\dfrac{3}{4}\right)} = \dfrac{60+8}{9} = \dfrac{68}{9}$

62. $\dfrac{1+\dfrac{5}{8}}{3-\dfrac{9}{16}} = \dfrac{16\left(1+\dfrac{5}{8}\right)}{16\left(3-\dfrac{9}{16}\right)}$

$= \dfrac{16+10}{48-9}$

$= \dfrac{26}{39}$

$= \dfrac{2}{3}$

63. $\dfrac{\dfrac{12ab}{9c}}{\dfrac{4a}{c^2}} = \dfrac{12ab}{9c} \cdot \dfrac{c^2}{4a} = \dfrac{bc}{3}$

64. $\dfrac{\dfrac{18x^4y^2}{9xy^5}}{\dfrac{4z^2}{4z^2}} = \dfrac{18x^4y^2 \cdot 4z^2}{9xy^5 \cdot 4z^2} = \dfrac{72x^4y^2z^2}{9xy^5} = \dfrac{8x^3z^2}{y^3}$

65. $\dfrac{a-\dfrac{a}{b}}{\dfrac{1+a}{b}} = \dfrac{\left(a-\dfrac{a}{b}\right)b}{\left(\dfrac{1+a}{b}\right)b} = \dfrac{ab-a}{1+a}$

66. $\dfrac{r^2+\dfrac{7}{s}}{\dfrac{s^2}{s}} = \dfrac{\left(r^2+\dfrac{7}{s}\right)s}{\left(s^2\right)s} = \dfrac{r^2s+7}{s^3}$

67. $\dfrac{\dfrac{3}{x}+\dfrac{2}{x^2}}{5-\dfrac{1}{x}} = \dfrac{\left(\dfrac{3}{x}+\dfrac{2}{x^2}\right)x^2}{\left(5-\dfrac{1}{x}\right)x^2} = \dfrac{3x+2}{5x^2-x} = \dfrac{3x+2}{x(5x-1)}$

68. $\dfrac{\dfrac{x}{x+y}}{\dfrac{x^2}{4x+4y}} = \dfrac{x}{x+y} \cdot \dfrac{4x+4y}{x^2}$

$= \dfrac{1}{\cancel{x+y}} \cdot \dfrac{4\cancel{(x+y)}}{x}$

$= \dfrac{4}{x}$

69. $\dfrac{\dfrac{9}{x}}{\dfrac{9}{x^2}} = \dfrac{9}{x} \cdot \dfrac{x^2}{9} = x$

70. $\dfrac{\dfrac{1}{a}+2}{\dfrac{1}{a}+\dfrac{3}{a}} = \dfrac{\dfrac{1}{a}+2}{\dfrac{4}{a}} = \dfrac{\left(\dfrac{1}{a}+2\right)a}{\left(\dfrac{4}{a}\right)a} = \dfrac{1+2a}{4}$

71. $\dfrac{\dfrac{1}{x^2}-\dfrac{1}{x}}{\dfrac{1}{x^2}+\dfrac{1}{x}} = \dfrac{x^2\left(\dfrac{1}{x^2}-\dfrac{1}{x}\right)}{x^2\left(\dfrac{1}{x^2}+\dfrac{1}{x}\right)}$

$= \dfrac{1-x}{1+x}$

$= \dfrac{-x+1}{x+1}$

72. $\dfrac{\dfrac{8x}{y}-x}{\dfrac{y}{x}-1} = \dfrac{\left(\dfrac{8x}{y}-x\right)xy}{\left(\dfrac{y}{x}-1\right)xy}$

$= \dfrac{8x^2 - x^2 y}{y^2 - xy}$

$= \dfrac{8x^2 - x^2 y}{y(y-x)}$

73. $\dfrac{5}{9} = \dfrac{10}{x+3}$

$5(x+3) = 10(9)$

$5x + 15 = 90$

$5x = 75$

$x = 15$

74. $\dfrac{x}{4} = \dfrac{x-3}{2}$

$2x = 4(x-3)$

$2x = 4x - 12$

$12 = 2x$

$6 = x$

75. $\dfrac{12}{n} + 2 = \dfrac{n}{4}$

$4n\left(\dfrac{12}{n}+2\right) = 4n\left(\dfrac{n}{4}\right)$

$48 + 8n = n^2$

$0 = n^2 - 8n - 48$

$0 = (n-12)(n+4)$

$n - 12 = 0 \quad \text{or} \quad n + 4 = 0$

$n = 12 \qquad\qquad n = -4$

Since –4 is an extraneous root, $n = 12$ is the solution.

76. $\dfrac{10}{m} + \dfrac{3}{2} = \dfrac{m}{10}$

$10m\left(\dfrac{10}{m}+\dfrac{3}{2}\right) = 10m\left(\dfrac{m}{10}\right)$

$100 + 15m = m^2$

$0 = m^2 - 15m - 100$

$0 = (m-20)(m+5)$

$m - 20 = 0 \quad \text{or} \quad m + 5 = 0$

$m = 20 \qquad\qquad m = -5$

Since –5 is an extraneous root, $m = 20$ is the solution.

77. $\dfrac{-4}{d} = \dfrac{3}{2} + \dfrac{4-d}{d}$

$2d\left(\dfrac{-4}{d}\right) = 2d\left(\dfrac{3}{2}+\dfrac{4-d}{d}\right)$

$-8 = 3d + 8 - 2d$

$-8 = d + 8$

$-16 = d$

78.
$$\frac{1}{x-7}+\frac{1}{x+7}=\frac{1}{x^2-49}$$

$$\frac{1}{x-7}+\frac{1}{x+7}=\frac{1}{(x-7)(x+7)}$$

$$(x-7)(x+7)\left[\frac{1}{x-7}+\frac{1}{x+7}\right]=\left[\frac{1}{(x-7)(x+7)}\right](x-7)(x+7)$$

$$x+7+x-7=1$$

$$2x=1$$

$$x=\frac{1}{2}$$

79.
$$\frac{x-3}{x-2}+\frac{x+1}{x+3}=\frac{2x^2+x+1}{x^2+x-6}$$

$$\frac{x-3}{x-2}+\frac{x+1}{x+3}=\frac{2x^2+x+1}{(x-2)(x+3)}$$

$$(x-2)(x+3)\left(\frac{x-3}{x-2}+\frac{x+1}{x+3}\right)=(x-2)(x+3)\left[\frac{2x^2+x+1}{(x-2)(x+3)}\right]$$

$$(x+3)(x-3)+(x-2)(x+1)=2x^2+x+1$$

$$x^2-9+x^2-x-2=2x^2+x+1$$

$$2x^2-x-11=2x^2+x+1$$

$$-12=2x$$

$$-6=x$$

80.
$$\frac{a}{a^2-64}+\frac{4}{a+8}=\frac{3}{a-8}$$

$$\frac{a}{(a+8)(a-8)}+\frac{4}{a+8}=\frac{3}{a-8}$$

$$(a+8)(a-8)\left[\frac{a}{(a+8)(a-8)}+\frac{4}{a+8}\right]=(a+8)(a-8)\left(\frac{3}{a-8}\right)$$

$$a+4(a-8)=3(a+8)$$

$$a+4a-32=3a+24$$

$$5a-32=3a+24$$

$$2a=56$$

$$a=28$$

81.
$$\frac{d}{d-4} - 4 = \frac{4}{d-4}$$
$$(d-4)\left(\frac{d}{d-4} - 4\right) = (d-4)\left(\frac{4}{d-4}\right)$$
$$d - 4(d-4) = 4$$
$$d - 4d + 16 = 4$$
$$-3d + 16 = 4$$
$$-3d = -12$$
$$d = 4$$

Since $\dfrac{4}{0}$ is not a real number, there is no solution.

82. John and Amy rate $= \dfrac{1}{6}$

Paul and Cindy rate $= \dfrac{1}{4}$

$$\frac{t}{6} + \frac{t}{4} = 1$$
$$24\left(\frac{t}{6} + \frac{t}{4}\right) = 24(1)$$
$$4t + 6t = 24$$
$$10t = 24$$
$$t = \frac{24}{10} = 2.4$$

It will take the 4 people 2.4 hours.

83. $\dfrac{3}{4}$-inch hose's rate $= \dfrac{1}{7}$

$\dfrac{5}{16}$-inch hose's rate $= \dfrac{1}{12}$

$$\frac{t}{7} - \frac{t}{12} = 1$$
$$\frac{12t - 7t}{84} = 1$$
$$5t = 84$$
$$t = \frac{84}{5} = 16\frac{4}{5}$$

It will take $16\dfrac{4}{5}$ hours to fill the pool.

84. Let x be one number then, $6x$ is the other number.
$$\frac{1}{x} + \frac{1}{6x} = 7$$
$$6x\left(\frac{1}{x} + \frac{1}{6x}\right) = 6x(7)$$
$$6 + 1 = 42x$$
$$7 = 42x$$
$$\frac{7}{42} = x$$
$$\frac{1}{6} = x$$
$$6x = 6\left(\frac{1}{6}\right) = 1$$

The numbers are $\dfrac{1}{6}$ and 1.

85. Let $x =$ Robert's speed, then $3.5 + x =$ Tran's speed
$$t = \frac{d}{r}$$
Robert's time = Tran's time
$$\frac{3}{x} = \frac{8}{3.5 + x}$$
$$3(3.5 + x) = 8x$$
$$10.5 + 3x = 8x$$
$$10.5 = 5x$$
$$2.1 = x$$
$$x + 3.5 = 2.1 + 3.5 = 5.6$$
Robert's speed is 2.1 mph and Tran's speed is 5.6 mph.

86. The equation is $W = \dfrac{kL^2}{A}$. To find k, substitute 4 for W, 2 for L, and 10 for A.
$$4 = \frac{k(2)^2}{10}$$
$$4 = \frac{4k}{10}$$
$$40 = 4k$$
$$10 = k$$
Thus $W = \dfrac{10L^2}{A}$. Now substitute 5 for L and 20 for A.
$$W = \frac{10 \cdot (5)^2}{20} = \frac{250}{20} = \frac{25}{2}$$

87. The equation is $z = \dfrac{kxy}{r^2}$. To find k, substitute 12 for z, 20 for x, 8 for y, and 8 for r.

$$12 = \frac{k(20)(8)}{(8)^2}$$

$$12 = \frac{160k}{64}$$

$$12(64) = 160k$$

$$768 = 160k$$

$$\frac{768}{160} = k$$

$$k = 4.8$$

Thus $z = \dfrac{4.8xy}{r^2}$. Now substitute 10 for x, 80 for y, and 3 for r.

$$z = \frac{4.8(10)(80)}{3^2} \approx 426.7$$

88.
$$d = kw$$
$$182 = k \cdot 132$$
$$182 = 132k$$
$$1.379 \approx k$$

Now we have to substitute 198 for w and 1.379 for k to find the recommended dosage for Bill.

$$d = kw$$
$$d = 1.379 \cdot 198$$
$$d \approx 273$$

Thus, 273 mg is needed for Bill.

89.
$$t = \frac{k}{s}$$
$$1.4 = \frac{k}{6}$$
$$8.4 = k$$

Now we have to substitute 5 for s and 8.4 for k to find Leif's time.

$$t = \frac{k}{s}$$
$$t = \frac{8.4}{5}$$
$$t = 1.68$$

Thus, it will take Leif 1.68 hours.

Chapter 7 Practice Test

1. $\dfrac{-8+x}{x-8} = \dfrac{x-8}{x-8} = 1$

2. $\dfrac{x^3-1}{x^2-1} = \dfrac{\cancel{(x-1)}(x^2+x+1)}{\cancel{(x-1)}(x+1)} = \dfrac{x^2+x+1}{x+1}$

3. $\dfrac{20x^2y^3}{4z^2} \cdot \dfrac{8xz^3}{5xy^4} = \dfrac{4 \cdot 5x^2 y^3}{4z^2} \cdot \dfrac{2 \cdot 4xz^3}{5xy^4}$

$$= \frac{8x^3 y^3 z^3}{xy^4 z^2}$$

$$= \frac{8x^2 z}{y}$$

4. $\dfrac{a^2 - 9a + 14}{a-2} \cdot \dfrac{a^2 - 4a - 21}{(a-7)^2}$

$$= \frac{\cancel{(a-7)}\cancel{(a-2)}}{\cancel{a-2}} \cdot \frac{\cancel{(a-7)}(a+3)}{\cancel{(a-7)^2}}$$

$$= a + 3$$

5. $\dfrac{x^2 - x - 6}{x^2 - 9} \cdot \dfrac{x^2 - 6x + 9}{x^2 + 4x + 4}$

$$= \frac{\cancel{(x-3)}\cancel{(x+2)}}{\cancel{(x-3)}(x+3)} \cdot \frac{(x-3)(x-3)}{\cancel{(x+2)}(x+2)}$$

$$= \frac{(x-3)^2}{(x+3)(x+2)}$$

$$= \frac{x^2 - 6x + 9}{(x+3)(x+2)}$$

6. $\dfrac{x^2 - 1}{x+2} \cdot \dfrac{x+2}{1 - x^2}$

$$= \frac{\cancel{(x-1)}\cancel{(x+1)}}{\cancel{x+2}} \cdot \frac{\cancel{x+2}}{-1\cancel{(x-1)}\cancel{(x+1)}}$$

$$= -1$$

7. $\dfrac{x^2 - 4y^2}{5x + 20y} \div \dfrac{x+2y}{x+4y} = \dfrac{(x-2y)\cancel{(x+2y)}}{5\cancel{(x+4y)}} \cdot \dfrac{\cancel{x+4y}}{\cancel{x+2y}}$

$$= \frac{x - 2y}{5}$$

8. $\dfrac{15}{y^2+2y-15} \div \dfrac{5}{y-3} = \dfrac{\overset{3}{\cancel{15}}}{(\cancel{y-3})(y+5)} \cdot \dfrac{\cancel{y-3}}{\cancel{5}_1}$

$= \dfrac{3}{y+5}$

9. $\dfrac{m^2+3m-18}{m-3} \div \dfrac{m^2-8m+15}{3-m}$

$= \dfrac{(m+6)(m-3)}{m-3} \cdot \dfrac{-1(m-3)}{(m-5)(m-3)}$

$= \dfrac{-(m+6)}{m-5}$

$= -\dfrac{m+6}{m-5}$

10. $\dfrac{4x+3}{8y} + \dfrac{2x-5}{8y} = \dfrac{4x+3+2x-5}{8y}$

$= \dfrac{6x-2}{8y}$

$= \dfrac{2(3x-1)}{8y}$

$= \dfrac{3x-1}{4y}$

11. $\dfrac{7x^2-4}{x+3} - \dfrac{6x+9}{x+3} = \dfrac{7x^2-4-(6x+9)}{x+3}$

$= \dfrac{7x^2-4-6x-9}{x+3}$

$= \dfrac{7x^2-6x-13}{x+3}$

12. $\dfrac{2}{xy} - \dfrac{8}{xy^3} = \dfrac{2}{xy} \cdot \dfrac{y^2}{y^2} - \dfrac{8}{xy^3}$

$= \dfrac{2y^2}{xy^3} - \dfrac{8}{xy^3}$

$= \dfrac{2y^2-8}{xy^3}$

13. $3 - \dfrac{5z}{z-5} = 3\left(\dfrac{z-5}{z-5}\right) - \dfrac{5z}{z-5}$

$= \dfrac{3z-15}{z-5} - \dfrac{5z}{z-5}$

$= \dfrac{3z-15-5z}{z-5}$

$= \dfrac{-2z-15}{z-5}$

$= -\dfrac{2z+15}{z-5}$

14. $\dfrac{x-5}{x^2-16} - \dfrac{x-2}{x^2+2x-8}$

$= \dfrac{x-5}{(x-4)(x+4)} - \dfrac{x-2}{(x-2)(x+4)}$

$= \dfrac{x-5}{(x-4)(x+4)} - \dfrac{1}{x+4}$

$= \dfrac{x-5}{(x-4)(x+4)} - \dfrac{1}{x+4} \cdot \dfrac{x-4}{x-4}$

$= \dfrac{x-5-(x-4)}{(x-4)(x+4)}$

$= \dfrac{x-5-x+4}{(x-4)(x+4)}$

$= \dfrac{-1}{(x-4)(x+4)}$

15. $\dfrac{2+\dfrac{1}{2}}{3-\dfrac{1}{5}} = \dfrac{10\left(2+\dfrac{1}{2}\right)}{10\left(3-\dfrac{1}{5}\right)} = \dfrac{20+5}{30-2} = \dfrac{25}{28}$

16. $\dfrac{x+\dfrac{x}{y}}{\dfrac{7}{x}} = \left(x+\dfrac{x}{y}\right)\dfrac{x}{7}$

$= \left(\dfrac{xy+x}{y}\right)\left(\dfrac{x}{7}\right)$

$= \dfrac{yx^2+x^2}{7y}$

17. $\dfrac{4+\dfrac{3}{x}}{\dfrac{9}{x}-5} = \dfrac{x\left(4+\dfrac{3}{x}\right)}{x\left(\dfrac{9}{x}-5\right)} = \dfrac{4x+3}{9-5x}$

18.
$$2 + \frac{8}{x} = 6$$
$$x\left(2 + \frac{8}{x}\right) = 6x$$
$$2x + 8 = 6x$$
$$8 = 4x$$
$$2 = x$$

19.
$$\frac{2x}{3} - \frac{x}{4} = x + 1$$
$$12\left(\frac{2x}{3} - \frac{x}{4}\right) = 12(x+1)$$
$$8x - 3x = 12x + 12$$
$$5x = 12x + 12$$
$$-7x = 12$$
$$x = -\frac{12}{7}$$

20.
$$\frac{x}{x-8} + \frac{6}{x-2} = \frac{x^2}{x^2 - 10x + 16}$$
$$\frac{x}{x-8} + \frac{6}{x-2} = \frac{x^2}{(x-8)(x-2)}$$
$$(x-8)(x-2)\left(\frac{x}{x-8} + \frac{6}{x-2}\right) = (x-8)(x-2)\left[\frac{x^2}{(x-8)(x-2)}\right]$$
$$x(x-2) + 6(x-8) = x^2$$
$$x^2 - 2x + 6x - 48 = x^2$$
$$4x - 48 = 0$$
$$4x = 48$$
$$x = 12$$

21.
$$\frac{t}{10} + \frac{t}{15} = 1$$
$$30\left(\frac{t}{10} + \frac{t}{15}\right) = 30(1)$$
$$3t + 2t = 30$$
$$5t = 30$$
$$t = 6$$
It will take them 6 hours to level one acre together.

22. Let x be the number.
$$x + \frac{1}{x} = 2$$
$$x\left(x + \frac{1}{x}\right) = x(2)$$
$$x^2 + 1 = 2x$$
$$x^2 - 2x + 1 = 0$$
$$(x-1)(x-1) = 0$$
$$x - 1 = 0$$
$$x = 1$$
The number is 1.

23. Let $x =$ base, then $2x - 2 =$ height.

$$\text{area} = \frac{1}{2} \cdot \text{base} \cdot \text{height}$$

$$30 = \frac{1}{2} x (2x - 2)$$

$$2(30) = 2\left[\frac{1}{2} x (2x - 2)\right]$$

$$60 = x(2x - 2)$$

$$60 = 2x^2 - 2x$$

$$0 = 2x^2 - 2x - 60$$

$$0 = 2\left(x^2 - x - 30\right)$$

$$0 = 2(x - 6)(x + 5)$$

$$x - 6 = 0 \quad \text{or} \quad x + 5 = 0$$

$$x = 6 \qquad\quad x = -5$$

Since the base cannot be negative, the base is 6 inches and the height is $2(6) - 2 = 10$ inches.

24. Let $d =$ the distance she rollerblades, then $12 - d$ is the distance she bicycles.

$$t = \frac{d}{r}$$

$$\frac{d}{4} + \frac{12 - d}{10} = 1.5$$

$$20\left(\frac{d}{4} + \frac{12 - d}{10}\right) = 20(1.5)$$

$$5d + 2(12 - d) = 30$$

$$5d + 24 - 2d = 30$$

$$3d = 6$$

$$d = 2$$

She rollerblades for 2 miles.

25.
$$w = \frac{k}{f}$$

$$4.3 = \frac{k}{263}$$

$$1130.9 = k$$

Now substitute 1000 for f and 1130.9 for k.

$$w = \frac{k}{f}$$

$$w = \frac{1130.9}{1000}$$

$$w \approx 1.1309$$

The wavelength would be about 1.13 feet.

Chapter 7 Cumulative Review Test

1.
$$3x^2 - 5xy^2 - 7 = 3(-4)^2 - 5(-4)(-2)^2 - 7$$
$$= 3(16) - 5(-4)(4) - 7$$
$$= 48 + 80 - 7$$
$$= 121$$

2.
$$[6 - [3(8 \div 4)]^2 + 9 \cdot 4]^2$$
$$= [6 - [3(2)]^2 + 9 \cdot 4]^2$$
$$= [6 - (6)^2 + 9 \cdot 4]^2$$
$$= [6 - 36 + 9 \cdot 4]^2$$
$$= [6 - 36 + 36]^2$$
$$= [6]^2$$
$$= 36$$

3.
$$5z + 4 = -3(z - 7)$$
$$5z + 4 = -3z + 21$$
$$5z + 3z = 21 - 4$$
$$8z = 17$$
$$z = \frac{17}{8}$$

4. $c + (c + 0.012c)$

5. Let $(-7, 8)$ be (x_1, y_1) and $(3, 8)$ be (x_2, y_2).

$$m = \frac{y_2 - y_1}{x_2 - x_1}$$

$$m = \frac{8 - 8}{3 - (-7)}$$

$$m = \frac{0}{10} = 0$$

The slope is 0.

6. To put in slope-intercept form, solve for y.
$$3x - 4y = 12$$
$$3x - 3x - 4y = -3x + 12$$
$$-4y = -3x + 12$$
$$\frac{-4y}{-4} = \frac{-3x}{-4} + \frac{12}{-4}$$
$$y = \frac{3}{4}x - 3$$

7. $\left(6x^2 - 3x - 5\right) - \left(-2x^2 - 8x - 19\right)$

$= 6x^2 - 3x - 5 + 2x^2 + 8x + 19$

$= 6x^2 + 2x^2 - 3x + 8x - 5 + 19$

$= 8x^2 + 5x + 14$

8. $\left(3n^2 - 4n + 3\right)\left(2n - 5\right)$

$= 3n^2\left(2n - 5\right) - 4n\left(2n - 5\right) + 3\left(2n - 5\right)$

$= 6n^3 - 15n^2 - 8n^2 + 20n + 6n - 15$

$= 6n^3 - 23n^2 + 26n - 15$

9. $\dfrac{4x - 38}{8} = \dfrac{4x}{8} - \dfrac{38}{8} = \dfrac{1}{2}x - \dfrac{19}{4}$

10. $8a^2 - 8a - 5a + 5 = 8a\left(a - 1\right) - 5\left(a - 1\right)$

$= \left(a - 1\right)\left(8a - 5\right)$

11. $13x^2 + 26x - 39 = 13\left(x^2 + 2x - 3\right)$

$= 13\left(x + 3\right)\left(x - 1\right)$

12. $\qquad 2x^2 = 11x - 12$

$2x^2 - 11x + 12 = 0$

$\left(x - 4\right)\left(2x - 3\right) = 0$

$x - 4 = 0 \quad \text{or} \quad 2x - 3 = 0$

$\qquad x = 4 \qquad\qquad x = \dfrac{3}{2}$

13. $\dfrac{x^2 + x - 12}{x^2 - x - 6} \cdot \dfrac{x^2 - 2x - 8}{2x^2 - 7x - 4}$

$= \dfrac{(x + 4)\cancel{(x - 3)}}{\cancel{(x - 3)}\cancel{(x + 2)}} \cdot \dfrac{\cancel{(x - 4)}\cancel{(x + 2)}}{(2x + 1)\cancel{(x - 4)}}$

$= \dfrac{x + 4}{2x + 1}$

14. $\dfrac{r}{r + 2} - \dfrac{3}{r - 5} = \dfrac{r}{r + 2} \cdot \dfrac{r - 5}{r - 5} - \dfrac{3}{r - 5} \cdot \dfrac{r + 2}{r + 2}$

$= \dfrac{r(r - 5)}{(r + 2)(r - 5)} - \dfrac{3(r + 2)}{(r + 2)(r - 5)}$

$= \dfrac{r^2 - 5r - (3r + 6)}{(r + 2)(r - 5)}$

$= \dfrac{r^2 - 5r - 3r - 6}{(r + 2)(r - 5)}$

$= \dfrac{r^2 - 8r - 6}{(r + 2)(r - 5)}$

15. $\dfrac{4}{x^2 - 3x - 10} + \dfrac{6}{x^2 + 5x + 6}$

$= \dfrac{4}{(x - 5)(x + 2)} + \dfrac{6}{(x + 2)(x + 3)}$

$= \dfrac{4(x + 3)}{(x - 5)(x + 2)(x + 3)} + \dfrac{6(x - 5)}{(x - 5)(x + 2)(x + 3)}$

$= \dfrac{4(x + 3) + 6(x - 5)}{(x - 5)(x + 2)(x + 3)}$

$= \dfrac{4x + 12 + 6x - 30}{(x - 5)(x + 2)(x + 3)}$

$= \dfrac{10x - 18}{(x - 5)(x + 2)(x + 3)}$

16. $\qquad \dfrac{x}{9} - \dfrac{x}{6} = \dfrac{1}{12}$

$36\left(\dfrac{x}{9} - \dfrac{x}{6}\right) = 36\left(\dfrac{1}{12}\right)$

$\qquad 4x - 6x = 3$

$\qquad\qquad -2x = 3$

$\qquad\qquad\qquad x = -\dfrac{3}{2}$

17.

$$\frac{7}{x+3}+\frac{5}{x+2}=\frac{5}{x^2+5x+6}$$

$$\frac{7}{x+3}+\frac{5}{x+2}=\frac{5}{(x+3)(x+2)}$$

$$(x+3)(x+2)\left(\frac{7}{x+3}+\frac{5}{x+2}\right)=(x+3)(x+2)\left[\frac{5}{(x+3)(x+2)}\right]$$

$$7(x+2)+5(x+3)=5$$

$$7x+14+5x+15=5$$

$$12x+29=5$$

$$12x=-24$$

$$x=-2$$

Check:

$$\frac{7}{x+3}+\frac{5}{x+2}=\frac{5}{x^2+5x+6}$$

$$\frac{7}{-2+3}+\frac{5}{-2+2}=\frac{5}{(-2)^2+5(-2)+6}$$

$$\frac{7}{1}+\frac{5}{0}=\frac{5}{0}$$

Since $\frac{5}{0}$ is not a real number, there is no solution.

18. Let x = the total medical bills. The cost under plan 1 is $0.10x$, while the cost under plan 2 is $100 + 0.05x$.

$$0.10x=150+0.05x$$

$$0.05x=150$$

$$x=3000$$

The cost under both plans is the same for $3000 in total medical bills.

19. Let x = pounds of sunflower seed and
y = pounds of premixed assorted seed mix
$x+y=50$
$0.50x+0.20y=16.00$

Solve the first equation for y.

$y=50-x$

Substitute $50-x$ for y in the second equation.

$0.50x+0.20(50-x)=16$

$$0.50x+10-0.20x=16$$

$$0.30x=6$$

$$x=20$$

$y=50-x=50-20=30$

He will have to use 20 pounds of sunflower seed and 30 pounds of premixed assorted seed mix.

20. Let d = distance on first leg, then the distance on the second leg is $12.75-d$.

$$t=\frac{d}{r}$$

Time for first leg + time for second leg = total time

$$\frac{d}{6.5}+\frac{12.75-d}{9.5}=1.5$$

$$(9.5)(6.5)\left[\frac{d}{6.5}+\frac{12.75-d}{9.5}\right]=(9.5)(6.5)(1.5)$$

$$9.5d+6.5(12.75-d)=92.625$$

$$9.5d+82.875-6.5d=92.625$$

$$3d=9.75$$

$$d=3.25$$

$12.75-d=12.75-3.25=9.5$

The distance traveled during the first leg of the race was 3.25 miles and the distance traveled in the second leg of the race was 9.5 miles.

Chapter 8

1. No, a nonlinear equation will not always have a
   y-intercept because the graph does not have to
   intersect the y-axis. For example, the graph of
   $y = \dfrac{1}{x}$ does not have a y-intercept.

2. No, plotting only integer values will not always
   produce accurate graphs. In many situations it is
   necessary to plot fraction values.

3. When graphing $y = \dfrac{1}{x}$, we cannot substitute 0
   for x because $\dfrac{1}{0}$ is undefined.

4. A horizontal line would represent a constant
   speed.

5.

6.

7.

8.

9.

10.

11.

12.

13.

$y = \frac{1}{2}x - 1$

14.

$y = -\frac{1}{2}x - 3$

15.

$y = -\frac{1}{3}x + 2$

16.

$y = -\frac{1}{3}x + 4$

17.

$y = x^2$

18.

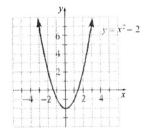

$y = x^2 - 2$

19.

$y = -x^2$

20.

$y = -x^2 + 4$

21.

$y = |x| + 1$

22.

$y = |x| + 2$

23.

$y = -|x|$

24.

$y = -|x| - 3$

383

25.

26.

27.

28.

29.

30.

31.

32.

33.

34.

35.

36.

384

37.

38.

39.

40.

41. $y = \dfrac{x^2}{x+1}$

$$\left(\frac{1}{12}\right) \overset{?}{=} \frac{\left(\frac{1}{3}\right)^2}{\left(\frac{1}{3}\right)+1}$$

$$\frac{1}{12} \overset{?}{=} \frac{\frac{1}{9}}{\frac{4}{3}}$$

$$\frac{1}{12} \overset{?}{=} \frac{1}{9}\cdot\frac{3}{4}$$

$$\frac{1}{12} = \frac{1}{12} \quad \text{True}$$

Yes, $\left(\dfrac{1}{3},\dfrac{1}{12}\right)$ is on the graph of the equation

$y = \dfrac{x^2}{x+1}$.

42. $y = \dfrac{x^2+1}{x^2-1}$

$$\left(-\frac{3}{5}\right) \overset{?}{=} \frac{\left(-\frac{1}{2}\right)^2+1}{\left(-\frac{1}{2}\right)^2-1}$$

$$-\frac{3}{5} \overset{?}{=} \frac{\frac{1}{4}+1}{\frac{1}{4}-1}$$

$$-\frac{3}{5} \overset{?}{=} \frac{\frac{5}{4}}{-\frac{3}{4}}$$

$$-\frac{3}{5} \overset{?}{=} \frac{5}{4}\cdot\frac{-4}{3}$$

$$-\frac{3}{5} = -\frac{5}{3} \quad \text{False}$$

No, $\left(-\dfrac{1}{2},-\dfrac{3}{5}\right)$ is not on the graph of the equation

$y = \dfrac{x^2+1}{x^2-1}$.

43. a.

b. Area $= \dfrac{1}{2}bh = \dfrac{1}{2}(4)(4) = 8$

The area is 8 square units.

44. a.

b. Area $= lw = 6(8) = 48$

The area is 48 square units.

45. a. The average length of the golf course at the majors in 1980 was about 6875 yards.

b. The average length of the golf course at the majors in 2005 was about 7300 yards.

c. The average length of the golf course at the majors was greater than 7000 yards for the years 1990, 2000, and 2005.

d. No, the average length of the golf courses in the majors from 1995 to 2005 does not appear to be linear. The increase in length is not the same from 1995 to 2000 as it is from 2000 to 2005. That is, the increase in the length is not constant.

46. a. Internet sales in the first quarter of 2000 was approximately $5.7 billion.

b. Internet sales in the first quarter of 2005 was approximately $20 billion.

c. First quarter Internet sales were greater than $12 billion in the years 2003, 2004, and 2005.

d. Yes, Internet sales in the first quarter from 2000 to 2005 appear to be approximately linear. Internet sales appear to be increasing at approximately $2.9 billion per year from 2000 to 2005. That is, the increase in first quarter sales is approximately constant.

47.

$y = x + 3$
$y = x + 1$
$y = x - 1$

a. Each graph crosses the y-axis at the point corresponding to the constant term in the graph's equation.

b. Yes, all the equations seem to have the same slant or slope.

48.

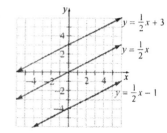

$y = \frac{1}{2}x + 3$
$y = \frac{1}{2}x$
$y = \frac{1}{2}x - 1$

a. Each graph crosses the y-axis at the point corresponding to the constant term in the graph's equation.

b. Yes, all the equations seem to have the same slant or slope.

49.

$y = 2x$

2 units
1 unit

For each unit change in x, y changes 2 units. Thus, the rate of change of y with respect to x is 2.

50.

$y = 4x$

4 units
1 unit

For each unit change in x, y changes 4 units. Thus, the rate of change of y with respect to x is 4.

51.

3 units
1 unit

$y = 3x + 2$

For each unit change in x, y changes 3 units. Thus, the rate of change of y with respect to x is 3.

52.

$y = \frac{1}{2}x$

1/2 unit
1 unit

For each unit change in x, y changes $\dfrac{1}{2}$ unit. Thus, the rate of change of y with respect to x is $\dfrac{1}{2}$.

53. Answers may vary. One possible answer is the points $(4, -3)$ and $(5, 1)$.

    Starting at $(3, -7)$: For a unit change, x changes from 3 to $3 + 1 = 4$. At the same time, y changes from -7 to $-7 + 4 = -3$. So, $(4, -3)$ is a solution to the equation.

    Starting at $(4, -3)$: For a unit change, x changes from 4 to $4 + 1 = 5$. At the same time, y changes from -3 to $-3 + 4 = 1$. So, $(5, 1)$ is a solution to the equation.

54. Answers may vary. One possible answer is the points $(2, -1)$ and $(3, 2)$.

    Starting at $(1, -4)$: For a unit change, x changes from 1 to $1 + 1 = 2$. At the same time, y changes from -4 to $-4 + 3 = -1$. So, $(2, -1)$ is a solution to the equation.

    Starting at $(2, -1)$: For a unit change, x changes from 2 to $2 + 1 = 3$. At the same time, y changes from -1 to $-1 + 3 = 2$. So, $(3, 2)$ is a solution to the equation.

55. c

56. d

57. a

58. b

59. d

60. c

61. b

62. a

63. b

64. a

65. d

66. c

67. b

68. a

69. d

70. c

71.

72.

73.

74.

75.

76.

77.

78.

79. a. Group member 1:
$$\left(\frac{-2+6}{2},\frac{4+8}{2}\right)=\left(\frac{4}{2},\frac{12}{2}\right)=(2,6)$$

Group member 2:
$$\left(\frac{-3+5}{2},\frac{-2+6}{2}\right)=\left(\frac{2}{2},\frac{4}{2}\right)=(1,2)$$

Group member 3:
$$\left(\frac{4+(-2)}{2},\frac{1+4}{2}\right)=\left(\frac{2}{2},\frac{5}{2}\right)=\left(1,\frac{5}{2}\right)$$

b. Midpoint $=\left(\dfrac{x_1+x_2}{2},\dfrac{y_1+y_2}{2}\right)$

80. a. $(4,-3)$ or $(-6,-3)$ or $(12,13)$.

b. 40 square units

c. Answers will vary.

d. Yes. See part (a). Each parallelogram has an area of 40 square units.

81. $x^2-4x+5=(-3)^2-4(-3)+5=9+12+5=26$

82. $m=\dfrac{y_2-y_1}{x_2-x_1}=\dfrac{7-3}{6-(-5)}=\dfrac{7-3}{6+5}=\dfrac{4}{11}$

83.
$$\frac{2x}{x^2-4}+\frac{1}{x-2}=\frac{2}{x+2}$$
$$\frac{2x}{(x-2)(x+2)}+\frac{1}{x-2}=\frac{2}{x+2}$$
$$(x-2)(x+2)\left(\frac{2x}{(x-2)(x+2)}+\frac{1}{x-2}\right)=(x-2)(x+2)\left(\frac{2}{x+2}\right)$$
$$2x+(x+2)=2(x-2)$$
$$3x+2=2x-4$$
$$x+2=-4$$
$$x=-6$$

Note that -6 does not cause a denominator to be zero, so it is not extraneous.
In other words -6 checks, so the solution to the equation is $x=-6$.

84.

$$\frac{4x}{x^2+6x+9} - \frac{2x}{x+3} = \frac{x+1}{x+3}$$

$$\frac{4x}{(x+3)^2} - \frac{2x}{x+3} = \frac{x+1}{x+3}$$

$$(x+3)^2\left(\frac{4x}{(x+3)^2} - \frac{2x}{x+3}\right) = (x+3)^2\left(\frac{x+1}{x+3}\right)$$

$$4x - 2x(x+3) = (x+3)(x+1)$$

$$4x - 2x^2 - 6x = x^2 + x + 3x + 3$$

$$4x - 2x^2 - 6x = x^2 + x + 3x + 3$$

$$-2x^2 - 2x = x^2 + 4x + 3$$

$$0 = 3x^2 + 6x + 3$$

$$0 = 3(x^2 + 2x + 1)$$

$$0 = 3(x+1)^2$$

$$x + 1 = 0$$

$$x = -1$$

Note that −1 does not cause a denominator to be zero, so it is not extraneous. In other words, −1 checks. The solution to the equation is $x = -1$.

Exercise Set 8.2

1. A function is a correspondence between a first set of elements, the domain, and a second set of elements, the range, such that each element of the domain corresponds to exactly one element in the range.

2. A relation is any set of ordered pairs.

3. Yes, all functions are also relations. A function is a set of ordered pairs so it is a relation.

4. No, all relations are not functions. A relation can have two ordered pairs with the same first element but a function cannot.

5. $\{5, 6, 7, 8\}$

6. $\{4, 5, 6, 7, 8, 9\}$

7. If each vertical line drawn through any part of the graph intersects the graph in at most one point, the graph represents a function. If any vertical line intersects the graph at more than one point, then the graph is not a function.

8. The domain is the set of values for the independent variable.

9. The range is the set of values for the dependent variable.

10. Domain: $\mathbb{R}$ or $(-\infty, \infty)$
There are no restrictions on values of x that can be used.
Range: $\mathbb{R}$ or $(-\infty, \infty)$
All values of y are represented in the function.

11. Domain: $\mathbb{R}$ or $(-\infty, \infty)$
There are no restrictions on values of x that can be used.
Range: $\mathbb{R}$ or $(-\infty, \infty)$
All values of y are represented in the function.

12. Domain: $\mathbb{R}$ or $(-\infty, \infty)$
There are no restrictions on values of x that can be used.
Range: $\{y \,|\, y \geq 0\}$
The absolute value of any number is never negative.

13. If y depends on x, then y is the dependent variable.

14. If y depends on x, then x is the independent variable.

15. "$f(x)$" is read "f of x."

16. Yes, all functions that are given in function notation are also equations. The function notation essentially represents the y variable of an equation.

17. **a.** Yes, the relation is a function.

    b. Domain: $\{3, 5, 11\}$,
    Range: $\{6, 10, 22\}$

18. **a.** No, the relation is not a function.

    b. Domain: $\{$Robert, Margaret$\}$,
    Range: $\{$Bobby, Rob, Peggy, Maggie$\}$

19. **a.** Yes, the relation is a function.

    b. Domain: $\{$Cameron, Tyrone, Vishnu$\}$,
    Range: $\{3, 6\}$

20. **a.** Yes, the relation is a function.

    b. Domain: $\{4, 5, 7\}$, Range: $(16, 25, 49\}$

21. **a.** No, the relation is not a function.

    b. Domain: $\{1990, 2001, 2002\}$,
    Range: $\{20, 34, 37\}$

22. a. Yes, the relation is a function.

    b. Domain: $\{|-8|, |8|, |0|\}$,
Range: $\{0, 8\}$

23. a. The relation is a function.

    b. Domain: $\{1, 2, 3, 4, 5\}$,
Range: $\{1, 2, 3, 4, 5\}$

24. a. The relation is not a function.

    b. Domain: $\{1, 4, 9\}$,
Range: $\{-3, -2, -1, 0, 2, 3\}$

25. a. The relation is a function.

    b. Domain: $\{1, 2, 3, 4, 5, 7\}$,
Range: $\{-1, 0, 2, 4, 9\}$

26. a. The relation is a function.

    b. Domain: $\{-2, -1, 0, 3, 4\}$,
Range: $\{-3, -2, 1, 4, 5\}$

27. a. The relation is not a function.

    b. Domain: $\{1, 2, 3\}$,
Range: $\{1, 2, 4, 5, 6\}$

28. a. The relation is a function.

    b. Domain: $\{-3, 0, 2, 3, 5, 6\}$,
Range: $\{2, 3, 4, 5, 8\}$

29. a. The relation is not a function.

    b. Domain: $\{0, 1, 2\}$, Range: $\{-7, -1, 2, 3\}$

30. a. The relation is a function.

    b. Domain: $\{-1, 0, 1, 2, 3\}$, Range: $\{5\}$

31. $A = \{0\}$

32. $B = \{1, 3, 5\}$

33. $C = \{18, 20\}$

34. $D = \{-3, -2, -1, 0, 1, 2, ...\}$

35. $E = \{0, 1, 2\}$

36. $F = \{1, 2, 3\}$

37. $H = \{0, 7, 14, 21, 28, ...\}$

38. $L = \{-4, -3, -2, -1, ...\}$

39. $J = \{1, 2, 3, 4, ...\}$ or $J = N$

40. $K = \{\ \}$ or $\varnothing$

41. a. Set A is the set of all x such that x is a natural number less than 7.

    b. $A = \{1, 2, 3, 4, 5, 6\}$

42. a. Set B is the set of all x such that x is one of the last five capital letters in the English alphabet.

    b. $B = \{V, W, X, Y, Z\}$

43. $\{x \mid x \geq 0\}$

44. $\{w \mid w > -5\}$

45. $\{z \mid z \leq 2\}$

46. $\{y \mid y < 4\}$

47. $\{p \mid -6 \leq p < 3\}$

48. $\{x \mid -1.67 \leq x < 5.02\}$

49. $\{q \mid q > -3 \text{ and } q \in N\}$

50. $\{x \mid -1.93 \leq x \leq 2 \text{ and } x \in I\}$

51. $\{r \mid r \leq \pi \text{ and } r \in W\}$

52. $\left\{ x \mid \dfrac{5}{12} < x \leq \dfrac{7}{12} \text{ and } x \in N \right\}$

53. $\left\{x \mid x \geq 1\right\}$

54. $\left\{x \mid x \leq 6\right\}$

55. $\left\{x \mid x \leq 4 \text{ and } x \in I\right\}$ or $\left\{x \mid x < 5 \text{ and } x \in I\right\}$

56. $\left\{x \mid x \leq -6 \text{ and } x \in I\right\}$ or $\left\{x \mid x < -5 \text{ and } x \in I\right\}$

57. $\left\{x \mid -3 < x \leq 5\right\}$

58. $\left\{x \mid 4 \leq x < 7.7\right\}$

59. $\left\{x \mid -2.5 \leq x < 4.2\right\}$

60. $\left\{x \mid x \in I\right\}$

61. $\left\{x \mid -3 \leq x \leq 1 \text{ and } x \in I\right\}$

62. $\left\{x \mid -\dfrac{12}{5} \leq x \leq \dfrac{4}{11}\right\}$.

63. **a.** The graph represents a function.
  b. Domain: $\mathbb{R}$, Range: $\mathbb{R}$
  c. $x = 2$

64. **a.** The graph represents a function.
  b. Domain: $\mathbb{R}$, Range: {2}
  c. All real numbers

65. **a.** The graph does not represent a function.
  b. Domain: $\left\{x \mid 0 \leq x \leq 2\right\}$,
    Range: $\left\{y \mid -3 \leq y \leq 3\right\}$
  c. $x \approx 1.5$

66. **a.** The graph does not represent a function.
  b. Domain: $\left\{x \mid -4 \leq x \leq 4\right\}$,
    Range: $\left\{y \mid -2 \leq y \leq 2\right\}$
  c. $x = 0$

67. **a.** The graph represents a function.
  b. Domain: $\mathbb{R}$, Range: $\left\{y \mid y \geq 0\right\}$
  c. $x = -3$ or $x = -1$

68. **a.** The graph does not represent a function.
  b. Domain: {−2} , Range: $\mathbb{R}$
  c. $x = -2$

69. **a.** The graph represents a function.
  b. Domain: {−1, 0, 1, 2, 3},
    Range: {−1, 0, 1, 2, 3}
  c. $x = 2$

70. **a.** The graph represents a function.
  b. Domain: {1, 2, 3, 4}, Range: {1}
  c. No values of x

71. **a.** The graph does not represent a function.
  b. Domain: $\left\{x \mid x \geq 2\right\}$, Range: $\mathbb{R}$
  c. $x = 3$

72. **a.** The graph represents a function.
  b. Domain: $\left\{x \mid -20 \leq x \leq 10\right\}$,
    Range : $\left\{y \mid -2 \leq y \leq 2\right\}$
  c. $x = -17.5$ or $x = -7.5$ or $x = 2.5$

73. **a.** The graph represents a function.
  b. Domain: $\left\{x \mid -2 \leq x \leq 2\right\}$,
    Range : $\left\{y \mid -1 \leq y \leq 2\right\}$
  c. $x = -2$ or $x = 2$

74. **a.** The graph does not represent a function.
  b. Domain: $\mathbb{R}$, Range: $\mathbb{R}$
  c. $x = 2$

75. **a.** $f(2) = -2(2) + 7 = -4 + 7 = 3$
  b. $f(-3) = -2(-3) + 7 = 6 + 7 = 13$

76. **a.** $f(0) = \dfrac{1}{3}(0) + 4 = 0 + 4 = 4$
  b. $f(-12) = \dfrac{1}{3}(-12) + 4 = -4 + 4 = 0$

77. **a.** $h(0) = (0)^2 - (0) - 6 = -6$
  b. $h(-1) = (-1)^2 - (-1) - 6 = 1 + 1 - 6 = -4$

78. a. $g(2) = -2(2)^2 + 7(2) - 11$
$= -2(4) + 7(2) - 11$
$= -8 + 14 - 11$
$= -5$

b. $g\left(\dfrac{1}{2}\right) = -2\left(\dfrac{1}{2}\right)^2 + 7\left(\dfrac{1}{2}\right) - 11$
$= -2\left(\dfrac{1}{4}\right) + 7\left(\dfrac{1}{2}\right) - 11$
$= -\dfrac{1}{2} + \dfrac{7}{2} - 11$
$= \dfrac{6}{2} - 11$
$= 3 - 11$
$= -8$

79. a. $r(1) = -(1)^3 - 2(1)^2 + (1) + 4$
$= -(1) - 2(1) + (1) + 4$
$= -1 - 2 + 1 + 4$
$= 2$

b. $r(-2) = -(-2)^3 - 2(-2)^2 + (-2) + 4$
$= -(-8) - 2(4) + (-2) + 4$
$= 8 - 8 - 2 + 4$
$= 2$

80. a. $g(0) = 4 - 3(0) + 16(0)^2 - 2(0)^3$
$= 4 - 0 + 0 - 0$
$= 4$

b. $g(3) = 4 - 3(3) + 16(3)^2 - 2(3)^3$
$= 4 - 3(3) + 16(9) - 2(27)$
$= 4 - 9 + 144 - 54$
$= 85$

81. a. $h(6) = |5 - 2(6)| = |5 - 12| = |-7| = 7$

b. $h\left(\dfrac{5}{2}\right) = \left|5 - 2\left(\dfrac{5}{2}\right)\right| = |5 - 5| = 0$

82. a. $q(0) = -2|(0) + 8| + 13$
$= -2|8| + 13$
$= -2(8) + 13$
$= -16 + 13$
$= -3$

b. $q(-4) = -2|(-4) + 8| + 13$
$= -2|4| + 13$
$= -2(4) + 13$
$= -8 + 13$
$= 5$

83. a. $s(-3) = \sqrt{(-3) + 3} = \sqrt{0} = 0$

b. $s(6) = \sqrt{(6) + 3} = \sqrt{9} = 3$

84. a. $f(-2) = \sqrt{5 - 2(-2)} = \sqrt{5 + 4} = \sqrt{9} = 3$

b. $f(2) = \sqrt{5 - 2(2)} = \sqrt{5 - 4} = \sqrt{1} = 1$

85. a. $g(0) = \dfrac{(0)^3 - 2}{(0) - 2} = \dfrac{-2}{-2} = 1$

b. $g(0) = \dfrac{(2)^3 - 2}{2 - 2} = \dfrac{8 - 2}{0} = \dfrac{6}{0}$ undefined

86. a. $h(-3) = \dfrac{(-3)^2 + 4(-3)}{(-3) + 6} = \dfrac{9 - 12}{3} = \dfrac{-3}{3} = -1$

b. $h\left(\dfrac{2}{5}\right) = \dfrac{\left(\dfrac{2}{5}\right)^2 + 4\left(\dfrac{2}{5}\right)}{\left(\dfrac{2}{5}\right) + 6} = \dfrac{\dfrac{4}{25} + \dfrac{8}{5}}{\dfrac{2}{5} + 6} = \dfrac{\dfrac{4 + 40}{25}}{\dfrac{2 + 30}{5}}$
$= \dfrac{\dfrac{44}{25}}{\dfrac{32}{5}} = \dfrac{44}{25} \cdot \dfrac{5}{32} = \dfrac{11}{40}$ or 0.275

87. a. $A(4) = 6(4) = 24$
The area is 24 square feet.

b. $A(6.5) = 6(6.5) = 39$
The area is 39 square feet.

88. a. $i(2.5\%) = i(0.025) = 1000(0.025) = 25$
With a 2.5% interest rate, the interest will be $25.

b. $i(4.25\%) = i(0.0425) = 1000(0.0425) = 42.5$
With a 4.25% interest rate, the interest will be $42.50.

89. a. $A(r) = \pi r^2$

b. $A(12) = \pi(12)^2 = 144\pi \approx 452.4$
The area is about 452.4 square yards.

90. a. $P(s) = 4s$

b. $P(7) = 4(7) = 28$
The perimeter is 28 meters.

91. a. $C(F) = \dfrac{5}{9}(F - 32)$

 b. $C(-31) = \dfrac{5}{9}(-31 - 32) = \dfrac{5}{9}(-63) = -35$

 The Celsius temperature that corresponds to $-31°F$ is $-35°C$.

92. a. $V(r) = 3\pi r^2$

 b. $V(2) = 3\pi(2)^2 = 12\pi \approx 37.7$

 The volume is about 37.7 cubic feet.

93. a. $T(3) = -0.03(3)^2 + 1.5(3) + 14$
 $= -0.27 + 4.5 + 14$
 $= 18.23$

 The temperature is $18.23°C$.

 b. $T(12) = -0.03(12)^2 + 1.5(12) + 14$
 $= -4.32 + 18 + 14$
 $= 27.68$

 The temperature is $27.68°C$.

94. a. $d(60) = 0.18(60) + 0.01(60)^2$
 $= 10.8 + 36$
 $= 46.8$

 The stopping distance is 46.8 meters.

 b. $d(25) = 0.18(25) + 0.01(25)^2$
 $= 4.5 + 6.25$
 $= 10.75$

 The stopping distance is 10.75 meters.

95. a. $T(4) = -0.02(4)^2 - 0.34(4) + 80$
 $= -0.32 - 1.36 + 80$
 $= 78.32$

 The temperature is $78.32°$.

 b. $T(12) = -0.02(12)^2 - 0.34(12) + 80$
 $= -2.88 - 4.08 + 80$
 $= 73.04$

 The temperature is $73.04°$.

96. a. $n(18) = 2(18)^2 - 150(18) + 4000$
 $= 648 - 2700 + 4000$
 $= 1948$

 In 1 month, there are about 1948 accidents involving 18-year-olds.

 b. $n(25) = 2(25)^2 - 150(25) + 4000$
 $= 1250 - 3750 + 4000$
 $= 1500$

 In 1 month, there are about 1500 accidents involving 25-year-olds.

97. a. $T(6) = \dfrac{1}{3}(6)^3 + \dfrac{1}{2}(6)^2 + \dfrac{1}{6}(6)$
 $= 72 + 18 + 1$
 $= 91$

 If the base is 6 by 6 oranges, then there will be 91 oranges in the pyramid.

 b. $T(8) = \dfrac{1}{3}(8)^3 + \dfrac{1}{2}(8)^2 + \dfrac{1}{6}(8)$
 $= \dfrac{512}{3} + 32 + \dfrac{4}{3}$
 $= 204$

 If the base is 8 by 8 oranges, then there will be 204 oranges in the pyramid.

98. a. $R(1) = 24 + 5(1) - (1)^2 = 24 + 5 - 1 = 28$

 The increase in revenue will be \$28,000.

 b. $R(4) = 24 + 5(4) - (4)^2 = 24 + 20 - 16 = 28$

 The increase in revenue will be \$28,000.

99. Answers will vary. One possible interpretation: The person warms up slowly, possibly by walking for 5 minutes, then begins jogging slowly over a period of 5 minutes. For the next 15 minutes, the person jogs at a steady pace. For the next 5 minutes, he walks slowly and his heart rate decreases to his normal resting heart rate. The rate stays the same for the next 5 minutes.

100. Answers will vary. One possible interpretation: During the past hour there is no water. During the next 2 hours water builds up to 0.5 feet. During the next 2 hours it rains more heavily and the rain builds up to 2.0 feet. During the next hour the rain slows down a bit, but the water is still accumulating. During the last 4 hours the rain stops and the water level drops to about 1.25 feet.

101. Answers will vary. One possible interpretation: The man walks on level ground, about 30 feet above sea level, for 5 minutes. For the next 5 minutes he walks uphill to 45 feet above sea level. For 5 minutes he walks on level ground then walks quickly downhill for 3 minutes to an elevation of 20 feet above sea level. For 7 minutes he walks on level ground. Then he walks quickly uphill.

102. Answers may vary. One possible interpretation: The water is turned on full-force. After four minutes, the hot or cold water is turned down a little; and after three more minutes, it is turned off. Six minutes later, someone gets in the tub, soaks for six minutes, makes waves for seven minutes, soaks for two minutes, then gets out. The person then pulls the plug and the water drains out for the next ten minutes.

103. Answers may vary. One possible interpretation: A woman drives in stop-and-go traffic for five minutes. Then she drives on the highway for fifteen minutes, gets off onto a country road for a few minutes, stops for a couple of minutes, and returns to stop-and-go traffic.

104. Answers may vary. One possible interpretation: The person travels at 30 mph for one hour, then at 60 mph for two hours, then stops. An hour later, the person continues the trip at 80 mph for two hours.

105. **a.** Yes, both graphs pass the vertical line test.

    b. The independent variable is the year.

    c. $f(2005) = \$218,600$.

    d. $g(2005) = \$865,000$.

    e. percent increase $= \dfrac{218,600 - 89,300}{89,300}$

$$\approx 1.448$$
$$\approx 144.8\%$$

    The percent increase from 1988 through 2005 was about 144.8%.

106. **a.** Yes, the graph passes the vertical line test.

    b. The dependent variable is the number of accounts.

    c. $n(2005) = 7.5$ million accounts

    d. percent increase $= \dfrac{7.5 - 3.1}{3.1} \approx 1.419 \approx 141.9\%$

    The percent increase from 2002 through 2005 was about 141.9%.

107. **a.** Yes, both graphs pass the vertical line test.

    b. $f(1998) \approx 6.0$ million viewers.

    c. $g(1998) \approx 4.4$ million viewers.

    d. Yes, both graphs are approximately linear from 1998 to 2005. The number of Today Show viewers is remained relatively constant, while the number of Good Morning America viewers increased at a relatively constant rate.

    e. The two shows will have the same number of viewers around the year 2006 or 2007.

108. **a.**

    b. Yes, the points do seem to lie on a straight line.

    c. If the trend continues, the number of LCD monitors that will be shipped in 2009 will be approximately 150 million.

    d. Yes, the bar graph represents a function. Each year has one output (that is, one number of shipments of LCD panels.

    e. Yes, the line graph represents a function. It passes the vertical line test.

109. **a.**

    b. No, the points don't lie on a straight line.

    c. The cost of a 30-second commercial in 2004 was about $2,300,000.

110. **a.**

    b. $f(30,000) = 0.6(30,000) + 5000$

$$= 18,000 + 5000$$
$$= 23,000$$

    For a family whose average household income is $30,000, the average household expenditure is approximately $23,000.

111. a.

Annual number of bushels of soybeans (1000)

b. $f(40,000) = -0.00004(40,000) + 4.25$

$$= -1.6 + 4.25$$

$$= 2.65$$

The cost of a bushel of soybeans if 40,000 bushels are produced is approximately \$2.65 per bushel.

112.

113.

114. $3x - 2 = \dfrac{1}{3}(3x - 3)$

$$3x - 2 = \dfrac{1}{3}(3x) - \dfrac{1}{3}(3)$$

$$3x - 2 = x - 1$$

$$3x - x = -1 + 2$$

$$2x = 1$$

$$x = \dfrac{1}{2}$$

The solution set is $\left\{\dfrac{1}{2}\right\}$.

115.

$$E = a_1 p_1 + a_2 p_2 + a_3 p_3$$

$$E - a_1 p_1 - a_3 p_3 = a_2 p_2$$

$$p_2 = \dfrac{E - a_1 p_1 - a_3 p_3}{a_2}$$

116. $3x + 6y = 9$

$$6y = -3x + 9$$

$$y = \dfrac{-3x + 9}{6}$$

$$y = \dfrac{-3x}{6} + \dfrac{9}{6}$$

$$y = -\dfrac{1}{2}x + \dfrac{3}{2}$$

The slope is $m = -\dfrac{1}{2}$ and the y-intercept is $\left(0, \dfrac{3}{2}\right)$.

117. $\dfrac{3x^2 - 16x - 12}{3x^2 - 10x - 8} \div \dfrac{x^2 - 7x + 6}{3x^2 - 11x - 4}$

$$= \dfrac{3x^2 - 16x - 12}{3x^2 - 10x - 8} \cdot \dfrac{3x^2 - 11x - 4}{x^2 - 7x + 6}$$

$$= \dfrac{(3x + 2)(x - 6)}{(3x + 2)(x - 4)} \cdot \dfrac{(3x + 1)(x - 4)}{(x - 1)(x - 6)}$$

$$= \dfrac{(3x+2)(x-6)}{(3x+2)(x-4)} \cdot \dfrac{(3x+1)(x-4)}{(x-1)(x-6)}$$

$$= \dfrac{3x + 1}{x - 1}$$

Exercise Set 8.3

1. The graph of a linear function will be a straight line.

2. To write a linear equation in standard form using function notation, solve the equation for y, then substitute $f(x)$ for y.

3. To find the x-intercept, set $y = 0$ and solve for x. To find the y-intercept, set $x = 0$ and solve for y.

4. Graphing calculators call the x-intercepts zeros or roots.

5. To solve an equation in one variable graphically, graph both sides of the equation. The solution is the x-coordinate of the point of intersection.

6. To solve $2(x - 1) = 3x - 5$ graphically, graph $Y_1 = 2(x - 1)$ and $Y_2 = 3x - 5$. The x-coordinate of the point of intersection is the solution.

7. $f(x) = 3x - 2$

x	calculation	$f(x)$
0	$3(0) - 2$	-2
1	$3(1) - 2$	1
2	$3(2) - 2$	4

$f(x) = 3x - 2$

8. $g(x) = -2x + 3$

x	calculation	$g(x)$
0	$-2(0) + 3$	3
1	$-2(1) + 3$	1
2	$-2(2) + 3$	-1

$g(x) = -2x + 3$

9. $g(x) = -\dfrac{2}{3}x + 4$

x	calculation	$g(x)$
-3	$-\dfrac{2}{3}(-3) + 4$	6
0	$-\dfrac{2}{3}(0) + 4$	4
3	$-\dfrac{2}{3}(0) + 4$	2

$g(x) = -\dfrac{2}{3}x + 4$

10. $f(x) = \dfrac{1}{2}x - 6$

x	calculation	$f(x)$
0	$\dfrac{1}{2}(0) - 6$	-6
4	$\dfrac{1}{2}(4) - 6$	-4
6	$\dfrac{1}{2}(6) - 6$	-3

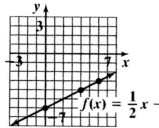

$f(x) = \dfrac{1}{2}x - 6$

11. $f(x) = \dfrac{3}{4}x + 1$

x	calculation	$f(x)$
-4	$\dfrac{3}{4}(-4) + 1$	-2
0	$\dfrac{3}{4}(0) + 1$	1
4	$\dfrac{3}{4}(4) + 1$	4

$f(x) = \dfrac{3}{4}x + 1$

12. $g(x) = 6x - 6$

x	calculation	$g(x)$
0	$6(0) - 6$	-6
1	$6(1) - 6$	0
2	$6(2) - 6$	6

$g(x) = 6x - 6$

13. $f(x) = 3x - 6$

    For the y-intercept, set $x = 0$:
    $$f(0) = 3(0) - 6 = 0 - 6 = -6$$
    The y-intercept is $(0, -6)$.

    For the x-intercept, set $f(x) = 0$ and solve for x:
    $$0 = 3x - 6$$
    $$6 = 3x$$
    $$2 = x$$
    The x-intercept is $(2, 0)$.

14. $g(x) = -2x + 6$

    For the y-intercept, set $x = 0$:
    $$g(0) = -2(0) + 6 = 0 + 6 = 6$$
    The y-intercept is $(0, 6)$.

    For the x-intercept, set $g(x) = 0$ and solve for x:
    $$0 = -2x + 6$$
    $$2x = 6$$
    $$x = 3$$
    The x-intercept is $(3, 0)$.

15. $f(x) = 2x + 3$

    For the y-intercept, set $x = 0$:
    $$f(0) = 2(0) + 3 = 0 + 3 = 3$$
    The y-intercept is $(0, 3)$.

    For the x-intercept, set $f(x) = 0$ and solve for x:
    $$0 = 2x + 3$$
    $$-3 = 2x$$
    $$-\frac{3}{2} = x$$
    The x-intercept is $\left(-\frac{3}{2}, 0\right)$.

16. $f(x) = -6x + 5$

    For the y-intercept, set $x = 0$:
    $$f(0) = -6(0) + 5 = 0 + 5 = 5$$
    The y-intercept is $(0, 5)$.

    For the x-intercept, set $f(x) = 0$ and solve for x:
    $$0 = -6x + 5$$
    $$6x = 5$$
    $$x = \frac{5}{6}$$
    The x-intercept is $\left(\frac{5}{6}, 0\right)$.

17. $g(x) = 4x - 8$

    For the y-intercept, set $x = 0$:
    $$g(0) = 4(0) - 8 = 0 - 8 = -8$$
    The y-intercept is $(0, -8)$.

    For the x-intercept, set $g(x) = 0$ and solve for x:
    $$0 = 4x - 8$$
    $$8 = 4x$$
    $$2 = x$$
    The x-intercept is $(2, 0)$.

18. $p(x) = -\dfrac{3}{4}x + 3$

For the *y*-intercept, set *x* = 0:

$$p(0) = -\dfrac{3}{4}(0) + 3 = 0 + 3 = 3$$

The *y*-intercept is (0, 3).
For the *x*-intercept, set *p*(*x*) = 0 and solve for *x*:

$$0 = -\dfrac{3}{4}x + 3$$

$$\dfrac{3}{4}x = 3$$

$$\dfrac{4}{3}\left(\dfrac{3}{4}x\right) = \dfrac{4}{3}(3)$$

$$x = 4$$

The *x*-intercept is (4, 0).

19. $s(x) = \dfrac{4}{3}x + 3$

For the *y*-intercept, set *x* = 0:

$$s(0) = \dfrac{4}{3}(0) + 3 = 0 + 3 = 3$$

The *y*-intercept is (0, 3).
For the *x*-intercept, set *s*(*x*) = 0 and solve for *x*:

$$0 = \dfrac{4}{3}x + 3$$

$$-\dfrac{4}{3}x = 3$$

$$-\dfrac{3}{4}\left(-\dfrac{4}{3}x\right) = -\dfrac{3}{4}(3)$$

$$x = -\dfrac{9}{4}$$

The *x*-intercept is $\left(-\dfrac{9}{4}, 0\right)$.

20. $g(x) = -\dfrac{1}{4}x + 2$

For the *y*-intercept, set *x* = 0:

$$g(0) = -\dfrac{1}{4}(0) + 2 = 0 + 2 = 2$$

The *y*-intercept is (0, 2).
For the *x*-intercept, set *g*(*x*) = 0 and solve for *x*:

$$0 = -\dfrac{1}{4}x + 2$$

$$\dfrac{1}{4}x = 2$$

$$4\left(\dfrac{1}{4}x\right) = 4(2)$$

$$x = 8$$

The *x*-intercept is (8, 0).

21. $h(x) = -\dfrac{6}{5}x + 2$

For the *y*-intercept, set *x* = 0:

$$h(0) = -\dfrac{6}{5}(0) + 2 = 0 + 2 = 2$$

The *y*-intercept is (0, 2).
For the *x*-intercept, set *h*(*x*) = 0 and solve for *x*:

$$0 = -\dfrac{6}{5}x + 2$$

$$\dfrac{6}{5}x = 2$$

$$\dfrac{5}{6}\left(\dfrac{6}{5}x\right) = \dfrac{5}{6}(2)$$

$$x = \dfrac{5}{3}$$

The *x*-intercept is $\left(\dfrac{5}{3}, 0\right)$.

22. $f(x) = \dfrac{1}{2}x - 2$

For the y-intercept, set $x = 0$:

$$f(0) = \frac{1}{2}(0) - 2 = 0 - 2 = -2$$

The y-intercept is $(0, -2)$.

For the x-intercept, set $f(x) = 0$ and solve for x:

$$0 = \frac{1}{2}x - 2$$

$$2 = \frac{1}{2}x$$

$$2(2) = 2\left(\frac{1}{2}x\right)$$

$$4 = x$$

The x-intercept is $(4, 0)$.

23. $g(x) = -\dfrac{1}{2}x + 2$

For the y-intercept, set $x = 0$:

$$g(0) = -\frac{1}{2}(0) + 2 = 0 + 2 = 2$$

The y-intercept is $(0, 2)$.

For the x-intercept, set $g(x) = 0$ and solve for x:

$$0 = -\frac{1}{2}x + 2$$

$$\frac{1}{2}x = 2$$

$$2\left(\frac{1}{2}x\right) = 2(2)$$

$$x = 4$$

The x-intercept is $(4, 0)$.

24. $p(x) = -\dfrac{1}{4}x - 6$

For the y-intercept, set $x = 0$:

$$p(0) = -\frac{1}{4}(0) - 6 = 0 - 6 = -6$$

The y-intercept is $(0, -6)$.

For the x-intercept, set $p(x) = 0$ and solve for x:

$$0 = -\frac{1}{4}x - 6$$

$$\frac{1}{4}x = -6$$

$$4\left(\frac{1}{4}x\right) = 4(-6)$$

$$x = -24$$

The x-intercept is $(-24, 0)$.

25. $w(x) = \dfrac{1}{3}x - 2$

For the y-intercept, set $x = 0$:

$$w(0) = \frac{1}{3}(0) - 2 = 0 - 2 = -2$$

The y-intercept is $(0, -2)$.

For the x-intercept, set $w(x) = 0$ and solve for x:

$$0 = \frac{1}{3}x - 2$$

$$2 = \frac{1}{3}x$$

$$3(2) = 3\left(\frac{1}{3}x\right)$$

$$6 = x$$

The x-intercept is $(6, 0)$.

26. $h(x) = -\dfrac{1}{3}x + 4$

For the *y*-intercept, set $x = 0$:

$$h(0) = -\dfrac{1}{3}(0) + 4 = 0 + 4 = 4$$

The *y*-intercept is $(0, 4)$.

For the *x*-intercept, set $h(x) = 0$ and solve for *x*:

$$0 = -\dfrac{1}{3}x + 4$$

$$\dfrac{1}{3}x = 4$$

$$3\left(\dfrac{1}{3}x\right) = 3(4)$$

$$x = 12$$

The *x*-intercept is $(12, 0)$.

27. $s(x) = -\dfrac{4}{3}x + 48$

For the *y*-intercept, set $x = 0$:

$$s(0) = -\dfrac{4}{3}(0) + 48 = 0 + 48 = 48$$

The *y*-intercept is $(0, 48)$.

For the *x*-intercept, set $s(x) = 0$ and solve for *x*:

$$0 = -\dfrac{4}{3}x + 48$$

$$\dfrac{4}{3}x = 48$$

$$\dfrac{3}{4}\left(\dfrac{4}{3}x\right) = \dfrac{3}{4}(48)$$

$$x = 36$$

The *x*-intercept is $(36, 0)$.

28. $d(x) = -\dfrac{1}{3}x - 2$

For the *y*-intercept, set $x = 0$:

$$d(0) = -\dfrac{1}{3}(0) - 2 = 0 - 2 = -2$$

The *y*-intercept is $(0, -2)$.

For the *x*-intercept, set $d(x) = 0$ and solve for *x*:

$$0 = -\dfrac{1}{3}x - 2$$

$$\dfrac{1}{3}x = -2$$

$$3\left(\dfrac{1}{3}x\right) = 3(-2)$$

$$x = -6$$

The *x*-intercept is $(-6, 0)$.

29. The equation is $d = 30t$. To graph, plot a few points.

t	Calculation	d
0	30(0)	0
1	30(1)	30
4	30(4)	120

30. The equation is $i = (1000)(0.03)t$, or $i = 30t$. To graph, plot a few points.

t	Calculation	i
0	15(0)	0
1	15(1)	15
5	15(5)	75
10	15(10)	150

31. a. $p = 60x - 80,000$. To graph, plot a few points.

x	Calculation	p
0	60(0) – 80,000	–80,000
2500	60(2500) – 80,000	70,000
5000	60(5000) – 80,000	220,000

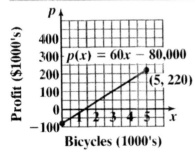

b. To break even, the profit would be zero. That is, set $p = 0$ and solve for x:
$$0 = 60x - 80,000$$
$$80,000 = 60x$$
$$x = \frac{-80,000}{-60} \approx 1333$$
The company must sell about 1,300 bicycles to break even.

c. To earn a profit of \$150,000, set $p = 150,000$ and solve for x:
$$150,000 = 60x - 80,000$$
$$230,000 = 60x$$
$$x = \frac{230,000}{60} \approx 3833$$
The company must sell about 3,800 bicycles to make a \$150,000 profit.

32. a. $c(m) = 75 + 0.15m$

b. To graph, plot a few points.

m	Calculation	c
0	75 + 0.15(0)	75
100	75 + 0.15(100)	90
200	75 + 0.15(200)	105

c. Find the value of the function at $m = 150$.
$$c(150) = 75 + 0.15(150) = 75 + 22.50 = 97.50$$
The cost would be \$97.50.

d. For a cost of \$135, set $c = 135$ and solve for m:
$$135 = 75 + 0.15m$$
$$60 = 0.15m$$
$$400 = m$$
Raul would have to drive 400 miles.

33. a. $s(x) = 500 + 0.15x$

b. To graph, plot a few points.

x	Calculation	s
0	500 + 0.15(0)	500
1000	500 + 0.15(1000)	650
5000	500 + 0.15(5000)	1250

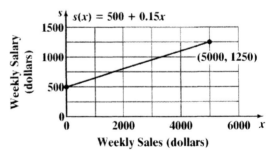

c. For weekly sales of \$3000,
$$s(3000) = 500 + 0.15(3000)$$
$$= 500 + 450$$
$$= 950$$
Her salary is \$950.

d. For a salary of $1100, set $s = 1100$ and solve for x.

$$1100 = 500 + 0.15x$$
$$600 = 0.15x$$
$$4000 = x$$

Her weekly sales are $4000.

34. a. $s(x) = 100 + 0.03x$

b. To graph, plot a few points.

x	Calculation	s
0	100 + 0.03(0)	100
50,000	100 + 0.03(50,000)	1600
100,000	100 + 0.03(100,000)	3100

Sales (thousands of dollars)

c. For weekly sales of $75,000, her salary will be

$$s(75,000) = 100 + 0.03(75,000)$$
$$= 100 + 2250$$
$$= 2350$$

Her salary will be $2350.

35. a. There is only one y-value for each x-value. (It passes the vertical line test.)

b. The independent variable is length. The dependent variable is weight.

c. Yes, the graph of weight versus length is approximately linear.

d. The weight of the average girl who is 85 centimeters long is 11.5 kilograms.

e. The average length of a girl with a weight of 7 kilograms is 65 centimeters.

f. For a girl 95 centimeters long, the weights 12.0 – 15.5 kilograms are considered normal.

g. As the lengths increase, the normal range of weights increases. Yes, this is expected: as the girls grow, it is reasonable that their weights will vary more.

36. a. For each graph there is only one y-value for each x-value. (Each graph passes the vertical line test.)

b. The independent variable is years. The dependent variable is dollars.

c. It would take 60 years to save $600 using the linear growth curve.

d. Using the exponential growth curve, it would take about 26 years for the amount to reach $600.

e. At year 20, the savings amount is $200. This is doubled when the savings amount grows to $400, which occurs at year 40 (that is, 20 years after year 20). Thus, starting at year 20, it would take 20 years for the money to double growing at a linear rate.

f. At year 20, the savings amount is about $200. This is doubled when the savings grows to about $400, which occurs around year 30 (that is, 10 years after year 20). Thus, starting at year 20, it would take about 10 years for the money to double growing exponentially.

37. The x- and y-intercepts of a graph will be the same when the graph goes through the origin.

38. Answers may vary. One possible answer is, $f(x) = x$ and $g(x) = 2x$ are two linear functions whose x- and y-intercepts are both $(0, 0)$.

39. Answers may vary. One possible answer is, $f(x) = 4$ is a function whose graph has no x-intercept but has a y-intercept of $(0, 4)$.

40. Answers may vary. One possible answer is, $x = -5$ is an equation whose graph has no y-intercept but has an x-intercept of $(-5, 0)$.

41. The x- and y-intercepts will both be $(0, 0)$.

42.

The x- and y-intercepts will be $\left(\dfrac{1}{3}, 0\right)$ and $(0, -1)$, respectively.

43. a.

b. vertical change = 2 – 0 = 2

c. horizontal change = 0 – (–4) = 4

d. $\dfrac{\text{vertical change}}{\text{horizontal change}} = \dfrac{2}{4} = \dfrac{1}{2}$

The ratio represents the slope of the line.

44. a.

b. vertical change = 5 – (–1) = 6

c. horizontal change = 3 – (–1) = 4

d. $\dfrac{\text{vertical change}}{\text{horizontal change}} = \dfrac{6}{4} = \dfrac{3}{2}$

The ratio represents the slope of the line.

45. Graph $Y_1 = 2x + 5$ and $Y_2 = 8x - 1$, and find the intersection.

The solution is $x = 1$.

46. Graph $Y_1 = 3(x + 2) + 1$ and $Y_2 = 2(x - 1) + 7$, and find the intersection.

The solution is $x = -2$.

47. Graph $Y_1 = 0.3(x + 5)$ and $Y_2 = -0.6(x + 2)$, and find the intersection.

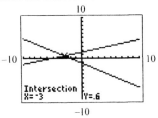

The solution is $x = -3$.

48. Graph $Y_1 = 2x + \dfrac{1}{4}$ and $Y_2 = 5x - \dfrac{1}{2}$, and find the intersection.

The solution is $x = 0.25$.

49. Let $Y_1 = 2(x + 3.2)$.

Window: –10,10,1,–10,10,1

The *x*-intercept is (–3.2, 0), and the *y*-intercept is (0, 6.4).

50. To use the graphing calculator, we must rewrite the equation in the form $y = f(x)$.

$$5x - 2y = 7$$
$$-2y = -5x + 7$$
$$\frac{-2y}{-2} = \frac{-5x + 7}{-2}$$
$$y = \frac{5}{2}x - \frac{7}{2}$$

Let $Y_1 = \dfrac{5}{2}x - \dfrac{7}{2}$.

Window: –10,10,1,–10,10,1

The *x*-intercept is (1.4, 0), and the *y*-intercept is (0, –3.5).

51. To use the graphing calculator, we must rewrite the equation in the form $y = f(x)$.

$$-4x - 3.2y = 8$$
$$-3.2y = 4x + 8$$
$$y = \frac{4x + 8}{-3.2}$$
$$y = -1.25x - 2.5$$

Let $Y_1 = -1.25x - 2.5$.

Window: $-10, 10, 1, -10, 10, 1$

The x-intercept is $(-2, 0)$, and the y-intercept is $(0, -2.5)$.

52. Let $Y_1 = \frac{3}{5}x - \frac{1}{2}$.

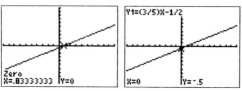

Window: $-10, 10, 1, -10, 10, 1$

The x-intercept is $(0.8\overline{3}, 0)$, and the y-intercept is $(0, -0.5)$.

53. $(7x^2 - 3x - 100) + (-4x^2 - 9x + 12)$
$= 7x^2 - 3x - 100 - 4x^2 - 9x + 12$
$= 7x^2 - 4x^2 - 3x - 9x - 100 + 12$
$= 3x^2 - 12x - 88$

54. $3x^2 - 12x - 96 = 3(x^2 - 4x - 32)$
$= 3(x + 4)(x - 8)$

55. $\dfrac{x - 2}{x^2 - 4} = \dfrac{x - 2}{(x + 2)(x - 2)} = \dfrac{1}{x + 2}$

56. $x + \dfrac{24}{x} = 10$

$$x\left(x + \frac{24}{x}\right) = x(10)$$
$$x^2 + 24 = 10x$$
$$x^2 - 10x + 24 = 0$$
$$(x - 4)(x - 6) = 0$$

$x - 4 = 0$ or $x - 6 = 0$
$x = 4$ $x = 6$

Note that neither 4 nor 6 is extraneous. In other words, both 4 and 6 check. The solutions to the equation are $x = 4$ and $x = 6$.

Mid-Chapter Test: 8.1-8.3

1.

$y = 3x + 2$

2.

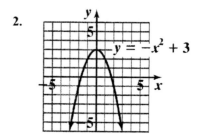

$y = -x^2 + 3$

3.

$y = |x| - 4$

4.

$y = \sqrt{x - 4}$

5. a. A relation is any set of ordered pairs.

  b. A function is a correspondence between a first set of elements, the domain, and a second set of elements, the range, such that each element of the domain corresponds to exactly one element in the range.

404

c. No, every relation is not a function. A relation can have two ordered pairs with the same first element but a function cannot.

d. Yes, every function is also a relation. A function is a set of ordered pairs so it is a relation.

6. The relation is a function.

Domain: $\{1, 2, 7, -5\}$

Range: $\{5, -3, -1, 6\}$

7. The relation is not a function.

Domain: $\{x \mid -2 \le x \le 2\}$

Range: $\{y \mid -4 \le y \le 4\}$

8. The relation is a function.

Domain: $\{x \mid -5 \le x \le 3\}$

Range: $\{y \mid -1 \le y \le 3\}$

9. $E = \{0, 9, 18, 27, 36, \ldots\}$

10. $\{z \mid z \le -5\}$

11. $g(-2) = 2(-2)^2 + 8(-2) - 13$

$\qquad = 2(4) + 8(-2) - 13$

$\qquad = 8 - 16 - 13$

$\qquad = -21$

12. $h(3) = -6(3)^2 + 3(3) + 150$

$\qquad = -6(9) + 3(3) + 150$

$\qquad = -54 + 9 + 150$

$\qquad = 105$

At $t = 3$ seconds, the apple is 105 feet above the ground.

13. $f(x) = 2x + 3$

For the y-intercept, set $x = 0$:

$f(0) = 2(0) + 3 = 0 + 3 = 3$

The y-intercept is $(0, 3)$.

For the x-intercept, set $f(x) = 0$ and solve for x:

$0 = 2x + 3$

$-3 = 2x$

$-\dfrac{3}{2} = x$

The x-intercept is $\left(-\dfrac{3}{2}, 0\right)$.

14. $g(x) = \dfrac{1}{2}x - 4$

For the y-intercept, set $x = 0$:

$g(0) = \dfrac{1}{2}(0) - 4 = 0 - 4 = -4$

The y-intercept is $(0, -4)$.

For the x-intercept, set $g(x) = 0$ and solve for x:

$0 = \dfrac{1}{2}x - 4$

$4 = \dfrac{1}{2}x$

$2(4) = 2\left(\dfrac{1}{2}\right)x$

$8 = x$

The x-intercept is $(8, 0)$.

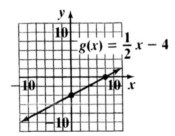

15. $m(x) = -\dfrac{1}{3}x + 2$

For the y-intercept, set $x = 0$:

$m(0) = -\dfrac{1}{3}(0) + 2 = 0 + 2 = 2$

The y-intercept is $(0, 2)$.

For the x-intercept, set $m(x) = 0$ and solve for x:

$0 = -\dfrac{1}{3}x + 2$

$\dfrac{1}{3}x = 2$

$3\left(\dfrac{1}{3}\right)x = 3(2)$

$x = 6$

The x-intercept is $(6, 0)$.

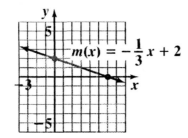

16. **a.** Let $x = 0$: $p(0) = 30(0) - 660$
$$= 0 - 660$$
$$= -660$$
Let $x = 40$: $p(40) = 30(40) - 660$
$$= 1200 - 660$$
$$= 540$$
Plots the points $(0, -660)$ and $(40, 540)$ and connect to obtain the graph.

b. $p(x) = 0$
$$30x - 660 = 0$$
$$30x = 660$$
$$x = 22$$
The company will break even if 22 pairs of shoes are produced and sold.

c. $p(x) = 360$
$$30x - 660 = 360$$
$$30x = 1020$$
$$x = 34$$
The company will make a $360 daily profit if 34 pairs of shoes are produced and sold.

Exercise Set 8.4

1. When the slope is given as a rate of change it means the change in y for a unit change in x.

2. The slope of a constant function is $m = 0$, because the vertical change (or rise) is 0.

3. **a.** If a graph is translated up 3 units, it is lifted or moved up 3 units.

   b. If the y-intercept is $(0, -4)$ and the graph is translated up 5 units, the new y-intercept will be at $y = -4 + 5 = 1$. The new y-intercept is $(0, 1)$.

4. **a.** If a graph is translated down 4 units, it is lowered or moved down 4 units.

   b. If the y-intercept is $(0, -3)$ and the graph is translated down 4 units, the new y-intercept will be at $y = -3 - 4 = -7$. The new y-intercept is $(0, -7)$.

5. Two lines are perpendicular if their slopes are negative reciprocals, or if one line is horizontal and the other is vertical.

6. A vertical line has an undefined slope; the negative reciprocal is undefined. A horizontal line has zero slope; the negative reciprocal is undefined. In short, we cannot divide by 0.

7. The slope is negative and y decreases 6 units when x increases 2 units. Thus, $m = -\dfrac{6}{2} = -3$. The line crosses the y-axis at 0 so $b = 0$. Hence, $m = -3$ and $b = 0$, and the equation of the line is $f(x) = -3x + 0$ or $f(x) = -3x$.

8. The slope is positive and y changes 2 units when x changes 2 units. Thus, $m = 1$. The line crosses the y-axis at -1 so $b = -1$. Hence, $m = 1$ and $b = -1$, and the equation of the line is $f(x) = x - 1$.

9. The slope is undefined since the change in x is 0. The equation of this vertical line is $x = -2$.

10. The line is horizontal so $m = 0$. The line crosses the y-axis at 3 so $b = 3$. Hence, $m = 0$ and $b = 3$, and the equation of the line is $f(x) = 3$.

11. The slope is negative and y decreases 1 unit when x increases 3 units. Thus, $m = -\dfrac{1}{3}$. The line crosses the y-axis at 2 so $b = 2$. Hence, $m = -\dfrac{1}{3}$ and $b = 2$, and the equation of the line is
$$f(x) = -\frac{1}{3}x + 2.$$

12. The slope is positive and y changes 4 units when x changes 2 units. Thus, $m = 2$. The line crosses the y-axis at 3 so $b = 3$. Hence, $m = 2$ and $b = 3$, and the equation of the line is $f(x) = 2x + 3$.

13. The slope is negative and y decreases 15 units when x increases 10 units. Thus, $m = -\dfrac{15}{10} = -\dfrac{3}{2}$. The line crosses the y-axis at 15 so $b = 15$. Hence, $m = -\dfrac{3}{2}$ and $b = 15$, and the equation of the line is $f(x) = -\dfrac{3}{2}x + 15$.

14. The slope is positive and y changes 5 units when x changes 15 units. Thus, $m = \dfrac{5}{15} = \dfrac{1}{3}$. The line crosses the y-axis at 5 so $b = 5$. Hence, $m = \dfrac{1}{3}$ and $b = 5$. The equation of the line is $f(x) = \dfrac{1}{3}x + 5$.

15. The graph of $f(x) = -5$ is a horizontal line with y-intercept $(0, -5)$.

16. The graph of $g(x) = 2$ is a horizontal line with y-intercept $(0, 2)$.

17. The graph of $g(x) = -15$ is a horizontal line with y-intercept $(0, -15)$.

18. The graph of $h(x) = 75$ is a horizontal line with y-intercept $(0, 75)$.

19. $m_1 = \dfrac{2-0}{0-2} = \dfrac{2}{-2} = -1$; $m_2 = \dfrac{3-0}{0-3} = \dfrac{3}{-3} = -1$
Since their slopes are equal, l_1 and l_2 are parallel.

20. $m_1 = \dfrac{9-6}{3-7} = \dfrac{3}{-4} = -\dfrac{3}{4}$; $m_2 = \dfrac{-4-(-1)}{9-5} = \dfrac{-3}{4} = -\dfrac{3}{4}$
Since their slopes are equal, l_1 and l_2 are parallel.

21. $m_1 = \dfrac{7-6}{5-4} = \dfrac{1}{1} = 1$; $m_2 = \dfrac{4-(-1)}{1-(-1)} = \dfrac{5}{2}$
Since their slopes are different and since the product of their slopes is not -1, l_1 and l_2 are neither parallel nor perpendicular.

22. $m_1 = \dfrac{-3-4}{4-(-3)} = \dfrac{-7}{7} = -1$; $m_2 = \dfrac{-5-(-6)}{6-(-5)} = \dfrac{1}{11}$
Since their slopes are different and since the product of their slopes is not -1, l_1 and l_2 are neither parallel nor perpendicular.

23. $m_1 = \dfrac{-2-2}{-1-3} = \dfrac{-4}{-4} = 1$; $m_2 = \dfrac{-1-0}{3-2} = \dfrac{-1}{1} = -1$
Since the product of their slopes is -1, the lines are perpendicular.

24. $m_1 = \dfrac{1-5}{9-3} = \dfrac{-4}{6} = -\dfrac{2}{3}$; $m_2 = \dfrac{3-0}{6-4} = \dfrac{3}{2}$

Since the product of their slopes is -1, the lines are perpendicular.

25. $y = \dfrac{1}{5}x + 9$, so $m_1 = \dfrac{1}{5}$

$y = -5x + 2$, so $m_2 = -5$

Since the product of their slopes is -1, the lines are perpendicular.

26.
$2x + 3y = 11$ $y = -\dfrac{2}{3}x + 4$

$3y = -2x + 11$

$y = -\dfrac{2}{3}x + \dfrac{11}{3}$ $m_2 = -\dfrac{2}{3}$

$m_1 = -\dfrac{2}{3}$

Since their slopes are equal and their y-intercepts are different, the lines are parallel.

27.
$4x + 2y = 8$ $8x = 4 - 4y$

$2y = -4x + 8$ $4y = -8x + 4$

$y = -2x + 4$ $y = -2x + 1$

$m_1 = -2$ $m_2 = -2$

Since their slopes are equal and their y-intercepts are different, the lines are parallel.

28.
$2x - y = 4$ $3x + 6y = 18$

$-y = -2x + 4$ $6y = -3x + 18$

$y = 2x - 4$ $y = \dfrac{-3x + 18}{6}$

$m_1 = 2$ $y = -\dfrac{1}{2}x + 3$

            $m_2 = -\dfrac{1}{2}$

Since the product of their slopes is -1, the lines are perpendicular.

29.
$2x - y = 4$ $-x + 4y = 4$

$-y = -2x + 4$ $4y = x + 4$

$y = 2x - 4$ $y = \dfrac{1}{4}x + 1$

$m_1 = 2$ $m_2 = \dfrac{1}{4}$

Since their slopes are different and since the product of their slopes is not -1, the lines are neither parallel nor perpendicular.

30.
$6x + 2y = 8$ $4x - 5 = -y$

$2y = -6x + 8$ $y = -4x + 5$

$y = -3x + 4$ $m_2 = -4$

$m_1 = -3$

Since their slopes are different and since the product of their slopes is not -1, the lines are neither parallel nor perpendicular.

31.
$y = \dfrac{1}{2}x - 6$ $-4y = 8x + 15$

$m_1 = \dfrac{1}{2}$ $y = \dfrac{8x + 15}{-4}$

            $y = -2x - \dfrac{15}{4}$

            $m_2 = -2$

Since the product of their slopes is -1, the lines are perpendicular.

32.
$2y - 8 = -5x$ $y = -\dfrac{5}{2}x - 2$

$2y = -5x + 8$ $m_2 = -\dfrac{5}{2}$

$y = -\dfrac{5}{2}x + 4$

$m_1 = -\dfrac{5}{2}$

Since their slopes are equal and their y-intercepts are different, the lines are parallel.

33.
$y = \dfrac{1}{2}x + 6$ $-2x + 4y = 8$

$m_1 = \dfrac{1}{2}$ $4y = 2x + 8$

            $y = \dfrac{1}{2}x + 2$

            $m_2 = \dfrac{1}{2}$

Since their slopes are equal and their y-intercepts are different, the lines are parallel.

34.
$-4x + 6y = 11$ $2x - 3y = 5$

$6y = 4x + 11$ $-3y = -2x + 5$

$y = \dfrac{4x + 11}{6}$ $y = \dfrac{-2x + 5}{-3}$

$y = \dfrac{2}{3}x + \dfrac{11}{6}$ $y = \dfrac{2}{3}x - \dfrac{5}{3}$

$m_1 = \dfrac{2}{3}$ $m_2 = \dfrac{2}{3}$

Since their slopes are equal and their y-intercepts are different, the lines are parallel.

35.
$$x - 2y = -9$$
$$-2y = -x - 9$$
$$y = \frac{-x - 9}{-2}$$
$$y = \frac{1}{2}x + \frac{9}{2}$$
$$m_1 = \frac{1}{2}$$

$$y = x + 6$$
$$m_2 = 1$$

Since their slopes are different and since the product of their slopes is not -1, the lines are neither parallel nor perpendicular.

36.
$$\frac{1}{2}x - \frac{3}{4}y = 1$$
$$4\left(\frac{1}{2}x - \frac{3}{4}y\right) = 4(1)$$
$$2x - 3y = 4$$
$$-3y = -2x + 4$$
$$y = \frac{2}{3}x - \frac{4}{3}$$
$$m_1 = \frac{2}{3}$$

$$\frac{3}{5}x + \frac{2}{5}y = -1$$
$$5\left(\frac{3}{5}x + \frac{2}{5}y\right) = 5(-1)$$
$$3x + 2y = -5$$
$$2y = -3x - 5$$
$$y = -\frac{3}{2}x - \frac{5}{2}$$
$$m_2 = -\frac{3}{2}$$

Since the product of their slopes is -1, the lines are perpendicular.

37. The slope of the given line, $y = 2x + 4$, is $m_1 = 2$. So $m_2 = 2$. Now use the point-slope form with $m = 2$ and $(x_1, y_1) = (2, 5)$ to obtain the slope-intercept form.
$$y - y_1 = m(x - x_1)$$
$$y - 5 = 2(x - 2)$$
$$y - 5 = 2x - 4$$
$$y = 2x + 1$$

38. Find the slope of the given line.
$$4x - 2y = 6$$
$$-2y = -4x + 6$$
$$y = 2x - 3$$
$m_1 = 2$, so $m_2 = 2$. Now use the point-slope form with $m = 2$ and $(x_1, y_1) = (-1, 6)$ to obtain the slope-intercept form.
$$y - y_1 = m(x - x_1)$$
$$y - 6 = 2(x - (-1))$$
$$y - 6 = 2(x + 1)$$
$$y - 6 = 2x + 2$$
$$y = 2x + 8$$

39. Find the slope of the given line.
$$2x - 5y = 7$$
$$-5y = -2x + 7$$
$$y = \frac{-2x + 7}{-5}$$
$$y = \frac{2}{5}x - \frac{7}{5}$$
$m_1 = \frac{2}{5}$, so $m_2 = \frac{2}{5}$. Now use the point-slope form with $m = \frac{2}{5}$ and $(x_1, y_1) = (-3, -5)$ to obtain the standard form.

$$y - y_1 = m(x - x_1)$$
$$y - (-5) = \frac{2}{5}(x - (-3))$$
$$y + 5 = \frac{2}{5}(x + 3)$$
$$y + 5 = \frac{2}{5}x + \frac{6}{5}$$
$$5(y + 5) = 5\left(\frac{2}{5}x + \frac{6}{5}\right)$$
$$5y + 25 = 2x + 6$$
$$-2x + 5y = -19$$
$$2x - 5y = 19$$

40. The slope of the given line, $y = -2x - 1$, is $m_1 = -2$. So, $m_2 = \frac{1}{2}$. Now use the point-slope form with $m = \frac{1}{2}$ and $(x_1, y_1) = (-1, 4)$ to obtain the standard form.

$$y - y_1 = m(x - x_1)$$
$$y - 4 = \frac{1}{2}(x + 1)$$
$$y - 4 = \frac{1}{2}x + \frac{1}{2}$$
$$2(y - 4) = 2\left(\frac{1}{2}x + \frac{1}{2}\right)$$
$$2y - 8 = x + 1$$
$$-x + 2y = 9$$
$$x - 2y = -9$$

41. Find the slope of the line with the given intercepts:

$m = \dfrac{5-0}{0-3} = -\dfrac{5}{3}$. The y-intercept $(0, 5)$, so $b = 5$.

Thus, the slope-intercept form of the equation is

$y = -\dfrac{5}{3}x + 5$.

42. The slope of the given line $f(x) = -\dfrac{1}{5}x + 1$ is

$m_1 = -\dfrac{1}{5}$. So $m_2 = 5$. Now use the point-slope

form with $m = 5$ and $(x_1, y_1) = (-2, -1)$ to

obtain the function notation.

$y - y_1 = m(x - x_1)$

$y - (-1) = 5\big(x - (-2)\big)$

$y + 1 = 5(x + 2)$

$y + 1 = 5x + 10$

$y = 5x + 9$

$f(x) = 5x + 9$

43. The slope of the given line $y = \dfrac{1}{3}x + 1$ is

$m_1 = \dfrac{1}{3}$. So m_2 is the negative reciprocal, or

$m_2 = -\dfrac{1}{m_1} = -\dfrac{1}{\frac{1}{3}} = -1 \cdot 3 = -3$. Use the point-

slope form with $m = -3$ and $(x_1, y_1) = (5, -2)$ to

obtain the function notation.

$y - y_1 = m(x - x_1)$

$y - (-2) = -3(x - 5)$

$y + 2 = -3x + 15$

$y = -3x + 13$

$f(x) = -3x + 13$

44. Find the slope of the line with the given intercepts:

$m_1 = \dfrac{2-0}{0-2} = -1$. So m_2 is the negative reciprocal,

or $m_2 = -\dfrac{1}{m_1} = -\dfrac{1}{-1} = 1$. Now use the point-slope

form with $m_2 = 1$ and $(x_1, y_1) = (-3, 5)$ to obtain

the standard form.

$y - y_1 = m(x - x_1)$

$y - 5 = 1\big(x - (-3)\big)$

$y - 5 = x + 3$

$-x + y = 8$

$x - y = -8$

45. Find the slope of the line with the given intercepts:

$m_1 = \dfrac{-3-0}{0-2} = \dfrac{-3}{-2} = \dfrac{3}{2}$. So m_2 is the negative

reciprocal, or $m_2 = -\dfrac{1}{m_1} = -\dfrac{1}{\frac{3}{2}} = -\dfrac{2}{3}$. Now use the

point-slope form with $m = -\dfrac{2}{3}$ and

$(x_1, y_1) = (6, 2)$ and obtain the slope-intercept

form.

$y - y_1 = m(x - x_1)$

$y - 2 = -\dfrac{2}{3}(x - 6)$

$y - 2 = -\dfrac{2}{3}x + 4$

$y = -\dfrac{2}{3}x + 6$

46. Find the slope of the line passing through $(3, 5)$

and $(-2, 3)$: $m_1 = \dfrac{3-5}{-2-3} = \dfrac{-2}{-5} = \dfrac{2}{5}$. So $m_2 = \dfrac{2}{5}$.

Now use the point-slope form with $m = \dfrac{2}{5}$ and

$(x_1, y_1) = (1, 2)$ to obtain the function notation.

$y - y_1 = m(x - x_1)$

$y - 2 = \dfrac{2}{5}(x - 1)$

$y - 2 = \dfrac{2}{5}x - \dfrac{2}{5}$

$y = \dfrac{2}{5}x + \dfrac{8}{5}$

$f(x) = \dfrac{2}{5}x + \dfrac{8}{5}$

47. $m = \dfrac{2-4}{-4-6} = \dfrac{-2}{-10} = \dfrac{1}{5}$

For a 1-unit change in x, y changes $\dfrac{1}{5}$ or 0.2

unit.

48. $m = \dfrac{2-(-4)}{5-(-3)} = \dfrac{6}{8} = \dfrac{3}{4}$

For a 1-unit change in x, y changes $\dfrac{3}{4}$ or 0.75

unit.

49. a. Let $(x_1, y_1) = (2005, 19.7)$ and

$(x_2, y_2) = (2006, 31.0)$. Then

$$m = \frac{31.0 - 19.7}{2006 - 2005} = \frac{11.3}{1} = 11.3 \, .$$

b. positive

c. Let $(x_1, y_1) = (2004, 7.3)$ and

$(x_2, y_2) = (2008, 35.6)$. Then

$$m = \frac{35.6 - 7.3}{2008 - 2004} = \frac{28.3}{4} = 7.075 \, .$$

The average rate of change in digital TV sales from 2004 to 2008 is 7.075 million sales per year.

50. a. Let $(x_1, y_1) = (2005, 10.1)$ and

$(x_2, y_2) = (2006, 4.7)$. Then

$$m = \frac{4.7 - 10.1}{2006 - 2005} = \frac{-5.4}{1} = -5.4 \, .$$

b. negative

c. Let $(x_1, y_1) = (2004, 23.5)$ and

$(x_2, y_2) = (2008, 1.3)$. Then

$$m = \frac{1.3 - 23.5}{2008 - 2004} = \frac{-22.2}{4} = -5.55 \, .$$

The average rate of change in analog TV sales from 2004 to 2008 is -5.55 million sales per year.

51. a, b.

c. From 1995 to 2000,

$$m = \frac{2876 - 2257}{2000 - 1995} = \frac{619}{5} = 123.8$$

From 2000 to 2004,

$$m = \frac{3133 - 2876}{2004 - 2000} = \frac{257}{4} = 64.25$$

From 2004 to 2008,

$$m = \frac{3260 - 3133}{2008 - 2004} = \frac{127}{4} = 31.75$$

d. The greatest average rate of change occurred during the period 1995 to 2000,

because the largest slope corresponds to these years.

52. a.

b. From 2001 to 2002,

$$m = \frac{810 - 740}{2002 - 2001} = \frac{70}{1} = 70$$

From 2002 to 2003,

$$m = \frac{880 - 810}{2003 - 2002} = \frac{70}{1} = 70$$

From 2003 to 2004,

$$m = \frac{950 - 880}{2004 - 2003} = \frac{70}{1} = 70$$

c. Yes, this graph is a linear function. The points are in a straight line. That is the slope between each pair of points is constant.

d. From part (b), we know that $m = 70$. Since 2001 corresponds to $t = 0$, then the y-intercept is $(0, 740)$, so $b = 740$. Thus, the linear function is $d(t) = 70t + 740$.

e. Note that the year 2016 corresponds to $t = 15$:

$d(15) = 70(15) + 740 = 1050 + 740 = 1790$.

Assuming the trend continues, the demand for steel in 2016 will be 1790 metric tons.

f.

$$d(t) = 1230$$
$$70t + 740 = 1230$$
$$70t = 490$$
$$t = 7$$

Now $t = 7$ corresponds to the year 2008. Thus, assuming the trend continues, the demand for steel will be 1230 metric tons in the year 2008.

53. a. If x is the number of years after age 20, two points on the graph are $(0, 200)$ and $(50, 150)$.

The slope is $m = \frac{150 - 200}{50 - 0} = \frac{-50}{50} = -1$ and the y-intercept is $(0, 200)$, so $b = 200$. Thus, the equation for the line is $h(x) = -1x + 200$, or $h(x) = -x + 200$.

b. Note that a 34-year-old man is represented by
$x = 14$. Now, $h(14) = -(14) + 200 = 186$.
Thus, the maximum recommended heart rate
for a 34-year-old man is 186 beats per
minute.

54. a. Note that $t = 0$ represents 2000 and that $t = 4$
represents 2004. Thus, two ordered pairs of
the function are (0, 17603) and (5, 19484).
The slope of the line is
$m = \dfrac{19484 - 17603}{2004 - 2000} = \dfrac{1881}{4} = 470.25$. Now,
the y-intercept is (0, 17603), so $b = 17,603$.
The linear function is
$P(t) = 470.25t + 17,603$.

b. Note the year 2003 is represented by $t = 3$:
$P(3) = 470.25(3) + 17,603$
$= 1410.75 + 17,603$
$= 19,013.75$
The function indicates the poverty threshold
for 2003 was approximately \$19,013.75. This
is a slight overestimate since the graph shows
the poverty level a little below \$19,000.

c. Note the year 2010 is represented by $t = 10$:
$P(10) = 470.25(10) + 17,603$
$= 4702.5 + 17,603$
$= 22,305.5$
The function indicates the poverty threshold
for 2010 will be \$22,305.50.

d. $P(t) = 20,424.50$
$470.25t + 17,603 = 20,424.50$
$470.25t = 2821.50$
$t = 6$
The function indicates the poverty threshold
for a family of four reached \$20,424.50 six
years after 2000, which was the year 2006.

55. a. Note that $t = 0$ represents 1997 and $t = 7$
represents 2004. Thus, two ordered pairs of
the function are (0, 159.5) and (7, 294.9).
The slope of the line is
$m = \dfrac{294.9 - 159.50}{2004 - 1997} = \dfrac{135.4}{7} \approx 19.34$
The y-intercept is (0, 159.5), so $b = 159.5$.
The linear function is $M(t) \approx 19.34t + 159.5$.

b. Note that 2003 is represented by $t = 6$:
$M(6) = 19.34(6) + 159.5$
$= 116.04 + 159.5$
$= 275.54$
The function indicates that Medicaid spending

for 2003 was \$275.54 billion. This estimate is
similar to the spending shown in the graph.

c. Note that 2010 is represented by $t = 13$:
$M(13) = 19.34(13) + 159.5$
$= 251.42 + 159.5$
$= 410.92$
The function indicates that Medicaid spending
for 2010 will be \$410.92 billion.

d. $M(t) = 340$
$19.34t + 159.5 = 340$
$19.34t = 180.5$
$t = \dfrac{180.5}{19.34} \approx 9.3$
Note that $t = 9$ represents the year 2006.
Thus, according to the function, Medicaid
spending reached \$340 billion during the
year 2006.

56. a. Note that $t = 0$ represents 1990 and $t = 13$
represents 2003. Thus, two ordered pairs of
the function are (0, 0.766) and (13, 0.544).
The slope of the line is
$m = \dfrac{0.544 - 0.766}{13 - 0} = \dfrac{-0.222}{13} \approx -0.017$
The y-intercept is (0, 0.766), so $b = 0.766$.
The linear function is $P(t) \approx -0.017t + 0.766$.

b. Note that 1994 is represented by $t = 4$:
$P(4) = -0.017(4) + 0.766$
$= -0.068 + 0.766$
$= 0.698$
According to the function, the purchasing
power of the dollar in 1994 was \$0.698.
This estimate is close to the purchasing
power shown in the graph.

c. Note that 2006 is represented by $t = 16$:
$P(16) = -0.017(16) + 0.766$
$= -0.272 + 0.766$
$= 0.494$
According to the function, the purchasing
power of the dollar in 2006 was \$0.494.

d. $P(t) = 0.426$
$-0.017t + 0.766 = 0.426$
$-0.017t = -0.340$
$t = 20$
Note that $t = 20$ represents the year 2010.
From the function, the purchasing power of
the dollar will drop to \$0.426 in 2010.

57. a. Note that $t = 0$ represents 2001 and $t = 3$ represents 2004. Thus, two ordered pairs of the function are (0, 19.4) and (3, 16.1). The slope of the line is
$$m = \frac{16.1 - 19.4}{3 - 0} = \frac{-3.3}{3} = -1.1$$
The y-intercept is (0, 19.4), so , $b = 19.4$. The linear function is $P(t) = -1.1t + 19.4$.

b. Negative. The negative slope occurs because the percent of teenagers who used illicit drugs decreased from 2001 through 2004.

c. Note that 2003 is represented by $t = 2$:
$$P(2) = -1.1(2) + 19.4 = -2.2 + 19.4 = 17.2$$
According to the function, 17.2% of teenagers used illicit drugs in 2003. This estimate is close to the percent shown in the graph.

d. Note that 2010 is represented by $t = 9$:
$$P(9) = -1.1(9) + 19.4 = -9.9 + 19.4 = 9.5$$
According to the function, 9.5% of teenagers will be using illicit drugs in 2010.

58. a. Note that $t = 0$ represents June 2003 and $t = 17$ represents November 2004. Thus, two ordered pairs of the function are (0, 9.15) and (17, 9.79). The slope of the line is
$$m = \frac{9.79 - 9.15}{17 - 0} = \frac{0.64}{17} \approx 0.0376$$
The y-intercept is (0, 9.15), so $b = 9.15$. The linear function is $P(t) \approx 0.0376t + 9.15$.

b. Positive. The slope is positive because personal income increased from June 2003 to November 2004.

c. February 2004 is represented by $t = 8$:
$$P(8) = 0.0376(8) + 9.15 \approx 0.30 + 9.15 = 9.45$$
From the function, the personal income for February 2004 was $9.45 trillion. This is close to the amount shown in the graph.

d. Using $t = 30$:
$$P(30) = 0.0376(30) + 9.15 \approx 10.28$$
From the function, the personal income for December 2005 was $10.28 trillion.

59. a. Note that $t = 0$ represents 1995 and that $t = 9$ represents 2004. Thus, two ordered pairs of the function are (0, 110500) and (9, 185200). The slope of the line is
$$m = \frac{185,200 - 110,500}{9 - 0} = \frac{74,700}{9} = 8300$$
The y-intercept is (0, 110500), so $b = 110,500$. The linear function is $P(t) = 8300t + 110,500$.

b. Note that $t = 5$ represents 2000:
$$P(5) = 8300(5) + 110,500$$
$$= 41,500 + 110,500$$
$$= 152,000$$
The median home sale price in the year 2000 was about $152,000.

c. Note that $t = 15$ represents 2010:
$$P(15) = 8300(15) + 110,500$$
$$= 124,500 + 110,500$$
$$= 235,000$$
The median home sale price in the year 2010 will be about $235,000.

d. $8300t + 110,500 = 200,000$
$$8300t = 89,500$$
$$t = \frac{89,500}{8300} \approx 10.8$$
Now $t \approx 10.8$ corresponds to the year 2005. Thus, assuming the trend continues, the median home sale price will reach $200,000 near the end of the year 2005.

60. a. Note that $t = 0$ represents 1970 and that $t = 80$ represents 2050. Thus, two ordered pairs of the function are (0, 3.7) and (80, 2.0). The slope of the line is
$$m = \frac{2.0 - 3.7}{2050 - 1970} = \frac{-1.7}{80} \approx -0.021$$
The y-intercept is (0, 3.7), so $b = 3.7$. The linear function is $W(t) \approx -0.021t + 3.7$.

b. Note that $t = 50$ represents 2020:
$$W(50) = -0.021(50) + 3.7 = -1.05 + 3.7 = 2.65$$
According to the function, there will be about 2.65 workers per beneficiary in 2020.

61. a. To find the function, use the points (2.5, 210) and (6, 370) to determine the slope.
$$m = \frac{370 - 210}{6 - 2.5} = \frac{160}{3.5} \approx 45.7$$
Now use the point-slope form with $m = 45.7$ and $(s_1, C_1) = (2.5, 210)$
$$C - C_1 = m(s - s_1)$$
$$C - 210 = 45.7(s - 2.5)$$
$$C - 210 = 45.7s - 114.25$$
$$C = 45.7s + 95.75$$
$$C(s) \approx 45.7s + 95.8$$

b. $C(5) \approx 45.7(5) + 95.8 = 228.5 + 95.8 = 324.3$
The average person will burn about 324.3 calories.

62. a. To find the function, use the points $(5, 525)$ and $(15, 880)$ to determine the slope:

$$m = \frac{880 - 525}{15 - 5} = \frac{355}{10} = 35.5$$

Now use the point-slope form with $m = 35.5$ and $(d_1, C_1) = (5, 525)$.

$$C - C_1 = m(d - d_1)$$
$$C - 525 = 35.5(d - 5)$$
$$C - 525 = 35.5d - 177.5$$
$$C = 35.5d + 347.5$$
$$C(d) = 35.5d + 347.5$$

b. $C(9) = 35.5(9) + 347.5 = 319.5 + 347.5 = 667$

The average person will burn about 667 calories.

63. a. To find the function, use the points $(200, 50)$ and $(300, 30)$ to determine the

slope: $m = \frac{30 - 50}{300 - 200} = \frac{-20}{100} = -0.20$

Now use the point-slope form with $m = -0.20$ and $(p_1, d_1) = (200, 50)$

$$d - d_1 = m(p - p_1)$$
$$d - 50 = -0.20(p - 200)$$
$$d - 50 = -0.20p + 40$$
$$d = -0.20p + 90$$
$$d(p) = -0.20p + 90$$

b. $d(260) = -0.20(260) + 90 = -52 + 90 = 38$

When the price is $260, the demand will be 38 DVD players.

c.
$$d(p) = 45$$
$$-0.20p + 90 = 45$$
$$-0.20p = -45$$
$$p = 225$$

In order to have a demand of 45 DVD players, the price should be $225.

64. a. To find the function, use the points $(1, 530)$ and $(2, 400)$ to determine the slope:

$$m = \frac{400 - 530}{2 - 1} = \frac{-130}{1} = -130 \ .$$

Now use the point-slope form with $m = -130$ and $(p_1, d_1) = (1, 530)$:

$$d - d_1 = m(p - p_1)$$
$$d - 530 = -130(p - 1.00)$$
$$d - 530 = -130p + 130$$
$$d = -130p + 660$$
$$d(p) = -130p + 660$$

b.
$$d(2.60) = -130(2.60) + 660$$
$$= -338 + 660$$
$$= 322$$

When the price is $2.60, the demand will be 322 chicken sandwiches.

c.
$$d(p) = 244$$
$$-130p + 660 = 244$$
$$-130p = -416$$
$$p = 3.2$$

For demand to be 244 chicken sandwiches, the price should be $3.20.

65. a. To find the function, use the points $(2, 130)$ and $(4, 320)$ to determine the slope:

$$m = \frac{320 - 130}{4 - 2} = \frac{190}{2} = 95 \ .$$

Now use the point-slope form with $m = 95$ and $(p_1, s_1) = (2, 130)$.

$$s - s_1 = m(p - p_1)$$
$$s - 130 = 95(p - 2.00)$$
$$s - 130 = 95p - 190$$
$$s = 95p - 60$$
$$s(p) = 95p - 60$$

b. $s(2.80) = 95(2.80) - 60 = 266 - 60 = 206$

If the price is $2.80, the supply will be 206 kites.

c.
$$s(p) = 255$$
$$95p - 60 = 225$$
$$95p = 285$$
$$p = 3$$

For the supply to be 225 kites, the price should be $3.00.

66. a. To find the function, use the points $(210, 20)$ and $(230, 30)$ to determine the slope:

$$m = \frac{30 - 20}{230 - 210} = \frac{10}{20} = 0.5 \ .$$

Now use the point-slope form with $m = 0.5$ and $(p_1, s_1) = (210, 20)$

$$s - s_1 = m(p - p_1)$$
$$s - 20 = 0.5(p - 210)$$
$$s - 20 = 0.5p - 105$$
$$s = 0.5p - 85$$
$$s(p) = 0.5p - 85$$

b. $s(220) = 0.5(220) - 85 = 1110 - 85 = 25$

When the price is \$220.00, the supply will be 25 strollers.

c.
$$s(p) = 35$$
$$0.5p - 85 = 35$$
$$0.5p = 120$$
$$p = 240$$

For the supply to be 35 strollers, the price should be \$240.

67. a. To find the function, use the points (80, 1000) and (200, 2500) to determine the slope:
$$m = \frac{2500 - 1000}{200 - 80} = \frac{1500}{120} = 12.5.$$
Now use the point-slope form with $m = 12.5$ and $(t_1, i_1) = (80, 1000)$.
$$i - i_1 = m(t - t_1)$$
$$i - 1000 = 12.5(t - 80)$$
$$i - 1000 = 12.5t - 1000$$
$$i = 12.5t$$
$$i(t) = 12.5t$$

b. $i(120) = 12.5(120) = 1500$

If 120 tickets are sold, the income will be \$1500.

c.
$$i(t) = 2200$$
$$12.5t = 2200$$
$$t = 176$$

If the income is \$2200, then 176 tickets were sold.

68. a. To find the function, use the points (30, 35) and (60, 20) to determine the slope:
$$m = \frac{20 - 35}{60 - 30} = \frac{-15}{30} = -\frac{1}{2}.$$

Now use the point-slope form with $m = -\frac{1}{2}$

and $(s_1, m_1) = (30, 35)$.
$$m - m_1 = m(s - s_1)$$
$$m - 35 = -\frac{1}{2}(s - 30)$$
$$m - 35 = -\frac{1}{2}s + 15$$
$$m = -\frac{1}{2}s + 50$$
$$m(s) = -\frac{1}{2}s + 50$$

b. $m(48) = -\frac{1}{2}(48) + 50 = -24 + 50 = 26$

If the car is driven at 48 miles per hour, then its gas mileage will be 26 miles per gallon.

c.
$$m(s) = 40$$
$$-\frac{1}{2}s + 50 = 40$$
$$-\frac{1}{2}s = -10$$
$$s = 20$$

If the gas mileage is 40 miles per gallon, then the speed is 20 miles per hour.

69. a. To find the function, use the points (2000, 30) and (4000, 50) to determine the slope:
$$m = \frac{50 - 30}{4000 - 2000} = \frac{20}{2000} = 0.01.$$
Now use the point-slope form with $m = 0.01$ and $(w_1, r_1) = (2000, 30)$.
$$r - r_1 = m(w - w_1)$$
$$r - 30 = 0.01(w - 2000)$$
$$r - 30 = 0.01w - 20$$
$$r = 0.01w + 10$$
$$r(w) = 0.01w + 10$$

b. $r(3613) = 0.01(3613) + 10$
$$= 36.13 + 10$$
$$= 46.13$$
If the weight of the care is 3613 pounds, then the registration fee will be \$46.13.

c.
$$r(w) = 60$$
$$0.01w + 10 = 60$$
$$0.01w = 50$$
$$w = 5000$$
If the registration fee is \$60, then the weight of the car is 5000 pounds.

70. a. To find the function, use the points (9, 41350) and (15, 46687) to determine the slope:
$$m = \frac{46,687 - 41,350}{15 - 9} = \frac{5,337}{6} = 889.5.$$
Now use the point-slope form with $m = 889.5$ and $(n_1, s_1) = (9, 41350)$:
$$s - s_1 = m(n - n_1)$$
$$s - 41,350 = 889.5(n - 9)$$
$$s - 41,350 = 889.5n - 8,005.5$$
$$s = 889.5n + 33,344.5$$
$$s(n) = 889.50n + 33,344.50$$

b. For 10 years of teaching:

$$s(10) = 889.50(10) + 33,344.50$$
$$= 8895.00 + 33,344.50$$
$$= 42,239.50$$

The annual salary for a lecturer with 10 years of teaching experience will be \$42,239.50.

c.
$$s(n) = 44,908$$
$$889.50n + 33,344.50 = 44,908$$
$$889.50n = 11,563.50$$
$$n = 13$$

In order to have an annual salary of \$44,908, a lecturer would need 13 years of teaching.

71. a. To find the function, use the points (50, 36.0) and (70, 18.7) to determine the slope:

$$m = \frac{18.7 - 36.0}{70 - 50} = \frac{-17.3}{20} = -0.865 .$$

Now use the point-slope form with $m = -0.865$ and $(a_1, y_1) = (50, 36.0)$:

$$y - y_1 = m(a - a_1)$$
$$y - 36.0 = -0.865(a - 50)$$
$$y - 36.0 = -0.865a + 43.25$$
$$y = -0.865a + 79.25$$
$$y(a) = -0.865a + 79.25$$

b.
$$y(37) = -0.865(37) + 79.25$$
$$= -32.005 + 79.25$$
$$= 47.245$$

The additional life expectancy will be about 47.2 years.

c.
$$y(a) = 25$$
$$-0.865a + 79.25 = 25$$
$$-0.865a = -54.25$$
$$a \approx 62.7$$

In order to have an additional life expectancy of 25 years, one would need to be currently about 62.7 years old.

72. a. To find the function, use the points (261, 3.5) and (275, 10.5) to determine the slope:

$$m = \frac{10.5 - 3.5}{275 - 261} = \frac{7}{14} = 0.5 .$$

Now use the point-slope form with $m = 0.5$ and $(a_1, v_1) = (261, 3.5)$:

$$v - v_1 = m(a - a_1)$$
$$v - 3.5 = 0.5(a - 261)$$
$$v - 3.5 = 0.5a - 130.5$$
$$v = 0.5a - 127$$
$$v(a) = 0.5a - 127$$

b. $v(265) = 0.5(265) - 127 = 132.5 - 127 = 5.5$

The value of a 265-year-old Guarneri de Gesù violin will be about \$5.5 million.

c.
$$v(a) = 15$$
$$0.5a - 127 = 15$$
$$0.5a = 142$$
$$a = 284$$

For a Guarneri de Gesù violin to be worth \$15 million, it must be about 284 years old.

73. a. To find the function, use the points (18, 14) and (36, 17.4) to determine the slope:

$$m = \frac{17.4 - 14}{36 - 18} = \frac{3.4}{18} \approx 0.189 .$$

Now use the point-slope form with $m = 0.189$ and $(a_1, w_1) = (18, 14)$:

$$w - w_1 = m(a - a_1)$$
$$w - 14 = 0.189(a - 18)$$
$$w - 14 = 0.189a - 3.402$$
$$w = 0.189a + 10.598$$
$$w(a) \approx 0.189a + 10.6$$

b.
$$w(22) = 0.189(22) + 10.6$$
$$= 4.158 + 10.6$$
$$= 14.758$$

A 22-month-old boy who is in the 95th percentile will weigh about 14.758 kg. This is close to the weight shown in the graph.

74. a. To find the function, use the points (18, 87) and (36, 102) to determine the slope:

$$m = \frac{102 - 87}{36 - 18} = \frac{15}{18} \approx 0.833 .$$

Now use the point-slope form with $m = 0.833$ and $(a_1, l_1) = (18, 87)$:

$$l - l_1 = m(a - a_1)$$
$$l - 87 = 0.833(a - 18)$$
$$l - 87 = 0.833a - 14.994$$
$$l = 0.833a + 72.006$$
$$l(a) \approx 0.833a + 72$$

b. $l(21) = 0.833(21) + 72 = 17.493 + 72 = 89.493$

The length of a 21-month-old boy who is in the 95th percentile will be about 89.493 cm.

75. If the y-intercept is $(0, -13)$ and the line is translated up 17 units, the new y-intercept will be at $y = -13 + 17 = 4$. The y-intercept of the translated graph is (0, 4).

76. If the y-intercept is $(0, 17)$ and the line is translated up 38 units, the new y-intercept will be at $y = 17 + 38 = 55$. The y-intercept of the translated graph is $(0, 55)$.

77. If the y-intercept is $(0, 6)$ and the line is translated down 9 units, the new y-intercept will be at $y = 6 - 9 = -3$. The y-intercept of the translated graph is $(0, -3)$.

78. If the y-intercept is $(0, -9)$ and the line is translated down 8 units, the new y-intercept will be at $y = -9 - 8 = -17$. The y-intercept of the translated graph is $(0, -17)$.

79. a. The slope is 3 and the y-intercept is $(0, 1)$, so the equation is $y = 3x + 1$.

    b. The slope is 3 and the y-intercept is $(0, -5)$, so the equation is $y = 3x - 5$.

80. a. The slope is $-\dfrac{3}{4}$ and the y-intercept is $(0, -1)$, so the equation is $y = -\dfrac{3}{4}x - 1$.

    b. The slope is $-\dfrac{3}{4}$ and the y-intercept is $\left(0, \dfrac{7}{2}\right)$, so the equation is $y = -\dfrac{3}{4}x + \dfrac{7}{2}$.

81. a. The slope of the translated graph is 1.

    b. If the y-intercept $b = -1$ is translated up 3 units, the y-intercept of the translated graph is at $y = -1 + 3 = 2$. The new y-intercept is $(0, 2)$.

    c. Using $m = 1$ and $b = 2$, the equation of the translated graph is $y = x + 2$.

82. a. The slope of the translated graph is $-\dfrac{3}{2}$.

    b. If the y-intercept $b = 3$ is translated down 4 units, the y-intercept of the translated graph is at $y = 3 - 4 = -1$. The new y-intercept is $(0, -1)$.

    c. Using $m = -\dfrac{3}{2}$ and $b = -1$, the equation of the translated graph is $y = -\dfrac{3}{2}x - 1$.

83. First, rewrite the equation in the slope-intercept form by solving for y in terms of x.
$$3x - 2y = 6$$
$$-2y = -3x + 6$$
$$y = \frac{-3x + 6}{-2}$$
$$y = \frac{3}{2}x - 3$$
Thus, $m = \dfrac{3}{2}$ and $b = -3$. If the graph is translated down 4 units, then the y-intercept of the translated graph is at $y = -3 - 4 = -7$. Hence, the equation of the translated graph is $y = \dfrac{3}{2}x - 7$.

84. First, rewrite the equation in the slope-intercept form by solving for y in term of x.
$$-3x - 5y = 15$$
$$-5y = 3x + 15$$
$$y = \frac{3x + 15}{-5}$$
$$y = -\frac{3}{5}x - 3$$
Thus, $m = -\dfrac{3}{5}$ and $b = -3$. If the graph is translated up 2 units, then the y-intercept of the translated graph is at $y = -3 + 2 = -1$. Hence, the equation of the translated graph is $y = -\dfrac{3}{5}x - 1$.

85. The y-intercept of $y = 3x + 6$ is 6. On the screen, the y-intercept is not 6. The y-intercept is wrong.

86. The slope of $y = -2x - 4$ is -2. On the screen, the slope is not -2. The slope is wrong.

87. The slope of $y = \dfrac{1}{2}x + 4$ is $\dfrac{1}{2}$. On the screen, the slope is not $\dfrac{1}{2}$. The slope is wrong.

88. The y-intercept of $y = -4x - 1$ is -1. On the screen, the y-intercept is not -1. The y-intercept is wrong.

89. There are 91 steps and the total vertical distance is 1292.2 in. Thus, the average height of a step is $\frac{1292.2}{91} = 14.2$ inches. If the slope is 2.21875 and the average height, or "rise", is 14.2 inches, the average width, or "run", is found as follows:

$$\text{slope} = \frac{\text{rise}}{\text{run}}$$
$$m = \frac{\text{height}}{\text{width}}$$
$$2.21875 = \frac{14.2}{\text{width}}$$
$$\text{width} = \frac{14.2}{2.21875} = 6.4$$

The average width is 6.4 inches.

90. The tangent lines have a positive slope on the intervals (b, c) and (d, e). They have a slope of 0 at the points b, c, and d. And they have a negative slope on the intervals (a, b) and (c, d).

91. a. A car depreciates the most (about 26%) during the first year, from 0 to 1.

b. The depreciation appears nearly linear between years 1 and 3.

c. The depreciation is the lowest between years 4 and 5.

d. The graph appears to contain the points $(0, 100)$ and $(1, 74)$, so the slope of the line segment from year 0 to year 1 is:

$$m = \frac{100\% - 74\%}{0 - 1} = \frac{26\%}{-1} = -26\% = -0.26$$

From year 0 to year 1, the car loses about 26% of its value.

92. a. The graph represents a function because each age has a unique average head circumference. That is, the graph passes the vertical line test.

b. The independent variable is age. The dependent variable is head circumference.

c. Domain: $\{a \mid 2 \le a \le 18\}$

Range: $\{c \mid 48 \le a \le 55\}$

d. The interval for normal head circumferences of 18-year-old girls is 52 to 58 cm.

e. Head circumference is a function of age because age is the independent variable and head circumference is the dependent variable.

f. Age 10: $c \approx 52$ cm; Age 14: $c \approx 54$ cm

g. $m = \frac{55 - 48}{18 - 2} = \frac{7}{16} = 0.4375$

Now use the point-slope form with $m = 0.4375$ and $(a_1, c_1) = (2, 48)$:

$$c - c_1 = m(a - a_1)$$
$$c - 48 = 0.4375(a - 2)$$
$$c - 48 = 0.4375a - 0.875$$
$$c = 0.4375a - 47.125$$
$$c(a) = 0.4375a - 47.125$$

93.
$$\frac{-6^2 - 16 \div 2 \div |-4|}{5 - 3 \cdot 2 - 4 \div 2^2} = \frac{-36 - 16 \div 2 \div 4}{5 - 6 - 4 \div 4}$$
$$= \frac{-36 - 8 \div 4}{5 - 6 - 1}$$
$$= \frac{-36 - 2}{-1 - 1}$$
$$= \frac{-38}{-2}$$
$$= 19$$

94.
$$2.6x - (-1.4x + 3.4) = 6.2$$
$$2.6x + 1.4x - 3.4 = 6.2$$
$$4.0x - 3.4 = 6.2$$
$$4.0x = 9.6$$
$$x = 2.4$$

95.
$$\frac{3}{4}x + \frac{1}{5} = \frac{2}{3}(x - 2)$$
$$60\left[\frac{3}{4}x + \frac{1}{5}\right] = 60\left[\frac{2}{3}(x - 2)\right]$$
$$45x + 12 = 40(x - 2)$$
$$45x + 12 = 40x - 80$$
$$5x + 12 = -80$$
$$5x = -92$$
$$x = -\frac{92}{5}$$

96. a. A relation is any set of ordered pairs.

b. A function is a correspondence between a first set of elements, the domain, and a second set of elements, the range, such that each element of the domain corresponds to exactly one element in the range.

c. Answers will vary.

97. Domain: $\{3, 4, 5, 6\}$; Range: $\{-2, -1, 2, 3\}$

Exercise Set 8.5

1. Yes, $f(x) + g(x) = (f + g)(x)$ for all values of x. This is how addition of functions is defined.

2. Yes, $f(x) - g(x) = (f - g)(x)$ for all values of x. This is how subtraction of functions is defined.

3. $f(x)/g(x) = (f/g)(x)$ provided $g(x) \neq 0$. This is because division by zero is undefined.

4. Yes, $(f + g)(x) = (g + f)(x)$ for all values of x since addition is commutative. . For example, if $f(x) = x^2 + 1$ and $g(x) = x$, then
$$(f + g)(x) = f(x) + g(x)$$
$$= (x^2 + 1) + (x)$$
$$= x^2 + x + 1$$
$$(g + f)(x) = g(x) + f(x)$$
$$= (x) + (x^2 + 1)$$
$$= x^2 + x + 1$$
So, $(f + g)(x) = (g + f)(x)$.

5. No, $(f - g)(x) \neq (g - f)(x)$ for all values of x since subtraction is not commutative. For example, if $f(x) = x^2 + 1$ and $g(x) = x$, then
$$(f - g)(x) = f(x) - g(x)$$
$$= (x^2 + 1) - (x)$$
$$= x^2 - x + 1$$
$$(g - f)(x) = g(x) - f(x)$$
$$= (x) - (x^2 + 1)$$
$$= -x^2 + x - 1$$
So, $(f - g)(x) \neq (g - f)(x)$.

6. a. $(f + g)(2) = f(2) + g(2) = 9 + (-3) = 6$

  b. $(f - g)(2) = f(2) - g(2) = 9 - (-3) = 12$

  c. $(f \cdot g)(2) = f(2) \cdot g(2) = 9 \cdot (-3) = -27$

  d. $(f/g)(2) = f(2)/g(2) = 9/(-3) = -3$

7. a. $(f + g)(-2) = f(-2) + g(-2) = (-3) + 5 = 2$

  b. $(f - g)(-2) = f(-2) - g(-2) = (-3) - 5 = -8$

  c. $(f \cdot g)(-2) = f(-2) \cdot g(-2) = (-3) \cdot 5 = -15$

  d. $(f/g)(-2) = f(-2)/g(-2) = (-3)/5 = -\dfrac{3}{5}$

8. a. $(f + g)(7) = f(7) + g(7) = 10 + 0 = 10$

  b. $(f - g)(7) = f(7) - g(7) = 10 - 0 = 10$

  c. $(f \cdot g)(7) = f(7) \cdot g(7) = 10 \cdot 0 = 0$

  d. $(f/g)(7) = f(7)/g(7) = 10/0$, which is undefined.

9. a. $(f + g)(x) = f(x) + g(x)$
$$= (x + 5) + (x^2 + x)$$
$$= x^2 + 2x + 5$$

  b. $(f + g)(a) = a^2 + 2a + 5$

  c. $(f + g)(2) = (2)^2 + 2(2) + 5$
$$= 4 + 2(2) + 5$$
$$= 4 + 4 + 5$$
$$= 13$$

10. a. $(f + g)(x) = f(x) + g(x)$
$$= (x^2 - x - 8) + (x^2 + 1)$$
$$= 2x^2 - x - 7$$

  b. $(f + g)(a) = 2a^2 - a - 7$

  c. $(f + g)(2) = 2(2)^2 - (2) - 7$
$$= 2(4) - 2 - 7$$
$$= 8 - 2 - 7$$
$$= 6 - 7$$
$$= -1$$

11. a. $(f + g)(x) = f(x) + g(x)$
$$= (-3x^2 + x - 4) + (x^3 + 3x^2)$$
$$= x^3 + x - 4$$

  b. $(f + g)(a) = a^3 + a - 4$

  c. $(f + g)(2) = (2)^3 + (2) - 4$
$$= 8 + 2 - 4$$
$$= 6$$

12. a. $(f + g)(x) = f(x) + g(x)$
$$= (4x^3 + 2x^2 - x - 1) + (x^3 - x^2 + 2x + 6)$$
$$= 5x^3 + x^2 + x + 5$$

  b. $(f + g)(a) = 5a^3 + a^2 + a + 5$

  c. $(f + g)(2) = 5(2)^3 + (2)^2 + (2) + 5$
$$= 5(8) + 4 + 2 + 5$$
$$= 40 + 4 + 2 + 5$$
$$= 51$$

13. a. $(f+g)(x) = f(x)+g(x)$
$= (4x^3 - 3x^2 - x)+(3x^2+4)$
$= 4x^3 - x + 4$

b. $(f+g)(a) = 4a^3 - a + 4$

c. $(f+g)(2) = 4(2)^3 - (2)+4$
$= 4(8) - 2 + 4$
$= 32 - 2 + 4$
$= 30 + 4$
$= 34$

14. a. $(f+g)(x) = f(x)+g(x)$
$= (3x^2 - x + 2)+(6 - 4x^2)$
$= -x^2 - x + 8$

b. $(f+g)(a) = -a^2 - a + 8$

c. $(f+g)(2) = -(2)^2 - (2)+8$
$= -4 - 2 + 8$
$= -6 + 8$
$= 2$

15. $f(2) = (2)^2 - 4 = 4 - 4 = 0$
$g(2) = -5(2)+3 = -10 + 3 = -7$
$f(2)+g(2) = 0 + (-7) = -7$

16. $f(5) = (5)^2 - 4 = 25 - 4 = 21$
$g(5) = -5(5)+3 = -25 + 3 = -22$
$f(5)+g(5) = 21 + (-22) = -1$

17. $f(4) = (4)^2 - 4 = 16 - 4 = 12$
$g(4) = -5(4)+3 = -20 + 3 = -17$
$f(4)-g(4) = 12 - (-17) = 29$

18. $f\left(\frac{1}{4}\right) = \left(\frac{1}{4}\right)^2 - 4 = \frac{1}{16} - \frac{64}{16} = -\frac{63}{16}$
$g\left(\frac{1}{4}\right) = -5\left(\frac{1}{4}\right)+3 = \frac{-5}{4} + \frac{12}{4} = \frac{7}{4}$
$f\left(\frac{1}{4}\right) - g\left(\frac{1}{4}\right) = -\frac{63}{16} - \frac{7}{4} = -\frac{63}{16} - \frac{28}{16} = -\frac{91}{16}$

19. $f(3) = (3)^2 - 4 = 9 - 4 = 5$
$g(3) = -5(3)+3 = -15 + 3 = -12$
$f(3)\cdot g(3) = 5(-12) = -60$

20. $f(-1) = (-1)^2 - 4 = 1 - 4 = -3$
$g(-1) = -5(-1)+3 = 5 + 3 = 8$
$f(-1)\cdot g(-1) = (-3)(8) = -24$

21. $f\left(\frac{3}{5}\right) = \left(\frac{3}{5}\right)^2 - 4 = \frac{9}{25} - \frac{100}{25} = -\frac{91}{25}$
$g\left(\frac{3}{5}\right) = -5\left(\frac{3}{5}\right)+3 = -3 + 3 = 0$
$\dfrac{f\left(\frac{3}{5}\right)}{g\left(\frac{3}{5}\right)} = \dfrac{-\frac{91}{25}}{0}$ which is undefined.

22. $f(-1) = (-1)^2 - 4 = 1 - 4 = -3$
$g(-1) = -5(-1)+3 = 5 + 3 = 8$
$f(-1)/g(-1) = -3/8 = -\frac{3}{8}$

23. $f(-3) = (-3)^2 - 4 = 9 - 4 = 5$
$g(-3) = -5(-3)+3 = 15 + 3 = 18$
$g(-3) - f(-3) = 18 - 5 = 13$

24. $f(6) = (6)^2 - 4 = 36 - 4 = 32$
$g(6) = -5(6)+3 = -30 + 3 = -27$
$g(6)\cdot g(6) = (-27)(32) = -864$

25. $f(0) = (0)^2 - 4 = 0 - 4 = -4$
$g(0) = -5(0)+3 = 0 + 3 = 3$
$g(0)/f(0) = 3/-4 = -\frac{3}{4}$

26. $f(2) = (2)^2 - 4 = 4 - 4 = 0$
$g(2) = -5(2)+3 = -10 + 3 = -7$
$f(2)/g(2) = 0/(-7) = 0$

27. $(f+g)(x) = f(x)+g(x)$
$= (2x^2 - x)+(x-6)$
$= 2x^2 - 6$

28. $(f+g)(x) = 2x^2 - 6$
$(f+g)(a) = 2a^2 - 6$

29. $(f+g)(x) = 2x^2 - 6$

$$(f+g)(2) = 2(2)^2 - 6$$
$$= 2(4) - 6$$
$$= 8 - 6$$
$$= 2$$

30. $(f+g)(x) = 2x^2 - 6$

$$(f+g)(-3) = 2(-3)^2 - 6$$
$$= 2(9) - 6$$
$$= 18 - 6$$
$$= 12$$

31. $(f-g)(-2) = f(-2) - g(-2)$

$$= \left(2\cdot(-2)^2 - (-2)\right) - \left((-2) - 6\right)$$
$$= (8+2) - (-8)$$
$$= 10 + 8$$
$$= 18$$

32. $(f-g)(1) = f(1) - g(1)$

$$= \left(2\cdot 1^2 - 1\right) - (1 - 6)$$
$$= (2-1) - (-5)$$
$$= 1 + 5$$
$$= 6$$

33. $(f\cdot g)(0) = f(0)\cdot g(0)$

$$= \left(2\cdot 0^2 - 0\right)\cdot(0 - 6)$$
$$= (0)(-6)$$
$$= 0$$

34. $(f\cdot g)(3) = f(3)\cdot g(3)$

$$= \left(2\cdot 3^2 - 3\right)\cdot(3 - 6)$$
$$= (18 - 3)(-3)$$
$$= (15)(-3)$$
$$= -45$$

35. $(f/g)(-1) = f(-1)/g(-1)$

$$= \left(2\cdot(-1)^2 - (-1)\right)\big/\left((-1) - 6\right)$$
$$= (2+1)/(-7)$$
$$= 3/(-7)$$
$$= -\frac{3}{7}$$

36. $(f/g)(6) = f(6)/g(6)$

$$= \left(2\cdot 6^2 - 6\right)\big/\left(6 - 6\right)$$
$$= (72 - 6)/0$$
$$= 66/0,\ \text{which is undefined}$$

37. $(g/f)(5) = g(5)/f(5)$

$$= (5 - 6)\big/\left(2\cdot 5^2 - 5\right)$$
$$= (-1)/(50 - 5)$$
$$= (-1)/45$$
$$= -\frac{1}{45}$$

38. $(g-f)(4) = g(4) - f(4)$

$$= (4 - 6) - \left(2\cdot 4^2 - 4\right)$$
$$= (-2) - (32 - 4)$$
$$= -2 - 28$$
$$= -30$$

39. $(g-f)(x) = g(x) - f(x)$

$$= (x - 6) - (2x^2 - x)$$
$$= x - 6 - 2x^2 + x$$
$$= -2x^2 + 2x - 6$$

40. $(g-f)(x) = -2x^2 + 2x - 6$

$$(g-f)(r) = -2r^2 + 2r - 6$$

41. $(f+g)(0) = f(0) + g(0) = 2 + 1 = 3$

42. $(f-g)(0) = f(0) - g(0) = 2 - 1 = 1$

43. $(f\cdot g)(2) = f(2)\cdot g(2) = 4\cdot(-1) = -4$

44. $(f/g)(1) = f(1)/g(1) = 3/0$, which is undefined

45. $(g-f)(-1) = g(-1) - f(-1) = 2 - 1 = 1$

46. $(g+f)(-3) = g(-3) - f(-3) = 4 + (-1) = 3$

47. $(g/f)(4) = g(4)/f(4) = 1/0$, which is undefined

48. $(g\cdot f)(-1) = g(-1)\cdot f(-1) = 2\cdot 1 = 2$

49. $(f+g)(-2) = f(-2) + g(-2) = 1 + (-1) = 0$

50. $(f-g)(-1) = f(-1) - g(-1) = 3 - 2 = 1$

51. $(f\cdot g)(1) = f(1)\cdot g(1) = 0\cdot 1 = 0$

52. $(g-f)(3) = g(3) - f(3) = 3 - 1 = 2$

53. $(f/g)(4) = f(4)/g(4) = -3/1 = -3$

54. $(g/f)(5) = g(5)/f(5) = 1/(-2) = -\dfrac{1}{2}$

55. $(g/f)(2) = g(2)/f(2) = 2/(-1) = -2$

56. $(g \cdot f)(0) = g(0) \cdot f(0) = (-2) \cdot 3 = -6$

57. a. Frank contributed $1000 in 2004.

  b. $1400 - 600 = 800$
  In 2006, Sharon contributed about $800 more than Frank.

  c. $1600 + 2000 + 1400 + 900 + 2000 = 7900$
  Frank and Sharon contributed about $7900 over the five-year period.

  d. $(F + S)(2005) = \$900$

58. a. About 16 million hectares of land in developing nations were devoted to genetically modified crops in 2002.

  b. About 43 million hectares of land in developing nations were devoted to genetically modified crops in 2002.

  c. The total area devoted to genetically modified crops was less than 23 million hectares in years 1995, 1996, and 1997.

  d. The total area devoted to genetically modified crops was greater than 50 million hectares in years 2001, 2002, and 2003.

59. a. The import of crude oil to China was the greatest in 2003. That year approximately 1.8 million barrels per day were imported.

  b. In 1998 and 2001, the import of crude oil decrease from the year before.

  c. $I(2002) \approx 1.4$ million barrels

  d. $5.8 - 1.8 = 4.0$
  In 2003, about 4.0 million barrels of crude oil were produced in China per day.

60. a. The projected global population in 2050 is about 9.1 billion people.

  b. The projected number of children 0–14 years of age in 2050 is about 1.9 billion.

  c. $9.1 - 1.9 = 7.2$
  The projected number of people 15 years of age and older in 2050 is about 7.2 billion.

  d. $9.1 - 6.2 = 2.9$
  The difference in the total global population between 2002 and 2050 is about 2.9 billion people.

61. a. About 20 houses were sold in Fuller in the summer of 2006.

  b. $28 - 20 = 8$
  About 8 houses were sold in Fuller at other times in 2006.

  c. $Y(2005) \approx 30 - 18 = 12$ houses

  d. $(S + Y)(2003) \approx 23$ houses

62. a. The total income for 2006 is about $45,000.

  b. $L(2002) \approx \$15,000$

  c. $S(2005) \approx \$32,000 - \$17,000 = \$15,000$

  d. $(L + S)(2003) \approx \$25,000$

63. a.

  b.

  c.

64. a.

b.

c.

65. a.

b.

c.

66. a.

b.

c.
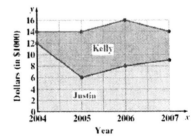

67. If $(f + g)(a) = 0$, then, $f(a)$ and $g(a)$ must either be opposites or both be equal to 0.

68. If $(f \cdot g)(a) = 0$, then either $f(a)$ or $g(a)$ must be equal to 0.

69. If $(f - g)(a) = 0$, then $f(a) = g(a)$.

70. If $(f - g)(a) < 0$, then $f(a) < g(a)$.

71. If $(f / g)(a) < 0$, then $f(a)$ and $g(a)$ must have opposite signs.

72. If $(f \cdot g)(a) < 0$, then $f(a)$ and $g(a)$ must have opposite signs.

73.

74.

75.

76.

77.

78. $(-4)^{-3} = \dfrac{1}{(-4)^3} = \dfrac{1}{-64} = -\dfrac{1}{64}$

79.
$$A = \frac{1}{2}bh$$
$$2 \cdot A = 2 \cdot \frac{1}{2}bh$$
$$2A = bh$$
$$\frac{2A}{b} = \frac{bh}{b}$$
$$\frac{2A}{b} = h \text{ or } h = \frac{2A}{b}$$

80. Let the pre-tax cost of the washing machine be x.
$$x + 0.06x = 477$$
$$1.06x = 477$$
$$x = 450$$
The pre-tax cost of the washing machine was $450.

81. Set $y = 0$ to find the x-intercept.
$$3x - 4(0) = 12$$
$$3x = 12$$
$$x = 4$$
The x-intercept is (4, 0).
Set $x = 0$ to find the y-intercept.
$$3(0) - 4y = 12$$
$$-4y = 12$$
$$y = -3$$
The y-intercept is (0, –3).

82. $2,960,000 = 2.96 \times 10^6$

83.

x	y
–3	1
–2	0
–1	–1
0	–2
1	–1
2	0
3	1

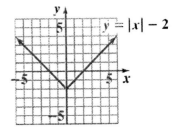

$$y = |x| - 2$$

Chapter 8 Review Exercises

1. $y = \dfrac{1}{2}x$

x	y
-2	$y = \dfrac{1}{2}(-2) = -1$
0	$y = \dfrac{1}{2}(0) = 0$
2	$y = \dfrac{1}{2}(2) = 1$

$$y = \dfrac{1}{2}x$$

2. $y = -2x - 1$

x	y
0	$y = -2(0) - 1 = -1$
1	$y = -2(1) - 1 = -3$
2	$y = -2(2) - 1 = -4$

$$y = -2x - 1$$

3. $y = \dfrac{1}{2}x + 3$

x	y
0	$y = \dfrac{1}{2}(0) + 3 = 3$
-2	$y = \dfrac{1}{2}(-2) + 3 = 2$
-4	$y = \dfrac{1}{2}(-4) + 3 = 1$

$$y = \dfrac{1}{2}x + 3$$

4. $y = -\dfrac{3}{2}x + 1$

x	y
-2	$y = -\dfrac{3}{2}(-2) + 1 = 4$
0	$y = -\dfrac{3}{2}(0) + 1 = 1$
2	$y = -\dfrac{3}{2}(2) + 1 = -2$

$$y = -\dfrac{3}{2}x + 1$$

5. $y = x^2$

x	y
-3	$y = (-3)^2 = 9$
-1	$y = (-1)^2 = 1$
0	$y = 0^2 = 0$
2	$y = 2^2 = 4$

6. $y = x^2 - 1$

x	y
-3	$y = (-3)^2 - 1 = 8$
-1	$y = (-1)^2 - 1 = 0$
0	$y = 0^2 - 1 = 0$
1	$y = 1^2 - 1 = 0$
2	$y = 2^2 - 1 = 3$

7. $y = |x|$

x	y
-4	$y = |-4| = 4$
-1	$y = |-1| = 1$
0	$y = |0| = 0$
2	$y = |2| = 2$

8. $y = |x| - 1$

x	y
-4	$y = |-4| - 1 = 3$
-1	$y = |-1| - 1 = 0$
0	$y = |0| - 1 = -1$
2	$y = |2| - 1 = 1$

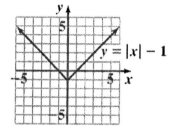

9. $y = x^3$

x	y
-2	$y = (-2)^3 = -8$
-1	$y = (-1)^3 = -1$
0	$y = 0^3 = 0$
1	$y = 1^3 = 1$
2	$y = 2^3 = 8$

426

10. $y = x^3 + 4$

x	y
-2	$y = (-2)^3 + 4 = -4$
-1	$y = (-1)^3 + 4 = 3$
0	$y = 0^3 + 4 = 4$
1	$y = 1^3 + 4 = 5$

11. A function is a correspondence between a first set of elements, the domain, and a second set of elements, the range, such that each element of the domain corresponds to exactly one element in the range.

12. No, every relation is not a function. For example, $\{(4, 2), (4, -2)\}$ is a relation but not a function.

Yes, every function is a relation because it is a set of ordered pairs.

13. Yes, each member of the domain corresponds to exactly one member of the range.

14. No, the domain element 2 corresponds to more than one member of the range (5 and -2).

15. $A = \{3, 4, 5, 6\}$

16. $B = \{6, 7, 8, ...\}$

17. $(4, \infty)$

18. $(-\infty, -2]$

19. $(-1.5, 2.7]$

20. a. Yes, the relation is a function.

　　b. Domain: $\mathbb{R}$; Range: $\mathbb{R}$

21. a. Yes, the relation is a function.

　　b. Domain: $\mathbb{R}$; Range: $\{y \mid y \leq 0\}$

22. a. No, the relation is not a function.

　　b. Domain: $\{x \mid -3 \leq x \leq 3\}$;
　　　　Range: $\{y \mid -3 \leq y \leq 3\}$

23. a. No, the relation is not a function.

　　b. Domain: $\{x \mid -2 \leq x \leq 2\}$;
　　　　Range: $\{y \mid -1 \leq y \leq 1\}$

24. $f(x) = -x^2 + 3x - 4$

　　a. $f(2) = -(2)^2 + 3(2) - 4 = -4 + 6 - 4 = -2$

　　b. $f(h) = -h^2 + 3h - 4$

25. $g(t) = 2t^3 - 3t^2 + 6$

　　a. $g(-1) = 2(-1)^3 - 3(-1)^2 + 6 = -2 - 3 + 6 = 1$

　　b. $g(a) = 2a^3 - 3a^2 + 6$

26. Answers will vary. One possible interpretation: Car speeds up to 50 mph and stays at 50 mph for about 11 minutes. It then speeds up to about 68 mph and stays at that speed for 5 minutes. It then stops quickly and stays stopped for 5 minutes. It then travels through stop and go traffic for 5 minutes.

27. $N(x) = 40x - 0.2x^2$

　　a. $N(30) = 40(30) - 0.2(30)^2$
　　　　　$= 1200 - 180$
　　　　　$= 1020$
　　　1020 baskets of apples are produced by 20 trees.

　　b. $N(50) = 40(50) - 0.2(50)^2$
　　　　　$= 2000 - 500$
　　　　　$= 1500$
　　　1500 baskets of apples are produced by 50 trees.

28. $h(t) = -16t^2 + 196$

　　a. $h(1) = -16(1)^2 + 196 = -16 + 196 = 180$
　　　After 1 second, the height of the ball is 180 feet.

　　b. $h(3) = -16(3)^2 + 196 = -144 + 196 = 52$
　　　After 3 seconds, the height of the ball is 52 feet.

29. $f(x) = \frac{1}{2}x - 4$

For the y-intercept, set $x = 0$:

$f(0) = \frac{1}{2}(0) - 4 = 0 - 4 = -4$

The y-intercept is $(0, -4)$.

For the x-intercept, set $f(x) = 0$ and solve for x:

$0 = \frac{1}{2}x - 4$

$4 = \frac{1}{2}x$

$2(4) = 2\left(\frac{1}{2}\right)x$

$8 = x$

The x-intercept is $(8, 0)$.

30. $f(x) = \frac{8}{3}x - 80$

For the y-intercept, set $x = 0$:

$f(0) = \frac{8}{3}(0) - 80 = 0 - 80 = -80$

The y-intercept is $(0, -80)$.

For the x-intercept, set $f(x) = 0$ and solve for x:

$0 = \frac{8}{3}x - 80$

$80 = \frac{8}{3}x$

$\frac{3}{8}(80) = \frac{3}{8}\left(\frac{8}{3}x\right)$

$30 = x$

The x-intercept is $(4, 0)$.

31. $f(x) = 4$ is a horizontal line 4 units above the x-axis.

32. **a.** $p(x) = 0.1x - 5000$

x	p
0	$p = 0.1(0) - 5000 = -5000$
50,000	$p = 0.1(50,000) - 5000 = 0$
100,000	$p = 0.1(100,000) - 5000 = 5000$

Bagels sold (1000s)

b. Approximately 50,000 bagels are sold when the company breaks even.

c. If the company has $22,000 profit, then approximately 270,000 bagels were sold.

33. The principle is $12,000 and the time is one year. Use the decimal form of the interest rate.
$I = 12,000r$

Rate (as a decimal)

34. **a.** Yes, the graph represents a function. It passes the vertical line test.

b. This is a horizontal line (constant function), so the slope is 0. The y-intercept is $(0, 3)$, so the equation is $f(x) = 3$.

35. a. No, the graph does not represent a function. It fails the vertical line test.

36. a. Yes, the graph represents a function. It passes the vertical line test.

b. The x-intercept is (4, 0) and the y-intercept is (0, 2), so $m = \dfrac{2-0}{0-4} = \dfrac{2}{-4} = -\dfrac{1}{2}$ and $b = 2$.

Thus, the equation is $f(x) = -\dfrac{1}{2}x + 2$.

37. a. The slope of the translated graph is the same as the slope of the original graph: $m = -2$.

b. The y-intercept of the translated graph is the 4 less than the y-intercept of the original graph: $5 - 4 = 1$. The y-intercept of the translated graph is (0, 1).

c. Since $m = -2$ and $b = 1$, the equation of the translated graph is $y = -2x + 1$.

38. Use the point-slope form.
$$y - y_1 = m(x - x_1)$$
$$y - (-4) = \frac{2}{3}\left(x - (-6)\right)$$
$$y + 4 = \frac{2}{3}(x + 6)$$
$$y + 4 = \frac{2}{3}x + 4$$
$$y = \frac{2}{3}x$$

Since $b = 0$, the y-intercept is (0, 0).

39. a.

b. 1970 to 1980:
$$m_1 = \frac{510 - 346}{1980 - 1970} = \frac{164}{10} = 16.4$$
1980 to 1990:
$$m_2 = \frac{552 - 510}{1990 - 1980} = \frac{42}{10} = 4.2$$
1990 to 2000:
$$m_3 = \frac{317 - 552}{2000 - 1990} = \frac{-235}{10} = -23.5$$

c. The number of reported cases of typhoid fever increased the most during the 10-year period of 1970 – 1980.

40. Let t represent the number of years after 1980. Then 1980 is represented by $t = 0$ and 2070 is represented by $t = 90$. Therefore, the points (0, 35.6) and (90, 98.2) are on the line. Find the slope: $m = \dfrac{98.2 - 35.6}{2070 - 1980} = \dfrac{62.6}{90} \approx 0.7$.

The t-intercept is (0, 35,6), so $b = 35.6$. Thus, the equation of the line is: $n = 0.7t + 35.6$. With function notation, we have $n(t) = 0.7t + 35.6$.

41.
$$\begin{array}{ll} 2x - 3y = 10 & y = \dfrac{2}{3}x - 5 \\ -3y = -2x + 10 & \\ \dfrac{-3y}{-3} = \dfrac{-2x + 10}{-3} & m_2 = \dfrac{2}{3} \\ y = \dfrac{2}{3}x - \dfrac{10}{3} & \\ m_1 = \dfrac{2}{3} & \end{array}$$

Since their slopes are equal and their y-intercepts are different, the lines are parallel.

42.
$$\begin{array}{ll} 2x - 3y = 7 & -3x - 2y = 8 \\ -3y = -2x + 7 & -2y = 3x + 8 \\ y = \dfrac{-2x + 7}{-3} & y = \dfrac{3x + 8}{-2} \\ y = \dfrac{2}{3}x - \dfrac{7}{3} & y = -\dfrac{3}{2}x - 4 \\ m_1 = \dfrac{2}{3} & m_2 = -\dfrac{3}{2} \end{array}$$

Since the slopes are negative reciprocals, the lines are perpendicular.

43.
$$\begin{array}{ll} 4x - 2y = 13 & -2x + 4y = -9 \\ -2y = -4x + 13 & 4y = 2x - 9 \\ y = \dfrac{-4x + 13}{-2} & y = \dfrac{2x - 9}{4} \\ y = 2x - \dfrac{13}{2} & y = \dfrac{1}{2}x - \dfrac{9}{4} \\ m_1 = 2 & m_2 = \dfrac{1}{2} \end{array}$$

Since the slopes not equal and are not negative reciprocals, the lines are neither parallel nor perpendicular.

44. Use the point-slope form with $m = \frac{1}{2}$ and

$(x_1, y_1) = (4, 9)$.

$$y - 9 = \frac{1}{2}(x - 4)$$

$$y - 9 = \frac{1}{2}x - 2$$

$$y = \frac{1}{2}x + 7$$

45. First, find the slope: $m = \frac{-6 - 1}{4 - (-3)} = \frac{-7}{7} = -1$.

Now, use the point-slope form with $m = -1$ and $(x_1, y_1) = (-3, 1)$.

$$y - 1 = -1(x - (-3))$$

$$y - 1 = -1(x + 3)$$

$$y - 1 = -x - 3$$

$$y = -x - 2$$

46. The slope of the line $y = -\frac{2}{3}x + 1$ is $-\frac{2}{3}$. Since

the new line is parallel to this line, its slope is

also $-\frac{2}{3}$. Use the slope-intercept form with

$m = -\frac{2}{3}$ and y-intercept of $(0, 6)$.

$$y = -\frac{2}{3}x + 6$$

47. $-2y = -5x + 7$

$$y = \frac{-5x + 7}{-2}$$

$$y = \frac{5}{2}x - \frac{7}{2}$$

The slope of this line is $\frac{5}{2}$. The new line is

parallel to this line, so its slope is also $\frac{5}{2}$. Use

the point-slope form with $m = \frac{5}{2}$ and

$(x_1, y_1) = (2, 8)$.

$$y - 8 = \frac{5}{2}(x - 2)$$

$$y - 8 = \frac{5}{2}x - 5$$

$$y = \frac{5}{2}x + 3$$

48. The slope of the line $y = \frac{3}{5}x + 5$ is $\frac{3}{5}$. Since the

new line is perpendicular to this line, its slope is

$-\frac{5}{3}$. Use the point-slope form with $m = -\frac{5}{3}$ and

$(x_1, y_1) = (-3, 1)$.

$$y - 1 = -\frac{5}{3}(x - (-3))$$

$$y - 1 = -\frac{5}{3}(x + 3)$$

$$y - 1 = -\frac{5}{3}x - 5$$

$$y = -\frac{5}{3}x - 4$$

49. $4x - 2y = 8$

$$-2y = -4x + 8$$

$$y = \frac{-4x + 8}{-2}$$

$$y = 2x - 4$$

The slope of this line is 2. Since the new line is

perpendicular to this line, its slope is $-\frac{1}{2}$. Use

the point-slope form with $m = -\frac{1}{2}$ and

$(x_1, y_1) = (4, 5)$.

$$y - 5 = -\frac{1}{2}(x - 4)$$

$$y - 5 = -\frac{1}{2}x + 2$$

$$y = -\frac{1}{2}x + 7$$

50. $m_1 = \frac{-3 - 3}{0 - 5} = \frac{-6}{-5} = \frac{6}{5}$

$m_2 = \frac{-2 - (-1)}{2 - 1} = \frac{-2 + 1}{2 - 1} = \frac{-1}{1} = -1$

Since the slopes are not equal and are not
negative reciprocals, the lines are neither parallel
nor perpendicular.

51. $m_1 = \frac{3 - 2}{2 - 3} = \frac{1}{-1} = -1$

$m_2 = \frac{4 - 1}{1 - 4} = \frac{3}{-3} = -1$

Since the slopes are equal, the lines are parallel.

52. $m_1 = \dfrac{6-3}{4-7} = \dfrac{3}{-3} = -1$

$m_2 = \dfrac{3-2}{6-5} = \dfrac{1}{1} = 1$

Since the slopes are negative reciprocals, the lines are perpendicular.

53. $m_1 = \dfrac{3-5}{2-(-3)} = \dfrac{3-5}{2+3} = \dfrac{-2}{5} = -\dfrac{2}{5}$

$m_2 = \dfrac{2-(-2)}{-1-(-4)} = \dfrac{2+2}{-1+4} = \dfrac{4}{3}$

Since the slopes are not equal and are not negative reciprocals, the lines are neither parallel nor perpendicular.

54. a. First, find the slope of the linear function using the points (35, 10.76) and (50, 19.91):

$m = \dfrac{19.91-10.76}{50-35} = \dfrac{9.15}{15} = 0.61$.

Use the point-slope form with $m = 0.61$ and $(a_1, r_1) = (35, 10.76)$:

$r - r_1 = m(a - a_1)$

$r - 10.76 = 0.61(a - 35)$

$r - 10.76 = 0.61a - 21.35$

$r = 0.61a - 10.59$

$r(a) = 0.61a - 10.59$

b. $r(40) = 0.61(40) - 10.59$

$= 24.40 - 10.59$

$= 13.81$

The monthly rate for a 40-year-old man is about $13.81.

55. a. First, find the slope of the linear function using the points (30, 489) and (50, 525):

$m = \dfrac{525-489}{50-30} = \dfrac{36}{20} = 1.8$.

Use the point-slope form with $m = 1.8$ and $(r_1, C_1) = (30, 489)$:

$C - C_1 = m(r - r_1)$

$C - 489 = 1.8(r - 30)$

$C - 489 = 1.8r - 54$

$C = 1.8r + 435$

$C(r) = 1.8r + 435$

b. $C(40) = 1.8(40) + 435 = 72 + 435 = 507$

When a person swims at 40 yards per minute for one hour, he or she will burn 507 calories.

c. $C(r) = 600$

$1.8r + 435 = 600$

$1.8r = 165$

$r \approx 91.7$

To burn 600 calories in 1 hour, the person needs to swim at a speed of about 91.7 yards per minute.

56. $(f+g)(x) = f(x) + g(x)$

$= (x^2 - 3x + 4) + (2x - 5)$

$= x^2 - x - 1$

57. $(f+g)(x) = x^2 - x - 1$

$(f+g)(4) = (4)^2 - 4 - 1 = 16 - 4 - 1 = 11$

58. $(g-f)(x) = (2x-5) - (x^2 - 3x + 4)$

$= 2x - 5 - x^2 + 3x - 4$

$= -x^2 + 5x - 9$

59. $(g-f)(x) = -x^2 + 5x - 9$

$(g-f)(-1) = -(-1)^2 + 5(-1) - 9$

$= -1 - 5 - 9$

$= -15$

60. $(f \cdot g)(-1) = f(-1) \cdot g(-1)$

$= \big((-1)^2 - 3(-1) + 4\big) \cdot \big(2(-1) - 5\big)$

$= (1 + 3 + 4) \cdot (-2 - 5)$

$= 8(-7)$

$= -56$

61. $(f \cdot g)(3) = f(3) \cdot g(3)$

$= \big(3^2 - 3(3) + 4\big) \cdot \big(2(3) - 5\big)$

$= (9 - 9 + 4) \cdot (6 - 5)$

$= 4(1)$

$= 4$

62. $(f/g)(1) = \dfrac{f(1)}{g(1)}$

$= \dfrac{1^2 - 3(1) + 4}{2(1) - 5}$

$= \dfrac{1 - 3 + 4}{2 - 5}$

$= \dfrac{2}{-3}$

$= -\dfrac{2}{3}$

63. $(f/g)(2) = \dfrac{f(2)}{g(2)}$

$= \dfrac{2^2 - 3(2) + 4}{2(2) - 5}$

$= \dfrac{4 - 6 + 4}{4 - 5}$

$= \dfrac{2}{-1}$

$= -2$

64. a. The projected female population worldwide in 2050 is about 4.6 billion.

b. 2.9 billion $-$ 0.8 billion $=$ 2.1 billion
The projected number of women 15–49 years of age in 2050 about 2.1 billion.

c. 3.5 billion $-$ 2.7 billion $=$ 0.8 billion
The number of women who are projected to be in the 50 years and older age group in 2010 is about 0.8 billion.

d. 2002: 3.1 billion $-$ 2.5 billion $=$ 0.6 billion
2010: 3.5 billion $-$ 2.7 billion $=$ 0.8 billion
$\dfrac{0.8 \text{ billion} - 0.6 \text{ billion}}{0.6 \text{ billion}} = \dfrac{0.2 \text{ billion}}{0.6 \text{ billion}} \approx 0.33$
There is approximately a 33% increase in the projected number of women 50 years and older from 2002 to 2010.

65. a. Ginny's total retirement income in 2006 was about $47,000.

b. Ginny's pension income in 2005 was about $28,000.

c. $25,000 - 22,000 = 3000$
Ginny's interest and dividend income in 2003 was about $3000.

Chapter 8 Practice Test

1. $y = -2x + 1$

x	y
-1	$y = -2(-1) + 1 = 3$
0	$y = -2(0) + 1 = 1$
1	$y = -2(1) + 1 = -1$

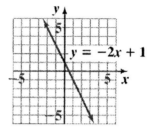

2. $y = \sqrt{x}$

x	y
-1	$y = \sqrt{-1}$ undefined
0	$y = \sqrt{0} = 0$
1	$y = \sqrt{1} = 1$
4	$y = \sqrt{4} = 2$

3. $y = x^2 - 4$

x	y
-2	$y = (-2)^2 - 4 = 0$
-1	$y = (-1)^2 - 4 = -3$
0	$y = (0)^2 - 4 = -4$
1	$y = (1)^2 - 4 = -3$
2	$y = (2)^2 - 4 = 0$

432

4. $y = |x|$

x	y
−3	$y = |-3| = 3$
0	$y = |0| = 0$
4	$y = |4| = 4$

5. A function is a correspondence between a first set of elements, the domain, and a second set of elements, the range, such that each element of the domain corresponds to exactly one element in the range.

6. Yes, the set of ordered pairs represents a function because each member in the domain corresponds with exactly one member in the range.

7. Yes, the graph represents a function because it passes the vertical line test.
Domain: $\mathbb{R}$
Range: $\{y \mid y \le 4\}$

8. No, the graph does not represent a function because it fails the vertical line test.
Domain: $\{x \mid -3 \le x \le 3\}$
Range: $\{y \mid -2 \le y \le 2\}$

9. $f(x) = 3x^2 - 6x + 5$
$f(-2) = 3(-2)^2 - 6(-2) + 5 = 12 + 12 + 5 = 29$

10. The graph of $f(x) = -3$ is a horizontal line 3 units below the x-axis.

11. a. $p(x) = 10.2x - 50,000$

b. The company breaks even when $p(x) = 0$.
$$10.2x - 50,000 = 0$$
$$10.2x = 50,000$$
$$x = \frac{50,000}{10.2} = 4900$$
The company breaks even when it sells 4900 books.

c. $10.2x - 50,000 = 100,000$
$$10.2x = 150,000$$
$$x = \frac{150,000}{10.2} \approx 14,700$$
The company needs to sell about 14,700 books to break even.

12. The year 2000 correspond to $t = 0$, and the year 2050 corresponds to $t = 50$. Thus, the points $(0, 274.634)$ and $(50, 419.854)$ lie on the graph.
$$m = \frac{419.854 - 274.634}{50 - 0} = \frac{145.220}{50} = 2.9044$$
The y-intercept is $(0, 274.634)$, so $b = 274.634$.
Thus, the equation is $p(t) = 2.9044t + 274.634$.

13. Write each equation in slope-intercept form by solving for y.

$$2x - 3y = 12$$
$$-3y = -2x + 12$$
$$y = \frac{-2x + 12}{-3}$$
$$y = \frac{2}{3}x - 4$$

$$4x + 10 = 6y$$
$$\frac{4x + 10}{6} = y$$
$$\frac{4}{6}x + \frac{10}{6} = y$$
$$y = \frac{2}{3}x + \frac{5}{3}$$

Since the slopes are the same and the y-intercepts are different, the lines are parallel.

14. The slope of $y = \frac{1}{2}x + 1$ is $\frac{1}{2}$. Any line perpendicular to this line must have slope -2. Use the point-slope form with $m = -2$ and $(x_1, y_1) = (6, -5)$.

$$y - y_1 = m(x - x_1)$$
$$y - (-5) = -2(x - 6)$$
$$y + 5 = -2x + 12$$
$$y = -2x + 7$$

15. a. Let t be the number of years since 2000. Then 2000 is represented by $t = 0$ and 2010 is represented by $t = 10$. Find the slope of the linear function using the points (0, 266) and (10, 236).

$$m = \frac{236 - 266}{10 - 0} = \frac{-30}{10} = -3$$

The y-intercept is (0, 266), so $b = 266$. Thus, the equation is $r(t) = -3t + 266$.

b. Note that 2006 is represented by $t = 6$:
$$r(6) = -3(6) + 266 = -18 + 266 = 248$$

From the function, the death rate due to heart disease in 2006 was 248 per 100,000.

c. Note that 2020 is represented by $t = 20$:
$$r(20) = -3(20) + 266 = -60 + 266 = 206$$

Assuming the trend continues, the death rate due to heart disease in 2020 will be 206 per 100,000.

16. $(f + g)(3) = f(3) + g(3)$
$$= \left(2(3)^2 - (3)\right) + \left((3) - 6\right)$$
$$= (2(9) - 3) + (3 - 6)$$
$$= (18 - 3) + (3 - 6)$$
$$= 15 + (-3)$$
$$= 12$$

17. $(f / g)(-1) = \dfrac{f(-1)}{g(-1)}$
$$= \frac{2(-1)^2 - (-1)}{(-1) - 6}$$
$$= \frac{2 + 1}{-7}$$
$$= -\frac{3}{7}$$

18. $f(a) = 2a^2 - a$

19. a. The total number of tons of paper to be used in 2010 will be about 44 million tons.

b. The number of tons of paper to be used by businesses in 2010 will be about 18 million tons.

c. The number of tons of paper to be used for reference, print media, and household use in 2010 will be about $44 - 18 = 26$, or 26 million tons.

Chapter 8 Cumulative Review Test

1. Substitute -3 for x and -2 for y and simplify:
$$4x^2 - 7xy^2 + 6 = 4(-3)^2 - 7(-3)(-2)^2 + 6$$
$$= 4(9) - 7(-3)(4) + 6$$
$$= 36 + 84 + 6$$
$$= 126$$

2. $2 - \{3[6 - 4(6^2 \div 4)]\} = 2 - \{3[6 - 4(36 \div 4)]\}$
$$= 2 - \{3[6 - 4(9)]\}$$
$$= 2 - \{3[6 - 36]\}$$
$$= 2 - \{3[-30]\}$$
$$= 2 - \{-90\}$$
$$= 2 + 90$$
$$= 92$$

3. $2(x + 4) - 5 = -3\left[x - (2x + 1)\right]$
$$2x + 8 - 5 = -3\left[x - 2x - 1\right]$$
$$2x + 3 = -3\left[-x - 1\right]$$
$$2x + 3 = 3x + 3$$
$$3 = x + 3$$
$$0 = x$$

4.
$$P = 2E + 3R$$
$$P - 2E = 2E + 3R - 2E$$
$$P - 2E = 3R$$
$$\frac{P - 2E}{3} = \frac{3R}{3}$$
$$\frac{P - 2E}{3} = R \quad \text{or} \quad R = \frac{P - 2E}{3}$$

5.
$$5x - 2y = 12$$
$$-5x + 5x - 2y = -5x + 12$$
$$-2y = -5x + 12$$
$$\frac{-2y}{-2} = \frac{-5x + 12}{-2}$$
$$y = \frac{5}{2}x - 6$$

6.
$$\left(\frac{6x^2 y^3}{2x^5 y}\right)^3 = \left(\frac{6}{2} \cdot \frac{y^{3-1}}{x^{5-2}}\right)^3$$
$$= \left(\frac{3y^2}{x^3}\right)^3$$
$$= \frac{3^3 (y^2)^3}{(x^3)^3}$$
$$= \frac{27 y^{2(3)}}{x^{3(3)}}$$
$$= \frac{27 y^6}{x^9}$$

7.
$$(6x^2 - 3x - 2) - (-2x^2 - 8x - 1)$$
$$= 6x^2 - 3x - 2 + 2x^2 + 8x + 1$$
$$= 6x^2 + 2x^2 - 3x + 8x - 2 + 1$$
$$= 8x^2 + 5x - 1$$

8.
$$(4x^2 - 6x + 3)(3x - 5)$$
$$= 4x^2(3x - 5) - 6x(3x - 5) + 3(3x - 5)$$
$$= 12^3 - 20x^2 - 18x^2 + 30x + 9x - 15$$
$$= 12x^3 - 38x^2 + 39x - 15$$

9.
$$6a^2 - 6a - 5a + 5 = 6a(a - 1) - 5(a - 1)$$
$$= (a - 1)(6a - 5)$$

10.
$$2x^2 = x + 15$$
$$2x^2 - x - 15 = 0$$
$$(x - 3)(2x + 5) = 0$$
$$x - 3 = 0 \quad \text{or} \quad 2x + 5 = 0$$
$$x = 3 \qquad\qquad x = -\frac{5}{2}$$

11.
$$\frac{x^2 - 9}{x^2 - x - 6} \cdot \frac{x^2 - 2x - 8}{2x^2 - 7x - 4}$$
$$= \frac{(x+3)(x-3)}{(x-3)(x+2)} \cdot \frac{(x-4)(x+2)}{(2x+1)(x-4)}$$
$$= \frac{x+3}{2x+1}$$

12.
$$\frac{x}{x+4} - \frac{3}{x-5} = \frac{x}{x+4} \cdot \frac{x-5}{x-5} - \frac{3}{x-5} \cdot \frac{x+4}{x+4}$$
$$= \frac{x(x-5)}{(x+4)(x-5)} - \frac{3(x+4)}{(x+4)(x-5)}$$
$$= \frac{x^2 - 5x - (3x + 12)}{(x+4)(x-5)}$$
$$= \frac{x^2 - 5x - 3x - 12}{(x+4)(x-5)}$$
$$= \frac{x^2 - 8x - 12}{(x+4)(x-5)}$$

13.
$$\frac{4}{x^2 - 3x - 10} + \frac{2}{x^2 + 5x + 6}$$
$$= \frac{4}{(x-5)(x+2)} + \frac{2}{(x+2)(x+3)}$$
$$= \frac{4(x+3)}{(x-5)(x+2)(x+3)} + \frac{2(x-5)}{(x-5)(x+2)(x+3)}$$
$$= \frac{4(x+3) + 2(x-5)}{(x-5)(x+2)(x+3)}$$
$$= \frac{4x + 12 + 2x - 10}{(x-5)(x+2)(x+3)}$$
$$= \frac{6x + 2}{(x-5)(x+2)(x+3)}$$

14.
$$\frac{x}{9} - \frac{x}{6} = \frac{1}{12}$$
$$36\left(\frac{x}{9} - \frac{x}{6}\right) = 36\left(\frac{1}{12}\right)$$
$$4x - 6x = 3$$
$$-2x = 3$$
$$x = -\frac{3}{2}$$

15.
$$\frac{7}{x+3}+\frac{5}{x+2}=\frac{5}{x^2+5x+6}$$
$$\frac{7}{x+3}+\frac{5}{x+2}=\frac{5}{(x+3)(x+2)}$$
$$(x+3)(x+2)\left(\frac{7}{x+3}+\frac{5}{x+2}\right)=(x+3)(x+2)\left[\frac{5}{(x+3)(x+2)}\right]$$
$$7(x+2)+5(x+3)=5$$
$$7x+14+5x+15=5$$
$$12x+29=5$$
$$12x=-24$$
$$x=-2$$

Check:
$$\frac{7}{x+3}+\frac{5}{x+2}=\frac{5}{x^2+5x+6}$$
$$\frac{7}{-2+3}+\frac{5}{-2+2}=\frac{5}{(-2)^2+5(-2)+6}$$
$$\frac{7}{1}+\frac{5}{0}=\frac{5}{0}$$

Since $\frac{5}{0}$ is not a real number, there is no solution.

16. a. The graph is not a function because it fails the vertical line test.

b. Domain: $\{x\,|\,x\le 2\}$

Range: $\mathbb{R}$

17. Write each equation in slope-intercept form by solving for y.

$2x-5y=6 \qquad\qquad 5x-2y=9$

$-5y=-2x+6 \qquad -2y=-5x+9$

$y=\dfrac{-2x+6}{-5} \qquad y=\dfrac{-5x+9}{-2}$

$y=\dfrac{2}{5}x-\dfrac{6}{5} \qquad y=\dfrac{5}{2}x-\dfrac{9}{2}$

Since the slopes are $\frac{2}{5}$ and $\frac{5}{2}$ which are neither equal nor negative reciprocals, the lines are neither parallel nor perpendicular.

18. $(f+g)(x)=f(x)+g(x)$
$$=(x^2+3x-2)+(4x-6)$$
$$=x^2+7x-8$$

19. $(f\cdot g)(4)=f(4)\cdot g(4)$
$$=[(4)^2+3(4)-2]\cdot[4(4)-6]$$
$$=(16+12-2)(16-6)$$
$$=(26)(10)$$
$$=260$$

20. a. Commercial Sector $=14\%$ of 2.18×10^{13}
$$=0.14\times 2.18\times10^{13}$$
$$=0.3052\times10^{13}$$
$$=3.052\times10^{12}$$
Commercial sector consumption of natural gas in 2003 was 3.052×10^{12} cubic feet.

b. Industrial Sector $=37\%$ of 2.18×10^{13}
$$=0.37\times 2.18\times10^{13}$$
$$=0.8066\times10^{13}$$
$$=8.066\times10^{12}$$
Transportation Sector $=3\%$ of 2.18×10^{13}
$$=0.03\times 2.18\times10^{13}$$
$$=0.0654\times10^{13}$$
$$=6.54\times10^{11}$$
$$8.066\times10^{12}-6.54\times10^{11}$$
$$=8.066\times10^{12}-0.654\times10^{12}$$
$$=(8.066-0.654)\times10^{12}$$
$$=7.412\times10^{12}$$
In 2003, the industrial sector consumed 7.412×10^{12} cubic feet more of natural gas than the transportation sector.

c. $2.18\times10^{13}+10\%$ of 2.18×10^{13}
$$=110\%\text{ of }2.18\times10^{13}$$
$$=1.1\times 2.18\times10^{13}$$
$$=2.398\times10^{13}$$
Consumption of natural gas in 2006 will be 2.398×10^{13} cubic feet.

Chapter 9

1. The solution to a system of equations represents the ordered pairs that satisfy all the equations in the system.

2. **a.** A consistent system of equations has a solution.

   b. An inconsistent system of equations has no solution.

   c. A dependent system of equations has an infinite number of solutions.

3. Write the equation in slope-intercept form and compare their slopes and y-intercepts. If the slopes are different, the system has exactly one solution. If the slopes and y-intercepts are the same, the system has an infinite number of solutions. If the slopes are the same and the y-intercepts are different, the system has no solution.

4. The graph will be a single line.

5. The point of intersection can only be estimated.

6. A dependent system of equations is consistent. It is consistent since it has a solution.

7. **a.**
   $y = 3x - 6$ $y = -3x$
   $0 = 3(2) - 6$ $0 = -3(2)$
   $0 = 6 - 6$ $0 = -6$ False
   $0 = 0$ True
   Since (2, 0) does not satisfy both equations, it is not a solution to the system of equations.

   b.
   $y = 3x - 6$
   $0 = 3(0) - 6$
   $0 = -6$ False
   Since (0, 0) does not satisfy the first equation, it is not a solution to the system of equations.

   c.
   $y = 3x - 6$ $y = -3x$
   $-3 = 3(1) - 6$ $-3 = -3(1)$
   $-3 = 3 - 6$ $-3 = -3$ True
   $-3 = -3$ True
   Since (1, –3) satisfies both equations, it is a solution to the system of equations.

8. **a.**
   $y = -4x$
   $8 = -4(0)$
   $8 = 0$ False
   Since (0, 8) does not satisfy the first equation, it is not a solution to the system of equations.

   b.
   $y = -4x$ $y = -2x + 8$
   $16 = -4(-4)$ $16 = -2(-4) + 8$
   $16 = 16$ True $16 = 16$ True
   Since (–4, 16) satisfies both equations, it is a solution to the system of equations.

   c.
   $y = -4x$ $y = -2x + 8$
   $-12 = -4(3)$ $-12 = -2(3) + 8$
   $-12 = -12$ True $-12 = 2$ False
   Since (3, –12) does not satisfy both equations, it is not a solution to the system of equations.

9. **a.**
   $y = 2x - 3$ $y = x + 5$
   $13 = 2(8) - 3$ $13 = 8 + 5$
   $13 = 13$ True $13 = 13$ True
   Since (8, 13) satisfies both equations, it is a solution to the system.

   b.
   $y = 2x - 3$ $y = x + 5$
   $5 = 2(4) - 3$ $5 = 4 + 5$
   $5 = 5$ True $5 = 9$ False
   Since (4, 5) does not satisfy both equations, it is not a solution to the system.

   c.
   $y = 2x - 3$ $y = x + 5$
   $7 = 2(5) - 3$ $7 = 5 + 5$
   $7 = 7$ True $7 = 10$ False
   Since (5, 7) does not satisfy both equations, it is not a solution to the system.

10. **a.**
    $x + 2y = 4$ $y = 3x - 5$
    $0 + 2(2) = 4$ $2 = 3(0) - 5$
    $4 = 4$ True $2 = -5$ False
    Since (0, 2) does not satisfy both equations, it is not a solution to the system.

    b.
    $x + 2y = 4$ $y = 3x - 5$
    $2 + 2(1) = 4$ $1 = 3(2) - 5$
    $4 = 4$ True $1 = 1$ True
    Since (2, 1) satisfies both equations, it is a solution to the system.

    c.
    $x + 2y = 4$ $y = 3x - 5$
    $4 + 2(0) = 4$ $0 = 3(4) - 5$
    $4 = 4$ True $0 = 7$ False
    Since (4, 0) does not satisfy both equations, it is not a solution to the system.

11. a.
$$4x+y=15 \qquad 5x+y=10$$
$$4(3)+3=15 \qquad 5(3)+3=10$$
$$15=15 \;\; \text{True} \qquad 18=10 \;\; \text{False}$$
Since (3, 3) does not satisfy both equations, it is not a solution to the system.

b.
$$4x+y=15$$
$$4(2)+(0)=15$$
$$8=15 \;\; \text{False}$$
Since (2, 0) does not satisfy the first equation, it is not a solution to the system.

c.
$$4x+y=15 \qquad 5x+y=10$$
$$4(-1)+19=15 \qquad 5(-1)+19=10$$
$$15=15 \;\; \text{True} \qquad 14=10 \;\; \text{False}$$
Since (–1, 19) does not satisfy both equations, it is not a solution to the system.

12. a.
$$y=2x+6 \qquad y=2x-1$$
$$6=2(0)+6 \qquad 6=2(0)-1$$
$$6=6 \;\; \text{True} \qquad 6=-1 \;\; \text{False}$$
Since (0, 6) does not satisfy both equations, it is not a solution to the system.

b.
$$y=2x+6$$
$$5=2(3)+6$$
$$5=12 \;\; \text{False}$$
Since (3, 5) does not satisfy the first equation, it is not a solution to the system.

c.
$$y=2x+6$$
$$0=2(-2)+6$$
$$0=2 \;\; \text{False}$$
Since (–2, 0) does not satisfy the first equation, it is not a solution to the system.

13. Solve the first equation for y.
$$4x-6y=12$$
$$-6y=-4x+12$$
$$y=\frac{2}{3}x-2$$
Notice that it is the same as the second equation. If the ordered pair satisfies the first equation, then it also satisfies the second equation.

a.
$$4x-6y=12$$
$$4(3)-6(0)=12$$
$$12=12 \;\; \text{True}$$
Since (3, 0) satisfies both equations, it is a solution to the system.

b.
$$4x-6y=12$$
$$4(9)-6(4)=12$$
$$12=12 \;\; \text{True}$$
Since (9, 4) satisfies both equations, it is a solution to the system.

c.
$$4x-6y=12$$
$$4(6)-6(1)=12$$
$$18=12 \;\; \text{False}$$
Since (6, 1) does not satisfy the first equation, it is not a solution to the system.

14. Solve the second equation for y.
$$2y=-2x+10$$
$$\frac{2y}{2}=\frac{-2x+10}{2}$$
$$y=-x+5$$
Notice that this is the same as the first equation. If the ordered pair satisfies the first equation, then it also satisfies the second equation.

a.
$$y=-x+5$$
$$6=-(-1)+5$$
$$6=6 \;\; \text{True}$$
Since (6, –1) satisfies both equations, it is a solution to the system.

b.
$$y=-x+5$$
$$5=-0+5$$
$$5=5 \;\; \text{True}$$
Since (0, 5) satisfies both equations, it is a solution to the system.

c.
$$y=-x+5$$
$$3=-(-2)+5$$
$$3=7 \;\; \text{False}$$
Since (–2, 3) does not satisfy the first equation, it is not a solution to the system.

15. a.
$$3x-4y=8 \qquad 2y=\frac{2}{3}x-4$$
$$3(0)-4(-2)=8$$
$$8=8 \;\; \text{True} \qquad 2(-2)=\frac{2}{3}(0)-4$$
$$-4=-4 \;\; \text{True}$$
Since (0, –2) satisfies both equations, it is a solution to the system.

b.
$$3x-4y=8$$
$$3(1)-4(-6)=8$$
$$27=8 \;\; \text{False}$$
Since (1, –6) does not satisfy the first equation, it is not a solution to the system.

c.
$$3x - 4y = 8 \qquad\qquad 2y = \frac{2}{3}x - 4$$
$$3\left(-\frac{1}{3}\right) - 4\left(-\frac{9}{4}\right) = 8 \qquad 2\left(-\frac{9}{4}\right) = \frac{2}{3}\left(-\frac{1}{3}\right) - 4$$
$$8 = 8 \qquad\qquad\qquad -\frac{9}{2} = -\frac{38}{9} \text{ False}$$
$$\text{True}$$

Since $\left(-\frac{1}{3}, -\frac{9}{4}\right)$ does not satisfy both equations, it is not a solution to the system.

16. a.
$$2x + 3y = 6 \qquad\qquad -x + \frac{5}{2} = \frac{1}{2}y$$
$$2\left(\frac{1}{2}\right) + 3\left(\frac{5}{3}\right) = 6 \qquad -\frac{1}{2} + \frac{5}{2} = \frac{1}{2}\left(\frac{5}{3}\right)$$
$$6 = 6 \qquad\qquad\qquad 2 = \frac{5}{6} \text{ False}$$
$$\text{True}$$

Since $\left(\frac{1}{2}, \frac{5}{3}\right)$ does not satisfy both equations, it is not a solution to the system.

b.
$$2x + 3y = 6$$
$$2(-2) + 3\left(\frac{10}{3}\right) = 6$$
$$6 = 6 \text{ True}$$
$$-x + \frac{5}{2} = \frac{1}{2}y$$
$$-(-2) + \frac{5}{2} = \frac{1}{2}\left(\frac{10}{3}\right)$$
$$\frac{9}{2} = \frac{5}{3} \text{ False}$$

Since $\left(-2, \frac{10}{3}\right)$ does not satisfy both equations, it is not a solution to the system.

c.
$$2x + 3y = 6 \qquad\qquad -x + \frac{5}{2} = \frac{1}{2}y$$
$$2\left(\frac{9}{4}\right) + 3\left(\frac{1}{2}\right) = 6 \qquad -\frac{9}{4} + \frac{5}{2} = \frac{1}{2}\left(\frac{1}{2}\right)$$
$$6 = 6 \qquad\qquad\qquad \frac{1}{4} = \frac{1}{4} \text{ True}$$
$$\text{True}$$

Since $\left(\frac{9}{4}, \frac{1}{2}\right)$ satisfies both equations, it is a solution to the system.

17. consistent—one solution

18. consistent—one solution

19. dependent—infinite number of solutions

20. dependent—infinite number of solutions

21. consistent—one solution

22. consistent —one solution

23. inconsistent—no solution

24. inconsistent—no solution

25. Write each equation in slope-intercept form.
$$y = 2x - 1 \qquad\qquad 3y = 5x - 6$$
$$y = \frac{5}{3}x - 2$$

Since the slopes of the lines are not the same, the lines intersect to produce one solution. This is a consistent system.

26. Write each equation in slope-intercept form.
$$x + y = 8 \qquad\qquad x - y = 8$$
$$y = -x + 8 \qquad\qquad -y = -x + 8$$
$$y = x - 8$$

Since the slopes of the lines are not the same, the lines intersect to produce one solution. This is a consistent system.

27. Write each equation in slope-intercept form.
$$2y = 3x + 3 \qquad\qquad y = \frac{3}{2}x - 2$$
$$y = \frac{3}{2}x + \frac{3}{2}$$

Since the lines have the same slope, $\frac{3}{2}$, and different y-intercepts, the lines are parallel. There is no solution. This is an inconsistent system.

28. Express each equation in slope-intercept form.
$$y = \frac{1}{2}x + 3 \qquad\qquad 2y = x + 6$$
$$y = \frac{1}{2}x + 3$$

Since both equations are identical, the line is the same for both of them. There are an infinite number of solutions. This is a dependent system.

29. Write each equation in slope-intercept form.
$$2x = y - 6 \qquad\qquad 3x = 3y + 5$$
$$y = 2x + 6 \qquad\qquad 3y = 3x - 5$$
$$y = x - \frac{5}{3}$$

Since the slopes of the lines are not the same, the lines intersect to produce one solution. This is a consistent system.

30. Write each equation in slope-intercept form.

$$x + 3y = 6 \qquad\qquad 4x + y = 4$$
$$3y = -x + 6 \qquad\qquad y = -4x + 4$$
$$y = -\frac{1}{3}x + 2$$

Since the slopes of the lines are not the same, the lines intersect to produce one solution. This is a consistent system.

31. Write each equation in slope-intercept form.

$$3x + 5y = -7 \qquad\qquad -3x - 5y = -10$$
$$5y = -3x - 7 \qquad\qquad -5y = 3x - 10$$
$$y = -\frac{3}{5}x - \frac{7}{5} \qquad\qquad y = -\frac{3}{5}x + 2$$

Since the lines have the same slope and different y-intercepts, the lines are parallel. There is no solution. This is an inconsistent system.

32. Write each equation in slope-intercept form.

$$x - y = 2 \qquad\qquad 2x - 2y = -6$$
$$y = x - 2 \qquad\qquad -2y = -2x - 6$$
$$\qquad\qquad\qquad y = x + 3$$

Since the lines have the same slope, 1, and different y-intercepts, the lines are parallel. There is no solution. This is an inconsistent system.

33. Write each equation in slope-intercept form.

$$x = 3y + 5 \qquad\qquad 2x - 6y = 10$$
$$x - 5 = 3y \qquad\qquad -6y = -2x + 10$$
$$\frac{1}{3}x - \frac{5}{3} = y \qquad\qquad y = \frac{1}{3}x - \frac{5}{3}$$

Since both equations are identical, the line is the same for both of them. There are an infinite number of solutions. This is a dependent system.

34. Write each equation in slope-intercept form.

$$x - y = 3 \qquad\qquad \frac{1}{2}x - 2y = -8$$
$$-y = -x + 3 \qquad\qquad$$
$$y = x - 3 \qquad\qquad -2y = -\frac{1}{2}x - 8$$
$$\qquad\qquad\qquad y = \frac{1}{4}x + 4$$

Since the slopes of the lines are not the same, the lines intersect to produce one solution. This is a consistent system.

35. Write each equation in slope-intercept form.

$$y = \frac{3}{2}x + \frac{1}{2} \qquad\qquad 3x - 2y = \frac{5}{2}$$
$$\qquad\qquad\qquad -2y = -3x - \frac{5}{2}$$
$$\qquad\qquad\qquad y = \frac{3}{2}x + \frac{5}{4}$$

Since the lines have the same slope and different y-intercepts, the lines are parallel. There is no solution. This is an inconsistent system.

36. Write each equation in slope-intercept form.

$$2y = \frac{7}{3}x - 9 \qquad\qquad 4y = 8x + 9$$
$$y = \frac{7}{6}x - \frac{9}{2} \qquad\qquad y = 2x + \frac{9}{4}$$

Since the slopes of the lines are not the same, the lines intersect to produce one solution. This is a consistent system.

37. Graph the equations $y = x + 3$ and $y = -x + 3$.

The lines intersect and the point of intersection is (0, 3). This is a consistent system.

38. Graph the equations $y = 2x + 4$ and $y = -3x - 6$.

The lines intersect and the point of intersection is (–2, 0). This is a consistent system.

39. Graph the equations $y = 3x - 6$ and $y = -x + 6$.

The lines intersect and the point of intersection is (3, 3). This is a consistent system.

40. Graph the equations $y = 3x - 4$ and $y = -x$.

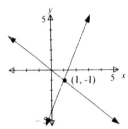

The lines intersect and the point of intersection is $(1, -1)$. This is a consistent system.

41. Graph the equations $4x = 8$ or $x = 2$ and $y = -3$.

The lines intersect and the point of intersection is $(2, -3)$. This is a consistent system.

42. Graph the equations $2x - y = 7$ or $y = 2x - 7$ and $2y = 2x - 6$ or $y = x - 3$.

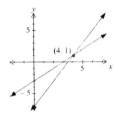

The lines intersect and the point of intersection is $(4, 1)$. This is a consistent system.

43. Graph the equations $x + y = 5$ or $y = -x + 5$ and $-x + y = 1$ or $y = x + 1$.

The lines intersect and the point of intersection is $(2, 3)$. This is a consistent system.

44. Graph the equations $-x + 2y = 7$ or $y = \dfrac{1}{2}x + \dfrac{7}{2}$ and $2x - y = -2$ or $y = 2x + 2$.

The lines intersect and the point of intersection is $(1, 4)$. This is a consistent system.

45. Graph the equations $y = -\dfrac{1}{2}x + 4$ and $x + 2y = 6$ or $y = -\dfrac{1}{2}x + 3$.

The lines are parallel. The system is inconsistent and there is no solution.

46. Graph the equations $-x + 2y = 0$ or $y = \dfrac{1}{2}x$ and $2x - y = -3$ or $y = 2x + 3$.

The lines intersect and the point of intersection is $(-2, -1)$. This is a consistent system.

47. Graph the equations $x + 2y = 8$ or $y = -\dfrac{1}{2}x + 4$ and $5x + 2y = 0$ or $y = -\dfrac{5}{2}x$.

The lines intersect and the point of intersection is $(-2, 5)$. This is a consistent system.

48. Graph the equations $3x + y = -6$ or $y = -3x - 6$ and $2x = 1 + y$ or $y = 2x - 1$.

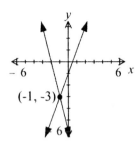

The lines intersect and the point of intersection is $(-1, -3)$. This is a consistent system.

49. Graph the equations $2x + 3y = 6$ or

$y = -\frac{2}{3}x + 2$ and $4x = -6y + 12$

or $y = -\frac{2}{3}x + 2$.

The lines are identical. There are an infinite number of solutions. This is a dependent system.

50. Graph the equations $2x + 5y - 6 = 0$ or

$y = -\frac{2}{5}x + \frac{6}{5}$ and $2x - 3y = 6$ or $y = \frac{2}{3}x - 2$.

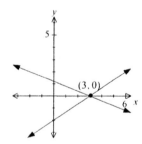

The lines intersect and the point of intersection is $(3, 0)$. This is a consistent system.

51. Graph the equations $y = 3$ and $y = 2x - 3$.

The lines intersect and the point of intersection is $(3, 3)$. This is a consistent system.

52. Graph the equations $x = 5$ and $y = 2x - 8$.

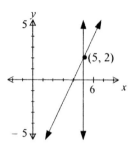

The lines intersect and the point of intersection is $(5, 2)$. This is a consistent system.

53. Graph the equations $x - 2y = 4$ or $y = \frac{1}{2}x - 2$

and $2x - 4y = 8$ or $y = \frac{1}{2}x - 2$.

The lines are identical. There are an infinite number of solutions. This is a dependent system.

54. Graph the equations $4x - y = 6$ or $y = 4x - 6$ and $2y = 8x - 12$ or $y = 4x - 6$.

The lines are identical. There are an infinite number of solutions. This is a dependent system.

55. Graph the equations $2x + y = -2$ or $y = -2x - 2$ and $6x + 3y = 6$ or $y = -2x + 2$.

The lines are parallel. The system is inconsistent and there is no solution.

56. Graph the equations $y = 2x - 1$ and $2y = 4x + 5$.

The lines are parallel. The system is inconsistent and there is no solution.

57. Graph the equations $4x - 3y = 6$ or $y = \frac{4}{3}x - 2$

and $2x + 4y = 14$ or $y = -\frac{1}{2}x + \frac{7}{2}$.

The lines intersect and the point of intersection is $(3, 2)$. This is a consistent system.

58. Graph the equations $2x + 6y = 12$ or

$y = -\frac{1}{3}x + 2$ and $y = -\frac{1}{3}x + 2$.

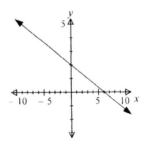

The lines are identical. There are an infinite number of solutions. This is a dependent system.

59. Graph the equations $2x - 3y = 0$ or $y = \frac{2}{3}x$ and

$x + 2y = 0$ or $y = -\frac{1}{2}x$.

The lines intersect and the point of intersection is $(0, 0)$. This is a consistent system.

60. Graph the equations $4x = 4y - 12$ or $y = x + 3$
and $-8x + 8y = 8$ or $y = x + 1$.

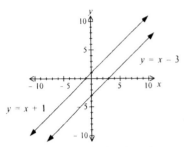

The lines are parallel. There is no solution. The system is inconsistent.

61. Write each equation in slope-intercept form.

$6x - 4y = 12$ $\qquad$ $12y = 18x - 24$

$\qquad -4y = -6x + 12$

$\qquad\qquad y = \frac{3}{2}x - 2$

$\qquad\qquad y = \frac{3}{2}x - 3$

The lines are parallel because they have the same

slope, $\frac{3}{2}$, and different y-intercepts.

62. Write each equation in slope-intercept form.

$4x - 8y = 12$ $\qquad$ $2x - 8 = 4y$

$\qquad -8y = -4x + 12$ $\qquad$ $4y = 2x - 8$

$\qquad\qquad y = \frac{1}{2}x - \frac{3}{2}$ $\qquad$ $y = \frac{1}{2}x - 2$

The lines are parallel because they have the same

slope, $\frac{1}{2}$, and different y-intercepts.

63. The system has an infinite number of solutions. If the two lines have two points in common then they must be the same line.

64. The system has one solution. If the slopes are different, then the lines intersect in one point.

65. The system has no solutions. Distinct parallel lines do not intersect.

66. Yes; If each line passes through the origin, but the slopes are different, then their point of intersection (and therefore the solution) is $(0, 0)$.

67. $x = 5$, $y = 3$ has one solution, $(5, 3)$.

68. $(3, -1)$ is the solution, so the system is:
$x = 3$
$y = -1$

69. (repair) $c = 600 + 650n$
(replacement) $c = 1800 + 450n$
Graph the equations and determine the intersection.

The solution is (6, 4500). Therefore, the total cost of repair equals the total cost of replacement at 6 years.

70. Moneywell $c = 4400 + 15n$
Doile $c = 3400 + 25n$
Graph the equations and determine the intersection.

The solution is (100, 5900).
Therefore, the cost of the two systems will be the same after 100 months or 8 years 4 months.

71. $c = 25h$

$c = 21h + 28$

Graph the equations and determine the intersection.

The solution (6, 150). Therefore, the boats must be rented for 6 hours for the cost to be the same.

72. $c = 200 + 50h$

$c = 300 + 40h$

Graph the equations and determine the intersection.

The solution is (10, 700).
Therefore, the two services will have the same cost at 10 hours.

73. 0

74. infinite number

75. 2

76. 1

77. 3

78. 3

79. $3x - (x - 6) + 4(3 - x) = 3x - x + 6 + 12 - 4x$
$$= 3x - x - 4x + 6 + 12$$
$$= -2x + 18$$

80. $2(x + 3) - x = 5x + 2$
$$2x + 6 - x = 5x + 2$$
$$x + 6 = 5x + 2$$
$$-4x = -4$$
$$x = 1$$

81.
$$A = p(1 + rt)$$
$$1000 = 500(1 + r \cdot 20)$$
$$1000 = 500(1 + 20r)$$
$$1000 = 500(1) + 500(20r)$$
$$1000 = 500 + 10,000r$$
$$1000 - 500 = 500 + 10,000r - 500$$
$$500 = 10,000r$$
$$\frac{500}{10,000} = \frac{10,000r}{10,000}$$
$$0.05 = r$$

82. a. For the *x*-intercept, set $y = 0$.

$$2x + 3y = 12$$
$$2x + 3(0) = 12$$
$$2x = 12$$
$$x = 6$$

The *x*-intercept is (6, 0).

For the *y*-intercept, set $x = 0$.

$$2x + 3y = 12$$
$$2(0) + 3y = 12$$
$$3y = 12$$
$$y = 4$$

The *y*-intercept is (0, 4).

b.

83. $\dfrac{x^2 - 9x + 14}{2 - x} = \dfrac{(x-7)(x-2)}{-(x-2)} = -(x-7)$

84.
$$\frac{4}{b} + 2b = \frac{38}{3}$$
$$3b\left(\frac{4}{b} + 2b\right) = 3b\left(\frac{38}{3}\right)$$
$$12 + 6b^2 = 38b$$
$$6b^2 - 38b + 12 = 0$$
$$2(3b^2 - 19b + 6) = 0$$
$$2(3b - 1)(b - 6) = 0$$
$$3b - 1 = 0 \quad \text{or} \quad b - 6 = 0$$
$$b = \frac{1}{3} \qquad\qquad b = 6$$

Exercise Set 9.2

1. The *x* in the first equation, since both 6 and 12 are divisible by 3.

2. The *y* in the first equation, since both 4 and 8 are divisible by 2.

3. You will obtain a false statement, such as $3 = 0$.

4. You will obtain a true statement, such as $2 = 2$

5. $x + 2y = 6$

$2x - 3y = 5$

Solve the first equation for *x*, $x = 6 - 2y$.

Substitute $6 - 2y$ for *x* in the second equation.

$$2(6 - 2y) - 3y = 5$$
$$12 - 4y - 3y = 5$$
$$-7y = -7$$
$$y = 1$$

Substitute 1 for *y* in the equation $x = 6 - 2y$.

$$x = 6 - 2(1) = 4$$

The solution is (4, 1).

6. $y = 2x + 7$

$y = -x - 5$

Substitute $-x - 5$ for *y* in the first equation.

$$-x - 5 = 2x + 7$$
$$-3x = 12$$
$$x = -4$$

Substitute –4 for *x* in the first equation.

$$y = 2x + 7$$
$$y = 2(-4) + 7 = -1$$

The solution is (–4, –1).

7. $x + y = -2$

$x - y = 0$

Solve the first equation for *y*, $y = -2 - x$.

Substitute $-2 - x$ for *y* in the second equation.

$$x - (-2 - x) = 0$$
$$x + 2 + x = 0$$
$$2x = -2$$
$$x = -1$$

Substitute –1 for *x* in the equation $y = -2 - x$.

$$y = -2 - (-1) = -2 + 1 = -1$$

The solution is (–1, –1).

8. $x + 2y = 6$

$4y = 12 - 2x$

Solve the first equation for *x*, $x = 6 - 2y$.

Substitute $6 - 2y$ for *x* in the second equation.

$$4y = 12 - 2x$$
$$4y = 12 - 2(6 - 2y)$$
$$4y = 12 - 12 + 4y$$
$$4y = 4y$$

Since this is a true statement, there are an infinite number of solutions. This is a dependent system.

445

9. $3x + y = 3$

$3x + y + 5 = 0$

Solve the first equation for y, $y = -3x + 3$.

Substitute $-3x + 3$ for y in the second equation.

$3x + y + 5 = 0$

$3x - 3x + 3 + 5 = 0$

$\qquad 8 = 0$ False

There is no solution.

10. $3x - y = 8$

$6x - 2y = 10$

First solve the first equation for y.

$3x - y = 8$

$\quad y = 3x - 8$

Now substitute $3x - 8$ for y in the second equation.

$\qquad 6x - 2y = 10$

$6x - 2(3x - 8) = 10$

$\quad 6x - 6x + 16 = 10$

$\qquad\qquad 16 = 10$ False

There is no solution.

11. $x = 3$

$x + y + 5 = 0$

Substitute 3 for x in the second equation.

$x + y + 5 = 0$

$3 + y + 5 = 0$

$\qquad y = -8$

The solution is (3, –8).

12. $y = 2x + 4$

$y = -2$

Substitute –2 for y in the first equation.

$\ y = 2x + 4$

$-2 = 2x + 4$

$-6 = 2x$

$-3 = x$

The solution is (–3, –2).

13. $x = y + 1$

$4x + 2y = -14$

Substitute $y + 1$ for x in the second equation.

$\quad 4x + 2y = -14$

$4(y + 1) + 2y = -14$

$\ 4y + 4 + 2y = -14$

$\qquad 6y + 4 = -14$

$\qquad\quad 6y = -18$

$\qquad\quad y = \dfrac{-18}{6} = -3$

Now, substitute –3 for y in the first equation.

$x = y + 1$

$x = -3 + 1 = -2$

The solution is (–2, –3).

14. $2x + 3y = 7$

$6x - y = 1$

Solve the second equation for y.

$6x - y = 1$

$\quad -y = -6x + 1$

$\quad\ y = 6x - 1$

Substitute $6x - 1$ for y in the first equation.

$\quad 2x + 3y = 7$

$2x + 3(6x - 1) = 7$

$\ 2x + 18x - 3 = 7$

$\qquad 20x - 3 = 7$

$\qquad\quad 20x = 10$

$\qquad\quad x = \dfrac{10}{20} = \dfrac{1}{2}$

Substitute $\dfrac{1}{2}$ for x in the equation $y = 6x - 1$.

$y = 6\left(\dfrac{1}{2}\right) - 1 = 3 - 1 = 2$

The solution is $\left(\dfrac{1}{2}, 2\right)$.

15. $2x + y = 11$

$\quad\quad y = 3x - 4$

Substitute $3x - 4$ for y in the first equation.

$\quad 2x + y = 11$

$2x + 3x - 4 = 11$

$\quad\quad 5x - 4 = 11$

$\quad\quad\quad 5x = 15$

$\quad\quad\quad\quad x = 3$

Now substitute 3 for x in the second equation.

$y = 3x - 4$

$y = 3(3) - 4$

$y = 9 - 4$

$y = 5$

The solution is (3, 5).

16. $\quad\quad y = -2x + 7$

$\quad x + 4y = 0$

Substitute $-2x + 7$ for y in the second equation.

$\quad\quad\quad x + 4y = 0$

$x + 4(-2x + 7) = 0$

$\quad\quad x - 8x + 28 = 0$

$\quad\quad\quad -7x + 28 = 0$

$\quad\quad\quad\quad -7x = -28$

$\quad\quad\quad\quad\quad x = 4$

Now, substitute 4 for x in the first equation.

$y = -2x + 7$

$y = -2(4) + 7$

$y = -8 + 7$

$y = -1$

The solution is (4, –1).

17. $\quad\quad y = \dfrac{1}{3}x - 2$

$x - 3y = 6$

Substitute $\dfrac{1}{3}x - 2$ for y in the second equation.

$\quad\quad x - 3y = 6$

$x - 3\left(\dfrac{1}{3}x - 2\right) = 6$

$\quad\quad x - x + 6 = 6$

$\quad\quad\quad\quad 6 = 6$

Since this is a true statement, there are an infinite number of solutions. This is a dependent system.

18. $x - \dfrac{1}{2}y = 7$

$\quad y = 2x - 14$

Substitute $2x - 14$ for y in the first equation.

$\quad\quad x - \dfrac{1}{2}y = 7$

$x - \dfrac{1}{2}(2x - 14) = 7$

$\quad\quad x - x + 7 = 7$

$\quad\quad\quad\quad 7 = 7$

Since this is a true statement, there are an infinite number of solutions. This is a dependent system.

19. $2x + 5y = 9$

$6x - 2y = 10$

First solve the second equation for y.

$\dfrac{1}{2}(6x - 2y) = \dfrac{1}{2}(10)$

$\quad\quad 3x - y = 5$

$\quad\quad\quad y = 3x - 5$

Now substitute $3x - 5$ for y in the first equation.

$\quad\quad 2x + 5y = 9$

$2x + 5(3x - 5) = 9$

$2x + 15x - 25 = 9$

$\quad\quad\quad 17x = 34$

$\quad\quad\quad\quad x = 2$

Finally substitute 2 for x in the equation $y = 3x - 5$.

$y = 3(2) - 5$

$y = 6 - 5$

$y = 1$

The solution is (2, 1).

20. $3x - 3y = 4$

$2x + 3y = 5$

Solve the first equation for x.

$3x - 3y = 4$

$3x = 3y + 4$

$x = y + \dfrac{4}{3}$

Now, substitute $y + \dfrac{4}{3}$ for x in the second equation.

$2x + 3y = 5$

$2\left(y + \dfrac{4}{3}\right) + 3y = 5$

$2y + \dfrac{8}{3} + 3y = 5$

$5y + \dfrac{8}{3} = 5$

$3\left(5y + \dfrac{8}{3}\right) = 3(5)$

$15y + 8 = 15$

$15y = 7$

$y = \dfrac{7}{15}$

Finally, substitute $\dfrac{7}{15}$ for y in the equation $x = \dfrac{5}{2} - 2y$.

$x = y + \dfrac{4}{3}$

$x = \dfrac{7}{15} + \dfrac{4}{3}$

$x = \dfrac{7}{15} + \dfrac{20}{15}$

$x = \dfrac{27}{15} = \dfrac{9}{5}$

The solution is $\left(\dfrac{9}{5}, \dfrac{7}{15}\right)$.

21. $y = 2x - 13$

$-4x - 7 = 9y$

Substitute $2x - 13$ for y in the second equation.

$-4x - 7 = 9y$

$-4x - 7 = 9(2x - 13)$

$-4x - 7 = 18x - 117$

$-22x - 7 = -117$

$-22x = -110$

$x = \dfrac{-110}{-22} = 5$

Now substitute 5 for x in the first equation.

$y = 2x - 13$

$y = 2(5) - 13$

$y = 10 - 13$

$y = -3$

The solution is $(5, -3)$.

22. $5x - 2y = -7$

$8 = y - 4x$

First, solve the second equation for y.

$8 = y - 4x$

$4x + 8 = y$

Then substitute $4x + 8$ for y in the first equation.

$5x - 2y = -7$

$5x - 2(4x + 8) = -7$

$5x - 8x - 16 = -7$

$-3x - 16 = -7$

$-3x = 9$

$x = -3$

Finally, substitute -3 for x in the equation $y = 4x + 8$.

$y = 4(-3) + 8$

$y = -4$

The solution is $(-3, -4)$.

23. $4x - 5y = -4$

$3x = 2y - 3$

First solve the second equation for x.

$\dfrac{1}{3}(3x) = \dfrac{1}{3}(2y - 3)$

$x = \dfrac{2}{3}y - 1$

Now substitute $\dfrac{2}{3}y - 1$ for x in the first equation.

$$4x - 5y = -4$$

$$4\left(\frac{2}{3}y - 1\right) - 5y = -4$$

$$\frac{8}{3}y - 4 - 5y = -4$$

$$\frac{8}{3}y - \frac{15}{3}y = 0$$

$$-\frac{7}{3}y = 0$$

$$y = 0$$

Finally substitute 0 for y in the

equation $x = \frac{2}{3}y - 1$.

$$x = \frac{2}{3}(0) - 1 = -1$$

The solution is $(-1, 0)$.

24. $2x - 3y = 9$

$5x + 2y = -6$

First solve the first equation for x.

$2x - 3y = 9$

$$2x = 3y + 9$$

$$x = \frac{3}{2}y + \frac{9}{2}$$

Now substitute $\frac{3}{2}y + \frac{9}{2}$ for x in the second

equation.

$$5x + 2y = -6$$

$$5\left(\frac{3}{2}y + \frac{9}{2}\right) + 2y = -6$$

$$\frac{15}{2}y + \frac{45}{2} + 2y = -6$$

$$2\left(\frac{15}{2}y + \frac{45}{2} + 2y\right) = 2(-6)$$

$$15y + 45 + 4y = -12$$

$$19y + 45 = -12$$

$$19y = -57$$

$$y = -3$$

Finally substitute -3 for y in the equation

$x = \frac{3}{2}y + \frac{9}{2}$.

$$x = \frac{3}{2}(-3) + \frac{9}{2} = -\frac{9}{2} + \frac{9}{2} = 0$$

The solution is $(0, -3)$.

25. $4x + 5y = -6$

$$2x - \frac{10}{3}y = -4$$

First solve the second equation for x,

$$2x - \frac{10}{3}y = -4$$

$$3\left(2x - \frac{10}{3}y\right) = 3(-4)$$

$$6x - 10y = -12$$

$$6x = 10y - 12$$

$$x = \frac{5}{3}y - 2$$

Now substitute $\frac{5}{3}y - 2$ for x in the first

equation.

$$4x + 5y = -6$$

$$4\left(\frac{5}{3}y - 2\right) + 5y = -6$$

$$\frac{20}{3}y - 8 + 5y = -6$$

$$\frac{20}{3}y + \frac{15}{3}y = 8 - 6$$

$$\frac{35}{3}y = 2$$

$$y = \frac{6}{35}$$

Finally, substitute $\frac{9}{37}$ for y in the

equation $x = \frac{5}{3}y - 2$.

$$x = \frac{5}{3}\left(\frac{6}{35}\right) - 2$$

$$x = \frac{2}{7} - \frac{14}{7}$$

$$x = -\frac{12}{7}$$

The solution is $\left(-\frac{12}{7}, \frac{6}{35}\right)$.

26. $4x + y = 1$
$10x - 5y = -2$
First solve the first equation for y,
$y = -4x + 1$.
Now substitute $-4x + 1$ for y in the second equation.
$$10x - 5y = -2$$
$$10x - 5(-4x + 1) = -2$$
$$10x + 20x - 5 = -2$$
$$30x - 5 = -2$$
$$30x = 3$$
$$x = \frac{3}{30} = \frac{1}{10}$$
Finally, substitute $\frac{1}{10}$ for x in the equation
$y = -4x + 1$.
$$y = -4\left(\frac{1}{10}\right) + 1 = -\frac{4}{10} + \frac{10}{10} = \frac{6}{10} = \frac{3}{5}$$
The solution is $\left(\frac{1}{10}, \frac{3}{5}\right)$.

27. $3x - 4y = 15$
$-6x + 8y = -14$
First solve the second equation for y,
$-6x + 8y = -14$
$$8y = 6x - 14$$
$$y = \frac{3}{4}x - \frac{7}{4}$$
Now substitute $\frac{3}{4}x - \frac{7}{4}$ for y in the first equation.
$$3x - 4\left(\frac{3}{4}x - \frac{7}{4}\right) = 15$$
$$3x - 3x + 7 = 15$$
$$7 = 15 \text{ False}$$
Since this is a false statement, there is no solution to this system.

28. $\frac{1}{2}x + 2y = 5$
$3x - \frac{1}{2}y = 5$
First solve the second equation for y,
$$3x - \frac{1}{2}y = 5$$
$$-\frac{1}{2}y = -3x + 5$$
$$y = 6x - 10$$

Now substitute $6x - 10$ for x in the first equation.
$$\frac{1}{2}x + 2(6x - 10) = 5$$
$$\frac{1}{2}x + 12x - 20 = 5$$
$$\frac{25}{2}x - 20 = 5$$
$$\frac{25}{2}x = 25$$
$$\frac{2}{25}\left(\frac{25}{2}x\right) = \frac{2}{25}(25)$$
$$x = 2$$
Finally substitute 2 for x in the equation
$y = 6x - 10$
$$y = 6(2) - 10 = 2$$
The solution is (2, 2).

29. $4x - y = 1$
$10x + \frac{1}{2}y = 1$
Solve the first equation for y.
$y = 4x - 1$
Now substitute $4x - 1$ for y in the second equation.
$$10x + \frac{1}{2}(4x - 1) = 1$$
$$10x + 2x - \frac{1}{2} = 1$$
$$12x - \frac{1}{2} = 1$$
$$12x = \frac{3}{2}$$
$$\frac{1}{12}(12x) = \frac{1}{12}\left(\frac{3}{2}\right)$$
$$x = \frac{1}{8}$$
Now substitute $\frac{1}{8}$ for x in the first equation;
$y = 4x - 1$
$$y = 4\left(\frac{1}{8}\right) - 1 = \frac{1}{2} - 1 = -\frac{1}{2}$$
The solution to the system is $\left(\frac{1}{8}, -\frac{1}{2}\right)$.

30. $-\dfrac{1}{5}x+\dfrac{3}{7}y=2$

$\dfrac{3}{5}x-\dfrac{2}{7}y=1$

Solve the first equation for y.

$-\dfrac{1}{5}x+\dfrac{3}{7}y=2$

$\dfrac{3}{7}y=\dfrac{1}{5}x+2$

$\dfrac{7}{3}\left(\dfrac{3}{7}y\right)=\dfrac{7}{3}\left(\dfrac{1}{5}x+2\right)$

$y=\dfrac{7}{15}x+\dfrac{14}{3}$

Now substitute $\dfrac{7}{15}x+\dfrac{14}{3}$ for y in the second

equation.

$\dfrac{3}{5}x-\dfrac{2}{7}\left(\dfrac{7}{15}x+\dfrac{14}{3}\right)=1$

$\dfrac{3}{5}x-\dfrac{2}{15}x-\dfrac{4}{3}=1$

$\dfrac{7}{15}x-\dfrac{4}{3}=1$

$\dfrac{7}{15}x=\dfrac{7}{3}$

$\dfrac{15}{7}\left(\dfrac{7}{15}x\right)=\dfrac{15}{7}\left(\dfrac{7}{3}\right)$

$x=5$

Finally substitute 5 for x in the equation:

$y=\dfrac{7}{15}x+\dfrac{14}{3}$

$y=\dfrac{7}{15}(5)+\dfrac{14}{3}$

$y=\dfrac{7}{3}+\dfrac{14}{3}$

$y=\dfrac{21}{3}=7$

The solution is $(5, 7)$.

31. Let x = the smaller number,
then y = the larger number.
$x+y=80$
$x+8=y$
Substitute $x+8$ for y in the first equation.

$x+y=80$

$x+(x+8)=80$

$2x+8=80$

$2x=72$

$x=36$

Now substitute 36 for x in the second equation:

$x+8=y$

$36+8=y$

$44=y$

The two integers are 36 and 44.

32. Let x = the smaller number,
then y = the larger number.
$y-x=44$
$y=2x$
Substitute $2x$ for y in the first equation.

$y-x=44$

$2x-x=44$

$x=44$

Now substitute 44 for x in the second equation.
$y=2x=2(44)=88$
The two numbers are 44 and 88.

33. Let l = the length of the rectangle,
then w = the width.
$2l+2w=50$
$l=9+w$
Substitute $9+w$ for l in the first equation and
solve for w.

$2l+2w=50$

$2(9+w)+2w=50$

$18+2w+2w=50$

$4w=32$

$w=8$

Now substitute 8 for w in the second equation to find l.
$l=9+w$

$l=9+8=17$

The length of the rectangle is 17 feet and the width is 8 feet.

34. Let l = the length of the rectangle,
then w = the width.
$2l + 2w = 60$
$l = 5(w)$
Substitute $5(w)$ for l in the first equation and solve for w.
$$2l + 2w = 60$$
$$2(5w) + 2w = 60$$
$$10w + 2w = 60$$
$$12w = 60$$
$$w = 5$$
Now substitute 5 for w in the second equation to find l.
$$l = 5w = 5(5) = 25$$
The length of the rectangle is 25 feet and the width is 5 feet.

35. Let f = the number of attendees who paid the full fee and d = the number of attendees who received the discount.
$f + d = 2500$
$d = f - 622$
Substitute $f - 622$ for d in the first equation.
$$f + d = 2500$$
$$f + (f - 622) = 2500$$
$$2f - 622 = 2500$$
$$2f = 3122$$
$$f = 1561$$
Now substitute 1561 for f in the second equation and solve for d.
$$d = f - 622 = 1561 - 622 = 939$$
The number of attendees who paid the full amount was 1561 and then 939 got the discount fee.

36. Let b = the amount of money Billy had and j = the amount of money Jean had.
$b + j = 530$
$j = 130 + b$
Substitute $130 + b$ for j in the first equation.
$$b + j = 530$$
$$b + (130 + b) = 530$$
$$2b + 130 = 530$$
$$2b = 400$$
$$b = 200$$
Now substitute 200 for b in the first equation and solve for j.
$$b + j = 530$$
$$200 + j = 530$$
$$j = 330$$
Billy had $200 and Jean had $330.

37. Let c = the client's portion of the award and a = the attorneys portion.
$c + a = 40,000$
$c = 3a$
Now solve the first equation for a and substitute it for a in the second equation.
$$c + a = 40000$$
$$a = 40000 - c$$

$$c = 3a$$
$$c = 3(40000 - c)$$
$$c = 120,000 - 3c$$
$$4c = 120,000$$
$$c = 30,000$$
The client received $30,000.

38. Let g = the number of pounds of green jelly beans and r = the number of pounds of red jelly beans.
$g + r = 42$
$g = 3r$
Substitute $3r$ for g in the first equation.
$$g + r = 42$$
$$3r + r = 42$$
$$4r = 42$$
$$r = \frac{42}{4} = 10.5$$
Now substitute 10.5 for r in the second equation and solve for g.
$$g = 3r = 3(10.5) = 31.5$$
There were 10.5 pounds of red jelly beans and 31.5 pounds green jelly beans.

39. $c = 1280 + 794n$
$c = 874n$

a. Substitute $874n$ for c in the first equation.
$$874n = 1280 + 794n$$
$$80n = 1280$$
$$n = 16$$
The mortgage plans will have the same total cost at 16 months.

b. $12 \text{ years} \cdot \left(\dfrac{12 \text{ months}}{1 \text{ year}} \right) = 144 \text{ months}$

$c = 1280 + 794(144) = 115,616$
$c = 874(144) = 125,856$
Yes, since $115,616 is less than $125,856, she should refinance.

40. $T = 86 - 2t$

$T = 59 + 2.5t$

a. Substitute $86 - 2t$ for T in the second equation.

$86 - 2t = 59 + 2.5t$

$86 - 59 = 2.5t + 2t$

$27 = 4.5t$

$6 = t$

The cities will have the same temperature in 6 hours.

b. Substitute 6 for t in the first equation.

$T = 86 - 2t$

$T = 86 - 2(6) = 86 - 12 = 74$

The temperature will be 74°F.

41. a. Substitute $65 + 72t$ for m in the first equation and solve for t.

$65 + 72t = 80 + 60t$

$12t = 15$

$t = \dfrac{15}{12} = 1.25$

It will take Roberta 1.25 hours to catch up to Jean.

b. Now substitute 1.25 for t in one of the original equtions.

$m = 80 + 60(1.25)$

$m = 80 + 75$

$m = 155$

They will be at mile marker 155 when they meet.

42. $s = 300 + 20n$

$s = 400 + 10n$

Substitute $300 + 20n$ for s in the second equation.

$300 + 20n = 400 + 10n$

$20n - 10n = 400 - 300$

$10n = 100$

$n = 10$

The salaries will be the same if 10 computer systems are sold.

43. a. $T = 180 - 10t$

b. $T = 20 + 6t$

c. $T = 180 - 10t$

$T = 20 + 6t$

Substitute $20 + 6t$ for T in the first equation.

$20 + 6t = 180 - 10t$

$16t = 160$

$t = 10$

It will take 10 minutes for the ball and oil to reach the same temperature.

d. Substitute 10 for t in one of the original equations.

$T = 180 - 10t$

$T = 180 - 10(10)$

$T = 180 - 100$

$T = 80$

The temperature will be 80°F.

44. $x = 4$

$2x - y = 6$

$-x + y + z = -3$

Substitute 4 for x in the second equation and solve for y.

$2(4) - y = 6$

$8 - y = 6$

$-y = -2$

$y = 2$

Now substitute 4 for x and 2 for y in the third equation and solve for z.

$-4 + 2 + z = -3$

$-2 + z = -3$

$z = -1$

$(4, 2, -1)$ is the solution.

45. $\dfrac{27.6}{1.2} = 23$

The willow tree is about 23 years old.

46. $4x + 5y = 22$

Substitute 3 for x and solve for y.

$4(3) + 5y = 22$

$12 + 5y = 22$

$5y = 10$

$y = 2$

The ordered pair is $(3, 2)$.

47. $4x - 8y = 16$

Let $x = 0$ and solve for y.

$4(0) - 8y = 16$

$\quad -8y = 16$

$\quad\quad y = -2$

Let $y = 0$ and solve for x.

$4x - 8(0) = 16$

$\quad\quad 4x = 16$

$\quad\quad x = 4$

The intercepts are $(0, -2)$ and $(4, 0)$.

48. $3x - 5y = 25$

Write in slope-intercept form.

$-5y = -3x + 25$

$y = \dfrac{3}{5}x - 5$

The slope is $\dfrac{3}{5}$ and the y intercept is $(0, -5)$.

49. Use the points $(-2, 0)$ and $(0, 4)$ to find the slope

of the line: $m = \dfrac{4 - 0}{0 - (-2)} = \dfrac{4}{2} = 2$

The y-intercept is 4, so $b = 4$.

Thus, the equation of the line is:

$y = mx + b$

$y = 2x + 4$

50. $(6x + 7)(3x - 2) = 18x^2 - 12x + 21x - 14$

$\quad\quad\quad\quad\quad\quad = 18x^2 + 9x - 14$

Exercise Set 9.3

1. Multiply the top equation by 2.
Now the top equation contains a $-2x$ and the bottom equation contains a $2x$. When the equations are added together, the variable x will be eliminated.

2. Multiply the bottom equation by 2.
Now the top equation contains a $4y$ and the bottom equation contains a $-4y$. When the equations are added together, the variable y will be eliminated.

3. You will obtain a false statement, such as $0 = 6$

4. You will obtain a true statement, such as $0 = 0$.

5. $\quad\quad x + y = 6$

$\quad\quad\quad x - y = 4$

Add: $2x \quad = 10$

$\quad\quad\quad x = 5$

Substitute 5 for x in the first equation.

$x + y = 6$

$5 + y = 6$

$\quad\quad y = 1$

The solution is $(5, 1)$.

6. $\quad\quad x - y = 10$

$\quad\quad\quad x + y = 8$

Add: $2x \quad = 18$

$\quad\quad\quad x = 9$

Substitute 9 for x in the second equation.

$x + y = 8$

$9 + y = 8$

$\quad\quad y = -1$

The solution is $(9, -1)$.

7. Add: $\quad x + y = 9$

$\quad\quad\quad -x + y = 1$

$\quad\quad\quad\quad 2y = 10$

$\quad\quad\quad\quad y = 5$

Substitute 5 for y in the first equation.

$x + y = 9$

$x + 5 = 9$

$\quad x = 4$

The solution is $(4, 5)$.

8. $\quad\quad 5x + y = 14$

$\quad\quad\quad 4x - y = 4$

Add: $9x \quad = 18$

$\quad\quad\quad x = 2$

Substitute 2 for x in the first equation.

$5x + y = 14$

$5(2) + y = 14$

$10 + y = 14$

$\quad\quad y = 4$

The solution is $(2, 4)$.

9. Add: $x + 2y = 21$

$\underline{2x - 2y = -6}$

$3x \quad = 15$

$x = 5$

Substitute 5 for x in the first equation.

$x + 2y = 21$

$5 + 2y = 21$

$2y = 16$

$y = 8$

The solution is $(5, 8)$.

10. Add: $x - y = 3$

$\underline{x + y = -3}$

$2x \quad = 0$

$x = 0$

Substitute 0 for x in the second equation.

$x + y = -3$

$0 + y = -3$

$y = -3$

The solution is $(0, -3)$.

11. $4x + y = 6 \quad (eq. 1)$

$-8x - 2y = 20 \quad (eq. 2)$

Multiply the first equation by 2, then add to the second equation.

$2[4x + y = 6]$

gives

$8x + 2y = 12$

$\underline{-8x - 2y = 20}$

$0 = 32$ False

There is no solution.

12. $x - y = 2 \quad (eq. 1)$

$3x - 3y = 1 \quad (eq. 2)$

Multiply the first equation by -3 and then add.

$-3[x - y = 2]$

gives

$-3x + 3y = -6$

$\underline{3x - 3y = 1}$

$0 = -5$ False

There is no solution.

13. $-5x + y = 14 \quad (eq. 1)$

$-3x + y = -2 \quad (eq. 2)$

To eliminate y, multiply the first equation by -1 and then add.

$-1[-5x + y = 14]$

gives

$5x - y = -14$

$\underline{-3x + y = -2}$

$2x \quad = -16$

$x = -8$

Substitute -8 for x in the first equation.

$-5x + y = 14$

$-5(-8) + y = 14$

$40 + y = 14$

$y = -26$

The solution is $(-8, -26)$.

14. $6x + 3y = 30 \quad (eq. 1)$

$2x + 3y = 18 \quad (eq. 2)$

To eliminate y multiply the first equation by -1 and then add.

$-1[6x + 3y = 30]$

gives

$-6x - 3y = -30$

$\underline{2x + 3y = 18}$

$-4x \quad = -12$

$x = 3$

Substitute 3 for x in the first equation.

$6x + 3y = 30$

$6(3) + 3y = 30$

$18 + 3y = 30$

$3y = 12$

$y = 4$

The solution is $(3, 4)$.

15. $2x + y = -6$

$2x - 2y = 3$

To eliminate y, multiply the first equation by 2 and then add.

$2[2x + y = -6]$

gives

$4x + 2y = -12$

$\underline{2x - 2y = 3}$

$6x = -9$

$x = -\dfrac{3}{2}$

Substitute $-\dfrac{3}{2}$ for x in the first equation.

$2x + y = -6$

$2\left(-\dfrac{3}{2}\right) + y = -6$

$-3 + y = -6$

$y = -3$

The solution is $\left(-\dfrac{3}{2}, -3\right)$.

16. $-4x + 3y = 0 \quad (eq. 1)$

$7x - 6y = 3 \quad (eq. 2)$

To eliminate y, multiply the first equation by 2 and then add.

$2[-4x + 3y = 0]$

gives

$-8x + 6y = 0$

$\underline{7x - 6y = 3}$

$-x = 3$

$x = -3$

Substitute -3 for x in the first equation.

$-4x + 3y = 0$

$-4(-3) + 3y = 0$

$12 + 3y = 0$

$3y = -12$

$y = -4$

The solution is $(-3, -4)$.

17. $2y = 6x + 16 \quad (eq. 1)$

$y = -3x - 4 \quad (eq. 2)$

Rewrite the equations to align the variables on the left hand side of the equal sign.

$-6x + 2y = 16$

$3x + y = -4$

To eliminate x, multiply the second equation by 2, then add.

$2[3x + y = -4]$

gives

$-6x + 2y = 16$

$\underline{6x + 2y = -8}$

$4y = 8$

$y = 2$

Substitute 2 for y in the second equation.

$3x + y = -4$

$3x + 2 = -4$

$3x = -6$

$x = -2$

The solution is $(-2, 2)$.

18. $2x - 3y = 4 \quad (eq. 1)$

$2x + y = -4 \quad (eq. 2)$

To eliminate y, multiply the second equation by 3, then add.

$3[2x + y = -4]$

gives

$2x - 3y = 4$

$\underline{6x + 3y = -12}$

$8x = -8$

$x = -1$

Substitute -1 for x in the second equation.

$2x + y = -4$

$2(-1) + y = -4$

$-2 + y = -4$

$y = -2$

The solution is $(-1, -2)$.

19. $5x + 3y = 12 \quad (eq.\ 1)$

$3x - 6y = 15 \quad (eq.\ 2)$

To eliminate y, multiply the first equation by 2 and then add.

$2[5x + 3y = 12]$

gives

$10x + 6y = 24$

$\underline{3x - 6y = 15}$

$13x \quad\ = 39$

$x = 3$

Substitute 3 for x in the first equation.

$5x + 3y = 12$

$5(3) + 3y = 12$

$15 + 3y = 12$

$3y = -3$

$y = -1$

The solution is $(3, -1)$.

20. $8x - 4y = 12 \quad (eq.\ 1)$

$2x - 8y = 3 \quad (eq.\ 2)$

To eliminate x, multiply the second equation by -4, then add.

$-4[2x - 8y = 3]$

gives

$8x - 4y = 12$

$\underline{-8x + 32y = -12}$

$28y = 0$

$y = 0$

Substitute 0 for y in the first equation.

$8x - 4y = 12$

$8x - 4(0) = 12$

$8x = 12$

$x = \dfrac{3}{2}$

The solution is $\left(\dfrac{3}{2},\ 0\right)$.

21. $-2y = -4x + 12$

$y = 2x - 6$

Align x- and y-terms on the left side.

$4x - 2y = 12 \quad (eq.\ 1)$

$-2x + y = -6 \quad (eq.\ 2)$

To eliminate x, multiply the second equation by 2 and then add.

$2[-2x + y = -6]$

gives

$4x - 2y = \ \ 12$

$\underline{-4x + 2y = -12}$

$0 = 0$

Since this is a true statement, there are an infinite number of solutions. This is a dependent system.

22. $4x - 2y = 12$

$4y = 8x - 24$

Align x- and y-terms on the left side.

$4x - 2y = 12 \quad (eq.\ 1)$

$-8x + 4y = -24 \quad (eq.\ 2)$

Multiply the first equation by 2 and add.

$2[4x - 2y = 12]$

gives

$8x - 4y = 24$

$\underline{-8x + 4y = -24}$

$0 = 0$

Since this is a true statement, there are an infinite number of solutions. This is a dependent system.

23. $5x - 4y = -3$

$7y = 2x + 12$

Align x- and y-terms on the left side.

$5x - 4y = -3 \quad (eq.\ 1)$

$-2x + 7y = 12 \quad (eq.\ 2)$

To eliminate x, multiply the first equation by 2 and the second equation by 5 and then add.

$2[5x - 4y = -3]$

$5[-2x + 7y = 12]$

gives

$10x - \ \ 8y = -6$

$\underline{-10x + 35y = 60}$

$27y = 54$

$y = \ \ 2$

Substitute 2 for y in the first equation.

$5x - 4y = -3$

$5x - 4(2) = -3$

$5x - 8 = -3$

$5x = 5$

$x = 1$

The solution is $(1, 2)$.

24. $2x + 3y = -3 \quad (eq.\ 1)$

$-3x - 5y = 7 \quad (eq.\ 2)$

To eliminate x, multiply the first equation by 5 and the second equation by 3 and then add.

$5[2x + 3y = -3]$

$3[-3x - 5y = 7]$

gives

$10x + 15y = -15$

$\underline{-9x - 15y = 21}$

$x = 6$

Substitute 6 for y in the first equation.

$2x + 3y = -3$

$2(6) + 3y = -3$

$12 + 3y = -3$

$3y = -15$

$y = -5$

The solution is (6, –5).

25. $5x - 4y = 1 \quad (eq.\ 1)$

$-10x + 8y = -3 \quad (eq.\ 2)$

Multiply the first equation by 2, then add.

$2[5x - 4y = 1]$

gives

$10x - 8y = \ \ 1$

$\underline{-10x + 8y = -3}$

$0 = -2 \quad \text{False}$

There is no solution.

26. $2x - 3y = 11$

$5y = 3x - 17$

Align x- and y-terms on the left side.

$2x - 3y = 11 \quad (eq.\ 1)$

$-3x + 5y = -17 \quad (eq.\ 2)$

To eliminate x, multiply the first equation by 3 and the second equation by 2 and then add.

$3[2x - 3y = 11]$

$2[-3x + 5y = -17]$

gives

$6x - 9y = 33$

$\underline{-6x + 10y = -34}$

$y = -1$

Substitute –1 for y in the first equation.

$2x - 3y = 11$

$2x - 3(-1) = 11$

$2x + 3 = 11$

$2x = 8$

$x = 4$

The solution is (4, –1).

27. $5x - 6y = 0 \quad (eq.\ 1)$

$3x + 4y = 0 \quad (eq.\ 2)$

To eliminate y, multiply the first equation by 3 and the second equation by –5 and then add.

$3[5x - 6y = 0]$

$-5[3x + 4y = 0]$

gives

$15x - 18y = 0$

$\underline{-15x - 20y = 0}$

$-38y = 0$

$y = 0$

Substitute 0 for y in the second equation.

$3x + 4y = 0$

$3x + 4(0) = 0$

$3x = 0$

$x = 0$

The solution is (0, 0).

28. $4x - 2y = -4 \quad (eq.\ 1)$

$5x - 6y = -26 \quad (eq.\ 2)$

To eliminate y, multiply the first equation by –3, then add.

$-3[4x - 2y = -4]$

gives

$-12x + 6y = 12$

$\underline{5x - 6y = -26}$

$-7x \quad\ \ = -14$

$x = 2$

Substitute 2 for x in the first equation.

$4x - 2y = -4$

$4(2) - 2y = -4$

$8 - 2y = -4$

$-2y = -12$

$y = 6$

The solution is (2, 6).

29. $-5x + 4y = -20 \quad (eq.\ 1)$

$3x - 2y = 15 \quad (eq.\ 2)$

To eliminate y, multiply the second equation by 2, then add.

$2[3x - 2y = 15]$

gives

$-5x + 4y = -20$

$\underline{6x - 4y = \ \ 30}$

$x \quad\ \ = 10$

Substitute 10 for x in the first equation.
$$-5x + 4y = -20$$
$$-5(10) + 4y = -20$$
$$-50 + 4y = -20$$
$$4y = 30$$
$$y = \frac{15}{2}$$
The solution is $\left(10, \frac{15}{2}\right)$.

30. $4x - 3y = -4$

$3x - 5y = 10$

To eliminate x, multiply the first equation by -3 and the second equation by 4 and then add.
$$-3[4x - 3y = -4]$$
$$4[3x - 5y = 10]$$
gives
$$-12x + 9y = 12$$
$$\underline{12x - 20y = 40}$$
$$-11y = 52$$
$$y = -\frac{52}{11}$$
Substitute $-\frac{52}{11}$ for y in the first equation.
$$4x - 3y = -4$$
$$4x - 3\left(-\frac{52}{11}\right) = -4$$
$$4x + \frac{156}{11} = -4$$
$$4x = \frac{-44}{11} - \frac{156}{11}$$
$$4x = -\frac{200}{11}$$
$$x = -\frac{50}{11}$$
The solution is $\left(-\frac{50}{11}, -\frac{52}{11}\right)$.

31. $6x = 4y + 12$

$3y - 5x = -6$

Align the x- and y-terms on the left side.
$$6x - 4y = 12$$
$$5x - 3y = 6$$
To eliminate x, multiply the first equation by 5 and the second equation by -6 and then add.

$$5(6x - 4y = 12)$$
$$-6(5x - 3y = 6)$$
gives
$$30x - 20y = 60$$
$$\underline{-30x + 18y = -36}$$
$$-2y = 24$$
$$y = -12$$
Substitute -12 for y in the first equation.
$$6x - 4y = 12$$
$$6x - 4(-12) = 12$$
$$6x + 48 = 12$$
$$6x = -36$$
$$x = -6$$
The solution is $(-6, -12)$.

32. $5x = 2y - 4$

$3x - 5y = 6$

Align the x- and y-terms on the left side.
$$5x - 2y = -4$$
$$3x - 5y = 6$$
To eliminate x, multiply the first equation by -3 and the second equation by 5 and then add.
$$-3[5x - 2y = -4]$$
$$5[3x - 5y = 6]$$
gives
$$-15x + 6y = 12$$
$$\underline{15x - 25y = 30}$$
$$-19y = 42$$
$$y = -\frac{42}{19}$$
Substitute $-\frac{42}{19}$ for y in the first equation.
$$5x = 2y - 4$$
$$5x = 2\left(-\frac{42}{19}\right) - 4$$
$$5x = -\frac{84}{19} - \frac{76}{19}$$
$$5x = -\frac{160}{19}$$
$$x = -\frac{32}{19}$$
The solution is $\left(-\frac{32}{19}, -\frac{42}{19}\right)$.

33. $4x + 5y = 0$

$3x = 6y + 4$

Align the x- and y-terms on the left side.

$4x + 5y = 0$

$3x - 6y = 4$

To eliminate y, multiply the first equation by 6 and the second equation by 5 and then add.

$6[4x + 5y = 0]$

$5[3x - 6y = 4]$

gives

$24x + 30y = 0$

$\underline{15x - 30y = 20}$

$39x \qquad = 20$

$x = \dfrac{20}{39}$

Substitute $\dfrac{20}{39}$ for x in the first equation.

$4x + 5y = 0$

$4\left(\dfrac{20}{39}\right) + 5y = 0$

$5y = -\dfrac{80}{39}$

$y = -\dfrac{16}{39}$

The solution is $\left(\dfrac{20}{39}, -\dfrac{16}{39}\right)$

34. $4x - 3y = 8$

$-3x + 4y = 9$

To eliminate y, multiply the first equation by 4 and the second equation by 3 and then add.

$4[4x - 3y = 8]$

$3[-3x + 4y = 9]$

gives

$16x - 12y = 32$

$\underline{-9x + 12y = 27}$

$7x \qquad = 59$

$x = \dfrac{59}{7}$

To find y, it may be easier to return to the system and eliminate x. To do this, multiply the first equation by 3 and the second equation by 4 and then add.

$3[4x - 3y = 8]$

$4[-3x + 4y = 9]$

gives

$12x - 9y = 24$

$\underline{-12x + 16y = 36}$

$7y = 60$

$y = \dfrac{60}{7}$

The solution is $\left(\dfrac{59}{7}, \dfrac{60}{7}\right)$.

35. $x - \dfrac{1}{2}y = 4$

$3x + y = 6$

To eliminate y, multiply the first equation by 2 and then add.

$2\left[x - \dfrac{1}{2}y = 4\right]$

gives

$2x - y = 8$

$\underline{3x + y = 6}$

$5x \quad = 14$

$x = \dfrac{14}{5}$

Substitute $\dfrac{14}{5}$ for x in the second equation.

$3x + y = 6$

$3\left(\dfrac{14}{5}\right) + y = 6$

$\dfrac{42}{5} + y = 6$

$y = 6 - \dfrac{42}{5}$

$y = \dfrac{30}{5} - \dfrac{42}{5}$

$y = -\dfrac{12}{5}$

The solution is $\left(\dfrac{14}{5}, -\dfrac{12}{5}\right)$

36. $2x - \dfrac{1}{3}y = 6$

$3x - \dfrac{5}{6}y = -13$

To eliminate x, multiply the first equation by 3 and the second equation by -2, then add.

$3\left[2x - \dfrac{1}{3}y = 6\right]$

$-2\left[3x - \dfrac{5}{6}y = -13\right]$

gives

$6x - y = 18$

$-6x + \dfrac{5}{3}y = 26$

_____

$\dfrac{2}{3}y = 44$

$\dfrac{3}{2}\left(\dfrac{2}{3}y\right) = \dfrac{3}{2}(44)$

$y = 66$

Substitute 66 for y in the first equation.

$2x - \dfrac{1}{3}(66) = 6$

$2x - 22 = 6$

$2x = 28$

$x = 14$

The solution is $(14, 66)$.

37. $3x - y = 4$

$2x - \dfrac{2}{3}y = 8$

To eliminate y, multiply the first equation by $-\dfrac{2}{3}$ and then add.

$-\dfrac{2}{3}[3x - y = 4]$

gives

$-2x + \dfrac{2}{3}y = \dfrac{8}{3}$

$2x - \dfrac{2}{3}y = 8$

_____

$0 = \dfrac{32}{3}$ False

There is no solution.

38. $-5x + 6y = -12$

$\dfrac{5}{3}x - 4 = 2y$

Align x and y terms on the left hand side.

$5x + 6y = -12$

$\dfrac{5}{3}x - 2y = 4$

To eliminate x, multiply the second equation by 3 then add.

$3\left[\dfrac{5}{3}x - 4 = 2y\right]$

gives

$5x - 6y = -12$

$5x - 6y = -12$

_____

$0 = 0$ True

Since this is a true statement, there are an infinite number of solutions. This is a dependent system.

39. Add: $x + y = 20$

$x - y = 8$

_____

$2x = 28$

$x = 14$

Substitute 14 for x in the first equation to find the second number.

$x + y = 20$

$14 + y = 20$

$y = 6$

The numbers are 14 and 6.

40. Add: $x + y = 46$

$x - y = 6$

_____

$2x = 52$

$x = 26$

Substitute 26 for x in the first equation to find the second number.

$x + y = 42$

$26 + y = 46$

$y = 20$

The numbers are 26 and 20.

41. $x + 2y = 14$

$x - y = 2$

To eliminate y, multiply the second equation by 2 and then add.

$2[x - y = 2]$

gives

$x + 2y = 14$

$\underline{2x - 2y = 4}$

$\quad\; 3x = 18$

$\quad\;\; x = 6$

Substitute 6 for x in the second equation to find the other number.

$x - y = 2$

$6 - y = 2$

$\quad y = 4$

The numbers are 6 and 4.

42. $x + y = 9$

$3y - 2x = 7$

Align x and y terms on the left hand side.

$x + y = 9$

$\underline{-2x + 3y = 7}$

To eliminate x, multiply the first equation by 2 and then add.

$2[x + y = 9]$

gives

$2x + 2y = 18$

$\underline{-2x + 3y = 7}$

$\quad\;\; 5y = 25$

$\quad\;\;\; y = 5$

Substitute 5 for y in the first equation to find the other number.

$x + y = 9$

$x + 5 = 9$

$\quad x = 4$

The first number is 4 and the second number is 5.

43. Let x be the length of the rectangle and y be the width.

$2x + 2y = 18$

$\qquad x = 2y$

Align the x and y variables on the left hand side of the equal sign.

$2x + 2y = 18$

$\underline{x - 2y = 0}$

Now add the equations to eliminate the y.

$3x = 18$

$\;\; x = 6$

Substitute 6 for x in the second equation and solve for y.

$x = 2y$

$6 = 2y$

$3 = y$

The width is 3 inches and the length is 6 inches.

44. $2x + 2y = 28$

$4x + 6y = 66$

To eliminate x, multiply the first equation by -2 and then add.

$-2[2x + 2y = 28]$

gives

$-4x - 4y = -56$

$\underline{\;\; 4x + 6y = 66}$

$\qquad 2y = 10$

$\qquad\; y = 5$

Now substitute 5 for y in the first equation and find x.

$2x + 2y = 28$

$2x + 2(5) = 28$

$2x + 10 = 28$

$\quad 2x = 18$

$\quad\;\; x = 9$

The length is 9 inches and the width is 5 inches.

45. Let l = the length and w = the width of the photograph.

$2l + 2w = 36$

$l - w = 2$

Multiply the second equation by 2

$2[l - w = 2]$

gives

$2l + 2w = 36$

$\underline{2l - 2w = \;\; 4}$

$\qquad 4l = 40$

$\qquad\; l = 10$

$10 - w = 2$

$\qquad\; w = 8$

The length is 10 inches and the width is 8 inches.

46. Let l = the length and w = the width of the garden.

$$2l + 2w = 82$$
$$l - w = 11$$

Multiply the second equation by 2

$$2[l - w = 11]$$

gives

$$\begin{aligned} 2l + 2w &= 82 \\ \underline{2l - 2w} &= 22 \\ 4l &= 104 \\ l &= 26 \end{aligned}$$

Substitute 26 for l in the second equation.

$$l - w = 11$$
$$26 - w = 11$$
$$w = 15$$

The length is 26 feet and the width is 15 feet.

47 – 48. Answers will vary.

49. a.
$$4x + 2y = 1000$$
$$2x + 4y = 800$$

To eliminate x, multiply the first equation by -2.

$$-2[4x + 2y = 1000]$$

gives

$$\begin{aligned} -8x - 4y &= -2000 \\ \underline{2x + 4y} &= 800 \\ -6x &= -1200 \\ x &= 200 \end{aligned}$$

Substitute 200 for x in the first equation.

$$4x + 2y = 1000$$
$$4(200) + 2y = 1000$$
$$800 + 2y = 1000$$
$$2y = 200$$
$$y = 100$$

The solution is (200, 100).

b. They will have the same solution. Dividing an equation by a nonzero number does not change the solutions.

$$2x + y = 500$$
$$2x + 4y = 800$$

To eliminate x, multiply the first equation by -1 and then add.

$$-1[2x + y = 500]$$

gives

$$\begin{aligned} -2x - y &= -500 \\ \underline{2x + 4y} &= 800 \\ 3y &= 300 \\ y &= 100 \end{aligned}$$

Substitute 100 for y in the first equation.

$$2x + y = 500$$
$$2x + 100 = 500$$
$$2x = 400$$
$$x = 200$$

The solution is (200, 100).

50. They will have the same solution. Dividing the equations by a nonzero number does not change the solutions to the equations or the system.

The new system is:

$$2x + y = 500$$
$$x + 2y = 400$$

To eliminate y, multiply the first equation by -2 and then add.

$$-2[2x + y = 500]$$

gives

$$\begin{aligned} -4x - 2y &= -1000 \\ \underline{x + 2y} &= 400 \\ -3x &= -600 \\ x &= 200 \end{aligned}$$

Substitute 200 for x in the second equation.

$$x + 2y = 400$$
$$200 + 2y = 400$$
$$2y = 200$$
$$y = 100$$

The solution is (200, 100).

51.
$$\frac{x+2}{2} - \frac{y+4}{3} = 4$$

$$\frac{x+y}{2} = \frac{1}{2} + \frac{x-y}{3}$$

Start by writing each equation in standard form after clearing fractions.

For the first equation:

$$6\left[\frac{x+2}{2} - \frac{y+4}{3} = 4\right]$$
$$3(x+2) - 2(y+4) = 24$$
$$3x + 6 - 2y - 8 = 24$$
$$3x - 2y - 2 = 24$$
$$3x - 2y = 26$$

For the second equation:

$$6\left[\frac{x+y}{2} = \frac{1}{2} + \frac{x-y}{3}\right]$$
$$3(x+y) = 3 + 2(x-y)$$
$$3x + 3y = 3 + 2x - 2y$$
$$x + 5y = 3$$

The new system is:

$3x - 2y = 26$

$x + 5y = 3$

To eliminate x, multiply the second equation by -3 and then add.

$-3[x + 5y = 3]$

gives

$3x - 2y = 26$

$\underline{-3x - 15y = -9}$

$-17y = 17$

$y = -1$

Now, substitute -1 for y in the equation $x + 5y = 3$.

$x + 5(-1) = 3$

$x - 5 = 3$

$x = 8$

The solution is $(8, -1)$.

52. $\frac{5}{2}x + 3y = \frac{9}{2} + y$

$\frac{1}{4}x - \frac{1}{2}y = 6x + 12$

Start by writing each equation in standard form after clearing fractions.

For the first equation:

$2\left[\frac{5}{2}x + 3y = \frac{9}{2} + y\right]$

$5x + 6y = 9 + 2y$

$5x + 4y = 9$

For the second equation:

$4\left[\frac{1}{4}x - \frac{1}{2}y = 6x + 12\right]$

$x - 2y = 24x + 48$

$-23x - 2y = 48$

The new system is:

$5x + 4y = 9$

$-23x - 2y = 48$

To eliminate y, multiply the second equation by 2 and then add.

$2[-23x - 2y = 48]$

gives

$5x + 4y = 9$

$\underline{-46x - 4y = 96}$

$-41x = 105$

$x = -\frac{105}{41}$

Now, substitute $-\frac{105}{41}$ for x in the second equation.

$-23x - 2y = 48$

$-23\left(-\frac{105}{41}\right) - 2y = 48$

$\frac{2415}{41} - 2y = 48$

$-2y = \frac{1968}{41} - \frac{2415}{41}$

$-2y = -\frac{447}{41}$

$y = \frac{447}{82}$

The solution is $\left(-\frac{105}{41}, \frac{447}{82}\right)$.

53. $x + 2y - z = 2$

$2x - y + z = 3$

$3x + y + z = 8$

Add the second and third equations to eliminate y.

$2x - y + z = 3$

$\underline{3x + y + z = 8}$

$5x + 2z = 11$

Multiply the second equation by 2 and then add the first equation to eliminate y.

$2[2x - y + z = 3]$

gives

$4x - 2y + 2z = 6$

$\underline{x + 2y - z = 2}$

$5x + z = 8$

Now we have two equations with two unknowns.

$5x + 2z = 11$

$5x + z = 8$

To eliminate z, multiply the second equation by -2 and then add.

$-2[5x + z = 8]$

gives

$5x + 2z = 11$

$\underline{-10x - 2z = -16}$

$-5x = -5$

$x = 1$

Substitute 1 for x in the second equation and solve for z

$5x + z = 8$

$5(1) + z = 8$

$5 + z = 8$

$z = 3$

Now go back to one of the original equations and substitute 1 for x and 3 for z and then find y. The third equation is used below.

$3x + y + z = 8$

$3(1) + y + 3 = 8$

$3 + y + 3 = 8$

$y + 6 = 8$

$y = 2$

The solution to the system is $(1, 2, 3)$.

54. Answers will vary.

55. $5^3 = 5 \cdot 5 \cdot 5 = 125$

56. $2(2x - 3) = 2x + 8$

$4x - 6 = 2x + 8$

$4x - 2x = 6 + 8$

$2x = 14$

$x = 7$

57. $\left(4x^2 y - 3xy + y\right) - \left(2x^2 y + 6xy - 3y\right)$

$= 4x^2 y - 3xy + y - 2x^2 y - 6xy + 3y$

$= 4x^2 y - 2x^2 y - 3xy - 6xy + y + 3y$

$= 2x^2 y - 9xy + 4y$

58. $\left(8a^4 b^2 c\right)\left(4a^2 b^7 c^4\right) = 8 \cdot 4 \cdot a^4 \cdot a^2 \cdot b^2 \cdot b^7 \cdot c \cdot c^4$

$= 32 a^{4+2} b^{2+7} c^{1+4}$

$= 32 a^6 b^9 c^5$

59. $xy + xc - ay - ac = x(y + c) - a(y + c)$

$= (y + c)(x - a)$

60. $f(x) = 2x^2 - 4$

$f(-3) = 2(-3)^2 - 4$

$= 2(9) - 4$

$= 18 - 4$

$= 14$

Exercise Set 9.4

1. The graph will be a plane.

2. The three planes intersect at this point.

3. $x = 1$

$2x - y = 4$

$-3x + 2y - 2z = 1$

Substitute 1 for x in the second equation.

$2(1) - y = 4$

$2 - y = 4$

$-y = 2$

$y = -2$

Substitute 1 for x and -2 for y in the third equation.

$-3(1) + 2(-2) - 2z = 1$

$-3 - 4 - 2z = 1$

$-7 - 2z = 1$

$-2z = 8$

$z = -4$

The solution is $(1, -2, -4)$.

4. $-x + 3y - 5z = -7$

$2y - z = -1$

$z = 3$

Substitute 3 for z in the second equation.

$2y - (3) = -1$

$2y = 2$

$y = 1$

Substitute 1 for y, and a 3 for z in the first equation.

$-x + 3(1) - 5(3) = -7$

$-x + 3 - 15 = -7$

$-x - 12 = -7$

$-x = 5$

$x = -5$

The solution is $(-5, 1, 3)$.

5.
$$5x - 6z = -17$$
$$3x - 4y + 5z = -1$$
$$2z = -6$$

Solve the third equation for z.
$$2z = -6$$
$$z = -3$$

Substitute -3 for z in the first equation.
$$5x - 6z = -17$$
$$5x - 6(-3) = -17$$
$$5x + 18 = -17$$
$$5x = -35$$
$$x = -7$$

Substitute -7 for x and -3 for z in the second equation.
$$3x - 4y + 5z = -1$$
$$3(-7) - 4y + 5(-3) = -1$$
$$-21 - 4y - 15 = -1$$
$$-4y - 36 = -1$$
$$-4y = 35$$
$$y = \frac{35}{-4} = -\frac{35}{4}$$

The solution is $\left(-7, -\dfrac{35}{4}, -3\right)$.

6.
$$2x - 5y = 12$$
$$-3y = -9$$
$$2x - 3y + 4z = 8$$

Solve the second equation for y.
$$-3y = -9 \implies y = 3$$

Substitute 3 for y in the first equation.
$$2x - 5y = 12$$
$$2x - 5(3) = 12$$
$$2x - 15 = 12$$
$$2x = 27$$
$$x = \frac{27}{2}$$

Substitute $\dfrac{27}{2}$ for x and 3 for y in the third equation.
$$2x - 3y + 4z = 8$$
$$2\left(\frac{27}{2}\right) - 3(3) + 4z = 8$$
$$27 - 9 + 4z = 8$$
$$18 + 4z = 8$$
$$4z = -10$$
$$z = \frac{-10}{4} = -\frac{5}{2}$$

The solution is $\left(\dfrac{27}{2}, 3, -\dfrac{5}{2}\right)$.

7.
$$x + 2y = 6$$
$$3y = 9$$
$$x + 2z = 12$$

Solve the second equation for y.
$$3y = 9$$
$$y = 3$$

Substitute 3 for y in the first equation.
$$x + 2y = 6$$
$$x + 2(3) = 6$$
$$x + 6 = 6$$
$$x = 0$$

Substitute 0 for x in the third equation.
$$x + 2z = 12$$
$$0 + 2z = 12$$
$$2z = 12$$
$$z = 6$$

The solution is $(0, 3, 6)$.

8.
$$x - y + 5z = -4$$
$$3x - 2z = 6$$
$$4z = 2$$

Solve the last equation for z.
$$4z = 2$$
$$z = \frac{2}{4} = \frac{1}{2}$$

Substitute $\dfrac{1}{2}$ for z in the second equation.
$$3x - 2z = 6$$
$$3x - 2\left(\frac{1}{2}\right) = 6$$
$$3x - 1 = 6$$
$$3x = 7$$
$$x = \frac{7}{3}$$

Substitute $\dfrac{7}{3}$ for x and $\dfrac{1}{2}$ for z in the first equation.
$$x - y + 5z = -4$$
$$\frac{7}{3} - y + 5\left(\frac{1}{2}\right) = -4$$
$$\frac{7}{3} - y + \frac{5}{2} = -4$$

To clear fractions, multiply this equation by 6.
$$6\left(\frac{7}{3} - y + \frac{5}{2} = -4\right)$$

$14 - 6y + 15 = -24$

$-6y + 29 = -24$

$-6y = -53$

$y = \dfrac{-53}{-6} = \dfrac{53}{6}$

The solution is $\left(\dfrac{7}{3}, \dfrac{53}{6}, \dfrac{1}{2}\right)$.

9. $x - 2y = -3$ (1)

$3x + 2y = 7$ (2)

$2x - 4y + z = -6$ (3)

To eliminate y between equations (1) and (2), add equations (1) and (2).

$x - 2y = -3$

$\underline{3x + 2y = \ 7}$

Add: $4x = 4$

$x = 1$

Substitute 1 for x in equation (1).

$(1) - 2y = -3$

$-2y = -4$

$y = 2$

Substitute 1 for x, and 2 for y in equation (3).

$2(1) - 4(2) + z = -6$

$2 - 8 + z = -6$

$-6 + z = -6$

$z = 0$

The solution is (1, 2, 0).

10. $x - y + 2z = 1$ (1)

$y - 4z = 2$ (2)

$-2x + 2y - 5z = 2$ (3)

To eliminate x between equations (1) and (3), multiply equation (1) by 2 and then add.

$2[x - y + 2z = 1]$

$-2x + 2y - 5z = 2$

gives

$2x - 2y + 4z = 2$

$\underline{-2x + 2y - 5z = 2}$

Add: $-z = 4$

$z = -4$

Substitute −4 for z in equation (2).

$y - 4(-4) = 2$

$y + 16 = 2$

$y = -14$

Substitute −14 for y and −4 for z in equation (3).

$-2x + 2(-14) - 5(-4) = 2$

$-2x - 28 + 20 = 2$

$-2x - 8 = 2$

$x = -5$

The solution is (−5, −14, −4).

11. $2y + 4z = 2$ (1)

$x + y + 2z = -2$ (2)

$2x + y + z = 2$ (3)

To eliminate x between equations (2) and (3), multiply equation (2) by −2 and then add.

$-2[x + y + 2z = -2]$

$2x + y + z = \ 2$

gives

$-2x - 2y - 4z = \ 4$

$\underline{2x + y \ \ + z = \ 2}$

Add: $-y - 3z = \ 6$ (4)

To eliminate y between equations (1) and (4), multiply equation (4) by 2 and then add.

$2y + 4z = 2$

$2\left[-y - 3z = 6\right]$

gives

$2y + 4z = 2$

$\underline{-2y - 6z = 12}$

Add: $-2z = 14$

$z = -7$

Substitute −7 for z in equation (1).

$2y + 4(-7) = 2$

$2y - 28 = 2$

$2y = 30$

$y = 15$

Substitute 15 for y, and −7 for z in equation (3).

$2x + (15) + (-7) = 2$

$2x + 8 = 2$

$2x = -6$

$x = -3$

The solution is (−3, 15, −7).

12. $2x + y - 8 = 0$ (1)

$\quad\quad 3x - 4z = -3$ (2)

$\quad\quad 2x - 3z = 1$ (3)

To eliminate x between equations (2) and (3), multiply equation (2) by –2, multiply equation (3) by 3, and then add.

$-2\left[3x - 4z = -3\right]$

$\quad 3\left[2x - 3z = 1\right]$

gives

$\quad\quad -6x + 8z = 6$

$\quad\quad \underline{6x - 9z = 3}$

Add: $\quad -z = 9$

$\quad\quad\quad z = -9$

Now, substitute –9 for z in equation (3).

$2x - 3(-9) = 1$

$\quad 2x + 27 = 1$

$\quad\quad 2x = -26$

$\quad\quad\quad x = -13$

Finally, substitute –13 for x in equation (1).

$2(-13) + y - 8 = 0$

$\quad -26 + y - 8 = 0$

$\quad\quad y - 34 = 0$

$\quad\quad\quad y = 34$

The solution is $(-13, 34, -9)$.

13. $3p + 2q = 11$ (1)

$\quad\quad 4q - r = 6$ (2)

$\quad\quad 6p + 7r = 4$ (3)

To eliminate r between equations (2) and (3), multiply equation (2) by 7 and add to equation (3).

$7[4q - r = 6]$

$6p + 7r = 4$

gives

$\quad\quad 28q - 7r = 42$

$\quad\quad \underline{6p + 7r = 4}$

Add: $6p + 28q = 46$ (4)

Equations (1) and (4) are two equations in two unknowns. To eliminate p, multiply equation (1) by –2 and add to equation (4).

$-2[3p + 2q = 11]$

$\quad 6p + 28q = 46$

gives

$\quad\quad -6p - 4q = -22$

$\quad\quad \underline{6p + 28q = 46}$

Add: $\quad 24q = 24$

$\quad\quad\quad q = 1$

Substitute 1 for q in equation (1).

$3p + 2q = 11$

$3p + 2(1) = 11$

$\quad 3p + 2 = 11$

$\quad\quad 3p = 9$

$\quad\quad\quad p = 3$

Substitute 1 for q in equation (2).

$4q - r = 6$

$4(1) - r = 6$

$\quad 4 - r = 6$

$\quad\quad -r = 2$

$\quad\quad\quad r = -2$

The solution is $(3, 1, -2)$.

14. $3s + 5t = -12$ (1)

$\quad\quad 2t - 2u = 2$ (2)

$\quad\quad -s + 6u = -2$ (3)

To eliminate u between equations (2) and (3), multiply equation (2) by 3 and add to equation (3).

$3[2t - 2u = 2]$

$\quad -s + 6u = -2$

gives

$\quad\quad 6t - 6u = 6$

$\quad\quad \underline{-s \quad\quad + 6u = -2}$

Add: $-s + 6t \quad\quad = 4$ (4)

Equations (1) and (4) are two equations in two unknowns. To eliminate s, multiply equation (4) by 3 and add to equation (1).

$3s + 5t = -12$

$3\left[-s + 6t = 4\quad\right]$

gives:

$\quad\quad 3s + 5t = -12$

$\quad\quad \underline{-3s + 18t = 12}$

Add: $\quad\quad 23t = 0$

$\quad\quad\quad\quad t = 0$

Substitute 0 for t in equation (1).

$3s + 5t = -12$

$3s + 5(0) = -12$

$\quad\quad 3s = -12$

$\quad\quad\quad s = -4$

Substitute 0 for t in equation (2).

$2t - 2u = 2$

$2(0) - 2u = 2$

$\quad\quad -2u = 2$

$\quad\quad\quad u = -1$

The solution is $(-4, 0, -1)$.

15.
$$p+q+r=4 \quad (1)$$
$$p-2q-r=1 \quad (2)$$
$$2p-q-2r=-1 \quad (3)$$

To eliminate q between equations (1) and (3), simply add.
$$p+q+r=4$$
$$2p-q-2r=-1$$
Add: $3p \quad -r=3 \quad (4)$

To eliminate q between equations (1) and (2), multiply equation (1) by 2 and then add.
$$2[p+q+r=4]$$
$$p-2q-r=1$$
gives
$$2p+2q+2r=8$$
$$p-2q-r=1$$
Add: $3p \quad +r=9 \quad (5)$

Equations (4) and (5) are two equations in two unknowns.
$$3p-r=3$$
$$3p+r=9$$
To eliminate r, simply add these two equations.
$$3p-r=3$$
$$3p+r=9$$
Add: $6p \quad =12$
$$p=2$$

Substitute 2 for p in equation (5).
$$3p+r=9$$
$$3(2)+r=9$$
$$6+r=9$$
$$r=3$$
Substitute 2 for p and 3 for r in equation (1).
$$p+q+r=4$$
$$2+q+3=4$$
$$q+5=4$$
$$q=-1$$
The solution is $(2, -1, 3)$.

16.
$$x-2y+3z=-7 \quad (1)$$
$$2x-y-z=7 \quad (2)$$
$$-4x+3y+2z=-14 \quad (3)$$

To eliminate x between equations (1) and (3), multiply equation (1) by 4 and add to equation (3).
$$4[x-2y+3z=-7]$$
$$-4x+3y+2z=-14$$
gives:

$$4x-8y+12z=-28$$
$$-4x+3y+2z=-14$$
Add: $-5y+14z=-42 \quad (4)$

To eliminate x between equations (2) and (3), multiply equation (2) by 2 and then add:
$$2[2x-y-z=7]$$
$$-4x+3y+2z=-14$$
gives
$$4x-2y-2z=14$$
$$-4x+3y+2z=-14$$
Add: $y=0$

Substitute 0 for y in equation (4).
$$-5y+14z=-42$$
$$-5(0)+14z=-42$$
$$14z=-42$$
$$z=-3$$
Substitute 0 for y and -3 for z in equation (1).
$$x-2y+3z=-7$$
$$x-2(0)+3(-3)=-7$$
$$x-0-9=-7$$
$$x-9=-7$$
$$x=2$$
The solution is $(2, 0, -3)$.

17.
$$2x-2y+3z=5 \quad (1)$$
$$2x+y-2z=-1 \quad (2)$$
$$4x-y-3z=0 \quad (3)$$

To eliminate y between equations (2) and (3), simply add.
$$2x+y-2z=-1$$
$$4x-y-3z=0$$
Add: $6x \quad -5z=-1 \quad (4)$

To eliminate y between equations (1) and (2), multiply equation (2) by 2 and then add.
$$2x-2y+3z=5$$
$$2[2x+y-2z=-1]$$
gives
$$2x-2y+3z=5$$
$$4x+2y-4z=-2$$
Add: $6x \quad -z=3 \quad (5)$

Equations (4) and (5) are two equations in two unknowns.
$$6x-5z=-1$$
$$6x-z=3$$
To eliminate x, multiply equation (5) by -1 and then add.

$$6x - 5z = -1$$
$$-1[6x - z = 3]$$
gives
$$6x - 5z = -1$$
$$\underline{-6x + z = -3}$$
Add: $-4z = -4$
$$z = 1$$
Substitute 1 for z in equation (5).
$$6x - z = 3$$
$$6x - 1 = 3$$
$$6x = 4$$
$$x = \frac{4}{6} = \frac{2}{3}$$
Substitute $\frac{2}{3}$ for x and 1 for z in equation (2).
$$2x + y - 2z = -1$$
$$2\left(\frac{2}{3}\right) + y - 2(1) = -1$$
$$\frac{4}{3} + y - 2 = -1$$
$$y - \frac{2}{3} = -1$$
$$y = -1 + \frac{2}{3} = -\frac{1}{3}$$
The solution is $\left(\frac{2}{3}, -\frac{1}{3}, 1\right)$.

18. $2x - y - 2z = 3$ (1)
$\quad\ x - 3y - 4z = 2$ (2)
$\quad\ x + y + 2z = -1$ (3)
To eliminate x between equations (1) and (2), multiply equation (2) by -2 and then add.
$$2x - y - 2z = 3$$
$$-2\left[x - 3y - 4z = 2\right]$$
gives
$$2x - y - 2z = 3$$
$$\underline{-2x + 6y + 8z = -4}$$
Add: $\quad 5y + 6z = -1$ (4)
To eliminate x between equations (2) and (3), multiply equation (2) by -1 and then add.
$$-1[x - 3y - 4z = 2]$$
$$x + y + 2z = -1$$
gives

$$-x + 3y + 4z = -2$$
$$\underline{x + y + 2z = -1}$$
Add: $\quad 4y + 6z = -3$ (5)
To eliminate z between equations (4) and (5), multiply equation (4) by -1 and then add.
$$-1[5y + 6z = -1]$$
$$4y + 6z = -3$$
gives
$$-5y - 6z = 1$$
$$\underline{4y + 6z = -3}$$
Add: $\quad -y = -2$
$$y = 2$$
Now substitute 2 for y in equation (4).
$$5(2) + 6z = -1$$
$$10 + 6z = -1$$
$$6z = -11$$
$$z = -\frac{11}{6}$$
Finally, substitute $-\frac{11}{6}$ for z and 2 for y in equation (3).
$$x + (2) + 2\left(-\frac{11}{6}\right) = -1$$
$$x + 2 - \frac{11}{3} = -1$$
$$x = -1 - 2 + \frac{11}{3}$$
$$x = \frac{2}{3}$$
The solution is $\left(\frac{2}{3}, 2, -\frac{11}{6}\right)$.

19. $r - 2s + t = 2$ (1)
$\quad 2r + 3s - t = -3$ (2)
$\quad 2r - s - 2t = 1$ (3)
To eliminate t between equations (1) and (2), add the two equations.
$$r - 2s + t = 2$$
$$\underline{2r + 3s - t = -3}$$
Add: $\quad 3r + s = -1$ (4)
To eliminate t between equations (2) and (3), multiply equation (2) by -2 and then add.
$$-2[2r + 3s - t = -3]$$
$$2r - s - 2t = -1$$
gives

$$-4r - 6s + 2t = 6$$
$$\underline{2r - s - 2t = 1}$$
Add: $\quad -2r - 7s = 7 \quad (5)$

Equations (4) and (5) make a system of two equations in two variables. To eliminate r, multiply equation (4) by 2 and equation (5) by 3, then add the equations.
$$2\left[3r + s = -1\right]$$
$$3\left[-2r - 7s = 7\right]$$
gives:
$$6r + 2s = -2$$
$$\underline{-6r - 21s = 21}$$
Add: $\quad -19s = 19$
$$s = -1$$

Substitute -1 for s into equation (4) and solve for r.
$$3r + s = -1$$
$$3r - 1 = -1$$
$$3r = 0$$
$$r = 0$$

Finally, substitute 0 for r and -1 for s into equation (1)
$$r - 2s + t = 2$$
$$(0) - 2(-1) + t = 2$$
$$2 + t = 2$$
$$t = 0$$
The solution is $(0, -1, 0)$.

20. $\quad 3a - 3b + 4c = -1 \quad (1)$
$$a - 2b + 2c = 2 \quad (2)$$
$$2a - 2b - c = 3 \quad (3)$$

To eliminate a between equations (1) and (2), multipy equation (2) by -3 then add.
$$3a - 3b + 4c = -1$$
$$\underline{-3a + 6b - 6c = -6}$$
Add: $\quad 3b - 2c = -7 \quad (4)$

To eliminate a between equations (2) and (3), multiply equation (2) by -2 and then add.
$$-2a + 4b - 4c = -4$$
$$\underline{2a - 2b - c = 3}$$
Add: $\quad 2b - 5c = -1 \quad (5)$

Equations (4) and (5) are two equations in two unknowns.
$$3b - 2c = -7 \quad (4)$$
$$2b - 5c = -1 \quad (5)$$

To eliminate c, multiply equation (4) by -5, multiply equation (5) by 2 and then add.
$$-5\left[3b - 2c = -7\right]$$
$$2\left[2b - 5c = -1\right]$$
gives
$$-15b + 10c = 35$$
$$\underline{4b - 10c = -2}$$
Add: $\quad -11b = 33$
$$b = -3$$

Substitute -3 for b in equation (4).
$$3(-3) - 2c = -7$$
$$-9 - 2c = -7$$
$$-2c = 2$$
$$c = -1$$

Substitute -1 for c and -3 for b in equation (2).
$$a - 2(-3) + 2(-1) = 2$$
$$a + 6 - 2 = 2$$
$$a + 4 = 2$$
$$a = -2$$
The solution is $(-2, -3, -1)$.

21. $\quad 2a + 2b - c = 2 \quad (1)$
$$3a + 4b + c = -4 \quad (2)$$
$$5a - 2b - 3c = 5 \quad (3)$$

To eliminate c between equations (1) and (2), simply add.
$$2a + 2b - c = 2$$
$$\underline{3a + 4b + c = -4}$$
Add: $5a + 6b = -2 \quad (4)$

To eliminate c between equations (2) and (3), multiply equation (2) by 3 and then add.
$$3[3a + 4b + c = -4]$$
$$5a - 2b - 3c = 5$$
gives
$$9a + 12b + 3c = -12$$
$$\underline{5a - 2b - 3c = 5}$$
Add: $14a + 10b = -7 \quad (5)$

Equations (4) and (5) are two equations in two unknowns.
$$5a + 6b = -2$$
$$14a + 10b = -7$$

To eliminate b, multiply equation (4) by -5 and multiply equation (5) by 3 and then add.
$$-5[5a + 6b = -2]$$
$$3[14a + 10b = -7]$$
gives

$$-25a - 30b = 10$$
$$\underline{42a + 30b = -21}$$
Add: $17a \qquad = -11$
$$a = -\frac{11}{17}$$

Substitute $-\frac{11}{17}$ for a in equation (4).

$$5a + 6b = -2$$
$$5\left(-\frac{11}{17}\right) + 6b = -2$$
$$-\frac{55}{17} + 6b = -2$$
$$6b = -2 + \frac{55}{17}$$
$$b = \frac{1}{6} \cdot \frac{21}{17} = \frac{7}{34}$$

Substitute $-\frac{11}{17}$ for a and $\frac{7}{34}$ for b in equation (2).

$$3a + 4b + c = -4$$
$$3\left(-\frac{11}{17}\right) + 4\left(\frac{7}{34}\right) + c = -4$$
$$-\frac{33}{17} + \frac{14}{17} + c = -4$$
$$-\frac{19}{17} + c = -4$$
$$c = -4 + \frac{19}{17}$$
$$c = -\frac{49}{17}$$

The solution is $\left(-\frac{11}{17}, \frac{7}{34}, -\frac{49}{17}\right)$.

22. $x - 2y + 2z = 3$ (1)
$2x - 3y + 2z = 5$ (2)
$x + y + 6z = -2$ (3)

To eliminate x between equations (1) and (2), multiply equation (1) by -2 then add.

$$-2x + 4y - 4z = -6 \quad (1)\times -2$$
$$\underline{2x - 3y + 2z = 5 \qquad (2)}$$
$$y - 2z = -1 \qquad (4)$$

To eliminate x between equations (2) and (3), multiply equation (3) by -2 and then add.

$$2x - 3y + 2z = 5 \qquad (2)$$
$$\underline{-2x - 2y - 12z = 4 \quad (3)\times -2}$$
$$-5y - 10z = 9 \qquad (5)$$

Equations (4) and (5) are two equations in two unknowns.

$$y - 2z = -1$$
$$-5y - 10z = 9$$

To eliminate y, multiply equation (4) by 5 and add the equations.

$$5[y - 2z = -1]$$
$$-5y - 10z = 9$$

gives

$$5y - 10z = -5$$
$$\underline{-5y - 10z = 9}$$
Add: $\qquad -20z = 4$
$$z = -\frac{1}{5}$$

Substitute $-\frac{1}{5}$ for z in equation (4) and solve for y.

$$y - 2z = -1$$
$$y - 2\left(-\frac{1}{5}\right) = -1$$
$$y + \frac{2}{5} = -1$$
$$y = -\frac{7}{5}$$

Substitute $-\frac{1}{5}$ for z and $-\frac{7}{5}$ for y in equation (3).

$$x + \left(-\frac{7}{5}\right) + 6\left(-\frac{1}{5}\right) = -2$$
$$x - \frac{13}{5} = -2$$
$$x = \frac{3}{5}$$

The solution is $\left(\frac{3}{5}, -\frac{7}{5}, -\frac{1}{5}\right)$.

23. $-x + 3y + z = 0$ (1)

$-2x + 4y - z = 0$ (2)

$3x - y + 2z = 0$ (3)

To eliminate z between equations (1) and (2), simply add.

$-x + 3y + z = 0$

$\underline{-2x + 4y - z = 0}$

Add: $-3x + 7y \quad = 0$ (4)

To eliminate z between equations (2) and (3), multiply equation (2) by 2 and then add.

$2[-2x + 4y - z] = 0$

$3x - y + 2z = 0$

gives

$-4x + 8y - 2z = 0$

$\underline{3x - \; y + 2z = 0}$

Add: $-x + 7y \quad = 0$ (5)

Equations (4) and (5) are two equations in two unknowns.

$-3x + 7y = 0$

$-x + 7y = 0$

To eliminate y, multiply equation (4) by -1 and then add.

$-1[-3x + 7y = 0]$

$-x + 7y = 0$

gives

$3x - 7y = 0$

$\underline{-x + 7y = 0}$

Add: $2x \quad = 0$

$x = 0$

Substitute 0 for x in equation (5).

$-x + 7y = 0$

$-0 + 7y = 0$

$7y = 0$

$y = 0$

Finally, substitute 0 for x and 0 for y into equation (1).

$-x + 3y + z = 0$

$-0 + 3(0) + z = 0$

$0 + z = 0$

$z = 0$

The solution is $(0, 0, 0)$.

24. $x + y + z = 0$ (1)

$-x - y + z = 0$ (2)

$-x + y + z = 0$ (3)

To eliminate x and y between equations (1) and (2), simply add.

$x + y + z = 0$

$\underline{-x - y + z = 0}$

Add: $\quad 2z = 0$

$z = 0$

Substitute 0 for z in equations (2) and (3) to obtain a system of two equations in two unknowns. Equation (2) becomes

$-x - y + z = 0$

$-x - y + 0 = 0$

$-x - y = 0$ (4)

Equation (3) becomes

$-x + y + z = 0$

$-x + y + 0 = 0$

$-x + y = 0$ (5)

Equations (4) and (5) are two equations in two unknowns. To eliminate y, simply add.

$-x - y = 0$

$\underline{-x + y = 0}$

Add: $-2x \quad = 0$

$x = 0$

Substitute 0 for x and 0 for z in equation (1).

$x + y + z = 0$

$0 + y + 0 = 0$

$y + 0 = 0$

$y = 0$

The solution is $(0, 0, 0)$.

25. $-\dfrac{1}{4}x + \dfrac{1}{2}y - \dfrac{1}{2}z = -2$ (1)

$\dfrac{1}{2}x + \dfrac{1}{3}y - \dfrac{1}{4}z = 2$ (2)

$\dfrac{1}{2}x - \dfrac{1}{2}y + \dfrac{1}{4}z = 1$ (3)

To clear fractions, multiply equation (1) by 4, equation (2) by 12, and equation (3) by 4.

$4\left(-\dfrac{1}{4}x + \dfrac{1}{2}y - \dfrac{1}{2}z = -2\right)$

$12\left(\dfrac{1}{2}x + \dfrac{1}{3}y - \dfrac{1}{4}z = 2\right)$

$4\left(\dfrac{1}{2}x - \dfrac{1}{2}y + \dfrac{1}{4}z = 1\right)$

gives

$-x + 2y - 2z = -8$ (4)

$6x + 4y - 3z = 24$ (5)

$2x - 2y + z = 4$ (6)

To eliminate y between equations (4) and (6), simply add.

$-x + 2y - 2z = -8$

$\underline{2x - 2y + z = 4}$

Add: $x \quad - z = -4$ (7)

To eliminate y between equations (5) and (6), multiply equation (6) by 2 and then add to equation (5).

$6x + 4y - 3z = 24$

$2[2x - 2y + z = 4]$

gives

$6x + 4y - 3z = 24$

$\underline{4x - 4y + 2z = 8}$

Add: $10x \quad - z = 32$ (8)

Equations (7) and (8) are two equations in two unknowns.

$x - z = -4$

$10x - z = 32$

To eliminate z, multiply equation (7) by -1 and then add.

$-1[x - z = -4]$

$10x - z = 32$

gives

$-x + z = 4$

$\underline{10x - z = 32}$

Add: $9x \quad = 36$

$$x = \frac{36}{9} = 4$$

Substitute 4 for x in equation (7).

$x - z = -4$

$4 - z = -4$

$-z = -8$

$z = 8$

Finally, substitute 4 for x and 8 for z in equation (4).

$-x + 2y - 2z = -8$

$-4 + 2y - 2(8) = -8$

$-4 + 2y - 16 = -8$

$2y - 20 = -8$

$2y = 12$

$$y = \frac{12}{2} = 6$$

The solution is (4, 6, 8).

26. $\frac{2}{3}x + y - \frac{1}{3}z = \frac{1}{3}$ (1)

$\frac{1}{2}x + y + z = \frac{5}{2}$ (2)

$\frac{1}{4}x - \frac{1}{4}y + \frac{1}{4}z = \frac{3}{2}$ (3)

To clear fractions, multiply equation (1) by 3, equation (2) by 2, and equation (3) by 4. The resulting system is:

$3\left(\frac{2}{3}x + y - \frac{1}{3}z = \frac{1}{3}\right)$

$2\left(\frac{1}{2}x + y + z = \frac{5}{2}\right)$

$4\left(\frac{1}{4}x - \frac{1}{4}y + \frac{1}{4}z = \frac{3}{2}\right)$

gives

$2x + 3y - z = 1 \,(4)$

$x + 2y + 2z = 5 \,(5)$

$x - y + z = 6 \,(6)$

To eliminate z between equations (4) and (6), simply add.

$2x + 3y - z = 1$

$\underline{x - y + z = 6}$

Add: $3x + 2y = 7$ (7)

To eliminate z between equations (4) and (5), multiply equation (4) by 2 and then add.

$2[2x + 3y - z = 1]$

$x + 2y + 2z = 5$

gives

$4x + 6y - 2z = 2$

$\underline{x + 2y + 2z = 5}$

Add: $5x + 8y = 7$ (8)

Equations (7) and (8) are two equations in two unknowns.

$3x + 2y = 7$

$5x + 8y = 7$

To eliminate y, multiply equation (7) by -4 and then add.

$-4[3x + 2y = 7]$

$5x + 8y = 7$

gives

$-12x - 8y = -28$

$\underline{5x + 8y = 7}$

Add: $-7x = -21$

$$x = \frac{-21}{-7} = 3$$

Substitute 3 for x in equation (7).

$3x + 2y = 7$

$3(3) + 2y = 7$

$9 + 2y = 7$

$2y = -2$

$y = -1$

Substitute 3 for x and -1 for y in equation (6).

$x - y + z = 6$

$3 - (-1) + z = 6$

$3 + 1 + z = 6$

$4 + z = 6$

$z = 2$

The solution is $(3, -1, 2)$.

27. $\quad x - \dfrac{2}{3}y - \dfrac{2}{3}z = -2 \quad (1)$

$\qquad \dfrac{2}{3}x + y - \dfrac{2}{3}z = \dfrac{1}{3} \quad (2)$

$\qquad -\dfrac{1}{4}x + y - \dfrac{1}{4}z = \dfrac{3}{4} \quad (3)$

To clear fractions, multiply equation (1) by 3, equation (2) by 3, and equation (3) by 4. The resulting system is

$3\left(x - \dfrac{2}{3}y - \dfrac{2}{3}z = -2 \right)$

$3\left(\dfrac{2}{3}x + y - \dfrac{2}{3}z = \dfrac{1}{3} \right)$

$4\left(-\dfrac{1}{4}x + y - \dfrac{1}{4}z = \dfrac{3}{4} \right)$

gives

$3x - 2y - 2z = -6 \, (4)$

$2x + 3y - 2z = 1 \quad (5)$

$-x + 4y - z = 3 \quad (6)$

To eliminate x between equations (4) and (6), multiply equation (6) by 3 and then add.

$3x - 2y - 2z = -6$

$3[-x + 4y - z = 3]$

gives

$\quad 3x - 2y - 2z = -6$

$\underline{-3x + 12y - 3z = 9}$

Add: $\quad 10y - 5z = 3 \quad (7)$

To eliminate x between equations (5) and (6), multiply equation (6) by 2 and then add.

$2x + 3y - 2z = 1$

$2[-x + 4y - z = 3]$

gives

$2x + 3y - 2z = 1$

$\underline{-2x + 8y - 2z = 6}$

Add: $\quad 11y - 4z = 7 \quad (8)$

Equations (7) and (8) are two equations in two unknowns.

$10y - 5z = 3$

$11y - 4z = 7$

To eliminate z, multiply equation (7) by -4 and equation (8) by 5 and then add.

$-4[10y - 5z = 3]$

$5[11y - 4z = 7]$

gives

$\quad -40y + 20z = -12$

$\underline{55y - 20z = 35}$

Add: $15y = 23$

$\qquad\qquad y = \dfrac{23}{15}$

Substitute $\dfrac{23}{15}$ for y into equation (7).

$10y - 5z = 3$

$10\left(\dfrac{23}{15} \right) - 5z = 3$

$\dfrac{46}{3} - 5z = 3$

$-5z = -\dfrac{37}{3}$

$z = \left(-\dfrac{1}{5} \right)\left(-\dfrac{37}{3} \right) = \dfrac{37}{15}$

Substitute $\dfrac{23}{15}$ for y and $\dfrac{37}{15}$ for z in equation (6).

$-x + 4y - z = 3$

$-x + 4\left(\dfrac{23}{15} \right) - \dfrac{37}{15} = 3$

$-x + \dfrac{92}{15} - \dfrac{37}{15} = 3$

$-x + \dfrac{11}{3} = 3$

$-x = -\dfrac{2}{3}$

$x = \dfrac{2}{3}$

The solution is $\left(\dfrac{2}{3}, \dfrac{23}{15}, \dfrac{37}{15} \right)$.

28.

$$\frac{1}{8}x+\frac{1}{4}y+z = 2 \quad (1)$$

$$\frac{1}{3}x+\frac{1}{4}y+z = \frac{17}{6} \quad (2)$$

$$-\frac{1}{4}x+\frac{1}{3}y-\frac{1}{2}z =-\frac{5}{6} \quad (3)$$

To clear fractions, multiply equation (1) by 8, equation (2) by 12, and equation (3) by 12. The resulting system is

$$8\left(\frac{1}{8}x+\frac{1}{4}y+ z = 2\right)$$

$$12\left(\frac{1}{3}x+\frac{1}{4}y+ z = \frac{17}{6}\right)$$

$$12\left(-\frac{1}{4}x+\frac{1}{3}y-\frac{1}{2}z =-\frac{5}{6}\right)$$

gives

$$x+2y+8z = 16 \quad (4)$$
$$4x+3y+12z = 34 \quad (5)$$
$$-3x+4y-6z = -10 \quad (6)$$

To eliminate z between equations (4) and (5), multiply equation (4) by -3 and multiply equation (5) by 2, then add.

$$-3\left[x+2y+8z = 16\right]$$
$$2\left[4x+3y+12z = 34\right]$$

gives

$$-3x-6y-24z = -48$$
$$\underline{8x+6y+24z = 68}$$

Add: $5x = 20$

$$x = 4$$

To eliminate z between equations (5) and (6), multiply equation (6) by 2 and then add.

$$4x+3y+12z = 34$$
$$2\left[-3x+4y-6z = -10\right]$$

gives

$$4x+3y+12z = 34$$
$$\underline{-6x+8y-12z = -20}$$

Add: $-2x+11y = 14 \quad (7)$

Substitute 4 for x in equation (7) and solve for y.

$$-2x+11y = 14$$
$$-2(4)+11y = 14$$
$$-8+11y = 14$$
$$11y = 22$$
$$y = 2$$

Substitute 4 for x and 2 for y in equation (4).

$$x+2y+8z = 16$$
$$(4)+2(2)+8z = 16$$
$$4+4+8z = 16$$
$$8z = 8$$
$$z = 1$$

The solution is (4, 2, 1).

29.

$$0.2x+0.3y+0.3z = 1.1$$
$$0.4x-0.2y+0.1z = 0.4$$
$$-0.1x-0.1y+0.3z = 0.4$$

Multiply each equation by 10.

$$10(0.2x+0.3y+0.3z = 1.1)$$
$$10(0.4x-0.2y+0.1z = 0.4)$$
$$10(-0.1x-0.1y+0.3z = 0.4)$$

gives

$$2x+3y+3z = 11 \quad (1)$$
$$4x-2y+z = 4 \quad (2)$$
$$-x-y+3z = 4 \quad (3)$$

To eliminate z between equations (1) and (2), multiply equation (2) by -3 and then add.

$$2x+3y+3z = 11$$
$$-3[4x-2y+z = 4]$$

gives

$$2x+3y+3z = 11$$
$$\underline{-12x+6y-3z = -12}$$

Add: $-10x+9y = -1 \quad (4)$

To eliminate z between equations (1) and (3) multiply equation (1) by -1 and then add.

$$-1[2x+3y+3z = 11]$$
$$-x-y+3z = 4$$

gives

$$-2x-3y-3z = -11$$
$$\underline{-x-y+3z = 4}$$

Add: $-3x-4y = -7 \quad (5)$

Equations (4) and (5) are two equations in two unknowns.

$$-10x+9y = -1$$
$$-3x-4y = -7$$

To eliminate x, multiply equation (4) by -3 and equation (5) by 10.

$$-3[-10x+9y = -1]$$
$$10[-3x-4y = -7]$$

gives

$$30x - 27y = 3$$
$$-30x - 40y = -70$$

Add: $\qquad -67y = -67$

$$y = 1$$

Substitute 1 for y in equation (4).

$$-10x + 9y = -1$$
$$-10x + 9(1) = -1$$
$$-10x = -10$$
$$x = 1$$

Substitute 1 for x and 1 for y in equation (1).

$$2x + 3y + 3z = 11$$
$$2(1) + 3(1) + 3z = 11$$
$$5 + 3z = 11$$
$$3z = 6$$
$$z = 2$$

The solution is (1, 1, 2).

30.
$$0.6x - 0.4y + 0.2z = 2.2$$
$$-0.1x - 0.2y + 0.3z = 0.9$$
$$-0.2x - 0.1y - 0.3z = -1.2$$

Multiply each equation by 10.

$$10(0.6x - 0.4y + 0.2z = 2.2)$$
$$10(-0.1x - 0.2y + 0.3z = 0.9)$$
$$10(-0.2x - 0.1y - 0.3z = -1.2)$$

gives

$$6x - 4y + 2z = 22 \quad (1)$$
$$-x - 2y + 3z = 9 \quad (2)$$
$$-2x - y - 3z = -12 \,(3)$$

To eliminate y between equations (1) and (2) multiply equation (2) by -2 and then add.

$$6x - 4y + 2z = 22$$
$$-2[-x - 2y + 3z = 9]$$

gives

$$6x - 4y + 2z = 22$$
$$2x + 4y - 6z = -18$$

Add: $8x \qquad - 4z = 4 \qquad (4)$

To eliminate y between equations (1) and (3), multiply equation (3) by -4 and then add.

$$6x - 4y + 2z = 22$$
$$-4[-2x - y - 3z = -12]$$

gives

$$6x - 4y + 2z = 22$$
$$8x + 4y + 12z = 48$$

Add: $14x \qquad + 14z = 70 \quad (5)$

Equations (4) and (5) are two equations in two unknowns.

$$8x - 4z = 4$$
$$14x + 14z = 70$$

To eliminate z, multiply equation (4) by 7 and equation (5) by 2.

$$7[8x - 4z = 4]$$
$$2[14x + 14z = 70]$$

gives

$$56x - 28z = 28$$
$$28x + 28z = 140$$

Add: $\qquad 84x = 168$

$$x = 2$$

Substitute 2 for x in equation (4).

$$8x - 4z = 4$$
$$8(2) - 4z = 4$$
$$16 - 4z = 4$$
$$-4z = -12$$
$$z = 3$$

Substitute 2 for x and 3 for z in equation (3).

$$-2x - y - 3z = -12$$
$$-2(2) - y - 3(3) = -12$$
$$-4 - y - 9 = -12$$
$$-13 - y = -12$$
$$-y = 1$$
$$y = -1$$

The solution is (2, -1, 3).

31.
$$2x + y + 2z = 1 \qquad (1)$$
$$x - 2y - z = 0 \qquad (2)$$
$$3x - y + z = 2 \qquad (3)$$

To eliminate z between equations (2) and (3), simply add.

$$x - 2y - z = 0$$
$$3x - y + z = 2$$

Add: $4x - 3y \quad = 2 \quad (4)$

To eliminate z between equations (1) and (2), multiply equation (2) by 2 and then add.

$$2x + y + 2z = 1$$
$$2[x - 2y - z = 0]$$

gives

$$2x + y + 2z = 1$$
$$2x - 4y - 2z = 0$$

Add: $4x - 3y \quad = 1 \quad (5)$

Equations (4) and (5) are two equations in two unknowns.

$$4x - 3y = 2$$
$$4x - 3y = 1$$

To eliminate x, multiply equation (4) by -1 and then add.

$$-1[4x - 3y = 2]$$
$$4x - 3y = 1$$

gives

$$-4x + 3y = -2$$
$$\underline{4x - 3y = 1}$$

Add: $\qquad 0 = -1 \quad$ False

Since this is a false statement, there is no solution and the system is inconsistent.

32. $2p - 4q + 6r = 8 \qquad$ (1)

$-p + 2q - 3r = 6 \qquad$ (2)

$3p + 4q + 5r = 8 \qquad$ (3)

To eliminate p between equations (1) and (2), Multiply equation (2) by 2 and then add to equation (1).

$$2p - 4q + 6r = 8$$
$$2[-p + 2q - 3r = 6]$$

gives

$$2p - 4q + 6r = 8$$
$$\underline{-2p + 4q - 6r = 12}$$

Add: $\qquad 0 = 20 \quad$ False

Since this is a false statement, there is no solution and the system is inconsistent.

33. $x - 4y - 3z = -1 \quad$ (1)

$-3x + 12y + 9z = 3 \quad$ (2)

$2x - 10y - 7z = 5 \quad$ (3)

To eliminate x between equations (1) and (2), multiply equation (1) by 3 and then add.

$$3[x - 4y - 3z = -1]$$
$$-3x + 12y + 9z = 3$$

gives

$$3x - 12y - 9z = -3$$
$$\underline{-3x + 12y + 9z = 3}$$

Add: $\qquad\qquad 0 = 0$

Since $0 = 0$ is a true statement, we suspect that the system is dependent and therefore has infinitely many solutions. However, we could still encounter a contradiction if we used a different pair of equations.

To eliminate x from equations (1) and (3), multiply equation (1) by -2 and add.

$$-2[x - 4y - 3z = -1]$$
$$2x - 10y - 7z = 5$$

gives

$$-2x + 8y + 6z = 2$$
$$\underline{2x - 10y - 7z = 5}$$

Add: $\qquad -2y - z = 7$

To eliminate x from equations (2) and (3), multiply equation (2) by 2 and equation (3) by 3, then add.

$$2[-3x + 12y + 9z = 3]$$
$$3[2x - 10y - 7z = 5]$$

gives

$$-6x + 24y + 18z = 6$$
$$\underline{6x - 30y - 21z = 15}$$

Add: $\qquad -6y - 3z = 21$

Since neither of the remaining pairs yields a contradiction, the system is indeed dependent and has an infinite number of solutions.

34. $5a - 4b + 2c = 5 \qquad$ (1)

$-10a + 8b - 4c = -10 \quad$ (2)

$-7a - 4b + c = 7 \qquad$ (3)

Notice that if you multiply equation (1) by -2, the result is exactly the same as equation (2). This implies that this is a dependent system and therefore has infinitely many solutions. However, we should still check the other pairings to ensure there are no contradictions.

To eliminate b from equations (1) and (3), multiply equation (3) by -1 and add.

$$5a - 4b + 2c = 5$$
$$-1[-7a - 4b + c = 7]$$

gives

$$5a - 4b + 2c = 5$$
$$\underline{7a + 4b - c = -7}$$

Add: $\qquad 7a + c = -2$

To eliminate b from equations (2) and (3), multiply equation (3) by 2 and then add.

$$-10a + 8b - 4c = -10$$
$$2[-7a - 4b + c = 7]$$

gives

$$-10a + 8b - 4c = -10$$
$$\underline{-14a - 8b + 2c = 14}$$

Add: $\qquad -24a - 2c = 4$

Since neither of the remaining pairs yields a contradiction, the system is indeed dependent and has an infinite number of solutions.

35.
$$x + 3y + 2z = 6 \quad (1)$$
$$x - 2y - z = 8 \quad (2)$$
$$-3x - 9y - 6z = -7 \quad (3)$$

To eliminate x between equations (1) and (3), multiply equation (1) by 3 and then add.
$$3[x + 3y + 2z = 6]$$
$$-3x - 9y - 6z = -7$$
gives
$$3x + 9y + 6z = 18$$
$$\underline{-3x - 9y - 6z = -7}$$
Add: $\qquad\qquad 0 = 11$

Since 0 = 11 is a false statement, the system is inconsistent.

36.
$$2x - 2y + 4z = 2 \quad (1)$$
$$-3x + y = -9 \quad (2)$$
$$2x - y + z = 5 \quad (3)$$

To eliminate z between equations (1) and (3), multiply equation (3) by –4 and then add.
$$2x - 2y + 4z = 2$$
$$-4[2x - y + z = 5]$$
gives
$$2x - 2y + 4z = \quad 2$$
$$\underline{-8x + 4y - 4z = -20}$$
Add: $-6x + 2y \qquad = -18$

Divide by 2: $-3x + y = -9 \qquad (4)$

Equations (4) and (2) are two equations in two unknowns.
$$-3x + y = -9$$
$$-3x + y = -9$$
Since both equations are identical, subtracting one equation from the other produces 0 = 0. Thus, there are an infinite number of solutions and the system is dependent.

37. No point is common to all three planes. Therefore, the system is inconsistent.

38. There is no point common to all three planes. Thus, there is no solution and the system is inconsistent.

39. One point is common to all three planes. There is one solution and the system is consistent.

40. A straight line is common to all three planes. Therefore, there are an infinite number of points common to all three planes and the system is dependent.

41. a. Yes, if two or more of the planes are parallel, there will be no solution.

b. Yes, three planes may intersect at a single point.

c. No, the possibilities are no solution, one solution, or infinitely many solutions.

42. a. No, if two of the planes are parallel, no points can be common to all three planes.

b. No, if two of the planes are parallel, no points can be common to all three planes.

c. Yes, if two of the planes are parallel, no points will be common to all three planes.

43. $Ax + By + Cz = 1$

Substitute $(-1, 2, -1)$, $(-1, 1, 2)$, and $(1, -2, 2)$ into the equation forming three equations in the three unknowns A, B, and C.
$$A(-1) + B(2) + C(-1) = 1$$
$$A(-1) + B(1) + C(2) = 1$$
$$A(1) + B(-2) + C(2) = 1$$
gives
$$-A + 2B - C = 1 \quad (1)$$
$$-A + B + 2C = 1 \quad (2)$$
$$A - 2B + 2C = 1 \quad (3)$$

To eliminate A between equations (1) and (2), multiply equation (2) by –1 and then add.
$$-A + 2B - C = 1$$
$$-1[-A + B + 2C = 1]$$
gives
$$-A + 2B - C = \quad 1$$
$$\underline{A - B - 2C = -1}$$
Add: $\qquad\qquad B - 3C = \quad 0 \quad (4)$

To eliminate A between equations (1) and (3), simply add.
$$-A + 2B \quad - C = 1$$
Add: $\underline{A - 2B + 2C = 1}$
$$\qquad\qquad C = 2$$

Substitute 2 for C in equation (4).
$$B - 3(2) = 0$$
$$B - 6 = 0$$
$$B = 6$$

Substitute 6 for B and 2 for C in equation (1).

$$-A + 2B - C = 1$$
$$-A + 2(6) - (2) = 1$$
$$-A + 12 - 2 = 1$$
$$-A + 10 = 1$$
$$-A = -9$$
$$A = 9$$

The equation is $9x + 6y + 2z = 1$.

44. $Ax + By + Cz = 14$

Substitute $(3, -1, 2)$, $(2, -2, 1)$ and $(-5, 3, -24)$ into the equation forming three equations in the three unknowns A, B, and C.

$$A(3) + B(-1) + C(2) = 14$$
$$A(2) + B(-2) + C(1) = 14$$
$$A(-5) + B(3) + C(-24) = 14$$

gives

$$3A - B + 2C = 14 \ (1)$$
$$2A - 2B + C = 14 \ (2)$$
$$-5A + 3B - 24C = 14 \ (3)$$

To eliminate C between equations (1) and (2), multiply equation (2) by -2 and add.

$$3A - B + 2C = 14$$
$$-2[2A - 2B + C = 14]$$

gives

$$3A - B + 2C = \ \ 14$$
$$\underline{-4A + 4B - 2C = -28}$$

Add: $\ -A + 3B \qquad = -14 \quad (4)$

To eliminate C between equations (1) and (3), multiply equation (1) by 12 and add.

$$12[3A - B + 2C = 14]$$
$$-5A + 3B - 24C = 14$$

gives

$$36A - 12B + 24C = 168$$
$$\underline{-5A + \ \ 3B - 24C = \ \ 14}$$

Add: $31A - \ \ 9B \qquad = 182 \quad (5)$

Equations (4) and (5) are two equations in two unknowns.

$$-A + 3B = -14$$
$$31A - 9B = 182$$

To eliminate B, multiply equation (4) by 3 and then add.

$$3[-A + 3B = -14]$$
$$31A - 9B = 182$$

gives

$$-3A + 9B = -42$$
$$\underline{31A - 9B = 182}$$

Add: $28A \qquad = 140$
$$A = 5$$

Substitute 5 for A in equation (4).
$$-A + 3B = -14$$
$$-5 + 3B = -14$$
$$3B = -9$$
$$B = -3$$

Substitute 5 for A and -3 for B in equation (2).
$$2A - 2B + C = 14$$
$$2(5) - 2(-3) + C = 14$$
$$16 + C = 14$$
$$C = -2$$

Therefore, $A = 5$, $B = -3$, and $C = -2$ and the equation is $5x - 3y - 2z = 14$.

45. Answers will vary. One example is
$$x + y + z = 10$$
$$x + 2y + z = 11$$
$$x + y + 2z = 16$$

Choose coefficients for x, y, and z, then use the given coordinates to find the constants.

46. Answers will vary. One example is
$$x + y + z = 6$$
$$x - y + z = -4$$
$$x - y - z = -10$$

Choose coefficients for x, y, and z, then use the given coordinates to find the constants.

47. a. $y = ax^2 + bx + c$

For the point $(1, -1)$,
let $y = -1$ and $x = 1$.
$$-1 = a(1)^2 + b(1) + c$$
$$-1 = a + b + c \qquad (1)$$

For the point $(-1, -5)$,
let $y = -5$ and $x = -1$.
$$-5 = a(-1)^2 + b(-1) + c$$
$$-5 = a - b + c \qquad (2)$$

For the point $(3, 11)$,
let $y = 11$ and $x = 3$.
$$11 = a(3)^2 + b(3) + c$$
$$11 = 9a + 3b + c \qquad (3)$$

Equations (1), (2), and (3) give us a system of three equations.

$a+b+c=-1\,(1)$

$a-b+c=-5\,(2)$

$9a+3b+c=11\,(3)$

To eliminate a and c between equations (1) and (2) multiply equation (2) by -1 and then add.

$a+b+c=-1$

$-1[a-b+c=-5]$

gives

$\qquad a+b+c=-1$

$\qquad \underline{-a+b-c=\ \ 5}$

Add: $\qquad 2b\ \ \ \ =\ 4$

$\qquad\qquad\quad b=2$

Substitute 2 for b in equations (1) and (3).

Equation (1) becomes

$a+b+c=-1$

$a+2+c=-1$

$\qquad a+c=-3\qquad(4)$

Equation (3) becomes

$9a+3b+c=11$

$9a+3(2)+c=11$

$\qquad 9a+c=5\qquad(5)$

Equations (4) and (5) are two equations in two unknowns. To eliminate c, multiply equation (4) by -1 and then add.

$-1[a+c=-3]$

$\quad 9a+c=5$

gives

$\qquad -a-c=\ 3$

$\qquad \underline{9a+c=5}$

Add: $8a\qquad =8$

$\qquad\qquad a=1$

Finally, substitute 1 for a in equation (4).

$a+c=-3$

$1+c=-3$

$\qquad c=-4$

Thus, $a=1$, $b=2$, and $c=-4$.

b. The quadratic equation is $y=x^2+2x-4$.

This is the equation determined by the values found in part (a).

48. a. $y=ax^2+bx+c$

For the point $(1,7)$, let $y=7$ and $x=1$.

$7=a(1)^2+b(1)+c$

$7=a+b+c\qquad\qquad(1)$

For the point $(-2,-5)$, let $y=-5$ and $x=-2$.

$-5=a(-2)^2+b(-2)+c$

$-5=4a-2b+c\qquad\qquad(2)$

For the point $(3,5)$, let $y=5$ and $x=3$.

$5=a(3)^2+b(3)+c$

$5=9a+3b+c\qquad\qquad(3)$

Equations (1), (2), and (3) give us a system of three equations.

$a+b+c=7\ \ (1)$

$4a-2b+c=-5\,(2)$

$9a+3b+c=5\ \ (3)$

To eliminate c between equations (1) and (2), multiply equation (1) by -1 and then add.

$-1[a+b+c=7]$

$\quad 4a-2b+c=-5$

gives

$\qquad -a\ -b-c=\ -7$

$\qquad \underline{4a-2b+c=\ -5}$

Add: $3a-3b\qquad =-12$

or $\qquad a-\ b\quad =\ -4\ \ (4)$

To eliminate c between equations (1) and (3), multiply equation (1) by -1 and then add.

$-1[a+b+c=7]$

$\ \ 9a+3b+c=5$

gives

$\qquad -a\ -b-c=-7$

$\qquad \underline{9a+3b+c=\ \ 5}$

Add: $8a+2b\qquad =-2$

or $\quad 4a+\ b\quad =-1\ \ (5)$

Equations (4) and (5) are a system of two equations in two unknowns. To eliminate b, simply add.

$\qquad a-b=-4$

$\qquad \underline{4a+b=-1}$

Add: $5a\quad\ \ =-5$

$\qquad\qquad a=-1$

Substitute $a=-1$ in equation (4).

$$a - b = -4$$
$$-1 - b = -4$$
$$-b = -3$$
$$b = 3$$

Finally, substitute -1 for a and 3 for b into equation (1).

$$a + b + c = 7$$
$$-1 + 3 + c = 7$$
$$c = 5$$

Thus, $a = -1$, $b = 3$, $c = 5$.

b. The quadratic equation is $y = -x^2 + 3x + 5$. This is the equation determined by the values found in part (a).

49.
$$3p + 4q = 11 \quad (1)$$
$$2p + r + s = 9 \quad (2)$$
$$q - s = -2 \quad (3)$$
$$p + 2q - r = 2 \quad (4)$$

To eliminate r between equations (2) and (4), simply add.

$$2p \quad + r + s = 9$$
$$\underline{p + 2q - r \quad = 2}$$

Add: $3p + 2q \quad + s = 11 \quad (5)$

To eliminate s between equations (3) and (5), simply add.

$$q - s = -2$$
$$\underline{3p + 2q + s = 11}$$

Add: $3p + 3q \quad = 9 \quad (6)$

Equations (1) and (6) give us a system of two equations in two unknowns.
To eliminate p, multiply equation (6) by -1 and then add.

$$3p + 4q = 11$$
$$-1[3p + 3q = 9]$$

gives

$$3p + 4q = 11$$
$$\underline{-3p - 3q = -9}$$

Add: $\quad q = 2$

Substitute 2 for q in equation (3).

$$q - s = -2$$
$$2 - s = -2$$
$$-s = -4$$
$$s = 4$$

Substitute 2 for q in equation (1).

$$3p + 4q = 11$$
$$3p + 4(2) = 11$$
$$3p + 8 = 11$$
$$3p = 3$$
$$p = 1$$

Finally, substitute 1 for p and 4 for s in equation (2).

$$2p + r + s = 9$$
$$2(1) + r + 4 = 9$$
$$r + 6 = 9$$
$$r = 3$$

The solution is $(1, 2, 3, 4)$.

50.
$$3a + 2b - c = 0 \quad (1)$$
$$2a + 2c + d = 5 \quad (2)$$
$$a + 2b - d = -2 \quad (3)$$
$$2a - b + c + d = 2 \quad (4)$$

To eliminate d between equations (2) and (3), simply add.

$$2a \quad + 2c + d = 5$$
$$\underline{a + 2b \quad - d = -2}$$

Add: $3a + 2b + 2c \quad = 3 \quad (5)$

Using equations (1) and (5), we can eliminate a and b and then solve for c.
To do this, multiply equation (1) by -1 and then add.

$$-1[3a + 2b - c = 0]$$
$$3a + 2b + 2c = 3$$

gives

$$-3a - 2b + c = 0$$
$$\underline{3a + 2b + 2c = 3}$$

Add: $\qquad 3c = 3$
$$c = 1$$

To eliminate d from equations (3) and (4), simply add.

$$a + 2b \quad - d = -2$$
$$\underline{2a - b + c + d = 2}$$

Add: $3a + b + c \quad = 0 \quad (6)$

Since $c = 1$, equation (6) becomes
$$3a + b + 1 = 0$$
$$3a + b = -1 \quad (7)$$

Substitute 1 for c in equation (1).
$$3a + 2b - c = 0$$
$$3a + 2b - 1 = 0$$
$$3a + 2b = 1 \quad (8)$$

Using equations (7) and (8), we now have two equations system in two unknowns.

$3a + b = -1$

$3a + 2b = 1$

To eliminate a, multiply equation (7) by -1 and then add.

$-1[3a + b = -1]$

$3a + 2b = 1$

gives

$-3a - b = 1$

$3a + 2b = 1$

Add: $b = 2$

Now, substitute 2 for b in equation (7).

$3a + b = -1$

$3a + 2 = -1$

$3a = -3$

$a = -1$

Finally, substitute -1 for a and 1 for c in equation (2).

$2a + 2c + d = 5$

$2(-1) + 2(1) + d = 5$

$-2 + 2 + d = 5$

$d = 5$

The solution is $(-1, 2, 1, 5)$.

51. a. commutative property of addition

b. associative property of multiplication

c. distributive property

52. $3x + 4 = -(x - 6)$

$3x + 4 = -x + 6$

$3x + x = 6 - 4$

$4x = 2$

$x = \frac{2}{4} = \frac{1}{2}$

53. Let t be the time for Margie.

Then, $t - \frac{1}{6}$ is the time for David.

	rate	time	distance
David	5	t	$5t$
Margie	3	$t + \frac{1}{6}$	$3\left(t + \frac{1}{6}\right)$

a. The distances traveled are the same.

$3\left(t + \frac{1}{6}\right) = 5t$

$3t + \frac{1}{2} = 5t$

$\frac{1}{2} = 2t$

$t = \frac{1}{4}$ hour (or 15 minutes)

b. The distance is

$5t = 5\left(\frac{1}{4}\right) = \frac{5}{4} = 1\frac{1}{4}$ or 1.25 miles.

54. Let w = the width of the rectangle. Then $2w + 2$ = the length of the rectangle.

$2(2w + 2) + 2w = 22$

$4w + 4 + 2w = 22$

$6w + 4 = 22$

$6w = 18$

$w = 3$

The width is 3 ft, and the length is $2(3) + 2 = 8$ ft.

Mid-Chapter Test: 9.1-9.4

1. a. $(-1, 1)$

$4(-1) + 3(1) = -1$

$-4 + 3 = -1$

$-1 = -1$ True

$-1 - 2(1) = 8$

$-1 - 2 = 8$

$-3 = 8$ False

$(-1, 1)$ is not a solution.

b. $(2, -3)$

$4(2) + 3(-3) = -1$

$8 - 9 = -1$

$-1 = -1$ True

$2 - 2(-3) = 8$

$2 + 6 = 8$

$8 = 8$ True

$(2, -3)$ is a solution.

2. a. $\left(\frac{1}{2},5\right)$

$$6\left(\frac{1}{2}\right)-5=-2$$

$$3-5=-2$$

$$-2=-2 \quad \text{True}$$

$$7\left(\frac{1}{2}\right)+\frac{1}{2}(5)=6$$

$$\frac{7}{2}+\frac{5}{2}=6$$

$$6=6 \quad \text{True}$$

$\left(\frac{1}{2},5\right)$ is a solution.

b. $\left(\frac{1}{3},4\right)$

$$6\left(\frac{1}{3}\right)-4=-2$$

$$2-4=-2$$

$$-2=-2 \quad \text{True}$$

$$7\left(\frac{1}{3}\right)+\frac{1}{2}(4)=6$$

$$\frac{7}{3}+2=6$$

$$\frac{13}{3}=6 \quad \text{False}$$

$\left(\frac{1}{3},4\right)$ is not a solution.

3. Solve each equation for y.

$$2x+y=8 \qquad 3x-4y=1$$

$$y=-2x+8 \qquad -4y=-3x+1$$

$$y=\frac{3}{4}x-\frac{1}{4}$$

Since the equations have different slopes the system will have one solution.

4. Solve each equation for y.

$$\frac{1}{2}x-3y=5 \qquad -2x+12y=-20$$

$$-3y=-\frac{1}{2}x+5 \qquad 12y=2x-20$$

$$y=\frac{1}{6}x-\frac{5}{3} \qquad y=\frac{1}{6}x-\frac{5}{3}$$

Since both equations are the same, the system has infinite solutions.

5. Solve each equation for y.

$$y=\frac{3}{2}x+\frac{5}{2} \qquad 3x-2y=7$$

$$-2y=-3x+7$$

$$y=\frac{3}{2}x-\frac{7}{2}$$

Since the two equations have the same slope but different y-intercepts, the lines are parallel which means there is no solution.

6. $y=2x+1$ has slope of 2 and y-intercept of 1.

$y=-x+4$ has slope of -1 and y-intercept of 4.

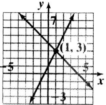

The solution is (1, 3).

7. $x=5$ is a vertical line with x-intercept (5, 0).

$y=-3$ is a horizontal line with y-intercept (0,-3).

The solution is (5, -3)

8. $$3x+y=-2$$

$$2x-3y=-16$$

Solve the first equation for y, $y=-3x-2$.

Substitute $-3x-2$ for y in the second equation.

$$2x-3(-3x-2)=-16$$

$$2x+9x+6=-16$$

$$11x+6=-16$$

$$11x=-22$$

$$x=-2$$

To find y, substitute -2 for x in the equation $y=-3x-2$.

$$y=-3(-2)-2=6-2=4$$

The solution is (-2, 4).

9. $x - 3y = 2$

$4x + 9y = 1$

Solve the first equation for x, $x = 3y + 2$.

Substitute $-3x - 2$ for x in the second equation.

$4(3y + 2) + 9y = 1$

$12y + 8 + 9y = 1$

$21y + 8 = 1$

$21y = -7$

$y = -\dfrac{1}{3}$

To find x, substitute $-\dfrac{1}{3}$ for y in the equation

$x = 3\left(-\dfrac{1}{3}\right) + 2 = -1 + 2 = 1$.

The solution is $\left(1, -\dfrac{1}{3}\right)$.

10. $3x - y = 5$

$x - \dfrac{1}{3}y = 2$

Solve the second equation for x, $x = \dfrac{1}{3}y + 2$.

Substitute $\dfrac{1}{3}y + 2$ for x in the first equation.

$3\left(\dfrac{1}{3}y + 2\right) - y = 5$

$y + 2 - y = 5$

$2 = 5$ False

Since this is a false statement the system has no solution.

11. Let l be the length and w be the width of the rectangle.

$2l + 2w = 44$

$l = w + 8$

Substitute $w + 8$ for l in the first equation and solve for w.

$2(w + 8) + 2w = 44$

$2w + 16 + 2w = 44$

$4w + 16 = 44$

$4w = 28$

$w = 7$

Now substitute 7 for w in the equation $l = w + 8$.

$l = 7 + 8 = 15$.

The length of the rectangle is 15 feet and the width is 7 feet.

12. $x + 3y = 1$

$\underline{2x - 3y = 11}$

$3x \quad\;\; = 12$

$x = 4$

Substitute 4 for x in the first equation and then find y.

$4 + 3y = 1$

$3y = -3$

$y = -1$

The solution is $(4, -1)$.

13. $4x + 3y = 4$ (1)

$-8x + 5y = 14$ (2)

Multiply equation 1 by 2 giving $8x + 6y = 8$.

Now add the two equations to eliminate x and solve for y.

$8x + 6y = 8$

$\underline{-8x + 5y = 14}$

$11y = 22$

$y = 2$

Substitute 2 for y in equation 1 and solve for x.

$4x + 3(2) = 4$

$4x + 6 = 4$

$4x = -2$

$x = -\dfrac{1}{2}$

The solution is $\left(-\dfrac{1}{2}, 2\right)$.

14. $5x - 2y = 1$ (1)

$-10x + 4y = -2$ (2)

Multiply equation 1 by 2 giving $10x - 4y = 2$.

Now add the two equations.

$10x - 4y = 2$

$\underline{-10x + 4y = -2}$

$0 = 0$

The system has an infinite number of solutions.

485

15. A system's solution has to have two values, one for x and one for y.

$$3x - 5y = -16 \quad (1)$$
$$2x + 3y = 21 \quad (2)$$

Multiply equation 1 by 3 and equation 2 by 5, then add to eliminate y and solve for x.

$$3(3x - 5y = -16)$$
$$\underline{5(2x + 3y = 21)}$$

$$9x - 15y = -48$$
$$\underline{10x + 15y = 105}$$
$$19x = 57$$
$$x = 3$$

Substitute 3 for x in equation 2 and solve for y.

$$2(3) + 3y = 21$$
$$6 + 3y = 21$$
$$3y = 15$$
$$y = 5$$

The solution is $(3, 5)$.

16.
$$x + y + z = 2 \quad (1)$$
$$2x - y + 2z = -2 \quad (2)$$
$$3x + 2y + 6z = 1 \quad (3)$$

To eliminate y between equations (1) and (2), simply add.

$$x + y + z = 2$$
$$\text{Add: } \underline{2x - y + 2z = -2}$$
$$3x + 3z = 0 \quad (4)$$

To eliminate y between equations (2) and (3), multiply equation (2) by 2 and then add.

$$4x - 2y + 4z = -4$$
$$\underline{3x + 2y + 6z = 1}$$
$$\text{Add: } \quad 7x + 10z = -3 \quad (5)$$

Equations (4) and (5) are two equations in two unknowns.

$$3x + 3z = 0 \quad (4)$$
$$7x + 10z = -3 \quad (5)$$

To eliminate x, multiply equation (4) by -7, multiply equation (5) by 3 and then add.

$$-21x - 21z = 0$$
$$\underline{21x + 30z = -9}$$
$$\text{Add: } \quad 9z = -9$$
$$z = -1$$

Substitute -1 for z in equation (4).

$$3x + 3(-1) = 0$$
$$3x - 3 = 0$$
$$3x = 3$$
$$x = 1$$

Substitute 1 for x and -1 for z in equation (1).

$$x + y + z = 2$$
$$1 + y + (-1) = 2$$
$$y = 2$$

The solution is $(1, 2, -1)$.

17.
$$2x - y - z = 1 \quad (1)$$
$$3x + 5y + 2z = 12 \quad (2)$$
$$-6x - 4y + 5z = 3 \quad (3)$$

To eliminate x between equations (1) and (2), multiply equation (1) by -3 and equation (2) by 2, then add.

$$-6x + 3y + 3z = -3$$
$$\underline{6x + 10y + 4z = 24}$$
$$\text{Add: } \quad 13y + 7z = 21 \quad (4)$$

To eliminate x between equations (2) and (3), multiply equation (2) by 2 and then add.

$$6x + 10y + 4z = 24$$
$$\underline{-6x - 4y + 5z = 3}$$
$$\text{Add: } \quad 6y + 9z = 27 \quad (5)$$

Equations (4) and (5) are two equations in two unknowns.

$$13y + 7z = 21 \quad (4)$$
$$6y + 9z = 27 \quad (5)$$

To eliminate z, multiply equation (4) by -9, multiply equation (5) by 7 and then add.

$$-117y - 63z = -189$$
$$\underline{42y + 63z = 189}$$
$$\text{Add: } \quad -75y = 0$$
$$y = 0$$

Substitute 0 for y in equation (4).

$$13(0) + 7z = 21$$
$$7z = 21$$
$$z = 3$$

Substitute 0 for y and 3 for z in equation (1).

$$2x - y - z = 1$$
$$2x - 0 - 3 = 1$$
$$2x - 3 = 1$$
$$2x = 4$$
$$x = 2$$

The solution is $(2, 0, 3)$.

Exercise Set 9.5

1. Let x = the land area of Georgia and y = the land area of Ireland.
$$x + y = 139,973$$
$$y = x + 573$$
Substitute $x + 573$ for y in the first equation.
$$x + (x + 573) = 139,973$$
$$2x + 573 = 139,973$$
$$2x = 139,400$$
$$x = 69,700$$
Substitute 69,700 for x in the second equation.
$$y = 69,700 + 573 = 70,273$$

The land area of Georgia is 69,700 km^2 and the land area of Ireland is 70,273 km^2.

2. Let x = the number of wins by Petty and y = the number of wins by Yarborough.
$$x + y = 11$$
$$x = 2y - 1$$
Substitute $2y - 1$ for x in the first equation.
$$(2y - 1) + y = 11$$
$$3y - 1 = 11$$
$$3y = 12$$
$$y = 4$$
Substitute 4 for y in the second equation.
$$x = 2(4) - 1 = 7$$
Richard Petty had 7 wins and Dale Yarborough had 4 wins.

3. Let F = grams of fat in fries and H = grams of fat in hamburger
$$F = 3H + 4$$
$$F - H = 46$$
Substitute $3H + 4$ for F in the second equation.
$$F - H = 46$$
$$3H + 4 - H = 46$$
$$2H = 42$$
$$H = 21$$
Substitute 21 for H in the first equation.
$$F = 3H + 4$$
$$F = 3(21) + 4 = 63 + 4 = 67$$
The hamburger has 21 grams of fat and the fries have 67 grams of fat.

4. Let x = number who visited Disneyland and y = number who visited Magic Kingdom
$$x + y = 28.4$$
$$y = x + 1.8$$
Substitute $x + 1.8$ for y in the first equation.

$$x + (x + 1.8) = 28.4$$
$$2x + 1.8 = 28.4$$
$$2x = 26.6$$
$$x = 13.3$$
Substitute 13.3 for x in the second equation.
$$y = (13.3) + 1.8 = 15.1$$

15.1 million people visited Magic Kingdom and 13.3 million people visited Disneyland.

5. Let h = the cost of a hot dog and s = the cost of a soda.
$$2h + 3s = 7$$
$$4h + 2s = 10$$
Multiply the first equation by –2 and then add.
$$-2[2h + 3s = 7]$$
$$4h + 2s = 10$$
gives
$$-4h - 6s = -14$$
$$\underline{4h + 2s = 10}$$
Add: $\qquad -4s = -4$
$$s = 1$$
Substitute 1 for s in the first equation.
$$2h + 3(1) = 7$$
$$2h + 3 = 7$$
$$2h = 4$$
$$h = 2$$
Each hot dog costs \$2 and each soda costs \$1.

6. Let w = the cost of a water bottle and p = the cost of a pretzel.
$$2w + 3p = 16.50$$
$$4w + p = 15.50$$
Multiply the first equation by –2 and add.
$$-2[2w + 3p = 16.50]$$
$$4w + p = 15.50$$
gives
$$-4w - 6p = -33.00$$
$$\underline{4w + p = 15.50}$$
Add: $\qquad -5p = -17.50$
$$p = 3.50$$
Substitute 3.50 for p in the second equation.
$$4w + (3.50) = 15.50$$
$$4w = 12.00$$
$$w = 3.00$$
Each water bottle costs \$3.00 and each pretzel costs \$3.50.

7. Let x = the number of photos on the 128MB card and y = the number on the 516MB card.
$$y = 4x$$
$$x + y = 360$$
Substitute $4x$ for y in the second equation.
$$x + 4x = 360$$
$$5x = 360$$
$$x = 72$$
Substitute 72 for x in the first equation.
$$y = 4(72) = 288$$
The 128-megabyte memory card can store 72 photos and the 516-megabyte card can store 288 photos.

8. Let x = the cost to print a photo on the Olympus printer and y = the cost to print a photo on the Epson printer.
$$x + y = 0.80$$
$$x = 2y + 0.20$$
Substitute $2y + 0.20$ for x in the first equation.
$$2y + 0.20 + y = 0.80$$
$$3y + 0.20 = 0.80$$
$$3y = 0.60$$
$$y = 0.20$$
Substitute 0.20 for y in the second equation.
$$x = 2(0.20) + 0.20 = 0.60$$
It costs \$0.60 to print a photo on the Olympus printer and \$0.20 to print a photo on the Epson printer.

9. Let x = the measure of the larger angle and y = the measure of the smaller angle.
$$x + y = 90$$
$$x = 2y + 15$$
Substitute $2y + 15$ for x in the first equation.
$$x + y = 90$$
$$2y + 15 + y = 90$$
$$3y + 15 = 90$$
$$3y = 75$$
$$y = 25$$
Now, substitute 25 for y in the second equation.
$$x = 2y + 15$$
$$x = 2(25) + 15 = 50 + 15 = 65$$
The two angles measure 25° and 65°.

10. Let x = the measure of the larger angle and y = the measure of the smaller angle.
$$x + y = 90$$
$$x - y = 46 \implies x = y + 46$$
Substitute $y + 46$ for x in the first equation.
$$(y + 46) + y = 90$$
$$2y + 46 = 90$$
$$2y = 44$$
$$y = 22$$
Now, substitute 22 for y in the second equation.
$$x = (22) + 46 = 68$$
The two angles measure 22° and 68°.

11. Let A and B be the measures of the two angles.
$$A + B = 180$$
$$A = 3B - 28$$
Substitute $3B - 28$ for A in the first equation.
$$A + B = 180$$
$$3B - 28 + B = 180$$
$$4B - 28 = 180$$
$$4B = 208$$
$$B = 52$$
Now substitute 52 for B in the second equation.
$$A = 3B - 28$$
$$A = 3(52) - 28 = 128$$
The two angles measure 52° and 128°.

12. Let A and B be the measures of the two angles.
$$A + B = 180$$
$$A = 3.5B$$
Substitute $3.5B$ for A in the first equation.
$$(3.5B) + B = 180$$
$$4.5B = 180$$
$$B = 40$$
Now substitute 40 for B in the second equation.
$$A = 3.5(40) = 140$$
The two angles measure 40° and 140°.

13. Let t = team's rowing speed in still water and
c = speed of current
$t + c = 15.6$
$t - c = 8.8$
Add the equations to eliminate variable c.
$t + c = 15.6$
$\underline{t - c = 8.8}$
$2t = 24.4$
$t = 12.2$
Substitute 12.2 for t in the first equation.
$(12.2) + c = 15.6$
$c = 3.4$
The team's speed in still water is 12.2 mph and the speed of the current is 3.4 mph.

14. Let p = plane's speed in still air and w = speed of wind
$p + w = 121$
$p - w = 87$
Add the equations to eliminate variable w.
$p + w = 121$
$\underline{p - w = 87}$
$2p = 208$
$p = 104$
Substitute 104 for p in the first equation.
$(104) + w = 121$
$w = 17$
The plane's speed in still air is 104 mph and the speed of the wind is 17 mph.

15. Let x = the weekly salary and y = the commission rate.
$x + 4000y = 660$
$x + 6000y = 740$
Multiply the first equation by -1 and then add.
$-1[x + 4000y = 660]$
$x + 6000y = 740$
gives
$-x - 4000y = -660$
$\underline{x + 6000y = 740}$
Add: $2000y = 80$
$y = \dfrac{80}{2000} = 0.04$
Substitute 0.04 for y in the first equation.

$x + 4000y = 660$
$x + 4000(0.04) = 660$
$x + 160 = 660$
$x = 500$ dollars
His weekly salary is \$500 and the commission rate is 4%.

16. Let x = the daily fee and y = the mileage fee.
$2x + 100y = 85$
$3x + 400y = 165$
To solve, multiply the first equation by -4 and then add.
$-4[2x + 100y = 85]$
$3x + 400y = 165$
gives
$-8x - 400y = -340$
$\underline{3x + 400y = 165}$
Add: $-5x = -175$
$x = \dfrac{-175}{-5} = 35$
Now substitute 35 for x in the first equation.
$2x + 100y = 85$
$2(35) + 100y = 85$
$70 + 100y = 85$
$100y = 15$
$y = 0.15$
Thus the daily fee is \$35 and the mileage fee is 15¢ per mile.

17. Let x = the amount of 5% solution and y = the amount of 30% solution.
$x + y = 3$
$0.05x + 0.30y = 0.20(3)$
Solve the first equation for x.
$x = 3 - y$
Substitute $3 - y$ for x in the second equation.
$0.05x + 0.30y = 0.20(3)$
$0.05(3 - y) + 0.30y = 0.6$
$0.15 - 0.05y + 0.30y = 0.6$
$0.25y = 0.45$
$y = 1.8$
Substitute 1.8 for y in the first equation.
$x + y = 3$
$x + 1.8 = 3$
$x = 1.2$
Pola should mix 1.2 ounces of the 5% solution with 1.8 ounces of the 30% solution.

18. Let x = amount of 4% nitrogen fertilizer
and y = amount of 20% nitrogen fertilizer
$$x + y = 10$$
$$0.04x + 0.20y = 0.10(10)$$
Solve the first equation for y.
$$y = 10 - x$$
Substitute $10 - x$ for y in the second equation.
$$0.04x + 0.20(10 - x) = 0.10(10)$$
$$0.04x + 2 - 0.20x = 1$$
$$-0.16x = -1$$
$$x = 6.25$$
Substitute 6.25 for x in the first equation.
$$(6.25) + y = 10$$
$$y = 3.75$$
Frank Ditlman should mix 6.25 gallons of 4% nitrogen with 3.75 gallons of 20% nitrogen.

19. Let x = gallons of concentrate (18% solution)
and y = gallons of water (0% solution).
$$x + y = 200$$
$$0.18x + 0y = 0.009(200)$$
Solve the second equation for x.
$$0.18x + 0y = 0.009(200)$$
$$0.18x = 1.8$$
$$x = 10$$
Substitute 10 for x in the first equation.
$$x + y = 200$$
$$10 + y = 200$$
$$y = 190$$
The mixture should contain 10 gallons of concentrate and 190 gallons of water.

20. Let x = amount of 22% nitrogen fertilizer
and y = amount of 4% nitrogen fertilizer
$$x + y = 400$$
$$0.22x + 0.04y = 0.10(400)$$
Solve the first equation for y.
$$y = 400 - x$$
Substitute $400 - x$ for y in the second equation.
$$0.22x + 0.04y = 0.10(400)$$
$$0.22x + 0.04(400 - x) = 0.10(400)$$
$$0.22x + 16 - 0.04x = 40$$
$$0.18x = 24$$
$$x = 133\frac{1}{3}$$
Substitute $133\frac{1}{3}$ for x in the first equation.

$$x + y = 400$$
$$133\frac{1}{3} + y = 400$$
$$y = 266\frac{2}{3}$$
William Weaver should mix $133\frac{1}{3}$ pounds of 22% nitrogen with $266\frac{2}{3}$ pounds of 4% nitrogen.

21. Let x = pounds of birdseed and y = pounds of sunflower seeds
$$0.59x + 0.89y = 0.76(40)$$
$$x + y = 40$$
Solve the second equation for y.
$$y = 40 - x$$
Substitute $40 - x$ for y in the first equation.
$$0.59x + 0.89y = 0.76(40)$$
$$0.59x + 0.89(40 - x) = 30.4$$
$$0.59x + 35.6 - 0.89x = 30.4$$
$$-0.3x = -5.2$$
$$x = 17\frac{1}{3}$$
Substitute $17\frac{1}{3}$ for x in the second equation.
$$x + y = 40$$
$$17\tfrac{1}{3} + y = 40$$
$$y = 22\tfrac{2}{3}$$

Angela Leinenbach should mix $17\frac{1}{3}$ pounds of birdseed at \$0.59 per pound with $22\frac{2}{3}$ pounds of sunflower seeds at \$0.89 per pound.

22. Let x be the amount of the \$5.20 coffee and y be the amount of the \$6.30 coffee.
$$x + y = 30$$
$$5.2x + 6.3y = 170$$
Solve the first equation for x.
$$x + y = 30$$
$$x = 30 - y$$
Substitute $30 - y$ for x in the second equation.

$$5.2x + 6.3y = 170$$
$$5.2(30 - y) + 6.3y = 170$$
$$156 - 5.2y + 6.3y = 170$$
$$156 + 1.1y = 170$$
$$1.1y = 14$$
$$y = \frac{14}{1.1} \approx 12.7 \text{ lb}$$

Substitute 12.7 for y in the equation $x = 30 - y$.
$$x = 30 - y$$
$$x \approx 30 - 12.7 \approx 17.3$$

Mr. Manue needs to mix about 17.3 lb of the \$5.20 coffee with about 12.7 lb of the \$6.30 coffee.

23. Let x = the price of an adult ticket and y = the price of a child ticket.
$$3x + 4y = 159$$
$$2x + 3y = 112$$

Multiply the first equation by 2 and the second equation by -3, then add.
$$2[3x + 4y = 159]$$
$$-3[2x + 3y = 112]$$
gives
$$6x + 8y = 318$$
$$-6x - 9y = -336$$

Add: $\quad -y = -18$
$$y = 18$$

Substitute 18 for y in the second equation.
$$2x + 3(18) = 112$$
$$2x + 54 = 112$$
$$2x = 58$$
$$x = 29$$

Adult tickets cost \$29 and child tickets cost \$18.

24. Let R = cost of regular wings and J = cost of jumbo wings
$$3R + 5J = 67$$
$$4R + 4J = 64$$

Multiply the first equation by 4 and the second equation by -3, then add.
$$4[3R + 5J = 67]$$
$$-3[4R + 4J = 64]$$
gives
$$12R + 20J = 268$$
$$-12R - 12J = -192$$

Add: $\quad 8J = 76$
$$J = 9.50$$

Substitute 9.50 for J in the first equation.

$$3R + 5(9.50) = 67$$
$$3R + 47.50 = 67$$
$$3R = 19.50$$
$$R = 6.50$$

A regular order of wings costs \$6.50 and a jumbo order costs \$9.50.

25. Let x = amount invested at 5% and y = amount invested at 6%
$$x + y = 10,000$$
$$0.05x + 0.06y = 540$$

Solve the first equation for y.
$$y = 10,000 - x$$
Substitute $10,000 - x$ for y in the second equation.
$$0.05x + 0.06y = 540$$
$$0.05x + 0.06(10,000 - x) = 540$$
$$0.05x + 600 - 0.06x = 540$$
$$-0.01x = -60$$
$$x = 6000$$

Substitute 6000 for x in the first equation.
$$x + y = 10,000$$
$$6000 + y = 10,000$$
$$y = 4000$$

Mr. and Mrs. Gamton invested \$6000 at 5% and \$4000 at 6%.

26. Let x = the amount invested at 9% and y = the amount invested at 5%.
$$x + y = 30,000$$
$$0.09x + 0.05y = 30,000(0.065)$$

Solve the first equation for x.
$$x + y = 30,000$$
$$x = 30,000 - y$$
Substitute $30,000 - y$ for x in the second equation.
$$0.09x + 0.05y = 30,000(0.065)$$
$$0.09(30,000 - y) + 0.05y = 30,000(0.065)$$
$$2700 - 0.09y + 0.05y = 1950$$
$$2700 - 0.04y = 1950$$
$$-0.04y = -750$$
$$y = \frac{-750}{-0.04} = 18,750$$

Substitute 18,750 for y in the equation
$$x = 30,000 - y$$
$$x = 30,000 - 18,750 = 11,250$$

Louis Okonkwo invested \$11,250 at 9% and \$18,750 at 5%.

27. Let x = the amount of the whole milk (3.25% fat) and y = the amount of the skim milk (0% fat).
$$x + y = 260$$
$$0.0325x + 0y = 0.02(260)$$
Solve the second equation for x.
$$0.0325x + 0y = 0.02(260)$$
$$0.0325x = 5.2$$
$$x = 160$$
Now substitute 160 for x in the first equation.
$$(160) + y = 260$$
$$y = 100$$
Becky needs to mix 160 gallons of the whole milk with 100 gallons of skim milk to produce 260 gallons of 2% fat milk.

28. Let x = the amount of heavy cream and y = the amount of half-and-half.
$$x + y = 16$$
$$0.36x + 0.105y = 0.2(16)$$
Solve the first equation for x.
$$x + y = 16$$
$$x = 16 - y$$
Substitute $16 - y$ for x in the second equation.
$$0.36x + 0.105y = 0.2(16)$$
$$0.36(16 - y) + 0.105y = 0.2(16)$$
$$5.76 - 0.36y + 0.105y = 3.2$$
$$-0.255y + 5.76 = 3.2$$
$$-0.255y = -2.56$$
$$y = \frac{-2.56}{-0.255} \approx 10.04$$
Now substitute 10.04 for y in the first equation.
$$x + y = 16$$
$$x + 10.04 \approx 16$$
$$x \approx 5.96 \text{ ounces}$$
Lambert needs to mix about 5.96 ounces of heavy cream with about 10.04 ounces of half-and-half to produce 16 ounces of 20% butterfat.

29. Let x = pounds of *Season's Choice* birdseed at $1.79/lb and y = pounds of *Garden Mix* birdseed at $1.19/lb
$$1.79x + 1.19y = 28.00$$
$$x + y = 20$$
Solve the second equation for y.
$$y = 20 - x$$
Substitute $20 - x$ for y in the first equation.

$$1.79x + 1.19(20 - x) = 28.00$$
$$1.79x + 23.80 - 1.19x = 28.00$$
$$0.60x = 4.20$$
$$x = 7$$
Substitute 7 for x in the second equation.
$$(7) + y = 20$$
$$y = 13$$
The Carters should buy 7 pounds *of Season's Choice* and 13 pounds of *Garden Mix*.

30. Let x = the amount of apple juice and y = the amount of raspberry juice.
$$x + y = 8$$
$$8.3x + 9.3y = 8(8.7)$$
Solve the first equation for y.
$$x + y = 8$$
$$y = 8 - x$$
Substitute $8 - x$ for y in the second equation.
$$8.3x + 9.3y = 8(8.7)$$
$$8.3x + 9.3(8 - x) = 8(8.7)$$
$$8.3x + 74.4 - 9.3x = 69.6$$
$$74.4 - 1.0x = 69.6$$
$$-x = -4.8$$
$$x = 4.8$$
Substitute 4.8 for x in the equation $y = 8 - x$.
$$y = 8 - 4.8 = 3.2$$
The company should mix 4.8 ounces of apple juice with 3.2 ounces of raspberry juice.

31. Let x = the rate of the slower car and y = the rate of the faster car.
$$4x + 4y = 420$$
$$y = x + 5$$
Substitute $x + 5$ for y in the first equation.
$$4x + 4y = 420$$
$$4x + 4(x + 5) = 420$$
$$4x + 4x + 20 = 420$$
$$8x + 20 = 420$$
$$8x = 400$$
$$x = 50$$
Now substitute 50 for x in the second equation.
$$y = x + 5$$
$$y = 50 + 5 = 55$$
The rate of the slower car is 50 mph and the rate of the faster car is 55 mph.

32. Let x be the amount of time traveled at 50 mph and y be the amount of time traveled at 70 mph.

$$50x + 70y = 430$$
$$x + y = 7$$

Solve the second equation for y.

$$x + y = 7$$
$$y = -x + 7$$

Substitute $-x + 7$ for y in the first equation.

$$50x + 70y = 430$$
$$50x + 70(-x + 7) = 430$$
$$50x - 70x + 490 = 430$$
$$-20x = -60$$
$$x = 3$$

Substiute 3 for x in the equation solved for y.

$$y = -x + 7$$
$$y = -(3) + 7 = 4$$

Kip Ortiz traveled for 3 hours at 50 mph and for 4 hours at 70 mph.

33. Let x = the amount of time traveled at 65 mph and y = the amount of time traveled at 50 mph.

$$x + y = 11.4$$
$$65x + 50y = 690$$

Solve the first equation for x

$$x = 11.4 - y$$

Now substitute $11.4 - y$ into x in the second equation.

$$65(11.4 - y) + 50y = 690$$
$$741 - 65y + 50y = 690$$
$$-15y = -51$$
$$y = 3.4$$

Substitute 3.4 for y in the first equation.

$$x + (3.4) = 11.4$$
$$x = 8$$

Cabrina traveled for 8 hours at 65 mph and Dabney traveled for 3.4 hours at 50 mph.

34. Let x = the rollerblading rate and y = the bicycling rate. Then, since she rollerblades and cycles each for half an hour, the distance that she rollerblades is $0.5x$ miles and the distance that she cycles is $0.5y$ miles. Therefore the system of equations is

$$y = 2x$$
$$0.5x + 0.5y = 12$$

Now substitute $y = 2x$ into y in the second equation.

$$0.5x + 0.5(2x) = 12$$
$$0.5x + x = 12$$
$$1.5x = 12$$
$$x = 8$$

Substitute 8 for x in the first equation.

$$y = 2(8) = 16$$

Cynthia rollerblades at a rate of 8 mph and cycles at a rate of 16 mph.

35. Let x = the number of grams of Mix A and y = the number of grams of Mix B.

$$0.1x + 0.2y = 20$$
$$0.06x + 0.02y = 6$$

To solve, multiply the second equation by -10 and then add.

$$0.1x + 0.2y = 20$$
$$-10[0.06x + 0.02y = 6]$$

gives

$$0.1x + 0.2y = 20$$
$$-0.6x - 0.2y = -60$$

Add: $\quad -0.5x \qquad = -40$

$$x = \frac{-40}{-0.5} = 80$$

Now substitute 80 for x in the first equation.

$$0.1x + 0.2y = 20$$
$$0.1(80) + 0.2y = 20$$
$$8 + 0.2y = 20$$
$$0.2y = 12$$
$$y = \frac{12}{0.2} = 60$$

The scientist should feed each animal 80 grams of Mix A and 60 grams of Mix B.

36. Let x = the number of Model A chairs and y = the number of Model B chairs.

Model	Assemble	Paint
A	1	0.5
B	3.2	0.4

$$1x + 3.2y = 46.4$$
$$0.5x + 0.4y = 8.8$$

To solve, multiply the second equation by -2 and then add.

$$1x + 3.2y = 46.4$$
$$-2[0.5x + 0.4y = 8.8]$$

gives

$$x + 3.2y = 46.4$$
$$-x - 0.8y = -17.6$$

Add: $\quad 2.4y = 28.8$

$$y = \frac{28.8}{2.4} = 12$$

Substitute 12 for y in the first equation.

$$x + 3.2y = 46.4$$
$$x + 3.2(12) = 46.4$$
$$x + 38.4 = 46.4$$
$$x = 8$$

The company should make 8 Model A chairs and 12 Model B.

37. Let x = the amount of the first alloy and y = the amount of the second alloy.

$$0.7x + 0.4y = 0.6(300)$$
$$0.3x + 0.6y = 0.4(300)$$

To solve, multiply the first equation by 3 and the second equation by –2 and then add.

$$3[0.7x + 0.4y = 0.6(300)]$$
$$-2[0.3x + 0.6y = 0.4(300)]$$

gives

$$2.1x + 1.2y = 540$$
$$\underline{-0.6x - 1.2y = -240}$$

Add: $1.5x = 300$

$$x = \frac{300}{1.5} = 200$$

Now substitute 200 for x in the first equation.

$$0.7x + 0.4y = 0.6(300)$$
$$0.7(200) + 0.4y = 0.6(300)$$
$$140 + 0.4y = 180$$
$$0.4y = 40$$
$$y = \frac{40}{0.4} = 100$$

200 grams of the first alloy should be combined with 100 grams of the second alloy to produce the desired mixture.

38. Let x = the number of grams of the sterling silver (92.5% silver) and y = the number of grams of the pure silver.

$$x + y = 250$$
$$0.925x + 1.00y = 0.94(250)$$

To solve, multiply the first equation by –1 and then add.

$$-1[x + y = 250]$$
$$0.925x + 1.00y = 0.94(250)$$

gives

$$-x - y = -250$$
$$\underline{0.925x + 1.00y = 235}$$

Add: $-0.075x = -15$

$$x = 200$$

Now substitute 200 for x in the first equation.

$$(200) + y = 250$$
$$y = 50$$

200 grams of the sterling silver should be combined with 50 grams of pure silver to produce the desired mixture.

39. Let t = the number of years since 2002 and y = the number of returns filed. We can use the given functions to form a system of equations.

Paper $\quad y = -2.73t + 58.37$

Online $\quad y = 1.95t + 10.58$

Subsitute $-2.73t + 58.37$ for y in the second equation.

$$-2.73t + 58.37 = 1.95t + 10.58$$
$$58.37 = 4.68t + 10.58$$
$$47.79 = 4.68t$$
$$\frac{47.79}{4.68} = t \quad \text{or} \quad t \approx 10.2$$

Thus, if the trends continue, the number of paper Form 1040 returns will be about the same as the number of online Form 1040, 1040A, 1040EZ returns in 2012 (2002 + 10 = 2012).

40. Let t = time spent jogging then $0.9 - t$ = time spent walking
Remember that $d = rt$.

$$3.5 = 3(0.9 - t) + 5t$$
$$3.5 = 2.7 - 3t + 5t$$
$$0.8 = 2t$$
$$0.4 = t$$

He spent 0.4 hour jogging.

41. Let x = speed of Melissa's car and y = speed of Tom's car

$$x = y + 15$$
$$\frac{150}{x} = \frac{120}{y} \quad \text{(travel times are equal)}$$

Substitute $y + 15$ for x in the second equation.

$$\frac{150}{y + 15} = \frac{120}{y}$$
$$150y = 120y + 1800$$
$$30y = 1800$$
$$y = 60$$

Substitute 60 for y in the first equation.

$$x = y + 15$$
$$x = 60 + 15$$
$$x = 75$$

Tom traveled at 60 mph and Melissa traveled at 75 mph.

42. a. Let c = cost and n = number of copies in 1 yr
Plan 1: $c = 0.10n$
Plan 2: $c = 0.04n + 120$

b.

Copies

c. The graphs intersect at approximately $n = 2000$. Therefore, the costs are the same for approximately 2000 copies in one year.

d. $0.10n = 0.04n + 120$
$$0.06n = 120$$
$$n = 2000$$
The cost is the same for 2000 copies.

43. Let x = pieces of personal mail
y = number of bills and statements
z = number of advertisements
$$x + y + z = 24$$
$$y = 2x - 2$$
$$z = 5x + 2$$
Substitute $2x - 2$ for y and $5x + 2$ for z in the first equation.
$$x + y + z = 24$$
$$x + 2x - 2 + 5x + 2 = 24$$
$$8x = 24$$
$$x = 3$$
Substitute 3 for x in the second and third equations.

$y = 2x - 2$ $\qquad$ $z = 5x + 2$
$y = 2(3) - 2$ $\qquad$ $z = 5(3) + 2$
$y = 4$ $\qquad$ $z = 17$

An average American household receives 3 pieces of personal mail, 4 bills and statements, and 17 advertisements per week.

44. Let x = number of chief petty officers
y = number of commissioned officers
z = number of other enlisted men
$$x + y + z = 141$$
$$x = y + 4$$
$$z = 8y - 3$$
Substitute $y + 4$ for x and $8y - 3$ for z in the first equation.
$$x + y + z = 141$$
$$y + 4 + y + 8y - 3 = 141$$
$$10y = 140$$
$$y = 14$$
Substitute 14 for y in the second and third equations.

$x = y + 4$ $\qquad$ $z = 8y - 3$
$x = 14 + 4$ $\qquad$ $z = 8(14) - 3$
$x = 18$ $\qquad$ $z = 109$

There are 14 commissioned officers, 18 chief petty officers, and 109 other enlisted men.

45. Let x = the number of bowl game appearances by Alabama, y = the number of bowl game appearnces by Tennessee, and z = the number of bowl game appearances by Texas.
$$x + y + z = 141$$
$$x = z + 8$$
$$y + z = x + 37$$
Solve the third equation for y.
$$y + z = x + 37$$
$$y = x + 37 - z$$
Substitute $x + 37 - z$ for y in the first equation.
$$x + (x + 37 - z) + z = 141$$
$$2x + 37 = 141$$
$$2x = 104$$
$$x = 52$$
Substitute 52 for x in the second equation.
$$52 = z + 8$$
$$44 = z$$
Substitute 44 for z and 52 for x in the third equation.
$$y + 44 = 52 + 37$$
$$y + 44 = 89$$
$$y = 45$$
Through 2004, Alabama has appeared in 52 bowl games, Tennessee has appeared in 45 bowl games, and Texas has appeared in 44 bowl games.

46. Let x = the number of gold medals earned by the United States, y = the number of gold medals earned by China, and z = the number of gold medals earned by Russia.

$$x + y + z = 94$$
$$x = y + 3$$
$$x + z = 2y - 2$$

Write the equations in standard form.

$$x + y + z = 94 \quad (1)$$
$$x - y \quad = 3 \quad (2)$$
$$x - 2y + z = -2 \quad (3)$$

First eliminate x and z from equations (1) and (3). Multiply equation (3) by -1 and add to equation (1).

$$x + y + z = 94$$
$$-1\left[x - 2y + z = -2 \right]$$

gives

$$x + y + z = 94$$
$$\underline{-x + 2y - z = 2}$$
Add: $\qquad 3y = 96$
$$y = 32$$

Substitute 32 for y in equation (2).

$$x - 32 = 3$$
$$x = 35$$

Substitute 35 for x and 32 for y in equation (1).

$$35 + 32 + z = 94$$
$$67 + z = 94$$
$$z = 27$$

The United States earned 35 gold medals, China earned 32 gold medals, and Russia earned 27 gold medals.

47. Let x = the number of top-ten finishes for Vijay Singh, y = the number of top-ten finishes for Tiger Woods, and z = the number of top-ten finishes for Phil Mickelson.

$$x + y + z = 191$$
$$y = z + 8$$
$$x = z + 12$$

Substitute $z + 8$ for y and $z + 12$ for x in the first equation.

$$(z + 12) + (z + 8) + z = 191$$
$$3z + 20 = 191$$
$$3z = 171$$
$$z = 57$$

Substitute 57 for z in the second equation.
$$y = 57 + 8 = 65$$

Substitute 57 for z in the third equation.
$$x = 57 + 12 = 69$$

Vijay Singh had 69 top-ten finishes, Tiger Woods had 65 top-ten finishes, and Phil Mickelson had 57 top-ten finishes.

48. Let x = the number of wins for Tony Stewart, y = the number of wins for Greg Biffle, and z = the number of wins for Carl Edwards.

$$x + y + z = 15$$
$$x = z + 1$$
$$y = z + 2$$

Substitute $z + 1$ for x and $z + 2$ for y in the first equation.

$$(z + 1) + (z + 2) + z = 15$$
$$3z + 3 = 15$$
$$3z = 12$$
$$z = 4$$

Substitute 4 for z in the second and third equations.

$$x = 4 + 1 \qquad y = 4 + 2$$
$$x = 5 \qquad y = 6$$

Tony Stewart had 5 wins, Greg Biffle had 6 wins, and Carl Edwards had 4 wins.

49. Let x = the amount of snowfall (inches) in Haverhill, y = the amount of snowfall in Plymouth, and z = the amount of snowfall in Salem.

$$x + y + z = 112.5$$
$$y = z$$
$$y = x + 1.5$$

Substitute $x + 1.5$ for both y and z in the first equation.

$$x + (x + 1.5) + (x + 1.5) = 112.5$$
$$3x + 3 = 112.5$$
$$3x = 109.5$$
$$x = 36.5$$

Substitute 36.5 for x in the third equation.

$$y = 36.5 + 1.5$$
$$y = 38$$

Haverhill received 36.5 inches of snow while Plymouth and Salem each received 38 inches.

50. Let x = the points scored by Adam Vinatieri, y = the points scored by Jason Elam, and z = the points scored by Jeff Reed.

$$x + y + z = 394$$
$$x = z + 17$$
$$x + z = 2y + 7$$

Write the equations in standard form.

$$x + y + z = 394 \quad (1)$$
$$x \quad\quad - z = 17 \quad (2)$$
$$x - 2y + z = 7 \quad (3)$$

Add equations (1) and (2):

$$x + y + z = 394$$
$$\underline{x \quad\quad - z = 17}$$

Add: $\quad 2x + y = 411 \quad (4)$

Add equations (2) and (3):

$$x \quad\quad - z = 17$$
$$\underline{x - 2y + z = 7}$$

Add: $\quad 2x - 2y = 24 \quad (5)$

Equations (4) and (5) are two equations in two unknowns.

$$2x + y = 411$$
$$2x - 2y = 24$$

Eliminate y by multiplying equation (4) by 2 and adding to equation (5).

$$2\left[2x + y = 411\right]$$
$$2x - 2y = 24$$

gives

$$4x + 2y = 822$$
$$\underline{2x - 2y = 24}$$

Add: $\quad 6x = 846$

$$x = 141$$

Substitute 141 for x in equation (2).

$$141 - z = 17$$
$$-z = -124$$
$$z = 124$$

Substitute 141 for x and 124 for z in equation (1).

$$141 + y + 124 = 394$$
$$y + 265 = 394$$
$$y = 129$$

Adam Vinatieri scored 141 points, Jason Elam scored 129 points, and Jeff Reed scored 124 points.

51. Let F = the number of Super Bowls held in Florida, L = the number held in Louisiana, and C = the number held in California.

$$F + L + C = 32 \quad (1)$$
$$F = L + 3 \quad (2)$$
$$F + L = 2C - 1 \quad (3)$$

Substitute $L + 3$ for F in the first and third equations.

$$(L + 3) + L + C = 32 \qquad\qquad (L + 3) + L = 2C - 1$$
$$2L + C + 3 = 32 \qquad\qquad\quad 2L + 3 = 2C - 1$$
$$2L + C = 29 \qquad\qquad\quad\quad 2L - 2C = -4$$

We now have two equations in two unknowns.

$$2L + C = 29 \quad (4)$$
$$2L - 2C = -4 \quad (5)$$

Eliminate L by multiplying equation (5) by -1 and adding to equation (4).

$$2L + C = 29$$
$$-1\left[2L - 2C = -4\right]$$

gives

$$2L + C = 29$$
$$\underline{-2L + 2C = 4}$$

Add: $\quad 3C = 33$

$$C = 11$$

Substitute 11 for C in equation (4).

$$2L + 11 = 29$$
$$2L = 18$$
$$L = 9$$

Substitute 9 for L in equation (2).

$$F = 9 + 3 = 12$$

Florida hosted 12 Super Bowls, Louisiana hosted 9 Super Bowls, and California hosted 11 Super Bowls.

52. Let x = the cost of an up-front, y = the cost of a main-floor ticket, and z = the price of a balcony ticket.

$$x = 2z$$
$$z = y - 10$$
$$z = x - 30$$

Substitute $x - 30$ for z in the first equation.

$$x = 2z$$
$$x = 2(x - 30)$$
$$x = 2x - 60$$
$$-x = -60$$
$$x = 60$$

Substitute 60 for x in the first equation.

$60 = 2z$

$30 = z$

Finally, substitute 30 for z in the second equation.

$30 = y - 10$

$40 = y$

The tickets cost \$30 for a balcony seat, \$40 for a main-floor seat, and \$60 for an up-front seat.

53. Let x be the smallest angle measure, y the second smallest, and z the largest.

$x + y + z = 180$

$x = \dfrac{2}{3}y$

$z = 3y - 30$

Substitute $\dfrac{2}{3}y$ for x and $3y - 30$ for z in the first equation.

$x + y + z = 180$

$\dfrac{2}{3}y + y + 3y - 30 = 180$

$\dfrac{14}{3}y - 30 = 180$

$\dfrac{14}{3}y = 210$

$y = 45$

Substitute 45 for y in the second equation.

$x = \dfrac{2}{3}y$

$x = \dfrac{2}{3}(45) = 30$

Substitute 45 for y in the third equation.

$z = 3y - 30$

$z = 3(45) - 30 = 135 - 30 = 105$

The three angles are 30°, 45°, and 105°.

54. Let x be the smallest angle measure, y the second smallest, and z the largest.

$x + y + z = 180$ (1)

$z = 3y - 10$ (2)

$x = z - 2y$ (3)

Substitute $3y - 10$ for z in equation (1).

$x + y + (3y - 10) = 180$

$x + 4y = 190$ (4)

Substitute $3y - 10$ for z in equation (3).

$x = (3y - 10) - 2y$

$x = y - 10$

Substitute $y - 10$ for x in equation (4).

$(y - 10) + 4y = 190$

$5y - 10 = 190$

$5y = 200$

$y = 40$

Substitute 40 for y in equation (4).

$x + 4(40) = 190$

$x + 160 = 190$

$x = 30$

Substitute 40 for y and 30 for x in equation (1).

$(30) + (40) + z = 180$

$z = 110$

The three angles are 30°, 40°, and 110°.

55. Let x = the amount invested at 3%, y = the amount invested at 5%, and z = the amount invested at 6%.

$y = 2x$ (1)

$x + y + z = 10,000$ (2)

$0.03x + 0.05y + 0.06z = 525$ (3)

Substitute $2x$ for y in equation (2).

$x + y + z = 10,000$

$x + 2x + z = 10,000$

$3x + z = 10,000$ (4)

Substitute $2x$ for y in equation (3).

$0.03x + 0.05y + 0.06z = 525$

$0.03x + 0.05(2x) + 0.06z = 525$

$0.03x + 0.10x + 0.06z = 525$

$0.13x + 0.06z = 525$ (5)

Equations (4) and (5) are a system of two equations in two unknowns.

$3x + z = 10,000$

$0.13x + 0.06z = 525$

To eliminate z, multiply equation (4) by –3 and equation (5) by 50 and add.

$-3[3x + z = 10,000]$

$50[0.13x + 0.06x = 525]$

gives

$-9x - 3z = -30,000$

$6.5x + 3z = 26,250$

Add: $-2.5x = -3750$

$x = \dfrac{-3750}{-2.5} = 1500$

Substitute 1500 for x in equation (4).

$$3x + z = 10,000$$
$$3(1500) + z = 10,000$$
$$4500 + z = 10,000$$
$$z = 5500$$

Substitute 1500 for x and 5500 for z in equation (2).

$$x + y + z = 10,000$$
$$1500 + y + 5500 = 10,000$$
$$y + 7000 = 10,000$$
$$y = 3000$$

Tam invested $1500 at 3%, $3000 at 5%, and $5500 at 6%.

56. Let x = the amount invested at 5.5%, y = the amount invested at 4.5%, and z = the amount invested at 3.75%.

$$x + y + z = 15,000 \quad (1)$$
$$y = 2x \quad (2)$$
$$0.055x + 0.045y + 0.0375z = 692.50 \quad (3)$$

Substitute $2x$ for y in equation (1).

$$x + (2x) + z = 15,000$$
$$3x + z = 15,000 \quad (4)$$

Substitute $2x$ for y in equation (3).

$$0.055x + 0.045(2x) + 0.0375z = 692.50$$
$$0.055x + 0.09x + 0.0375z = 692.50$$
$$0.145x + 0.0375z = 692.50 \quad (5)$$

Equations (4) and (5) are a system of two equations in two unknowns.

$$3x + z = 15,000 \quad (4)$$
$$0.145x + 0.0375z = 692.50 \quad (5)$$

To solve, multiply equation (4) by –0.0375 and then add.

$$-0.0375[3x + z = 15,000]$$
$$0.145x + 0.0375z = 692.50$$

gives

$$-0.1125x - 0.0375y = -562.50$$
$$\underline{0.145x + 0.0375z = 692.50}$$

Add: $0.0325x \qquad = 130$

$$x = 4,000$$

Substitute 4,000 for x in equation (4).

$$3(4,000) + z = 15,000$$
$$12,000 + z = 15,000$$
$$z = 3,000$$

Finally, substitute 4,000 for x and 3,000 for z in equation (1).

$$(4,000) + y + (3,000) = 15,000$$
$$y + 7,000 = 15,000$$
$$y = 8,000$$

Nick invested $4,000 at 5.5%, $8,000 at 4.5%, and $3,000 at 3.75%.

57. Let x = the amount of the 10% solution, y = the amount of the 12% solution, and z = the amount of the 20% solution.

$$x + y + z = 8 \qquad (1)$$
$$0.10x + 0.12y + 0.20z = (0.13)8 \, (2)$$
$$z = x - 2 \qquad (3)$$

Substitute $x - 2$ for z in equation (1).

$$x + y + z = 8$$
$$x + y + (x - 2) = 8$$
$$2x + y - 2 = 8$$
$$2x + y = 10 \qquad (4)$$

Substitute $x - 2$ for z in equation (2).

$$0.10x + 0.12y + 0.20z = (0.13)8$$
$$0.10x + 0.12y + 0.20(x - 2) = (0.13)8$$
$$0.10x + 0.12y + 0.20x - 0.40 = 1.04$$
$$0.30x + 0.12y = 1.44 \qquad (5)$$

Equations (4) and (5) are a system of two equations in two unknowns.

$$2x + y = 10$$
$$0.30x + 0.12y = 1.44$$

To solve, multiply equation (5) by 100 and equation (4) by –12 and then add.

$$-12[2x + y = 10]$$
$$100[0.30x + 0.12y = 1.44]$$

gives

$$-24x - 12y = -120$$
$$\underline{30x + 12y = 144}$$

Add: $6x \qquad = 24$

$$x = 4$$

Substitute 4 for x in equation (4).

$$2x + y = 10$$
$$2(4) + y = 10$$
$$8 + y = 10$$
$$y = 2$$

Finally, substitute 4 for x in equation (3).

$$z = x - 2$$
$$z = 4 - 2$$
$$z = 2$$

The mixture consists of 4 liters of the 10% solution, 2 liters of the 12% solution, and 2 liters of the 20% solution.

58. Let x = the amount of 8% solution, y = the amount of the 10% solution, and z = the amount of the 20% solution.

$$x + y + z = 100$$

$$0.08x + 0.10y + 0.20z = 0.12(100)$$

$$0.08x = \frac{0.10y + 0.20z}{2}$$

Write this system in standard form and multiply the second equation by 50 and the third equation by 100 to clear decimals.

$$x + y + z = 100 \quad (1)$$

$$4x + 5y + 10z = 600 \,(2)$$

$$8x - 5y - 10z = 0 \quad (3)$$

To eliminate y and z from equations (2) and (3), simply add.

$$4x + 5y + 10z = 600$$

$$\underline{8x - 5y - 10z = \quad 0}$$

Add: $12x \qquad\qquad = 600$

$$x = \frac{600}{12} = 50$$

Substitute 50 for x in both equations (1) and (2).
Equation (1) becomes

$$x + y + z = 100$$

$$50 + y + z = 100$$

$$y + z = 50 \quad (4)$$

Equation (2) becomes

$$4x + 5y + 10z = 600$$

$$4(50) + 5y + 10z = 600$$

$$200 + 5y + 10z = 600$$

$$5y + 10z = 400$$

Divide by 5.

$y + 2z = 80 \qquad (5)$

Equations (4) and (5) are a system of two equations in two unknowns.

$$y + z = 50$$

$$y + 2z = 80$$

To eliminate y, multiply equation (4) by –1 and then add.

$$-1[y + z = 50] \quad \Rightarrow \quad -y - z = -50$$

$$\underline{y + 2z = 80 \quad \Rightarrow \quad y + 2z = \quad 80}$$

Add: $\quad z = \quad 30$

Finally, substitute 30 for z in equation (4).

$$y + z = 50$$

$$y + 30 = 50$$

$$y = 20$$

Combine 50 ml of the 8% solution, 20 ml of the 10% solution, and 30 ml of the 20% solution to obtain the desired results.

59. Let x = the number of children's chairs, y = the number of standard chairs, and z = the number of executive chairs.

$$5x + 4y + 7z = 154\,(1)$$

$$3x + 2y + 5z = 94 \quad (2)$$

$$2x + 2y + 4z = 76 \quad (3)$$

To eliminate y between equations (1) and (2), multiply equation (2) by –2 and add.

$$5x + 4y + 7z = 154$$

$$-2[3x + 2y + 5z = 94]$$

gives

$$5x + 4y + 7z = \quad 154$$

$$\underline{-6x - 4y - 10z = -188}$$

Add: $-x \quad - 3z = -34 \quad (4)$

To eliminate y between equations (2) and (3), multiply equation (3) by –1 and add.

$$3x + 2y + 5z = 94$$

$$-1[2x + 2y + 4z = 76]$$

gives

$$3x + 2y + 5z = \quad 94$$

$$\underline{-2x - 2y - 4z = -76}$$

Add: $x \qquad + z = \quad 18 \qquad (5)$

Equations (4) and (5) are a system of two equations in two unknowns. To eliminate x, simply add.

$$-x - 3z = -34$$

$$\underline{x + \quad z = \quad 18}$$

Add: $\qquad -2z = -16$

$$z = \frac{-16}{-2} = 8$$

Substitute 8 for z in equation (5).

$$x + z = 18$$

$$x + 8 = 18$$

$$x = 10$$

Substitute 10 for x and 8 for z in equation (3).

$$2x + 2y + 4z = 76$$

$$2(10) + 2y + 4(8) = 76$$

$$20 + 2y + 32 = 76$$

$$2y + 52 = 76$$

$$2y = 24$$

$$y = 12$$

The Donaldson Furniture Company should produce 10 children's chairs, 12 standard chairs, and 8 executive chairs.

60. Let x = the number of Dakars produced, y = the number of Komodos produced, and z = the number of Aragons produced.

$$2x + 3y + 4z = 133 \qquad (1)$$
$$x + 2y + 2.5z = 78 \qquad (2)$$
$$1.5x + 2y + 3z = 96 \qquad (3)$$

To eliminate x between equations (1) and (2), multiply equation (2) by -2 and add.

$$2x + 3y + 4z = 133$$
$$-2[x + 2y + 2.5z = 78]$$

gives

$$2x + 3y + 4z = 133$$
$$\underline{-2x - 4y - 5z = -156}$$
Add: $\qquad -y - z = -23 \quad (4)$

To eliminate x between equations (2) and (3), multiply equation (2) by -1.5 and add.

$$-1.5[x + 2y + 2.5z = 78]$$
$$1.5x + 2y + 3z = 96$$

gives

$$-1.5x - 3y - 3.75z = -117$$
$$\underline{1.5x + 2y + 3z = 96}$$
Add: $\qquad -y - 0.75z = -21 \quad (5)$

Equations (4) and (5) are a system of two equations in two unknowns. To eliminate y, multiply equation (4) by -1 and add.

$$-1[-y - z = -23] \Rightarrow \quad y + z = 23$$
$$\underline{-y - 0.75z = -21}$$
Add: $\qquad\qquad\qquad 0.25z = 2$
$$z = 8$$

Substitute 8 for z in equation (4).

$$-y - (8) = -23$$
$$-y = -15$$
$$y = 15$$

Substitute 15 for y and 8 for z in equation (1).

$$2x + 3(15) + 4(8) = 133$$
$$2x + 45 + 32 = 133$$
$$2x + 77 = 133$$
$$2x = 56$$
$$x = 28$$

The Jamis Bicycle Company should produce 28 Dakars, 15 Komodos, and 8 Aragons.

61.
$$I_A + I_B + I_C = 0 \,(1)$$
$$-8I_B + 10I_C = 0 \,(2)$$
$$4I_A - 8I_B = 6 \,(3)$$

To eliminate I_A between equations (1) and (3), multiply equation (1) by -4 and add.

$$-4[I_A + I_B + C = 0]$$
$$4I_A - 8I_B = 6$$

gives

$$-4I_A - 4I_B - 4I_C = 0$$
$$\underline{4I_A - 8I_B \qquad = 6}$$
Add: $\qquad -12I_B - 4I_C = 6$
or $\qquad -6I_B - 2I_C = 3 \quad (4)$

Equations (4) and (2) are a system of two equations in two unknowns.

$$-8I_B + 10I_C = 0$$
$$-6I_B - 2I_C = 3$$

Multiply equation (4) by 5 and add this result to equation (2).

$$-8I_B + 10I_C = 0$$
$$5[-6I_B - 2I_C = 3]$$

gives

$$-8I_B + 10I_C = 0$$
$$\underline{-30I_B - 10I_C = 15}$$
Add: $-38I_B \qquad = 15$

$$I_B = \frac{15}{-38} = -\frac{15}{38}$$

Substitute $-\dfrac{15}{38}$ for I_B in equation (2).

$$-8I_B + 10I_C = 0$$
$$-8\left(-\frac{15}{38}\right) + 10I_C = 0$$
$$\frac{120}{38} + 10I_C = 0$$
$$10I_C = -\frac{120}{38}$$
$$\frac{1}{10}(10I_C) = \frac{1}{10}\left(-\frac{120}{38}\right)$$
$$I_C = -\frac{12}{38} = -\frac{6}{19}$$

Finally, substitute $-\dfrac{15}{38}$ for I_B in equation (3).

$$4I_A - 8I_B = 6$$

$$4I_A - 8\left(-\frac{15}{38}\right) = 6$$

$$4I_A + \frac{120}{38} = 6$$

$$4I_A = 6 - \frac{120}{38}$$

$$4I_A = 6 - \frac{60}{19}$$

$$4I_A = \frac{114}{19} - \frac{60}{19}$$

$$4I_A = \frac{54}{19}$$

$$\frac{1}{4}(4I_A) = \frac{1}{4}\left(\frac{54}{19}\right)$$

$$I_A = \frac{27}{38}$$

The current in branch A is $\frac{27}{38}$, the current in branch B is $-\frac{15}{38}$ and the current in branch C is $-\frac{6}{19}$.

62. $3F_1 + F_2 - F_3 = 2$ (1)

$F_1 - 2F_2 + F_3 = 0$ (2)

$4F_1 - F_2 + F_3 = 3$ (3)

To eliminate F_3 between equations (1) and (2), simply add.

$$3F_1 + F_2 - F_3 = 2$$
$$\underline{F_1 - 2F_2 + F_3 = 0}$$

Add: $4F_1 - F_2 \qquad = 2$ (4)

To eliminate F_3 between equations (1) and (3), simply add.

$$3F_1 + F_2 - F_3 = 2$$
$$\underline{4F_1 - F_2 + F_3 = 3}$$

Add: $7F_1 \qquad\qquad = 5$

$$F_1 = \frac{5}{7}$$

Substitute $\frac{5}{7}$ for F_1 in equation (4).

$$4F_1 - F_2 = 2$$

$$4\left(\frac{5}{7}\right) - F_2 = 2$$

$$\frac{20}{7} - F_2 = 2$$

$$-F_2 = 2 - \frac{20}{7}$$

$$-F_2 = \frac{14}{7} - \frac{20}{7}$$

$$-F_2 = -\frac{6}{7}$$

$$F_2 = \frac{6}{7}$$

Finally, substitute $\frac{5}{7}$ for F_1 and $\frac{6}{7}$ for F_2 in equation (2).

$$F_1 - 2F_2 + F_3 = 0$$

$$\frac{5}{7} - 2\left(\frac{6}{7}\right) + F_3 = 0$$

$$\frac{5}{7} - \frac{12}{7} + F_3 = 0$$

$$-1 + F_3 = 0$$

$$F_3 = 1$$

The three forces are $F_1 = \frac{5}{7}$, $F_2 = \frac{6}{7}$, and $F_3 = 1$.

63. a. Yes; the graphs pass the vertical line test.

b. Answers will vary. One possibility follows: Car A's speed is increasing at a decreasing rate (decelerating). Car B's speed is increasing at an increasing rate (accelerating).

c. At $t = 0.5$ hours, car A is traveling at a higher speed since the graph for car A is above the graph for car B.

d. Car A traveled farther. Car A had greater speed than Car B for the same period of time.

64. Substitute -2 for x and 5 for y.

$$\frac{1}{2}x + \frac{2}{5}xy + \frac{1}{8}y = \frac{1}{2}(-2) + \frac{2}{5}(-2)(5) + \frac{1}{8}(5)$$

$$= -1 - 4 + \frac{5}{8}$$

$$= -5 + \frac{5}{8}$$

$$= -\frac{35}{8}$$

65. $4 - 2\big[(x-5)+2x\big] = -(x+6)$

$4 - 2(x-5+2x) = -x-6$

$4 - 2(3x-5) = -x-6$

$4 - 6x + 10 = -x-6$

$-6x + 14 = -x - 6$

$-6x + x = -6 - 14$

$-5x = -20$

$x = 4$

66. The slope is $m = \dfrac{-8-(-4)}{2-6} = \dfrac{-8+4}{2-6} = \dfrac{-4}{-4} = 1$.

Use the point-slope form with $m = 1$ and $(x_1, y_1) = (6, -4)$.

$y - y_1 = m(x - x_1)$

$y - (-4) = 1(x-6)$

$y + 4 = x - 6$

$y = x - 10$

67. Use the vertical line test. If a vertical line cannot be drawn to intersect the graph in more than one point, the graph represents a fimction.

Exercise Set 9.6

1. A square matrix has the same number of rows and columns.

2. Answers will vary.

3. $-\dfrac{1}{2}R_2$. The next step is to change the -2 in the second row to 1 by multiplying the second row of numbers by $-\dfrac{1}{2}$.

4. $-2R_1 + R_3$. The next step is to change the 2 in the third row to 0 by multiplying the first row of numbers by -2 and then adding these products to the third row of numbers.

5. Switch R_1 and R_2 in order to continue placing ones along the diagonal.

6. $-\dfrac{1}{4}R_3$. Multiply row (3) by $-\dfrac{1}{4}$ in order to obtain ones along the diagonal.

7. Dependent (assuming no contradictions exist)

8. a. A row contains all zeros.

b. All the numbers in a row on the left side of the augmented matrix are 0's, but the number on the right side is not 0.

9. $\begin{bmatrix} 5 & -10 & | & -25 \\ 3 & -7 & | & -4 \end{bmatrix} \Rightarrow \begin{bmatrix} 1 & -2 & | & -5 \\ 3 & -7 & | & -4 \end{bmatrix} \tfrac{1}{5}R_1$

10. $\begin{bmatrix} 1 & 8 & | & 3 \\ 0 & 4 & | & -3 \end{bmatrix} \Rightarrow \begin{bmatrix} 1 & 8 & | & 3 \\ 0 & 1 & | & -\tfrac{3}{4} \end{bmatrix} \tfrac{1}{4}R_2$

11. $\begin{bmatrix} 4 & 7 & 2 & | & -1 \\ 3 & 2 & 1 & | & -5 \\ 1 & 1 & 3 & | & -8 \end{bmatrix} \Rightarrow \begin{bmatrix} 1 & 1 & 3 & | & -8 \\ 3 & 2 & 1 & | & -5 \\ 4 & 7 & 2 & | & -1 \end{bmatrix} \begin{matrix} \text{switch} \\ \\ R_1 \text{ and } R_3 \end{matrix}$

12. $\begin{bmatrix} 1 & 5 & 7 & | & 2 \\ 0 & 8 & -1 & | & -6 \\ 0 & 1 & 3 & | & -4 \end{bmatrix} \Rightarrow \begin{bmatrix} 1 & 5 & 7 & | & 2 \\ 0 & 1 & 3 & | & -4 \\ 0 & 8 & -1 & | & -6 \end{bmatrix} \begin{matrix} \text{switch} \\ \\ R_2 \text{ and } R_3 \end{matrix}$

13. $\begin{bmatrix} 1 & 3 & | & 12 \\ -4 & 11 & | & -6 \end{bmatrix} \Rightarrow \begin{bmatrix} 1 & 3 & | & 12 \\ 0 & 23 & | & 42 \end{bmatrix} 4R_1 + R_2$

14. $\begin{bmatrix} 1 & 5 & | & 6 \\ \tfrac{1}{2} & 10 & | & -4 \end{bmatrix} \Rightarrow \begin{bmatrix} 1 & 5 & | & 6 \\ 0 & \tfrac{15}{2} & | & -7 \end{bmatrix} -\tfrac{1}{2}R_1 + R_2$

15. $\begin{bmatrix} 1 & 0 & 8 & | & \tfrac{1}{4} \\ 5 & 2 & 2 & | & -2 \\ 6 & -3 & 1 & | & 0 \end{bmatrix} \Rightarrow$

$\begin{bmatrix} 1 & 0 & 8 & | & \tfrac{1}{4} \\ 0 & 2 & -38 & | & -\tfrac{13}{4} \\ 6 & -3 & 1 & | & 0 \end{bmatrix} -5R_1 + R_2$

16. $\begin{bmatrix} 1 & 2 & -1 & | & 6 \\ 0 & 1 & 5 & | & 0 \\ 0 & 0 & 3 & | & 12 \end{bmatrix} \Rightarrow \begin{bmatrix} 1 & 2 & -1 & | & 6 \\ 0 & 1 & 5 & | & 0 \\ 0 & 0 & 1 & | & 4 \end{bmatrix} \tfrac{1}{3}R_3$

17. $x + 3y = 3$
$-x + y = -3$

$$\begin{bmatrix} 1 & 3 & | & 3 \\ -1 & 1 & | & -3 \end{bmatrix}$$

$$\begin{bmatrix} 1 & 3 & | & 3 \\ 0 & 4 & | & 0 \end{bmatrix} R_1 + R_2$$

$$\begin{bmatrix} 1 & 3 & | & 3 \\ 0 & 1 & | & 0 \end{bmatrix} \frac{1}{4} R_2$$

The system is
$x + 3y = 3$
$y = 0$

Substitute 0 for y in the first equation.
$x + 3y = 3$
$x + 3(0) = 3$
$x + 0 = 3$
$x = 3$

The solution is $(3, 0)$.

18. $x + 2y = 10$
$3x - y = 9$

$$\begin{bmatrix} 1 & 2 & | & 10 \\ 3 & -1 & | & 9 \end{bmatrix}$$

$$\begin{bmatrix} 1 & 2 & | & 10 \\ 0 & -7 & | & -21 \end{bmatrix} -3R_1 + R_2$$

$$\begin{bmatrix} 1 & 2 & | & 10 \\ 0 & 1 & | & 3 \end{bmatrix} -\frac{1}{7} R_2$$

The system is
$x + 2y = 10$
$y = 3$

Substitute 3 for y in the first equation.
$x + 2(3) = 10$
$x + 6 = 10$
$x = 4$

The solution is $(4, 3)$.

19. $x + 3y = -2$
$-2x - 7y = 3$

$$\begin{bmatrix} 1 & 3 & | & -2 \\ -2 & -7 & | & 3 \end{bmatrix}$$

$$\begin{bmatrix} 1 & 3 & | & -2 \\ 0 & -1 & | & -1 \end{bmatrix} 2R_1 + R_2$$

$$\begin{bmatrix} 1 & 3 & | & -2 \\ 0 & 1 & | & 1 \end{bmatrix} -R_2$$

The system is
$x + 3y = -2$
$y = 1$

Substitute 1 for y in the first equation.
$x + 3(1) = -2$
$x + 3 = -2$
$x = -5$

The solution is $(-5, 1)$.

20. $3x + 6y = 0$
$2x - y = 10$

$$\begin{bmatrix} 3 & 6 & | & 0 \\ 2 & -1 & | & 10 \end{bmatrix}$$

$$\begin{bmatrix} 1 & 2 & | & 0 \\ 2 & -1 & | & 10 \end{bmatrix} \frac{1}{3} R_1$$

$$\begin{bmatrix} 1 & 2 & | & 0 \\ 0 & -5 & | & 10 \end{bmatrix} -2R_1 + R_2$$

$$\begin{bmatrix} 1 & 2 & | & 0 \\ 0 & 1 & | & -2 \end{bmatrix} -\frac{1}{5} R_2$$

The system is
$x + 2y = 0$
$y = -2$

Substitute -2 for y in the first equation.
$x + 2(-2) = 0$
$x - 4 = 0$
$x = 4$

The solution is $(4, -2)$.

21. $5a - 10b = -10$
$2a + b = 1$

$$\begin{bmatrix} 5 & -10 & | & -10 \\ 2 & 1 & | & 1 \end{bmatrix}$$

$$\begin{bmatrix} 1 & -2 & | & -2 \\ 2 & 1 & | & 1 \end{bmatrix} \frac{1}{5} R_1$$

$$\begin{bmatrix} 1 & -2 & | & -2 \\ 0 & 5 & | & 5 \end{bmatrix} -2R_1 + R_2$$

$$\begin{bmatrix} 1 & -2 & | & -2 \\ 0 & 1 & | & 1 \end{bmatrix} \frac{1}{5} R_2$$

The system is
$a - 2b = -2$
$b = 1$

Substitute 1 for b in the first equation.
$a - 2(1) = -2$
$a - 2 = -2$
$a = 0$

The solution is $(0, 1)$.

22. $3s - 2t = 1$

$-2s + 4t = -6$

$$\begin{bmatrix} 3 & -2 & | & 1 \\ -2 & 4 & | & -6 \end{bmatrix}$$

$$\begin{bmatrix} 1 & -\frac{2}{3} & | & \frac{1}{3} \\ -2 & 4 & | & -6 \end{bmatrix} \frac{1}{3}R_1$$

$$\begin{bmatrix} 1 & -\frac{2}{3} & | & \frac{1}{3} \\ 0 & \frac{8}{3} & | & -\frac{16}{3} \end{bmatrix} 2R_1 + R_2$$

$$\begin{bmatrix} 1 & -\frac{2}{3} & | & \frac{1}{3} \\ 0 & 1 & | & -2 \end{bmatrix} \frac{3}{8}R_2$$

The system is

$$s - \frac{2}{3}t = \frac{1}{3}$$

$$t = -2$$

Substitute -2 for t in the first equation.

$$s - \frac{2}{3}(-2) = \frac{1}{3}$$

$$s + \frac{4}{3} = \frac{1}{3}$$

$$s = -\frac{3}{3}$$

$$s = -1$$

The solution is $(-1, -2)$.

23. $2x - 5y = -6$

$-4x + 10y = 12$

$$\begin{bmatrix} 2 & -5 & | & -6 \\ -4 & 10 & | & 12 \end{bmatrix}$$

$$\begin{bmatrix} 1 & -\frac{5}{2} & | & -3 \\ -4 & 10 & | & 12 \end{bmatrix} \frac{1}{2}R_1$$

$$\begin{bmatrix} 1 & -\frac{5}{2} & | & -3 \\ 0 & 0 & | & 0 \end{bmatrix} 4R_1 + R_2$$

Since the last row contains all 0's, this is a dependent system of equations.

24. $-2m - 4n = 7$

$3m + 6n = -8$

$$\begin{bmatrix} -2 & -4 & | & 7 \\ 3 & 6 & | & -8 \end{bmatrix}$$

$$\begin{bmatrix} 1 & 2 & | & -\frac{7}{2} \\ 3 & 6 & | & -8 \end{bmatrix} -\frac{1}{2}R_1$$

$$\begin{bmatrix} 1 & 2 & | & -\frac{7}{2} \\ 0 & 0 & | & -\frac{5}{2} \end{bmatrix} -3R_1 + R_2$$

Since the last row contains zeros on the left and a nonzero number on the right, this is an inconsistent system and there is no solution.

25. $12x + 2y = 2$

$6x - 3y = -11$

$$\begin{bmatrix} 12 & 2 & | & 2 \\ 6 & -3 & | & -11 \end{bmatrix}$$

$$\begin{bmatrix} 1 & \frac{1}{6} & | & \frac{1}{6} \\ 6 & -3 & | & -11 \end{bmatrix} \frac{1}{12}R_1$$

$$\begin{bmatrix} 1 & \frac{1}{6} & | & \frac{1}{6} \\ 0 & -4 & | & -12 \end{bmatrix} -6R_1 + R_2$$

$$\begin{bmatrix} 1 & \frac{1}{6} & | & \frac{1}{6} \\ 0 & 1 & | & 3 \end{bmatrix} -\frac{1}{4}R_2$$

The system is

$$x + \frac{1}{6}y = \frac{1}{6}$$

$$y = 3$$

Substitute 3 for y in the first equation.

$$x + \frac{1}{6}y = \frac{1}{6}$$

$$x + \frac{1}{6}(3) = \frac{1}{6}$$

$$x + \frac{3}{6} = \frac{1}{6}$$

$$x = -\frac{2}{6}$$

$$x = -\frac{1}{3}$$

The solution is $\left(-\frac{1}{3}, 3\right)$.

26. $4r + 2s = -10$

$-2r + s = -7$

$$\begin{bmatrix} 4 & 2 & | & -10 \\ -2 & 1 & | & -7 \end{bmatrix}$$

$$\begin{bmatrix} 1 & \frac{1}{2} & | & -\frac{5}{2} \\ -2 & 1 & | & -7 \end{bmatrix} \frac{1}{4}R_1$$

$$\begin{bmatrix} 1 & \frac{1}{2} & | & -\frac{5}{2} \\ 0 & 2 & | & -12 \end{bmatrix} 2R_1 + R_2$$

$$\begin{bmatrix} 1 & \frac{1}{2} & | & -\frac{5}{2} \\ 0 & 1 & | & -6 \end{bmatrix} \frac{1}{2}R_2$$

The system is

$$r + \frac{1}{2}s = -\frac{5}{2}$$

$$s = -6$$

Substitute -6 for s in the first equation.

$$r + \frac{1}{2}s = -\frac{5}{2}$$

$$r + \frac{1}{2}(-6) = -\frac{5}{2}$$

$$r - 3 = -\frac{5}{2}$$

$$r = -\frac{5}{2} + 3$$

$$r = -\frac{5}{2} + \frac{6}{2}$$

$$r = \frac{1}{2}$$

The solution is $\left(\frac{1}{2}, -6 \right)$.

27. $-3x + 6y = 5$

$\quad\ 2x - 4y = 7$

$$\begin{bmatrix} -3 & 6 & | & 5 \\ 2 & -4 & | & 7 \end{bmatrix}$$

$$\begin{bmatrix} 1 & -2 & | & -\frac{5}{3} \\ 2 & -4 & | & 7 \end{bmatrix} -\frac{1}{3}R_1$$

$$\begin{bmatrix} 1 & -2 & | & -\frac{5}{3} \\ 0 & 0 & | & \frac{31}{3} \end{bmatrix} -2R_1 + R_2$$

Since the last row contains zeros on the left and a nonzero number on the right, this is an inconsistent system and there is no solution.

28. $8x = 4y + 12 \quad \rightarrow \quad 8x - 4y = 12$

$\quad\ -2x + y = -3 \qquad\qquad -2x + y = -3$

$$\begin{bmatrix} 8 & -4 & | & 12 \\ -2 & 1 & | & -3 \end{bmatrix}$$

$$\begin{bmatrix} 1 & -\frac{1}{2} & | & \frac{3}{2} \\ -2 & 1 & | & -3 \end{bmatrix} \frac{1}{8}R_1$$

$$\begin{bmatrix} 1 & -\frac{1}{2} & | & \frac{3}{2} \\ 0 & 0 & | & 0 \end{bmatrix} 2R_1 + R_2$$

Since the last row contains all 0's, this is a dependent system of equations.

29. $12x - 8y = 6$

$\quad\ -3x + 4y = -1$

$$\begin{bmatrix} 12 & -8 & | & 6 \\ -3 & 4 & | & -1 \end{bmatrix}$$

$$\begin{bmatrix} 1 & -\frac{2}{3} & | & \frac{1}{2} \\ -3 & 4 & | & -1 \end{bmatrix} \frac{1}{12}R_1$$

$$\begin{bmatrix} 1 & -\frac{2}{3} & | & \frac{1}{2} \\ 0 & 2 & | & \frac{1}{2} \end{bmatrix} 3R_1 + R_2$$

$$\begin{bmatrix} 1 & -\frac{2}{3} & | & \frac{1}{2} \\ 0 & 1 & | & \frac{1}{4} \end{bmatrix} \frac{1}{2}R_2$$

The system is

$$x - \frac{2}{3}y = \frac{1}{2}$$

$$y = \frac{1}{4}$$

Substitute $\frac{1}{4}$ for y in the first equation.

$$x - \frac{2}{3}y = \frac{1}{2}$$

$$x - \frac{2}{3}\left(\frac{1}{4} \right) = \frac{1}{2}$$

$$x - \frac{1}{6} = \frac{1}{2}$$

$$x = \frac{1}{2} + \frac{1}{6}$$

$$x = \frac{4}{6}$$

$$x = \frac{2}{3}$$

The solution is $\left(\frac{2}{3}, \frac{1}{4} \right)$.

30. $2x - 3y = 3$

$\quad\ -5x + 9y = -7$

$$\begin{bmatrix} 2 & -3 & | & 3 \\ -5 & 9 & | & -7 \end{bmatrix}$$

$$\begin{bmatrix} 1 & -\frac{3}{2} & | & \frac{3}{2} \\ -5 & 9 & | & -7 \end{bmatrix} \frac{1}{2}R_1$$

$$\begin{bmatrix} 1 & -\frac{3}{2} & | & \frac{3}{2} \\ 0 & \frac{3}{2} & | & \frac{1}{2} \end{bmatrix} 5R_1 + R_2$$

$$\begin{bmatrix} 1 & -\frac{3}{2} & | & \frac{3}{2} \\ 0 & 1 & | & \frac{1}{3} \end{bmatrix} \frac{2}{3}R_2$$

The system is
$$x - \frac{3}{2}y = \frac{3}{2}$$
$$y = \frac{1}{3}$$
Substitute $\frac{1}{3}$ for y in the first equation.
$$x - \frac{3}{2}y = \frac{3}{2}$$
$$x - \frac{3}{2}\left(\frac{1}{3}\right) = \frac{3}{2}$$
$$x - \frac{1}{2} = \frac{3}{2}$$
$$x = \frac{4}{2}$$
$$x = 2$$
The solution is $\left(2, \frac{1}{3}\right)$.

31. $10m = 8n + 15$
$16n = -15m - 2$
Write the system in standard form.
$$10m - 8n = 15$$
$$15m + 16n = -2$$
$$\begin{bmatrix} 10 & -8 & | & 15 \\ 15 & 16 & | & -2 \end{bmatrix}$$
$$\begin{bmatrix} 1 & -\frac{4}{5} & | & \frac{3}{2} \\ 15 & 16 & | & -2 \end{bmatrix} \frac{1}{10}R_1$$
$$\begin{bmatrix} 1 & -\frac{4}{5} & | & \frac{3}{2} \\ 0 & 28 & | & -\frac{49}{2} \end{bmatrix} -15R_1 + R_2$$
$$\begin{bmatrix} 1 & -\frac{4}{5} & | & \frac{3}{2} \\ 0 & 1 & | & -\frac{7}{8} \end{bmatrix} \frac{1}{28}R_2$$
The system is
$$m - \frac{4}{5}n = \frac{3}{2}$$
$$n = -\frac{7}{8}$$
Substitute $-\frac{7}{8}$ for n in the first equation.

$$m - \frac{4}{5}n = \frac{3}{2}$$
$$m - \frac{4}{5}\left(-\frac{7}{8}\right) = \frac{3}{2}$$
$$m + \frac{7}{10} = \frac{3}{2}$$
$$m = \frac{3}{2} - \frac{7}{10} = \frac{15}{10} - \frac{7}{10} = \frac{8}{10} = \frac{4}{5}$$
The solution is $\left(\frac{4}{5}, -\frac{7}{8}\right)$.

32. $8x = 9y + 4$
$16x - 27y = 11$
Write the system in standard form.
$$8x - 9y = 4$$
$$16x - 27y = 11$$
$$\begin{bmatrix} 8 & -9 & | & 4 \\ 16 & -27 & | & 11 \end{bmatrix}$$
$$\begin{bmatrix} 1 & -\frac{9}{8} & | & \frac{1}{2} \\ 16 & -27 & | & 11 \end{bmatrix} \frac{1}{8}R_1$$
$$\begin{bmatrix} 1 & -\frac{9}{8} & | & \frac{1}{2} \\ 0 & -9 & | & 3 \end{bmatrix} -16R_1 + R_2$$
$$\begin{bmatrix} 1 & -\frac{9}{8} & | & \frac{1}{2} \\ 0 & 1 & | & -\frac{1}{3} \end{bmatrix} -\frac{1}{9}R_2$$
The system is
$$x - \frac{9}{8}y = \frac{1}{2}$$
$$y = -\frac{1}{3}$$
Substitute $-\frac{1}{3}$ for y in the first equation.
$$x - \frac{9}{8}y = \frac{1}{2}$$
$$x - \frac{9}{8}\left(-\frac{1}{3}\right) = \frac{1}{2}$$
$$x + \frac{3}{8} = \frac{1}{2}$$
$$x = \frac{1}{8}$$
The solution is $\left(\frac{1}{8}, -\frac{1}{3}\right)$.

33. $x - 3y + 2z = 5$
$2x + 5y - 4z = -3$
$-3x + y - 2z = -11$

$$\begin{bmatrix} 1 & -3 & 2 & | & 5 \\ 2 & 5 & -4 & | & -3 \\ -3 & 1 & -2 & | & -11 \end{bmatrix}$$

$$\begin{bmatrix} 1 & -3 & 2 & | & 5 \\ 0 & 11 & -8 & | & -13 \\ -3 & 1 & -2 & | & -11 \end{bmatrix} -2R_1 + R_2$$

$$\begin{bmatrix} 1 & -3 & 2 & | & 5 \\ 0 & 11 & -8 & | & -13 \\ 0 & -8 & 4 & | & 4 \end{bmatrix} 3R_1 + R_3$$

$$\begin{bmatrix} 1 & -3 & 2 & | & 5 \\ 0 & 1 & -\frac{8}{11} & | & -\frac{13}{11} \\ 0 & -8 & 4 & | & 4 \end{bmatrix} \frac{1}{11}R_2$$

$$\begin{bmatrix} 1 & -3 & 2 & | & 5 \\ 0 & 1 & -\frac{8}{11} & | & -\frac{13}{11} \\ 0 & 0 & -\frac{20}{11} & | & -\frac{60}{11} \end{bmatrix} 8R_2 + R_3$$

$$\begin{bmatrix} 1 & -3 & 2 & | & 5 \\ 0 & 1 & -\frac{8}{11} & | & -\frac{13}{11} \\ 0 & 0 & 1 & | & 3 \end{bmatrix} -\frac{11}{20}R_3$$

The system is
$x - 3y + 2z = 5$
$$y - \frac{8}{11}z = -\frac{13}{11}$$
$$z = 3$$
Substitute 3 for z in the second equation.
$$y - \frac{8}{11}(3) = -\frac{13}{11}$$
$$y - \frac{24}{11} = -\frac{13}{11}$$
$$y = \frac{11}{11}$$
$$y = 1$$
Substitute 1 for y and 3 for z in the first equation.
$x - 3(1) + 2(3) = 5$
$x - 3 + 6 = 5$
$x + 3 = 5$
$x = 2$
The solution is $(2, 1, 3)$.

34. $a - 3b + 4c = 7$
$4a + b + c = -2$
$-2a - 3b + 5c = 12$

$$\begin{bmatrix} 1 & -3 & 4 & | & 7 \\ 4 & 1 & 1 & | & -2 \\ -2 & -3 & 5 & | & 12 \end{bmatrix}$$

$$\begin{bmatrix} 1 & -3 & 4 & | & 7 \\ 0 & 13 & -15 & | & -30 \\ -2 & -3 & 5 & | & 12 \end{bmatrix} -4R_1 + R_2$$

$$\begin{bmatrix} 1 & -3 & 4 & | & 7 \\ 0 & 13 & -15 & | & -30 \\ 0 & -9 & 13 & | & 26 \end{bmatrix} 2R_1 + R_3$$

$$\begin{bmatrix} 1 & -3 & 4 & | & 7 \\ 0 & 1 & -\frac{15}{13} & | & -\frac{30}{13} \\ 0 & -9 & 13 & | & 26 \end{bmatrix} \frac{1}{13}R_2$$

$$\begin{bmatrix} 1 & -3 & 4 & | & 7 \\ 0 & 1 & -\frac{15}{13} & | & -\frac{30}{13} \\ 0 & 0 & \frac{34}{13} & | & \frac{68}{13} \end{bmatrix} 9R_2 + R_3$$

$$\begin{bmatrix} 1 & -3 & 4 & | & 7 \\ 0 & 1 & -\frac{15}{13} & | & -\frac{30}{13} \\ 0 & 0 & 1 & | & 2 \end{bmatrix} \frac{13}{34}R_3$$

The system is
$a - 3b + 4c = 7$
$$b - \frac{15}{13}c = -\frac{30}{13}$$
$$c = 2$$
Substitute 2 for c in the second equation.
$$b - \frac{15}{13}(2) = -\frac{30}{13}$$
$$b - \frac{30}{13} = -\frac{30}{13}$$
$$b = -\frac{30}{13} + \frac{30}{13}$$
$$b = 0$$
Substitute 0 for b and 2 for c in the first equation.
$a - 3(0) + 4(2) = 7$
$a + 0 + 8 = 7$
$a = -1$
The solution is $(-1, 0, 2)$.

35. $x + 2y = 5$

$y - z = -1$

$2x - 3z = 0$

Write the system in standard form.

$x + 2y + 0z = 5$

$0x + y - z = -1$

$2x + 0y - 3z = 0$

$$\begin{bmatrix} 1 & 2 & 0 & | & 5 \\ 0 & 1 & -1 & | & -1 \\ 2 & 0 & -3 & | & 0 \end{bmatrix}$$

$$\begin{bmatrix} 1 & 2 & 0 & | & 5 \\ 0 & 1 & -1 & | & -1 \\ 0 & -4 & -3 & | & -10 \end{bmatrix} -2R_1 + R_3$$

$$\begin{bmatrix} 1 & 2 & 0 & | & 5 \\ 0 & 1 & -1 & | & -1 \\ 0 & 0 & -7 & | & -14 \end{bmatrix} 4R_2 + R_3$$

$$\begin{bmatrix} 1 & 2 & 0 & | & 5 \\ 0 & 1 & -1 & | & -1 \\ 0 & 0 & 1 & | & 2 \end{bmatrix} -\frac{1}{7}R_3$$

The system is

$x + 2y = 5$

$y - z = -1$

$z = 2$

Substitute 2 for z in the second equation.

$y - z = -1$

$y - 2 = -1$

$y = 1$

Substitute 1 for y in the first equation.

$x + 2y = 5$

$x + 2(1) = 5$

$x = 3$

The solution is $(3, 1, 2)$.

36. $3a - 5c = 3$

$a + 2b = -6$

$7b - 4c = 5$

Write the system in standard form.

$3a + 0b - 5c = 3$

$a + 2b + 0c = -6$

$0a + 7b - 4c = 5$

$$\begin{bmatrix} 3 & 0 & -5 & | & 3 \\ 1 & 2 & 0 & | & -6 \\ 0 & 7 & -4 & | & 5 \end{bmatrix}$$

$$\begin{bmatrix} 1 & 0 & -\frac{5}{3} & | & 1 \\ 1 & 2 & 0 & | & -6 \\ 0 & 7 & -4 & | & 5 \end{bmatrix} \frac{1}{3}R_1$$

$$\begin{bmatrix} 1 & 0 & -\frac{5}{3} & | & 1 \\ 0 & 2 & \frac{5}{3} & | & -7 \\ 0 & 7 & -4 & | & 5 \end{bmatrix} -1R_1 + R_2$$

$$\begin{bmatrix} 1 & 0 & -\frac{5}{3} & | & 1 \\ 0 & 1 & \frac{5}{6} & | & -\frac{7}{2} \\ 0 & 7 & -4 & | & 5 \end{bmatrix} \frac{1}{2}R_1$$

$$\begin{bmatrix} 1 & 0 & -\frac{5}{3} & | & 1 \\ 0 & 1 & \frac{5}{6} & | & -\frac{7}{2} \\ 0 & 0 & -\frac{59}{6} & | & \frac{59}{2} \end{bmatrix} -7R_2 + R_3$$

$$\begin{bmatrix} 1 & 0 & -\frac{5}{3} & | & 1 \\ 0 & 1 & \frac{5}{6} & | & -\frac{7}{2} \\ 0 & 0 & 1 & | & -3 \end{bmatrix} -\frac{6}{59}R_3$$

The system is

$a - \dfrac{5}{3}c = 1$

$b + \dfrac{5}{6}c = -\dfrac{7}{2}$

$c = -3$

Substitute -3 for c in the second equation.

$b + \dfrac{5}{6}(-3) = -\dfrac{7}{2}$

$b - \dfrac{5}{2} = -\dfrac{7}{2}$

$b = -\dfrac{7}{2} + \dfrac{5}{2}$

$b = -1$

Substitute -3 for c in the first equation.

$a - \dfrac{5}{3}(-3) = 1$

$a + 5 = 1$

$a = -4$

The solution is $\left(-4, -1, -3\right)$.

37. $x - 2y + 4z = 5$

$-3x + 4y - 2z = -8$

$4x + 5y - 4z = -3$

$$\begin{bmatrix} 1 & -2 & 4 & | & 5 \\ -3 & 4 & -2 & | & -8 \\ 4 & 5 & -4 & | & -3 \end{bmatrix}$$

$$\begin{bmatrix} 1 & -2 & 4 & | & 5 \\ 0 & -2 & 10 & | & 7 \\ 4 & 5 & -4 & | & -3 \end{bmatrix} 3R_1 + R_2$$

$$\begin{bmatrix} 1 & -2 & 4 & | & 5 \\ 0 & -2 & 10 & | & 7 \\ 0 & 13 & -20 & | & -23 \end{bmatrix} -4R_1 + R_3$$

$$\begin{bmatrix} 1 & -2 & 4 & | & 5 \\ 0 & 1 & -5 & | & -\frac{7}{2} \\ 0 & 13 & -20 & | & -23 \end{bmatrix} -\frac{1}{2}R_2$$

$$\begin{bmatrix} 1 & -2 & 4 & | & 5 \\ 0 & 1 & -5 & | & -\frac{7}{2} \\ 0 & 0 & 45 & | & \frac{45}{2} \end{bmatrix} -13R_2 + R_3$$

$$\begin{bmatrix} 1 & -2 & 4 & | & 5 \\ 0 & 1 & -5 & | & -\frac{7}{2} \\ 0 & 0 & 1 & | & \frac{1}{2} \end{bmatrix} \frac{1}{45}R_3$$

The system is

$x - 2y + 4z = 5$

$y - 5z = -\dfrac{7}{2}$

$z = \dfrac{1}{2}$

Substitute $\dfrac{1}{2}$ for z in the second equation.

$y - 5\left(\dfrac{1}{2}\right) = -\dfrac{7}{2}$

$y - \dfrac{5}{2} = -\dfrac{7}{2}$

$y = -1$

Substitute -1 for y and $\dfrac{1}{2}$ for z in the first equation.

$x - 2(-1) + 4\left(\dfrac{1}{2}\right) = 5$

$x + 2 + 2 = 5$

$x + 4 = 5$

$x = 1$

The solution is $\left(1, -1, \dfrac{1}{2}\right)$.

38. $3x + 5y + 2z = 3$

$-x - y - z = -2$

$2x - 2y + 5z = 11$

$$\begin{bmatrix} 3 & 5 & 2 & | & 3 \\ -1 & -1 & -1 & | & -2 \\ 2 & -2 & 5 & | & 11 \end{bmatrix}$$

$$\begin{bmatrix} 1 & \frac{5}{3} & \frac{2}{3} & | & 1 \\ -1 & -1 & -1 & | & -2 \\ 2 & -2 & 5 & | & 11 \end{bmatrix} \frac{1}{3}R_1$$

$$\begin{bmatrix} 1 & \frac{5}{3} & \frac{2}{3} & | & 1 \\ 0 & \frac{2}{3} & -\frac{1}{3} & | & -1 \\ 2 & -2 & 5 & | & 11 \end{bmatrix} R_1 + R_2$$

$$\begin{bmatrix} 1 & \frac{5}{3} & \frac{2}{3} & | & 1 \\ 0 & \frac{2}{3} & -\frac{1}{3} & | & -1 \\ 0 & -\frac{16}{3} & \frac{11}{3} & | & 9 \end{bmatrix} -2R_1 + R_3$$

$$\begin{bmatrix} 1 & \frac{5}{3} & \frac{2}{3} & | & 1 \\ 0 & 1 & -\frac{1}{2} & | & -\frac{3}{2} \\ 0 & -\frac{16}{3} & \frac{11}{3} & | & 9 \end{bmatrix} \frac{3}{2}R_2$$

$$\begin{bmatrix} 1 & \frac{5}{3} & \frac{2}{3} & | & 1 \\ 0 & 1 & -\frac{1}{2} & | & -\frac{3}{2} \\ 0 & 0 & 1 & | & 1 \end{bmatrix} \frac{16}{3}R_2 + R_3$$

The system is

$x + \dfrac{5}{3}y + \dfrac{2}{3}z = 1$

$y - \dfrac{1}{2}z = -\dfrac{3}{2}$

$z = 1$

Substitute 1 for z in the second equation.

$y - \dfrac{1}{2}z = -\dfrac{3}{2}$

$y - \dfrac{1}{2}(1) = -\dfrac{3}{2}$

$y = -1$

Substitute -1 for y and 1 for z in the second equation.

$-x - y - z = -2$

$-x - (-1) - 1 = -2$

$-x = -2$

$x = 2$

The solution is $(2, -1, 1)$.

39.
$$2x - 5y + z = 1$$
$$3x - 5y + z = 3$$
$$-4x + 10y - 2z = -2$$

$$\begin{bmatrix} 2 & -5 & 1 & | & 1 \\ 3 & -5 & 1 & | & 3 \\ -4 & 10 & -2 & | & -2 \end{bmatrix}$$

$$\begin{bmatrix} 1 & -\frac{5}{2} & \frac{1}{2} & | & \frac{1}{2} \\ 3 & -5 & 1 & | & 3 \\ -4 & 10 & -2 & | & -2 \end{bmatrix} \frac{1}{2}R_1$$

$$\begin{bmatrix} 1 & -\frac{5}{2} & \frac{1}{2} & | & \frac{1}{2} \\ 0 & \frac{5}{2} & -\frac{1}{2} & | & \frac{3}{2} \\ -4 & 10 & -2 & | & -2 \end{bmatrix} -3R_1 + R_2$$

$$\begin{bmatrix} 1 & -\frac{5}{2} & \frac{1}{2} & | & \frac{1}{2} \\ 0 & \frac{5}{2} & -\frac{1}{2} & | & \frac{3}{2} \\ 0 & 0 & 0 & | & 0 \end{bmatrix} 4R_1 + R_3$$

Since there is a row of all zeros, the system is dependent.

40.
$$x + 2y + 3z = 1$$
$$4x + 5y + 6z = -3$$
$$7x + 8y + 9z = 0$$

$$\begin{bmatrix} 1 & 2 & 3 & | & 1 \\ 4 & 5 & 6 & | & -3 \\ 7 & 8 & 9 & | & 0 \end{bmatrix}$$

$$\begin{bmatrix} 1 & 2 & 3 & | & 1 \\ 0 & -3 & -6 & | & -7 \\ 7 & 8 & 9 & | & 0 \end{bmatrix} -4R_1 + R_2$$

$$\begin{bmatrix} 1 & 2 & 3 & | & 1 \\ 0 & -3 & -6 & | & -7 \\ 0 & -6 & -12 & | & -7 \end{bmatrix} -7R_1 + R_3$$

$$\begin{bmatrix} 1 & 2 & 3 & | & 1 \\ 0 & 1 & 2 & | & \frac{7}{3} \\ 0 & -6 & -12 & | & -7 \end{bmatrix} -\frac{1}{3}R_2$$

$$\begin{bmatrix} 1 & 2 & 3 & | & 1 \\ 0 & 1 & 2 & | & \frac{7}{3} \\ 0 & 0 & 0 & | & 7 \end{bmatrix} 6R_2 + R_3$$

Since the last row contains zeros on the left and a nonzero number on the right, the system is inconsistent and there is no solution.

41.
$$4p - q + r = 4$$
$$-6p + 3q - 2r = -5$$
$$2p + 5q - r = 7$$

$$\begin{bmatrix} 4 & -1 & 1 & | & 4 \\ -6 & 3 & -2 & | & -5 \\ 2 & 5 & -1 & | & 7 \end{bmatrix}$$

$$\begin{bmatrix} 1 & -\frac{1}{4} & \frac{1}{4} & | & 1 \\ -6 & 3 & -2 & | & -5 \\ 2 & 5 & -1 & | & 7 \end{bmatrix} \frac{1}{4}R_1$$

$$\begin{bmatrix} 1 & -\frac{1}{4} & \frac{1}{4} & | & 1 \\ 0 & \frac{3}{2} & -\frac{1}{2} & | & 1 \\ 2 & 5 & -1 & | & 7 \end{bmatrix} 6R_1 + R_2$$

$$\begin{bmatrix} 1 & -\frac{1}{4} & \frac{1}{4} & | & 1 \\ 0 & \frac{3}{2} & -\frac{1}{2} & | & 1 \\ 0 & \frac{11}{2} & -\frac{3}{2} & | & 5 \end{bmatrix} -2R_1 + R_3$$

$$\begin{bmatrix} 1 & -\frac{1}{4} & \frac{1}{4} & | & 1 \\ 0 & 1 & -\frac{1}{3} & | & \frac{2}{3} \\ 0 & \frac{11}{2} & -\frac{3}{2} & | & 5 \end{bmatrix} \frac{2}{3}R_2$$

$$\begin{bmatrix} 1 & -\frac{1}{4} & \frac{1}{4} & | & 1 \\ 0 & 1 & -\frac{1}{3} & | & \frac{2}{3} \\ 0 & 0 & \frac{1}{3} & | & \frac{4}{3} \end{bmatrix} -\frac{11}{2}R_2 + R_3$$

$$\begin{bmatrix} 1 & -\frac{1}{4} & \frac{1}{4} & | & 1 \\ 0 & 1 & -\frac{1}{3} & | & \frac{2}{3} \\ 0 & 0 & 1 & | & 4 \end{bmatrix} 3R_3$$

The system is
$$x - \frac{1}{4}y + \frac{1}{4}z = 1$$
$$y - \frac{1}{3}z = \frac{2}{3}$$
$$z = 4$$

Substitute 4 for z in the second equation.
$$y - \frac{1}{3}z = \frac{2}{3}$$
$$y - \frac{1}{3}(4) = \frac{2}{3}$$
$$y - \frac{4}{3} = \frac{2}{3}$$
$$y = \frac{6}{3}$$
$$y = 2$$

Substitute 2 for y and 4 for z in the first equation.

$$x - \frac{1}{4}y + \frac{1}{4}z = 1$$

$$x - \frac{1}{4}(2) + \frac{1}{4}(4) = 1$$

$$x - \frac{1}{2} + 1 = 1$$

$$x + \frac{1}{2} = 1$$

$$x = \frac{1}{2}$$

The solution is $\left(\frac{1}{2}, 2, 4\right)$.

42. $-4r + 3s - 6t = 14$

$4r + 2s - 2t = -3$

$2r - 5s - 8t = -23$

$$\begin{bmatrix} -4 & 3 & -6 & | & 14 \\ 4 & 2 & -2 & | & -3 \\ 2 & -5 & -8 & | & -23 \end{bmatrix}$$

$$\begin{bmatrix} 1 & -\frac{3}{4} & \frac{3}{2} & | & -\frac{7}{2} \\ 4 & 2 & -2 & | & -3 \\ 2 & -5 & -8 & | & -23 \end{bmatrix} -\frac{1}{4}R_1$$

$$\begin{bmatrix} 1 & -\frac{3}{4} & \frac{3}{2} & | & -\frac{7}{2} \\ 0 & 5 & -8 & | & 11 \\ 2 & -5 & -8 & | & -23 \end{bmatrix} -4R_1 + R_2$$

$$\begin{bmatrix} 1 & -\frac{3}{4} & \frac{3}{2} & | & -\frac{7}{2} \\ 0 & 5 & -8 & | & 11 \\ 0 & -\frac{7}{2} & -11 & | & -16 \end{bmatrix} -2R_1 + R_3$$

$$\begin{bmatrix} 1 & -\frac{3}{4} & \frac{3}{2} & | & -\frac{7}{2} \\ 0 & 1 & -\frac{8}{5} & | & \frac{11}{5} \\ 0 & -\frac{7}{2} & -11 & | & -16 \end{bmatrix} \frac{1}{5}R_2$$

$$\begin{bmatrix} 1 & -\frac{3}{4} & \frac{3}{2} & | & -\frac{7}{2} \\ 0 & 1 & -\frac{8}{5} & | & \frac{11}{5} \\ 0 & 0 & -\frac{83}{5} & | & -\frac{83}{10} \end{bmatrix} \frac{7}{2}R_2 + R_3$$

$$\begin{bmatrix} 1 & -\frac{3}{4} & \frac{3}{2} & | & -\frac{7}{2} \\ 0 & 1 & -\frac{8}{5} & | & \frac{11}{5} \\ 0 & 0 & 1 & | & \frac{1}{2} \end{bmatrix} -\frac{5}{83}R_3$$

The system is

$$r - \frac{3}{4}s + \frac{3}{2}t = -\frac{7}{2}$$

$$s - \frac{8}{5}t = \frac{11}{5}$$

$$t = \frac{1}{2}$$

Substitute $\frac{1}{2}$ for t in the second equation.

$$s - \frac{8}{5}t = \frac{11}{5}$$

$$s - \frac{8}{5}\left(\frac{1}{2}\right) = \frac{11}{5}$$

$$s - \frac{4}{5} = \frac{11}{5}$$

$$s = \frac{15}{5}$$

$$s = 3$$

Substitute 3 for s and $\frac{1}{2}$ for t in the first equation.

$$r - \frac{3}{4}s + \frac{3}{2}t = -\frac{7}{2}$$

$$r - \frac{3}{4}(3) + \frac{3}{2}\left(\frac{1}{2}\right) = -\frac{7}{2}$$

$$r - \frac{9}{4} + \frac{3}{4} = -\frac{7}{2}$$

$$r - \frac{6}{4} = -\frac{7}{2}$$

$$r - \frac{3}{2} = -\frac{7}{2}$$

$$r = -2$$

The solution is $\left(-2, 3, \frac{1}{2}\right)$.

43. $2x - 4y + 3z = -12$

$3x - y + 2z = -3$

$-4x + 8y - 6z = 10$

$$\begin{bmatrix} 2 & -4 & 3 & | & -12 \\ 3 & -1 & 2 & | & -3 \\ -4 & 8 & -6 & | & 10 \end{bmatrix}$$

$$\begin{bmatrix} 1 & -2 & \frac{3}{2} & | & -6 \\ 3 & -1 & 2 & | & -3 \\ -4 & 8 & -6 & | & 10 \end{bmatrix} \frac{1}{2}R_1$$

$$\begin{bmatrix} 1 & -2 & \frac{3}{2} & | & -6 \\ 0 & 5 & -\frac{5}{2} & | & 15 \\ -4 & 8 & -6 & | & 10 \end{bmatrix} -3R_1 + R_2$$

$$\begin{bmatrix} 1 & -2 & \frac{3}{2} & | & -6 \\ 0 & 5 & -\frac{5}{2} & | & 15 \\ 0 & 0 & 0 & | & -14 \end{bmatrix} 4R_1 + R_3$$

Since the last row contains zeros on the left and a nonzero number on the right, the system is inconsistent and there is no solution.

44. $3x - 2y + 4z = -1$
$5x + 2y - 4z = 9$
$-6x + 4y - 8z = 2$

$$\begin{bmatrix} 3 & -2 & 4 & | & -1 \\ 5 & 2 & -4 & | & 9 \\ -6 & 4 & -8 & | & 2 \end{bmatrix}$$

$$\begin{bmatrix} 1 & -\frac{2}{3} & \frac{4}{3} & | & -\frac{1}{3} \\ 5 & 2 & -4 & | & 9 \\ -6 & 4 & -8 & | & 2 \end{bmatrix} \frac{1}{3}R_1$$

$$\begin{bmatrix} 1 & -\frac{2}{3} & \frac{4}{3} & | & -\frac{1}{3} \\ 0 & \frac{16}{3} & -\frac{32}{3} & | & \frac{32}{3} \\ -6 & 4 & -8 & | & 2 \end{bmatrix} -5R_1 + R_2$$

$$\begin{bmatrix} 1 & -\frac{2}{3} & \frac{4}{3} & | & -\frac{1}{3} \\ 0 & \frac{16}{3} & -\frac{32}{3} & | & \frac{32}{3} \\ 0 & 0 & 0 & | & 0 \end{bmatrix} 6R_1 + R_3$$

Since there is a row of all zeros, the system is dependent.

45. $5x - 3y + 4z = 22$
$-x - 15y + 10z = -15$
$-3x + 9y - 12z = -6$

$$\begin{bmatrix} 5 & -3 & 4 & | & 22 \\ -1 & -15 & 10 & | & -15 \\ -3 & 9 & -12 & | & -6 \end{bmatrix}$$

$$\begin{bmatrix} 1 & -\frac{3}{5} & \frac{4}{5} & | & \frac{22}{5} \\ -1 & -15 & 10 & | & -15 \\ -3 & 9 & -12 & | & -6 \end{bmatrix} \frac{1}{5}R_1$$

$$\begin{bmatrix} 1 & -\frac{3}{5} & \frac{4}{5} & | & \frac{22}{5} \\ 0 & -\frac{78}{5} & \frac{54}{5} & | & -\frac{53}{5} \\ -3 & 9 & -12 & | & -6 \end{bmatrix} R_1 + R_2$$

$$\begin{bmatrix} 1 & -\frac{3}{5} & \frac{4}{5} & | & \frac{22}{5} \\ 0 & -\frac{78}{5} & \frac{54}{5} & | & -\frac{53}{5} \\ 0 & \frac{36}{5} & -\frac{48}{5} & | & \frac{36}{5} \end{bmatrix} 3R_1 + R_3$$

$$\begin{bmatrix} 1 & -\frac{3}{5} & \frac{4}{5} & | & \frac{22}{5} \\ 0 & 1 & -\frac{9}{13} & | & \frac{53}{78} \\ 0 & \frac{36}{5} & -\frac{48}{5} & | & \frac{36}{5} \end{bmatrix} -\frac{5}{78}R_2$$

$$\begin{bmatrix} 1 & -\frac{3}{5} & \frac{4}{5} & | & \frac{22}{5} \\ 0 & 1 & -\frac{9}{13} & | & \frac{53}{78} \\ 0 & 0 & -\frac{60}{13} & | & \frac{30}{13} \end{bmatrix} -\frac{36}{5}R_2 + R_3$$

$$\begin{bmatrix} 1 & -\frac{3}{5} & \frac{4}{5} & | & \frac{22}{5} \\ 0 & 1 & -\frac{9}{13} & | & \frac{53}{78} \\ 0 & 0 & 1 & | & -\frac{1}{2} \end{bmatrix}$$

The system is
$$x - \frac{3}{5}y + \frac{4}{5}z = \frac{22}{5}$$
$$y - \frac{9}{13}z = \frac{53}{78}$$
$$z = -\frac{1}{2}$$

Substitute $-\frac{1}{2}$ for z in the second equation.
$$y - \frac{9}{13}z = \frac{53}{78}$$
$$y - \frac{9}{13}\left(-\frac{1}{2}\right) = \frac{53}{78}$$
$$y + \frac{9}{26} = \frac{53}{78}$$
$$y = \frac{53}{78} - \frac{27}{78} = \frac{26}{78} = \frac{1}{3}$$

Substitute $\frac{1}{3}$ for y and $-\frac{1}{2}$ for z in the first equation.
$$x - \frac{3}{5}y + \frac{4}{5}z = \frac{22}{5}$$
$$x - \frac{3}{5}\left(\frac{1}{3}\right) + \frac{4}{5}\left(-\frac{1}{2}\right) = \frac{22}{5}$$
$$x - \frac{1}{5} - \frac{2}{5} = \frac{22}{5}$$
$$x = \frac{22}{5} + \frac{1}{5} + \frac{2}{5} = \frac{25}{5} = 5$$

The solution is $\left(5, \frac{1}{3}, -\frac{1}{2}\right)$.

46.
$$9x - 4y + 5z = -2$$
$$-9x + 5y - 10z = -1$$
$$9x + 3y + 10z = 1$$

$$\begin{bmatrix} 9 & -4 & 5 & | & -2 \\ -9 & 5 & -10 & | & -1 \\ 9 & 3 & 10 & | & 1 \end{bmatrix}$$

$$\begin{bmatrix} 1 & -\frac{4}{9} & \frac{5}{9} & | & -\frac{2}{9} \\ -9 & 5 & -10 & | & -1 \\ 9 & 3 & 10 & | & 1 \end{bmatrix} \frac{1}{9}R_1$$

$$\begin{bmatrix} 1 & -\frac{4}{9} & \frac{5}{9} & | & -\frac{2}{9} \\ 0 & 1 & -5 & | & -3 \\ 9 & 3 & 10 & | & 1 \end{bmatrix} 9R_1 + R_2$$

$$\begin{bmatrix} 1 & -\frac{4}{9} & \frac{5}{9} & | & -\frac{2}{9} \\ 0 & 1 & -5 & | & -3 \\ 0 & 7 & 5 & | & 3 \end{bmatrix} -9R_1 + R_3$$

$$\begin{bmatrix} 1 & -\frac{4}{9} & \frac{5}{9} & | & -\frac{2}{9} \\ 0 & 1 & -5 & | & -3 \\ 0 & 0 & 40 & | & 24 \end{bmatrix} -7R_2 + R_3$$

$$\begin{bmatrix} 1 & -\frac{4}{9} & \frac{5}{9} & | & -\frac{2}{9} \\ 0 & 1 & -5 & | & -3 \\ 0 & 0 & 1 & | & \frac{3}{5} \end{bmatrix} \frac{1}{40}R_3$$

The system is
$$x - \frac{4}{9}y + \frac{5}{9}z = -\frac{2}{9}$$
$$y - 5z = -3$$
$$z = \frac{3}{5}$$

Substitute $\frac{3}{5}$ for z in the second equation.

$$y - 5\left(\frac{3}{5}\right) = -3$$
$$y - 3 = -3$$
$$y = 0$$

Substitute 0 for y and $\frac{3}{5}$ for z in the first equation.

$$x - \frac{4}{9}(0) + \frac{5}{9}\left(\frac{3}{5}\right) = -\frac{2}{9}$$
$$x + \frac{3}{9} = -\frac{2}{9}$$
$$x = -\frac{5}{9}$$

The solution is $\left(-\frac{5}{9}, 0, \frac{3}{5}\right)$.

47. No, this is the same as switching the order of the equations.

48. Answers may vary; one possible answer is: Generally not, but if two equations are identical and there are no contradictions, the system is dependent.

49. Let x = smallest angle
y = remaining angle
z = largest angle
$$z = x + 55$$
$$z = y + 20$$
$$x + y + z = 180$$

Write the system in standard form:
$$x - z = -55$$
$$y - z = -20$$
$$x + y + z = 180$$

$$\begin{bmatrix} 1 & 0 & -1 & | & -55 \\ 0 & 1 & -1 & | & -20 \\ 1 & 1 & 1 & | & 180 \end{bmatrix}$$

$$\begin{bmatrix} 1 & 0 & -1 & | & -55 \\ 0 & 1 & -1 & | & -20 \\ 0 & 1 & 2 & | & 235 \end{bmatrix} -1R_1 + R_3$$

$$\begin{bmatrix} 1 & 0 & -1 & | & -55 \\ 0 & 1 & -1 & | & -20 \\ 0 & 0 & 3 & | & 255 \end{bmatrix} -1R_2 + R_3$$

$$\begin{bmatrix} 1 & 0 & -1 & | & -55 \\ 0 & 1 & -1 & | & -20 \\ 0 & 0 & 1 & | & 85 \end{bmatrix} \frac{1}{3}R_3$$

The system is
$$x - z = -55$$
$$y - z = -20$$
$$z = 85$$

Substitute 85 for z in the second equation.
$$y - z = -20$$
$$y - 85 = -20$$
$$y = 65$$

Substitute 85 for z in the first equation.
$$x - z = -55$$
$$x - 85 = -55$$
$$x = 30$$

The angles are 30°, 65°, and 85°.

50. Let x = smallest angle

y = remaining angle

z = largest angle

$z = 2x$

$y = x + 10$

$x + y + z = 90$

Write the system in standard form.

$2x - z = 0$

$x - y = -10$

$x + y + z = 90$

$$\begin{bmatrix} 2 & 0 & -1 & | & 0 \\ 1 & -1 & 0 & | & -10 \\ 1 & 1 & 1 & | & 90 \end{bmatrix}$$

$$\begin{bmatrix} 1 & 0 & -\frac{1}{2} & | & 0 \\ 1 & -1 & 0 & | & -10 \\ 1 & 1 & 1 & | & 90 \end{bmatrix} \frac{1}{2} R_1$$

$$\begin{bmatrix} 1 & 0 & -\frac{1}{2} & | & 0 \\ 0 & -1 & \frac{1}{2} & | & -10 \\ 1 & 1 & 1 & | & 90 \end{bmatrix} -1R_1 + R_2$$

$$\begin{bmatrix} 1 & 0 & -\frac{1}{2} & | & 0 \\ 0 & -1 & \frac{1}{2} & | & -10 \\ 0 & 1 & \frac{3}{2} & | & 90 \end{bmatrix} -1R_1 + R_3$$

$$\begin{bmatrix} 1 & 0 & -\frac{1}{2} & | & 0 \\ 0 & 1 & -\frac{1}{2} & | & 10 \\ 0 & 1 & \frac{3}{2} & | & 90 \end{bmatrix} -1R_2$$

$$\begin{bmatrix} 1 & 0 & -\frac{1}{2} & | & 0 \\ 0 & 1 & -\frac{1}{2} & | & 10 \\ 0 & 0 & 2 & | & 80 \end{bmatrix} -1R_2 + R_3$$

$$\begin{bmatrix} 1 & 0 & -\frac{1}{2} & | & 0 \\ 0 & 1 & -\frac{1}{2} & | & 10 \\ 0 & 0 & 1 & | & 40 \end{bmatrix} \frac{1}{2} R_3$$

The system is

$x - \frac{1}{2}z = 0$

$y - \frac{1}{2}z = 10$

$z = 40$

Substitute 40 for z in the second equation.

$y - \frac{1}{2}(40) = 10$

$y - 20 = 10$

$y = 30$

Substitute 40 for z in the first equation.

$x - \frac{1}{2}(40) = 0$

$x - 20 = 0$

$x = 20$

The angles are 20°, 30°, and 40°.

51. Let x = amount Chiquita controls,

y = amount Dole controls,

z = amount Del Monte controls

$x = z + 12$

$y = 2z - 3$

$x + y + z = 65$

Write the system in standard form.

$x - z = 12$

$y - 2z = -3$

$x + y + z = 65$

$$\begin{bmatrix} 1 & 0 & -1 & | & 12 \\ 0 & 1 & -2 & | & -3 \\ 1 & 1 & 1 & | & 65 \end{bmatrix}$$

$$\begin{bmatrix} 1 & 0 & -1 & | & 12 \\ 0 & 1 & -2 & | & -3 \\ 0 & 1 & 2 & | & 53 \end{bmatrix} -1R_1 + R_3$$

$$\begin{bmatrix} 1 & 0 & -1 & | & 12 \\ 0 & 1 & -2 & | & -3 \\ 0 & 0 & 4 & | & 56 \end{bmatrix} -1R_2 + R_3$$

$$\begin{bmatrix} 1 & 0 & -1 & | & 12 \\ 0 & 1 & -2 & | & -3 \\ 0 & 0 & 1 & | & 14 \end{bmatrix} \frac{1}{4} R_3$$

The system is

$x - z = 12$

$y - 2z = -3$

$z = 14$

Substitute 14 for z in the second equation.

$y - 2z = -3$

$y - 2(14) = -3$

$y - 28 = -3$

$y = 25$

Substitute 14 for z in the first equation.

$x - z = 12$

$x - 14 = 12$

$x = 26$

Del Monte controls 14% of the bananas, Dole controls 25%, Chiquita controls 26%, and others controlling the remaining 100% – 65% = 35%.

52. Let T = the percent that selected reducing taxes, H = the percent that selected reforming health care insurance, and D = the percent that selected strengthening the U.S. dollar.

$$T + H + D = 77$$
$$T = H + 4$$
$$T = 3D + 2$$

Write the system in standard form.

$$T + H + D = 77$$
$$T - H + 0D = 4$$
$$T + 0H - 3D = 2$$

$$\begin{bmatrix} 1 & 1 & 1 & | & 77 \\ 1 & -1 & 0 & | & 4 \\ 1 & 0 & -3 & | & 2 \end{bmatrix}$$

$$\begin{bmatrix} 1 & 1 & 1 & | & 77 \\ 0 & -2 & -1 & | & -73 \\ 1 & 0 & -3 & | & 2 \end{bmatrix} -R_1 + R_2$$

$$\begin{bmatrix} 1 & 1 & 1 & | & 77 \\ 0 & -2 & -1 & | & -73 \\ 0 & -1 & -4 & | & -75 \end{bmatrix} -R_1 + R_3$$

$$\begin{bmatrix} 1 & 1 & 1 & | & 77 \\ 0 & 1 & \frac{1}{2} & | & \frac{73}{2} \\ 0 & -1 & -4 & | & -75 \end{bmatrix} -\frac{1}{2}R_2$$

$$\begin{bmatrix} 1 & 1 & 1 & | & 77 \\ 0 & 1 & \frac{1}{2} & | & \frac{73}{2} \\ 0 & 0 & -\frac{7}{2} & | & -\frac{77}{2} \end{bmatrix} R_2 + R_3$$

$$\begin{bmatrix} 1 & 1 & 1 & | & 77 \\ 0 & 1 & \frac{1}{2} & | & \frac{73}{2} \\ 0 & 0 & 1 & | & 11 \end{bmatrix} -\frac{2}{7}R_3$$

The system is

$$T + H + D = 77$$
$$H + \frac{1}{2}D = \frac{73}{2}$$
$$D = 11$$

Substitute 11 for D in the second equation.

$$H + \frac{1}{2}(11) = \frac{73}{2}$$
$$H + \frac{11}{2} = \frac{73}{2}$$
$$H = 31$$

Substitute 11 for D and 31 for H in the first equation.

$$T + (31) + (11) = 77$$
$$T + 42 = 77$$
$$T = 35$$

35% of CEOs selected reducing taxes, 31% selected reform health care insurance, and 11% selected strengthening the U.S. dollar.

53. $\dfrac{3x^2 + 4x - 23}{x + 4}$

$$\begin{array}{r} 3x - 8 \\ x+4{\overline{\smash{\big)}\,3x^2 + 4x - 23}} \\ \underline{3x^2 + 12x} \\ -8x - 23 \\ \underline{-8x - 32} \\ 9 \end{array}$$

$$\frac{3x^2 + 4x - 23}{x + 4} = 3x - 8 + \frac{9}{x + 4}$$

54. $2x^2 - x - 36 = 0$

$$(2x - 9)(x + 4) = 0$$

$2x - 9 = 0$ $\quad$ or $\quad$ $x + 4 = 0$

$\quad\quad x = \dfrac{9}{2}$ $\quad\quad\quad\quad$ $x = -4$

55. $\dfrac{1}{x^2 - 4} - \dfrac{2}{x - 2} = \dfrac{1}{(x+2)(x-2)} - \dfrac{2}{x - 2}$

$$= \frac{1}{(x+2)(x-2)} - \frac{2(x+2)}{(x+2)(x-2)}$$

$$= \frac{1 - 2(x+2)}{(x+2)(x-2)}$$

$$= \frac{1 - 2x - 4}{(x+2)(x-2)}$$

$$= \frac{-2x - 3}{(x+2)(x-2)}$$

56. Let b be the time (in minutes) it takes Terry to stach the wood by herself.

$$\frac{t}{a} + \frac{t}{b} = 1$$
$$\frac{12}{20} + \frac{12}{b} = 1$$
$$20b\left(\frac{12}{20} + \frac{12}{b}\right) = 20b(1)$$
$$12b + 240 = 20b$$
$$240 = 8b$$
$$30 = b$$

It will take Terry 30 minutes to stach the wood by herself.

Exercise Set 9.7

1 – 2. Answers will vary.

3. If $D = 0$ and D_x, D_y, or D_z is not equal to 0, the system is inconsistent.

4. If $D = 0$ and D_x, D_y, and D_z all also equal 0, the system is dependent.

5. $x = \dfrac{D_x}{D} = \dfrac{12}{4} = 3$

$y = \dfrac{D_y}{D} = \dfrac{-2}{4} = -\dfrac{1}{2}$

The solution is $\left(3, -\dfrac{1}{2}\right)$.

6. $x = \dfrac{D_x}{D} = \dfrac{8}{-2} = -4$

$y = \dfrac{D_y}{D} = \dfrac{14}{-2} = -7$

$z = \dfrac{D_z}{D} = \dfrac{-2}{-2} = 1$

The solution is $(-4, -7, 1)$.

7. $\begin{vmatrix} 2 & 4 \\ 1 & 5 \end{vmatrix} = (2)(5) - (1)(4) = 10 - 4 = 6$

8. $\begin{vmatrix} 3 & 5 \\ -1 & -2 \end{vmatrix} = (3)(-2) - (-1)(5) = -6 - (-5) = -1$

9. $\begin{vmatrix} \frac{1}{2} & 3 \\ 2 & -4 \end{vmatrix} = \dfrac{1}{2}(-4) - (2)(3) = -2 - 6 = -8$

10. $\begin{vmatrix} 13 & -\frac{2}{3} \\ -1 & 0 \end{vmatrix} = 13(0) - (-1)\left(-\dfrac{2}{3}\right) = 0 - \dfrac{2}{3} = -\dfrac{2}{3}$

11. $\begin{vmatrix} 3 & 2 & 0 \\ 0 & 5 & 3 \\ -1 & 4 & 2 \end{vmatrix} = 3\begin{vmatrix} 5 & 3 \\ 4 & 2 \end{vmatrix} - 0\begin{vmatrix} 2 & 0 \\ 4 & 2 \end{vmatrix} + (-1)\begin{vmatrix} 2 & 0 \\ 5 & 3 \end{vmatrix}$

$= 3(10 - 12) - 0(4 - 0) - 1(6 - 0)$

$= 3(-2) - 0(4) - 1(6)$

$= -6 - 0 - 6$

$= -12$

12. We will use expansion by the minor determinants of the second row.

$\begin{vmatrix} 4 & 1 & 1 \\ 0 & 0 & 3 \\ 2 & 2 & 9 \end{vmatrix} = -0\begin{vmatrix} 1 & 1 \\ 2 & 9 \end{vmatrix} + 0\begin{vmatrix} 4 & 1 \\ 2 & 9 \end{vmatrix} - 3\begin{vmatrix} 4 & 1 \\ 2 & 2 \end{vmatrix}$

$= -0(9 - 2) + 0(36 - 2) - 3(8 - 2)$

$= -0(7) + 0(34) - 3(6)$

$= 0 + 0 - 18$

$= -18$

13. $\begin{vmatrix} 2 & 3 & 1 \\ 1 & -3 & -6 \\ -4 & 5 & 9 \end{vmatrix}$

$= 2\begin{vmatrix} -3 & -6 \\ 5 & 9 \end{vmatrix} - 1\begin{vmatrix} 3 & 1 \\ 5 & 9 \end{vmatrix} + (-4)\begin{vmatrix} 3 & 1 \\ -3 & -6 \end{vmatrix}$

$= 2[-27 - (-30)] - 1(27 - 5) - 4[-18 - (-3)]$

$= 2(3) - 1(22) - 4(-15)$

$= 6 - 22 + 60$

$= 44$

14. $\begin{vmatrix} 5 & -8 & 6 \\ 3 & 0 & 4 \\ -5 & -2 & 1 \end{vmatrix}$

$= 5\begin{vmatrix} 0 & 4 \\ -2 & 1 \end{vmatrix} - 3\begin{vmatrix} -8 & 6 \\ -2 & 1 \end{vmatrix} + (-5)\begin{vmatrix} -8 & 6 \\ 0 & 4 \end{vmatrix}$

$= 5[0 - (-8)] - 3[-8 - (-12)] - 5(-32 - 0)$

$= 5(8) - 3(4) - 5(-32)$

$= 40 - 12 + 160$

$= 188$

15. $x + 3y = 1$

$-2x - 3y = 4$

To solve, first calculate D, D_x, and D_y.

$D = \begin{vmatrix} 1 & 3 \\ -2 & -3 \end{vmatrix} = (1)(-3) - (-2)(3) = -3 - (-6) = 3$

$D_x = \begin{vmatrix} 1 & 3 \\ 4 & -3 \end{vmatrix} = (1)(-3) - (4)(3) = -15$

$D_y = \begin{vmatrix} 1 & 1 \\ -2 & 4 \end{vmatrix} = (1)(4) - (-2)(1) = 4 - (-2) = 6$

$x = \dfrac{D_x}{D} = \dfrac{-15}{3} = -5$ and $y = \dfrac{D_y}{D} = \dfrac{6}{3} = 2$

The solution is $(-5, 2)$.

16. $2x + 4y = -2$
$-5x - 2y = 13$

To solve, first calculate D, D_x, and D_y.

$D = \begin{vmatrix} 2 & 4 \\ -5 & -2 \end{vmatrix} = (2)(-2) - (-5)(4)$

$\quad = -4 - (-20) = 16$

$D_x = \begin{vmatrix} -2 & 4 \\ 13 & -2 \end{vmatrix} = (-2)(-2) - (13)(4)$

$\quad = 4 - 52 = -48$

$D_y = \begin{vmatrix} 2 & -2 \\ -5 & 13 \end{vmatrix} = (2)(13) - (-5)(-2)$

$\quad = 26 - 10 = 16$

$x = \dfrac{D_x}{D} = \dfrac{-48}{16} = -3$ and $y = \dfrac{D_y}{D} = \dfrac{16}{16} = 1$

The solution is $(-3, 1)$.

17. $-x - 2y = 2$
$x + 3y = -6$

To solve, first calculate D, D_x, and D_y.

$D = \begin{vmatrix} -1 & -2 \\ 1 & 3 \end{vmatrix} = (-1)(3) - (1)(-2) = -3 + 2 = -1$

$D_x = \begin{vmatrix} 2 & -2 \\ -6 & 3 \end{vmatrix}$

$\quad = (2)(3) - (-6)(-2)$

$\quad = 6 - 12$

$\quad = -6$

$D_y = \begin{vmatrix} -1 & 2 \\ 1 & -6 \end{vmatrix} = (-1)(-6) - (1)(2) = 6 - 2 = 4$

$x = \dfrac{D_x}{D} = \dfrac{-6}{-1} = 6$ and $y = \dfrac{D_y}{D} = \dfrac{4}{-1} = -4$

The solution is $(6, -4)$.

18. $2r + 3s = -9$
$3r + 5s = -16$

To solve first calculate D, D_r, and D_s.

$D = \begin{vmatrix} 2 & 3 \\ 3 & 5 \end{vmatrix} = (2)(5) - (3)(3) = 10 - 9 = 1$

$D_r = \begin{vmatrix} -9 & 3 \\ -16 & 5 \end{vmatrix} = (-9)(5) - (-16)(3)$

$\quad = -45 - (-48) = -45 + 48 = 3$

$D_s = \begin{vmatrix} 2 & -9 \\ 3 & -16 \end{vmatrix} = (2)(-16) - (3)(-9)$

$\quad = -32 - (-27) = -32 + 27 = -5$

$r = \dfrac{D_r}{D} = \dfrac{3}{1} = 3$ and $s = \dfrac{D_s}{D} = \dfrac{-5}{1} = -5$

The solution is $(3, -5)$.

19. $6x = 4y + 7$
$8x - 1 = -3y$

Rewrite the system in standard form:
$6x - 4y = 7$
$8x + 3y = 1$

Now calculate D, D_x, and D_y.

$D = \begin{vmatrix} 6 & -4 \\ 8 & 3 \end{vmatrix} = (6)(3) - (8)(-4) = 18 + 32 = 50$

$D_x = \begin{vmatrix} 7 & -4 \\ 1 & 3 \end{vmatrix} = (7)(3) - (1)(-4) = 21 + 4 = 25$

$D_y = \begin{vmatrix} 6 & 7 \\ 8 & 1 \end{vmatrix} = (6)(1) - (8)(7) = 6 - 56 = -50$

$x = \dfrac{D_x}{D} = \dfrac{25}{50} = \dfrac{1}{2}$ and $y = \dfrac{D_y}{D} = \dfrac{-50}{50} = -1$

The solution is $\left(\dfrac{1}{2}, -1 \right)$.

20. $6x + 3y = -4$
$9x + 5y = -6$

To solve, first calculate D, D_x, and D_y.

$D = \begin{vmatrix} 6 & 3 \\ 9 & 5 \end{vmatrix} = (6)(5) - (9)(3) = 30 - 27 = 3$

$D_x = \begin{vmatrix} -4 & 3 \\ -6 & 5 \end{vmatrix} = (-4)(5) - (-6)(3) = -20 + 18 = -2$

$D_y = \begin{vmatrix} 6 & -4 \\ 9 & -6 \end{vmatrix} = (6)(-6) - (9)(-4) = -36 + 36 = 0$

$x = \dfrac{D_x}{D} = \dfrac{-2}{3} = -\dfrac{2}{3}$ and $y = \dfrac{D_y}{D} = \dfrac{0}{3} = 0$

The solution is $\left(-\dfrac{2}{3}, 0 \right)$.

21. $5p - 7q = -21$

$-4p + 3q = 22$

To solve, first calculate D, D_p, and D_q.

$D = \begin{vmatrix} 5 & -7 \\ -4 & 3 \end{vmatrix} = (5)(3) - (-4)(-7)$

$\quad = 15 - 28$

$\quad = -13$

$D_p = \begin{vmatrix} -21 & -7 \\ 22 & 3 \end{vmatrix} = (-21)(3) - (22)(-7)$

$\quad = -63 - (-154)$

$\quad = 91$

$D_q = \begin{vmatrix} 5 & -21 \\ -4 & 22 \end{vmatrix} = (5)(22) - (-4)(-21)$

$\quad = 110 - 84$

$\quad = 26$

$p = \dfrac{D_p}{D} = \dfrac{91}{-13} = -7$ and $q = \dfrac{D_q}{D} = \dfrac{26}{-13} = -2$

The solution is $(-7, -2)$.

22. $4x = -5y - 2$

$-2x = y + 4$

Rewrite the system in standard form:

$4x + 5y = -2$

$2x + y = -4$

Now calculate D, D_x, and D_y.

$D = \begin{vmatrix} 4 & 5 \\ 2 & 1 \end{vmatrix} = (4)(1) - (2)(5)$

$\quad = 4 - 10 = -6$

$D_x = \begin{vmatrix} -2 & 5 \\ -4 & 1 \end{vmatrix} = (-2)(1) - (-4)(5)$

$\quad = -2 - (-20)$

$\quad = 18$

$D_y = \begin{vmatrix} 4 & -2 \\ 2 & -4 \end{vmatrix} = (4)(-4) - (2)(-2)$

$\quad = -16 - (-4)$

$\quad = -12$

$x = \dfrac{D_x}{D} = \dfrac{18}{-6} = -3$ and $y = \dfrac{D_y}{D} = \dfrac{-12}{-6} = 2$

The solution is $(-3, 2)$.

23. $x + 5y = 3$

$2x - 6 = -10y$

Rewrite the system in standard form:

$x + 5y = 3$

$2x + 10y = 6$

To solve, first calculate D, D_x, and D_y.

$D = \begin{vmatrix} 1 & 5 \\ 2 & 10 \end{vmatrix} = (1)(10) - (2)(5) = 10 - 10 = 0$

$D_x = \begin{vmatrix} 3 & 5 \\ 6 & 10 \end{vmatrix} = (3)(10) - (6)(5) = 30 - 30 = 0$

$D_y = \begin{vmatrix} 1 & 3 \\ 2 & 6 \end{vmatrix} = (1)(6) - (2)(3) = 6 - 6 = 0$

Since $D = 0$, $D_x = 0$, and $D_y = 0$, the system is dependent so there are an infinite number of solutions.

24. $9x + 6y = -3$

$6x + 4y = -2$

Now calculate D, D_x, and D_y.

$D = \begin{vmatrix} 9 & 6 \\ 6 & 4 \end{vmatrix} = (9)(4) - (6)(6) = 36 - 36 = 0$

$D_x = \begin{vmatrix} -3 & 6 \\ -2 & 4 \end{vmatrix} = (-3)(4) - (-2)(6) = -12 + 12 = 0$

$D_y = \begin{vmatrix} 9 & -3 \\ 6 & -2 \end{vmatrix} = (9)(-2) - (6)(-3) = -18 + 18 = 0$

Since $D = 0$, $D_x = 0$, and $D_y = 0$, the system is dependent so there are an infinite number of solutions.

25. $3r = -4s - 6$

$3s = -5r + 1$

Rewrite the system in standard form.

$3r + 4s = -6$

$5r + 3s = 1$

Now calculate D, D_r, and D_s.

$D = \begin{vmatrix} 3 & 4 \\ 5 & 3 \end{vmatrix} = (3)(3) - (5)(4) = 9 - 20 = -11$

$D_r = \begin{vmatrix} -6 & 4 \\ 1 & 3 \end{vmatrix} = (-6)(3) - (1)(4) = -18 - 4 = -22$

$D_s = \begin{vmatrix} 3 & -6 \\ 5 & 1 \end{vmatrix} = (3)(1) - (5)(-6) = 3 + 30 = 33$

$r = \dfrac{D_r}{D} = \dfrac{-22}{-11} = 2$ and $s = \dfrac{D_s}{D} = \dfrac{33}{-11} = -3$

The solution is $(2, -3)$.

26. $x = y - 1$

$3y = 2x + 9$

Rewrite the system in standard form.

$x - y = -1$

$2x - 3y = -9$

Now calculate D, D_x, and D_y.

$D = \begin{vmatrix} 1 & -1 \\ 2 & -3 \end{vmatrix} = (1)(-3) - (2)(-1) = -3 + 2 = -1$

$D_x = \begin{vmatrix} -1 & -1 \\ -9 & -3 \end{vmatrix} = (-1)(-3) - (-9)(-1) = 3 - 9 = -6$

$D_y = \begin{vmatrix} 1 & -1 \\ 2 & -9 \end{vmatrix} = (1)(-9) - (2)(-1) = -9 + 2 = -7$

$x = \dfrac{D_x}{D} = \dfrac{-6}{-1} = 6$ and $y = \dfrac{D_y}{D} = \dfrac{-7}{-1} = 7$

The solution is $(6, 7)$.

27. $5x - 5y = 3$

$-x + y = -4$

To solve, first calculate D, D_x, and D_y.

$D = \begin{vmatrix} 5 & -5 \\ -1 & 1 \end{vmatrix} = (5)(1) - (-1)(-5) = 5 - 5 = 0$

$D_x = \begin{vmatrix} 3 & -5 \\ -4 & 1 \end{vmatrix} = (3)(1) - (-4)(-5) = 3 - 20 = -17$

Since $D = 0$ and $D_x \neq 0$, the system is inconsistent, so there is no solution.

28. $2x - 5y = -3$

$-4x + 10y = 7$

To solve, first calculate D, D_x, and D_y.

$D = \begin{vmatrix} 2 & -5 \\ -4 & 10 \end{vmatrix} = (2)(10) - (-4)(-5) = 20 - 20 = 0$

$D_x = \begin{vmatrix} -3 & -5 \\ 7 & 10 \end{vmatrix} = (-3)(10) - (7)(-5)$

$= -30 + 35 = 5$

Since $D = 0$ and $D_x \neq 0$, the system is inconsistent, so there is no solution.

29. $6.3x - 4.5y = -9.9$

$-9.1x + 3.2y = -2.2$

Here, you can work with decimals in the determinants. If you do not want to use decimals, then you need to multiply each equation by 10 to clear the decimals.

First, calculate D, D_x, and D_y.

$D = \begin{vmatrix} 6.3 & -4.5 \\ -9.1 & 3.2 \end{vmatrix} = (6.3)(3.2) - (-9.1)(-4.5)$

$= 20.16 - 40.95 = -20.79$

$D_x = \begin{vmatrix} -9.9 & -4.5 \\ -2.2 & 3.2 \end{vmatrix} = (-9.9)(3.2) - (-2.2)(-4.5)$

$= -31.68 - 9.90 = -41.58$

$D_y = \begin{vmatrix} 6.3 & -9.9 \\ -9.1 & -2.2 \end{vmatrix} = (6.3)(-2.2) - (-9.1)(-9.9)$

$= -13.86 - 90.09 = -103.95$

$x = \dfrac{D_x}{D} = \dfrac{-41.58}{-20.79} = 2$ and

$y = \dfrac{D_y}{D} = \dfrac{-103.95}{-20.79} = 5$

The solution is $(2, 5)$.

30. $-1.1x + 8.3y = 36.5$

$3.5x + 1.6y = -4.1$

Here, you can work with decimals in the determinants. If you do not want to use decimals, then you need to multiply each equation by 10 to clear the decimals.

First, calculate D, D_x, and D_y.

$D = \begin{vmatrix} -1.1 & 8.3 \\ 3.5 & 1.6 \end{vmatrix} = (-1.1)(1.6) - (3.5)(8.3)$

$= -1.76 - 29.05 = -30.81$

$D_x = \begin{vmatrix} 36.5 & 8.3 \\ -4.1 & 1.6 \end{vmatrix} = (36.5)(1.6) - (-4.1)(8.3)$

$= 58.4 + 34.03 = 92.43$

$D_y = \begin{vmatrix} -1.1 & 36.5 \\ 3.5 & -4.1 \end{vmatrix} = (-1.1)(-4.1) - (3.5)(36.5)$

$= 4.51 - 127.75 = -123.24$

$x = \dfrac{D_x}{D} = \dfrac{92.43}{-30.81} = -3$ and

$y = \dfrac{D_y}{D} = \dfrac{-123.24}{-30.81} = 4$

The solution is $(-3, 4)$.

31.
$$x + y + z = 3$$
$$0x - 3y + 4z = 15$$
$$-3x + 4y - 2z = -13$$

To solve, first calculate D, D_x, D_y, and D_z.

$$D = \begin{vmatrix} 1 & 1 & 1 \\ 0 & -3 & 4 \\ -3 & 4 & -2 \end{vmatrix} \text{ (using first column)}$$

$$= 1\begin{vmatrix} -3 & 4 \\ 4 & -2 \end{vmatrix} - 0\begin{vmatrix} 1 & 1 \\ 4 & -2 \end{vmatrix} + (-3)\begin{vmatrix} 1 & 1 \\ -3 & 4 \end{vmatrix}$$

$$= 1(6-16) - 0(-2-4) - 3(4+3)$$

$$= 1(-10) - 0(-6) - 3(7)$$

$$= -10 - 0 - 21$$

$$= -31$$

$$D_x = \begin{vmatrix} 3 & 1 & 1 \\ 15 & -3 & 4 \\ -13 & 4 & -2 \end{vmatrix} \text{ (using first row)}$$

$$= 3\begin{vmatrix} -3 & 4 \\ 4 & -2 \end{vmatrix} - 1\begin{vmatrix} 15 & 4 \\ -13 & -2 \end{vmatrix} + 1\begin{vmatrix} 15 & -3 \\ -13 & 4 \end{vmatrix}$$

$$= 3(6-16) - 1(-30+52) + 1(60-39)$$

$$= 3(-10) - 1(22) + 1(21)$$

$$= -30 - 22 + 21$$

$$= -31$$

$$D_y = \begin{vmatrix} 1 & 3 & 1 \\ 0 & 15 & 4 \\ -3 & -13 & -2 \end{vmatrix} \text{ (using first column)}$$

$$= 1\begin{vmatrix} 15 & 4 \\ -13 & -2 \end{vmatrix} - 0\begin{vmatrix} 3 & 1 \\ -13 & -2 \end{vmatrix} + (-3)\begin{vmatrix} 3 & 1 \\ 15 & 4 \end{vmatrix}$$

$$= 1(-30+52) - 0(-6+13) - 3(12-15)$$

$$= 1(22) - 0(7) - 3(-3)$$

$$= 22 - 0 + 9$$

$$= 31$$

$$D_z = \begin{vmatrix} 1 & 1 & 3 \\ 0 & -3 & 15 \\ -3 & 4 & -13 \end{vmatrix} \text{ (using first column)}$$

$$= 1\begin{vmatrix} -3 & 15 \\ 4 & -13 \end{vmatrix} - 0\begin{vmatrix} 1 & 3 \\ 4 & -13 \end{vmatrix} + (-3)\begin{vmatrix} 1 & 3 \\ -3 & 15 \end{vmatrix}$$

$$= 1(39-60) - 0(-13-12) - 3(15+9)$$

$$= 1(-21) - 0(-25) - 3(24)$$

$$= -21 - 0 - 72$$

$$= -93$$

$$x = \frac{D_x}{D} = \frac{-31}{-31} = 1, \ y = \frac{D_y}{D} = \frac{31}{-31} = -1, \text{ and}$$

$$z = \frac{D_z}{D} = \frac{-93}{-31} = 3$$

The solution is $(1, -1, 3)$.

32.
$$2x + 3y + 0z = 4$$
$$3x + 7y - 4z = -3$$
$$x - y + 2z = 9$$

To solve, first calculate D, D_x, D_y, and D_z.

$$D = \begin{vmatrix} 2 & 3 & 0 \\ 3 & 7 & -4 \\ 1 & -1 & 2 \end{vmatrix} \text{ (using first row)}$$

$$= 2\begin{vmatrix} 7 & -4 \\ -1 & 2 \end{vmatrix} - 3\begin{vmatrix} 3 & -4 \\ 1 & 2 \end{vmatrix} + 0\begin{vmatrix} 3 & 7 \\ 1 & -1 \end{vmatrix}$$

$$= 2(14-4) - 3(6+4) + 0(-3-7)$$

$$= 2(10) - 3(10) + 0(-10)$$

$$= 20 - 30 + 0$$

$$= -10$$

$$D_x = \begin{vmatrix} 4 & 3 & 0 \\ -3 & 7 & -4 \\ 9 & -1 & 2 \end{vmatrix} \text{ (using first row)}$$

$$= 4\begin{vmatrix} 7 & -4 \\ -1 & 2 \end{vmatrix} - 3\begin{vmatrix} -3 & -4 \\ 9 & 2 \end{vmatrix} + 0\begin{vmatrix} -3 & 7 \\ 9 & -1 \end{vmatrix}$$

$$= 4(14-4) - 3(-6+36) + 0(3-63)$$

$$= 4(10) - 3(30) + 0(-60)$$

$$= 40 - 90 + 0$$

$$= -50$$

$$D_y = \begin{vmatrix} 2 & 4 & 0 \\ 3 & -3 & -4 \\ 1 & 9 & 2 \end{vmatrix} \text{ (using first row)}$$

$$= 2\begin{vmatrix} -3 & -4 \\ 9 & 2 \end{vmatrix} - 4\begin{vmatrix} 3 & -4 \\ 1 & 2 \end{vmatrix} + 0\begin{vmatrix} 3 & -3 \\ 1 & 9 \end{vmatrix}$$

$$= 2(-6+36) - 4(6+4) + 0(27+3)$$

$$= 2(30) - 4(10) + 0(30)$$

$$= 60 - 40 + 0$$

$$= 20$$

$$D_z = \begin{vmatrix} 2 & 3 & 4 \\ 3 & 7 & -3 \\ 1 & -1 & 9 \end{vmatrix} \text{ (using first row)}$$

$$= 2\begin{vmatrix} 7 & -3 \\ -1 & 9 \end{vmatrix} - 3\begin{vmatrix} 3 & -3 \\ 1 & 9 \end{vmatrix} + 4\begin{vmatrix} 3 & 7 \\ 1 & -1 \end{vmatrix}$$

$$= 2(63-3) - 3(27+3) + 4(-3-7)$$

$$= 2(60) - 3(30) + 4(-10)$$

$$= 120 - 90 - 40$$

$$= -10$$

$$x = \frac{D_x}{D} = \frac{-50}{-10} = 5, \quad y = \frac{D_y}{D} = \frac{20}{-10} = -2, \text{ and}$$

$$z = \frac{D_z}{D} = \frac{-10}{-10} = 1.$$

The solution is (5, –2, 1).

33. $3x - 5y - 4z = -4$
$4x + 2y + 0z = 1$
$0x + 6y - 4z = -11$

To solve, first calculate D, D_x, D_y, and D_z.

$$D = \begin{vmatrix} 3 & -5 & -4 \\ 4 & 2 & 0 \\ 0 & 6 & -4 \end{vmatrix} \text{ (using the first row)}$$

$$= 3\begin{vmatrix} 2 & 0 \\ 6 & -4 \end{vmatrix} - (-5)\begin{vmatrix} 4 & 0 \\ 0 & -4 \end{vmatrix} + (-4)\begin{vmatrix} 4 & 2 \\ 0 & 6 \end{vmatrix}$$

$$= 3(-8-0) + 5(-16-0) - 4(24-0)$$

$$= 3(-8) + 5(-16) - 4(24)$$

$$= -24 - 80 - 96$$

$$= -200$$

$$D_x = \begin{vmatrix} -4 & -5 & -4 \\ 1 & 2 & 0 \\ -11 & 6 & -4 \end{vmatrix} \text{ (using the first row)}$$

$$= -4\begin{vmatrix} 2 & 0 \\ 6 & -4 \end{vmatrix} - (-5)\begin{vmatrix} 1 & 0 \\ -11 & -4 \end{vmatrix} + (-4)\begin{vmatrix} 1 & 2 \\ -11 & 6 \end{vmatrix}$$

$$= -4(-8-0) + 5(-4+0) - 4(6+22)$$

$$= -4(-8) + 5(-4) - 4(28)$$

$$= 32 - 20 - 112$$

$$= -100$$

$$D_y = \begin{vmatrix} 3 & -4 & -4 \\ 4 & 1 & 0 \\ 0 & -11 & -4 \end{vmatrix} \text{ (using the first row)}$$

$$= 3\begin{vmatrix} 1 & 0 \\ -11 & -4 \end{vmatrix} - (-4)\begin{vmatrix} 4 & 0 \\ 0 & -4 \end{vmatrix} + (-4)\begin{vmatrix} 4 & 1 \\ 0 & -11 \end{vmatrix}$$

$$= 3(-4+0) + 4(-16-0) - 4(-44-0)$$

$$= 3(-4) + 4(-16) - 4(-44)$$

$$= -12 - 64 + 176$$

$$= 100$$

$$D_z = \begin{vmatrix} 3 & -5 & -4 \\ 4 & 2 & 1 \\ 0 & 6 & -11 \end{vmatrix} \text{ (using the first row)}$$

$$= 3\begin{vmatrix} 2 & 1 \\ 6 & -11 \end{vmatrix} - (-5)\begin{vmatrix} 4 & 1 \\ 0 & -11 \end{vmatrix} + (-4)\begin{vmatrix} 4 & 2 \\ 0 & 6 \end{vmatrix}$$

$$= 3(-22-6) + 5(-44-0) - 4(24-0)$$

$$= 3(-28) + 5(-44) - 4(24)$$

$$= -84 - 220 - 96$$

$$= -400$$

$$x = \frac{D_x}{D} = \frac{-100}{-200} = \frac{1}{2}, \quad y = \frac{D_y}{D} = \frac{100}{-200} = -\frac{1}{2}, \text{ and}$$

$$z = \frac{D_z}{D} = \frac{-400}{-200} = 2$$

The solution is $\left(\frac{1}{2}, -\frac{1}{2}, 2\right)$.

34. $2x + 5y + 3z = 2$
$6x - 9y + 0z = 5$
$0x + 3y + 2z = 1$

To solve, first calculate D, D_x, D_y, and D_z.

$$D = \begin{vmatrix} 2 & 5 & 3 \\ 6 & -9 & 0 \\ 0 & 3 & 2 \end{vmatrix} \text{ (using first row)}$$

$$= 2\begin{vmatrix} -9 & 0 \\ 3 & 2 \end{vmatrix} - 5\begin{vmatrix} 6 & 0 \\ 0 & 2 \end{vmatrix} + 3\begin{vmatrix} 6 & -9 \\ 0 & 3 \end{vmatrix}$$

$$= 2(-18-0) - 5(12-0) + 3(18-0)$$

$$= 2(-18) - 5(12) + 3(18)$$

$$= -36 - 60 + 54$$

$$= -42$$

$$D_x = \begin{vmatrix} 2 & 5 & 3 \\ 5 & -9 & 0 \\ 1 & 3 & 2 \end{vmatrix} \quad \text{(using first row)}$$

$$= 2\begin{vmatrix} -9 & 0 \\ 3 & 2 \end{vmatrix} - 5\begin{vmatrix} 5 & 0 \\ 1 & 2 \end{vmatrix} + 3\begin{vmatrix} 5 & -9 \\ 1 & 3 \end{vmatrix}$$

$$= 2(-18-0) - 5(10-0) + 3(15+9)$$

$$= 2(-18) - 5(10) + 3(24)$$

$$= -36 - 50 + 72$$

$$= -14$$

$$D_y = \begin{vmatrix} 2 & 2 & 3 \\ 6 & 5 & 0 \\ 0 & 1 & 2 \end{vmatrix} \quad \text{(using first row)}$$

$$= 2\begin{vmatrix} 5 & 0 \\ 1 & 2 \end{vmatrix} - 2\begin{vmatrix} 6 & 0 \\ 0 & 2 \end{vmatrix} + 3\begin{vmatrix} 6 & 5 \\ 0 & 1 \end{vmatrix}$$

$$= 2(10-0) - 2(12-0) + 3(6-0)$$

$$= 2(10) - 2(12) + 3(6)$$

$$= 20 - 24 + 18$$

$$= 14$$

$$D_z = \begin{vmatrix} 2 & 5 & 2 \\ 6 & -9 & 5 \\ 0 & 3 & 1 \end{vmatrix} \quad \text{(using first row)}$$

$$= 2\begin{vmatrix} -9 & 5 \\ 3 & 1 \end{vmatrix} - 5\begin{vmatrix} 6 & 5 \\ 0 & 1 \end{vmatrix} + 2\begin{vmatrix} 6 & -9 \\ 0 & 3 \end{vmatrix}$$

$$= 2(-9-15) - 5(6-0) + 2(18-0)$$

$$= 2(-24) - 5(6) + 2(18)$$

$$= -48 - 30 + 36$$

$$= -42$$

$$x = \frac{D_x}{D} = \frac{-14}{-42} = \frac{1}{3}, \quad y = \frac{D_y}{D} = \frac{14}{-42} = -\frac{1}{3}, \text{ and}$$

$$z = \frac{D_z}{D} = \frac{-42}{-42} = 1.$$

The solution is $\left(\dfrac{1}{3}, -\dfrac{1}{3}, 1 \right)$.

35. $x + 4y - 3z = -6$

$2x - 8y + 5z = 12$

$3x + 4y - 2z = -3$

To solve, first calculate D, D_x, D_y, and D_z

$$D = \begin{vmatrix} 1 & 4 & -3 \\ 2 & -8 & 5 \\ 3 & 4 & -2 \end{vmatrix} \quad \text{(using the first row)}$$

$$= 1\begin{vmatrix} -8 & 5 \\ 4 & -2 \end{vmatrix} - 4\begin{vmatrix} 2 & 5 \\ 3 & -2 \end{vmatrix} + (-3)\begin{vmatrix} 2 & -8 \\ 3 & 4 \end{vmatrix}$$

$$= 1(16-20) - 4(-4-15) - 3(8+24)$$

$$= 1(-4) - 4(-19) - 3(32)$$

$$= -4 + 76 - 96$$

$$= -24$$

$$D_x = \begin{vmatrix} -6 & 4 & -3 \\ 12 & -8 & 5 \\ -3 & 4 & -2 \end{vmatrix} \quad \text{(using the first row)}$$

$$= -6\begin{vmatrix} -8 & 5 \\ 4 & -2 \end{vmatrix} - 4\begin{vmatrix} 12 & 5 \\ -3 & -2 \end{vmatrix} + (-3)\begin{vmatrix} 12 & -8 \\ -3 & 4 \end{vmatrix}$$

$$= -6(16-20) - 4(-24+15) - 3(48-24)$$

$$= -6(-4) - 4(-9) - 3(24)$$

$$= 24 + 36 - 72$$

$$= -12$$

$$D_y = \begin{vmatrix} 1 & -6 & -3 \\ 2 & 12 & 5 \\ 3 & -3 & -2 \end{vmatrix} \quad \text{(using the first row)}$$

$$= 1\begin{vmatrix} 12 & 5 \\ -3 & -2 \end{vmatrix} - (-6)\begin{vmatrix} 2 & 5 \\ 3 & -2 \end{vmatrix} + (-3)\begin{vmatrix} 2 & 12 \\ 3 & -3 \end{vmatrix}$$

$$= 1(-24+15) + 6(-4-15) - 3(-6-36)$$

$$= 1(-9) + 6(-19) - 3(-42)$$

$$= -9 - 114 + 126$$

$$= 3$$

$$D_z = \begin{vmatrix} 1 & 4 & -6 \\ 2 & -8 & 12 \\ 3 & 4 & -3 \end{vmatrix} \quad \text{(using the first row)}$$

$$= 1\begin{vmatrix} -8 & 12 \\ 4 & -3 \end{vmatrix} - 4\begin{vmatrix} 2 & 12 \\ 3 & -3 \end{vmatrix} + (-6)\begin{vmatrix} 2 & -8 \\ 3 & 4 \end{vmatrix}$$

$$= 1(24-48) - 4(-6-36) - 6(8+24)$$

$$= 1(-24) - 4(-42) - 6(32)$$

$$= -24 + 168 - 192$$

$$= -48$$

$x = \dfrac{D_x}{D} = \dfrac{-12}{-24} = \dfrac{1}{2}$, $y = \dfrac{D_y}{D} = \dfrac{3}{-24} = -\dfrac{1}{8}$, and

$z = \dfrac{D_z}{D} = \dfrac{-48}{-24} = 2$.

The solution is $\left(\dfrac{1}{2}, -\dfrac{1}{8}, 2\right)$.

36. $2x + y - 2z = 4$

$2x + 2y - 4z = 1$

$-6x + 8y - 4z = 1$

To solve, first calculate D, D_x, D_y, and D_z.

$D = \begin{vmatrix} 2 & 1 & -2 \\ 2 & 2 & -4 \\ -6 & 8 & -4 \end{vmatrix}$ (using first row)

$= 2\begin{vmatrix} 2 & -4 \\ 8 & -4 \end{vmatrix} - 1\begin{vmatrix} 2 & -4 \\ -6 & -4 \end{vmatrix} + (-2)\begin{vmatrix} 2 & 2 \\ -6 & 8 \end{vmatrix}$

$= 2(-8 + 32) - 1(-8 - 24) - 2(16 + 12)$

$= 2(24) - 1(-32) - 2(28)$

$= 48 + 32 - 56$

$= 24$

$D_x = \begin{vmatrix} 4 & 1 & -2 \\ 1 & 2 & -4 \\ 1 & 8 & -4 \end{vmatrix}$ (using first row)

$= 4\begin{vmatrix} 2 & -4 \\ 8 & -4 \end{vmatrix} - 1\begin{vmatrix} 1 & -4 \\ 1 & -4 \end{vmatrix} + (-2)\begin{vmatrix} 1 & 2 \\ 1 & 8 \end{vmatrix}$

$= 4(-8 + 32) - 1(-4 + 4) - 2(8 - 2)$

$= 4(24) - 1(0) - 2(6)$

$= 96 - 0 - 12$

$= 84$

$D_y = \begin{vmatrix} 2 & 4 & -2 \\ 2 & 1 & -4 \\ -6 & 1 & -4 \end{vmatrix}$ (using first row)

$= 2\begin{vmatrix} 1 & -4 \\ 1 & -4 \end{vmatrix} - 4\begin{vmatrix} 2 & -4 \\ -6 & -4 \end{vmatrix} + (-2)\begin{vmatrix} 2 & 1 \\ -6 & 1 \end{vmatrix}$

$= 2(-4 + 4) - 4(-8 - 24) - 2(2 + 6)$

$= 2(0) - 4(-32) - 2(8)$

$= 0 + 128 - 16$

$= 112$

$D_z = \begin{vmatrix} 2 & 1 & 4 \\ 2 & 2 & 1 \\ -6 & 8 & 1 \end{vmatrix}$ (using first row)

$= 2\begin{vmatrix} 2 & 1 \\ 8 & 1 \end{vmatrix} - 1\begin{vmatrix} 2 & 1 \\ -6 & 1 \end{vmatrix} + 4\begin{vmatrix} 2 & 2 \\ -6 & 8 \end{vmatrix}$

$= 2(2 - 8) - 1(2 + 6) + 4(16 + 12)$

$= 2(-6) - 1(8) + 4(28)$

$= -12 - 8 + 112$

$= 92$

$x = \dfrac{D_x}{D} = \dfrac{84}{24} = \dfrac{7}{2}$, $y = \dfrac{D_y}{D} = \dfrac{112}{24} = \dfrac{14}{3}$, and

$z = \dfrac{D_z}{D} = \dfrac{92}{24} = \dfrac{23}{6}$.

The solution is $\left(\dfrac{7}{2}, \dfrac{14}{3}, \dfrac{23}{6}\right)$.

37. $a - b + 2c = 3$

$a - b + c = 1$

$2a + b + 2c = 2$

To solve, first calculate D, D_a, D_b, and D_c.

$D = \begin{vmatrix} 1 & -1 & 2 \\ 1 & -1 & 1 \\ 2 & 1 & 2 \end{vmatrix}$ (using first column)

$= 1\begin{vmatrix} -1 & 1 \\ 1 & 2 \end{vmatrix} - 1\begin{vmatrix} -1 & 2 \\ 1 & 2 \end{vmatrix} + 2\begin{vmatrix} -1 & 2 \\ -1 & 1 \end{vmatrix}$

$= 1(-2 - 1) - 1(-2 - 2) + 2(-1 + 2)$

$= 1(-3) - 1(-4) + 2(1)$

$= -3 + 4 + 2$

$= 3$

$D_a = \begin{vmatrix} 3 & -1 & 2 \\ 1 & -1 & 1 \\ 2 & 1 & 2 \end{vmatrix}$ (using first column)

$= 3\begin{vmatrix} -1 & 1 \\ 1 & 2 \end{vmatrix} - 1\begin{vmatrix} -1 & 2 \\ 1 & 2 \end{vmatrix} + 2\begin{vmatrix} -1 & 2 \\ -1 & 1 \end{vmatrix}$

$= 3(-2 - 1) - 1(-2 - 2) + 2(-1 + 2)$

$= 3(-3) - 1(-4) + 2(1)$

$= -9 + 4 + 2$

$= -3$

$$D_b = \begin{vmatrix} 1 & 3 & 2 \\ 1 & 1 & 1 \\ 2 & 2 & 2 \end{vmatrix} \text{ (using first column)}$$

$$= 1\begin{vmatrix} 1 & 1 \\ 2 & 2 \end{vmatrix} - 1\begin{vmatrix} 3 & 2 \\ 2 & 2 \end{vmatrix} + 2\begin{vmatrix} 3 & 2 \\ 1 & 1 \end{vmatrix}$$

$$= 1(2-2) - 1(6-4) + 2(3-2)$$

$$= 1(0) - 1(2) + 2(1)$$

$$= 0 - 2 + 2$$

$$= 0$$

$$D_c = \begin{vmatrix} 1 & -1 & 3 \\ 1 & -1 & 1 \\ 2 & 1 & 2 \end{vmatrix} \text{ (using first column)}$$

$$= 1\begin{vmatrix} -1 & 1 \\ 1 & 2 \end{vmatrix} - 1\begin{vmatrix} -1 & 3 \\ 1 & 2 \end{vmatrix} + 2\begin{vmatrix} -1 & 3 \\ -1 & 1 \end{vmatrix}$$

$$= 1(-2--1) - 1(-2-3) + 2(-1+3)$$

$$= 1(-3) - 1(-5) + 2(2)$$

$$= -3 + 5 + 4$$

$$= 6$$

$$a = \frac{D_a}{D} = \frac{-3}{3} = -1, \; b = \frac{D_b}{D} = \frac{0}{3} = 0 \text{, and}$$

$$c = \frac{D_c}{D} = \frac{6}{3} = 2$$

The solution is $(-1, 0, 2)$.

38. Write the system in standard form.

$$-2x + y + 0z = -10$$
$$3x + 2y + z = 3$$
$$x - 3y - 5z = 5$$

To solve, first calculate D, D_x, D_y, and D_z.

$$D = \begin{vmatrix} -2 & 1 & 0 \\ 3 & 2 & 1 \\ 1 & -3 & -5 \end{vmatrix} \text{ (using first column)}$$

$$= -2\begin{vmatrix} 2 & 1 \\ -3 & -5 \end{vmatrix} - 3\begin{vmatrix} 1 & 0 \\ -3 & -5 \end{vmatrix} + 1\begin{vmatrix} 1 & 0 \\ 2 & 1 \end{vmatrix}$$

$$= -2(-10+3) - 3(-5-0) + 1(1-0)$$

$$= -2(-7) - 3(-5) + 1(1)$$

$$= 14 + 15 + 1$$

$$= 30$$

$$D_x = \begin{vmatrix} -10 & 1 & 0 \\ 3 & 2 & 1 \\ 5 & -3 & -5 \end{vmatrix} \text{ (using first column)}$$

$$= -10\begin{vmatrix} 2 & 1 \\ -3 & -5 \end{vmatrix} - 3\begin{vmatrix} 1 & 0 \\ -3 & -5 \end{vmatrix} + 5\begin{vmatrix} 1 & 0 \\ 2 & 1 \end{vmatrix}$$

$$= -10(-10+3) - 3(-5-0) + 5(1-0)$$

$$= -10(-7) - 3(-5) + 5(1)$$

$$= 70 + 15 + 5$$

$$= 90$$

$$D_y = \begin{vmatrix} -2 & -10 & 0 \\ 3 & 3 & 1 \\ 1 & 5 & -5 \end{vmatrix} \text{ (using first column)}$$

$$= -2\begin{vmatrix} 3 & 1 \\ 5 & -5 \end{vmatrix} - 3\begin{vmatrix} -10 & 0 \\ 5 & -5 \end{vmatrix} + 1\begin{vmatrix} -10 & 0 \\ 3 & 1 \end{vmatrix}$$

$$= -2(-15-5) - 3(50-0) + 1(-10-0)$$

$$= -2(-20) - 3(50) + 1(-10)$$

$$= 40 - 150 - 10$$

$$= -120$$

$$D_z = \begin{vmatrix} -2 & 1 & -10 \\ 3 & 2 & 3 \\ 1 & -3 & 5 \end{vmatrix} \text{ (using first column)}$$

$$= -2\begin{vmatrix} 2 & 3 \\ -3 & 5 \end{vmatrix} - 3\begin{vmatrix} 1 & -10 \\ -3 & 5 \end{vmatrix} + 1\begin{vmatrix} 1 & -10 \\ 2 & 3 \end{vmatrix}$$

$$= -2(10+9) - 3(5-30) + 1(3+20)$$

$$= -2(19) - 3(-25) + 1(23)$$

$$= -38 + 75 + 23$$

$$= 60$$

$$x = \frac{D_x}{D} = \frac{90}{30} = 3, \; y = \frac{D_y}{D} = \frac{-120}{30} = -4 \text{, and}$$

$$z = \frac{D_z}{D} = \frac{60}{30} = 2$$

The solution is $(3, -4, 2)$.

39. $a + 2b + c = 1$
$a - b + 3c = 2$
$2a + b + 4c = 3$

To solve, first calculate D, D_a, D_b, and D_c.

$$D = \begin{vmatrix} 1 & 2 & 1 \\ 1 & -1 & 3 \\ 2 & 1 & 4 \end{vmatrix} \text{ (using first column)}$$

$$= 1 \begin{vmatrix} -1 & 3 \\ 1 & 4 \end{vmatrix} - 1 \begin{vmatrix} 2 & 1 \\ 1 & 4 \end{vmatrix} + 2 \begin{vmatrix} 2 & 1 \\ -1 & 3 \end{vmatrix}$$

$= 1(-4 - 3) - 1(8 - 1) + 2(6 + 1)$

$= 1(-7) - 1(7) + 2(7)$

$= -7 - 7 + 14 = 0$

$$D_a = \begin{vmatrix} 1 & 2 & 1 \\ 2 & -1 & 3 \\ 3 & 1 & 4 \end{vmatrix} \text{ (using first column)}$$

$$= 1 \begin{vmatrix} -1 & 3 \\ 1 & 4 \end{vmatrix} - 2 \begin{vmatrix} 2 & 1 \\ 1 & 4 \end{vmatrix} + 3 \begin{vmatrix} 2 & 1 \\ -1 & 3 \end{vmatrix}$$

$= 1(-4 - 3) - 2(8 - 1) + 3(6 + 1)$

$= 1(-7) - 2(7) + 3(7)$

$= -7 - 14 + 21 = 0$

$$D_b = \begin{vmatrix} 1 & 1 & 1 \\ 1 & 2 & 3 \\ 2 & 3 & 4 \end{vmatrix} \text{ (using first row)}$$

$$= 1 \begin{vmatrix} 2 & 3 \\ 3 & 4 \end{vmatrix} - 1 \begin{vmatrix} 1 & 3 \\ 2 & 4 \end{vmatrix} + 1 \begin{vmatrix} 1 & 2 \\ 2 & 3 \end{vmatrix}$$

$= 1(8 - 9) - 1(4 - 6) + 1(3 - 4)$

$= 1(-1) - 1(-2) + 1(-1)$

$= -1 + 2 - 1 = 0$

$$D_c = \begin{vmatrix} 1 & 2 & 1 \\ 1 & -1 & 2 \\ 2 & 1 & 3 \end{vmatrix} \text{ (using first column)}$$

$$= 1 \begin{vmatrix} -1 & 2 \\ 1 & 3 \end{vmatrix} - 1 \begin{vmatrix} 2 & 1 \\ 1 & 3 \end{vmatrix} + 2 \begin{vmatrix} 2 & 1 \\ -1 & 2 \end{vmatrix}$$

$= 1(-3 - 2) - 1(6 - 1) + 2(4 + 1)$

$= 1(-5) - 1(5) + 2(5)$

$= -5 - 5 + 10 = 0$

Since $D = 0$, $D_a = 0$, $D_b = 0$, and $D_c = 0$, there are an infinite number of solutions to the system and it is a dependent system.

40. $4x - 2y + 6z = 2$
$-6x + 3y - 9z = -3$
$2x - 7y + 11z = -5$

To solve, first calculate D, D_x, D_y, and D_z.

$$D = \begin{vmatrix} 4 & -2 & 6 \\ -6 & 3 & -9 \\ 2 & -7 & 11 \end{vmatrix} \text{ (using the first row)}$$

$$= 4 \begin{vmatrix} 3 & -9 \\ -7 & 11 \end{vmatrix} - (-2) \begin{vmatrix} -6 & -9 \\ 2 & 11 \end{vmatrix} + 6 \begin{vmatrix} -6 & 3 \\ 2 & -7 \end{vmatrix}$$

$= 4(33 - 63) + 2(-66 + 18) + 6(42 - 6)$

$= 4(-30) + 2(-48) + 6(36)$

$= -120 - 96 + 216 = 0$

$$D_x = \begin{vmatrix} 2 & -2 & 6 \\ -3 & 3 & -9 \\ -5 & -7 & 11 \end{vmatrix} \text{ (using the first row)}$$

$$= 2 \begin{vmatrix} 3 & -9 \\ -7 & 11 \end{vmatrix} - (-2) \begin{vmatrix} -3 & -9 \\ -5 & 11 \end{vmatrix} + 6 \begin{vmatrix} -3 & 3 \\ -5 & -7 \end{vmatrix}$$

$= 2(33 - 63) + 2(-33 - 45) + 6(21 + 15)$

$= 2(-30) + 2(-78) + 6(36)$

$= -60 - 156 + 216 = 0$

$$D_y = \begin{vmatrix} 4 & 2 & 6 \\ -6 & -3 & -9 \\ 2 & -5 & 11 \end{vmatrix} \text{ (using the first row)}$$

$$= 4 \begin{vmatrix} -3 & -9 \\ -5 & 11 \end{vmatrix} - (2) \begin{vmatrix} -6 & -9 \\ 2 & 11 \end{vmatrix} + 6 \begin{vmatrix} -6 & -3 \\ 2 & -5 \end{vmatrix}$$

$= 4(-33 - 45) - 2(-66 + 18) + 6(30 + 6)$

$= 4(-78) - 2(-48) + 6(36)$

$= -312 + 96 + 216 = 0$

$$D_z = \begin{vmatrix} 4 & -2 & 2 \\ -6 & 3 & -3 \\ 2 & -7 & -5 \end{vmatrix} \text{ (using the first row)}$$

$$= 4 \begin{vmatrix} 3 & -3 \\ -7 & -5 \end{vmatrix} - (-2) \begin{vmatrix} -6 & -3 \\ 2 & -5 \end{vmatrix} + 2 \begin{vmatrix} -6 & 3 \\ 2 & -7 \end{vmatrix}$$

$= 4(-15 - 21) + 2(30 + 6) + 2(42 - 6)$

$= 4(-36) + 2(36) + 2(36)$

$= -144 + 72 + 72 = 0$

Since $D = 0$, $D_x = 0$, $D_y = 0$, and $D_z = 0$, there are an infinite number of solutions to the system and it is a dependent system.

41. $1.1x + 2.3y - 4.0z = -9.2$

$-2.3x + 0y + 4.6z = 6.9$

$0x - 8.2y - 7.5z = -6.8$

Here, you can work with decimals in the determinants. If you do not want to use decimals, then you need to multiply each equation by 10 to clear the decimals. To solve, first calculate D, D_x, D_y, and D_z.

$$D = \begin{vmatrix} 1.1 & 2.3 & -4.0 \\ -2.3 & 0 & 4.6 \\ 0 & -8.2 & -7.5 \end{vmatrix} = 1.1\begin{vmatrix} 0 & 4.6 \\ -8.2 & -7.5 \end{vmatrix} - (-2.3)\begin{vmatrix} 2.3 & -4.0 \\ -8.2 & -7.5 \end{vmatrix} + 0\begin{vmatrix} 2.3 & -4.0 \\ 0 & 4.6 \end{vmatrix} \quad \text{(using first column)}$$

$= 1.1(0 + 37.72) + 2.3(-17.25 - 32.8) + 0(10.58 - 0)$

$= 1.1(37.72) + 2.3(-50.05) + 0(10.58)$

$= 41.492 - 115.115 + 0$

$= -73.623$

$$D_x = \begin{vmatrix} -9.2 & 2.3 & -4.0 \\ 6.9 & 0 & 4.6 \\ -6.8 & -8.2 & -7.5 \end{vmatrix} = -9.2\begin{vmatrix} 0 & 4.6 \\ -8.2 & -7.5 \end{vmatrix} - 6.9\begin{vmatrix} 2.3 & -4.0 \\ -8.2 & -7.5 \end{vmatrix} + (-6.8)\begin{vmatrix} 2.3 & -4.0 \\ 0 & 4.6 \end{vmatrix} \quad \text{(using first column)}$$

$= -9.2(0 + 37.72) - 6.9(-17.25 - 32.8) - 6.8(10.58 - 0)$

$= -9.2(37.72) - 6.9(-50.05) - 6.8(10.58)$

$= -347.024 + 345.345 - 71.944$

$= -73.623$

$$D_y = \begin{vmatrix} 1.1 & -9.2 & -4.0 \\ -2.3 & 6.9 & 4.6 \\ 0 & -6.8 & -7.5 \end{vmatrix} = 1.1\begin{vmatrix} 6.9 & 4.6 \\ -6.8 & -7.5 \end{vmatrix} - (-2.3)\begin{vmatrix} -9.2 & -4.0 \\ -6.8 & -7.5 \end{vmatrix} + 0\begin{vmatrix} -9.2 & -4.0 \\ 6.9 & 4.6 \end{vmatrix} \quad \text{(using first column)}$$

$= 1.1(-51.75 + 31.28) + 2.3(69 - 27.2) + 0(-42.32 + 27.6)$

$= 1.1(-20.47) + 2.3(41.8) + 0(-14.72)$

$= -22.517 + 96.14 + 0$

$= 73.623$

$$D_z = \begin{vmatrix} 1.1 & 2.3 & -9.2 \\ -2.3 & 0 & 6.9 \\ 0 & -8.2 & -6.8 \end{vmatrix} = 1.1\begin{vmatrix} 0 & 6.9 \\ -8.2 & -6.8 \end{vmatrix} - (-2.3)\begin{vmatrix} 2.3 & -9.2 \\ -8.2 & -6.8 \end{vmatrix} + 0\begin{vmatrix} 2.3 & -9.2 \\ 0 & 6.9 \end{vmatrix} \quad \text{(using first column)}$$

$= 1.1(0 + 56.58) + 2.3(-15.64 - 75.44) + 0(15.87 - 0)$

$= 1.1(56.58) + 2.3(-91.08) + 0(15.87)$

$= 62.238 - 209.484 + 0$

$= -147.246$

$x = \dfrac{D_x}{D} = \dfrac{-73.623}{-73.623} = 1$, $y = \dfrac{D_y}{D} = \dfrac{73.623}{-73.623} = -1$, and $z = \dfrac{D_z}{D} = \dfrac{-147.246}{-73.623} = 2$

The solution is $(1, -1, 2)$.

42. $0x + 4.6y - 2.1z = 24.3$

$-5.6x + 1.8y + 0.z = -5.8$

$2.8x - 4.7y - 3.1z = 7.0$

Here, you can work with decimals in the determinants. If you do not want to use decimals, then you need to multiply each equation by 10 to clear the decimals. To solve, first calculate D, D_x, D_y, and D_z.

To solve, first calculate D, D_x, D_y, and D_z.

$$D = \begin{vmatrix} 0 & 4.6 & -2.1 \\ -5.6 & 1.8 & 0 \\ 2.8 & -4.7 & -3.1 \end{vmatrix} = 0\begin{vmatrix} 1.8 & 0 \\ -4.7 & -3.1 \end{vmatrix} - (-5.6)\begin{vmatrix} 4.6 & -2.1 \\ -4.7 & -3.1 \end{vmatrix} + 2.8\begin{vmatrix} 4.6 & -2.1 \\ 1.8 & 0 \end{vmatrix} \text{ (using first column)}$$

$$= 0(-5.58 - 0) + 5.6(-14.26 - 9.87) + 2.8(0 + 3.78)$$

$$= 0(-5.58) + 5.6(-24.13) + 2.8(3.78)$$

$$= 0 - 135.128 + 10.584$$

$$= -124.544$$

$$D_x = \begin{vmatrix} 24.3 & 4.6 & -2.1 \\ -5.8 & 1.8 & 0 \\ 7.0 & -4.7 & -3.1 \end{vmatrix} = 24.3\begin{vmatrix} 1.8 & 0 \\ -4.7 & -3.1 \end{vmatrix} - (-5.8)\begin{vmatrix} 4.6 & -2.1 \\ -4.7 & -3.1 \end{vmatrix} + 7.0\begin{vmatrix} 4.6 & -2.1 \\ 1.8 & 0 \end{vmatrix} \text{ (using first column)}$$

$$= 24.3(-5.58 - 0) + 5.8(-14.26 - 9.87) + 7.0(0 + 3.78)$$

$$= 24.3(-5.58) + 5.8(-24.13) + 7.0(3.78)$$

$$= -135.594 - 139.954 + 26.46$$

$$= -249.088$$

$$D_y = \begin{vmatrix} 0 & 24.3 & -2.1 \\ -5.6 & -5.8 & 0 \\ 2.8 & 7.0 & -3.1 \end{vmatrix} = 0\begin{vmatrix} -5.8 & 0 \\ 7.0 & -3.1 \end{vmatrix} - (-5.6)\begin{vmatrix} 24.3 & -2.1 \\ 7.0 & -3.1 \end{vmatrix} + 2.8\begin{vmatrix} 24.3 & -2.1 \\ -5.8 & 0 \end{vmatrix} \text{ (using first column)}$$

$$= 0(17.98 - 0) + 5.6(-75.33 + 14.7) + 2.8(0 - 12.18)$$

$$= 0(17.98) + 5.6(-60.63) + 2.8(-12.18)$$

$$= 0 - 339.528 - 34.104 = -373.632$$

$$D_z = \begin{vmatrix} 0 & 4.6 & 24.3 \\ -5.6 & 1.8 & -5.8 \\ 2.8 & -4.7 & 7.0 \end{vmatrix} = 0\begin{vmatrix} 1.8 & -5.8 \\ -4.7 & 7.0 \end{vmatrix} - (-5.6)\begin{vmatrix} 4.6 & 24.3 \\ -4.7 & 7.0 \end{vmatrix} + 2.8\begin{vmatrix} 4.6 & 24.3 \\ 1.8 & -5.8 \end{vmatrix} \text{ (using first column)}$$

$$= 0(12.6 - 27.26) + 5.6(32.2 + 114.21) + 2.8(-26.68 - 43.74)$$

$$= 0(-14.66) + 5.6(146.41) + 2.8(-70.42)$$

$$= 0 + 819.896 - 197.176$$

$$= 622.72$$

$$x = \frac{D_x}{D} = \frac{-249.088}{-124.544} = 2, \quad y = \frac{D_y}{D} = \frac{-373.632}{-124.544} = 3, \text{ and } z = \frac{D_z}{D} = \frac{622.72}{-124.544} = -5$$

The solution is $(2, 3, -5)$.

43. $-6x + 3y - 12z = -13$

$\quad\quad 5x + 2y - 3z = 1$

$\quad\quad 2x - y + 4z = -5$

To solve, first calculate D, D_x, D_y, and D_z.

$D = \begin{vmatrix} -6 & 3 & -12 \\ 5 & 2 & -3 \\ 2 & -1 & 4 \end{vmatrix}$ (using the first row)

$= -6\begin{vmatrix} 2 & -3 \\ -1 & 4 \end{vmatrix} - 3\begin{vmatrix} 5 & -3 \\ 2 & 4 \end{vmatrix} + (-12)\begin{vmatrix} 5 & 2 \\ 2 & -1 \end{vmatrix}$

$= -6(8 - 3) - 3(20 + 6) - 12(-5 - 4)$

$= -6(5) - 3(26) - 12(-9)$

$= -30 - 78 + 108$

$= 0$

$D_x = \begin{vmatrix} -13 & 3 & -12 \\ 1 & 2 & -3 \\ -5 & -1 & 4 \end{vmatrix}$ (using the first row)

$= -13\begin{vmatrix} 2 & -3 \\ -1 & 4 \end{vmatrix} - 3\begin{vmatrix} 1 & -3 \\ -5 & 4 \end{vmatrix} + (-12)\begin{vmatrix} 1 & 2 \\ -5 & -1 \end{vmatrix}$

$= -13(8 - 3) - 3(4 - 15) - 12(-1 + 10)$

$= -13(5) - 3(-11) - 12(9)$

$= -65 + 33 - 108$

$= -140$

Since $D = 0$ and $D_x = -140 \neq 0$, there is no solution to the system and it is an inconsistent system.

44. $\quad\quad x - 2y + z = 2$

$\quad\quad 4x - 6y + 2z = 3$

$\quad\quad 2x - 3y + z = 0$

To solve, first calculate D, D_x, D_y, and D_z.

$D = \begin{vmatrix} 1 & -2 & 1 \\ 4 & -6 & 2 \\ 2 & -3 & 1 \end{vmatrix}$ (using first column)

$= 1\begin{vmatrix} -6 & 2 \\ -3 & 1 \end{vmatrix} - 4\begin{vmatrix} -2 & 1 \\ -3 & 1 \end{vmatrix} + 2\begin{vmatrix} -2 & 1 \\ -6 & 2 \end{vmatrix}$

$= 1(-6 + 6) - 4(-2 + 3) + 2(-4 + 6)$

$= 1(0) - 4(1) + 2(2)$

$= 0 - 4 + 4$

$= 0$

$D_x = \begin{vmatrix} 2 & -2 & 1 \\ 3 & -6 & 2 \\ 0 & -3 & 1 \end{vmatrix}$ (using first column)

$= 2\begin{vmatrix} -6 & 2 \\ -3 & 1 \end{vmatrix} - 3\begin{vmatrix} -2 & 1 \\ -3 & 1 \end{vmatrix} + 0\begin{vmatrix} -2 & 1 \\ -6 & 2 \end{vmatrix}$

$= 2(-6 + 6) - 3(-2 + 3) + 0(-4 + 6)$

$= 2(0) - 3(1) + 0(2)$

$= 0 - 3 + 0$

$= -3$

Since $D = 0$ and $D_x = -3 \neq 0$, there is no solution to the system and it is an inconsistent system.

45. $\quad 2x + \dfrac{1}{2}y - 3z = 5$

$\quad\quad -3x + 2y + 2z = 1$

$\quad\quad 4x - \dfrac{1}{4}y - 7z = 4$

To clear the system of fractions, multiply the first equation by 2 and the third equation by 4.

$\quad\quad 4x + y - 6z = 10$

$\quad\quad -3x + 2y + 2z = 1$

$\quad\quad 16x - y - 28z = 16$

To solve, first calculate D, D_x, D_y, and D_z.

$D = \begin{vmatrix} 4 & 1 & -6 \\ -3 & 2 & 2 \\ 16 & -1 & -28 \end{vmatrix}$ (use the first row)

$= 4\begin{vmatrix} 2 & 2 \\ -1 & -28 \end{vmatrix} - 1\begin{vmatrix} -3 & 2 \\ 16 & -28 \end{vmatrix} + (-6)\begin{vmatrix} -3 & 2 \\ 16 & -1 \end{vmatrix}$

$= 4(-56 + 2) - 1(84 - 32) - 6(3 - 32)$

$= 4(-54) - 1(52) - 6(-29)$

$= -216 - 52 + 174$

$= -94$

$D_x = \begin{vmatrix} 10 & 1 & -6 \\ 1 & 2 & 2 \\ 16 & -1 & -28 \end{vmatrix}$ (use the first row)

$= 10\begin{vmatrix} 2 & 2 \\ -1 & -28 \end{vmatrix} - 1\begin{vmatrix} 1 & 2 \\ 16 & -28 \end{vmatrix} + (-6)\begin{vmatrix} 1 & 2 \\ 16 & -1 \end{vmatrix}$

$= 10(-56 + 2) - 1(-28 - 32) - 6(-1 - 32)$

$= 10(-54) - 1(-60) - 6(-33)$

$= -540 + 60 + 198$

$= -282$

$$D_y = \begin{vmatrix} 4 & 10 & -6 \\ -3 & 1 & 2 \\ 16 & 16 & -28 \end{vmatrix} \text{ (use the first row)}$$

$$= 4\begin{vmatrix} 1 & 2 \\ 16 & -28 \end{vmatrix} - 10\begin{vmatrix} -3 & 2 \\ 16 & -28 \end{vmatrix} + (-6)\begin{vmatrix} -3 & 1 \\ 16 & 16 \end{vmatrix}$$

$$= 4(-28-32) - 10(84-32) - 6(-48-16)$$

$$= 4(-60) - 10(52) - 6(-64)$$

$$= -240 - 520 + 384$$

$$= -376$$

$$D_z = \begin{vmatrix} 4 & 1 & 10 \\ -3 & 2 & 1 \\ 16 & -1 & 16 \end{vmatrix} \text{ (use the first row)}$$

$$= 4\begin{vmatrix} 2 & 1 \\ -1 & 16 \end{vmatrix} - 1\begin{vmatrix} -3 & 1 \\ 16 & 16 \end{vmatrix} + 10\begin{vmatrix} -3 & 2 \\ 16 & -1 \end{vmatrix}$$

$$= 4(32+1) - 1(-48-16) + 10(3-32)$$

$$= 4(33) - 1(-64) + 10(-29)$$

$$= 132 + 64 - 290$$

$$= -94$$

$$x = \frac{D_x}{D} = \frac{-282}{-94} = 3, \quad y = \frac{D_y}{D} = \frac{-376}{-94} = 4,$$

$$z = \frac{D_z}{D} = \frac{-94}{-94} = 1$$

The solution is (3, 4, 1).

46. $\frac{1}{4}x - \frac{1}{2}y + 3z = -3$

$2x - 3y + 2z = -1$

$\frac{1}{6}x + \frac{1}{3}y - \frac{1}{3}z = 1$

To clear the system of fractions, multiply the first equation by 4 and the third equation by 6.

$x - 2y + 12z = -12$

$2x - 3y + 2z = -1$

$x + 2y - 2z = 6$

To solve, first calculate D, D_x, D_y, and D_z.

$$D = \begin{vmatrix} 1 & -2 & 12 \\ 2 & -3 & 2 \\ 1 & 2 & -2 \end{vmatrix} \text{ (use the first row)}$$

$$= 1\begin{vmatrix} -3 & 2 \\ 2 & -2 \end{vmatrix} - (-2)\begin{vmatrix} 2 & 2 \\ 1 & -2 \end{vmatrix} + 12\begin{vmatrix} 2 & -3 \\ 1 & 2 \end{vmatrix}$$

$$= 1(6-4) + 2(-4-2) + 12(4+3)$$

$$= 1(2) + 2(-6) + 12(7)$$

$$= 2 - 12 + 84$$

$$= 74$$

$$D_x = \begin{vmatrix} -12 & -2 & 12 \\ -1 & -3 & 2 \\ 6 & 2 & -2 \end{vmatrix} \text{ (use the first row)}$$

$$= -12\begin{vmatrix} -3 & 2 \\ 2 & -2 \end{vmatrix} - (-2)\begin{vmatrix} -1 & 2 \\ 6 & -2 \end{vmatrix} + 12\begin{vmatrix} -1 & -3 \\ 6 & 2 \end{vmatrix}$$

$$= -12(6-4) + 2(2-12) + 12(-2+18)$$

$$= -12(2) + 2(-10) + 12(16)$$

$$= -24 - 20 + 192$$

$$= 148$$

$$D_y = \begin{vmatrix} 1 & -12 & 12 \\ 2 & -1 & 2 \\ 1 & 6 & -2 \end{vmatrix} \text{ (use the first row)}$$

$$= 1\begin{vmatrix} -1 & 2 \\ 6 & -2 \end{vmatrix} - (-12)\begin{vmatrix} 2 & 2 \\ 1 & -2 \end{vmatrix} + 12\begin{vmatrix} 2 & -1 \\ 1 & 6 \end{vmatrix}$$

$$= 1(2-12) + 12(-4-2) + 12(12+1)$$

$$= 1(-10) + 12(-6) + 12(13)$$

$$= -10 - 72 + 156$$

$$= 74$$

$$D_z = \begin{vmatrix} 1 & -2 & -12 \\ 2 & -3 & -1 \\ 1 & 2 & 6 \end{vmatrix} \text{ (use the first row)}$$

$$= 1\begin{vmatrix} -3 & -1 \\ 2 & 6 \end{vmatrix} - (-2)\begin{vmatrix} 2 & -1 \\ 1 & 6 \end{vmatrix} + (-12)\begin{vmatrix} 2 & -3 \\ 1 & 2 \end{vmatrix}$$

$$= 1(-18+2) + 2(12+1) - 12(4+3)$$

$$= 1(-16) + 2(13) - 12(7)$$

$$= -16 + 26 - 84$$

$$= -74$$

$$x = \frac{D_x}{D} = \frac{148}{74} = 2, \quad y = \frac{D_y}{D} = \frac{74}{74} = 1,$$

$$z = \frac{D_z}{D} = \frac{-74}{74} = -1$$

The solution is (2, 1, –1).

47. $0.3x - 0.1y - 0.3z = -0.2$

$0.2x - 0.1y + 0.1z = -0.9$

$0.1x + 0.2y - 0.4z = 1.7$

To clear decimals multiply each equation by 10.

$3x - y - 3x = -2$

$2x - y + z = -9$

$x + 2y - 4z = 17$

To solve, first calculate D, D_x, D_y, and D_z.

$D = \begin{vmatrix} 3 & -1 & -3 \\ 2 & -1 & 1 \\ 1 & 2 & -4 \end{vmatrix}$ (use first column)

$= 3 \begin{vmatrix} -1 & 1 \\ 2 & -4 \end{vmatrix} - 2 \begin{vmatrix} -1 & -3 \\ 2 & -4 \end{vmatrix} + 1 \begin{vmatrix} -1 & -3 \\ -1 & 1 \end{vmatrix}$

$= 3(4 - 2) - 2(4 + 6) + 1(-1 - 3)$

$= 3(2) - 2(10) + 1(-4)$

$= 6 - 20 - 4$

$= -18$

$D_x = \begin{vmatrix} -2 & -1 & -3 \\ -9 & -1 & 1 \\ 17 & 2 & -4 \end{vmatrix}$ (use first column)

$= -2 \begin{vmatrix} -1 & 1 \\ 2 & -4 \end{vmatrix} - (-9) \begin{vmatrix} -1 & -3 \\ 2 & -4 \end{vmatrix} + 17 \begin{vmatrix} -1 & -3 \\ -1 & 1 \end{vmatrix}$

$= -2(4 - 2) + 9(4 + 6) + 17(-1 - 3)$

$= -2(2) + 9(10) + 17(-4)$

$= -4 + 90 - 68$

$= 18$

$D_y = \begin{vmatrix} 3 & -2 & -3 \\ 2 & -9 & 1 \\ 1 & 17 & -4 \end{vmatrix}$ (use first column)

$= 3 \begin{vmatrix} -9 & 1 \\ 17 & -4 \end{vmatrix} - 2 \begin{vmatrix} -2 & -3 \\ 17 & -4 \end{vmatrix} + 1 \begin{vmatrix} -2 & -3 \\ -9 & 1 \end{vmatrix}$

$= 3(36 - 17) - 2(8 + 51) + 1(-2 - 27)$

$= 3(19) - 2(59) + 1(-29)$

$= 57 - 118 - 29$

$= -90$

$D_z = \begin{vmatrix} 3 & -1 & -2 \\ 2 & -1 & -9 \\ 1 & 2 & 17 \end{vmatrix}$ (use first column)

$= 3 \begin{vmatrix} -1 & -9 \\ 2 & 17 \end{vmatrix} - 2 \begin{vmatrix} -1 & -2 \\ 2 & 17 \end{vmatrix} + 1 \begin{vmatrix} -1 & -2 \\ -1 & -9 \end{vmatrix}$

$= 3(-17 + 18) - 2(-17 + 4) + 1(9 - 2)$

$= 3(1) - 2(-13) + 1(7)$

$= 3 + 26 + 7$

$= 36$

$x = \dfrac{D_x}{D} = \dfrac{18}{-18} = -1$, $y = \dfrac{D_y}{D} = \dfrac{-90}{-18} = 5$, and

$z = \dfrac{D_z}{D} = \dfrac{36}{-18} = -2$

The solution is $(-1, 5, -2)$.

48. $0.6u - 0.4v + 0.5w = 3.1$

$0.5u + 0.2v + 0.2w = 1.3$

$0.1u + 0.1v + 0.1w = 0.2$

To clear decimals multiply each equation by 10.

$6u - 4v + 5w = 31$

$5u + 2v + 2w = 13$

$u + v + w = 2$

To solve, first calculate D, D_u, D_v, and D_w.

$D = \begin{vmatrix} 6 & -4 & 5 \\ 5 & 2 & 2 \\ 1 & 1 & 1 \end{vmatrix}$

$= 6 \begin{vmatrix} 2 & 2 \\ 1 & 1 \end{vmatrix} - 5 \begin{vmatrix} -4 & 5 \\ 1 & 1 \end{vmatrix} + 1 \begin{vmatrix} -4 & 5 \\ 2 & 2 \end{vmatrix}$

$= 6(2 - 2) - 5(-4 - 5) + 1(-8 - 10)$

$= 6(0) - 5(-9) + 1(-18)$

$= 0 + 45 - 18$

$= 27$

$D_u = \begin{vmatrix} 31 & -4 & 5 \\ 13 & 2 & 2 \\ 2 & 1 & 1 \end{vmatrix}$

$= 31 \begin{vmatrix} 2 & 2 \\ 1 & 1 \end{vmatrix} - 13 \begin{vmatrix} -4 & 5 \\ 1 & 1 \end{vmatrix} + 2 \begin{vmatrix} -4 & 5 \\ 2 & 2 \end{vmatrix}$

$= 31(2 - 2) - 13(-4 - 5) + 2(-8 - 10)$

$= 31(0) - 13(-9) + 2(-18)$

$= 0 + 117 - 36$

$= 81$

$$D_v = \begin{vmatrix} 6 & 31 & 5 \\ 5 & 13 & 2 \\ 1 & 2 & 1 \end{vmatrix}$$

$$= 6\begin{vmatrix} 13 & 2 \\ 2 & 1 \end{vmatrix} - 5\begin{vmatrix} 31 & 5 \\ 2 & 1 \end{vmatrix} + 1\begin{vmatrix} 31 & 5 \\ 13 & 2 \end{vmatrix}$$

$$= 6(13-4) - 5(31-10) + 1(62-65)$$

$$= 6(9) - 5(21) + 1(-3)$$

$$= 54 - 105 - 3$$

$$= -54$$

$$D_w = \begin{vmatrix} 6 & -4 & 31 \\ 5 & 2 & 13 \\ 1 & 1 & 2 \end{vmatrix}$$

$$= 6\begin{vmatrix} 2 & 13 \\ 1 & 2 \end{vmatrix} - 5\begin{vmatrix} -4 & 31 \\ 1 & 2 \end{vmatrix} + 1\begin{vmatrix} -4 & 31 \\ 2 & 13 \end{vmatrix}$$

$$= 6(4-13) - 5(-8-31) + 1(-52-62)$$

$$= 6(-9) - 5(-39) + 1(-114)$$

$$= -54 + 195 - 114$$

$$= 27$$

$$u = \frac{D_u}{D} = \frac{81}{27} = 3, \ v = \frac{D_v}{D} = \frac{-54}{27} = -2, \text{ and}$$

$$w = \frac{D_w}{D} = \frac{27}{27} = 1$$

The solution is $(3, -2, 1)$.

49. $\begin{vmatrix} a_1 & b_1 \\ a_2 & b_2 \end{vmatrix} = a_1 b_2 - a_2 b_1$

$\begin{vmatrix} a_2 & b_2 \\ a_1 & b_1 \end{vmatrix} = a_2 b_1 - a_1 b_2$

The second result is the negative of the first result. Thus, the second determinant has the opposite sign.

50. $\begin{vmatrix} a_1 & b_1 \\ a_2 & b_2 \end{vmatrix} = a_1 b_2 - a_2 b_1$

$\begin{vmatrix} b_1 & a_1 \\ b_2 & a_2 \end{vmatrix} = b_1 a_2 - b_2 a_1 = a_2 b_1 - a_1 b_2$

The second result is the negative of the first result. Thus, the second determinant has the opposite sign.

51. $0; \ \begin{vmatrix} a & b \\ a & b \end{vmatrix} = (a)(b) - (a)(b) = ab - ab = 0$

52. $0; \ $ for example, $\begin{vmatrix} 0 & 0 \\ a & b \end{vmatrix} = 0 \cdot b - a \cdot 0 = 0 - 0 = 0$

53. $0; \ $ for example

$$\begin{vmatrix} 0 & 0 & 0 \\ a & b & c \\ d & e & f \end{vmatrix} = 0\begin{vmatrix} b & c \\ e & f \end{vmatrix} - 0\begin{vmatrix} a & c \\ d & f \end{vmatrix} + 0\begin{vmatrix} a & b \\ d & e \end{vmatrix}$$

$$= 0 - 0 + 0 = 0$$

54. Yes, the determinant will become the opposite of the original value.

55. Yes, the determinant will become the opposite of the original value.

56. Yes, the value of the determinant is 0.

$$\begin{vmatrix} a & b & c \\ d & e & f \\ d & e & f \end{vmatrix} = a\begin{vmatrix} e & f \\ e & f \end{vmatrix} - b\begin{vmatrix} d & f \\ d & f \end{vmatrix} + c\begin{vmatrix} d & e \\ d & e \end{vmatrix}$$

$$= a(ef - ef) - b(df - df) + c(de - de)$$

$$= a(0) - b(0) + c(0) = 0$$

57. No; the value of the new determinant will be the same as the original value. Each time a row (or column) is multiplied by -1, the value of the determinant changes sign. Since two rows were multiplied by -1, the value of the determinant changes sign twice, which yields the original value.

58. No; the value of the new determinant will be the same as the original value. Each time a row (or column) is multiplied by -1, the value of the determinant changes sign. Since two rows were multiplied by -1, the value of the determinant changes sign twice, which yields the original value.

59. Yes; the value of the new determinant will be double the original value. That is, we would multiply the original determinant by 2 as well.

60. Yes; the value of the new determinant will be 12 times the original value. That is, we would multiply the original determinant by 4 and 3. Since $4 \cdot 3 = 12$, we multiply the original value by 12.

61.
$$\begin{vmatrix} 4 & 6 \\ -2 & y \end{vmatrix} = 32$$
$$(4)(y) - (-2)(6) = 32$$
$$4y + 12 = 32$$
$$4y = 20$$
$$y = \frac{20}{4} = 5$$

62.
$$\begin{vmatrix} b-3 & -4 \\ b+2 & -6 \end{vmatrix} = 14$$
$$(b-3)(-6) - (b+2)(-4) = 14$$
$$-6b + 18 + 4b + 8 = 14$$
$$-2b + 26 = 14$$
$$-2b = -12$$
$$b = \frac{-12}{-2} = 6$$

63.
$$\begin{vmatrix} 4 & 7 & y \\ 3 & -1 & 2 \\ 4 & 1 & 5 \end{vmatrix} = -35$$
$$4 \begin{vmatrix} -1 & 2 \\ 1 & 5 \end{vmatrix} - 3 \begin{vmatrix} 7 & y \\ 1 & 5 \end{vmatrix} + 4 \begin{vmatrix} 7 & y \\ -1 & 2 \end{vmatrix} = -35$$
$$4(-5 - 2) - 3(35 - y) + 4(14 + y) = -35$$
$$4(-7) - 3(35 - y) + 4(14 + y) = -35$$
$$-28 - 105 + 3y + 56 + 4y = -35$$
$$-77 + 7y = -35$$
$$7y = 42$$
$$y = 6$$

64.
$$\begin{vmatrix} 3 & 2 & -2 \\ 0 & 5 & -6 \\ -1 & x & -7 \end{vmatrix} = -31$$
$$3 \begin{vmatrix} 5 & -6 \\ x & -7 \end{vmatrix} - 0 \begin{vmatrix} 2 & -2 \\ x & -7 \end{vmatrix} + (-1) \begin{vmatrix} 2 & -2 \\ 5 & -6 \end{vmatrix} = -31$$
$$3(-35 + 6x) - 0(-14 + 2x) - 1(-12 + 10) = -31$$
$$3(-35 + 6x) - 0(-14 + 2x) - 1(-2) = -31$$
$$-105 + 18x - 0 + 2 = -31$$
$$18x - 103 = -31$$
$$18x = 72$$
$$x = \frac{72}{18} = 4$$

65. a. To eliminate y, multiply the first equation by b_2 and the second equation by $-b_1$ and then add.
$$b_2 [a_1 x + b_1 y = c_1]$$
$$-b_1 [a_2 x + b_2 y = c_2]$$
gives
$$a_1 b_2 x + b_1 b_2 y = c_1 b_2$$
$$\underline{-a_2 b_1 x - b_1 b_2 y = -c_2 b_1}$$
Add: $(a_1 b_2 - a_2 b_1)x \qquad = c_1 b_2 - c_2 b_1$
$$x = \frac{c_1 b_2 - c_2 b_1}{a_1 b_2 - a_2 b_1}$$

b. To eliminate x, multiply the first equation by $-a_2$ and the second equation by a_1 and then add.
$$-a_2 [a_1 x + b_1 y = c_1]$$
$$a_1 [a_2 x + b_2 y = c_2]$$
gives
$$-a_1 a_2 x - a_2 b_1 y = -a_2 c_1$$
$$\underline{a_1 a_2 x + a_1 b_2 y = a_1 c_2}$$
Add: $(a_1 b_2 - a_2 b_1)y = a_1 c_2 - a_2 c_1$
$$y = \frac{a_1 c_2 - a_2 c_1}{a_1 b_2 - a_2 b_1}$$

66. $2x - 5y = 6$
$$-5y = -2x + 6$$
$$y = \frac{-2x + 6}{-5}$$
$$y = \frac{2}{5}x - \frac{6}{5}$$

67. $3x + 4y = 8$
Solve for y.
$$4y = -3x + 8$$
$$y = -\frac{3}{4}x + 2$$

x	y
-4	$y = -\frac{3}{4}(-4) + 2 = 3 + 2 = 5$
0	$y = -\frac{3}{4}(0) + 2 = 0 + 2 = 2$
4	$y = -\frac{3}{4}(4) + 2 = -3 + 2 = -1$

68. $3x + 4y = 8$

For the *x*-intercept, let *y* = 0.

$3x + 4(0) = 8$

$3x + 0 = 8$

$3x = 8$

$x = \dfrac{8}{3} = 2\dfrac{2}{3}$

For the *y*-intercept, let *x* = 0.

$3(0) + 4y = 8$

$0 + 4y = 8$

$4y = 8$

$y = 2$

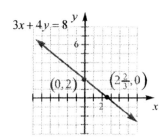

69. $3x + 4y = 8$

Solve for *y*.

$4y = -3x + 8$

$y = -\dfrac{3}{4}x + 2$

The slope is $-\dfrac{3}{4}$ and the *y*-intercept is 2.

Chapter 9 Review Exercises

1. a. $y = 4x - 2$ $2x + 3y = 8$

$6 = 4(2) - 2$ $2(2) + 3(6) = 8$

$6 = 6$ True $22 = 8$ False

Since (2, 6) does not satisfy both equations, it is not a solution to the system.

b. $y = 4x - 2$

$0 = 4(4) - 2$

$0 = 14$ False

Since (4, 0) does not satisfy the first equation, it is not a solution to the system.

c. $y = 4x - 2$ $2x + 3y = 8$

$2 = 4(1) - 2$ $2(1) + 3(2) = 8$

$2 = 2$ True $8 = 8$ True

Since (1, 2) satisfies both equations, it is a solution to the system.

2. a. $y = -x + 4$

$\dfrac{3}{2} = -\dfrac{5}{2} + 4$

$\dfrac{3}{2} = \dfrac{3}{2}$ True

$3x + 5y = 15$

$3\left(\dfrac{5}{2}\right) + 5\left(\dfrac{3}{2}\right) = 15$

$15 = 15$ True

Since $\left(\dfrac{5}{2}, \dfrac{3}{2}\right)$ satisfies both equations, it is a solution to the system.

b. $y = -x + 4$

$5 = -(-1) + 4$

$5 = 5$ True

$3x + 5y = 15$

$3(-1) + 5(5) = 15$

$22 = 15$ False

Since (−1, 5) does not satisfy both equations, it is not a solution to the system.

c. $y = -x + 4$

$\dfrac{3}{5} = -\dfrac{1}{2} + 4$

$\dfrac{3}{5} = \dfrac{7}{2}$ False

Since $\left(\dfrac{1}{2}, \dfrac{3}{5}\right)$ does not satisfy the first equation, it is not a solution to the system.

3. consistent, one solution

4. inconsistent, no solutions

5. dependent, infinite number of solutions

6. consistent, one solution

7. Write each equation in slope-intercept form.

$$x + 2y = 10 \qquad\qquad 4x = -8y + 16$$
$$\quad 2y = -x + 10 \qquad\quad 8y = -4x + 16$$
$$\quad y = -\frac{1}{2}x + 5 \qquad\quad y = -\frac{1}{2}x + 2$$

Since the slope of each line is $-\frac{1}{2}$ but the y-intercepts are different, the two lines are parallel. There is no solution. This is an inconsistent system.

8. Write each equation in slope-intercept form.

$y = -2x + 5$ is already in this form.

$$2x + 5y = 10$$
$$\quad 5y = -2x + 10$$
$$\quad y = -\frac{2}{5}x + 2$$

Since the slopes of the lines are different, the lines intersect to produce one solution. This is a consistent system.

9. Write each equation in slope-intercept form.

$y = \frac{1}{3}x + \frac{2}{3}$ is already in this form.

$$6y - 2x = 4$$
$$\quad 6y = 2x + 4$$
$$\quad y = \frac{1}{3}x + \frac{2}{3}$$

Since both equations are identical, the line is the same for both of them. There are an infinite number of solutions. This is a dependent system.

10. Write each equation in slope-intercept form.

$$6x = 4y - 20 \qquad\qquad 4x = 6y + 20$$
$$6x + 20 = 4y \qquad\quad 4x - 20 = 6y$$
$$\frac{3}{2}x + 5 = y \qquad\quad \frac{2}{3}x - \frac{10}{5} = y$$

Since the slopes of the lines are different, the lines intersect to produce one solution. This is a consistent system.

11. Graph $y = x - 4$ and $y = 2x - 7$.

The lines intersect and the point of intersection is $(3, -1)$. This is a consistent system.

12. Graph $x = -2$ and $y = 5$.

The lines intersect and the point of intersection is $(-2, 5)$. This is a consistent system.

13. Graph the equations $x + 2y = 8$ and $2x - y = -4$.

The lines intersect and the point of intersection is $(0, 4)$. This is a consistent system.

14. Graph $x + 4y = 8$ and $y = 2$.

The lines intersect and the point of intersection is $(0, 2)$. This is a consistent system.

15. Graph $y = 3$ and $y = -2x + 5$.

The lines intersect and the point of intersection is $(1, 3)$. This is a consistent system.

16. Graph the equations $y = x - 3$ and $3x - 3y = 9$.

Both equations produce the same line. This is a dependent system. There are an infinite number of solutions.

17. Graph $3x + y = 0$ and $3x - 3y = 12$.

The lines intersect and the point of intersection is $(1, -3)$. This is a consistent system.

18. Graph $x + 5y = 10$ and $\frac{1}{5}x + y = -1$.

The lines are parallel and do not intersect. The system is inconsistent and there is no solution.

19.
$$y = 4x - 18$$
$$2x - 5y = 0$$

Substitute $4x - 18$ for y in the second equation.
$$2x - 5y = 0$$
$$2x - 5(4x - 18) = 0$$
$$2x - 20x + 90 = 0$$
$$-18x + 90 = 0$$
$$-18x = -90$$
$$x = 5$$

Now, substitute 5 for x in the first equation.
$$y = 4x - 18$$
$$y = 4(5) - 18$$
$$y = 20 - 18$$
$$y = 2$$
The solution is $(5, 2)$.

20.
$$x = 3y - 9$$
$$x + 2y = 1$$

Substitute $3y - 9$ for x in the second equation.
$$x + 2y = 1$$
$$3y - 9 + 2y = 1$$
$$5y - 9 = 1$$
$$5y = 10$$
$$y = 2$$

Now substitute 2 for y in the first equation.
$$x = 3y - 9$$
$$x = 3(2) - 9$$
$$x = 6 - 9$$
$$x = -3$$
The solution is $(-3, 2)$.

21.
$$2x - y = 7$$
$$x + 2y = 6$$

Solve the second equation for x, $x = 6 - 2y$.
Substitute $6 - 2y$ for x in the first equation.
$$2x - y = 7$$
$$2(6 - 2y) - y = 7$$
$$12 - 4y - y = 7$$
$$-5y = -5$$
$$y = 1$$

Substitute 1 for y in the equation $x = 6 - 2y$.
$$x = 6 - 2(1)$$
$$x = 6 - 2$$
$$x = 4$$
The solution is $(4, 1)$.

22.
$$x = -3y$$
$$x + 4y = 5$$

Substitute $-3y$ for x in the second equation.
$$x + 4y = 5$$
$$-3y + 4y = 5$$
$$y = 5$$

Substitute 5 for y in the first equation.
$$x = -3y$$
$$x = -3(5)$$
$$x = -15$$
The solution is $(-15, 5)$.

23. $4x - 2y = 7$

$\quad y = 2x + 3$

Substitute $2x + 3$ for y in the first equation.

$\quad 4x - 2y = 7$

$4x - 2(2x + 3) = 7$

$\quad 4x - 4x - 6 = 7$

$\qquad -6 = 7$ False

There is no solution.

24. $2x - 4y = 7$

$\quad -4x + 8y = -14$

Solve the first equation for x.

$2x - 4y = 7$

$\quad 2x = 4y + 7$

$\quad x = 2y + \dfrac{7}{2}$

Substitute $2y + \dfrac{7}{2}$ for x in the second equation.

$\quad -4x + 8y = -14$

$-4\left(2y + \dfrac{7}{2}\right) + 8y = -14$

$\quad -8y - 14 + 8y = -14$

$\qquad\qquad -14 = -14$ True

There are an infinite number of solutions.

25. $2x - 3y = 8$

$\quad 6x - 5y = 20$

Solve the first equation for x.

$2x - 3y = 8$

$\quad 2x = 3y + 8$

$\quad x = \dfrac{3}{2}y + 4$

Substitute $\dfrac{3}{2}y + 4$ for x in the second equation.

$\quad 6x - 5y = 20$

$6\left(\dfrac{3}{2}y + 4\right) - 5y = 20$

$\quad 9y + 24 - 5y = 20$

$\qquad 4y + 24 = 20$

$\qquad\quad 4y = -4$

$\qquad\quad\; y = -1$

Substitute -1 for y in the equation $x = \dfrac{3}{2}y + 4$.

$x = \dfrac{3}{2}(-1) + 4 = -\dfrac{3}{2} + \dfrac{8}{2} = \dfrac{5}{2}$

The solution is $\left(\dfrac{5}{2}, -1\right)$.

26. $3x - y = -5$

$\quad x + 2y = 8$

Solve the second equation for x, $x = 8 - 2y$.

Substitute $8 - 2y$ for x in the first equation.

$\qquad 3x - y = -5$

$3(8 - 2y) - y = -5$

$\; 24 - 6y - y = -5$

$\qquad\quad -7y = -29$

$\qquad\qquad y = \dfrac{29}{7}$

Substitute $\dfrac{29}{7}$ for y in the equation $x = 8 - 2y$.

$x = 8 - 2\left(\dfrac{29}{7}\right)$

$x = \dfrac{56}{7} - \dfrac{58}{7}$

$x = -\dfrac{2}{7}$

The solution is $\left(-\dfrac{2}{7}, \dfrac{29}{7}\right)$.

27. $\quad x - y = -4$

$\underline{-x + 6y = -6}$

$\qquad\quad 5y = -10$

$\qquad\qquad y = -2$

Substitute -2 for y in the first equation.

$\quad x - y = -4$

$x - (-2) = -4$

$\quad x + 2 = -4$

$\qquad\; x = -6$

The solution is $(-6, -2)$.

28. $\quad x + 2y = -3$

$\underline{5x - 2y = \;\; 9}$

$\; 6x \qquad\; = 6$

$\qquad\quad x = 1$

Substitute 1 for x in the first equation.

$x + 2y = -3$

$1 + 2y = -3$

$\quad 2y = -4$

$\quad\; y = -2$

The solution is $(1, -2)$.

29. $x + y = 12$

$2x + y = 5$

To eliminate y, multiply the first equation by -1 and then add.

$-1[x + y = 12]$

gives

$-x - y = -12$

$\underline{2x + y = \quad 5}$

$x \quad = -7$

Substitute -7 for x in the first equation.

$x + y = 12$

$-7 + y = 12$

$y = 19$

The solution is $(-7, 19)$.

30. $4x - 3y = 8$

$2x + 5y = 8$

To eliminate x, multiply the second equation by -2 and then add.

$-2[2x + 5y = 8]$

gives

$4x - 3y = \quad 8$

$\underline{-4x - 10y = -16}$

$-13y = -8$

$y = \dfrac{8}{13}$

Substitute $\dfrac{8}{13}$ for y in the first equation.

$4x - 3y = 8$

$4x - 3\left(\dfrac{8}{13}\right) = 8$

$4x - \dfrac{24}{13} = 8$

$4x = \dfrac{104}{13} + \dfrac{24}{13}$

$4x = \dfrac{128}{13}$

$x = \dfrac{32}{13}$

The solution is $\left(\dfrac{32}{13}, \dfrac{8}{13}\right)$.

31. $-2x + 3y = 15$

$7x + 3y = 6$

To eliminate y, multiply the second equation by -1 and then add.

$-1[7x + 3y = 6]$

gives

$-2x + 3y = 15$

$\underline{-7x - 3y = -6}$

$-9x \quad = \quad 9$

$x = -1$

Substitute -1 for x in the second equation.

$7x + 3y = 6$

$7(-1) + 3y = 6$

$-7 + 3y = 6$

$3y = 13$

$y = \dfrac{13}{3}$

The solution is $\left(-1, \dfrac{13}{3}\right)$.

32. $2x + y = 3$

$-4x - 2y = 5$

Multiply the first equation by 2, and then add.

$2[2x + y = 3]$

gives

$4x + 2y = 6$

$\underline{-4x - 2y = 3}$

$0 = 9$ False

There is no solution.

33. $3x = -4y + 15$

$8y = -6x + 30$

Align the x and y terms.

$3x + 4y = 15$

$6x + 8y = 30$

To eliminate x, multiply the first equation by -2, and then add.

$-2[3x + 4y = 15]$

gives

$-6x - 8y = -30$

$\underline{6x + 8y = \quad 30}$

$0 = 0$ True

There are an infinite number of solutions.

34. $2x - 5y = 12$

$3x - 4y = -6$

To eliminate x, multiply the first equation by -3 and the second equation by 2 and then add.

$-3[2x - 5y = 12]$

$2[3x - 4y = -6]$

gives

$-6x + 15y = -36$

$\underline{6x - 8y = -12}$

$7y = -48$

$y = -\dfrac{48}{7}$

Now, substitute $-\dfrac{48}{7}$ for y in the first equation.

$2x - 5y = 12$

$2x - 5\left(-\dfrac{48}{7}\right) = 12$

$2x + \dfrac{240}{7} = 12$

$2x = \dfrac{84}{7} - \dfrac{240}{7}$

$2x = -\dfrac{156}{7}$

$x = -\dfrac{78}{7}$

The solution is $\left(-\dfrac{78}{7}, -\dfrac{48}{7}\right)$.

35. $x - 2y - 4z = 13$ (1)

$3y + 2z = -2$ (2)

$5z = -20$ (3)

Solve equation (3) for z.

$5z = -20$

$z = -4$

Substitute -4 for z in equation (2).

$3y + 2(-4) = -2$

$3y - 8 = -2$

$3y = 6$

$y = 2$

Substitute -4 for z and 2 for y in equation (1).

$x - 2(2) - 4(-4) = 13$

$x - 4 + 16 = 13$

$x + 12 = 13$

$x = 1$

The solution is $(1, 2, -4)$.

36. $2a + b - 2c = 5$

$3b + 4c = 1$

$3c = -6$

Solve the third equation for c.

$3c = -6$

$c = -2$

Substitute -2 for c in the second equation.

$3b + 4(-2) = 1$

$3b - 8 = 1$

$3b = 9$

$b = 3$

Substitute 3 for b and -2 for c in the first equation.

$2a + (3) - 2(-2) = 5$

$2a + 3 + 4 = 5$

$2a + 7 = 5$

$2a = -2$

$a = -1$

The solution is $(-1, 3, -2)$.

37. $x + 2y + 3z = 3$ (1)

$-2x - 3y - z = 5$ (2)

$3x + 3y + 7z = 2$ (3)

To eliminate x between equations (1) and (2), multiply equation (1) by 2 and then add.

$2[x + 2y + 3z = 3]$

$-2x - 3y - z = 5$

gives

$2x + 4y + 6z = 6$

$\underline{-2x - 3y - z = 5}$

Add: $y + 5z = 11$ (4)

To eliminate x between equations (2) and (3), multiply equation (2) by 3 and equation (3) by 2, then add.

$3[-2x - 3y - z = 5]$

$2[3x + 3y + 7z = 2]$

gives

$-6x - 9y - 3z = 15$

$\underline{6x + 6y + 14z = 4}$

Add: $-3y + 11z = 19$ (5)

Equations (4) and (5) are two equations in two unknowns.

$y + 5z = 11$ (4)

$-3y + 11z = 19$ (5)

To eliminate y, multiply equation (4) by 3 and then add.

$3[y + 5z = 11]$

$-3y + 11z = 19$

gives

$3y + 15z = 33$

$-3y + 11z = 19$

Add: $\qquad 26z = 52$

$z = 2$

Substitute 2 for z in equation (4).

$y + 5(2) = 11$

$y + 10 = 11$

$y = 1$

Finally, substitute 1 for y and 2 for z in equation (1).

$x + 2(1) + 3(2) = 3$

$x + 2 + 6 = 3$

$x + 8 = 3$

$x = -5$

The solution is $(-5, 1, 2)$.

38. $-x - 4y + 2z = 1$ (1)

$2x + 2y + z = 0$ (2)

$-3x - 2y - 5z = 5$ (3)

To eliminate y between equations (1) and (2), multiply equation (2) by 2 and add.

$-x - 4y + 2z = 1$

$2[2x + 2y + z = 0]$

gives

$-x - 4y + 2z = 1$

$4x + 4y + 2z = 0$

Add: $\qquad 3x \quad + 4z = 1$ (4)

To eliminate y between equations (2) and (3), simply add.

$2x + 2y + z = 0$

$-3x - 2y - 5z = 5$

Add: $\qquad -x \quad - 4z = 5$ (5)

Equations (4) and (5) are two equations in two unknowns.

$3x + 4z = 1$ (4)

$-x - 4z = 5$ (5)

To eliminate z, simply add equations (4) and (5).

$3x + 4z = 1$

$-x - 4z = 5$

Add: $2x \qquad = 6$

$x = 3$

Substitute 3 for x in equation (4).

$3(3) + 4z = 1$

$9 + 4z = 1$

$4z = -8$

$z = -2$

Finally, substitute 3 for x and -2 for z in equation (1).

$-(3) - 4y + 2(-2) = 1$

$-3 - 4y - 4 = 1$

$-7 - 4y = 1$

$-4y = 8$

$y = -2$

The solution is $(3, -2, -2)$.

39. $3y - 2z = -4$ (1)

$3x - 5z = -7$ (2)

$2x + y = 6$ (3)

To eliminate y between equations (1) and (3), multiply equation (3) by -3 and then add.

$3y - 2z = -4$

$-3[2x + y = 6]$

gives

$3y - 2z = -4$

$-6x - 3y \qquad = -18$

Add: $-6x \quad - 2z = -22$

or

$-3x - z = -11$ (4)

Equations (4) and (2) are two equations in two unknowns. To eliminate x, simply add.

$3x - 5z = -7$

$-3x - z = -11$

Add: $\qquad -6z = -18$

$z = 3$

Substitute 3 for z in equation (2).

$3x - 5z = -7$

$3x - 5(3) = -7$

$3x - 15 = -7$

$3x = 8$

$x = \dfrac{8}{3}$

Substitute $\dfrac{8}{3}$ for x in equation (3).

$$2x + y = 6$$

$$2\left(\frac{8}{3}\right) + y = 6$$

$$\frac{16}{3} + y = 6$$

$$y = 6 - \frac{16}{3}$$

$$y = \frac{18}{3} - \frac{16}{3}$$

$$y = \frac{2}{3}$$

The solution is $\left(\frac{8}{3}, \frac{2}{3}, 3\right)$.

40. $a + 2b - 5c = 19$ (1)

$2a - 3b + 3c = -15$ (2)

$5a - 4b - 2c = -2$ (3)

To eliminate a between equations (1) and (2), multiply equation (1) by -2 and then add.

$-2[a + 2b - 5c = 19]$

$2a - 3b + 3c = -15$

gives

$-2a - 4b + 10c = -38$

$\underline{2a - 3b + 3c = -15}$

Add: $-7b + 13c = -53$ (4)

To eliminate a between equations (1) and (3), multiply equation (1) by -5 and then add.

$-5[a + 2b - 5c = 19]$

$5a - 4b - 2c = -2$

gives

$-5a - 10b + 25c = -95$

$\underline{5a - 4b - 2c = -2}$

Add: $-14b + 23c = -97$ (5)

Equations (4) and (5) are two equations in two unknowns.

$-7b + 13c = -53$

$-14b + 23c = -97$

To eliminate b, multiply equation (4) by -2 and then add.

$-2[-7b + 13c = -53]$

$-14b + 23c = -97$

gives

$14b - 26c = 106$

$\underline{-14b + 23c = -97}$

Add: $-3c = 9$

$c = -3$

Substitute -3 for c in equation (4).

$-7b + 13c = -53$

$-7b + 13(-3) = -53$

$-7b - 39 = -53$

$-7b = -14$

$b = 2$

Finally, substitute 2 for b and -3 for c in equation (1).

$a + 2b - 5c = 19$

$a + 2(2) - 5(-3) = 19$

$a + 4 + 15 = 19$

$a + 19 = 19$

$a = 0$

The solution is $(0, 2, -3)$.

41. $x - y + 3z = 1$ (1)

$-x + 2y - 2z = 1$ (2)

$x - 3y + z = 2$ (3)

To eliminate x between equations (1) and (2), simply add.

$x - y + 3z = 1$

$\underline{-x + 2y - 2z = 1}$

Add: $y + z = 2$ (4)

To eliminate x between equations (2) and (3), simply add.

$-x + 2y - 2z = 1$

$\underline{x - 3y + z = 2}$

Add: $-y - z = 3$ (5)

Equations (4) and (5) are two equations in two unknowns. To eliminate y and z simply add.

$y + z = 2$

$\underline{-y - z = 3}$

Add: $0 = 5$ False

Since this is a false statement, there is no solution to the system. This is an inconsistent system.

42. $-2x + 2y - 3z = 6$ (1)

$\quad 4x - y + 2z = -2$ (2)

$\quad 2x + y - z = 4$ (3)

To eliminate x between equations (1) and (2), multiply equation (1) by 2 and then add.

$2[-2x + 2y - 3z = 6]$

$\quad 4x - y + 2z = -2$

gives

$\quad -4x + 4y - 6z = 12$

$\quad \underline{4x - y + 2z = -2}$

Add: $\quad 3y - 4z = 10$ (4)

To eliminate x between equations (1) and (3), simply add.

$\quad -2x + 2y - 3z = 6$

$\quad \underline{2x + y - z = 4}$

Add: $\quad 3y - 4z = 10$ (5)

Equations (4) and (5) are two equations in two unknowns.

$3y - 4z = 10$

$3y - 4z = 10$

Since they are identical, there are an infinite number of solutions. This is a dependent system.

43. Let x = Jennifer's age and y = Luan's age.

$y = x + 10$

$x + y = 66$

Substitute $x + 10$ for y in the second equation.

$x + (x + 10) = 66$

$\quad 2x + 10 = 66$

$\quad 2x = 56$

$\quad x = 28$

Now substitute 28 for x in the first equation.

$y = (28) + 10$

$y = 38$

Jennifer is 28 years old and Luan is 38 years old.

44. Let x = the speed of the plane in still air and y = the speed of the wind.

$x + y = 560$

$x - y = 480$

To eliminate y, simply add.

$\quad x + y = 560$

$\quad \underline{x - y = 480}$

Add: $2x \quad = 1040$

$\quad x \quad = 520$

Substitute 520 for x in the first equation.

$x + y = 560$

$(520) + y = 560$

$\quad y = 40$

The speed of the plane in still air is 520 mph and the speed of the wind is 40 mph.

45. Let x = the amount of 20% acid solution and y = the amount of 50% acid solution.

$\quad x + y = 6$

$0.2x + 0.5y = 0.4(6)$

To clear decimals, multiply the second equation by 10.

$\quad x + y = 6$

$2x + 5y = 24$

Solve the first equation for y.

$x + y = 6$

$\quad y = -x + 6$

Substitute $-x + 6$ for y in the second equation.

$\quad 2x + 5y = 24$

$2x + 5(-x + 6) = 24$

$\quad 2x - 5x + 30 = -24$

$\quad -3x + 30 = 24$

$\quad -3x = -6$

$\quad x = \dfrac{-6}{-3} = 2$

Finally, substitute 2 for x in the equation $y = -x + 6$.

$y = -x + 6$

$y = -2 + 6$

$y = 4$

Sally should combine 2 liters of solution A with 4 liters of solution B.

46. Let x = the number of adult tickets and y = the number of children's tickets.

$$x + y = 650$$
$$15x + 11y = 8790$$

To solve, multiply the first equation by -11 and then add.

$$-11[x + y = 650]$$
$$15x + 11y = 8790$$

gives

$$-11x - 11y = -7150$$
$$\underline{15x + 11y = 8790}$$

Add: $4x = 1640$

$$x = \frac{1640}{4} = 410$$

Substitute 410 for x in the first equation.

$$x + y = 650$$
$$410 + y = 650$$
$$y = 240$$

Thus, 410 adult tickets and 240 children's tickets were sold.

47. Let x = age at first time and y = age at second time.

$$y = 2x - 5$$
$$x + y = 118$$

Substitute $2x - 5$ for y in the second equation.

$$x + y = 118$$
$$x + 2x - 5 = 118$$
$$3x - 5 = 118$$
$$3x = 123$$
$$x = 41$$

Substitute 41 for x in the first equation.

$$y = 2x - 5$$
$$y = 2(41) - 5$$
$$y = 82 - 5$$
$$y = 77$$

His ages were 41 years and 77 years.

48. Let x = the amount invested at 7%, y = the amount invested at 5%, and z = the amount invested at 3%.

$$x + y + z = 40,000 \quad (1)$$
$$y = x - 5000 \,(2)$$
$$0.07x + 0.05y + 0.03z = 2300 \quad (3)$$

Substitute $x - 5000$ for y in equations (1) and (3). Equation (1) becomes

$$x + y + z = 40,000$$
$$x + x - 5000 + z = 40,000$$
$$2x + z = 45,000 \,(4)$$

Equation (3) becomes

$$0.07x + 0.05y + 0.03z = 2300$$
$$0.07x + 0.05(x - 5000) + 0.03z = 2300$$
$$0.07x + 0.05x - 250 + 0.03z = 2300$$
$$0.12x + 0.03z = 2550 \,(5)$$

Equation (4) and (5) are a system of two equations in two unknowns. Solve equation (4) for z.

$$2x + z = 45,000$$
$$z = -2x + 45,000$$

Substitute $-2x + 45,000$ for z in equation (5).

$$0.12x + 0.03z = 2550$$
$$0.12x + 0.03(-2x + 45,000) = 2550$$
$$0.12x - 0.06x + 1350 = 2550$$
$$0.06x = 1200$$
$$x = 20,000$$

Now substitute 20,000 for x in equation (2).

$$y = x - 5000$$
$$y = 20,000 - 5000 = 15,000$$

Finally, substitute 20,000 for x and 15,000 for y in equation (1).

$$x + y + z = 40,000$$
$$20,000 + 15,000 + z = 40,000$$
$$35,000 + z = 40,000$$
$$z = 5000$$

Thus, \$20,000 was invested at 7%, \$15,000 at 5%, and \$5000 at 3%.

49. $x + 5y = 1$

$-2x - 8y = -6$

$\begin{bmatrix} 1 & 5 & | & 1 \\ -2 & -8 & | & -6 \end{bmatrix}$

$\begin{bmatrix} 1 & 5 & | & 1 \\ 0 & 2 & | & -4 \end{bmatrix} 2R_1 + R_2$

$\begin{bmatrix} 1 & 5 & | & 1 \\ 0 & 1 & | & -2 \end{bmatrix} \frac{1}{2}R_2$

The system is

$x + 5y = 1$

$y = -2$

Substitute -2 for y in the first equation.

$x + 5(-2) = 1$

$x - 10 = 1$

$x = 11$

The solution is $(11, -2)$.

50. $2x - 5y = 1$

$2x + 4y = 10$

$\begin{bmatrix} 2 & -5 & | & 1 \\ 2 & 4 & | & 10 \end{bmatrix}$

$\begin{bmatrix} 1 & -\frac{5}{2} & | & \frac{1}{2} \\ 2 & 4 & | & 10 \end{bmatrix} \frac{1}{2}R_1$

$\begin{bmatrix} 1 & -\frac{5}{2} & | & \frac{1}{2} \\ 0 & 9 & | & 9 \end{bmatrix} -2R_1 + R_2$

$\begin{bmatrix} 1 & -\frac{5}{2} & | & \frac{1}{2} \\ 0 & 1 & | & 1 \end{bmatrix} \frac{1}{9}R_2$

The system is

$x - \frac{5}{2}y = \frac{1}{2}$

$y = 1$

Substitute 1 for y in the first equation.

$x - \frac{5}{2}(1) = \frac{1}{2}$

$x - \frac{5}{2} = \frac{1}{2}$

$x = \frac{6}{2}$

$x = 3$

The solution is $(3, 1)$.

51. $3y = 6x - 12$

$4x = 2y + 8$

Write the system in standard form.

$-6x + 3y = -12$

$4x - 2y = 8$

$\begin{bmatrix} -6 & 3 & | & -12 \\ 4 & -2 & | & 8 \end{bmatrix}$

$\begin{bmatrix} 1 & -\frac{1}{2} & | & 2 \\ 4 & -2 & | & 8 \end{bmatrix} -\frac{1}{6}R_1$

$\begin{bmatrix} 1 & -\frac{1}{2} & | & 2 \\ 0 & 0 & | & 0 \end{bmatrix} -4R_1 + R_2$

Since the last row is all zeros, the system is dependent. There are an infinite number of solutions.

52. $2x - y - z = 5$

$x + 2y + 3z = -2$

$3x - 2y + z = 2$

$\begin{bmatrix} 2 & -1 & -1 & | & 5 \\ 1 & 2 & 3 & | & -2 \\ 3 & -2 & 1 & | & 2 \end{bmatrix}$

$\begin{bmatrix} 1 & -\frac{1}{2} & -\frac{1}{2} & | & \frac{5}{2} \\ 1 & 2 & 3 & | & -2 \\ 3 & -2 & 1 & | & 2 \end{bmatrix} \frac{1}{2}R_1$

$\begin{bmatrix} 1 & -\frac{1}{2} & -\frac{1}{2} & | & \frac{5}{2} \\ 0 & \frac{5}{2} & \frac{7}{2} & | & -\frac{9}{2} \\ 3 & -2 & 1 & | & 2 \end{bmatrix} -1R_1 + R_2$

$\begin{bmatrix} 1 & -\frac{1}{2} & -\frac{1}{2} & | & \frac{5}{2} \\ 0 & \frac{5}{2} & \frac{7}{2} & | & -\frac{9}{2} \\ 0 & -\frac{1}{2} & \frac{5}{2} & | & -\frac{11}{2} \end{bmatrix} -3R_1 + R_3$

$\begin{bmatrix} 1 & -\frac{1}{2} & -\frac{1}{2} & | & \frac{5}{2} \\ 0 & 1 & \frac{7}{5} & | & -\frac{9}{5} \\ 0 & -\frac{1}{2} & \frac{5}{2} & | & -\frac{11}{2} \end{bmatrix} \frac{2}{5}R_2$

$\begin{bmatrix} 1 & -\frac{1}{2} & -\frac{1}{2} & | & \frac{5}{2} \\ 0 & 1 & \frac{7}{5} & | & -\frac{9}{5} \\ 0 & 0 & \frac{16}{5} & | & -\frac{32}{5} \end{bmatrix} \frac{1}{2}R_2 + R_3$

$\begin{bmatrix} 1 & -\frac{1}{2} & -\frac{1}{2} & | & \frac{5}{2} \\ 0 & 1 & \frac{7}{5} & | & -\frac{9}{5} \\ 0 & 0 & 1 & | & -2 \end{bmatrix} \frac{5}{16}R_3$

The system is

$$x - \frac{1}{2}y - \frac{1}{2}z = \frac{5}{2}$$
$$y + \frac{7}{5}z = -\frac{9}{5}$$
$$z = -2$$

Substitute –2 for z in the second equation.

$$y + \frac{7}{5}z = -\frac{9}{5}$$
$$y + \frac{7}{5}(-2) = -\frac{9}{5}$$
$$y - \frac{14}{5} = -\frac{9}{5}$$
$$y = \frac{5}{5} = 1$$

Substitute 1 for y and –2 for z in the first equation.

$$x - \frac{1}{2}y - \frac{1}{2}z = \frac{5}{2}$$
$$x - \frac{1}{2}(1) - \frac{1}{2}(-2) = \frac{5}{2}$$
$$x - \frac{1}{2} + 1 = \frac{5}{2}$$
$$x + \frac{1}{2} = \frac{5}{2}$$
$$x = \frac{4}{2} = 2$$

The solution is $(2, 1, -2)$.

53.
$$3a - b + c = 2$$
$$2a - 3b + 4c = 4$$
$$a + 2b - 3c = -6$$

$$\begin{bmatrix} 3 & -1 & 1 & | & 2 \\ 2 & -3 & 4 & | & 4 \\ 1 & 2 & -3 & | & -6 \end{bmatrix}$$

$$\begin{bmatrix} 1 & -\frac{1}{3} & \frac{1}{3} & | & \frac{2}{3} \\ 2 & -3 & 4 & | & 4 \\ 1 & 2 & -3 & | & -6 \end{bmatrix} \frac{1}{3}R_1$$

$$\begin{bmatrix} 1 & -\frac{1}{3} & \frac{1}{3} & | & \frac{2}{3} \\ 0 & -\frac{7}{3} & \frac{10}{3} & | & \frac{8}{3} \\ 1 & 2 & -3 & | & -6 \end{bmatrix} -2R_1 + R_2$$

$$\begin{bmatrix} 1 & -\frac{1}{3} & \frac{1}{3} & | & \frac{2}{3} \\ 0 & -\frac{7}{3} & \frac{10}{3} & | & \frac{8}{3} \\ 0 & \frac{7}{3} & -\frac{10}{3} & | & -\frac{20}{3} \end{bmatrix} -1R_1 + R_3$$

$$\begin{bmatrix} 1 & -\frac{1}{3} & \frac{1}{3} & | & \frac{2}{3} \\ 0 & 1 & -\frac{10}{7} & | & -\frac{8}{7} \\ 0 & \frac{7}{3} & -\frac{10}{3} & | & -\frac{20}{3} \end{bmatrix} -\frac{3}{7}R_2$$

$$\begin{bmatrix} 1 & -\frac{1}{3} & \frac{1}{3} & | & \frac{2}{3} \\ 0 & 1 & -\frac{10}{7} & | & -\frac{8}{7} \\ 0 & 0 & 0 & | & -4 \end{bmatrix} -\frac{7}{3}R_1 + R_3$$

Since the last row has all zeros on the left side and a nonzero number on the right side, the system is inconsistent and has no solution.

54. $x + y + z = 3$
$$3x + 4y = -1$$
$$y - 3z = -10$$

$$\begin{bmatrix} 1 & 1 & 1 & | & 3 \\ 3 & 4 & 0 & | & -1 \\ 0 & 1 & -3 & | & -10 \end{bmatrix}$$

$$\begin{bmatrix} 1 & 1 & 1 & | & 3 \\ 0 & 1 & -3 & | & -10 \\ 0 & 1 & -3 & | & -10 \end{bmatrix} -3R_1 + R_2$$

$$\begin{bmatrix} 1 & 1 & 1 & | & 3 \\ 0 & 1 & -3 & | & -10 \\ 0 & 0 & 0 & | & 0 \end{bmatrix} -1R_2 + R_3$$

Since the last row is all zeros and there are no contradictions, the system is dependent. There are an infinite number of solutions.

55. $7x - 8y = -10$
$$-5x + 4y = 2$$

To solve, first calculate D, D_x, and D_y.

$$D = \begin{vmatrix} 7 & -8 \\ -5 & 4 \end{vmatrix} = (7)(4) - (-5)(-8)$$
$$= 28 - 40 = -12$$

$$D_x = \begin{vmatrix} -10 & -8 \\ 2 & 4 \end{vmatrix} = (-10)(4) - (2)(-8)$$
$$= -40 + 16 = -24$$

$$D_y = \begin{vmatrix} 7 & -10 \\ -5 & 2 \end{vmatrix} = (7)(2) - (-5)(-10)$$
$$= 14 - 50 = -36$$

$$x = \frac{D_x}{D} = \frac{-24}{-12} = 2 \text{ and } y = \frac{D_y}{D} = \frac{-36}{-12} = 3$$

The solution is $(2, 3)$.

56. $x + 4y = 5$

$5x + 3y = -9$

To solve, first calculate D, D_x, and D_y.

$D = \begin{vmatrix} 1 & 4 \\ 5 & 3 \end{vmatrix}$

$\quad = (1)(3) - (5)(4)$

$\quad = 3 - 20$

$\quad = -17$

$D_x = \begin{vmatrix} 5 & 4 \\ -9 & 3 \end{vmatrix}$

$\quad = (5)(3) - (-9)(4)$

$\quad = 15 + 36$

$\quad = 51$

$D_y = \begin{vmatrix} 1 & 5 \\ 5 & -9 \end{vmatrix}$

$\quad = (1)(-9) - (5)(5)$

$\quad = -9 - 25$

$\quad = -34$

$x = \dfrac{D_x}{D} = \dfrac{51}{-17} = -3$ and $y = \dfrac{D_y}{D} = \dfrac{-34}{-17} = 2$

The solution is $(-3, 2)$.

57. $9m + 4n = -1$

$7m - 2n = -11$

To solve, first calculate D, D_m, and D_n.

$D = \begin{vmatrix} 9 & 4 \\ 7 & -2 \end{vmatrix}$

$\quad = (9)(-2) - (7)(4)$

$\quad = -18 - 28$

$\quad = -46$

$D_m = \begin{vmatrix} -1 & 4 \\ -11 & -2 \end{vmatrix}$

$\quad = (-1)(-2) - (-11)(4)$

$\quad = 2 + 44$

$\quad = 46$

$D_n = \begin{vmatrix} 9 & -1 \\ 7 & -11 \end{vmatrix}$

$\quad = (9)(-11) - (7)(-1)$

$\quad = -99 + 7$

$\quad = -92$

$m = \dfrac{D_m}{D} = \dfrac{46}{-46} = -1$ and $n = \dfrac{D_n}{D} = \dfrac{-92}{-46} = 2$.

The solution is $(-1, 2)$.

58. $p + q + r = 5$

$2p + q - r = -5$

$3p + 2q - 3r = -12$

To solve, calculate D, D_p, D_q, and D_r.

$D = \begin{vmatrix} 1 & 1 & 1 \\ 2 & 1 & -1 \\ 3 & 2 & -3 \end{vmatrix}$

$\quad = 1\begin{vmatrix} 1 & -1 \\ 2 & -3 \end{vmatrix} - 1\begin{vmatrix} 2 & -1 \\ 3 & -3 \end{vmatrix} + 1\begin{vmatrix} 2 & 1 \\ 3 & 2 \end{vmatrix}$

$\quad = 1(-3 + 2) - 1(-6 + 3) + 1(4 - 3)$

$\quad = 1(-1) - 1(-3) + 1(1)$

$\quad = -1 + 3 + 1 = 3$

$D_p = \begin{vmatrix} 5 & 1 & 1 \\ -5 & 1 & -1 \\ -12 & 2 & -3 \end{vmatrix}$

$\quad = 5\begin{vmatrix} 1 & -1 \\ 2 & -3 \end{vmatrix} - 1\begin{vmatrix} -5 & -1 \\ -12 & -3 \end{vmatrix} + 1\begin{vmatrix} -5 & 1 \\ -12 & 2 \end{vmatrix}$

$\quad = 5(-3 + 2) - 1(15 - 12) + 1(-10 + 12)$

$\quad = 5(-1) - 1(3) + 1(2)$

$\quad = -5 - 3 + 2 = -6$

$D_q = \begin{vmatrix} 1 & 5 & 1 \\ 2 & -5 & -1 \\ 3 & -12 & -3 \end{vmatrix}$

$\quad = 1\begin{vmatrix} -5 & -1 \\ -12 & -3 \end{vmatrix} - 5\begin{vmatrix} 2 & -1 \\ 3 & -3 \end{vmatrix} + 1\begin{vmatrix} 2 & -5 \\ 3 & -12 \end{vmatrix}$

$\quad = 1(15 - 12) - 5(-6 + 3) + 1(-24 + 15)$

$\quad = 1(3) - 5(-3) + 1(-9)$

$\quad = 3 + 15 - 9 = 9$

$D_r = \begin{vmatrix} 1 & 1 & 5 \\ 2 & 1 & -5 \\ 3 & 2 & -12 \end{vmatrix}$

$\quad = 1\begin{vmatrix} 1 & -5 \\ 2 & -12 \end{vmatrix} - 1\begin{vmatrix} 2 & -5 \\ 3 & -12 \end{vmatrix} + 5\begin{vmatrix} 2 & 1 \\ 3 & 2 \end{vmatrix}$

$\quad = 1(-12 + 10) - 1(-24 + 15) + 5(4 - 3)$

$\quad = 1(-2) - 1(-9) + 5(1)$

$\quad = -2 + 9 + 5 = 12$

$p = \dfrac{D_p}{D} = \dfrac{-6}{3} = -2$, $q = \dfrac{D_q}{D} = \dfrac{9}{3} = 3$, and

$r = \dfrac{D_r}{D} = \dfrac{12}{3} = 4$

The solution is $(-2, 3, 4)$.

59. $-2a + 3b - 4c = -7$

$2a + b + c = 5$

$-2a - 3b + 4c = 3$

To solve, calculate D, D_a, D_b, and D_c.

$$D = \begin{vmatrix} -2 & 3 & -4 \\ 2 & 1 & 1 \\ -2 & -3 & 4 \end{vmatrix}$$

$$= -2 \begin{vmatrix} 1 & 1 \\ -3 & 4 \end{vmatrix} - 3 \begin{vmatrix} 2 & 1 \\ -2 & 4 \end{vmatrix} + (-4) \begin{vmatrix} 2 & 1 \\ -2 & -3 \end{vmatrix}$$

$$= -2(4+3) - 3(8+2) - 4(-6+2)$$

$$= -2(7) - 3(10) - 4(-4)$$

$$= -14 - 30 + 16$$

$$= -28$$

$$D_a = \begin{vmatrix} -7 & 3 & -4 \\ 5 & 1 & 1 \\ 3 & -3 & 4 \end{vmatrix}$$

$$= -7 \begin{vmatrix} 1 & 1 \\ -3 & 4 \end{vmatrix} - 3 \begin{vmatrix} 5 & 1 \\ 3 & 4 \end{vmatrix} + (-4) \begin{vmatrix} 5 & 1 \\ 3 & -3 \end{vmatrix}$$

$$= -7(4+3) - 3(20-3) - 4(-15-3)$$

$$= -7(7) - 3(17) - 4(-18)$$

$$= -49 - 51 + 72$$

$$= -28$$

$$D_b = \begin{vmatrix} -2 & -7 & -4 \\ 2 & 5 & 1 \\ -2 & 3 & 4 \end{vmatrix}$$

$$= -2 \begin{vmatrix} 5 & 1 \\ 3 & 4 \end{vmatrix} - (-7) \begin{vmatrix} 2 & 1 \\ -2 & 4 \end{vmatrix} + (-4) \begin{vmatrix} 2 & 5 \\ -2 & 3 \end{vmatrix}$$

$$= -2(20-3) + 7(8+2) - 4(6+10)$$

$$= -2(17) + 7(10) - 4(16)$$

$$= -34 + 70 - 64$$

$$= -28$$

$$D_c = \begin{vmatrix} -2 & 3 & -7 \\ 2 & 1 & 5 \\ -2 & -3 & 3 \end{vmatrix}$$

$$= -2 \begin{vmatrix} 1 & 5 \\ -3 & 3 \end{vmatrix} - 3 \begin{vmatrix} 2 & 5 \\ -2 & 3 \end{vmatrix} + (-7) \begin{vmatrix} 2 & 1 \\ -2 & -3 \end{vmatrix}$$

$$= -2(3+15) - 3(6+10) - 7(-6+2)$$

$$= -2(18) - 3(16) - 7(-4)$$

$$= -36 - 48 + 28$$

$$= -56$$

$a = \dfrac{D_a}{D} = \dfrac{-28}{-28} = 1$, $b = \dfrac{D_b}{D} = \dfrac{-28}{-28} = 1$, and

$c = \dfrac{D_c}{D} = \dfrac{-56}{-28} = 2$

The solution is $(1, 1, 2)$.

60. $y + 3z = 4$

$-x - y + 2z = 0$

$x + 2y + z = 1$

To solve, first calculate D, D_x, D_y, and D_z.

$$D = \begin{vmatrix} 0 & 1 & 3 \\ -1 & -1 & 2 \\ 1 & 2 & 1 \end{vmatrix} = 0 \begin{vmatrix} -1 & 2 \\ 2 & 1 \end{vmatrix} - (-1) \begin{vmatrix} 1 & 3 \\ 2 & 1 \end{vmatrix} + 1 \begin{vmatrix} 1 & 3 \\ -1 & 2 \end{vmatrix}$$

$$= 0(-1-4) + 1(1-6) + 1(2+3)$$

$$= 0(-5) + 1(-5) + 1(5)$$

$$= 0 - 5 + 5$$

$$= 0$$

$$D_x = \begin{vmatrix} 4 & 1 & 3 \\ 0 & -1 & 2 \\ 1 & 2 & 1 \end{vmatrix} = 4 \begin{vmatrix} -1 & 2 \\ 2 & 1 \end{vmatrix} - 0 \begin{vmatrix} 1 & 3 \\ 2 & 1 \end{vmatrix} + 1 \begin{vmatrix} 1 & 3 \\ -1 & 2 \end{vmatrix}$$

$$= 4(-1-4) - 0(1-6) + 1(2+3)$$

$$= 4(-5) - 0(-5) + 1(5)$$

$$= -20 + 0 + 5$$

$$= -15$$

Since $D = 0$ and $D_x = -15$, the system is inconsistent and has no solution.

Chapter 9 Practice Test

1. a.

$x + 2y = -6$ $3x + 2y = -12$

$-6 + 2(0) = -6$ $3(-6) + 2(0) = -12$

$-6 = -6$ $-18 = -12$

True   False

Since $(-6, 0)$ does not satisfy both equations, it is not a solution to the system.

b.

$x + 2y = -6$ $3x + 2y = -12$

$-3 + 2\left(-\dfrac{3}{2}\right) = -6$ $3(-3) + 2\left(-\dfrac{3}{2}\right) = -12$

$-6 = -6$ $-12 = -12$

True   True

$\left(-3, -\dfrac{3}{2}\right)$ is a solution to the system.

c. $x + 2y = -6$ $\qquad$ $3x + 2y = -12$

$2 + 2(-4) = -6$ $\qquad$ $3(2) + 2(-4) = -12$

$-6 = -6$ $\qquad\qquad$ $-2 = -12$

$\qquad$ True $\qquad\qquad\qquad$ False

Since (2, –4) does not satisfy both equations, it is not a solution to the system.

2. The system is consistent; it has exactly one solution.

3. The system is inconsistent, it has no solution.

4. The system is dependent; it has an infinite number of solutions.

5. Write both equations in slope-intercept form.

$5x + 2y = 4$ $\qquad\qquad$ $6x = 3y - 7$

$2y = -5x + 4$ $\qquad$ $-3y = -6x - 7$

$y = \dfrac{-5x + 4}{2}$ $\qquad$ $y = \dfrac{-6x - 7}{-3}$

$y = -\dfrac{5}{2}x + 2$ $\qquad$ $y = 2x + \dfrac{7}{3}$

Since the slope of the first line is $-\dfrac{5}{2}$ and the slope of the second line is 2, the slopes are different so that the lines intersect to produce one solution. This is a consistent system.

6. Write both equations in slope-intercept form.

$5x + 3y = 9$

$3y = -5x + 9$ $\qquad\qquad$ $2y = -\dfrac{10}{3}x + 6$

$y = \dfrac{-5x + 9}{3}$ $\qquad$ $\dfrac{1}{2}(2y) = \dfrac{1}{2}\left(-\dfrac{10}{3}x + 6\right)$

$y = -\dfrac{5}{3}x + 3$ $\qquad$ $y = -\dfrac{5}{3}x + 3$

Since the equations are identical, there are an infinite number of solutions and this is a dependent system.

7. Write both equations in slope-intercept form.

$5x - 4y = 6$ $\qquad\qquad$ $-10x + 8y = -10$

$-4y = -5x + 6$ $\qquad$ $8y = 10x - 10$

$y = \dfrac{-5x + 6}{-4}$ $\qquad$ $y = \dfrac{10x - 10}{8}$

$y = \dfrac{5}{4}x - \dfrac{3}{2}$ $\qquad$ $y = \dfrac{5}{4}x - \dfrac{5}{4}$

Since the slope of each line is $\dfrac{5}{4}$, but the

y-intercepts are different $\left(b = -\dfrac{3}{2}\right.$ for the first equation, $b = -\dfrac{5}{4}$ for the second equation$\left.\right)$, for the second the two lines are parallel and produce no solution. This is an inconsistent system.

8. Graph the equations $y = 3x - 2$ and $y = -2x + 8$.

The lines intersect and the point of intersection is (2, 4).

9. Graph the equations $y = -x + 6$ and $y = 2x + 3$.

The lines intersect and the point of intersection is (1, 5).

10. $y = 4x - 3$

$y = 5x - 4$

Substitute $4x - 3$ for y in the second equation.

$4x - 3 = 5x - 4$

$-x - 3 = -4$

$-x = -1$

$x = 1$

Substitute 1 for x in the first equation.

$y = 4x - 3$

$y = 4(1) - 3$

$y = 4 - 3$

$y = 1$

The solution is (1, 1).

11. $4a + 7b = 2$

$5a + b = -13$

Solve the second equation for b.

$5a + b = -13$

$b = -5a - 13$

Substitute $-5a - 13$ for b in the first equation.

$4a + 7(-5a - 13) = 2$

$4a - 35a - 91 = 2$

$-31a - 91 = 2$

$-31a = 93$

$a = -3$

Substitute -3 for a in the equation $b = -5a - 13$.

$b = -5(-3) - 13$

$b = 2$

The solution is $(-3, 2)$.

12. $0.3x = 0.2y + 0.4$

$-1.2x + 0.8y = -1.6$

Write the system in standard form.

$0.3x - 0.2y = 0.4$

$-1.2x + 0.8y = -1.6$

To eliminate x, multiply the first equation by 4 and then add.

$4[0.3x - 0.2y = 0.4]$

$-1.2x + 0.8y = -1.6$

gives

$\quad 1.2x - 0.8y = \;\; 1.6$

$\underline{-1.2x + 0.8y = -1.6}$

Add: $\qquad\quad 0 = 0 \qquad$ True

Since this is a true statement, there are an infinite number of solutions and this is a dependent system.

13. $\dfrac{3}{2}a + b = 6$

$a - \dfrac{5}{2}b = -4$

To clear fractions, multiply both equations by 2.

$2\left[\dfrac{3}{2}a + b = 6\right]$

$2\left[a - \dfrac{5}{2}b = -4\right]$

gives

$3a + 2b = 12$

$2a - 5b = -8$

Now, to eliminate b, multiply the first equation by 5 and the second equation by 2 and then add.

$5[3a + 2b = 12]$

$2[2a - 5b = -8]$

gives

$\quad 15a + 10b = \;\; 60$

$\underline{\quad 4a - 10b = -16}$

Add: $19a \qquad\;\; = 44$

$a = \dfrac{44}{19}$

Substitute $\dfrac{44}{19}$ for a in the first equation.

$\dfrac{3}{2}a + b = 6$

$\dfrac{3}{2}\left(\dfrac{44}{19}\right) + b = 6$

$\dfrac{66}{19} + b = 6$

$b = 6 - \dfrac{66}{19}$

$b = \dfrac{114}{19} - \dfrac{66}{19}$

$b = \dfrac{48}{19}$

The solution is $\left(\dfrac{44}{19}, \dfrac{48}{19}\right)$.

14. $x + y + z = 2\;(1)$

$-2x - y + z = 1\;(2)$

$x - 2y - z = 1\;(3)$

To eliminate z between equations (1) and (3) simply add.

$x + \;\; y + z = 2$

$\underline{x - 2y - z = 1}$

Add: $2x - \; y \qquad = 3 \qquad (4)$

To eliminate z between equations (2) and (3) simply add.

$-2x - \; y + z = 1$

$\underline{\;\;\; x - 2y - z = 1}$

Add: $-x - 3y \qquad = 2 \qquad (5)$

Equations (4) and (5) are two equations in two unknowns.

$2x - y = 3$

$-x - 3y = 2$

To eliminate x, multiply equation (5) by 2 and then add.

$2x - y = 3$

$2[-x - 3y = 2]$

gives

$2x - \;\; y = 3$

$\underline{-2x - 6y = 4}$

Add: $\quad -7y = 7$

$$y = \frac{7}{-7} = -1$$

Substitute -1 for y in equation (4).

$2x - y = 3$

$2x - (-1) = 3$

$2x + 1 = 3$

$2x = 2$

$$x = \frac{2}{2} = 1$$

Finally, substitute 1 for x and -1 for y in equation (1).

$x + y + z = 2$

$1 - 1 + z = 2$

$0 + z = 2$

$z = 2$

The solution is $(1, -1, 2)$.

15. $-2x + 3y + 7z = 5$

$3x - 2y + z = -2$

$x - 6y + 9z = -13$

The augmented matrix is

$$\begin{bmatrix} -2 & 3 & 7 & 5 \\ 3 & -2 & 1 & -2 \\ 1 & -6 & 9 & -13 \end{bmatrix}$$

16. $\begin{bmatrix} 6 & -2 & 4 & 4 \\ 4 & 3 & 5 & 6 \\ 2 & -1 & 4 & -3 \end{bmatrix}$

$$\begin{bmatrix} 6 & -2 & 4 & 4 \\ 0 & 5 & -3 & 12 \\ 2 & -1 & 4 & -3 \end{bmatrix} -2R_3 + R_2$$

17. $2x + 7y = 1$

$3x + 5y = 7$

$$\begin{bmatrix} 2 & 7 & 1 \\ 3 & 5 & 7 \end{bmatrix}$$

$$\begin{bmatrix} 1 & \frac{7}{2} & \frac{1}{2} \\ 3 & 5 & 7 \end{bmatrix} \frac{1}{2}R_1$$

$$\begin{bmatrix} 1 & \frac{7}{2} & \frac{1}{2} \\ 0 & -\frac{11}{2} & \frac{11}{2} \end{bmatrix} -3R_1 + R_2$$

$$\begin{bmatrix} 1 & \frac{7}{2} & \frac{1}{2} \\ 0 & 1 & -1 \end{bmatrix} -\frac{2}{11}R_2$$

The system is

$$x + \frac{7}{2}y = \frac{1}{2}$$

$$y = -1$$

Substitute -1 for y in the first equation.

$$x + \frac{7}{2}(-1) = \frac{1}{2}$$

$$x - \frac{7}{2} = \frac{1}{2}$$

$$x = \frac{8}{2} = 4$$

The solution is $(4, -1)$.

18. $x - 2y + z = 7$

$-2x - y - z = -7$

$4x + 5y - 2z = 3$

$$\begin{bmatrix} 1 & -2 & 1 & 7 \\ -2 & -1 & -1 & -7 \\ 4 & 5 & -2 & 3 \end{bmatrix}$$

$$\begin{bmatrix} 1 & -2 & 1 & 7 \\ 0 & -5 & 1 & 7 \\ 4 & 5 & -2 & 3 \end{bmatrix} 2R_1 + R_2$$

$$\begin{bmatrix} 1 & -2 & 1 & 7 \\ 0 & -5 & 1 & 7 \\ 0 & 13 & -6 & -25 \end{bmatrix} -4R_1 + R_3$$

$$\begin{bmatrix} 1 & -2 & 1 & 7 \\ 0 & 1 & -\frac{1}{5} & -\frac{7}{5} \\ 0 & 13 & -6 & -25 \end{bmatrix} -\frac{1}{5}R_2$$

$$\begin{bmatrix} 1 & -2 & 1 & 7 \\ 0 & 1 & -\frac{1}{5} & -\frac{7}{5} \\ 0 & 0 & -\frac{17}{5} & -\frac{34}{5} \end{bmatrix} -13R_2 + R_3$$

$$\left[\begin{array}{ccc|c} 1 & -2 & 1 & 7 \\ 0 & 1 & -\frac{1}{5} & -\frac{7}{5} \\ 0 & 0 & 1 & 2 \end{array}\right] -\frac{5}{17}R_3$$

The system is

$x - 2y + z = 7$

$y - \dfrac{1}{5}z = -\dfrac{7}{5}$

$z = 2$

Substitute 2 for z in the second equation.

$y - \dfrac{1}{5}z = -\dfrac{7}{5}$

$y - \dfrac{1}{5}(2) = -\dfrac{7}{5}$

$y - \dfrac{2}{5} = -\dfrac{7}{5}$

$y = -1$

Substitute −1 for y and 2 for z in the first equation.

$x - 2y + z = 7$

$x - 2(-1) + 2 = 7$

$x + 2 + 2 = 7$

$x + 4 = 7$

$x = 3$

The solution is $(3, -1, 2)$.

19. $\begin{vmatrix} 3 & -1 \\ 5 & -2 \end{vmatrix} = (3)(-2) - (5)(-1)$

$= -6 - (-5)$

$= -6 + 5$

$= -1$

20. $\begin{vmatrix} 8 & 2 & -1 \\ 3 & 0 & 5 \\ 6 & -3 & 4 \end{vmatrix} = 8\begin{vmatrix} 0 & 5 \\ -3 & 4 \end{vmatrix} - 3\begin{vmatrix} 2 & -1 \\ -3 & 4 \end{vmatrix} + 6\begin{vmatrix} 2 & -1 \\ 0 & 5 \end{vmatrix}$

$= 8(0 + 15) - 3(8 - 3) + 6(10 - 0)$

$= 8(15) - 3(5) + 6(10)$

$= 120 - 15 + 60$

$= 165$

21. $4x + 3y = -6$

$-2x + 5y = 16$

To solve, first calculate D, D_x, and D_y.

$D = \begin{vmatrix} 4 & 3 \\ -2 & 5 \end{vmatrix} = (4)(5) - (-2)(3) = 20 + 6 = 26$

$D_x = \begin{vmatrix} -6 & 3 \\ 16 & 5 \end{vmatrix} = (-6)(5) - (16)(3) = -30 - 48 = -78$

$D_y = \begin{vmatrix} 4 & -6 \\ -2 & 16 \end{vmatrix} = (4)(16) - (-2)(-6) = 64 - 12 = 52$

$x = \dfrac{D_x}{D} = \dfrac{-78}{26} = -3$ and $y = \dfrac{D_y}{D} = \dfrac{52}{26} = 2$.

The solution is $(-3, 2)$.

22. $2r - 4s + 3t = -1$

$-3r + 5s - 4t = 0$

$-2r + s - 3t = -2$

To solve, first calculate D, D_r, D_s, and D_t.

$D = \begin{vmatrix} 2 & -4 & 3 \\ -3 & 5 & -4 \\ -2 & 1 & -3 \end{vmatrix}$

$= 2\begin{vmatrix} 5 & -4 \\ 1 & -3 \end{vmatrix} - (-4)\begin{vmatrix} -3 & -4 \\ -2 & -3 \end{vmatrix} + 3\begin{vmatrix} -3 & 5 \\ -2 & 1 \end{vmatrix}$

$= 2(-15 + 4) + 4(9 - 8) + 3(-3 + 10)$

$= 2(-11) + 4(1) + 3(7)$

$= -22 + 4 + 21$

$= 3$

$D_r = \begin{vmatrix} -1 & -4 & 3 \\ 0 & 5 & -4 \\ -2 & 1 & -3 \end{vmatrix}$

$= -1\begin{vmatrix} 5 & -4 \\ 1 & -3 \end{vmatrix} - (-4)\begin{vmatrix} 0 & -4 \\ -2 & -3 \end{vmatrix} + 3\begin{vmatrix} 0 & 5 \\ -2 & 1 \end{vmatrix}$

$= -1(-15 + 4) + 4(0 - 8) + 3(0 + 10)$

$= -1(-11) + 4(-8) + 3(10)$

$= 11 - 32 + 30$

$= 9$

$D_s = \begin{vmatrix} 2 & -1 & 3 \\ -3 & 0 & -4 \\ -2 & -2 & -3 \end{vmatrix}$

$= 2\begin{vmatrix} 0 & -4 \\ -2 & -3 \end{vmatrix} - (-1)\begin{vmatrix} -3 & -4 \\ -2 & -3 \end{vmatrix} + 3\begin{vmatrix} -3 & 0 \\ -2 & -2 \end{vmatrix}$

$= 2(0 - 8) + 1(9 - 8) + 3(6 - 0)$

$= 2(-8) + 1(1) + 3(6)$

$= -16 + 1 + 18$

$= 3$

$$D_t = \begin{vmatrix} 2 & -4 & -1 \\ -3 & 5 & 0 \\ -2 & 1 & -2 \end{vmatrix}$$

$$= 2\begin{vmatrix} 5 & 0 \\ 1 & -2 \end{vmatrix} - (-4)\begin{vmatrix} -3 & 0 \\ -2 & -2 \end{vmatrix} + (-1)\begin{vmatrix} -3 & 5 \\ -2 & 1 \end{vmatrix}$$

$$= 2(-10-0) + 4(6-0) - 1(-3+10)$$

$$= 2(-10) + 4(6) - 1(7)$$

$$= -20 + 24 - 7$$

$$= -3$$

$$r = \frac{D_r}{D} = \frac{9}{3} = 3, \quad s = \frac{D_s}{D} = \frac{3}{3} = 1, \quad t = \frac{D_t}{D} = \frac{-3}{3} = -1$$

The solution is $(3, 1, -1)$.

23. Let $x =$ the number of pounds of sunflower seeds and $y =$ the number of pounds of bird seed.
$$x + y = 20$$
$$0.49x + 0.89y = 0.73(20)$$
Solve the first equation for y.
$$x + y = 20$$
$$y = -x + 20$$
Substitute $-x + 20$ for y in the second equation.
$$0.49x + 0.89(-x + 20) = 0.73(20)$$
$$0.49x - 0.89x + 17.8 = 14.6$$
$$-0.4x = -3.2$$
$$x = 8$$
Substitute 8 for x in the equation for y.
$$y = -x + 20$$
$$y = -(8) + 20$$
$$y = 12$$
Thus, 8 pounds of sunflower seeds should be mixed with 12 pounds of the gourmet bird seed to obtain the desired mixture.

24. Let $x =$ amount of 6% solution
$y =$ amount of 15% solution
$$x + y = 10$$
$$0.06x + 0.15y = 0.09(10)$$
The system can be written as
$$x + y = 10$$
$$6x + 15y = 90$$
Solve the first equation for y.
$$y = 10 - x$$
Substitute $10 - x$ for y in the second equation.

$$6x + 15y = 90$$
$$6x + 15(10 - x) = 90$$
$$6x + 150 - 15x = 90$$
$$-9x = -60$$
$$x = \frac{-60}{-9} = \frac{20}{3} = 6\frac{2}{3}$$
Substitute $6\frac{2}{3}$ for x into $y = 10 - x$
$$y = 10 - 6\frac{2}{3}$$
$$y = 3\frac{1}{3}$$
She should mix $6\frac{2}{3}$ liters of 6% solution and $3\frac{1}{3}$ liters of 15% solution.

25. Let $x =$ smallest number
$y =$ remaining number
$z =$ largest number
$$x + y + z = 29$$
$$z = 4x$$
$$y = 2x + 1$$
Substitute $2x + 1$ for y and $4x$ for z in the first equation.
$$x + y + z = 29$$
$$x + 2x + 1 + 4x = 29$$
$$7x = 28$$
$$x = 4$$
Substitute 4 for x in the third equation.
$$y = 2(4) + 1$$
$$y = 9$$
Substitute 4 for x in the second equation.
$$z = 4(4)$$
$$z = 16$$
The three numbers are 4, 9, and 16.

Chapter 9 Cumulative Review Test

1. a. 9 and 1 are natural numbers.

  b. $\frac{1}{2}$, –4, 9, 0, –4.63, and 1 are rational numbers.

  c. $\frac{1}{2}$, –4, 9, 0, $\sqrt{3}$, –4.63, and 1 are real numbers.

2. $16 \div \left\{ 4 \left[3 + \left(\dfrac{5+10}{5} \right)^2 \right] - 32 \right\}$

$= 16 \div \left\{ 4 \left[3 + \left(\dfrac{15}{5} \right)^2 \right] - 32 \right\}$

$= 16 \div \left\{ 4 \left[3 + (3)^2 \right] - 32 \right\}$

$= 16 \div \left\{ 4 [3 + 9] - 32 \right\}$

$= 16 \div \left\{ 4 [12] - 32 \right\}$

$= 16 \div \left\{ 48 - 32 \right\}$

$= 16 \div \left\{ 16 \right\}$

$= 1$

3. $-7(3 - x) = 4(x + 2) - 3x$

$-21 + 7x = 4x + 8 - 3x$

$-21 + 7x = x + 8$

$6x = 29$

$x = \dfrac{29}{6}$

4. $4x - 8y = 16$

Find the x- and y-intercepts:

x-intercept	y-intercept
Let $y = 0$.	Let $x = 0$
$4x - 8(0) = 16$	$4(0) - 8y = 16$
$4x = 16$	$-8y = 16$
$x = 4$	$y = -2$

The intercepts are $(4, 0)$ and $(0, -2)$.

5. $y - y_1 = m(x - x_1)$

$y - 1 = \dfrac{2}{5} [x - (-3)]$

$y - 1 = \dfrac{2}{5} (x + 3)$

$y - 1 = \dfrac{2}{5} x + \dfrac{6}{5}$

$y = \dfrac{2}{5} x + \dfrac{6}{5} + 1$

$y = \dfrac{2}{5} x + \dfrac{11}{5}$

6. The line passes through the points $(1, 1)$ and $(0, -2)$. The y-intercept is $(0, -2)$, so $b = -2$.

The slope is $m = \dfrac{y_2 - y_1}{x_2 - x_1} = \dfrac{-2 - 1}{0 - 1} = \dfrac{-3}{-1} = 3$.

Thus, the equation of the line is:

$y = mx + b$

$y = 3x - 2$

7. $\dfrac{4a^3 b^{-5}}{28a^8 b} = \dfrac{a^{3-8} b^{-5-1}}{7} = \dfrac{a^{-5} b^{-6}}{7} = \dfrac{1}{7a^5 b^6}$

8. $3x^3 + 4x^2 + 6x + 8 = x^2 (3x + 4) + 2(3x + 4)$

$= (3x + 4)(x^2 + 2)$

9. Note that $(-14)(-2) = 28$ and $-14 + (-2) = -16$.

$x^2 - 16x + 28 = (x - 14)(x - 2)$

10. $x^2 - 5x = 0$

$x(x - 5) = 0$

$x = 0 \quad$ or $\quad x - 5 = 0$

$\qquad\qquad\qquad x = 5$

The solutions are 0 and 5.

11. $\dfrac{y - 5}{8} + \dfrac{2y + 7}{8} = \dfrac{y - 5 + 2y + 7}{8} = \dfrac{3y + 2}{8}$

12. $\dfrac{5}{y + 2} = \dfrac{3}{2y - 7}$

$5(2y - 7) = 3(y + 2)$

$10y - 35 = 3y + 6$

$7y = 41$

$y = \dfrac{41}{7}$

13. a. It is a function since it passes the vertical line test.

b. It is a function since it passes the vertical line test.

c. It is not a function since it fails the vertical line test.

14. $f(x) = \dfrac{x+3}{x^2-9}$

a. $f(-4) = \dfrac{(-4)+3}{(-4)^2-9} = \dfrac{-1}{16-9} = -\dfrac{1}{7}$

b. $f(h) = \dfrac{h+3}{h^2-9}$

c. $f(3) = \dfrac{(3)+3}{(3)^2-9} = \dfrac{6}{9-9} = \dfrac{6}{0}$ undefined

15. $3x+y=6$
$y=4x-1$
Substitute $4x-1$ for y in the first equation.
$3x+y=6$
$3x+4x-1=6$
$7x-1=6$
$7x=7$
$x=\dfrac{7}{7}=1$
Substitute 1 for x in the second equation.
$y=4x-1$
$y=4(1)-1$
$y=4-1$
$y=3$
The solution is $(1, 3)$.

16. $2p+3q=11$
$-3p-5q=-16$
To eliminate p, multiply the first equation by 3 and the second equation by 2 and then add.
$3[2p+3q=11]$
$2[-3p-5q=-16]$
gives
$6p+9q=33$
$\underline{-6p-10q=-32}$
Add: $\quad -q=1$
$q=-1$
Substitute -1 for q in the first equation.

$2p+3(-1)=11$
$2p-3=11$
$2p=14$
$p=7$
The solution is $(7, -1)$.

17. $x-2y=0$ (1)
$2x+z=7$ (2)
$y-2z=-5$ (3)
To eliminate z between equations (2) and (3), multiply equation (2) by 2 and then add.
$2[2x+z=7]$
$y-2z=-5$
gives
$4x\quad +2z=14$
$\underline{\quad\quad y-2z=-5}$
Add: $4x+y\quad =9$ (4)
Equations (4) and (1) are two equations in two unknowns:
$x-2y=0$
$4x+y=9$
To eliminate y, multiply equation (4) by 2 and then add.
$x-2y=0$
$2[4x+y=9]$
gives
$x-2y=0$
$\underline{8x+2y=18}$
Add: $9x\quad =18$
$x=\dfrac{18}{9}=2$
Substitute 2 for x in equation (4).
$4x+y=9$
$4(2)+y=9$
$8+y=9$
$y=1$
Finally, substitute 2 for x in equation (2).
$2x+z=7$
$2(2)+z=7$
$4+z=7$
$z=3$
The solution is $(2, 1, 3)$.

18. Let x be the measure of the smallest angle. Then $9x$ is the measure of the largest angle and $x + 70$ is the measure of the remaining angle. The sum of the measures of the three angles is $180°$.

$$x + (x + 70) + 9x = 180$$
$$11x + 70 = 180$$
$$11x = 110$$
$$x = 10$$

$x + 70 = 10 + 70 = 80;\quad 9x = 9(10) = 90$

The three angles are $10°$, $80°$, and $90°$.

19. Let t be the time for Judy to catch up to Dawn.

	rate	time	distance
Judy	6	t	$6t$
Mark	4	$t + \dfrac{1}{2}$	$4\left(t + \dfrac{1}{2}\right)$

$$6t = 4\left(t + \frac{1}{2}\right)$$
$$6t = 4t + 2$$
$$2t = 2$$
$$t = \frac{2}{2} = 1$$

It takes 1 hour for Judy to catch up to Mark.

20. Let $x =$ the number of $20 tickets sold and $y =$ the number of $16 tickets sold.
The system is

$$x + y = 1000$$
$$20x + 16y = 18,400$$

Solve the first equation for y.

$$x + y = 1000$$
$$y = -x + 1000$$

Substitute $-x + 1000$ for y in the second equation.

$$20x + 16(-x + 1,000) = 18,400$$
$$20x - 16x + 16,000 = 18,400$$
$$4x + 16,000 = 18,400$$
$$4x = 2400$$
$$x = \frac{2400}{4} = 600$$

Substitute 600 for x in the equation for y.

$$y = -x + 1000$$
$$y = -(600) + 1000$$
$$y = 400$$

Thus, 600 tickets sold at $20 and 400 tickets sold at $16 for the concert.

Chapter 10

Exercise Set 10.1

1. It is necessary to change the direction of the inequality symbol when multiplying or dividing by a negative number.

2. $x \leq 7$ includes 7 and $x < 7$ does not include 7.

3. **a.** Use open circles when the endpoints are not included.

   b. Use closed circles when the endpoints are included.

   c. Answers may vary. One possible answer is $x > 4$.

   d. Answers may vary. One possible answer is $x \geq 4$.

4. A compound inequality is an inequality formed from two inequalities joined with the word **and** or **or**. Sometimes the word **and** is implied but not written as in $-4 < x < 2$.

5. $a < x < b$ means $a < x$ and $x < b$.

6. There is no real number both greater than 5 and less than 3.

7. **a.**

   b. $(-2, \infty)$

   c. $\{x \mid x > -2\}$

8. **a.**

   b. $\left(\dfrac{5}{3}, \infty\right)$

   c. $\left\{t \mid t > \dfrac{5}{3}\right\}$

9. **a.**

   b. $(-\infty, \pi]$

   c. $\{w \mid w \leq \pi\}$

10. **a.**

    b. $(-4, 3)$

    c. $\{x \mid -4 < x < 3\}$

11. **a.**

    b. $\left(-3, \dfrac{4}{5}\right]$

    c. $\left\{q \mid -3 < q \leq \dfrac{4}{5}\right\}$

12. **a.**

    b. $\left[-\dfrac{6}{5}, \infty\right)$

    c. $\left\{x \mid x \geq -\dfrac{6}{5}\right\}$

13. **a.**

    b. $(-7, -4]$

    c. $\{x \mid -7 < x \leq -4\}$

14. **a.**

    b. $\left[-2\dfrac{7}{8}, -1\dfrac{2}{3}\right)$

    c. $\left\{k \mid -2\dfrac{7}{8} \leq k < -1\dfrac{2}{3}\right\}$

15. $x - 9 > -6$

    $x > 3$

16. $2x + 3 > 4$

$2x > 1$

$\dfrac{2x}{2} > \dfrac{1}{2}$

$x > \dfrac{1}{2}$

17. $3 - x < -4$

$-x < -7$

Reverse the inequality

$\dfrac{-x}{-1} > \dfrac{-7}{-1}$

$x > 7$

18. $12b - 5 \le 8b + 7$

$4b - 5 \le 7$

$4b \le 12$

$\dfrac{4b}{4} \le \dfrac{12}{4}$

$b \le 3$

19. $4.7x - 5.48 \ge 11.44$

$4.7x - 5.48 + 5.48 \ge 11.44 + 5.48$

$4.7x \ge 16.92$

$\dfrac{4.7x}{4.7} \ge \dfrac{16.92}{4.7}$

$x \ge 3.6$

20. $1.4x + 2.2 < 2.6x - 0.2$

$1.4x + 2.4 < 2.6x$

$2.4 < 1.2x$

$\dfrac{2.4}{1.2} < \dfrac{1.2x}{1.2}$

$2 < x$

21. $4(x + 2) \le 4x + 8$

$4x + 8 \le 4x + 8$

$8 \le 8$

Since this is a true statement, the solution is the entire real number line.

22. $15.3 > 3(a - 1.4)$

$15.3 > 3a - 4.2$

$19.5 > 3a$

$\dfrac{19.5}{3} > \dfrac{3a}{3}$

$6.5 > a$

23. $5b - 6 \ge 3(b + 3) + 2b$

$5b - 6 \ge 3b + 9 + 2b$

$5b - 6 \ge 5b + 9$

$-6 \ge 9$

Since this is a false statement, there is no solution.

24. $-6(d + 2) < -9d + 3(d - 1)$

$-6d - 12 < -9d + 3d - 3$

$-6d - 12 < -6d - 3$

$-12 < -3$

Since this is a true statement, the solution is all real numbers.

25. $2y - 6y + 8 \le 2(-2y + 9)$

$-4y + 8 \le -4y + 18$

$8 \le 18$

Since this is a true statement, the solution is all real numbers.

26.
$$\frac{y}{2}+\frac{4}{5}\le 3$$
$$10\left(\frac{y}{2}\right)+10\left(\frac{4}{5}\right)\le 10(3)$$
$$5y+8\le 30$$
$$5y\le 22$$
$$y\le \frac{22}{5}$$

$$\frac{22}{5}$$

27.
$$4+\frac{4x}{3}<6$$
$$\frac{4x}{3}<2$$
$$3\left(\frac{4x}{3}\right)<3(2)$$
$$4x<6$$
$$\frac{4x}{4}<\frac{6}{4}$$
$$x<\frac{3}{2}$$
$$\left(-\infty,\frac{3}{2}\right)$$

28.
$$4-3x<5+2x+17$$
$$4-3x<2x+22$$
$$4<5x+22$$
$$-18<5x$$
$$\frac{-18}{5}<\frac{5x}{5}$$
$$-\frac{18}{5}<x$$
$$\left(-\frac{18}{5},\infty\right)$$

29.
$$\frac{v-5}{3}-v\ge -3(v-1)$$
$$3\left[\frac{v-5}{3}-v\right]\ge 3\left[-3(v-1)\right]$$
$$v-5-3v\ge -9(v-1)$$
$$-5-2v\ge -9v+9$$
$$7v-5\ge 9$$
$$7v\ge 14$$
$$v\ge 2 \quad\Rightarrow\quad [2,\infty)$$

30.
$$\frac{h}{2}-\frac{5}{6}<\frac{7}{8}+h$$
$$24\left(\frac{h}{2}-\frac{5}{6}\right)<24\left(\frac{7}{8}+h\right)$$
$$12h-20<21+24h$$
$$-12h-20<21$$
$$-12h<41$$
$$\frac{-12h}{-12}>\frac{41}{-12}$$
$$h>-\frac{41}{12} \quad\Rightarrow\quad \left(-\frac{41}{12},\infty\right)$$

31.
$$\frac{t}{3}-t+7\le -\frac{4t}{3}+8$$
$$3\left(\frac{t}{3}-t+7\right)\le 3\left(-\frac{4t}{3}+8\right)$$
$$t-3t+21\le -4t+24$$
$$-2t+21\le -4t+24$$
$$2t\le 3$$
$$\frac{2t}{2}\le \frac{3}{2}$$
$$t\le \frac{3}{2} \quad\Rightarrow\quad \left(-\infty,\frac{3}{2}\right]$$

32. $\dfrac{6(x-2)}{5} > \dfrac{10(2-x)}{3}$

$15\left[\dfrac{6(x-2)}{5}\right] > 15\left[\dfrac{10(2-x)}{3}\right]$

$18(x-2) > 50(2-x)$

$18x-36 > 100-50x$

$68x-36 > 100$

$68x > 136$

$\dfrac{68x}{68} > \dfrac{136}{68}$

$x > 2 \;\Rightarrow\; (2,\infty)$

33. $-3x+1 < 3\big[(x+2)-2x\big]-1$

$-3x+1 < 3\big[x+2-2x\big]-1$

$-3x+1 < 3\big[2-x\big]-1$

$-3x+1 < 6-3x-1$

$-3x+1 < 5-3x$

$1 < 5 \;\Rightarrow\;$ a true statement

The solution set is $(-\infty,\infty)$.

34. $4\big[x-(3x-2)\big] > 3(x+5)-15$

$4\big[x-3x+2\big] > 3x+15-15$

$4\big[-2x+2\big] > 3x$

$-8x+8 > 3x$

$8 > 11x$

$\dfrac{8}{11} > x \;\Rightarrow\; \left(-\infty,\dfrac{8}{11}\right)$

35. $A=\{5,6,7\}$; $B=\{6,7,8\}$

$A\cup B=\{5,6,7,8\}$

$A\cap B=\{6,7\}$

36. $A=\{2,4,6,8\}$; $B=\{1,3,5,7\}$

$A\cup B=\{1,2,3,4,5,6,7,8\}$

$A\cap B=\{\ \}$

37. $A=\{-2,-4,-5\}$; $B=\{-1,-2,-4,-6\}$

$A\cup B=\{-1,-2,-4,-5,-6\}$

$A\cap B=\{-2,-4\}$

38. $A=\{-1,0,1\}$; $B=\{0,2,4,6\}$

$A\cup B=\{-1,0,1,2,4,6\}$

$A\cap B=\{0\}$

39. $A=\{\ \}$; $B=\{0,1,2,3\}$

$A\cup B=\{0,1,2,3\}$

$A\cap B=\{\ \}$

40. $A=\{2,4,6\}$; $B=\{2,4,6,8,...\}$

$A\cup B=\{2,4,6,8,...\}$

$A\cap B=\{2,4,6\}$

41. $A=\{0,2,4,6,8\}$; $B=\{1,3,5,7\}$

$A\cup B=\{0,1,2,3,4,5,6,7,8\}$

$A\cap B=\{\ \}$

42. $A=\{1,3,5\}$; $B=\{1,3,5,7,...\}$

$A\cup B=\{1,3,5,7,...\}$

$A\cap B=\{1,3,5\}$

43. $A=\{0.1,0.2,0.3\}$; $B=\{0.2,0.3,0.4,0.5,...\}$

$A\cup B=\{0.1,0.2,0.3,0.4,0.5,...\}$

$A\cap B=\{0.2,0.3\}$

44. $A=\left\{1,\dfrac{1}{2},\dfrac{1}{4},\dfrac{1}{6},...\right\}$; $B=\left\{\dfrac{1}{4},\dfrac{1}{6},\dfrac{1}{8}\right\}$

$A\cup B=\left\{1,\dfrac{1}{2},\dfrac{1}{4},\dfrac{1}{6},\dfrac{1}{8},...\right\}$

$A\cap B=\left\{\dfrac{1}{4},\dfrac{1}{6},\dfrac{1}{8}\right\}$

45. $-2 \le t+3 < 4$

$-2-3 \le t+3-3 < 4-3$

$-5 \le t < 1$

$[-5,1)$

46. $-7 < p-6 \le -5$

$-7+6 < p-6+6 \le -5+6$

$-1 < p \le 1$

$(-1,1]$

47. $-15 \le -3z \le 12$

Divide by -3 and reverse inequalities.

$\dfrac{-15}{-3} \ge \dfrac{-3z}{-3} \ge \dfrac{12}{-3}$

$5 \ge z \ge -4$

$-4 \le z \le 5$

$\left[-4, 5\right]$

48. $-16 < 5 - 3n \le 13$

$-16 - 5 < 5 - 3n - 5 \le 13 - 5$

$-21 < -3n \le 8$

Divide by -3 and reverse the inequalities.

$\dfrac{-21}{-3} > \dfrac{-3n}{-3} \ge \dfrac{8}{-3}$

$7 > n \ge -\dfrac{8}{3}$

$-\dfrac{8}{3} \le n < 7$

$\left[-\dfrac{8}{3}, 7\right)$

49. $4 \le 2x - 4 < 7$

$4 + 4 \le 2x - 4 + 4 < 7 + 4$

$8 \le 2x < 11$

$\dfrac{8}{2} \le \dfrac{2x}{2} < \dfrac{11}{2}$

$4 \le x < \dfrac{11}{2}$

$\left[4, \dfrac{11}{2}\right)$

50. $-12 < 3x - 5 \le -1$

$-12 + 5 < 3x - 5 + 5 \le -1 + 5$

$-7 < 3x \le 4$

$\dfrac{-7}{3} < \dfrac{3x}{3} \le \dfrac{4}{3}$

$-\dfrac{7}{3} < x \le \dfrac{4}{3}$

$\left(-\dfrac{7}{3}, \dfrac{4}{3}\right]$

51. $14 \le 2 - 3g < 15$

$14 - 2 \le 2 - 3g - 2 < 15 - 2$

$12 \le -3g < 13$

Divide by -3 and reverse inequalities.

$\dfrac{12}{-3} \ge \dfrac{-3g}{-3} > \dfrac{13}{-3}$

$-4 \ge g > -\dfrac{13}{3}$

$-\dfrac{13}{3} < g \le -4$

$\left(-\dfrac{13}{3}, -4\right]$

52. $\dfrac{1}{2} < 3x + 4 < 13$

$\dfrac{1}{2} - 4 < 3x + 4 - 4 < 13 - 4$

$-\dfrac{7}{2} < 3x < 9$

$\dfrac{-\frac{7}{2}}{3} < \dfrac{3x}{3} < 3$

$-\dfrac{7}{6} < x < 3$

$\left(-\dfrac{7}{6}, 3\right)$

53. $5 \le \dfrac{3x + 1}{2} < 11$

$2(5) \le 2\left(\dfrac{3x + 1}{2}\right) < 2(11)$

$10 \le 3x + 1 < 22$

$10 - 1 \le 3x + 1 - 1 < 22 - 1$

$9 \le 3x < 21$

$\dfrac{9}{3} \le \dfrac{3x}{3} < \dfrac{21}{3}$

$3 \le x < 7$

$\left\{x \mid 3 \le x < 7\right\}$

54. $\dfrac{3}{5} < \dfrac{-x-5}{3} < 2$

$15\left(\dfrac{3}{5}\right) < 15\left(\dfrac{-x-5}{3}\right) < 15(2)$

$9 < 5(-x-5) < 30$

$9 < -5x - 25 < 30$

$9 + 25 < -5x - 25 + 25 < 30 + 25$

$34 < -5x < 55$

Divide by -5 and reverse inequalities

$\dfrac{34}{-5} > \dfrac{-5x}{-5} > \dfrac{55}{-5}$

$-\dfrac{34}{5} > x > -11$

$-11 < x < -\dfrac{34}{5}$

$\left\{ x \mid -11 < x < -\dfrac{34}{5} \right\}$

55. $-6 \le -3(2x - 4) < 12$

$-6 \le -6x + 12 < 12$

$-6 - 12 \le -6x + 12 - 12 < 12 - 12$

$-18 \le -6x < 0$

Divide by -6 and reverse inequalities

$\dfrac{-18}{-6} \ge \dfrac{-6x}{-6} > \dfrac{0}{-6}$

$3 \ge x > 0$

$0 < x \le 3$

$\{x \mid 0 < x \le 3\}$

56. $-6 < \dfrac{4 - 3x}{2} < \dfrac{2}{3}$

$6(-6) < 6\left(\dfrac{4 - 3x}{2}\right) < 6\left(\dfrac{2}{3}\right)$

$-36 < 3(4 - 3x) < 2(2)$

$-36 < 12 - 9x < 4$

$-36 - 12 < 12 - 9x - 12 < 4 - 12$

$-48 < -9x < -8$

Divide by -9 and reverse inequalities.

$\dfrac{-48}{-9} > \dfrac{-9x}{-9} > \dfrac{-8}{-9}$

$\dfrac{16}{3} > x > \dfrac{8}{9}$

$\dfrac{8}{9} < x < \dfrac{16}{3}$

$\left\{ x \mid \dfrac{8}{9} < x < \dfrac{16}{3} \right\}$

57. $0 \le \dfrac{3(u - 4)}{7} \le 1$

$7(0) \le 7\left(\dfrac{3(u - 4)}{7}\right) \le 7(1)$

$0 \le 3(u - 4) \le 7$

$0 \le 3u - 12 \le 7$

$0 + 12 \le 3u - 12 + 12 \le 7 + 12$

$12 \le 3u \le 19$

$\dfrac{12}{3} \le \dfrac{3u}{3} \le \dfrac{19}{3}$

$4 \le u \le \dfrac{19}{3}$

$\left\{ u \mid 4 \le u \le \dfrac{19}{3} \right\}$

58. $-15 < \dfrac{3(x - 2)}{5} \le 0$

$5(-15) < 5\left[\dfrac{3(x - 2)}{5}\right] \le 5(0)$

$-75 < 3(x - 2) \le 0$

$-75 < 3x - 6 \le 0$

$-75 + 6 < 3x - 6 + 6 \le 0 + 6$

$-69 < 3x \le 6$

$\dfrac{-69}{3} < \dfrac{3x}{3} \le \dfrac{6}{3}$

$-23 < x \le 2$

$\{x \mid -23 < x \le 2\}$

59. $c \le 1$

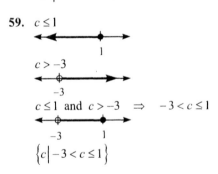

$c > -3$

$c \le 1$ and $c > -3$ $\Rightarrow$ $-3 < c \le 1$

$\{c \mid -3 < c \le 1\}$

60. $d > 0$

$d \le 8$

The union is the entire real number line.
Therefore, the solution set is all real numbers, or $\mathbb{R}$.

61. $x < 2$

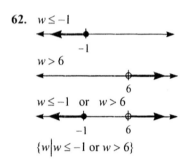

$x > 4$

$x < 2$ and $x > 4$

There is no overlap so the solution is the empty set, $\varnothing$.

62. $w \leq -1$

$w > 6$

$w \leq -1$ or $w > 6$

$\{w \mid w \leq -1 \text{ or } w > 6\}$

63. $x + 1 < 3$ and $x + 1 > -4$

$x < 2$ and $x > -5$

$x > -5$

$x < 2$

$x < -2$ and $x > -5$ which is $-5 < x < 2$ or

$\{x \mid -5 < x < 2\}$

64. $5x - 3 \leq 7$ or $-2x + 5 < -3$

$5x \leq 10$ or $-2x < -8$

$x \leq 2$ $x > 4$

$x \leq 2$

$x > 4$

$x \leq 2$ or $x > 4$

$\{x \mid x \leq 2 \text{ or } x > 4\}$

65. $2s + 3 < 7$ or $-3s + 4 \leq -17$

$2s < 4$ or $-3s \leq -21$

$\dfrac{2s}{2} < \dfrac{4}{2}$ or $\dfrac{-3s}{-3} \geq \dfrac{-21}{-3}$

$s < 2$ $s \geq 7$

$s < 2$ or $s \geq 7$ which is $(-\infty, 2) \cup [7, \infty)$.

66. $4a + 7 \geq 9$ and $-3a + 4 \leq -17$

$4a \geq 2$ $-3a \leq -21$

$\dfrac{4a}{4} \geq \dfrac{2}{4}$ $\dfrac{-3a}{-3} \geq \dfrac{-21}{-3}$

$a \geq \dfrac{1}{2}$ $a \geq 7$

$a \geq \dfrac{1}{2}$ and $a \geq 7$ $\Rightarrow$ $a \geq 7$

In interval notation: $[7, \infty)$

67. $4x + 5 \geq 5$ and $3x - 7 \leq -1$

$4x \geq 0$ and $3x \leq 6$

$x \geq 0$ and $x \leq 2$

$x \geq 0$

$x \leq 2$

$x \geq 0$ and $x \leq 2$ which is $0 \leq x \leq 2$

In interval notation: $[0, 2]$

68. $5 - 3x < -3$ and $5x - 3 > 10$

$-3x < -8$ and $5x > 13$

$x > \dfrac{8}{3}$ and $x > \dfrac{13}{5}$

$x > \dfrac{8}{3}$

$x > \dfrac{13}{5}$

$x > \dfrac{8}{3}$ and $x > \dfrac{13}{5}$ which is $x > \dfrac{8}{3}$

In interval notation: $\left(\dfrac{8}{3}, \infty\right)$

69. $4 - r < -2$ or $3r - 1 < -1$

$\qquad -r < -6 \qquad\qquad 3r < 0$

$\qquad\quad r > 6 \qquad\qquad\quad r < 0$

$r > 6$

$r < 0$

$r > 6$ or $r < 0$

In interval notation: $(-\infty, 0) \cup (6, \infty)$

70. $-x + 3 < 0$ or $2x - 5 \geq 3$

$\qquad -x < -3 \quad$ or $\qquad 2x \geq 8$

$\qquad\quad x > 3 \quad$ or $\qquad\quad x \geq 4$

$x > 3$

$x \geq 4$

$x > 3$ or $x \geq 4$ which is $x > 3$

In interval notation: $(3, \infty)$

71. $2k + 5 > -1$ and $7 - 3k \leq 7$

$\qquad 2k > -6 \qquad\qquad -3k \leq 0$

$\qquad \dfrac{2k}{2} > \dfrac{-6}{2} \qquad\qquad \dfrac{-3k}{-3} \geq \dfrac{0}{-3}$

$\qquad k > -3 \qquad\qquad\quad k \geq 0$

$k > -3$ and $k \geq 0 \;\Rightarrow\; k \geq 0$

In interval notation: $\left[0, \infty\right)$

72. $2q - 11 \leq -7$ or $2 - 3q < 11$

$\qquad 2q \leq 4 \qquad\qquad\quad -3q < 9$

$\qquad \dfrac{2q}{2} \leq \dfrac{4}{2} \qquad\qquad \dfrac{-3q}{-3} > \dfrac{9}{-3}$

$\qquad q \leq 2 \qquad\qquad\qquad q > -3$

$q \leq 2$ or $q > -3 \;\Rightarrow\; \left(-\infty, \infty\right)$

73. a. $l + g \leq 130$

$\quad$ **b.** $g = 2w + 2d$

$\qquad\qquad\quad l + g \leq 130$

$\qquad\qquad l + 2w + 2d \leq 130$

c. $l = 40$, $w = 20.5$

$\qquad\qquad l + 2w + 2d \leq 130$

$\qquad\quad 40 + 2(20.5) + 2d \leq 130$

$\qquad\qquad 40 + 41 + 2d \leq 130$

$\qquad\qquad\qquad 81 + 2d \leq 130$

$\qquad\qquad\qquad\qquad 2d \leq 49$

$\qquad\qquad\qquad\qquad\; d \leq 24.5$

The maximum depth is 24.5 inches.

74. a. $l + w + d \leq 45$

$\quad$ **b.** Substitute 23 for l, and 12 for w, then solve for d.

$\qquad\qquad l + w + d \leq 45$

$\qquad\quad 23 + 12 + d \leq 45$

$\qquad\qquad\; 35 + d \leq 45$

$\qquad\qquad\qquad d \leq 10$

The maximum depth is 10 inches.

75. Let x be the maximum number of boxes.

$70x \leq 800$

$\qquad x \leq \dfrac{800}{70}$

$\qquad x \leq 11.43$

The maximum number of boxes is 11.

76. Let x be the maximum number of boxes.

$70x + 195 \leq 800$

$\qquad 70x \leq 605$

$\qquad\quad x \leq \dfrac{605}{70} = \dfrac{121}{14} \approx 8.64$

The maximum number of boxes is 8.

77. Let $x =$ the number of minutes she talks beyond the first 20 minutes.

$0.99 + 0.07x \leq 5.00$

$\qquad 0.07x \leq 4.01$

$\qquad \dfrac{0.07x}{0.07} \leq \dfrac{4.01}{0.07}$

$\qquad\quad x \leq 57$ (to nearest whole number)

She can talk for 57 minutes beyond the first 20 minutes for a total of 77 minutes.

78. Let x be the additional hours to park in the garage.

$$1.25 + 0.75x \le 3.75$$
$$0.75x \le 2.5$$
$$x \le \frac{2.5}{0.75}$$
$$x \le 3.\overline{3}$$

You can park in the garage for the first (initial) hour plus 3 additional hours for a total of 4 hours.

79. To make a profit, the cost must be less than the revenue: cost < revenue.

$$10,025 + 1.09x < 6.42x$$
$$10,025 < 5.33x$$
$$\frac{10,025}{5.33} < x$$
$$1880.86 < x$$

She needs to sell a minimum of 1881 books to make a profit.

80. To make a profit, the cost must be less than the revenue: cost < revenue.

$$8000 + 0.08x < 1.85x$$
$$8000 < 1.77x$$
$$\frac{8000}{1.77} < x$$
$$4519.77 < x$$

He must clean a minimum of 4520 garments to make a profit.

81. Let x = the number of additional ounces beyond the first ounce.

$$0.39 + 0.24x \le 10.00$$
$$0.24x \le 9.61$$
$$\frac{0.24x}{0.24} \le \frac{9.61}{0.24}$$
$$x \le 40 \quad \text{(rounded down)}$$

The maximum weight is 41 ounces (the first ounce plus up to 40 additional ounces).

82. Let x = the number of pieces of mail sent. The cost of mailing x pieces of mail using *presorted first-class* mail is $150 + 0.275x$ dollars and the cost of mailing x pieces of mail without the bulk permit is $0.37x$ dollars. We want to know when "cost with permit" < "cost without permit".

$$150 + 0.275x < 0.37x$$
$$150 < 0.095x$$
$$\frac{150}{0.095} < \frac{0.095x}{0.095}$$
$$1579 < x \quad \text{(to nearest whole number)}$$
$$x > 1579$$

The company must send more than 1579 pieces of mail in order for the bulk permit to be financially worthwhile.

83. Let x be the amount of sales in dollars.

$$300 + 0.10x > 400 + 0.08x$$
$$0.10x > 100 + 0.08x$$
$$0.02x > 100$$
$$x > \frac{100}{0.02}$$
$$x > 5000$$

She will earn more by plan 1 if her weekly sales total more than $5000.

84. Let x be the maximum number of hours. The inequality is

$$6.25x + 8(90) \le 2000$$
$$6.25x + 720 \le 2000$$
$$6.25x \le 1280$$
$$x \le \frac{1280}{6.25}$$
$$x \le 204.8$$

Katie can work a maximum of 204 hours during the summer.

85. Let x be the minimum score for the sixth exam.

$$\frac{66 + 72 + 90 + 49 + 59 + x}{6} \ge 60$$
$$\frac{336 + x}{6} \ge 60$$
$$6\left(\frac{336 + x}{6}\right) \ge 6(60)$$
$$336 + x \ge 360$$
$$x \ge 24$$

She must make a 24 or higher on the sixth exam to pass the course.

86. Let x be the grade on the fifth exam. The average of the five grades must be greater than or equal to 90.

$$\frac{92 + 87 + 96 + 77 + x}{5} \geq 90$$

$$\frac{352 + x}{5} \geq 90$$

$$5\left(\frac{352 + x}{5}\right) \geq 5(90)$$

$$352 + x \geq 450$$

$$x \geq 98$$

Stephen must make a 98 or higher on the fifth exam to earn a final grade of A in the course.

87. Let x be the score on the fifth exam.

$$80 \leq \frac{85 + 92 + 72 + 75 + x}{5} < 90$$

$$80 \leq \frac{324 + x}{5} < 90$$

$$5(80) \leq 5\left(\frac{324 + x}{5}\right) < 5(90)$$

$$400 \leq 324 + x < 450$$

$$76 \leq x < 126$$

To receive a final grade of B, Ms. Mahoney must score 76 or higher on the fifth exam. That is, the score must be

$76 \leq x \leq 100$ (maximum grade is 100).

88. Let x be the value of the third pollutant. The inequality is

$$\frac{2.7 + 3.42 + x}{3} < 3.2$$

$$\frac{6.12 + x}{3} < 3.2$$

$$3\left(\frac{6.12 + x}{3}\right) < 3(3.2)$$

$$6.12 + x < 9.6$$

$$x < 3.48$$

Any value less than 3.48 parts per million of the third pollutant will result in the air being considered "clean."

89. a. The taxable income of $78,221 places a married couple filing jointly in the 25% tax bracket. The tax is $8,180.00 plus 25% of the taxable income over $59,400.
The tax is
$8,180.00 + 0.25(\$78,221 - \$59,400)$

$8,180.00 + 0.25(\$18,821)$

$8,180.00 + \$4,705.25$

$12,885.25$

They will owe $12,885.25 in taxes.

b. The taxable income of $301,233 places a married couple filing jointly in the 33% tax bracket. The tax is $40,915.50 plus 33% of the taxable income over $182,800.
The tax is
$40,915.5 + 0.33(\$301,233 - \$182,800)$

$40,915.5 + 0.33(\$118,433.00)$

$40,915.5 + \$39,082.89$

$79,998.39$

They will owe $79,998.39 in taxes.

90. a. The taxable income of $128,479 places a married couple filing jointly in the 28% tax bracket. The tax is $23,317.50 plus 28% of the taxable income over $119,950.
The tax is
$23,317.50 + 0.28(\$128,479 - \$119,950)$

$23,317.50 + 0.28(\$8,529)$

$23,317.50 + \$2,388.12$

$25,705.62$

They will owe $25,705.62 in taxes.

b. The taxable income of $275,248 places a married couple filing jointly in the 33% tax bracket. The tax is $40,915.50 plus 33% of the taxable income over $182,800.
The tax is
$40,915.5 + 0.33(\$275,248 - \$182,800)$

$40,915.5 + 0.33(\$92,448)$

$40,915.5 + \$30,507.84$

$71,423.34$

They will owe $71,423.34 in taxes.

91. a.
$$v(t) \geq 0$$
$$-32t + 96 \geq 0$$
$$-32t \geq -96$$
$$t \leq 3$$
The object is traveling upward on the interval $[0,3]$.

b.
$$v(t) \leq 0$$
$$-32t + 96 \leq 0$$
$$-32t \leq -96$$
$$t \geq 3$$
The object is traveling downward on the interval $[3,10]$.

92. a.
$$v(t) \geq 0$$
$$-32t + 172.8 \geq 0$$
$$-32t \geq -172.8$$
$$t \leq 5.4$$
The object is traveling upward on the interval $[0,5.4]$.

b.
$$v(t) \leq 0$$
$$-32t + 172.8 \leq 0$$
$$-32t \leq -172.8$$
$$t \geq 5.4$$
The object is traveling downward on the interval $[5.4,12]$.

93. a.
$$v(t) \geq 0$$
$$-9.8t + 49 \geq 0$$
$$-9.8t \geq -49$$
$$t \leq 5$$
The object is traveling upward on the interval $[0,5]$.

b.
$$v(t) \leq 0$$
$$-9.8t + 49 \leq 0$$
$$-9.8t \leq -49$$
$$t \geq 5$$
The object is traveling downward on the interval $[5,13]$.

94. a.
$$v(t) \geq 0$$
$$-9.8t + 31.36 \geq 0$$
$$-9.8t \geq -31.36$$
$$t \leq 3.2$$
The object is traveling upward on the interval $[0,3.2]$.

b.
$$v(t) \leq 0$$
$$-9.8t + 31.36 \leq 0$$
$$-9.8t \leq -31.36$$
$$t \geq 3.2$$
The object is traveling downward on the interval $[3.2,6]$.

95. a.
$$v(t) \geq 0$$
$$-32t + 320 \geq 0$$
$$-32t \geq -320$$
$$t \leq 10$$
The object is traveling upward on the interval $[0,8]$ (note: we restricted t to the interval $[0,8]$).

b. From part (a) we saw that the object was moving upward for all values of t on the interval $[0,8]$. Therefore, there are no values for t in that interval where the object is traveling downward.

96. a.
$$v(t) \geq 0$$
$$-9.8t + 68.6 \geq 0$$
$$-9.8t \geq -68.6$$
$$t \leq 7$$
The object is traveling upward on the interval $[0,5]$ (note: we restricted t to the interval $[0,5]$).

b. From part (a) we saw that the object was moving upward for all values of t on the interval $[0,5]$. Therefore, there are no values for t in that interval where the object is traveling downward.

97. Let x be the value of the third reading.

$$7.2 < \frac{7.48 + 7.15 + x}{3} < 7.8$$

$$7.2 < \frac{14.63 + x}{3} < 7.8$$

$$3(7.2) < 3\left(\frac{14.63 + x}{3}\right) < 3(7.8)$$

$$21.6 < 14.63 + x < 23.4$$

$$6.97 < x < 8.77$$

Any value between 6.97 and 8.77 would result in a normal pH reading.

98. a. 1995, 1996, 1997, 1998, and 1999

  b. 2000, 2001, 2002, 2003, 2004, and 2005

99. a. The goal is greater than 6000 for all five months shown and the enlisted number is greater than 4000 for all five months shown except for April. Thus, the goal is greater than 6000 and the number enlisted is greater than 4000 for the months January, February, March, and May.

  b. March, April, May

  c. April

100. No, $-1 > -2$ but $(-1)^2 < (-2)^2$

101. Answers may vary. The three components cover all possible total medical costs.

First piece: 0   if $c \le \$100$
There is a deductible of \$100 so for total costs less than or equal to \$100, the patient covers all costs.

Second piece: $0.80(c - 100)$ if $\$100 < c \le \$2100$

If total costs are more than \$100, but no more than \$2100, the patient pays the \$100 deductible and Blue Cross/Blue Shield pays 80% of the remaining amount.

Third piece: $c - 500$ if $c > \$2100$
The maximum out-of-pocket cost for the patient is \$500. For the second piece, the maximum cost to the patient occurs when $c = \$2100$. Since $0.80(2100 - 100) = 500$, this corresponds to the maximum amount a patient will have to pay. Thus, for any total medical cost over \$2100, the patient must pay the \$500 limit and Blue Cross/Blue Shield will pay the remaining amount.

102. The solution will involve dividing through by b. The direction of the inequalities will need to be changed if we divide by a negative number, but not if we divide by a positive number. Therefore, one needs to know whether $b > 0$ or $b < 0$.

103. a. From the chart, the 10th percentile is approximately 17.5 pounds and the 90th percentile is approximately 23.5 pounds. Therefore, 80% of the weights for 9 month old boys are in the interval $[17.5, 23.5]$ (in pounds).

  b. From the chart, the 10th percentile is approximately 23.5 pounds and the 90th percentile is approximately 31 pounds. Therefore, 80% of the weights for 21 month old boys are in the interval $[23.5, 31]$ (in pounds).

  c. From the chart, the 10th percentile is approximately 27.2 pounds and the 90th percentile is approximately 36.5 pounds. Therefore, 80% of the weights for 36 month old boys are in the interval $[27.2, 36.5]$ (in pounds).

104. a. From the chart, the 10th percentile is approximately 16.2 pounds and the 90th percentile is approximately 21.5 pounds. Therefore, 80% of the weights for 9 month old girls are in the interval $[16.2, 21.5]$ (in pounds).

  b. From the chart, the 10th percentile is approximately 22.4 pounds and the 90th percentile is approximately 29.4 pounds. Therefore, 80% of the weights for 21 month old girls are in the interval $[22.4, 29.4]$ (in pounds).

  c. From the chart, the 10th percentile is approximately 26.5 pounds and the 90th percentile is approximately 36 pounds. Therefore, 80% of the weights for 36 month old girls are in the interval $[26.5, 36]$ (in pounds).

105. First find the average of 82, 90, 74, 76, and 68.

$$\frac{82+90+74+76+68}{5} = \frac{390}{5} = 78$$

This represents $\frac{2}{3}$ of the final grade.

Let x be the score from the final exam. Since this represents $\frac{1}{3}$ of the final grade, the inequality is

$$80 \le \frac{2}{3}(78) + \frac{1}{3}x < 90$$

$$3(80) < 3\left[\frac{2}{3}(78) + \frac{1}{3}x\right] < 3(90)$$

$240 \le 2(78) + x < 270$
$240 \le 156 + x < 270$
$84 \le x < 114$

Stephen must score at least 84 points on the final exam to have a final grade of B. The range is $84 \le x \le 100$.

106. a. Answers may vary. One possible answer is:
Write $x < 3x - 10 < 2x$ as
$x < 3x - 10$ and $3x - 10 < 2x$

b. Solve each of the inequalities.
$\quad x < 3x - 10 \quad$ and $\quad 3x - 10 < 2x$

$\quad -2x < -10 \qquad\qquad -10 < -x$

$\quad\quad x > 5 \qquad\qquad\qquad 10 > x$

The final answer is $x > 5$ and $10 > x$ which is $5 < x < 10$ or (5, 10).

107. a. Answers may vary. One possible answer is:
Write $x < 2x + 3 < 2x + 5$ as $x < 2x + 3$ and $2x + 3 < 2x + 5$

b. Solve each of the inequalities.
$\quad x < 2x + 3 \quad$ and $\quad 2x + 3 < 2x + 5$

$\quad -x < 3 \qquad\qquad\qquad 3 < 5$

$\quad\quad x > -3 \qquad\qquad\quad$ All real numbers

The final answer is $x > -3$ or $(-3, \infty)$.

108. a. Answers may vary. One possible answer is:
Write $x + 5 < x + 3 < 2x + 2$ as
$x + 5 < x + 3$ and $x + 3 < 2x + 2$

b. Solve each of the inequalities
$\quad x + 5 < x + 3 \quad$ and $\quad x + 3 < 2x + 2$

$\quad\quad 5 < 3 \qquad\qquad\qquad 1 < x$

$\quad$ False $\qquad\qquad\qquad\quad x > 1$

The solution is the empty set or $\varnothing$.

109. a. 4 is a counting number.

b. 0 and 4 are whole numbers.

c. $-3, 4, \frac{5}{2}, 0$ and $-\frac{29}{80}$ are rational numbers.

d. $-3, 4, \frac{5}{2}, \sqrt{7}, 0$ and $-\frac{29}{80}$ are real numbers.

110. Associative property of addition.

111. Commutative property of addition

112.
$$R = L + (V - D)r$$
$$R = L + Vr - Dr$$
$$R - L + Dr = Vr$$
$$\frac{R - L + Dr}{r} = V \text{ or } V = \frac{R - L + Dr}{r}$$

113. a. $A \cup B = \{1, 2, 3, 4, 5, 6, 8, 9\}$

b. $A \cap B = \{1, 8\}$

Exercise Set 10.2

1. $|x| = a, a > 0$
Set $x = a$ or $x = -a$.

2. a. $\varnothing$ \qquad **b.** $\{0\}$ \qquad **c.** $\{-2, 2\}$

3. $|x| < a, a > 0$
Write $-a < x < a$.

4. Substitute -7 for x and check the equation.
$$|2x + 3| = 11$$
$$|2(-7) + 3| = 11$$
$$|-14 + 3| = 11$$
$$|-11| = 11$$
$$11 = 11$$
Yes, -7 is a solution.

5. $|x| > a, a > 0$
Write $x < -a$ or $x > a$.

6. The solution to $|x| < 0$ is $\varnothing$.

The absolute value of a number is never negative.

7. The solution to $|x| > 0$ is all real numbers except 0.

The absolute value of any real number, except 0, is greater than 0, i.e., positive.

8. a. $|ax + b| < c$

The solution is $m < x < n$ or

b. $|ax + b| > c$

The solution is $x < m$ or $x > n$ or

9. Set $x = y$ or $x = -y$.

10. a. $|ax + b| = k, a \neq 0$

If $k < 0$, there are no solutions.

b. $|ax + b| = k, a \neq 0$

If $k = 0$, there is one solution.

c. $|ax + b| = k, a \neq 0$

If $k > 0$, there are two solutions.

11. If $a \neq 0$, and $k > 0$,

a. $|ax + b| = k$ has 2 solutions.

b. $|ax + b| < k$ has an infinite number of solutions.

c. $|ax + b| > k$ has an infinite number of solutions.

12. a. $|x| = 4$, $x = -4$ or $x = 4$, C

b. $|x| < 4$, $(-4, 4)$, A

c. $|x| > 4$, $(-\infty, 4) \cup (4, \infty)$, D

d. $|x| \geq 4$, $(-\infty, 4] \cup [4, \infty)$, B

e. $|x| \leq 4$, $[-4, 4]$, E

13. a. $|x| = 5, \{-5, 5\}$, D

b. $|x| < 5, \{x | -5 < x < 5\}$, B

c. $|x| > 5, \{x | x < -5 \text{ or } x > 5\}$, E

d. $|x| \leq 5, \{x | -5 \leq x \leq 5\}$, C

e. $|x| \geq 5, \{x | x \leq -5 \text{ or } x \geq 5\}$, A

14. a. $x > y$

b. One example is $x = -1$ and $y = -2$. Note that $|-1| < |-2|$ and $-1 < 0$ and $-2 < 0$.

15. $|a| = 2$

$a = 2$ or $a = -2$
The solution set is $\{-2, 2\}$.

16. $|b| = 17$

$b = 17$ or $b = -17$
The solution set is $\{-17, 17\}$.

17. $|c| = \dfrac{1}{2}$

$c = \dfrac{1}{2}$ or $c = -\dfrac{1}{2}$

The solution set is $\left\{ -\dfrac{1}{2}, \dfrac{1}{2} \right\}$.

18. $|x| = 0$

$x = 0$ or $x = -0$
The solution set is $\{0\}$.

19. $|d| = -\dfrac{5}{6}$

There is no solution since the right side is a negative number and the absolute value can never be equal to a negative number. The solution set $\varnothing$.

20. $|l + 4| = 6$

$\quad l + 4 = 6 \qquad l + 4 = -6$

$\qquad x = 2 \quad$ or $\qquad x = -10$

The solution set is $\{-10, 2\}$.

21. $|x+5| = 8$

$\quad x+5 = 8 \qquad x+5 = -8$

$\qquad x = 3 \quad$ or $\qquad x = -13$

The solution set is $\{-13, 3\}$.

22. $|3+y| = \dfrac{3}{5}$

$\quad 3+y = \dfrac{3}{5} \qquad$ or $\quad 3+y = -\dfrac{3}{5}$

$\qquad y = -\dfrac{12}{5} \qquad\qquad\quad y = -\dfrac{18}{5}$

The solution set is $\left\{ -\dfrac{18}{5}, -\dfrac{12}{5} \right\}$.

23. $|4.5q+31.5| = 0$

$\quad 4.5q + 31.5 = 0$

$\qquad 4.5q = -31.5$

$\qquad\quad q = -7$

The solution set is $\{-7\}$.

24. $|4.7 - 1.6z| = 14.3$

$\quad 4.7 - 1.6z = 14.3 \quad$ or $\quad 4.7 - 1.6z = -14.3$

$\qquad -1.6z = 9.6 \qquad\qquad\quad -1.6z = -19$

$\qquad\quad z = -6 \qquad\qquad\qquad z = 11.875$

The solution set is $\{-6, 11.875\}$.

25. $|5 - 3x| = \dfrac{1}{2}$

$\quad 5 - 3x = \dfrac{1}{2} \qquad$ or $\qquad 5 - 3x = -\dfrac{1}{2}$

$\qquad -3x = \dfrac{1}{2} - 5 \qquad\qquad -3x = -\dfrac{1}{2} - 5$

$\qquad -3x = -\dfrac{9}{2} \qquad\qquad\quad -3x = -\dfrac{11}{2}$

$\quad -\dfrac{1}{3}(3x) = -\dfrac{1}{3}\left(-\dfrac{9}{2}\right) \qquad -\dfrac{1}{3}(-3x) = -\dfrac{1}{3}\left(-\dfrac{11}{2}\right)$

$\qquad\quad x = \dfrac{3}{2} \qquad\qquad\qquad x = \dfrac{11}{6}$

The solution set is $\left\{ \dfrac{3}{2}, \dfrac{11}{6} \right\}$.

26. $|6(y+4)| = 24$

$\quad |6y+24| = 24$

$\quad 6y+24 = 24 \quad$ or $\quad 6y+24 = -24$

$\qquad 6y = 0 \qquad\qquad\quad 6y = -48$

$\qquad\; y = 0 \qquad\qquad\qquad y = -8$

The solution set is $\{-8, 0\}$.

27. $\left|\dfrac{x-3}{4}\right| = 5$

$\quad \dfrac{x-3}{4} = 5 \qquad$ or $\qquad \dfrac{x-3}{4} = -5$

$\quad 4\left(\dfrac{x-3}{4}\right) = 4(5) \qquad 4\left(\dfrac{x-3}{4}\right) = 4(-5)$

$\qquad x-3 = 20 \qquad\qquad\quad x-3 = -20$

$\qquad\quad x = 23 \qquad\qquad\qquad x = -17$

The solution set is $\{-17, 23\}$.

28. $\left|\dfrac{3z+5}{6}\right| - 2 = 7$

$\qquad \left|\dfrac{3z+5}{6}\right| = 9$

$\quad \dfrac{3z+5}{6} = 9 \qquad$ or $\qquad \dfrac{3z+5}{6} = -9$

$\quad 6\left(\dfrac{3z+5}{6}\right) = 6(9) \qquad 6\left(\dfrac{3z+5}{6}\right) = 6(-9)$

$\qquad 3z+5 = 54 \qquad\qquad\quad 3z+5 = -54$

$\qquad 3z = 49 \qquad\qquad\qquad 3z = -59$

$\qquad\; z = \dfrac{49}{3} \qquad\qquad\qquad z = \dfrac{-59}{3} = -\dfrac{59}{3}$

The solution set is $\left\{ -\dfrac{59}{3}, \dfrac{49}{3} \right\}$.

29. $\left|\dfrac{x-3}{4}\right| + 8 = 8$

$\qquad \left|\dfrac{x-3}{4}\right| = 0$

$\qquad \dfrac{x-3}{4} = 0$

$\quad 4\left(\dfrac{x-3}{4}\right) = 4(0)$

$\qquad x-3 = 0$

$\qquad\quad x = 3$

The solution set is $\{3\}$.

30. $\left|\dfrac{5x-3}{2}\right|+5=9$

$\left|\dfrac{5x-3}{2}\right|=4$

$\dfrac{5x-3}{2}=4$ or $\dfrac{5x-3}{2}=-4$

$2\left(\dfrac{5x-3}{2}\right)=2(4)$ $2\left(\dfrac{5x-3}{2}\right)=2(-4)$

$5x-3=8$ $5x-3=-8$

$5x=11$ $5x=-5$

$x=\dfrac{11}{5}$ $x=\dfrac{-5}{5}=-1$

The solution set is $\left\{-1,\dfrac{11}{5}\right\}$.

31. $|w|<11$

$-11<w<11$

The solution set is $\{w|-11<w<11\}$.

32. $|p|\leq 9$

$-9\leq p\leq 9$

The solution set is $\{p|-9\leq p\leq 9\}$.

33. $|q+5|\leq 8$

$-8\leq q+5\leq 8$

$-8-5\leq q+5-5\leq 8-5$

$-13\leq q\leq 3$

The solution set is $\left\{q|-13\leq q\leq 3\right\}$.

34. $|7-x|<6$

$-6<7-x<6$

$-6-7<7-7-x<6-7$

$-13<-x<-1$

$\dfrac{-13}{-1}>\dfrac{-x}{-1}>\dfrac{-1}{-1}$

$13>x>1$

$1<x<13$

The solution set is $\{x|\ 1<x<13\}$.

35. $|5b-15|<10$

$-10<5b-15<10$

$-10+15<5b-15+15<10+15$

$5<5b<25$

$\dfrac{5}{5}<\dfrac{5b}{5}<\dfrac{25}{5}$

$1<b<5$

The solution set is $\left\{b|1<b<5\right\}$.

36. $|x-3|-7<-2$

$|x-3|<5$

$-5<x-3<5$

$-5+3<x-3+3<5+3$

$-2<x<8$

The solution set is $\{x|-2<x<8\}$.

37. $|2x+3|-5\leq 10$

$|2x+3|\leq 15$

$-15\leq 2x+3\leq 15$

$-15-3\leq 2x+3-3\leq 15-3$

$-18\leq 2x\leq 12$

$\dfrac{-18}{2}\leq\dfrac{2x}{2}\leq\dfrac{12}{2}$

$-9\leq x\leq 6$

The solution set is $\{x|-9\leq x\leq 6\}$

38. $|4-3x|-4<11$

$|4-3x|<15$

$-15<4-3x<15$

$-15-4<4-4-3x<15-4$

$-19<-3x<11$

$\dfrac{-19}{-3}>\dfrac{-3x}{-3}>\dfrac{11}{-3}$

$\dfrac{19}{3}>x>\dfrac{-11}{3}$

$\dfrac{-11}{3}<x<\dfrac{19}{3}$

The solution set is $\left\{x\left|-\dfrac{11}{3}<x<\dfrac{19}{3}\right.\right\}$.

39.
$$|3x - 7| + 8 < 14$$
$$|3x - 7| < 6$$
$$-6 < 3x - 7 < 6$$
$$-6 + 7 < 3x - 7 + 7 < 6 + 7$$
$$1 < 3x < 13$$
$$\frac{1}{3} < \frac{3x}{3} < \frac{13}{3}$$
$$\frac{1}{3} < x < \frac{13}{3}$$

The solution set is $\left\{x \middle| \frac{1}{3} < x < \frac{13}{3}\right\}$.

40.
$$\left|\frac{2x - 1}{9}\right| \leq \frac{5}{9}$$
$$-\frac{5}{9} \leq \frac{2x - 1}{9} \leq \frac{5}{9}$$
$$9\left(-\frac{5}{9}\right) \leq 9\left(\frac{2x - 1}{9}\right) \leq 9\left(\frac{5}{9}\right)$$
$$-5 \leq 2x - 1 \leq 5$$
$$-5 + 1 \leq 2x - 1 + 1 \leq 5 + 1$$
$$-4 \leq 2x \leq 6$$
$$\frac{-4}{2} \leq \frac{2x}{2} \leq \frac{6}{2}$$
$$-2 \leq x \leq 3$$

The solution set is $\{x | -2 \leq x \leq 3\}$.

41. $|2x - 6| + 5 \leq 1$
$$|2x - 6| \leq -4$$

There is no solution since the right side is negative whereas the left side is non-negative; zero or a positive number is never less than a negative number. The solution set is $\varnothing$.

42. $|2x - 3| < -10$

There is no solution since the right side is negative whereas the left side is positive or zero, hence, never less than a negative number. The solution set is $\varnothing$.

43.
$$\left|\frac{1}{2}j + 4\right| < 7$$
$$-7 < \frac{1}{2}j + 4 < 7$$
$$-7 - 4 < \frac{1}{2}j + 4 - 4 < 7 - 4$$
$$-11 < \frac{1}{2}j < 3$$
$$2(-11) < 2\left(\frac{1}{2}j\right) < 2(3)$$
$$-22 < j < 6$$

The solution set is $\left\{j | -22 < j < 6\right\}$.

44.
$$\left|\frac{k}{4} - \frac{3}{8}\right| < \frac{7}{16}$$
$$-\frac{7}{16} < \frac{k}{4} - \frac{3}{8} < \frac{7}{16}$$
$$16\left(-\frac{7}{16}\right) < 16\left(\frac{k}{4} - \frac{3}{8}\right) < 16\left(\frac{7}{16}\right)$$
$$-7 < 4k - 6 < 7$$
$$-7 + 6 < 4k - 6 + 6 < 7 + 6$$
$$-1 < 4k < 13$$
$$-\frac{1}{4} < k < \frac{13}{4}$$

The solution is $\left\{k \middle| -\frac{1}{4} < k < \frac{13}{4}\right\}$.

45.
$$\left|\frac{x - 3}{2}\right| - 4 \leq -2$$
$$\left|\frac{x - 3}{2}\right| \leq 2$$
$$-2 \leq \frac{x - 3}{2} \leq 2$$
$$2(-2) \leq 2\left(\frac{x - 3}{2}\right) \leq 2(2)$$
$$-4 \leq x - 3 \leq 4$$
$$-4 + 3 \leq x - 3 + 3 \leq 4 + 3$$
$$-1 \leq x \leq 7$$

The solution set is $\{x | -1 \leq x \leq 7\}$.

46. $\left|7x - \dfrac{1}{2}\right| < 0$

There is no solution since the right side is 0 and the left side is positive or zero, therefore, never less than 0. The solution set is $\varnothing$.

47. $|y| > 2$

$y < -2$ or $y > 2$

The solution set is $\{y | y < -2 \text{ or } y > 2\}$.

48. $|a| \geq 13$

$a \leq -13$ or $a \geq 13$

The solution set is $\{a | a \leq -13 \text{ or } a \geq 13\}$.

49. $|x + 4| > 5$

$\begin{array}{ll} x + 4 < -5 & \text{or} \quad x + 4 > 5 \\ x < -9 & \qquad\quad x > 1 \end{array}$

The solution set is $\{x | x < -9 \text{ or } x > 1\}$.

50. $|2b - 7| > 3$

$\begin{array}{ll} 2b - 7 < -3 & \text{or} \quad 2b - 7 > 3 \\ 2b < 4 & \qquad\quad 2b > 10 \\ b < \dfrac{4}{2} & \qquad\quad b > \dfrac{10}{2} \\ b < 2 & \qquad\quad b > 5 \end{array}$

The solution set is $\left\{b \,\middle|\, b < 2 \text{ or } b > 5\right\}$.

51. $|7 - 3b| > 5$

$\begin{array}{ll} 7 - 3b < -5 & \text{or} \quad 7 - 3b > 5 \\ -3b < -12 & \qquad\quad -3b > -2 \\ \dfrac{-3b}{-3} > \dfrac{-12}{-3} & \qquad\quad \dfrac{-3b}{-3} < \dfrac{-2}{-3} \\ b > 4 & \qquad\quad b < \dfrac{2}{3} \end{array}$

The solution set is $\left\{b \,\middle|\, b < \dfrac{2}{3} \text{ or } b > 4\right\}$.

52. $\left|\dfrac{6 + 2z}{3}\right| > 2$

$\begin{array}{ll} \dfrac{6 + 2z}{3} < -2 & \text{or} \quad \dfrac{6 + 2z}{3} > 2 \\ 3\left(\dfrac{6 + 2z}{3}\right) < 3(-2) & \quad 3\left(\dfrac{6 + 2z}{3}\right) > 3(2) \\ 6 + 2z < -6 & \qquad 6 + 2z > 6 \\ 2z < -12 & \qquad 2z > 0 \\ z < \dfrac{-12}{2} & \qquad z > \dfrac{0}{2} \\ z < -6 & \qquad z > 0 \end{array}$

The solution set is $\{z | z < -6 \text{ or } z > 0\}$.

53. $|2h - 5| > 3$

$\begin{array}{ll} 2h - 5 < -3 & \text{or} \quad 2h - 5 > 3 \\ 2h < 2 & \qquad\quad 2h > 8 \\ h < \dfrac{2}{2} & \qquad\quad h > \dfrac{8}{2} \\ h < 1 & \qquad\quad h > 4 \end{array}$

The solution set is $\left\{h \,\middle|\, h < 1 \text{ or } h > 4\right\}$.

54. $|2x - 1| \geq 12$

$\begin{array}{ll} 2x - 1 \leq -12 & \text{or} \quad 2x - 1 \geq 12 \\ 2x \leq -11 & \text{or} \quad 2x \geq 13 \\ x \leq -\dfrac{11}{2} & \qquad\quad x \geq \dfrac{13}{2} \end{array}$

The solution set is $\left\{x \,\middle|\, x \leq -\dfrac{11}{2} \text{ or } x \geq \dfrac{13}{2}\right\}$.

55. $|0.1x - 0.4| + 0.4 > 0.6$

$|0.1x - 0.4| > 0.2$

$\begin{array}{ll} 0.1x - 0.4 < -0.2 & \text{or} \quad 0.1x - 0.4 > 0.2 \\ 0.1x < 0.2 & \qquad 0.1x > 0.6 \\ x < \dfrac{0.2}{0.1} & \qquad x > \dfrac{0.6}{0.1} \\ x < 2 & \qquad x > 6 \end{array}$

The solution set is $\{x | x < 2 \text{ or } x > 6\}$.

56. $|3.7d + 6.9| - 2.1 > -5.4$

$|3.7d + 6.9| > -3.3$

Since the right side is negative whereas the left side is positive or zero and always greater than a negative number, the solution is the entire real number line. Thus, the solution is all real numbers, or $\mathbb{R}$.

57. $\left|\dfrac{x}{2} + 4\right| \geq 5$

$\dfrac{x}{2} + 4 \leq -5$ or $\dfrac{x}{2} + 4 \geq 5$

$2\left(\dfrac{x}{2} + 4\right) \leq 2(-5)$ $2\left(\dfrac{x}{2} + 4\right) \geq 2(5)$

$x + 8 \leq -10$ $x + 8 \geq 10$

$x \leq -18$ $x \geq 2$

The solution set is $\{x \mid x \leq -18 \text{ or } x \geq 2\}$.

58. $\left|4 - \dfrac{3x}{5}\right| \geq 9$

$4 - \dfrac{3x}{5} \leq -9$ or $4 - \dfrac{3x}{5} \geq 9$

$-\dfrac{3x}{5} \leq -13$ $-\dfrac{3x}{5} \geq 5$

$-\dfrac{5}{3}\left(-\dfrac{3x}{5}\right) \geq -\dfrac{5}{3}(-13)$ $-\dfrac{5}{3}\left(-\dfrac{3x}{5}\right) \leq -\dfrac{5}{3}(5)$

$x \geq \dfrac{65}{3}$ $x \leq -\dfrac{25}{3}$

The solution set is $\left\{x \mid x \leq -\dfrac{25}{3} \text{ or } x \geq \dfrac{65}{3}\right\}$.

59. $|7w + 3| - 12 \geq -12$

$|7w + 3| \geq 0$

Observe that the absolute value of a number is always greater than or equal to 0. Thus, the solution is the set of real numbers, or $\mathbb{R}$.

60. $|2.6 - x| \geq 0$

Since the right side is 0 whereas the left side is non-negative, and therefore always greater than or equal to 0, The solution is all real values, or $\mathbb{R}$.

61. $|4 - 2x| > 0$

$4 - 2x < 0$ or $4 - 2x > 0$

$-2x < -4$ $-2x > -4$

$x > \dfrac{-4}{-2}$ $x < \dfrac{-4}{-2}$

$x > 2$ $x < 2$

The solution set is $\{x \mid x < 2 \text{ or } x > 2\}$.

62. $|2c - 8| > 0$

$2c - 8 < 0$ or $2c - 8 > 0$

$2c < 8$ $2c > 8$

$c < \dfrac{8}{2}$ $c > \dfrac{8}{2}$

$c < 4$ $c > 4$

The solution set is

$\{c \mid c < 4 \text{ or } c > 4\}$ or $\{c \mid c \neq 4\}$.

63. $|3p - 5| = |2p + 10|$

$3p - 5 = -(2p + 10)$ or $3p - 5 = 2p + 10$

$3p - 5 = -2p - 10$ $p - 5 = 10$

$5p - 5 = -10$ $p = 15$

$5p = -5$

$p = -1$

The solution set is $\{-1, 15\}$.

64. $|6n + 3| = |4n - 13|$

$6n + 3 = -(4n - 13)$ $6n + 3 = (4n - 13)$

$6n + 3 = -4n + 13$ or $6n + 3 = 4n - 13$

$10n + 3 = 13$ $2n + 3 = -13$

$10n = 10$ $2n + -16$

$n = 1$ $n = -8$

The solution set is $\{-8, 1\}$.

65. $|6x| = |3x - 9|$

$6x = -(3x - 9)$ or $6x = 3x - 9$

$6x = -3x + 9$ $3x = -9$

$9x = 9$ $x = \dfrac{-9}{3}$

$x = \dfrac{9}{9}$ $x = -3$

$x = 1$

The solution set is $\{-3, 1\}$.

66. $|5t - 10| = |10 - 5t|$

$|5t - 10| = |-(5t - 10)|$

Since the $5t - 10$ and $-(5t - 10)$ are opposites,

the absolute value of each are equivalent.

Therefore, the solution is all real numbers or $\mathbb{R}$.

67. $\left|\dfrac{2r}{3} + \dfrac{5}{6}\right| = \left|\dfrac{r}{2} - 3\right|$

$\dfrac{2r}{3} + \dfrac{5}{6} = -\left(\dfrac{r}{2} - 3\right)$ or $\dfrac{2r}{3} + \dfrac{5}{6} = \dfrac{r}{2} - 3$

$\dfrac{2r}{3} + \dfrac{5}{6} = -\dfrac{r}{2} + 3$ $\qquad$ $6\left(\dfrac{2r}{3} + \dfrac{5}{6}\right) = 6\left(\dfrac{r}{2} - 3\right)$

$6\left(\dfrac{2r}{3} + \dfrac{5}{6}\right) = 6\left(-\dfrac{r}{2} + 3\right)$ $\qquad$ $4r + 5 = 3r - 18$

$4r + 5 = -3r + 18$ $\qquad\qquad$ $r + 5 = -18$

$7r + 5 = 18$ $\qquad\qquad\qquad$ $r = -23$

$7r = 13$

$r = \dfrac{13}{7}$

The solution set is $\left\{-23, \dfrac{13}{7}\right\}$.

68. $|3x - 8| = |3x + 8|$

$3x - 8 = 3x + 8$ or $3x - 8 = -(3x + 8)$

$-8 = 8$ False $\qquad$ $3x - 8 = -3x - 8$

$\qquad\qquad\qquad$ $6x - 8 = -8$

$\qquad\qquad\qquad$ $6x = 0$

$\qquad\qquad\qquad$ $x = 0$

The solution set is $\{0\}$.

69. $\left|-\dfrac{3}{4}m + 8\right| = \left|7 - \dfrac{3}{4}m\right|$

$-\dfrac{3}{4}m + 8 = -\left(7 - \dfrac{3}{4}m\right)$ or $-\dfrac{3}{4}m + 8 = 7 - \dfrac{3}{4}m$

$-\dfrac{3}{4}m + 8 = -7 + \dfrac{3}{4}m$ $\qquad$ $-\dfrac{3}{4}m + 8 = 7 - \dfrac{3}{4}m$

$-\dfrac{6}{4}m = -15$ $\qquad\qquad\qquad$ $8 = 7$ False!

$m = 10$

The solution set is $\{10\}$.

70. $\left|\dfrac{3}{2}r + 2\right| = \left|8 - \dfrac{3}{2}r\right|$

$\dfrac{3}{2}r + 2 = -\left(8 - \dfrac{3}{2}r\right)$ or $\dfrac{3}{2}r + 2 = 8 - \dfrac{3}{2}r$

$\dfrac{3}{2}r + 2 = -8 + \dfrac{3}{2}r$ $\qquad$ $3r + 2 = 8$

$\qquad\qquad\qquad$ $3r = 6$

$2 = -8$ $\qquad\qquad\qquad$ $r = 2$

False

The solution set is $\{2\}$.

71. $|h| = 1$

$h = 1$ or $h = -1$

The solution set is $\{-1, 1\}$.

72. $|y| \le 8$

$-8 \le y \le 8$

The solution set is $\{y \,|\, -8 \le y \le 8\}$.

73. $|q + 6| > 2$

$q + 6 < -2$ or $q + 6 > 2$

$q < -8$ $\qquad$ $q > -4$

The solution set is $\{q \,|\, q < -8 \ \text{ or } \ q > -4\}$.

74. $|9d + 7| \le -9$

There is no solution since the right side is
negative whereas the left side is non-negative
and, therefore, never less than a negative
number. The solution set is $\varnothing$.

75. $|2w - 7| \le 9$

$-9 \le 2w - 7 \le 9$

$-9 + 7 \le 2w - 7 + 7 \le 9 + 7$

$-2 \le 2w \le 16$

$\dfrac{-2}{2} \le \dfrac{2w}{2} \le \dfrac{16}{2}$

$-1 \le w \le 8$

The solution set is $\{w \,|\, -1 \le w \le 8\}$.

76. $|2z - 7| + 5 > 8$

$|2z - 7| > 3$

$2z - 7 < -3$ or $2z - 7 > 3$

$\qquad 2z < 4 \qquad\qquad 2z > 10$

$\qquad z < 2 \qquad\qquad z > 5$

The solution set is $\left\{ z \mid z < 2 \text{ or } z > 5 \right\}$.

77. $|5a - 1| = 9$

$5a - 1 = -9$ or $5a - 1 = 9$

$\qquad 5a = -8 \qquad\qquad 5a = 10$

$\qquad a = -\dfrac{8}{5} \qquad\qquad a = 2$

The solution set is $\left\{ -\dfrac{8}{5}, 2 \right\}$.

78. $|2x - 4| + 5 = 13$

$|2x - 4| = 8$

$2x - 4 = -8$ or $2x - 4 = 8$

$\qquad 2x = -4 \qquad\qquad 2x = 12$

$\qquad x = -2 \qquad\qquad x = 6$

The solution set is $\{-2, 6\}$.

79. $|5x + 2| > 0$

$5 + 2x < 0$ or $5 + 2x > 0$

$\qquad 2x < -5 \qquad\qquad 2x > -5$

$\qquad x < -\dfrac{5}{2} \qquad\qquad x > -\dfrac{5}{2}$

The solution set is $\left\{ x \mid x < -\dfrac{5}{2} \text{ or } x > -\dfrac{5}{2} \right\}$.

80. $|7 - 3b| = |5b + 15|$

$7 - 3b = -(5b + 15)$ or $7 - 3b = 5b + 15$

$\qquad 7 - 3b = -5b - 15 \qquad\qquad -8b = 8$

$\qquad 2b = -22 \qquad\qquad\qquad b = -1$

$\qquad b = -11$

The solution set is $\{-11, -1\}$.

81. $|4 + 3x| \le 9$

$-9 \le 4 + 3x \le 9$

$-13 \le 3x \le 5$

$-\dfrac{13}{3} \le x \le \dfrac{5}{3}$

The solution set is $\left\{ x \mid -\dfrac{13}{3} \le x \le \dfrac{5}{3} \right\}$.

82. $|2.4x + 4| + 4.9 > 3.9$

$|2.4x + 4| > -1.0$

Since the right side is negative whereas the left side is non-negative and always greater than a negative number, the solution is the entire real number line. Thus, the solution is the set of all real numbers or $\mathbb{R}$.

83. $|3n + 8| - 4 = -10$

$|3n + 8| = -6$

Since the right side is negative and the left side is non-negative, there is no solution since the absolute value can never equal a negative number. The solution set is $\varnothing$.

84. $|4 - 2x| - 3 = 7$

$|4 - 2x| = 10$

$4 - 2x = -10$ or $4 - 2x = 10$

$\qquad -2x = -14 \qquad\qquad -2x = 6$

$\qquad x = 7 \qquad\qquad\qquad x = -3$

The solution set is $\{-3, 7\}$.

85. $\left| \dfrac{w + 4}{3} \right| + 5 < 9$

$\left| \dfrac{w + 4}{3} \right| < 4$

$-4 < \dfrac{w + 4}{3} < 4$

$3(-4) < 3\left(\dfrac{w + 4}{3} \right) < 3(4)$

$-12 < w + 4 < 12$

$-16 < w < 8$

The solution set is $\{w \mid -16 < w < 8\}$.

86. $\left|\dfrac{5t-10}{6}\right| > \dfrac{5}{3}$

$\dfrac{5t-10}{6} < -\dfrac{5}{3}$ or $\dfrac{5t-10}{6} > \dfrac{5}{3}$

$6\left(\dfrac{5t-10}{6}\right) < 6\left(-\dfrac{5}{3}\right)$ $6\left(\dfrac{5t-10}{6}\right) > 6\left(\dfrac{5}{3}\right)$

$5t-10 < -10$ $5t-10 > 10$

$5t < 0$ $5t > 20$

$t < 0$ $t > 4$

The solution set is $\left\{ t \mid t < 0 \text{ or } t > 4\right\}$.

87. $\left|\dfrac{3x-2}{4}\right| - \dfrac{1}{3} \ge -\dfrac{1}{3}$

$\left|\dfrac{3x-2}{4}\right| \ge 0$

Since the absolute value of a number is always greater than or equal to zero, the solution is the set of all real numbers or $\mathbb{R}$.

88. $\left|\dfrac{2x-4}{5}\right| = 14$

$\dfrac{2x-4}{5} = -14$ or $\dfrac{2x-4}{5} = 14$

$5\left(\dfrac{2x-4}{5}\right) = 5(-14)$ $5\left(\dfrac{2x-4}{5}\right) = 5(14)$

$2x-4 = -70$ $2x-4 = 70$

$2x = -66$ $2x = 74$

$x = -33$ $x = 37$

The solution set is $\{-33, 37\}$.

89. $|2x-8| = \left|\dfrac{1}{2}x+3\right|$

$2x-8 = -\left(\dfrac{1}{2}x+3\right)$ or $2x-8 = \dfrac{1}{2}x+3$

$2x-8 = -\dfrac{1}{2}x-3$ $\dfrac{3}{2}x-8 = 3$

$\dfrac{5}{2}x-8 = -3$ $\dfrac{3}{2}x = 11$

$\dfrac{5}{2}x = 5$ $\dfrac{2}{3}\left(\dfrac{3}{2}x\right) = \dfrac{2}{3}(11)$

$\dfrac{2}{5}\left(\dfrac{5}{2}x\right) = \dfrac{2}{5}(5)$ $x = \dfrac{22}{3}$

$x = 2$

The solution set is $\left\{2, \dfrac{22}{3}\right\}$.

90. $\left|\dfrac{1}{3}y+3\right| = \left|\dfrac{2}{3}y-1\right|$

$\dfrac{1}{3}y+3 = \dfrac{2}{3}y-1$ or $\dfrac{1}{3}y+3 = -\left(\dfrac{2}{3}y-1\right)$

$3 = \dfrac{1}{3}y-1$ $\dfrac{1}{3}y+3 = -\dfrac{2}{3}y+1$

$4 = \dfrac{1}{3}y$ $y+3 = 1$

$3(4) = 3\left(\dfrac{1}{3}y\right)$ $y = -2$

$12 = y$

The solution set is $\{-2, 12\}$.

91. $\left| 2 - 3x \right| = \left| 4 - \dfrac{5}{3}x \right|$

$2 - 3x = -\left(4 - \dfrac{5}{3}x \right)$ or $2 - 3x = 4 - \dfrac{5}{3}x$

$2 - 3x = -4 + \dfrac{5}{3}x$ $\quad$ $-3x = 2 - \dfrac{5}{3}x$

$-3x = -6 + \dfrac{5}{3}x$ $\quad$ $-\dfrac{4}{3}x = 2$

$-\dfrac{14}{3}x = -6$ $\quad$ $-\dfrac{3}{4}\left(-\dfrac{4}{3}x \right) = -\dfrac{3}{2}(2)$

$\left(-\dfrac{3}{14} \right)\left(-\dfrac{14}{3} \right)x = \left(-\dfrac{3}{14} \right)(-6)$ $\quad$ $x = -\dfrac{3}{2}$

$x = \dfrac{9}{7}$

The solution set is $\left\{ -\dfrac{3}{2}, \dfrac{9}{7} \right\}$.

92. $\left| \dfrac{-2u + 3}{7} \right| \le 5$

$-5 \le \dfrac{-2u + 3}{7} \le 5$

$21(5) \le 21\left(\dfrac{-2u + 3}{7} \right) \le 21(5)$

$-105 \le -6u + 9 \le 105$

$-105 - 9 \le -6u + 9 - 9 \le 105 - 9$

$-114 \le -6u \le 96$

$\dfrac{-114}{-6} \ge \dfrac{-6u}{-6} \ge \dfrac{96}{-6}$

$19 \ge u \ge -16$

$-16 \le u \le 19$

The solution set is $\left\{ u \mid -16 \le u \le 19 \right\}$.

93. a. $\left| t - 0.089 \right| \le 0.004$

$-0.004 \le t - 0.089 \le 0.004$

$-0.004 + 0.089 \le t - 0.089 + 0.089 \le 0.004 + 0.089$

$0.085 \le t \le 0.093$

The solution is $\left[0.085, 0.093 \right]$.

b. 0.085 inches

c. 0.093 inches

94. a. $\left| t - \dfrac{5}{8} \right| \le \dfrac{1}{56}$

$-\dfrac{1}{56} \le t - \dfrac{5}{8} \le \dfrac{1}{56}$

$56\left(-\dfrac{1}{56} \right) \le 56\left(t - \dfrac{5}{8} \right) \le 56\left(\dfrac{1}{56} \right)$

$-1 \le 56t - 35 \le 1$

$-1 + 35 \le 56t - 35 + 35 \le 1 + 35$

$34 \le 56t \le 36$

$\dfrac{34}{56} \le \dfrac{56t}{56} \le \dfrac{36}{56}$

$\dfrac{17}{28} \le t \le \dfrac{9}{14}$

The solution is $\left[\dfrac{17}{28}, \dfrac{9}{14} \right]$.

b. $\dfrac{17}{28}$ inches

c. $\dfrac{9}{14}$ inches

95. a. $\left| d - 160 \right| \le 28$

$-28 \le d - 160 \le 28$

$-28 + 160 \le d - 160 + 160 \le 28 + 160$

$132 \le d \le 188$

The solution is [132, 188]

b. The submarine can move between 132 feet and 188 feet below sea level, inclusive.

96. a. $\left| d - 4 \right| \le \dfrac{1}{2}$

$-\dfrac{1}{2} \le d - 4 \le \dfrac{1}{2}$

$-\dfrac{1}{2} + 4 \le d - 4 + 4 \le \dfrac{1}{2} + 4$

$\dfrac{7}{2} \le d \le \dfrac{9}{2}$

The solution is $\left[\dfrac{7}{2}, \dfrac{9}{2} \right]$ or $[3.5, 4.5]$.

b. The spring will oscillate between 3.5 feet and 4.5 feet, inclusive.

97. $\{ -5, 5 \}$ is the solution set to the equation $\left| x \right| = 5$.

98. $\{x|-5 < x < 5\}$ is the solution set of $|x| < 5$.

99. $\{x|x \le -5 \text{ or } x \ge 5\}$ is the solution set of $|x| \ge 5$.

100. $\{x|-5 \le x \le 5\}$ is the solution set of $|x| \le 5$.

101. $|ax + b| \le 0$

$$0 \le ax + b \le 0$$

which is the same as

$$ax + b = 0$$
$$ax = -b$$
$$x = -\frac{b}{a}$$

102. $|ax + b| > 0$ is not true when $|ax + b| = 0$

$$ax + b = 0$$
$$ax = -b$$
$$x = -\frac{b}{a}$$

103. a. Set $ax + b = -c$ or $ax + b = c$ and solve each equation for x.

b. $ax + b = -c$ or $ax + b = c$
$$ax = -c - b \qquad\qquad ax = c - b$$
$$x = \frac{-c - b}{a} \qquad\qquad x = \frac{c - b}{a}$$

The solution is $x = \dfrac{-c - b}{a}$ or $x = \dfrac{c - b}{a}$.

104. a. Write the inequality as
$-c < ax + b < c$ and then solve for x.

b. $-c < ax + b < c$
$$-c - b < ax + b - b < c - b$$
$$-c - b < ax < c - b$$
$$\frac{-c - b}{a} < \frac{ax}{a} < \frac{c - b}{a}$$
$$\frac{-c - b}{a} < x < \frac{c - b}{a}$$

The solution is $\dfrac{-c - b}{a} < x < \dfrac{c - b}{a}$.

105. a. Write $ax + b < -c$ or $ax + b > c$ and solve each inequality for x.

b. $ax + b < -c$ or $ax + b > c$
$$ax < -c - b \qquad\qquad ax > c - b$$
$$x < \frac{-c - b}{a} \qquad\qquad x > \frac{c - b}{a}$$

The solution is $x < \dfrac{-c - b}{a}$ or $x > \dfrac{c - b}{a}$.

106. a. Divide both sides by -4 and change the direction of the inequality.

b. $-4|3x - 5| \le -12$
$$\frac{-4|3x - 5|}{-4} \ge \frac{-12}{-4}$$
$$|3x - 5| \ge 3$$
$$3x - 5 \le -3 \quad \text{or} \quad 3x - 5 \ge 3$$
$$3x \le 2 \qquad\qquad 3x \ge 8$$
$$x \le \frac{2}{3} \qquad\qquad x \ge \frac{8}{3}$$

The solution set is $\left\{x \middle| x \le \dfrac{2}{3} \text{ or } x \ge \dfrac{8}{3}\right\}$ or

$$\left(-\infty, \frac{2}{3}\right] \cup \left[\frac{8}{3}, \infty\right).$$

107. $|x - 4| = |4 - x|$
$$x - 4 = -(4 - x) \quad \text{or} \quad x - 4 = 4 - x$$
$$x - 4 = -4 + x \qquad\qquad 2x - 4 = 4$$
$$0 = 0 \qquad\qquad\qquad 2x = 8$$
$$\text{True} \qquad\qquad\qquad x = 4$$

Since the first statement is always true all real values work. The solution set is $\mathbb{R}$.

108. $|x - 4| = -|x - 4|$

This occurs only if $|x - 4| = 0$
$$x - 4 = 0$$
$$x = 4$$

The solution set is $\{4\}$.

109. $|x| = x$

By definition $|x| = \begin{cases} x, & x \ge 0 \\ -x, & x < 0 \end{cases}$

Thus, $|x| = x$ when $x \ge 0$

The solution set is $\{x|x \ge 0\}$.

110. $|x+2| = x+2$

By definition, $|x+2| = \begin{cases} x+2, & x+2 \geq 0 \\ -(x+2), & x+2 < 0 \end{cases}$

$= \begin{cases} x+2, & x \geq -2 \\ -(x+2), & x < -2 \end{cases}$

Thus, $|x+2| = x+2$ when $x \geq -2$.

The solution set is $\{x | x \geq -2\}$.

111. $|x+1| = 2x-1$

$\begin{array}{ll} x+1 = -(2x-1) & \text{or} \quad x+1=2x-1 \\ x+1 = -2x+1 & \qquad 1 = x-1 \\ 3x+1 = 1 & \qquad 2 = x \\ \quad 3x = 0 & \\ \quad\; x = 0 & \end{array}$

Checking both possible solutions, only $x = 2$ checks. The solution set is $\{2\}$.

112. $|3x+1| = x-3$

$\begin{array}{ll} 3x+1 = x-3 & \text{or} \quad 3x+1 = -(x-3) \\ 2x+1 = -3 & \qquad 3x+1 = -x+3 \\ \quad 2x = -4 & \qquad 4x+1 = 3 \\ \quad\; x = -2 & \qquad 4x = 2 \\ & \qquad x = \dfrac{2}{4} = \dfrac{1}{2} \end{array}$

Neither possible solution checks.
Thus, there are no values for x that make the equation true. The solution set is $\varnothing$.

113. $|x-4| = -(x-4)$

By the definition, $|x-4| = \begin{cases} x-4, & x-4 \geq 0 \\ -(x-4), & x-4 \leq 0 \end{cases}$

$= \begin{cases} x-4, & x \geq 4 \\ -(x-4), & x \leq 4 \end{cases}$

Thus, $|x-4| = -(x-4)$ for $x \leq 4$.

The solution set is $\{x | x \leq 4\}$.

114. $|x| + x = 8$

For $x \geq 0$: $|x| + x = 8$

$x + x = 8$

$2x = 8$

$x = 4$

For $x < 0$: $|x| + x = 8$

$-x + x = 8$

$0 = 8$ False

The solution set is $\{4\}$.

115. $x + |-x| = 8$

For $x \geq 0$, $x + |-x| = 8$

$x + x = 8$

$2x = 8$

$x = 4$

For $x < 0$, $x + |-x| = 8$

$x - x = 8$

$0 = 8$ False

The solution set is $\{4\}$.

116. $|x| - x = 8$

For $x \geq 0$, $|x| - x = 8$

$x - x = 8$

$0 = 8$ False

For $x < 0$, $|x| - x = 8$

$-x - x = 8$

$-2x = 8$

$x = -4$

The solution set is $\{-4\}$.

117. $x - |x| = 8$

For $x \geq 0$, $x - |x| = 8$

$x - x = 8$

$0 = 8$ False

For $x < 0$, $x - |x| = 8$

$x - (-x) = 8$

$x + x = 8$

$2x = 8$

$x = 4$ Contradicts $x < 0$

There are no values of x, so the solution set is $\varnothing$.

118. a. Answers will vary.

    b. All real numbers x and y.

    c. Only when $x = y$.

119.
$$\frac{1}{3}+\frac{1}{4}\div\frac{2}{5}\left(\frac{1}{3}\right)^2 = \frac{1}{3}+\frac{1}{4}\div\frac{2}{5}\cdot\frac{1}{9}$$
$$= \frac{1}{3}+\frac{1}{4}\cdot\frac{5}{2}\cdot\frac{1}{9}$$
$$= \frac{1}{3}+\frac{5}{72}$$
$$= \frac{1}{3}\cdot\frac{24}{24}+\frac{5}{72}$$
$$= \frac{24}{72}+\frac{5}{72}$$
$$= \frac{29}{72}$$

120. Substitute 1 for x and 3 for y.
$$4(x+3y)-5xy = 4(1+3\cdot3)-5(1)(3)$$
$$= 4(1+9)-5(1)(3)$$
$$= 4(10)-5(1)(3)$$
$$= 40-15$$
$$= 25$$

121. Let x be the time needed to swim across the lake. Then $1.5 - x$ is the time needed to make the return trip.

	Rate	Time	Distance
First Trip	2	x	$2x$
Return Trip	1.6	$1.5-x$	$1.6(1.5-x)$

The distances are the same.
$$2x = 1.6(1.5-x)$$
$$2x = 2.4-1.6x$$
$$3.6x = 2.4$$
$$x = \frac{2.4}{3.6} = \frac{2}{3}$$

The total distance across the lake is
$$2x = 2\left(\frac{2}{3}\right)=\frac{4}{3} \text{ or } 1.33 \text{ miles.}$$

122.
$$3(x-2)-4(x-3) > 2$$
$$3x-6-4x+12 > 2$$
$$-x+6 > 2$$
$$-x > -4$$
$$\frac{-x}{-1} < \frac{-4}{-1}$$
$$x < 4$$
The solution set is $\{x \mid x < 4\}$

Mid-Chapter Test: 10.1-10.2

1. $x > \dfrac{5}{2}$

2. $-4 \le w < 5$

    Interval notation: $[-4, 5)$

3.
$$6x-5 \le 4x+61$$
$$2x-5 \le 61$$
$$2x \le 66$$
$$x \le 33$$

4.
$$5y-9y+8 \le 2(-2y+1)$$
$$-4y+8 \le -4y+2$$
$$8 \le 2 \text{ false}$$
There is no solution to the inequality.

5.
$$2.4w-3.2 < 3.6w-0.8$$
$$-1.2w-3.2 < -0.8$$
$$-1.2w < 2.4$$
$$w > -2$$

6.
$$3-2x < 6+2x+1$$
$$3-2x < 2x+7$$
$$3 < 4x+7$$
$$-4 < 4x$$
$$-1 < x \text{ or } x > -1$$
Interval notation: $(-1, \infty)$

7. $-8 < p - 3 \le 4$

    $-5 < p \le 7$

    Interval notation: $(-5, 7]$

8. $\dfrac{1}{3} \le 4x + 1 < 5$

    $-\dfrac{2}{3} \le 4x < 4$

    $-\dfrac{2}{12} \le x < 1$

    $-\dfrac{1}{6} \le x < 1$

    Interval notation: $\left[-\dfrac{1}{6}, 1\right)$

9. $-3 \le \dfrac{2x+1}{5} \le 1$

    $-15 \le 2x + 1 \le 5$

    $-16 \le 2x \le 4$

    $-8 \le x \le 2$

    Solution set: $\{x \mid -8 \le x \le 2\}$

10. $m \le 7$ and $m > -6$

    We can rewrite this statement as a compound inequality:

    $-6 < m \le 7$

    Solution set: $\{m \mid -6 < m \le 7\}$

11. $9 - x < 3$ or $7x - 5 \le -5$

    $\quad -x < -6 \qquad 7x \le 0$

    $\quad x > 6 \qquad\quad x \le 0$

    We have $x \le 0$ or $x > 6$.

    Solution set: $\{x \mid x \le 0$ or $x > 6\}$.

12. $A \cup B = \{7, 8, 9, 10, 12, 15\}$

    $A \cap B = \{8, 10\}$

13. $|t - 4| = 6$

    $t - 4 = 6$ or $t - 4 = -6$

    $\quad t = 10 \qquad\quad t = -2$

    Solution set: $\{-2, 10\}$

14. $\left|\dfrac{w-5}{3}\right| \le 7$

    $-7 \le \dfrac{w-5}{3} \le 7$

    $-21 \le w - 5 \le 21$

    $-16 \le w \le 26$

    Solution set: $\{w \mid -16 \le w \le 26\}$

15. $|z| \ge 8$

    $z \le -8$ or $z \ge 8$

    Solution set: $\{z \mid z \le -8$ or $z \ge 8\}$

16. $|5 - 2x| \ge 0$

    Since absolute value is always nonnegative, the solution set is all real numbers.

    Solution set: $\mathbb{R}$

17. $|4 - 2x| = 5$

    $4 - 2x = -5$ or $4 - 2x = 5$

    $\quad -2x = -9 \qquad\quad -2x = 1$

    $\quad x = \dfrac{9}{2} \qquad\qquad x = -\dfrac{1}{2}$

    Solution set: $\left\{-\dfrac{1}{2}, \dfrac{9}{2}\right\}$

18. $|-3m + 4| < 7$

    $-7 < -3m + 4 < 7$

    $-11 < -3m < 3$

    $\dfrac{11}{3} > m > -1$

    $-1 < m < \dfrac{11}{3}$

    Solution set: $\left\{m \mid -1 < m < \dfrac{11}{3}\right\}$

19. $|6y + 9| = |4y - 1|$

    $6y + 9 = 4y - 1$ or $6y + 9 = -(4y - 1)$

    $\quad 2y = -10 \qquad\qquad 6y + 9 = -4y + 1$

    $\quad y = -5 \qquad\qquad\quad 10y = -8$

    $\qquad\qquad\qquad\qquad\qquad y = -\dfrac{4}{5}$

    Solution set: $\left\{-5, -\dfrac{4}{5}\right\}$

20. $\left|\dfrac{1}{2}z - 3\right| = \left|\dfrac{3}{2}z + 2\right|$

$\dfrac{1}{2}z - 3 = \dfrac{3}{2}z + 2$ or $\dfrac{1}{2}z - 3 = -\left(\dfrac{3}{2}z + 2\right)$

$-z = 5$ $\dfrac{1}{2}z - 3 = -\dfrac{3}{2}z - 2$

$z = -5$ $2z = 1$

$z = \dfrac{1}{2}$

Solution set: $\left\{-5, \dfrac{1}{2}\right\}$

Exercise Set 10.3

1. The inequalities > and < do not include the corresponding equation. The points on the line satisfy only the equation.

2. The inequalities ≥ and ≤ include the corresponding equation. The points on the line satisfy the equation.

3. $(0, 0)$ cannot be used as a test point if the line passes through the origin.

4. Yes, no matter what the values of a and b are, $y = ax + b$ is a non-vertical line and $y > ax + b$ will be the points that lie above the line.

5. Answers will vary.

6. No; the point of intersection of the boundary lines is only in the solution set if the inequalities are both non-strict.

7. Yes; the point of intersection of the boundary lines is in the solution set if the inequalities are both non-strict.

8. No; since the inequalities are strict, the points along the two boundary lines are ordered pairs which are not solutions to both inequalities.

9. $x > 1$
   Graph the line $x = 1$ (vertical line) using a dashed line. For the check point, select $(0, 0)$:
   $x > 1$
   $0 > 1$ ← Substitute 0 for x
   Since this is a false statement, shade the region which does not contain $(0, 0)$.

10. $x \geq 4$
    Graph the line $x = 4$ (vertical line) using a solid line. For the check point, select $(0, 0)$.
    $x \geq 4$
    $0 \geq 4$ ← Substitute 0 for x.
    Since this is a false statement, shade the region which does not contain $(0, 0)$.

11. $y < -2$
    Graph the line $y = -2$ (horizontal line) using a dashed line. For the check point, select $(0, 0)$.
    $y < -2$
    $0 < -2$ ← Substitute 0 for y.
    Since this is a false statement, shade the region which does not contain $(0, 0)$.

12. $y < x$

Graph the line $y = x$ using a dashed line. For the check point, select $(0, 1)$.

$y < x$

$1 < 0$ ← Substitute 0 for x and 1 for y

Since this is a false statement, shade the region which does not contain $(0, 1)$.

13. $y \geq -\dfrac{1}{2}x$

Graph the line $y = -\dfrac{1}{2}x$ using a solid line. For the check point, select $(0, 2)$.

$y \geq -\dfrac{1}{2}x$

$2 \geq -\dfrac{1}{2}(0)$ ← Substitute 0 for x and 2 for y

$2 \geq 0$

Since this is a true statement, shade the region which contains the point $(0, 2)$.

14. $y < \dfrac{1}{2}x$

Graph the line $y = \dfrac{1}{2}x$ using a dashed line. For a check point, select $(1, 1)$:

$y < \dfrac{1}{2}x$

$1 < \dfrac{1}{2}(1)$

$1 < \dfrac{1}{2}$ ← Substitute 1 for x and y

Since this a false statement, shade the region which does not contain the point $(1, 1)$.

15. $y < 2x + 1$

Graph the line $y = 2x + 1$ using a dashed line. For the check point, select $(0, 0)$.

$y < 2x + 1$

$0 < 2(0) + 1$ ← Substitute 0 for x and y

$0 < 1$

Since this is a true statement, shade the region which contains the point $(0, 0)$.

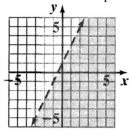

16. $y \geq 3x - 1$

Graph the line $y = 3x - 1$ using a solid line. For the check point, select $(0, 0)$.

$y \geq 3x - 1$

$0 \geq 3(0) - 1$ ← Substitute 0 for x and y

$0 \geq -1$

Since this is a true statement, shade the region which contains the point $(0, 0)$.

17. $y > 2x - 1$

Graph the line $y = 2x - 1$ using a dashed line.
For the check point, select $(0, 0)$.
$y > 2x - 1$
$0 > 2(0) - 1$ ← Substitute 0 for x and y
$0 > -1$
Since this is a true statement, shade the region
which contains the point $(0, 0)$.

18. $y \leq -x + 4$

Graph the line $y = -x + 4$ using a solid line. For
the check point, select $(0, 0)$.
$y \leq -x + 4$
$0 \leq -(0) + 4$ ← Substitute 0 for x and y
$0 \leq 4$
Since this is a true statement, shade the region
which contains the point $(0, 0)$.

19. $y \geq \dfrac{1}{2}x - 3$

Graph the line $y = \dfrac{1}{2}x - 3$ using a solid line. For
the check point, select $(0, 0)$.

$y \geq \dfrac{1}{2}x - 3$

$0 \geq \dfrac{1}{2}(0) - 3$ ← Substitute 0 for x and y

$0 \geq -3$
Since this is a true statement, shade the region

which contains the point $(0, 0)$.

20. $y < 3x + 2$

Graph the line $y = 3x + 2$ using a dashed line. For
the check point, select $(0, 0)$.
$y < 3x + 2$
$0 < 3(0) + 2$ ← Substitute 0 for x and y
$0 < 2$
Since this is a true statement, shade the region
which contains $(0, 0)$.

21. $2x + 3y > 6$

Graph the line $2x + 3y = 6$ using a dashed line.
For the check point, select $(0, 0)$.
$2x + 3y > 6$
$2(0) + 3(0) > 6$ ← Substitute 0 for x and y
$0 > 6$
Since this is a false statement, shade the region
which does not contain the point $(0, 0)$.

22. $2x - 3y \geq 12$

Graph the line $2x - 3y = 12$ using a solid line.

For the check point, select $(0, 0)$.

$$y \leq \frac{2}{3}x - 4$$

$$(0) \leq \frac{2}{3}(0) - 4 \leftarrow \text{Substitute 0 for } x \text{ and } y$$

$$0 \leq -4$$

Since this is a false statement, shade the region which does not contain the point $(0, 0)$.

23. $y \leq -3x + 5$

Graph the line $y = -3x + 5$ using a solid line.

For the check point, select $(0, 0)$.

$y \leq -3x + 5$

$0 \leq -3(0) + 5 \leftarrow$ Substitute 0 for x and y

$0 \leq 5$

Since this is a true statement, shade the region which contains the point $(0, 0)$.

24. $y \leq \frac{2}{3}x + 3$

Graph the line $y = \frac{2}{3}x + 3$ using a solid line. For the check point, select $(0, 0)$.

$$0 \leq \frac{2}{3}(0) + 3 \leftarrow \text{Substitute 0 for } x \text{ and } y$$

$$0 \leq 3$$

Since this is a true statement, shade the region

which contains the point $(0, 0)$.

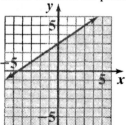

25. $2x + y < 4$

Graph the line $2x + y = 4$ using a dashed line.

For the check point, select $(0, 0)$.

$2x + y < 4$

$2(0) + 0 < 4 \leftarrow$ Substitute 0 for x and y

$0 < 4$

Since this is a true statement, shade the region which contains the point $(0, 0)$.

26. $3x - 4y \leq 12$

Graph the line $3x - 4y = 12$ using a solid line.

For the check point, select $(0, 0)$.

$3x - 4y \leq 12$

$3(0) - 4(0) \leq 12 \leftarrow$ Substitute 0 for x and y

$0 \leq 12$

Since this is a true statement, shade the region which contains the point $(0, 0)$.

27. $10 \geq 5x - 2y$

Graph the line $10 = 5x - 2y$ using a solid line.

For the check point, select $(0, 0)$.

$10 \geq 5x - 2y$

$10 \geq 5(0) - 2(0)$ ← Substitute 0 for x and y

$10 \geq 0$

Since this is a true statement, shade the region which contains the point $(0, 0)$.

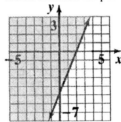

28. $-x - 2y > 4$

Graph the line $-x - 2y = 4$ using a dashed line. For the check point, select $(0, 0)$.

$-x - 2y > 4$

$-0 - 2(0) > 4$ ← Substitute 0 for x and y

$0 > 4$

Since this is a false statement, shade the region which does not contain the point $(0, 0)$.

29. $2x - y < 4$

$y \geq -x + 2$

For $2x - y < 4$, graph the line $2x - y = 4$ using a dashed line. For the check point, select $(0, 0)$:

$2x - y < 4$

$2(0) - (0) < 4$

$0 < 4$ True

Since this is a true statement, shade the region which contains the point $(0, 0)$. This is the region "above" the line.

For $y \geq -x + 2$, graph the line

$y = -x + 2$ using a solid line. For the check point, select $(0, 0)$:

$y \geq -x + 2$

$(0) \geq -(0) + 2$

$0 \geq 2$ False

Since this is a false statement, shade the region

which does not contain the point $(0, 0)$. This is the region "above" the line. To obtain the final region, take the intersection of the above two regions.

30. $y \leq -2x + 1$

$y > -3x$

For $y \leq -2x + 1$, graph the line

$y = -2x + 1$ using a solid line. For the check point, select $(0, 0)$:

$(0) \leq -2(0) + 1$

$0 \leq 1$ True

Since this is a true statement, shade the region which contains the point $(0, 0)$. This is the region "below" the line.

For $y > -3x$, graph the line $y = -3x$ using a dashed line. For the check point, select $(1, 1)$. Note that the point $(0,0)$ is on the line and therefore cannot be used as a check point.

$y > -3x$

$(1) > -3(1)$

$1 > -3$ True

Since this is a true statement, shade the region which contains the point $(1, 1)$. This is the region "above" the line. To obtain the final region, take the intersection of the above two regions.

31. $y < 3x - 2$

$y \leq -2x + 3$

For $y < 3x - 2$, graph the line $y = 3x - 2$ using a dashed line. For the check point, select (0, 0):

$y < 3x - 2$

$(0) < 3(0) - 2$

$0 < -2$ False

Since this is a false statement, shade the region which does not contain the point (0, 0). This is the region "below" the line.

For $y \leq -2x + 3$, graph the line $y = -2x + 3$ using a solid line. For the check point, use (0, 0):

$y \leq -2x + 3$

$(0) \leq -2(0) + 3$

$0 \leq 3$ True

Since this is a true statement, shade the region which contains the point (0, 0). This is the region "below" the line. To obtain the final region, take the intersection of the above two regions.

32. $y \geq 2x - 5$

$y > -3x + 5$

For $y \geq 2x - 5$, graph the line $y = 2x - 5$ using a solid line. For the check point, select (0, 0):

$y \geq 2x - 5$

$(0) \geq 2(0) - 5$

$0 \geq -5$ True

Since this is a true statement, shade the region which contains the point (0, 0). This is the region "above" the line.

For $y > -3x + 5$, graph the line $y = -3x + 5$ using a dashed line. For the check point, select (0, 0):

$y > -3x + 5$

$(0) > -3(0) + 5$

$0 > 5$ False

Since this is a false statement, shade the region which does not contain the point (0, 0). This is the region "above" the line. To obtain the final region, take the intersection of the above two

regions.

33. $y < x$

$y \geq 3x + 2$

For $y < x$, graph the line $y = x$ using a dashed line. For the check point, select (1, 0):

$y < x$

$0 < 1$ True

Since this is a true statement, shade the region which contains the point (1, 0). This is the region "below" the line.

For $y \geq 3x + 2$, graph the line $y = 3x + 2$ using a solid line. For the check point, select (0, 0):

$y \geq 3x + 2$

$(0) \geq 3(0) + 2$

$0 \geq 2$ False

Since this is a false statement, shade the region which does not contain the point (0, 0). This is the region "above" the line. To obtain the final region, take the intersection of the above two regions.

34. $-3x + 2y \geq -5$

$y \leq -4x + 7$

For $-3x + 2y \geq -5$, graph the line $-3x + 2y = -5$ using a solid line. For the check point, select (0, 0):

$-3x + 2y \geq -5$

$-3(0) + 2(0) \geq -5$

$0 \geq -5$ True

Since this is a true statement, shade the region which contains the point (0, 0). This is the region "above" the line.

For $y \leq -4x + 7$, graph the line $y = -4x + 7$ using a solid line. For the check point, select (0, 0):

$y \leq -4x + 7$

$(0) \leq -4(0) + 7$

$0 \leq 7$ True

Since this is a true statement, shade the region which contains the point (0, 0). This is the region "below" the line. To obtain the final region, take the intersection of the above two regions.

35. $-2x + 3y < -5$

$3x - 8y > 4$

For $-2x + 3y < -5$, graph the line $-2x + 3y = -5$ using a dashed line. For the check point, select (0, 0):

$-2x + 3y < -5$

$-2(0) + 3(0) < -5$

$0 < -5$ False

Since this is a false statement, shade the region which does not contain the point (0, 0). This is the region "below" the line.

For $3x - 8y > 4$, graph the line $3x - 8y = 4$ using a dashed line. For the check point, select (0, 0):

$3x - 8y > 4$

$3(0) - 8(0) > 4$

$0 > 4$ False

Since this is a false statement, shade the region which does not contain the point (0, 0). This is the region "below" the line. To obtain the final

region, take the intersection of the above two regions.

36. $-4x + 3y \geq -4$

$y > -3x + 3$

For $-4x + 3y \geq -4$, graph the line $-4x + 3y = -4$ using a solid line. For the check point, select (0, 0):

$-4x + 3y \geq -4$

$-4(0) + 3(0) \geq -4$

$0 \geq -4$ True

Since this is a true statement, shade the region which contains the point (0, 0). This is the region "above" the line.

For $y > -3x + 3$, graph the line $y = -3x + 3$ using a dashed line. For the check point, select (0, 0):

$y > -3x + 3$

$(0) > -3(0) + 3$

$0 > 3$ False

Since this is a false statement, shade the region which does not contain the point (0, 0). This is the region "above" the line. To obtain the final region, take the intersection of the above two regions.

37. $-4x + 5y < 20$

$x \geq -3$

For $-4x + 5y < 20$, graph the line $-4x + 5y = 20$ using a dashed line. For the check point, select $(0, 0)$:

$-4x + 5y < 20$

$-4(0) + 5(0) < 20$

$0 < 20$ True

Since this is a true statement, shade the region which contains the point $(0, 0)$. This is the region "below" the line.

For $x \geq -3$, the graph is the line $x = -3$ along with the region to the right of $x = -3$. To obtain the final region, take the intersection of the above two regions.

38. $y \geq -\dfrac{2}{3}x + 1$

$y > -4$

For $y \geq -\dfrac{2}{3}x + 1$, graph the line $y = -\dfrac{2}{3}x + 1$ using a solid line. For the check point, select $(0, 0)$:

$y \geq -\dfrac{2}{3}x + 1$

$(0) \geq -\dfrac{2}{3}(0) + 1$

$0 \geq 1$ False

Since this is a false statement, shade the region which does not contain the point $(0, 0)$. This is the region "above" the line.

For $y > -4$, graph the line $y = -4$ using a dashed line. For the check point, select $(0, 0)$:

$y > -4$

$(0) > -4$

$0 > -4$ True

Since this is a true statement, shade the region which contains the point $(0, 0)$. This is the region "above" the line. To obtain the final region, take

the intersection of the above two regions.

39. $x \leq 4$

$y \geq -2$

For $x \leq 4$, the graph is the line $x = 4$ along with the region to the left of $x = 4$.

For $y \geq -2$, the graph is the line $y = -2$ along with the region above the line $y = -2$. To obtain the final region, take the intersection of the above two regions.

40. $x \geq 0$

$x - 3y < 6$

For $x \geq 0$, shade the region to the right of the solid line $x = 0$. For $x - 3y < 6$, graph the line $x - 3y = 6$ using a dashed line. For the check point, select $(0, 0)$:

$x - 3y < 6$

$0 - 3(0) < 6$

$0 < 6$ True

Since this is a true statement, shade the region which contains the point $(0, 0)$. This is the region "above" the line. To obtain the final region, take the intersection of the above two regions.

41. $5x + 2y > 10$

$3x - y > 3$

For $5x + 2y > 10$, graph the line $5x + 2y = 10$ using a dashed line. For the check point, select $(0, 0)$:

$5x + 2y > 10$

$5(0) + 2(0) > 10$

$\qquad 0 > 10 \qquad$ False

Since this is a false statement, shade the region which does not contain the point $(0, 0)$. This is the region "above" the line.

For $3x - y > 3$, graph the line $3x - y = 3$ using a dashed line. For the check point, select $(0, 0)$:

$3x - y > 3$

$3(0) - 0 > 3$

$\qquad 0 > 3 \qquad$ False

Since this is a false statement, shade the region which does not contain the point $(0, 0)$. This is the region "below" the line. To obtain the final region, take the intersection of the above two regions.

42. $3x + 2y > 8$

$x - 5y < 5$

For $3x + 2y > 8$, graph the line $3x + 2y = 8$ using a dashed line. For the check point, select $(0, 0)$:

$3x + 2y > 8$

$3(0) + 2(0) > 8$

$\qquad 0 > 8 \qquad$ False

Since this is a false statement, shade the region which does not contain the point $(0, 0)$. This is the region "above" the line.

For $x - 5y < 5$, graph the line $x - 5y = 5$ using a dashed line. For the check point, select $(0, 0)$:

$x - 5y < 5$

$0 - 5(0) < 5$

$\qquad 0 < 5 \qquad$ True

Since this is a true statement, shade the region which contains the point $(0, 0)$. This is the region "above" the line. To obtain the final region, take

the intersection of the above two regions.

43. $-2x > y + 4$

$-x < \dfrac{1}{2}y - 1$

For $-2x > y + 4$, graph the line $-2x = y + 4$ using a dashed line. For the check point, select $(0, 0)$:

$-2x > y + 4$

$-2(0) > 0 + 4$

$\qquad 0 > 4 \qquad$ False

Since this is a false statement, shade the region which does not contain the point $(0, 0)$. This is the region "below" the line.

For $-x < \dfrac{1}{2}y - 1$, graph the line $-x = \dfrac{1}{2}y - 1$ using a dashed line. For the check point, select $(0, 0)$:

$-x < \dfrac{1}{2}y - 1$

$-0 < \dfrac{1}{2}(0) - 1$

$\qquad 0 < -1 \qquad$ False

Since this is a false statement, shade the region which does not contain the point $(0, 0)$. This is the region "above" the line. To obtain the final region take the intersection of the above two regions. Since the regions do not overlap, the final result is the empty set which means there is no solution.

44. $y \leq 3x - 2$

$\dfrac{1}{3} y < x + 1$

For $y \leq 3x - 2$, graph the line $y = 3x - 2$ using a solid line. For the check point, select (0, 0):

$y \leq 3x - 2$

$0 \leq 3(0) - 2$

$0 \leq -2$ False

Since this is a false statement, shade the region which does not contain the point (0, 0). This is the region "below" the line.

For $\dfrac{1}{3} y < x + 1$, graph the line $\dfrac{1}{3} y = x + 1$ using a dashed line. For the check point, select (0, 0):

$\dfrac{1}{3} y < x + 1$

$\dfrac{1}{3}(0) < 0 + 1$

$0 < 1$ True

Since this is a true statement, shade the region which contains the point (0, 0). This is the region "below" the line. To obtain the final region, take the intersection of the above two regions.

45. $y < 3x - 4$

$6x \geq 2y + 8$

Solve the second inequality for y.

$6x \geq 2y + 8$

$6x - 2y > 8$

$-2y \geq -6x + 8$

$y \leq 3x - 4$

The second inequality is now identical to the first except that the second inequality includes the line $y = 3x - 4$.

For $y < 3x - 4$, graph the line $y = 3x - 4$ using a dashed line. For the check point, select (0, 0):

$y < 3x - 4$

$0 < 3(0) - 4$

$0 < -4$ False

Since this is a false statement, shade the region which does not contain the point (0, 0). This is

the region "below" the line.

46. $\dfrac{1}{2} x + \dfrac{1}{2} y \geq 2$

$2x - 3y \leq -6$

For $\dfrac{1}{2} x + \dfrac{1}{2} y \geq 2$, graph the line $\dfrac{1}{2} x + \dfrac{1}{2} y = 2$ using a solid line.

For the check point, select (0, 0):

$\dfrac{1}{2} x + \dfrac{1}{2} y \geq 2$

$\dfrac{1}{2}(0) + \dfrac{1}{2}(0) \geq 2$

$0 \geq 2$ False

Since this is a false statement, shade the region which does not contain the point (0, 0). This is the region "above" the line.

For $2x - 3y \leq -6$ graph the line $2x - 3y = -6$ using a solid line. For the check point, select (0, 0):

$2x - 3y \leq -6$

$2(0) - 3(0) \leq -6$

$0 \leq -6$ False

Since this is a false statement, shade the region which does not contain the point (0, 0). This is the region "above" the line. To obtain the final region, take the intersection of the above two regions.

47. $x \geq 0$

$y \geq 0$

$2x + 3y \leq 6$

$4x + y \leq 4$

The first two inequalities indicate that the region must be in the first quadrant. For $2x + 3y \leq 6$, the graph is the line $2x + 3y = 6$ along with the region below this line. For $4x + y \leq 4$, the graph is the line $4x + y = 4$ along with the region below this line. To obtain the final region, take the intersection of these regions.

48. $x \geq 0$

$y \geq 0$

$x + y \leq 6$

$7x + 4y \leq 28$

The first two inequalities indicate that the region must be in the first quadrant. For $x + y \leq 6$, the graph is the line $x + y = 6$ along with the region below this line. For $7x + 4y \leq 28$, the graph is the line $7x + 4y = 28$ along with the region below the line. To obtain the final region, take the intersection of these regions.

49. $x \geq 0$

$y \geq 0$

$2x + 3y \leq 8$

$4x + 2y \leq 8$

The first two inequalities indicate that the region must be in the first quadrant. For $2x + 3y \leq 8$, the graph is the line $2x + 3y = 8$ along with the region below this line. For $4x + 2y \leq 8$, the graph is the line $4x + 2y = 8$ along with the region below this line. To obtain the final region, take the intersection of these regions.

50. $x \geq 0$

$y \geq 0$

$3x + 2y \leq 18$

$2x + 4y \leq 20$

The first two inequalities indicate that the region must be in the first quadrant.
For $3x + 2y \leq 18$, the graph is the line $3x + 2y = 18$ along with the region below this line. For $2x + 4y \leq 20$, the graph is the line $2x + 4y = 20$ along with the region below the line. To obtain the final region, take the intersection of these regions. The final answer is

51. $x \geq 0$

$y \geq 0$

$3x + y \leq 9$

$2x + 5y \leq 10$

The first two inequalities indicate that the region must be in the first quadrant. For $3x + y \leq 9$, the graph is the line $3x + y = 9$ along with the region below this line. For $2x + 5y \leq 10$, the graph is the line $2x + 5y = 10$ along with the region below this line. To obtain the final region, take the intersection of these regions.

52. $x \geq 0$

$y \geq 0$

$5x + 4y \leq 16$

$x + 6y \leq 18$

he first two inequalities indicate that the region must be in the first quadrant. For $5x + 4y \leq 16$, the graph is the line $5x + 4y = 16$ along with the region below this line. For $x + 6y \leq 18$, the graph is the line $x + 6y = 18$ along with the region below this line. To obtain the final region, take the intersection of these regions.

53. $x \geq 0$

$y \geq 0$

$x \leq 4$

$x + y \leq 6$

$x + 2y \leq 8$

The first two inequalities indicate that the region must be in the first quadrant. The third inequality indicates that the region must be on or to the left of the line $x = 4$. For $x + y \leq 6$, the graph is the line $x + y = 6$ along with the region below this line. For $x + 2y \leq 8$, the graph is the line $x + 2y = 8$ along with the region below the line. To obtain the final region, take the intersection of these regions.

54. $x \geq 0$

$y \geq 0$

$x \leq 4$

$2x + 3y \leq 18$

$4x + 2y \leq 20$

The first two inequalities indicate that the region must be in the first quadrant. The third inequality indicates that the region must be on or to the left of the line $x = 4$. For $2x + 3y \leq 18$, the graph is the line $2x + 3y = 18$ along with the region below this line. For $4x + 2y \leq 20$, the graph is the line $4x + 2y = 20$ along with the region below the line. To obtain the final region, take the intersection of these regions.

55. $x \geq 0$

$y \geq 0$

$x \leq 15$

$30x + 25y \leq 750$

$10x + 40y \leq 800$

The first two inequalities indicate that the region must be in the first quadrant. The third inequality indicates that the region must be on or to the left of the line $x = 15$. For $30x + 25y \leq 750$ the graph is the line $30x + 25y = 750$ along with the region below this line. For $10x + 40y \leq 800$, the graph is the line $10x + 40y = 800$ along with the region below the line. To obtain the final region, take the intersection of these regions.

56. $x \geq 0$

$y \geq 0$

$x \leq 15$

$40x + 25y \leq 1000$

$5x + 30y \leq 900$

The first two inequalities indicate that the region must be in the first quadrant. The third inequality indicates that the region must be on or to the left of the line $x = 15$. For $40x + 25y \leq 1000$, the graph is the line $40x + 25y = 1000$ along with the region below this line. For $5x + 30y \leq 900$, the graph is the line $5x + 30y = 900$ along with the region below this line. To obtain the final region, take the intersection of these regions.

57. $|x| < 2$

For $|x| < 2$, the graph is the region between the dashed lines $x = -2$ and $x = 2$.

58. $|x| > 1$

For $|x| > 1$, the graph is the region to the right of the dashed line $x = 1$ and to the left of the dashed line $x = -1$.

59. $|y - 2| \leq 4$

$-4 \leq y - 2 \leq 4$

$-2 \leq y \leq 6$

For $|y - 2| \leq 4$, the graph is the solid lines $y = -2$ and $y = 6$ along with the region between these lines.

60. $|y| \geq 2$

For $|y| \geq 2$, the graph is the solid line $y = 2$ and the region above this line, along with the solid line $y = -2$ and the region below this line.

61. $|y| > 2$

$y \leq x + 3$

For $|y| > 2$, the graph is the region above the dashed line $y = 2$ along with the region below the dashed line $y = -2$. For $y \leq x + 3$, the graph is the region below the solid line $y = x + 3$. To obtain the final region, take the intersection of these regions.

62. $|x| > 1$

$y \leq 3x + 2$

For $|x| > 1$, the graph is the region to the left of the dashed line $x = -1$ along with the region to the right of the dashed line $x = 1$. For $y < 3x + 2$, the graph is the region below the solid line $y = 3x + 2$. To obtain the final region, take the intersection of these regions.

63. $|y| < 4$

$y \geq -2x + 2$

For $|y| < 4$, the graph is the region between the dashed lines $y = -4$ and $y = 4$. For $y \geq -2x + 2$, the graph is the region above the solid line $y = -2x + 2$. To obtain the final region, take the intersection of these regions.

64. $|x - 2| \leq 3$

$x - y > 2$

$|x - 2| \leq 3$ can be written as

$-3 \leq x - 2 \leq 3$

$-1 \leq x \leq 5$

For $|x - 2| \leq 3$, the graph is the region between the solid lines $x = -1$ and $x = 5$. For $x - y > 2$, the graph is the region below the dashed line $x - y = 2$. To obtain the final region, take the intersection of these regions.

65. $|x+2| < 3$

$\quad |y| > 4$

$|x+2| < 3$ can be written as

$-3 < x+2 < 3$

$-5 < x < 1$

For $|x+2| < 3$, the graph is the region between the dashed lines $x = -5$ and $x = 1$. For $|y| > 4$, the graph is the region above the dashed line $y = 4$ along with the region below the dashed line $y = -4$. To obtain the final region, take the intersection of these regions.

66. $|x-2| > 1$

$\quad y > -2$

$|x-2| > 1$ can be written as

$x-2 < -1$ or $x-2 > 1$

$\quad x < 1 \qquad\quad x > 3$

For $|x-2| > 1$, the graph is the region to the left of the dashed line $x = 1$ along with the region to the right of the dashed line $x = 3$. For $y > -2$, the graph is the region above the dashed line $y = -2$. To obtain the final region, take the intersection of these regions.

67. $|x-3| \le 4$

$\quad |y+2| \le 1$

$|x-3| \le 4$ can be written as

$-4 \le x-3 \le 4$

$-1 \le x \le 7$

For $|x-3| \le 4$, the graph is the region between the solid lines $x = -1$ and $x = 7$.

$|y+2| \le 1$ can be written as

$-1 \le y+2 \le 1$

$-3 \le y \le -1$

For $|y+2| \le 1$, the graph is the region between the solid lines $y = -3$ and $y = -1$. To obtain the final region, take the intersection of these regions.

68. $|x+1| \le 2$

$\quad |y-3| \le 1$

$|x+1| \le 2$ can be written as

$-2 \le x+1 \le 2$

$-3 \le x \le 1$

For $|x+1| \le 2$, the graph is the region between the solid lines $x = -3$ and $x = 1$.

$|y-3| \le 1$ can be written as

$-1 \le y-3 \le 1$

$2 \le y \le 4$

For $|y-3| \le 1$, the graph is the region between the solid lines $y = 2$ and $y = 4$. To obtain the final region, take the intersection of these regions.

69. a,b.

  c.   The age at which the rate first exceeds $15 per month is 47.

70. a,b.

  c.   The year 2000 is the first year in which the CPI was greater than or equal to 171.

71. a,b.

  c.   The year 2003 is first year in which the percentage of Americans 18 and older who smoke was less than or equal to 23%.

72. a,b.

  c.   The year 2000 is the first year in which the number of Chinese travelers was greater than or equal to 12 million.

73. a.   Region A; we are looking for the region that lies below the graph for the paper returns and above the graph for the electronic returns.

    b.   Region B; we are looking for the region that lies above the graph for the paper returns and below the graph for the electronic returns.

74. a.   Region B; we are looking for the region that lies above the graph for May Department Stores and below the graph for Federated Department Stores.

    b.   Region A; we are looking for the region that lies below the graph for May Department Stores and above the graph for Federated Department Stores.

75. a.

    b.

76. a.

    b.

77. Yes; if the boundary lines are parallel, there may be no solution. For example, the system $y < x$ and $y > x + 1$ has no solution.

78. No; answers will vary. The solution of each inequality is a half-plane. It is not possible for two half-planes to intersect at a single point.

79. There are no solutions. Opposite sides of the same line are being shaded and only one inequality includes the line.

80. There are no solutions. Opposite sides of the same line are being shaded, but not the line itself.

81. There are an infinite number of solutions. Both inequalities include the line $5x - 2y = 3$.

82. There are an infinite number of solutions. The lines are parallel but the same side of each line is being shaded.

83. There are an infinite number of solutions. The lines are not parallel or identical.

84. There are an infinite number of solutions. The lines are not parallel or identical.

85. $y \geq x^2$

    $y \leq 4$

    For $y \geq x^2$, graph the equation $y = x^2$ using a solid line. For the check point, select $(0, 1)$.

    $y \geq x^2$

    $(1) \geq (0)^2$

    $1 \geq 0$ True

    Since this is a true statement, shade the region which contains the point $(0, 1)$. This is the region "above" the graph of $y \geq x^2$.

    For $y \leq 4$, the graph is the region below the solid line $y = 4$. To obtain the final region, take the intersection of these regions.

86. $y < 4 - x^2$

    $y > -5$

    For $y < 4 - x^2$, graph the equation $y = 4 - x^2$ using a dashed line. For the check point, select $(0, 0)$.

    $y < 4 - x^2$

    $(0) < 4 - (0)^2$

    $0 < 4$ True

    Since this is a true statement, shade the region which contains the point $(0, 0)$. This is the region "below" the graph of $y = 4 - x^2$.

    For $y > -5$, the graph is the region above the dashed line $y = -5$. To obtain the final region, take the intersection of these regions.

87. $y < |x|$

    $y < 4$

    For $y < |x|$, graph the equation $y = |x|$ using a dashed line. For the check point, select $(0, 3)$.

    $y < |x|$

    $3 < |0|$

    $3 < 0$ False

    Since this is a false statement, shade the region which does not contain the point $(0, 3)$. This is the region below the graph of $y = |x|$.

    For $y < 4$, the graph is the region below the dashed line $y = 4$. To obtain the final region, take the intersection of these regions.

88. $y \geq |x-2|$

$y \leq -|x-2|$

For $y \geq |x-2|$, graph the equation $y = |x-2|$ using a solid line. For the check point, select (0, 0):

$y \geq |x-2|$

$0 \geq |0-2|$

$0 \geq 2$ False

Since this is a false statement, shade the region which does not contain the point (0, 0). This is the region above the "V."

For $y \leq -|x-2|$, graph the equation $y = -|x-2|$ using a solid line. For the check point, select (0, 0):

$y \leq -|x-2|$

$0 \leq -|0-2|$

$0 \leq -2$ False

Since this is a false statement, shade the region which does not contain the point (0, 0). This is the region below the "V". To obtain the final region, take the intersection of these regions. In this case, the intersection is only the point (2, 0).

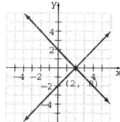

89.
$$f_1 d_1 + f_2 d_2 = f_3 d_3$$
$$f_1 d_1 - f_1 d_1 + f_2 d_2 = f_3 d_3 - f_1 d_1$$
$$f_2 d_2 = f_3 d_3 - f_1 d_1$$
$$\frac{f_2 d_2}{d_2} = \frac{f_3 d_3 - f_1 d_1}{d_2}$$
$$f_2 = \frac{f_3 d_3 - f_1 d_1}{d_2}$$

90. Domain: $\{-1, 0, 4, 5\}$
Range: $\{-5, -2, 2, 3\}$

91. Domain: $\mathbb{R}$
Range: $\mathbb{R}$

92. Domain: $\mathbb{R}$
Range: $\{y \mid y \geq -1\}$

Chapter 10 Review Exercises

1. $3z + 9 \leq 15$

$3z \leq 6$

$z \leq 2$

2. $8 - 2w > -4$

$-2w > -12$

$\dfrac{-2w}{-2} < \dfrac{-12}{-2}$

$w < 6$

3. $2x + 1 > 6$

$2x > 5$

$x > \dfrac{5}{2}$

4. $26 \leq 4x + 5$

$21 \leq 4x$

$\dfrac{21}{4} \leq x$

5. $\dfrac{4x+3}{3} > -5$

$3\left(\dfrac{4x+3}{3}\right) > 3(-5)$

$4x + 3 > -15$

$4x > -18$

$x > \dfrac{-18}{4}$

$x > -\dfrac{9}{2}$

6. $2(x-1) > 3x + 8$

$2x - 2 > 3x + 8$

$2x - 10 > 3x$

$-10 > x$

600

7. $-4(x-2) \geq 6x+8-10x$

$\quad -4x+8 \geq -4x+8$

$\qquad 8 \geq 8 \quad$ a true statement

The solution is all real numbers.

0

8. $\dfrac{x}{2}+\dfrac{3}{4} > x-\dfrac{x}{2}+1$

$4\left(\dfrac{x}{2}+\dfrac{3}{4}\right) > 4\left(x-\dfrac{x}{2}+1\right)$

$\quad 2x+3 > 4x-2x+4$

$\quad 2x+3 > 2x+4$

$\qquad 3 > 4$

This is a contradiction, so the solution is { }.

0

9. Let x be the maximum number of 40-pound boxes. Since the maximum load is 560 pounds, the total weight of Bob, Kathie, and the boxes must be less than or equal to 560 pounds.

$300+40x \leq 560$

$\quad 40x \leq 260$

$\qquad x \leq \dfrac{260}{40}$

$\qquad x \leq 6.5$

The maximum number of boxes that they can carry in the canoe is 6.

10. Let x be the number of additional minutes (beyond 3 minutes) of the phone call.

$4.50+0.95x \leq 8.65$

$\quad 0.95x \leq 4.15$

$\qquad x \leq \dfrac{4.15}{0.95}$

$\qquad x \leq 4.4$

The customer can talk for 3 minutes plus an additional 4 minutes for a total of 7 minutes.

11. Let x be the number of weeks (after the first week) needed to lose 27 pounds.

$5+1.5x \geq 27$

$\quad 1.5x \geq 22$

$\qquad x \geq \dfrac{22}{1.5}$

$\qquad x \geq 14\dfrac{2}{3} \approx 14.67$

The number of weeks is about 14.67 plus the initial week for a total of 15.67 weeks.

12. Let x be the grade from the 5th exam. The inequality is

$80 \leq \dfrac{94+73+72+80+x}{5} < 90$

$80 \leq \dfrac{319+x}{5} < 90$

$5(80) \leq 5\left(\dfrac{319+x}{5}\right) < 5(90)$

$400 \leq 319+x < 450$

$400-319 \leq 319+x < 450-319$

$81 \leq x < 131$

(must use 100 here since it is not possible to score 131)

Thus, Patrice needs to score 81 or higher on the 5th exam to receive a B.

$\{x \mid 81 \leq x \leq 100\}$

13. $A \cup B = \{1,2,3,4,5\}$

$A \cap B = \{2,3,4,5,\}$

14. $A \cup B = \{2,3,4,5,6,7,8,9\}$

$A \cap B = \{\ \ \}$

15. $A \cup B = \{1,2,3,4,...\}$

$A \cap B = \{2,4,6,...\}$

16. $A \cup B = \{3,4,5,6,9,10,11,12\}$

$A \cap B = \{9,10\}$

17. $1 < x-4 < 7$

$1+4 < x-4+4 < 7+4$

$5 < x < 11$

$(5, 11)$

18. $\qquad 8 < p+11 \leq 16$

$\quad 8-11 < p+11-11 \leq 16-11$

$\qquad -3 < p \leq 5$

$\qquad \left(-3, 5\right]$

19. $3 < 2x - 4 < 12$

$3 + 4 < 2x - 4 + 4 < 12 + 4$

$7 < 2x < 16$

$\dfrac{7}{2} < \dfrac{2x}{2} < \dfrac{16}{2}$

$\dfrac{7}{2} < x < 8$

$\left(\dfrac{7}{2}, 8\right)$

20. $-12 < 6 - 3x < -2$

$-12 - 6 < 6 - 6 - 3x < -2 - 6$

$18 < -3x < -8$

$\dfrac{-18}{-3} > \dfrac{-3x}{-3} > \dfrac{-8}{-3}$

$6 > x > \dfrac{8}{3}$

$\dfrac{8}{3} < x < 6$

$\left(\dfrac{8}{3}, 6\right)$

21. $-1 < \dfrac{5}{9}x + \dfrac{2}{3} \le \dfrac{11}{9}$

$9(-1) < 9\left(\dfrac{5}{9}x + \dfrac{2}{3}\right) \le 9\left(\dfrac{11}{9}\right)$

$-9 < 5x + 6 \le 11$

$-9 - 6 < 5x + 6 - 6 \le 11 - 6$

$-15 < 5x \le 5$

$\dfrac{-15}{5} < \dfrac{5x}{5} \le \dfrac{5}{5}$

$-3 < x \le 1$

$\left(-3, 1\right]$

22. $-8 < \dfrac{4 - 2x}{3} < 0$

$3(-8) < 3\left(\dfrac{4 - 2x}{3}\right) < 3(0)$

$-24 < 4 - 2x < 0$

$-24 - 4 < 4 - 4 - 2x < 0 - 4$

$-28 < -2x < -4$

$\dfrac{-28}{-2} > \dfrac{-2x}{-2} > \dfrac{-4}{-2}$

$14 > x > 2$

$2 < x < 14$

$(2, 14)$

23. $h \le 1$ and $7h - 4 > -25$

$\quad h \le 1$ and $\quad 7h > -21$

$\quad h \le 1$ and $\quad\quad h > -3$

$\quad h \le 1$

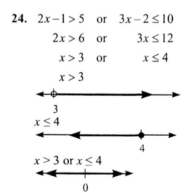

$h > -3$

$x \le 1$ and $x > -3$ which is $-3 < h \le 1$.

The solution set is $\left\{ h \mid -3 < h \le 1 \right\}$.

24. $2x - 1 > 5$ or $3x - 2 \le 10$

$\quad 2x > 6$ or $\quad 3x \le 12$

$\quad\quad x > 3$ or $\quad\quad x \le 4$

$\quad\quad x > 3$

$x \le 4$

$x > 3$ or $x \le 4$

which is the entire real number line or $\mathbb{R}$.

25. $4x - 5 < 11$ and $-3x - 4 \geq 8$

$\quad\quad 4x < 16$ and $\quad -3x \geq 12$

$\quad\quad\quad x < 4$ and $\quad\quad x \leq -4$

$x \leq 4$

$x \leq -4$

$x \leq -4$ and $x < 4$ which is $x \leq -4$

$\{x \mid x \leq -4\}$

26. $\dfrac{7-2g}{3} \leq -5$ or $\dfrac{3-g}{9} > 1$

$\quad 7 - 2g \leq -15$ or $\quad 3 - g > 9$

$\quad\quad -2g \leq -22$ or $\quad\quad -g > 6$

$\quad\quad\quad g \geq 11$ or $\quad\quad\quad g < -6$

$g < -6$

$g \geq 11$

$g < -6$ or $g \geq 11$

$\left\{ g \mid g < -6 \text{ or } g \geq 11 \right\}$

27. $|a| = 2$

$a = 2$ or $a = -2$

The solution set is $\{-2, 2\}$.

28. $|x| < 8$

$-8 < x < 8$

The solution set is $\{x \mid -8 < x < 8\}$.

29. $|x| \geq 9$

$x \leq -9$ or $x \geq 9$

The solution set is $\{x \mid x \leq -9 \text{ or } x \geq 9\}$.

30. $|l + 5| = 13$

$l + 5 = -13$ or $l + 5 = 13$

$\quad\quad l = -18$ or $\quad\quad l = 8$

The solution set is $\{-18, 8\}$.

31. $|x - 2| \geq 5$

$x - 2 \leq -5$ or $x - 2 \geq 5$

$\quad\quad x \leq -3$ or $\quad\quad x \geq 7$

The solution set is $\{x \mid x \leq -3 \text{ or } x \geq 7\}$.

32. $|4 - 2x| = 5$

$4 - 2x = 5$ or $4 - 2x = -5$

$\quad -2x = 1$ or $\quad -2x = -9$

$\quad\quad x = \dfrac{1}{-2}$ or $\quad x = \dfrac{-9}{-2}$

$\quad\quad x = -\dfrac{1}{2}$ or $\quad x = \dfrac{9}{2}$

The solution set is $\left\{ -\dfrac{1}{2}, \dfrac{9}{2} \right\}$.

33. $|-2q + 9| < 7$

$-7 < -2q + 9 < 7$

$-7 - 9 < -2q + 9 - 9 < 7 - 9$

$-16 < -2q < -2$

$\dfrac{-16}{-2} > \dfrac{-2q}{-2} > \dfrac{-2}{-2}$

$8 > q > 1$

$1 < q < 8$

The solution set is $\left\{ q \mid 1 < q < 8 \right\}$.

34. $\left| \dfrac{2x - 3}{5} \right| = 1$

$\dfrac{2x - 3}{5} = 1$ or $\dfrac{2x - 3}{5} = -1$

$2x - 3 = 5$ $\quad\quad 2x - 3 = -5$

$\quad 2x = 8$ $\quad\quad\quad 2x = -2$

$\quad\quad x = 4$ $\quad\quad\quad\quad x = -1$

The solution set is $\{-1, 4\}$.

35. $\left| \dfrac{x - 4}{3} \right| < 6$

$-6 < \dfrac{x - 4}{3} < 6$

$3(-6) < 3\left(\dfrac{x - 4}{3} \right) < 3(6)$

$-18 < x - 4 < 18$

$-14 < x < 22$

The solution set is $\{x \mid -14 < x < 22\}$.

36. $|4d - 1| = |6d + 9|$

$4d - 1 = -(6d + 9)$ or $4d - 1 = 6d + 9$

$4d - 1 = -6d - 9$ .... $4d - 10 = 6d$

$10d - 1 = -9$ .... $-10 = 2d$

$10d = -8$ .... $-5 = d$

$d = -\dfrac{4}{5}$

The solution set is $\left\{-5, -\dfrac{4}{5}\right\}$.

37. $|2x - 3| + 4 \ge -17$

$|2x - 3| \ge -21$

Since the right side is negative and the left side is non-negative, the solution is the entire real number line since the absolute value of a number is always greater than a negative number. The solution set is all real numbers, or $\mathbb{R}$.

38. $|3c + 8| - 6 \le 1$

$|3c + 8| \le 7$

$-7 \le 3c + 8 \le 7$

$-7 - 8 \le 3c + 8 - 8 \le 7 - 8$

$-15 \le 3c \le -1$

$\dfrac{-15}{3} \le \dfrac{3c}{3} \le \dfrac{-1}{3}$

$-5 \le c \le -\dfrac{1}{3}$

$\left[-5, -\dfrac{1}{3}\right]$

39. $3 < 2x - 5 \le 11$

$3 + 5 < 2x - 5 + 5 \le 11 + 5$

$8 < 2x \le 16$

$\dfrac{8}{2} < \dfrac{2x}{2} \le \dfrac{16}{2}$

$4 < x \le 8$

The solution is (4, 8].

40. $-6 \le \dfrac{3 - 2x}{4} < 5$

$4(-6) \le 4\left(\dfrac{3 - 2x}{4}\right) < 4(5)$

$-24 \le 3 - 2x < 20$

$-27 \le -2x < 17$

$\dfrac{-27}{-2} \ge \dfrac{-2x}{-2} > \dfrac{17}{-2}$

$\dfrac{27}{2} \ge x > -\dfrac{17}{2}$

$-\dfrac{17}{2} < x \le \dfrac{27}{2}$

The solution is $\left(-\dfrac{17}{2}, \dfrac{27}{2}\right]$.

41. $2p - 5 < 7$ or $9 - 3p \le 15$

$2p < 12$ or $-3p \le 6$

$p < 6$ or $p \ge -2$

$-2 \le p < 6$

The solution is $\left[-2, 6\right)$.

42. $x - 3 \le 4$ or $2x - 5 > 7$

$x - 3 + 3 \le 4 + 3$ .... $2x - 5 + 5 > 7 + 5$

$x \le 7$ .... $2x > 12$

.... $x > 6$

The solution is $(-\infty, \infty)$.

43. $-10 < 3(x - 4) \le 18$

$-10 < 3x - 12 \le 18$

$-10 + 12 < 3x - 12 + 12 \le 18 + 12$

$2 < 3x \le 30$

$\dfrac{2}{3} < x \le 10$

The solution is $\left(\dfrac{2}{3}, 10\right]$.

44. $y \ge -5$

Graph the line $y = -5$ using a solid line. For the check point, select $(0, 0)$.

$y \ge -5$

$0 \ge -5$ ← Substitute 0 for y

Since this is a true statement, shade the region which contains $(0, 0)$.

45. $x < 4$

Graph the line $x = 4$ using a dashed line. For the check point, select $(0, 0)$.

$x < 4$

$0 < 4$ ← Substitute 0 for x

Since this is a true statement, shade the region which contains $(0, 0)$.

46. $y \le 4x - 3$

Graph the line $y = 4x - 3$ using a solid line. For the check point, select $(0, 0)$.

$y \le 4x - 3$

$0 \le 4(0) - 3$ ← Substitute 0 for x and y

$0 \le -3$

Since this is a false statement, shade the region which does not contain $(0, 0)$.

47. $y < \dfrac{1}{3}x - 2$

Graph the line $y = \dfrac{1}{3}x - 2$ using a dashed line.

For the check point, select $(0, 0)$.

$y < \dfrac{1}{3}x - 2$

$0 < \dfrac{1}{3}(0) - 2$ ← Substitute 0 for x and y

$0 < -2$

Since this is a false statement, shade the region which does not contain $(0, 0)$.

48. $-x + 3y > 6$

$2x - y \le 2$

For $-x + 3y > 6$, graph the line $-x + 3y = 6$ using a dashed line. For the check point, select $(0, 0)$:

$-x + 3y > 6$

$-0 + 3(0) > 6$

$0 > 6$ False

Since this is a false statement, shade the region which does not contain the point $(0, 0)$.

For $2x - y \le 2$, graph the line $2x - y = 2$ using a solid line. For the check point, select $(0, 0)$:

$2x - y \le 2$

$2(0) - 0 \le 2$

$0 \le 2$ True

Since this is a true statement, shade the region which contains the point $(0, 0)$.

To obtain the final region, take the intersection of the above two regions.

49. $5x - 2y \leq 10$

$3x + 2y > 6$

For $5x - 2y \leq 10$, graph the line $5x - 2y = 10$ using a solid line.

For the check point, select $(0, 0)$:

$5x - 2y \leq 10$

$5(0) - 2(0) \leq 10$

$0 \leq 10$ True

Since this is a true statement, shade the region which contains the point $(0, 0)$.

For $3x + 2y > 6$, graph the line $3x + 2y = 6$ using a dashed line. For the check point, select $(0, 0)$:

$3x + 2y > 6$

$3(0) + 2(0) > 6$

$0 > 6$ False

Since this is a false statement, shade the region which does not contain the point $(0, 0)$. To obtain the final region, take the intersection of the above two regions.

50. $y > 2x + 3$

$y < -x + 4$

For $y > 2x + 3$, graph the line $y = 2x + 3$ using a dashed line. For the check point, select $(0, 0)$:

$y > 2x + 3$

$0 > 2(0) + 3$

$0 > 3$ False

Since this is a false statement, shade the region which does not contain the point $(0, 0)$.

For $y < -x + 4$, graph the line $y = -x + 4$ using a dashed line. For the check point, select $(0, 0)$:

$y < -x + 4$

$0 < -0 + 4$

$0 < 4$ True

Since this is a true statement, shade the region which contains the point $(0, 0)$. To obtain the final region, take the intersection of the above

two regions.

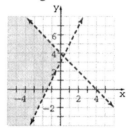

51. $x > -2y + 4$

$y < -\dfrac{1}{2}x - \dfrac{3}{2}$

For $x > -2y + 4$, graph the line $x = -2y + 4$ using a dashed line. For the check point, select $(0, 0)$:

$x > -2y + 4$

$0 > -2(0) + 4$

$0 > 4$ False

Since this is a false statement, shade the region which does not contain the point $(0, 0)$.

For $y < -\dfrac{1}{2}x - \dfrac{3}{2}$, graph the line $y = -\dfrac{1}{2}x - \dfrac{3}{2}$ using a dashed line. For the check point, select $(0, 0)$:

$y < -\dfrac{1}{2}x - \dfrac{3}{2}$

$0 < -\dfrac{1}{2}(0) - \dfrac{3}{2}$

$0 < -\dfrac{3}{2}$ False

Since this is a false statement, shade the region which does not contain the point $(0, 0)$. To obtain the final region, take the intersection of the above two regions. The regions do not overlap, so there are no solutions.

52. $x \geq 0$

$y \geq 0$

$x + y \leq 6$

$4x + y \leq 8$

The first two inequalities indicate that the solution must be in the first quadrant. For $x + y \leq 6$, the graph is the line $x + y = 6$ along with the region below this line. For $4x + y \leq 8$, the graph is the line $4x + y = 8$ along with the region below this line. To obtain the final region, take the intersection of these regions.

53. $x \geq 0$

$y \geq 0$

$2x + y \leq 6$

$4x + 5y \leq 20$

The first two inequalities indicate that the solution must be in the first quadrant. For $2x + y \leq 6$, graph the line $2x + y = 6$ along with the region below this line. For $4x + 5y \leq 20$, graph the line $4x + 5y = 20$ along with the region below this line. To obtain the final region, take the intersection of these regions.

54. $|x| \leq 3$

$|y| > 2$

For $|x| \leq 3$, the graph is the region between the solid lines $x = -3$ and $x = 3$. For $|y| > 2$, the graph is the region above the dashed line $y = 2$ along with the region below the dashed line $y = -2$. To obtain the final region, take the intersection of these regions.

55. $|x| > 4$

$|y - 2| \leq 3$

For $|x| > 4$, the graph is the region to the left of dashed line $x = -4$ along with the region to the right of the dashed line $x = 4$.

$|y - 2| \leq 3$ can be written as

$-3 \leq y - 2 \leq 3$

$-1 \leq y \leq 5$

For $|y - 2| \leq 3$, the graph is the region between the solid lines $y = -1$ and $y = 5$. To obtain the final region, take the intersection of these regions.

Chapter 10 Practice Test

1. $A \cup B = \{5, 7, 8, 9, 10, 11, 14\}$

$A \cap B = \{8, 10\}$

2. $A \cup B = \{1, 3, 5, 7, \ldots\}$

$A \cap B = \{3, 5, 7, 9, 11\}$

3. $3(2q+4) < 5(q-1)+7$

$6q+12 < 5q-5+7$

$6q+12 < 5q+2$

$q+12 < 2$

$q < -10$

-10

4. $\dfrac{6-2x}{5} \ge -12$

$5\left(\dfrac{6-2x}{5}\right) \ge 5(-12)$

$6-2x \ge -60$

$-2x \ge -66$

$\dfrac{-2x}{-2} \le \dfrac{-66}{-2}$

$x \le 33$

33

5. $x-3 \le 4 \qquad$ and $\qquad 2x+1 > 10$

$x-3+3 \le 4+3 \qquad\qquad 2x+1-1 > 10-1$

$x \le 7 \qquad\qquad\qquad 2x > 9$

$$x > \dfrac{9}{2}$$

The solution is $\left(\dfrac{9}{2}, 7\right]$.

6. $7 \le \dfrac{2u-5}{3} < 9$

$3(7) \le 3\left(\dfrac{2u-5}{3}\right) < 3(9)$

$21 \le 2u-5 < 27$

$21+5 \le 2u-5+5 < 27+5$

$26 \le 2u < 32$

$13 \le u < 16$

The solution is $[13, 16)$.

7. $|2b+5| = 9$

$2b+5 = -9 \quad$ or $\quad 2b+5 = 9$

$2b = -14 \qquad\qquad 2b = 4$

$b = -7 \qquad\qquad b = 2$

The solution set is $\{-7, 2\}$.

8. $|2x-3| = \left|\dfrac{1}{2}x-10\right|$

$2x-3 = -\left(\dfrac{1}{2}x-10\right) \quad$ or $\quad 2x-3 = \dfrac{1}{2}x-10$

$2x-3 = -\dfrac{1}{2}x+10 \qquad\qquad \dfrac{3}{2}x-3 = -10$

$\dfrac{5}{2}x-3 = 10 \qquad\qquad\qquad \dfrac{3}{2}x = -7$

$\dfrac{5}{2}x = 13 \qquad\qquad\qquad \dfrac{2}{3}\left(\dfrac{3}{2}x\right) = \dfrac{2}{3}(-7)$

$\dfrac{2}{5}\left(\dfrac{5}{2}x\right) = \dfrac{2}{5}(13) \qquad\qquad x = -\dfrac{14}{3}$

$x = \dfrac{26}{5}$

The solution set is $\left\{-\dfrac{14}{3}, \dfrac{26}{5}\right\}$.

9. $|4z+12| = 0$

$4z+12 = 0$

$4z = -12$

$z = -3$

The solution set is $\{-3\}$.

10. $|2x-3|+6 > 11$

$|2x-3| > 5$

$2x-3 < -5 \quad$ or $\quad 2x-3 > 5$

$2x < -2 \qquad\qquad 2x > 8$

$x < -1 \qquad\qquad x > 4$

The solution set is $\{x \mid x < -1 \text{ or } x > 4\}$.

11. $\left|\dfrac{2x-3}{8}\right| \le \dfrac{1}{4}$

$-\dfrac{1}{4} \le \dfrac{2x-3}{8} \le \dfrac{1}{4}$

$8\left(-\dfrac{1}{4}\right) \le 8\left(\dfrac{2x-3}{8}\right) \le 8\left(\dfrac{1}{4}\right)$

$-2 \le 2x-3 \le 2$

$1 \le 2x \le 5$

$\dfrac{1}{2} \le x \le \dfrac{5}{2}$

The solution set is $\left\{x \mid \dfrac{1}{2} \le x \le \dfrac{5}{2}\right\}$.

12. Graph the line $y = 3x - 2$ using a dashed line. For the check point, select $(0, 0)$.

$y < 3x - 2$

$0 < 3 \cdot 0 - 2 \leftarrow$ Substitute 0 for x and y

$0 < -2$

Since the statement is false, shade the region that does not contain $(0, 0)$.

13. $3x + 2y < 9$

$-2x + 5y \leq 10$

For $3x + 2y < 9$, graph the line $3x + 2y = 9$ using a dashed line. For the check point, select $(0, 0)$.

$3x + 2y < 9$

$3(0) + 2(0) < 9$

$\qquad 0 < 9 \qquad$ True

Since this is a true statement, shade the region which contains the point $(0, 0)$. this is the region "below" the line.

For $-2x + 5y \leq 10$, graph the line $-2x + 5y = 10$ using a solid line. For the check point, select $(0, 0)$.

$-2x + 5y \leq 10$

$-2(0) + 5(0) \leq 10$

$\qquad 0 \leq 10 \qquad$ True

Since this is a true statement, shade the region which contains the point $(0, 0)$. this is the region "below" the line. To obtain the final region, take the intersection of the above two regions.

14. $|x| > 3$

$|y| \leq 1$

For $|x| > 3$, the graph is the region to the left of the dashed line $x = -3$ along with the region to the right of the dashed line $x = 3$.

For $|y| \leq 1$, the graph is the region between the solid lines $y = -1$ and $y = 1$. To obtain the final region, take the intersection of these regions.

Chapter 10 Cumulative Review Test

1. $-40 - 3(4 - 8)^2$

$-40 - 3(-4)^2$

$-40 - 3(16)$

$-40 - 48$

-88

2. $2(x + 2y) + 4x - 5y$ for $x = 2$ and $y = 3$:

$2(2 + 2(3)) + 4(2) - 5(3)$

$2(2 + 6) + 8 - 15$

$2(8) - 7$

$16 - 7$

9

3. $\dfrac{1}{2}(x + 3) + \dfrac{1}{3}(3x + 6)$

$\dfrac{1}{2}x + \dfrac{3}{2} + x + 2$

$\dfrac{3}{2}x + \dfrac{7}{2}$

4. $\dfrac{a-7}{3} = \dfrac{a+5}{2} - \dfrac{7a-1}{6}$

$6\left(\dfrac{a-7}{3}\right) = 6\left(\dfrac{a+5}{2} - \dfrac{7a-1}{6}\right)$

$2(a-7) = 3(a+5) - (7a-1)$

$2a - 14 = 3a + 15 - 7a + 1$

$2a - 14 = -4a + 16$

$6a = 30$

$a = 5$

5. $\dfrac{40}{5000} = \dfrac{x}{26,000}$

$x = \dfrac{40(26,000)}{5000} = 208$

208 pounds of fertilizer are needed.

6. Let x = the amount of assets managed.

$1000 + 0.01x = 500 + 0.02x$

$500 = 0.01x$

$\dfrac{500}{0.01} = x$

$50,000 = x$

The plans will have the same total fee if she manages total assets of $50,000.

7. Let p = the price of the mixture.

$\text{Cost}_{\text{mix}} = \text{Cost}_{\text{sunflower}} + \text{Cost}_{\text{corn}}$

$3.5p = 1.80(2.5) + 1.40(1)$

$3.5p = 4.50 + 1.40$

$3.5p = 5.90$

$p \approx 1.69$

The mixture should be sold for $1.69 per pound.

8. $\left(\dfrac{4a^3b^{-2}}{2a^{-2}b^{-3}}\right)^{-2} = \left(2a^5b^1\right)^{-2} = \dfrac{1}{\left(2a^5b\right)^2} = \dfrac{1}{4a^{10}b^2}$

9. $(0.003)(0.00015) = \left(3.0 \times 10^{-3}\right)\left(1.5 \times 10^{-4}\right)$

$= (3)(1.5) \times 10^{-3} \cdot 10^{-4}$

$= 4.5 \times 10^{-7}$

10. $24p^3q + 16p^2q - 30pq$

$= 2pq\left(12p^2 + 8p - 15\right)$

$= 2pq(2p+3)(6p-5)$

11. $\dfrac{2b}{b+1} = 2 - \dfrac{5}{2b}$

$\dfrac{2b}{b+1} = \dfrac{4b-5}{2b}$

$4b^2 = (b+1)(4b-5)$

$4b^2 = 4b^2 - b - 5$

$b = -5$

12. $\dfrac{4}{r+5} + \dfrac{1}{r+3} = \dfrac{2}{r^2 + 8r + 15}$

LCD: $(r+5)(r+3)$ Domain: $x \neq -5, -3$

$(r+5)(r+3)\left(\dfrac{4}{r+5} + \dfrac{1}{r+3}\right) = (r+5)(r+3)\dfrac{2}{r^2+8r+15}$

$4(r+3) + 1(r+5) = 2$

$4r + 12 + r + 5 = 2$

$5r + 17 = 2$

$5r = -15$

$r = -3$

This value makes a denominator equal 0, so it must be excluded. Therefore, there is no solution to the equation.

13. $y = x^2 - 2$

14. a. Function; each input corresponds to exactly one output.

b. Not a function; fails the vertical line test.

c. Function; passes the vertical line test.

15. $3x - 5y = 7$

$-5y = -3x + 7$

$y = \dfrac{3}{5}x - \dfrac{7}{5} \quad \rightarrow \quad \text{slope} = \dfrac{3}{5}$

Since parallel lines have the same slope, the

slope of our line must also be $\dfrac{3}{5}$.

Using the slope, $m = \dfrac{3}{5}$, and the y-intercept,

$(0, -2)$, the equation of our line is

$y = \dfrac{3}{5}x - 2$.

16. $4x - 3y = 12$

$-3y = -4x + 12$

$y = \dfrac{4}{3}x - 4 \quad \rightarrow \quad \text{slope} = \dfrac{4}{3}$

Since perpendicular lines have opposite-reciprocal slopes, the slope of our line must be

$m = -\dfrac{3}{4}$.

$y - y_1 = m(x - x_1)$

$y - (-2) = -\dfrac{3}{4}(x - 3)$

$y + 2 = -\dfrac{3}{4}x + \dfrac{9}{4}$

$y = -\dfrac{3}{4}x + \dfrac{1}{4}$

17. a. $(f \cdot g)(x) = (x^2 - 11x + 30)(x - 5)$

$= x^3 - 5x^2 - 11x^2 + 55x + 30x - 150$

$= x^3 - 16x^2 + 85x - 150$

b. $(f / g)(x) = \dfrac{x^2 - 11x + 30}{x - 5}$

$= \dfrac{(x - 6)(x - 5)}{x - 5}$

$= x - 6$

c. Since $g(x) = 0$ when $x = 5$, this value must be excluded from the domain of (f / g). Therefore, the domain is $\{x \mid x \neq 5\}$.

18. $2a - b - 2c = -1$ (1)

$a - 2b - c = 1$ (2)

$a + b + c = 4$ (3)

Multiply equation (2) by -2 and add to equation (1).

$2a - b - 2c = -1$

$\underline{-2a + 4b + 2c = -2}$

$3b = -3$

$b = -1$

Substitute -1 for b in equations (2) and (3).

$a - 2(-1) - c = 1 \quad \rightarrow \quad a - c = -1$

$a + (-1) + c = 4 \quad \rightarrow \quad a + c = 5$

Add the resulting equations.

$a - c = -1$

$\underline{a + c = 5}$

$2a = 4$

$a = 2$

Substitute -1 for b and 2 for a in equation (3).

$2 + (-1) + c = 4$

$c = 3$

The solution is $(2, -1, 3)$.

19. $\dfrac{1}{2} < 3x + 4 < 6$

$-\dfrac{7}{2} < 3x < 2$

$-\dfrac{7}{6} < x < \dfrac{2}{3}$

Solution: $\left(-\dfrac{7}{6}, \dfrac{2}{3}\right)$

20. $y < 2x - 3$

Graph the line $y = 2x - 3$ with a dashed line since the inequality is strict. Select a test point, such as $(0, 0)$.

$0 < 2(0) - 3$

$0 < -3$ false

Since this resulted in a false statement, shade the half-plane that does not contain the point $(0, 0)$.

Chapter 11

1. a. Every real number has two square roots; a positive, or principal, square root and a negative square root.

   b. The square roots of 49 are 7 and –7.

   c. When we say square root, we are referring to the principal square root.

   d. $\sqrt{49} = 7$

2. a. Even roots are roots with even indices. Example: $\sqrt[4]{2}$ or $\sqrt{6}$

   b. Odd roots are roots with odd indices. Example: $\sqrt[3]{8}$

3. There is no real number which, when squared, results in -81.

4. Yes. It is only when the index is even that it is possible for the root of a real number to not be real.

5. No. If the number under the radical is negative, the answer is not a real number.

6. a. $\sqrt{a^2} = |a|$

   b. If $a \geq 0$ then $\sqrt{a^2} = |a|$ but since a is ≥ 0, $|a| = a$.

7. a. $\sqrt{(1.3)^2} = \sqrt{1.69} = 1.3$

   b. $\sqrt{(-1.3)^2} = \sqrt{1.69} = 1.3$

8. a. $\sqrt{(5.72)^2} = \sqrt{32.7184} = 5.72$

   b. $\sqrt{(-5.72)^2} = \sqrt{32.7184} = 5.72$

9. a. $\sqrt[3]{27} = 3$ since $3^3 = 27$

   b. $-\sqrt[3]{27} = -3$

   c. $\sqrt[3]{-27} = -3$ since $(-3)^3 = -27$

10. a. $\sqrt[4]{16} = 2$ since $(2)^4 = 16$

    b. $-\sqrt[4]{16} = -2$

    c. $\sqrt[4]{-16}$ is not a real number.

11. $\sqrt{36} = 6$ since $6^2 = 36$

12. $-\sqrt{36} = -6$

13. $\sqrt[3]{-64} = -4$ since $(-4)^3 = -64$

14. $\sqrt[3]{125} = 5$ since $5^3 = 125$

15. $\sqrt[3]{-125} = -5$ since $(-5)^3 = -125$

16. $-\sqrt[3]{-125} = -(-5) = 5$

17. $\sqrt[5]{-1} = -1$ since $(-1)^5 = -1$

18. $-\sqrt[5]{-1} = -(-1) = 1$

19. $\sqrt[5]{1} = 1$ since $1^5 = 1$

20. $\sqrt[6]{64} = 2$ since $2^6 = 64$

21. $\sqrt[6]{-64}$ is not a real number since an even root of a negative is not a real number.

22. $\sqrt[4]{-81}$ is not a real number since an even root of a negative is not a real number.

23. $\sqrt[3]{-343} = -7$ since $(-7)^3 = -343$

24. $\sqrt{121} = 11$ since $11^2 = 121$

25. $\sqrt{-36}$ is not a real number since an even root of a negative is not a real number.

26. $\sqrt{45.3} \approx 6.73$

27. $\sqrt{-45.3}$ is not a real number since an even root of a negative is not a real number.

28. $\sqrt{53.9} \approx 7.34$

29. $\sqrt{\dfrac{1}{25}} = \dfrac{1}{5}$ since $\left(\dfrac{1}{5}\right)^2 = \dfrac{1}{25}$

30. $\sqrt{-\dfrac{1}{25}}$ is not a real number since an even root of a negative is not a real number.

31. $\sqrt[3]{\dfrac{1}{8}} = \dfrac{1}{2}$ since $\left(\dfrac{1}{2}\right)^3 = \dfrac{1}{8}$

32. $\sqrt[3]{-\dfrac{1}{8}} = -\dfrac{1}{2}$ since $\left(-\dfrac{1}{2}\right)^3 = -\dfrac{1}{8}$

33. $\sqrt{\dfrac{4}{49}} = \dfrac{2}{7}$ since $\left(\dfrac{2}{7}\right)^2 = \dfrac{4}{49}$

34. $\sqrt[3]{\dfrac{8}{27}} = \dfrac{2}{3}$ since $\left(\dfrac{2}{3}\right)^3 = \dfrac{8}{27}$

35. $\sqrt[3]{-\dfrac{8}{27}} = -\dfrac{2}{3}$ since $\left(-\dfrac{2}{3}\right)^3 = -\dfrac{8}{27}$

36. $\sqrt[4]{-8.9}$ is not a real number since an even root of a negative is not a real number.

37. $-\sqrt[4]{18.2} \approx -2.07$

38. $\sqrt[5]{93} \approx 2.48$

39. $\sqrt{7^2} = |7| = 7$

40. $\sqrt{(-7)^2} = |-7| = 7$

41. $\sqrt{(19)^2} = |19| = 19$

42. $\sqrt{(-19)^2} = |-19| = 19$

43. $\sqrt{119^2} = |119| = 119$

44. $\sqrt{(-119)^2} = |-119| = 119$

45. $\sqrt{(235.23)^2} = |235.23| = 235.23$

46. $\sqrt{(-201.5)^2} = |-201.5| = 201.5$

47. $\sqrt{(0.06)^2} = |0.06| = 0.06$

48. $\sqrt{(-0.19)^2} = |-0.19| = 0.19$

49. $\sqrt{\left(\dfrac{12}{13}\right)^2} = \left|\dfrac{12}{13}\right| = \dfrac{12}{13}$

50. $\sqrt{\left(-\dfrac{101}{319}\right)^2} = \left|-\dfrac{101}{319}\right| = \dfrac{101}{319}$

51. $\sqrt{(x-4)^2} = |x-4|$

52. $\sqrt{(a+10)^2} = |a+10|$

53. $\sqrt{(x-3)^2} = |x-3|$

54. $\sqrt{(7a-11b)^2} = |7a-11b|$

55. $\sqrt{(3x^2-1)^2} = |3x^2-1|$

56. $\sqrt{(7y^2-3y)^2} = |7y^2-3y|$

57. $\sqrt{(6a^3-5b^4)^2} = |6a^3-5b^4|$

58. $\sqrt{(9y^4-2z^3)^2} = |9y^4-2z^3|$

59. $\sqrt{a^{14}} = \sqrt{(a^7)^2} = |a^7|$

60. $\sqrt{y^{22}} = \sqrt{(y^{11})^2} = |y^{11}|$

61. $\sqrt{z^{32}} = \sqrt{(z^{16})^2} = \left|z^{16}\right| = z^{16}$

62. $\sqrt{x^{200}} = \sqrt{(x^{100})^2} = \left|x^{100}\right| = x^{100}$

63. $\sqrt{a^2 - 8a + 16} = \sqrt{(a-4)^2} = \left|a-4\right|$

64. $\sqrt{x^2 - 12x + 36} = \sqrt{(x-6)^2} = \left|x-6\right|$

65. $\sqrt{9a^2 + 12ab + 4b^2} = \sqrt{(3a+2b)^2} = \left|3a+2b\right|$

66. $\sqrt{4x^2 + 20xy + 25y^2} = \sqrt{(2x+5y)^2} = \left|2x+5y\right|$

67. $\sqrt{49x^2} = \sqrt{(7x)^2} = 7x$

68. $\sqrt{100a^4} = \sqrt{(10a^2)^2} = 10a^2$

69. $\sqrt{16c^6} = \sqrt{(4c^3)^2} = 4c^3$

70. $\sqrt{121z^8} = \sqrt{(11z^4)^2} = 11z^4$

71. $\sqrt{x^2 + 4x + 4} = \sqrt{(x+2)^2} = x+2$

72. $\sqrt{9a^2 - 6a + 1} = \sqrt{(3a-1)^2} = \left|3a-1\right|$

73. $\sqrt{4x^2 + 4xy + y^2} = \sqrt{(2x+y)^2} = 2x+y$

74. $\sqrt{16b^2 - 40bc + 25c^2} = \sqrt{(4b-5c)^2} = \left|4b-5c\right|$

75. $f(x) = \sqrt{5x-6}$
$f(2) = \sqrt{5 \cdot 2 - 6}$
$\quad = \sqrt{10-6}$
$\quad = \sqrt{4}$
$\quad = 2$

76. $f(c) = \sqrt{7c+1}$
$f(5) = \sqrt{7 \cdot 5 + 1}$
$\quad = \sqrt{35+1}$
$\quad = \sqrt{36}$
$\quad = 6$

77. $q(x) = \sqrt{76-3x}$
$q(4) = \sqrt{76-3 \cdot 4}$
$\quad = \sqrt{76-12}$
$\quad = \sqrt{64}$
$\quad = 8$

78. $q(b) = \sqrt{9b+34}$
$q(-1) = \sqrt{9(-1)+34}$
$\quad = \sqrt{-9+34}$
$\quad = \sqrt{25}$
$\quad = 5$

79. $t(a) = \sqrt{-15a-9}$
$t(-6) = \sqrt{-15(-6)-9}$
$\quad = \sqrt{90-9}$
$\quad = \sqrt{81}$
$\quad = 9$

80. $f(a) = \sqrt{14a-36}$
$f(4) = \sqrt{14 \cdot 4 - 36}$
$\quad = \sqrt{56-36}$
$\quad = \sqrt{20}$
$\quad \approx 4.472$

81. $g(x) = \sqrt{64-8x}$
$g(-3) = \sqrt{64-8(-3)}$
$\quad = \sqrt{64+24}$
$\quad = \sqrt{88}$
$\quad \approx 9.381$

82. $p(x) = \sqrt[3]{8x + 9}$

$\quad p(2) = \sqrt[3]{8 \cdot 2 + 9}$

$\qquad = \sqrt[3]{16 + 9}$

$\qquad = \sqrt[3]{25}$

$\qquad \approx 2.924$

83. $h(x) = \sqrt[3]{9x^2 + 4}$

$\quad h(4) = \sqrt[3]{9(4)^2 + 4}$

$\qquad = \sqrt[3]{144 + 4}$

$\qquad = \sqrt[3]{148}$

$\qquad \approx 5.290$

84. $k(c) = \sqrt[4]{16c - 5}$

$\quad k(6) = \sqrt[4]{16 \cdot 6 - 5}$

$\qquad = \sqrt[4]{96 - 5}$

$\qquad = \sqrt[4]{91}$

$\qquad \approx 3.089$

85. $f(x) = \sqrt[3]{-2x^2 + x - 6}$

$\quad f(-3) = \sqrt[3]{-2(-3)^2 + (-3) - 6}$

$\qquad = \sqrt[3]{-18 - 3 - 6}$

$\qquad = \sqrt[3]{-27}$

$\qquad = -3$

86. $t(x) = \sqrt[4]{2x^3 - 3x^2 + 6x}$

$\quad t(2) = \sqrt[4]{2(2)^3 - 3(2)^2 + 6(2)}$

$\qquad = \sqrt[4]{16 - 12 + 12}$

$\qquad = \sqrt[4]{16}$

$\qquad = 2$

87. $f(x) = x + \sqrt{x} + 7$

$\quad f(81) = 81 + \sqrt{81} + 7$

$\qquad = 81 + 9 + 7$

$\qquad = 97$

88. $g(x) = x^2 + \sqrt{x} - 13$

$\quad g(25) = (25)^2 + \sqrt{25} - 13$

$\qquad = 625 + 5 - 13$

$\qquad = 617$

89. $t(x) = \dfrac{x}{2} + \sqrt{2x} - 4$

$\quad t(18) = \dfrac{18}{2} + \sqrt{2(18)} - 4$

$\qquad = 9 + \sqrt{36} - 4$

$\qquad = 9 + 6 - 4$

$\qquad = 11$

90. $m(x) = \dfrac{x}{3} + \sqrt{4x} + 10$

$\quad m(36) = \dfrac{36}{3} + \sqrt{4(36)} + 10$

$\qquad = 12 + \sqrt{144} + 10$

$\qquad = 12 + 12 + 10$

$\qquad = 34$

91. $k(x) = x^2 + \sqrt{\dfrac{x}{2}} - 21$

$\quad k(8) = (8)^2 + \sqrt{\dfrac{8}{2}} - 21$

$\qquad = 64 + \sqrt{4} - 21$

$\qquad = 64 + 2 - 21$

$\qquad = 45$

92. $r(x) = \dfrac{x}{9} + \sqrt{\dfrac{x}{5}} + 13$

$\quad r(45) = \dfrac{45}{9} + \sqrt{\dfrac{45}{5}} + 13$

$\qquad = 5 + \sqrt{9} + 13$

$\qquad = 5 + 3 + 13$

$\qquad = 21$

93. Choose a value for x that will make the expression $2x + 1$ a negative number. For example, select $x = -1$.

$\sqrt{(2(-1) + 1)^2} \neq 2(-1) + 1$

$\sqrt{(-1)^2} \neq -1$

$\sqrt{1} \neq -1$

$1 \neq -1$

Choosing any value for x less than $-\dfrac{1}{2}$ will show this inequality.

94. Choose a value of x that will make the expression $5x - 3$ a negative number. For example, use $x = -2$.

$\sqrt{(5x-3)^2}$ becomes

$\sqrt{[5(-2)-3]^2} = \sqrt{(-13)^2} = |-13| = 13$, whereas

$5x - 3$ becomes $5(-2) - 3 = -13$. Therefore,

$\sqrt{(5x-3)^2} \neq 5x - 3$. Choosing any value for x

less than $\dfrac{3}{5}$ will show this inequality.

95. $\sqrt{(x-1)^2} = x - 1$ for all $x \geq 1$. The expression

$\sqrt{(x-1)^2} = x - 1$, when $(x - 1)$ is equal to zero or a positive number. Therefore, solving for x,

$x - 1 \geq 0$
$\quad x \geq 1.$

96. $\sqrt{(x+3)^2} = x + 3$ for all values of x where $x + 3 \geq 0$. Therefore, solving for x,

$x + 3 \geq 0$
$\quad x \geq -3$

97. $\sqrt{(2x-6)^2} = 2x - 6$ for all $x \geq 3$. The expression

$\sqrt{(2x-6)^2} = 2x - 6$, when $(2x - 6)$ is positive or equal to 0. Therefore, solving for x,

$2x - 6 \geq 0$
$\quad x \geq 3$

98. $\sqrt{(3x-8)^2} = 3x - 8$ for all values of x where $3x - 8 \geq 0$. Therefore, solving for x,

$3x - 8 \geq 0$
$\quad 3x \geq 8$
$\quad x \geq \dfrac{8}{3}$

99. a. $\sqrt{a^2} = |a|$ for all real values

b. $\sqrt{a^2} = a$ when $a \geq 0$

c. $\sqrt[3]{a^3} = a$ for all real values

100. $\sqrt[n]{x}$ is not a real number when n is an even integer and $x < 0$.

101. If n is even, we are finding the even root of a positive number. If n is odd, the expression is a real number even if the radicand is negative.

102. $\sqrt[n]{x^m}$ is not a real number when n is an even integer, m is an odd integer and $x < 0$.

103. $\dfrac{\sqrt{x+5}}{\sqrt[3]{x+5}}$ The denominator cannot equal zero.

$\sqrt[3]{x+5} \neq 0$
$\quad\quad x \neq -5$

The radicand in the numerator must be greater than or equal to zero.

$x + 5 \geq 0$
$\quad\quad x \geq -5$

Therefore the domain is $\{x \mid x > -5\}$.

104. $\dfrac{\sqrt[3]{x-2}}{\sqrt[6]{x+1}}$

The radicand in the denominator must be greater than zero. There are no restrictions on the numerator since the index is odd.

$x + 1 > 0$
$\quad\quad x > -1$

Therefore, the domain is $\{x \mid x > -1\}$.

105. $f(x) = \sqrt{x}$ matches graph d).

The x-intercept is 0 and the domain is $x \geq 0$.

106. $f(x) = \sqrt{x^2}$ matches graph c). The x-intercept is 0 and the domain is all real numbers.

107. $f(x) = \sqrt{x-5}$ matches graph a). The x-intercept is 5 and the domain is $x - 5 \geq 0$, or $x \geq 5$.

108. $f(x) = \sqrt{x+5}$ matches graph b). The x-intercept is -5 and the domain is $x + 5 \geq 0$, or $x \geq -5$.

109. Answers may vary. One answer is
$f(x) = \sqrt{x-8}$

110. Answers may vary. One answer is
$f(x) = \sqrt{5-x}$

111. $f(x) = -\sqrt{x}$

a. No; since $\sqrt{x} \geq 0$, $-\sqrt{x}$ must be ≤ 0.

b. Yes, if $x = 0$.

c. Yes; since $\sqrt{x} \geq 0$, $-\sqrt{x}$ must be ≤ 0.

112. $f(x) = \sqrt{x+5}$

    a. No; $\sqrt{x+5} \geq 0$ for all x in the domain.

    b. Yes, if $x = -5$.

    c. Yes, $\sqrt{x+5} > 0$ for $x > -5$.

113. $V = \sqrt{64.4h}$

    a. $V = \sqrt{64.4(20)}$

       $= \sqrt{1288}$

       ≈ 35.89

       The velocity will be about 35.89 ft/sec.

    b. $V = \sqrt{64.4(40)}$

       $= \sqrt{2576}$

       ≈ 50.75

       The velocity will be about 50.75 ft/sec.

114. $u = \sqrt{\dfrac{H}{0.026}}$

    $u = \sqrt{\dfrac{15}{0.026}} \approx \sqrt{576.92} \approx 24.02$

    The wind speed is about 24.02 knots.

115. $f(x) = \sqrt{x+1}$

x	$f(x)$
-1	0
0	1
3	2
8	3

116. $g(x) = -\sqrt{x}$

x	$g(x)$
0	0
4	-2
9	-3

117. $g(x) = \sqrt{x} + 1$

x	$g(x)$
0	1
4	3
9	4

118. $f(x) = \sqrt{x-2}$

x	$f(x)$
2	0
3	1
6	2
11	3

119. $y_1 = \sqrt{x+1}$

120. $y_1 = \sqrt{x} + 1$

121. $y_1 = \dfrac{\sqrt{x+5}}{\sqrt[3]{x+5}}$

Yes, the domain is $x > -5$.

122. $y_1 = \dfrac{\sqrt[3]{x-2}}{\sqrt[6]{x+1}}$

Yes, the domain is $x > -1$.

123. $y = \sqrt[3]{x+4}$

124. $f(x) = \sqrt[3]{2x-3}$

125. $a \geq 0$ and $b \geq 0$

126. $a \geq 0$ and $b > 0$

127. $9ax - 3bx + 12ay - 4by$
$$= 3x(3a - b) + 4y(3a - b)$$
$$= (3a - b)(3x + 4y)$$

128. $3x^3 - 18x^2 + 24x = 3x\left(x^2 - 6x + 8\right)$
$$= 3x(x - 4)(x - 2)$$

129. $8x^4 + 10x^2 - 3$
$$= 8\left(x^2\right)^2 + 10\left(x^2\right) - 3 \;\leftarrow \text{use } y \text{ for } x^2$$
$$= 8y^2 + 10y - 3$$
$$= (4y - 1)(2y + 3) \qquad \leftarrow \text{use } x^2 \text{ for } y$$
$$= \left(4x^2 - 1\right)\left(2x^2 + 3\right)$$
$$= \left((2x)^2 - 1^2\right)\left(2x^2 + 3\right)$$
$$= (2x - 1)(2x + 1)\left(2x^2 + 3\right)$$

130. $x^3 - \dfrac{8}{27}y^3 = x^3 - \left(\dfrac{2}{3}y\right)^3$
$$= \left(x - \dfrac{2}{3}y\right)\left(x^2 + \dfrac{2}{3}xy + \left(\dfrac{2}{3}y\right)^2\right)$$
$$= \left(x - \dfrac{2}{3}y\right)\left(x^2 + \dfrac{2}{3}xy + \dfrac{4}{9}y^2\right)$$

Exercise Set 11.2

1. **a.** $\sqrt[n]{a}$ is a real number when n is even and $a \geq 0$, or n is odd.

   b. $\sqrt[n]{a}$ can be expressed with rational exponents as $a^{1/n}$.

2. **a.** $\sqrt[n]{a^m}$ is a real number when n and m are even, or n is even and $a \geq 0$, or n is odd.

   b. $\left(\sqrt[n]{a}\right)^m$ is a real number when n is even and $a \geq 0$, or n is odd.

   c. $\sqrt[n]{a^m}$ can be expressed with rational exponents as $a^{m/n}$.

3. **a.** $\sqrt[n]{a^n}$ is always real

   b. $\sqrt[n]{a^n} = a$ when $a \geq 0$ and n is even

   c. $\sqrt[n]{a^n} = a$ when n is odd

   d. $\sqrt[n]{a^n} = |a|$ when n is even and a is any real number

4. **a.** $-16^{1/2} = -\sqrt{16}, (-16)^{1/2} = \sqrt{-16}$

   b. $-16^{1/2} = -4, (-16)^{1/2}$ is not a real number

5. **a.** No, $(xy)^{1/2} = x^{1/2} y^{1/2} \neq xy^{1/2}$

   b. No, since $(xy)^{-1/2} = \dfrac{1}{(xy)^{1/2}} = \dfrac{1}{x^{1/2} y^{1/2}}$

   but $\dfrac{x^{1/2}}{y^{-1/2}} = x^{1/2} y^{1/2}$

6. **a.** No, since $\sqrt[6]{(3y)^3} = (3y)^{\frac{3}{6}} \neq (3y)^{\frac{6}{3}}$

   b. Yes, since $\sqrt{(ab)^4} = (ab)^{4/2} = (ab)^2$

7. $\sqrt{a^3} = a^{3/2}$

8. $\sqrt{y^7} = y^{7/2}$

9. $\sqrt{9^5} = 9^{5/2}$

10. $\sqrt[3]{y} = y^{1/3}$

11. $\sqrt[3]{z^5} = z^{5/3}$

12. $\sqrt[3]{x^{11}} = x^{11/3}$

13. $\sqrt[3]{7^{10}} = 7^{10/3}$

14. $\sqrt[5]{9^{11}} = 9^{11/5}$

15. $\sqrt[4]{9^7} = 9^{7/4}$

16. $\left(\sqrt{x}\right)^9 = x^{9/2}$

17. $\left(\sqrt[3]{y}\right)^{14} = y^{14/3}$

18. $\sqrt{ab^5} = \left(ab^5\right)^{1/2}$

19. $\sqrt[4]{a^3 b} = (a^3 b)^{1/4}$

20. $\sqrt[3]{x^4 y} = (x^4 y)^{1/3}$

21. $\sqrt[4]{x^9 z^5} = (x^9 z^5)^{1/4}$

22. $\sqrt[6]{y^{11} z} = (y^{11} z)^{1/6}$

23. $\sqrt[6]{3a + 8b} = (3a + 8b)^{1/6}$

24. $\sqrt[9]{3x + 5z^4} = (3x + 5z^4)^{1/9}$

25. $\sqrt[5]{\dfrac{2x^6}{11y^7}} = \left(\dfrac{2x^6}{11y^7}\right)^{1/5}$

26. $\sqrt[4]{\dfrac{3a^8}{11b^5}} = \left(\dfrac{3a^8}{11b^5}\right)^{1/4}$

27. $a^{1/2} = \sqrt{a}$

28. $b^{2/3} = \sqrt[3]{b^2}$

29. $c^{5/2} = \sqrt{c^5}$

30. $19^{1/2} = \sqrt{19}$

31. $18^{5/3} = \sqrt[3]{18^5}$

32. $y^{17/6} = \sqrt[6]{y^{17}}$

33. $(24x^3)^{1/2} = \sqrt{24x^3}$

34. $(85a^3)^{5/2} = \left(\sqrt{85a^3}\right)^5$

35. $(11b^2c)^{3/5} = \left(\sqrt[5]{11b^2c}\right)^3$

36. $(8x^3y^2)^{7/4} = \left(\sqrt[4]{8x^3y^2}\right)^7$

37. $(6a+5b)^{1/5} = \sqrt[5]{6a+5b}$

38. $(8x^2+9y)^{7/3} = \left(\sqrt[3]{8x^2+9y}\right)^7$

39. $(b^3-d)^{-1/3} = \dfrac{1}{\sqrt[3]{b^3-d}}$

40. $(7x^2-2y^3)^{-1/6} = \dfrac{1}{\sqrt[6]{7x^2-2y^3}}$

41. $\sqrt{a^6} = a^{6/2} = a^3$

42. $\sqrt[4]{a^8} = a^{8/4} = a^2$

43. $\sqrt[3]{x^9} = x^{9/3} = x^3$

44. $\sqrt[4]{x^{12}} = x^{12/4} = x^3$

45. $\sqrt[6]{y^2} = y^{2/6} = y^{1/3} = \sqrt[3]{y}$

46. $\sqrt[8]{b^4} = b^{4/8} = b^{1/2} = \sqrt{b}$

47. $\sqrt[6]{y^3} = y^{3/6} = y^{1/2} = \sqrt{y}$

48. $\sqrt[12]{z^4} = z^{4/12} = z^{1/3} = \sqrt[3]{z}$

49. $\left(\sqrt{19.3}\right)^2 = (19.3)^{2/2} = (19.3)^1 = 19.3$

50. $\sqrt[4]{(6.83)^4} = 6.83^{4/4} = 6.83^1 = 6.83$

51. $\left(\sqrt[3]{xy^2}\right)^{15} = (xy^2)^{15/3}$
$= (xy^2)^5$
$= x^5y^{10}$

52. $\left(\sqrt[4]{a^4bc^3}\right)^{40} = (a^4bc^3)^{40/4}$
$= (a^4bc^3)^{10}$
$= a^{40}b^{10}c^{30}$

53. $(\sqrt[8]{xyz})^4 = (xyz)^{4/8}$
$= (xyz)^{1/2}$
$= \sqrt{xyz}$

54. $\left(\sqrt[9]{a^2bc^4}\right)^3 = \left(a^2bc^4\right)^{3/9}$
$= \left(a^2bc^4\right)^{1/3}$
$= \sqrt[3]{a^2bc^4}$

55. $\sqrt{\sqrt{x}} = (\sqrt{x})^{1/2}$
$= (x^{1/2})^{1/2}$
$= x^{1/4}$
$= \sqrt[4]{x}$

56. $\sqrt{\sqrt[3]{a}} = \left(\sqrt[3]{a}\right)^{1/2}$
$= \left(a^{1/3}\right)^{1/2}$
$= a^{1/6}$
$= \sqrt[6]{a}$

57. $\sqrt{\sqrt[4]{y}} = \left(\sqrt[4]{y}\right)^{1/2}$
$= \left(y^{1/4}\right)^{1/2}$
$= y^{1/8}$
$= \sqrt[8]{y}$

58. $\sqrt[3]{\sqrt[4]{b}} = \left(\sqrt[4]{b}\right)^{1/3}$

$\quad\quad = (b)^{1/4 \cdot 1/3}$

$\quad\quad = (b)^{1/12}$

$\quad\quad = \sqrt[12]{b}$

59. $\sqrt[3]{\sqrt[3]{x^2 y}} = \left(\sqrt[3]{x^2 y}\right)^{1/3}$

$\quad\quad = (x^2 y)^{1/3 \cdot 1/3}$

$\quad\quad = (x^2 y)^{1/9}$

$\quad\quad = \sqrt[9]{x^2 y}$

60. $\sqrt[4]{\sqrt[3]{7 y}} = \left(\sqrt[3]{7 y}\right)^{1/4}$

$\quad\quad = (7 y)^{1/3 \cdot 1/4}$

$\quad\quad = (7 y)^{1/12}$

$\quad\quad = \sqrt[12]{7 y}$

61. $\sqrt{\sqrt[5]{a^9}} = \left(\sqrt[5]{a^9}\right)^{1/2}$

$\quad\quad = \left(a^{9/5}\right)^{1/2}$

$\quad\quad = a^{9/10}$

$\quad\quad = \sqrt[10]{a^9}$

62. $\sqrt[5]{\sqrt[4]{ab}} = \left(\sqrt[4]{ab}\right)^{1/5}$

$\quad\quad = (ab)^{1/4 \cdot 1/5}$

$\quad\quad = (ab)^{1/20}$

$\quad\quad = \sqrt[20]{ab}$

63. $25^{1/2} = \sqrt{25} = 5$

64. $121^{1/2} = \sqrt{121} = 11$

65. $64^{1/3} = \sqrt[3]{64} = 4$

66. $81^{1/4} = \sqrt[4]{81} = 3$

67. $64^{2/3} = \left(\sqrt[3]{64}\right)^2 = 4^2 = 16$

68. $27^{2/3} = \left(\sqrt[3]{27}\right)^2 = (3)^2 = 9$

69. $(-49)^{1/2} = \sqrt{-49}$ is not a real number.

70. $(-64)^{1/4} = \sqrt[4]{-64}$ is not a real number.

71. $\left(\dfrac{25}{9}\right)^{1/2} = \sqrt{\dfrac{25}{9}} = \dfrac{5}{3}$

72. $\left(\dfrac{100}{49}\right)^{1/2} = \sqrt{\dfrac{100}{49}} = \dfrac{10}{7}$

73. $\left(\dfrac{1}{8}\right)^{1/3} = \sqrt[3]{\dfrac{1}{8}} = \dfrac{1}{2}$

74. $\left(\dfrac{1}{32}\right)^{1/5} = \sqrt[5]{\dfrac{1}{32}} = \dfrac{1}{2}$

75. $-81^{1/2} = -\sqrt{81} = -9$

76. $(-81)^{1/2} = \sqrt{-81}$. is not a real number.

77. $-64^{1/3} = -\sqrt[3]{64} = -4$

78. $(-64)^{1/3} = \sqrt[3]{-64} = -4$

79. $64^{-1/3} = \dfrac{1}{64^{1/3}} = \dfrac{1}{\sqrt[3]{64}} = \dfrac{1}{4}$

80. $49^{-1/2} = \dfrac{1}{\sqrt{49}} = \dfrac{1}{7}$

81. $16^{-3/2} = \dfrac{1}{16^{3/2}} = \dfrac{1}{\left(\sqrt{16}\right)^3} = \dfrac{1}{4^3} = \dfrac{1}{64}$

82. $64^{-2/3} = \dfrac{1}{64^{2/3}} = \dfrac{1}{\left(\sqrt[3]{64}\right)^2} = \dfrac{1}{4^2} = \dfrac{1}{16}$

83. $\left(\dfrac{64}{27}\right)^{-1/3} = \left(\dfrac{27}{64}\right)^{1/3} = \sqrt[3]{\dfrac{27}{64}} = \dfrac{3}{4}$

84. $(-81)^{3/4} = \left(\sqrt[4]{-81}\right)^3$ is not a real number.

85. $(-100)^{3/2} = \left(\sqrt{-100}\right)^3$ is not a real number.

86. $-\left(\dfrac{25}{49}\right)^{-1/2} = -\dfrac{1}{\sqrt{25/49}} = -\dfrac{1}{\frac{5}{7}} = -\dfrac{7}{5}$ or

$-\left(\dfrac{25}{49}\right)^{-1/2} = -\left(\dfrac{49}{25}\right)^{1/2} = -\sqrt{\dfrac{49}{25}} = -\dfrac{7}{5}$

87. $121^{1/2} + 169^{1/2} = \sqrt{121} + \sqrt{169} = 11 + 13 = 24$

88. $49^{-1/2} + 36^{-1/2} = \dfrac{1}{\sqrt{49}} + \dfrac{1}{\sqrt{36}}$

$= \dfrac{1}{7} + \dfrac{1}{6}$

$= \dfrac{6}{42} + \dfrac{7}{42}$

$= \dfrac{13}{42}$

89. $343^{-1/3} + 16^{-1/2} = \dfrac{1}{343^{1/3}} + \dfrac{1}{16^{1/2}}$

$= \dfrac{1}{\sqrt[3]{343}} + \dfrac{1}{\sqrt{16}}$

$= \dfrac{1}{7} + \dfrac{1}{4}$

$= \dfrac{4}{28} + \dfrac{7}{28}$

$= \dfrac{11}{28}$

90. $16^{-1/2} - 256^{-3/4} = \dfrac{1}{16^{1/2}} - \dfrac{1}{256^{3/4}}$

$= \dfrac{1}{\sqrt{16}} - \dfrac{1}{\left(\sqrt[4]{256}\right)^3} = \dfrac{1}{4} - \dfrac{1}{4^3}$

$= \dfrac{1}{4} - \dfrac{1}{64} = \dfrac{16}{64} - \dfrac{1}{64} = \dfrac{15}{64}$

91. $x^4 \cdot x^{1/2} = x^{4+1/2} = x^{9/2}$

92. $x^6 \cdot x^{1/2} = x^{12/2+1/2}$

$= x^{13/2}$

93. $\dfrac{x^{1/2}}{x^{1/3}} = x^{1/2-1/3} = x^{3/6-2/6} = x^{1/6}$

94. $x^{-6/5} = \dfrac{1}{x^{6/5}}$

95. $\left(x^{1/2}\right)^{-2} = x^{1/2(-2)} = x^{-1} = \dfrac{1}{x}$

96. $\left(a^{-1/3}\right)^{-1/2} = a^{(-1/3)(-1/2)} = a^{1/6}$

97. $\left(9^{-1/3}\right)^0 = 9^{-1/3(0)} = 9^0 = 1$

98. $\dfrac{x^4}{x^{-1/2}} = x^{4-(-1/2)} = x^{4+1/2} = x^{9/2}$

99. $\dfrac{5y^{-1/3}}{60y^{-2}} = \dfrac{1}{12} y^{-1/3-(-2)} = \dfrac{1}{12} y^{5/3} = \dfrac{y^{5/3}}{12}$

100. $x^{-1/2} \cdot x^{-2/5} = x^{-1/2+(-2/5)} = x^{-5/10-4/10}$

$= x^{-9/10} = \dfrac{1}{x^{9/10}}$

101. $4x^{5/3} \cdot 3x^{-7/2} = 4 \cdot 3 \cdot x^{5/3} \cdot x^{-7/2} = 12x^{5/3-7/2}$

$= 12x^{10/6-21/6} = 12x^{-11/6} = \dfrac{12}{x^{11/6}}$

102. $\left(x^{-4/5}\right)^{1/3} = x^{(-4/5)(1/3)} = x^{-4/15} = \dfrac{1}{x^{4/15}}$

103. $\left(\dfrac{3}{24x}\right)^{1/3} = \left(\dfrac{1}{8x}\right)^{1/3} \dfrac{1^{1/3}}{8^{1/3}x^{1/3}} = \dfrac{1}{2x^{1/3}}$

104. $\left(\dfrac{52}{2x^4}\right)^{1/3} = \left(\dfrac{26}{x^4}\right)^{1/3} = \dfrac{26^{1/3}}{(x^4)^{1/3}} = \dfrac{26^{1/3}}{x^{4/3}}$

105. $\left(\dfrac{22x^{3/7}}{2x^{1/2}}\right)^2 = (11x^{3/7-1/2})^2 = (11x^{6/14-7/14})^2$

$= (11x^{-1/14})^2 = (11)^2(x^{-1/14})^2 = 121x^{-1/7}$

$= \dfrac{121}{x^{1/7}}$

106. $\left(\dfrac{x^{-1/3}}{x^{-2}}\right)^2 = [x^{-1/3-(-2)}]^2$

$= (x^{-1/3+2})^2$

$= (x^{5/3})^2$

$= x^{10/3}$

107. $\left(\dfrac{a^4}{4a^{-2/5}}\right)^{-3} = \dfrac{a^{-12}}{4^{-3}a^{6/5}}$

$= 4^3 a^{-12-6/5}$

$= 64a^{-66/5}$

$= \dfrac{64}{a^{66/5}}$

108. $\left(\dfrac{27z^{1/4}y^3}{3z^{1/4}}\right)^{1/2} = (9z^0 y^3)^{1/2} = (9y^3)^{1/2}$

$= 9^{1/2}(y^3)^{1/2} = 3y^{3/2}$

109. $\left(\dfrac{x^{3/4}y^{-3}}{x^{1/2}y^2}\right)^4 = \left(x^{3/4-1/2}y^{-3-2}\right)^4$

$= (x^{1/4}y^{-5})^4$

$= (x^{1/4})^4(y^{-5})^4$

$= xy^{-20}$

$= \dfrac{x}{y^{20}}$

110. $\left(\dfrac{250a^{-3/4}b^5}{2a^{-2}b^2}\right)^{2/3} = \left(\dfrac{250}{2}a^{-3/4+2}b^{5-2}\right)^{2/3}$

$= (125a^{5/4}b^3)^{2/3}$

$= (125)^{2/3}(a^{5/4})^{2/3}(b^3)^{2/3}$

$= 25a^{5/6}b^2$

111. $4z^{-1/2}(2z^4 - z^{1/2}) = 4z^{-1/2}\cdot 2z^4 - 4z^{-1/2}z^{1/2}$

$= 8z^{-1/2+4} - 4z^{-1/2+1/2}$

$= 8z^{7/2} - 4z^0$

$= 8z^{7/2} - 4$

112. $-3a^{-4/9}(5a^{1/9} - a^2) = -15a^{-3/9} + 3a^{-4/9+2}$

$= -15a^{-1/3} + 3a^{14/9}$

$= -\dfrac{15}{a^{1/3}} + 3a^{14/9}$

113. $5x^{-1}(x^{-4} + 4x^{-1/2}) = 5x^{-1}\cdot x^{-4} + 5x^{-1}\cdot 4x^{-1/2}$

$= 5x^{-1-4} + 20x^{-1-1/2}$

$= 5x^{-5} + 20x^{-3/2}$

$= \dfrac{5}{x^5} + \dfrac{20}{x^{3/2}}$

114. $-9z^{3/2}(z^{3/2} - z^{-3/2})$

$= (-9z^{3/2})(z^{3/2}) + (-9z^{3/2})(-z^{-3/2})$

$= -9z^{3/2+3/2} + 9z^{3/2-3/2}$

$= -9z^{6/2} + 9z^0$

$= -9z^3 + 9$

115. $-6x^{5/3}(-2x^{1/2} + 3x^{1/3})$

$= (-6x^{5/3})(-2x^{1/2}) + (-6x^{5/3})(3x^{1/3})$

$= 12x^{5/3+1/2} - 18x^{5/3+1/3}$

$= 12x^{13/6} - 18x^{6/3}$

$= 12x^{13/6} - 18x^2$

116. $\dfrac{1}{2}x^{-2}(10x^{4/3} - 38x^{-1/2})$

$= \dfrac{1}{2}x^{-2}\cdot 10x^{4/3} - \dfrac{1}{2}x^{-2}\cdot 38x^{-1/2}$

$= 5x^{-2+4/3} - 19x^{-2-1/2}$

$= 5x^{-2/3} - 19x^{-5/2}$

$= \dfrac{5}{x^{2/3}} - \dfrac{19}{x^{5/2}}$

117. $\sqrt{180} \approx 13.42$

118. $\sqrt[3]{168} \approx 5.52$

119. $\sqrt[5]{402.83} \approx 3.32$

120. $\sqrt[4]{1096} \approx 5.75$

121. $93^{2/3} \approx 20.53$

122. $(38.2)^{3/2} \approx 236.10$

123. $1000^{-1/2} \approx 0.03$

124. $(8060)^{-3/2} \approx 0.00$

125. $\sqrt[n]{a^n} = \left(\sqrt[n]{a}\right)^n = a$ when n is odd, or n is even with $a \geq 0$.

126. To show $(a^2 + b^2)^{1/2} \neq a + b$, use $a = 1$ and $b = 1$. Then $(a^2 + b^2)^{1/2}$ becomes $(1^2 + 1^2)^{1/2} = (1+1)^{1/2} = 2^{1/2} = \sqrt{2}$ whereas $a + b$ becomes $1 + 1 = 2$.
Since $\sqrt{2} \neq 2$, then $(a^2 + b^2)^{1/2} \neq a + b$.
Answers will vary.

127. To show $(a^{1/2} + b^{1/2})^2 \neq a + b$, use $a = 9$ and $b = 16$. Then $(a^{1/2} + b^{1/2})^2$ becomes $(9^{1/2} + 16^{1/2})^2 = (3+4)^2 = 7^2 = 49$ whereas $a + b$ becomes $9 + 16 = 25$. Since $49 \neq 25$, then $(a^{1/2} + b^{1/2})^2 \neq a + b$. Answers will vary.

128. To show $(a^3 + b^3)^{1/3} \neq a + b$, use $a = 1$ and $b = 1$. Then $(a^{1/2} + b^{1/2})^2$ becomes $(1^3 + 1^3)^{1/3} = (1+1)^{1/3} = 2^{1/3} = \sqrt[3]{2}$ whereas $a + b$ becomes $1 + 1 = 2$. Since $\sqrt[3]{2} \neq 2$, then $(a^3 + b^3)^{1/3} \neq a + b$. Answers will vary.

129. To show $(a^{1/3} + b^{1/3})^3 \neq a + b$, use $a = 1$ and $b = 1$. Then $(a^{1/3} + b^{1/3})^3$ becomes $(1^{1/3} + 1^{1/3})^3 = (\sqrt[3]{1} + \sqrt[3]{1})^3 = (1+1)^3 = 2^3 = 8$ whereas $a + b$ becomes $1 + 1 = 2$. Since $8 \neq 2$, then $(a^{1/3} + b^{1/3})^3 \neq a + b$. Answers will vary.

130. $\sqrt[3]{\sqrt{x}} = \sqrt{\sqrt[3]{x}}$ for $x \geq 0$ and both expressions equal $x^{1/6}$ when converted to exponential form.

131. $x^{3/2} + x^{1/2} = x^{1/2} \cdot x^1 + x^{1/2}$
$= x^{1/2}(x+1)$

132. $x^{1/4} - x^{5/4} = x^{1/4} - x^{1/4}x^1$
$= x^{1/4}(1-x)$

133. $y^{1/3} - y^{7/3} = y^{1/3} - y^{1/3}y^2$
$= y^{1/3}(1-y^2)$
$= y^{1/3}(1-y)(1+y)$

134. $x^{-1/2} + x^{1/2} = x^{-1/2} + x^{-1/2}x^1$
$= x^{-1/2}(1+x)$
$= \dfrac{1+x}{x^{1/2}}$

135. $y^{-2/5} + y^{8/5} = y^{-2/5} + y^{-2/5}y^2$
$= y^{-2/5}(1+y^2)$
$= \dfrac{1+y^2}{y^{2/5}}$

136. $a^{6/5} + a^{-4/5} = a^{-4/5}(a^{10/5}) + a^{-4/5}(1)$
$= a^{-4/5}(a^2 + 1)$
$= \dfrac{a^2 + 1}{a^{4/5}}$

137. a. $B(t) = 2^{10} \cdot 2^t$
$B(0) = 2^{10} \cdot 2^0$
$= 2^{10} \cdot 1$
$= 2^{10}$
Initially, there are 2^{10} or 1024 bacteria.

b. $B\left(\dfrac{1}{2}\right) = 2^{10} \cdot 2^{1/2}$
$= 2^{10}\sqrt{2}$
≈ 1448.15
After $\dfrac{1}{2}$ hour there are about 1448 bacteria.

138. $P = P_0 2^{-t/5600}$
$P = 10 \cdot 2^{-5000/5600}$
$P \approx 5.39$
In 5000 years, there will be about 5.39 mg of C_{14} present.

139. $A(t) = 2.69t^{3/2}$

a. $t = 200 - 1993 = 7$
$A(7) = 2.69(7)^{3/2}$
≈ 49.82
In 2000, there was about \$49.82 billion in total assets in the U.S. in 401(k) plans.

b. $t = 2009 - 1993 = 16$

$A(16) = 2.69(16)^{3/2}$

$= 172.16$

In 2009, there will be about \$172.16 billion in total assets in the U.S. in 401(k) plans.

140. $I(t) = 0.25t^{5/3}$

a. $t = 2000 - 1999 = 1$

$I(1) = 0.25(1)^{5/3} = 0.25$

In 2000, there was about \$0.25 billion in total internet sales.

b. $2008 - 1999 = 9$

$I(9) = 0.25(9)^{5/3} \approx 9.74$

In 2008, there will be about \$9.74 billion in total internet sales.

141. $(3^{\sqrt{2}})^{\sqrt{2}} = 3^{\sqrt{2} \cdot \sqrt{2}} = 3^2 = 9$

142. a. $3^\pi \approx 31.5442807$

b. Answers will vary. π is approximately equal to 3, and $3^3 = 27$, which is fairly close to 31. The value in part a) makes sense.

143. $f(x) = (x-7)^{1/2}(x+3)^{-1/2}$

$= \dfrac{(x-7)^{1/2}}{(x+3)^{1/2}}$

$= \dfrac{\sqrt{x-7}}{\sqrt{x+3}}$

The denominator must be greater than zero.

$\sqrt{x+3} > 0$

$x > -3$

The numerator must be greater than or equal to zero.

$\sqrt{x-7} \geq 0$

$x \geq 7$

Therefore, the domain is $\{x \mid x \geq 7\}$.

144. $f(x) = (x+4)^{1/2}(x-3)^{-1/2}$

$= \dfrac{(x+4)^{1/2}}{(x-3)^{1/2}}$

$= \dfrac{\sqrt{x+4}}{\sqrt{x-3}}$

The denominator must be greater than zero.

$\sqrt{x-3} > 0$

$x > 3$

The numerator must be greater than or equal to zero.

$\sqrt{x+4} \geq 0$

$x \geq -4$

Thus, the domain is $\{x \mid x > 3\}$.

145. a. If n is even: $\sqrt[n]{(x-6)^{2n}} = \sqrt[n]{\left((x-6)^2\right)^n}$

$= \left|(x-6)^2\right|$

$= (x-6)^2$

b. If n is odd: $\sqrt[n]{(x-6)^{2n}} = \sqrt[n]{\left((x-6)^2\right)^n}$

$= (x-6)^2$

146. Let a be the unknown index in the shaded area.

$\sqrt[4]{\sqrt[a]{\sqrt{x}}} = x^{1/24}$

$\left(\left(x^{1/2}\right)^{1/a}\right)^{1/4} = x^{1/24}$

$x^{1/2 \cdot 1/a \cdot 1/4} = x^{1/24}$

$x^{1/8a} = x^{1/24}$ $\leftarrow$ Equate exponents

$\dfrac{1}{8a} = \dfrac{1}{24}$

$8a = 24$

$a = 3$

147. Let a be the unknown index in the shaded area.

$$\sqrt[4]{\sqrt[5]{\sqrt[a]{\sqrt[3]{z}}}} = z^{1/120}$$

$$\left(\left(\left(z^{1/3}\right)^{1/a}\right)^{1/5}\right)^{1/4} = z^{1/120}$$

$$z^{1/60a} = z^{1/120}$$

$$\frac{1}{60a} = \frac{1}{120} \quad \leftarrow \text{ Equate exponents}$$

$$60a = 120$$

$$a = 2$$

148. a. $f(x) = \sqrt{2x+3} = (2x+3)^{1/2}$

b. $y_1 = \sqrt{2x+3}, y_2 = (2x+3)^{1/2}$

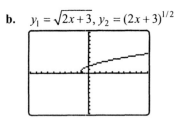

   $-10, \ 10, \ 1, \ -10, \ 10, \ 1$

a) is correct because the graphs are the same.

149. $\dfrac{a^{-2}+ab^{-1}}{ab^{-2}-a^{-2}b^{-1}} = \dfrac{\dfrac{1}{a^2}+\dfrac{a}{b}}{\dfrac{a}{b^2}-\dfrac{1}{a^2b}}$

$$= \frac{a^2b^2\left(\dfrac{1}{a^2}\right)+a^2b^2\left(\dfrac{a}{b}\right)}{a^2b^2\left(\dfrac{a}{b^2}\right)-a^2b^2\left(\dfrac{1}{a^2b}\right)}$$

$$= \frac{b^2+a^3b}{a^3-b}$$

150. $\dfrac{3x-2}{x+4} = \dfrac{2x+1}{3x-2}$

$$(3x-2)(3x-2) = (2x+1)(x+4)$$

$$9x^2-12x+4 = 2x^2+9x+4$$

$$7x^2-21x = 0$$

$$7x(x-3) = 0$$

$$7x = 0 \quad \text{or} \quad x-3 = 0$$

$$x = 0 \qquad\qquad x = 3$$

The solutions are 0 and 3.

151. Let y be the speed of the plane in still air. The table is

	d	r	$t = \dfrac{d}{r}$
With wind	560	$y+25$	$\dfrac{560}{y+25}$
Against wind	500	$y-25$	$\dfrac{500}{y-25}$

Since the time is the same for both parts of the trip. The equation is

$$\frac{560}{y+25} = \frac{500}{y-25}$$

$$560(y-25) = 500(y+25)$$

$$560y-14,000 = 500y+12,500$$

$$560y = 500y+26,500$$

$$60y = 26,500$$

$$y = \frac{26,500}{60}$$

$$\approx 441.67 \text{ mph}$$

The speed of the plane in still air is about 441.67 mph.

152. a. The graph is a relation but not a function because it fails the vertical line test.

b. The graph is a relation but not a function because it fails the vertical line test.

c. The graph is both a relation and a function. It passes the vertical line test.

Exercise Set 11.3

1. a. Square the natural numbers.

b. $1^2 = 1, 2^2 = 4, 3^2 = 9,$
   $4^2 = 16, 5^2 = 25, 6^2 = 36$

2. a. Cube the natural numbers.

b. $1^3 = 1, 2^3 = 8, 3^3 = 27,$
   $4^3 = 64, 5^3 = 125, 6^3 = 216$

3. **a.** Raise natural numbers to the fifth power.

   b. $1^5 = 1, 2^5 = 32, 3^5 = 243,$
   $4^5 = 1024, 5^5 = 3125$

4. Answers will vary.

5. If n is even and a is negative, $\sqrt[n]{a}$ is not a real number and the rule does not apply. Similarly for the case when b is negative.

6. Answers will vary.

7. If n is even and a is negative, $\sqrt[n]{a}$ is not a real number and the rule does not apply. Similarly for the case when b is negative.

8. Division by 0 is not possible.

9. $\sqrt{8} = \sqrt{4 \cdot 2} = \sqrt{4}\sqrt{2} = 2\sqrt{2}$

10. $\sqrt{28} = \sqrt{4 \cdot 7} = \sqrt{4}\sqrt{7} = 2\sqrt{7}$

11. $\sqrt{24} = \sqrt{4 \cdot 6} = 2\sqrt{6}$

12. $\sqrt{18} = \sqrt{9 \cdot 2} = 3\sqrt{2}$

13. $\sqrt{32} = \sqrt{16 \cdot 2} = \sqrt{16}\sqrt{2} = 4\sqrt{2}$

14. $\sqrt{12} = \sqrt{4 \cdot 3} = \sqrt{4}\sqrt{3} = 2\sqrt{3}$

15. $\sqrt{50} = \sqrt{25 \cdot 2} = \sqrt{25}\sqrt{2} = 5\sqrt{2}$

16. $\sqrt{72} = \sqrt{36 \cdot 2} = \sqrt{36}\sqrt{2} = 6\sqrt{2}$

17. $\sqrt{75} = \sqrt{25 \cdot 3} = \sqrt{25}\sqrt{3} = 5\sqrt{3}$

18. $\sqrt{300} = \sqrt{100 \cdot 3} = \sqrt{100}\sqrt{3} = 10\sqrt{3}$

19. $\sqrt{40} = \sqrt{4 \cdot 10} = \sqrt{4}\sqrt{10} = 2\sqrt{10}$

20. $\sqrt{600} = \sqrt{100 \cdot 6} = \sqrt{100}\sqrt{6} = 10\sqrt{6}$

21. $\sqrt[3]{16} = \sqrt[3]{8 \cdot 2} = \sqrt[3]{8}\sqrt[3]{2} = 2\sqrt[3]{2}$

22. $\sqrt[3]{24} = \sqrt[3]{8 \cdot 3} = \sqrt[3]{8}\sqrt[3]{3} = 2\sqrt[3]{3}$

23. $\sqrt[3]{54} = \sqrt[3]{27 \cdot 2} = \sqrt[3]{27}\sqrt[3]{2} = 3\sqrt[3]{2}$

24. $\sqrt[3]{81} = \sqrt[3]{27 \cdot 3} = \sqrt[3]{27}\sqrt[3]{3} = 3\sqrt[3]{3}$

25. $\sqrt[3]{32} = \sqrt[3]{8 \cdot 4} = \sqrt[3]{8}\sqrt[3]{4} = 2\sqrt[3]{4}$

26. $\sqrt[3]{108} = \sqrt[3]{27 \cdot 4} = \sqrt[3]{27}\sqrt[3]{4} = 3\sqrt[3]{4}$

27. $\sqrt[3]{40} = \sqrt[3]{8 \cdot 5} = \sqrt[3]{8}\sqrt[3]{5} = 2\sqrt[3]{5}$

28. $\sqrt[4]{80} = \sqrt[4]{16 \cdot 5} = \sqrt[4]{16}\sqrt[4]{5} = 2\sqrt[4]{5}$

29. $\sqrt[4]{48} = \sqrt[4]{16 \cdot 3} = \sqrt[4]{16}\sqrt[4]{3} = 2\sqrt[4]{3}$

30. $\sqrt[4]{162} = \sqrt[4]{81 \cdot 2} = \sqrt[4]{81}\sqrt[4]{2} = 3\sqrt[4]{2}$

31. $-\sqrt[5]{64} = -\sqrt[5]{32 \cdot 2} = -\sqrt[5]{32}\sqrt[5]{2} = -2\sqrt[5]{2}$

32. $-\sqrt[5]{243} = -3$

33. $\sqrt[3]{b^9} = b^3$

34. $6\sqrt{y^{12}} = 6y^6$

35. $\sqrt[3]{x^6} = x^2$

36. $\sqrt[5]{y^{20}} = \sqrt[5]{\left(y^4\right)^5} = y^4$

37. $\sqrt{x^3} = \sqrt{x^2 \cdot x} = \sqrt{x^2}\sqrt{x} = x\sqrt{x}$

38. $-\sqrt{x^5} = -\sqrt{x^4 \cdot x} = -\sqrt{x^4}\sqrt{x} = -x^2\sqrt{x}$

39. $\sqrt{a^{11}} = \sqrt{a^{10} \cdot a} = \sqrt{a^{10}}\sqrt{a} = a^5\sqrt{a}$

40. $\sqrt[3]{b^{13}} = \sqrt[3]{b^{12} \cdot b} = \sqrt[3]{b^{12}}\sqrt[3]{b} = b^4\sqrt[3]{b}$

41. $8\sqrt[3]{z^{32}} = 8\sqrt[3]{z^{30} \cdot z^2} = 8\sqrt[3]{z^{30}}\sqrt[3]{z^2} = 8z^{10}\sqrt[3]{z^2}$

42. $\sqrt[3]{a^7} = \sqrt[3]{a^6 \cdot a} = \sqrt[3]{a^6}\sqrt[3]{a} = a^2\sqrt[3]{a}$

43. $\sqrt[4]{b^{23}} = \sqrt[4]{b^{20} \cdot b^3} = \sqrt[4]{b^{20}}\sqrt[4]{b^3} = b^5\sqrt[4]{b^3}$

44. $\sqrt[5]{z^7} = \sqrt[5]{z^5 \cdot z^2} = \sqrt[5]{z^5}\sqrt[5]{z^2} = z\sqrt[5]{z^2}$

45. $\sqrt[6]{x^9} = \sqrt[6]{x^6 \cdot x^3} = \sqrt[6]{x^6}\sqrt[6]{x^3} = x\sqrt[6]{x^3}$ or $x\sqrt{x}$

46. $\sqrt[7]{y^{15}} = \sqrt[7]{y^{14} \cdot y} = \sqrt[7]{y^{14}}\sqrt[7]{y} = y^2\sqrt[7]{y}$

47. $3\sqrt[5]{y^{23}} = 3\sqrt[5]{y^{20} \cdot y^3} = 3\sqrt[5]{y^{20}}\sqrt[5]{y^3} = 3y^4\sqrt[5]{y^3}$

48. $\sqrt{24x^3} = \sqrt{4 \cdot 6 \cdot x^2 \cdot x}$
    $= \sqrt{4x^2 \cdot 6x}$
    $= \sqrt{4x^2}\sqrt{6x}$
    $= 2x\sqrt{6x}$

49. $2\sqrt{50y^9} = 2\sqrt{25 \cdot 2 \cdot y^8 \cdot y}$

$\qquad = 2\sqrt{25y^8 \cdot 2y}$

$\qquad = 2\sqrt{25y^8}\sqrt{2y}$

$\qquad = 10y^4\sqrt{2y}$

50. $\sqrt{75a^7b^{11}} = \sqrt{25 \cdot 3 \cdot a^6 \cdot a \cdot b^{10} \cdot b}$

$\qquad = \sqrt{25a^6b^{10} \cdot 3ab}$

$\qquad = \sqrt{25a^6b^{10}}\sqrt{3ab}$

$\qquad = 5a^3b^5\sqrt{3ab}$

51. $\sqrt[3]{x^3y^7} = \sqrt[3]{x^3 \cdot y^6 \cdot y}$

$\qquad = \sqrt[3]{x^3y^6 \cdot y}$

$\qquad = \sqrt[3]{x^3y^6}\sqrt[3]{y}$

$\qquad = xy^2\sqrt[3]{y}$

52. $\sqrt{x^5y^9} = \sqrt{x^4y^8 \cdot xy}$

$\qquad = \sqrt{x^4y^8} \cdot \sqrt{xy}$

$\qquad = x^2y^4\sqrt{xy}$

53. $\sqrt[5]{a^6b^{23}} = \sqrt[5]{a^5b^{20} \cdot ab^3}$

$\qquad = \sqrt[5]{a^5b^{20}} \cdot \sqrt[5]{ab^3}$

$\qquad = ab^4\sqrt[5]{ab^3}$

54. $-\sqrt{20x^6y^7z^{12}} = -\sqrt{4 \cdot 5 \cdot x^6 \cdot y^6 \cdot y \cdot z^{12}}$

$\qquad = -\sqrt{4x^6y^6z^{12} \cdot 5y}$

$\qquad = -\sqrt{4x^6y^6z^{12}}\sqrt{5y}$

$\qquad = -2x^3y^3z^6\sqrt{5y}$

55. $\sqrt{24x^{15}y^{20}z^{27}} = \sqrt{4 \cdot 6 \cdot x^{14} \cdot x \cdot y^{20} \cdot z^{26} \cdot z}$

$\qquad = \sqrt{4x^{14}y^{20}z^{26} \cdot 6xz}$

$\qquad = \sqrt{4x^{14}y^{20}z^{26}}\sqrt{6xz}$

$\qquad = 2x^7y^{10}z^{13}\sqrt{6xz}$

56. $\sqrt[3]{16x^3y^6} = \sqrt[3]{8 \cdot 2 \cdot x^3 \cdot y^6}$

$\qquad = \sqrt[3]{8x^3y^6 \cdot 2}$

$\qquad = \sqrt[3]{8x^3y^6}\sqrt[3]{2}$

$\qquad = 2xy^2\sqrt[3]{2}$

57. $\sqrt[3]{81a^6b^8} = \sqrt[3]{27 \cdot 3 \cdot a^6 \cdot b^6 \cdot b^2}$

$\qquad = \sqrt[3]{27a^6b^6 \cdot 3b^2}$

$\qquad = \sqrt[3]{27a^6b^6}\sqrt[3]{3b^2}$

$\qquad = 3a^2b^2\sqrt[3]{3b^2}$

58. $\sqrt[3]{128a^{10}b^{11}c^{12}} = \sqrt[3]{64 \cdot 2 \cdot a^9 \cdot a \cdot b^9 \cdot b^2 \cdot c^{12}}$

$\qquad = \sqrt[3]{64a^9b^9c^{12} \cdot 2ab^2}$

$\qquad = \sqrt[3]{64a^9b^9c^{12}}\sqrt[3]{2ab^2}$

$\qquad = 4a^3b^3c^4\sqrt[3]{2ab^2}$

59. $\sqrt[4]{32x^8y^9z^{19}} = \sqrt[4]{16 \cdot 2 \cdot x^8 \cdot y^8 \cdot y \cdot z^{16} \cdot z^3}$

$\qquad = \sqrt[4]{16x^8y^8z^{16} \cdot 2yz^3}$

$\qquad = \sqrt[4]{16x^8y^8z^{16}}\sqrt[4]{2yz^3}$

$\qquad = 2x^2y^2z^4\sqrt[4]{2yz^3}$

60. $\sqrt[4]{48x^{11}y^{21}} = \sqrt[4]{16 \cdot 3 \cdot x^8 \cdot x^3 \cdot y^{20} \cdot y}$

$\qquad = \sqrt[4]{16x^8y^{20} \cdot 3x^3y}$

$\qquad = \sqrt[4]{16x^8y^{20}}\sqrt[4]{3x^3y}$

$\qquad = 2x^2y^5\sqrt[4]{3x^3y}$

61. $\sqrt[4]{81a^8b^9} = \sqrt[4]{81 \cdot a^8 \cdot b^8 \cdot b}$

$\qquad = \sqrt[4]{81a^8b^8 \cdot b}$

$\qquad = \sqrt[4]{81a^8b^8}\sqrt[4]{b}$

$\qquad = 3a^2b^2\sqrt[4]{b}$

62. $-\sqrt[4]{32x^{18}y^{31}} = -\sqrt[4]{16 \cdot 2 \cdot x^{16} \cdot x^2 \cdot y^{28} \cdot y^3}$

$\qquad = -\sqrt[4]{16x^{16}y^{28} \cdot 2x^2y^3}$

$\qquad = -\sqrt[4]{16x^{16}y^{28}}\sqrt[4]{2x^2y^3}$

$\qquad = -2x^4y^7\sqrt[4]{2x^2y^3}$

63. $\sqrt[5]{32a^{10}b^{12}} = \sqrt[5]{32 \cdot a^{10} \cdot b^{10} \cdot b^2}$

$\qquad = \sqrt[5]{32a^{10}b^{10} \cdot b^2}$

$\qquad = \sqrt[5]{32a^{10}b^{10}} \sqrt[5]{b^2}$

$\qquad = 2a^2b^2\sqrt[5]{b^2}$

64. $\sqrt[6]{64x^{12}y^{23}z^{50}} = \sqrt[6]{64 \cdot x^{12} \cdot y^{18} \cdot y^5 \cdot z^{48} \cdot z^2}$

$\qquad = \sqrt[6]{64x^{12}y^{18}z^{48} \cdot y^5z^2}$

$\qquad = \sqrt[6]{64x^{12}y^{18}z^{48}} \sqrt[6]{y^5z^2}$

$\qquad = 2x^2y^3z^8\sqrt[6]{y^5z^2}$

65. $\sqrt{\dfrac{75}{3}} = \sqrt{25} = 5$

66. $\sqrt{\dfrac{36}{4}} = \sqrt{9} = 3$

67. $\sqrt{\dfrac{81}{100}} = \dfrac{\sqrt{81}}{\sqrt{100}} = \dfrac{9}{10}$

68. $\sqrt{\dfrac{8}{50}} = \sqrt{\dfrac{4}{25}} = \dfrac{\sqrt{4}}{\sqrt{25}} = \dfrac{2}{5}$

69. $\dfrac{\sqrt{27}}{\sqrt{3}} = \sqrt{\dfrac{27}{3}} = \sqrt{9} = 3$

70. $\dfrac{\sqrt{72}}{\sqrt{2}} = \sqrt{\dfrac{72}{2}} = \sqrt{36} = 6$

71. $\dfrac{\sqrt{3}}{\sqrt{48}} = \sqrt{\dfrac{3}{48}} = \sqrt{\dfrac{1}{16}} = \dfrac{1}{4}$

72. $\dfrac{\sqrt{15}}{\sqrt{60}} = \sqrt{\dfrac{15}{60}} = \sqrt{\dfrac{1}{4}} = \dfrac{1}{2}$

73. $\sqrt[3]{\dfrac{3}{24}} = \sqrt[3]{\dfrac{1}{8}} = \dfrac{\sqrt[3]{1}}{\sqrt[3]{8}} = \dfrac{1}{2}$

74. $\sqrt[3]{\dfrac{2}{54}} = \sqrt[3]{\dfrac{1}{27}} = \dfrac{1}{3}$

75. $\dfrac{\sqrt[3]{3}}{\sqrt[3]{81}} = \sqrt[3]{\dfrac{3}{81}} = \sqrt[3]{\dfrac{1}{27}} = \dfrac{1}{3}$

76. $\dfrac{\sqrt[3]{32}}{\sqrt[3]{4}} = \sqrt[3]{\dfrac{32}{4}} = \sqrt[3]{8} = 2$

77. $\sqrt[4]{\dfrac{3}{48}} = \sqrt[4]{\dfrac{1}{16}} = \dfrac{1}{2}$

78. $\dfrac{\sqrt[4]{243}}{\sqrt[4]{3}} = \sqrt[4]{\dfrac{243}{3}} = \sqrt[4]{81} = 3$

79. $\sqrt[5]{\dfrac{96}{3}} = \sqrt[5]{32} = 2$

80. $\dfrac{\sqrt[5]{2}}{\sqrt[5]{64}} = \sqrt[5]{\dfrac{2}{64}} = \sqrt[5]{\dfrac{1}{32}} = \dfrac{1}{2}$

81. $\sqrt{\dfrac{r^4}{4}} = \dfrac{\sqrt{r^4}}{\sqrt{4}} = \dfrac{r^2}{2}$

82. $\sqrt{\dfrac{100a^8}{49b^6}} = \dfrac{\sqrt{100a^8}}{\sqrt{49b^6}} = \dfrac{10a^4}{7b^3}$

83. $\sqrt{\dfrac{16x^4}{25y^{10}}} = \dfrac{\sqrt{16x^4}}{\sqrt{25y^{10}}} = \dfrac{4x^2}{5y^5}$

84. $\sqrt{\dfrac{49a^8b^{10}}{121c^{14}}} = \dfrac{\sqrt{49a^8b^{10}}}{\sqrt{121c^{14}}} = \dfrac{7a^4b^5}{11c^7}$

85. $\sqrt[3]{\dfrac{c^6}{64}} = \dfrac{\sqrt[3]{c^6}}{\sqrt[3]{64}} = \dfrac{c^2}{4}$

86. $\sqrt[3]{\dfrac{27x^6}{y^{12}}} = \dfrac{\sqrt[3]{27x^6}}{\sqrt[3]{y^{12}}} = \dfrac{3x^2}{y^4}$

87. $\sqrt[3]{\dfrac{a^8b^{12}}{b^{-8}}} = \sqrt[3]{a^8b^{12+8}}$

$\qquad = \sqrt[3]{a^8b^{20}}$

$\qquad = \sqrt[3]{a^6b^{18} \cdot a^2b^2}$

$\qquad = \sqrt[3]{a^6b^{18}} \cdot \sqrt[3]{a^2b^2}$

$\qquad = a^2b^6\sqrt[3]{a^2b^2}$

88. $\sqrt[4]{\dfrac{16x^{16}y^{32}}{81x^{-4}}} = \sqrt[4]{\dfrac{16}{81}x^{16+4}y^{32}}$

$\qquad = \sqrt[4]{\dfrac{16}{81}x^{20}y^{32}}$

$\qquad = \dfrac{2}{3}x^5y^8 \;\; \text{or} \;\; \dfrac{2x^5y^8}{3}$

89. $\dfrac{\sqrt{24}}{\sqrt{3}} = \sqrt{\dfrac{24}{3}} = \sqrt{8} = \sqrt{4\cdot 2} = 2\sqrt{2}$

90. $\dfrac{\sqrt{64x^5}}{\sqrt{2x^3}} = \sqrt{\dfrac{64x^5}{2x^3}} = \sqrt{32x^2} = \sqrt{16x^2\cdot 2} = 4x\sqrt{2}$

91. $\dfrac{\sqrt{27x^6}}{\sqrt{3x^2}} = \sqrt{\dfrac{27x^6}{3x^2}} = \sqrt{9x^4} = 3x^2$

92. $\dfrac{\sqrt{72x^3y^5}}{\sqrt{8x^3y^7}} = \sqrt{\dfrac{72x^3y^5}{8x^3y^7}} = \sqrt{\dfrac{9}{y^2}} = \dfrac{3}{y}$

93. $\dfrac{\sqrt{48x^6y^9}}{\sqrt{6x^2y^6}} = \sqrt{\dfrac{40x^6y^9}{5x^2y^6}}$

$\qquad = \sqrt{8x^4y^3}$

$\qquad = \sqrt{4x^4y^2\cdot 2y}$

$\qquad = 2x^2y\sqrt{2y}$

94. $\dfrac{\sqrt{300a^{10}b^{11}}}{\sqrt{2ab^4}} = \sqrt{\dfrac{300a^{10}b^{11}}{2ab^4}}$

$\qquad = \sqrt{150a^9b^7}$

$\qquad = \sqrt{25a^8b^6\cdot 6ab}$

$\qquad = 5a^4b^3\sqrt{6ab}$

95. $\sqrt[3]{\dfrac{5xy}{8x^{13}}} = \sqrt[3]{\dfrac{5y}{8x^{12}}} = \dfrac{\sqrt[3]{5y}}{\sqrt[3]{8x^{12}}} = \dfrac{\sqrt[3]{5y}}{2x^4}$

96. $\sqrt[3]{\dfrac{64a^5b^{12}}{27a^{14}b^5}} = \sqrt[3]{\dfrac{64b^7}{27a^9}}$

$\qquad = \dfrac{\sqrt[3]{64b^7}}{\sqrt[3]{27a^9}}$

$\qquad = \dfrac{\sqrt[3]{64b^6\cdot b}}{3a^3}$

$\qquad = \dfrac{4b^2\sqrt[3]{b}}{3a^3}$

97. $\sqrt[3]{\dfrac{25x^2y^9}{5x^8y^2}} = \sqrt[3]{\dfrac{5y^7}{x^6}}$

$\qquad = \dfrac{\sqrt[3]{5y^7}}{\sqrt[3]{x^6}}$

$\qquad = \dfrac{\sqrt[3]{y^6\cdot 5y}}{x^2}$

$\qquad = \dfrac{y^2\sqrt[3]{5y}}{x^2}$

98. $\sqrt[3]{\dfrac{54xy^4z^{17}}{18x^{13}z^4}} = \sqrt[3]{\dfrac{3y^4z^{12}}{x^{12}}}$

$\qquad = \dfrac{\sqrt[3]{3y^4z^{12}}}{\sqrt[3]{x^{12}}}$

$\qquad = \dfrac{\sqrt[3]{y^3z^{12}\cdot 3y}}{x^4}$

$\qquad = \dfrac{yz^4\sqrt[3]{3yz}}{x^4}$

99. $\sqrt[4]{\dfrac{10x^4y}{81x^{-8}}} = \sqrt[4]{\dfrac{10x^{12}y}{81}}$

$\qquad = \dfrac{\sqrt[4]{10x^{12}y}}{\sqrt[4]{81}}$

$\qquad = \dfrac{\sqrt[4]{x^{12}}\sqrt[4]{10y}}{\sqrt[4]{81}}$

$\qquad = \dfrac{x^3\sqrt[4]{10y}}{3}$

100. $\sqrt[4]{\dfrac{3a^6b^5}{16a^{-6}b^{13}}} = \sqrt[4]{\dfrac{3a^{12}}{16b^8}} = \dfrac{\sqrt[4]{3a^{12}}}{\sqrt[4]{16b^8}} = \dfrac{a^3\sqrt[4]{3}}{2b^2}$

101. $\sqrt{a \cdot b} = (a \cdot b)^{1/2} = a^{1/2} \cdot b^{1/2} = \sqrt{a} \cdot \sqrt{b}$

102. No, for example $\sqrt{3} \cdot \sqrt{12} = \sqrt{36} = 6$.

103. No, for example $\dfrac{\sqrt{18}}{\sqrt{2}} = \sqrt{\dfrac{18}{2}} = \sqrt{9} = 3$.

104. $\sqrt[n]{\dfrac{a}{b}} = \left(\dfrac{a}{b}\right)^{1/n} = \dfrac{a^{1/n}}{b^{1/n}} = \dfrac{\sqrt[n]{a}}{\sqrt[n]{b}}$

105. a. no

    b. $\dfrac{\sqrt[n]{x}}{\sqrt[n]{x}}$ is equal to 1 when $\sqrt[n]{x}$ is a real number

    and not equal to 0.

106. $F = \dfrac{9}{5}C + 32$

$F - 32 = \dfrac{9}{5}C$

$\dfrac{5}{9}(F - 32) = \dfrac{5}{9}\left(\dfrac{9}{5}C\right)$

$\dfrac{5}{9}(F - 32) = C$ or $C = \dfrac{5}{9}(F - 32)$

107. $\dfrac{15x^{12} - 5x^9 + 20x^6}{5x^6} = \dfrac{15x^{12}}{5x^6} - \dfrac{5x^9}{5x^6} + \dfrac{20x^6}{5x^6}$

$= 3x^6 - x^3 + 4$

108. $(x - 3)^3 + 8$

$= (x - 3)^3 + (2)^3$

$= ((x - 3) + 2)\left((x - 3)^2 - (x - 3)(2) + (2)^2\right)$

$= (x - 1)\left(x^2 - 6x + 9 - 2x + 6 + 4\right)$

$= (x - 1)\left(x^2 - 8x + 19\right)$

109. $(2x - 3)(x - 2) = 4x - 6$

$2x^2 - 7x + 6 = 4x - 6$

$2x^2 - 11x + 12 = 0$

$(2x - 3)(x - 4) = 0$

$2x - 3 = 0$ or $x - 4 = 0$

$2x = 3$ $x = 4$

$x = \dfrac{3}{2}$

110. $\left|\dfrac{2x - 4}{5}\right| = 12$

$\dfrac{2x - 4}{5} = -12$ or $\dfrac{2x - 4}{5} = 12$

$2x - 4 = -60$ $2x - 4 = 60$

$2x = -56$ $2x = 64$

$x = -28$ $x = 32$

The solution is $\{-28, 32\}$.

Exercise Set 11.4

1. Like radicals are radicals with the same radicands and index.

2. a. Answers will vary.

    b. $\dfrac{3}{5}\sqrt{5} + \dfrac{5}{4}\sqrt{5} = \left(\dfrac{3}{5} + \dfrac{5}{4}\right)\sqrt{5}$

$= \left(\dfrac{12}{20} + \dfrac{25}{20}\right)\sqrt{5}$

$= \dfrac{37}{20}\sqrt{5}$ or $\dfrac{37\sqrt{5}}{20}$

3. $\sqrt{3} + 3\sqrt{2} \approx 1.732 + 3(1.414)$

$\approx 1.732 + 4.242$

≈ 5.974 or 5.97

4. $2\sqrt{3} + \sqrt{5} \approx 2(1.732) + 2.236$

$\approx 3.464 + 2.236$

≈ 5.700 or 5.70

5. No. To see this, let $a = 16$ and $b = 9$. Then, the left side is $\sqrt{a} + \sqrt{b} = \sqrt{16} + \sqrt{9} = 4 + 3 = 7$ whereas the right side is

$\sqrt{a + b} = \sqrt{16 + 9} = \sqrt{25} = 5$.

6. No. The left side is $\sqrt{64} + \sqrt{36} = 8 + 6 = 14$ whereas the right side is $\sqrt{100} = 10$.

7. $\sqrt{3} - \sqrt{3} = 0$

8. $2\sqrt{6} - \sqrt{6} = 1\sqrt{6} = \sqrt{6}$

9. $6\sqrt{5} - 2\sqrt{5} = 4\sqrt{5}$

10. $3\sqrt{2} + 7\sqrt{2} - 11 = 10\sqrt{2} - 11$

11. $2\sqrt{3} - 2\sqrt{3} - 4\sqrt{3} + 5 = -4\sqrt{3} + 5$

12. $6\sqrt[3]{7} - 8\sqrt[3]{7} = -2\sqrt[3]{7}$

13. $2\sqrt[4]{y} - 9\sqrt[4]{y} = -7\sqrt[4]{y}$

14. $3\sqrt[5]{a} + 7 + 5\sqrt[5]{a} - 2 = 8\sqrt[5]{a} + 5$

15. $3\sqrt{5} - \sqrt[3]{x} + 6\sqrt{5} + 3\sqrt[3]{x} = 2\sqrt[3]{x} + 9\sqrt{5}$

16. $9 + 4\sqrt[4]{a} - 7\sqrt[4]{a} + 5 = -3\sqrt[4]{a} + 14$

17. $5\sqrt{x} - 8\sqrt{y} + 3\sqrt{x} + 2\sqrt{y} - \sqrt{x} = 7\sqrt{x} - 6\sqrt{y}$

18. $8\sqrt{a} + 4\sqrt[3]{b} + 7\sqrt{a} - 12\sqrt[3]{b} = 15\sqrt{a} - 8\sqrt[3]{b}$

19. $\sqrt{5} + \sqrt{20} = \sqrt{5} + \sqrt{4} \cdot \sqrt{5}$
$\qquad = \sqrt{5} + 2\sqrt{5}$
$\qquad = 3\sqrt{5}$

20. $\sqrt{75} + \sqrt{108} = \sqrt{25} \cdot \sqrt{3} + \sqrt{36} \cdot \sqrt{3}$
$\qquad = 5\sqrt{3} + 6\sqrt{3}$
$\qquad = 11\sqrt{3}$

21. $-6\sqrt{75} + 5\sqrt{125} = -6\sqrt{25} \cdot \sqrt{3} + 5\sqrt{25} \cdot \sqrt{5}$
$\qquad = -6\left(5\sqrt{3}\right) + 5\left(5\sqrt{5}\right)$
$\qquad = -30\sqrt{3} + 25\sqrt{5}$

22. $3\sqrt{250} + 4\sqrt{160} = 3\sqrt{25} \cdot \sqrt{10} + 4\sqrt{16} \cdot \sqrt{10}$
$\qquad = 3(5\sqrt{10}) + 4(4\sqrt{10})$
$\qquad = 15\sqrt{10} + 16\sqrt{10}$
$\qquad = 31\sqrt{10}$

23. $-4\sqrt{90} + 3\sqrt{40} + 2\sqrt{10}$
$\quad = -4\sqrt{9} \cdot \sqrt{10} + 3\sqrt{4} \cdot \sqrt{10} + 2\sqrt{10}$
$\quad = -4\left(3\sqrt{10}\right) + 3\left(2\sqrt{10}\right) + 2\left(\sqrt{10}\right)$
$\quad = -12\sqrt{10} + 6\sqrt{10} + 2\sqrt{10}$
$\quad = -4\sqrt{10}$

24. $3\sqrt{40x^2 y} + 2x\sqrt{490y}$
$\quad = 3\sqrt{4x^2}\sqrt{10y} + 2x\sqrt{49}\sqrt{10y}$
$\quad = 3\left(2x\sqrt{10y}\right) + 2x\left(7\sqrt{10y}\right)$
$\quad = 6x\sqrt{10y} + 14x\sqrt{10y}$
$\quad = 20x\sqrt{10y}$

25. $\sqrt{500xy^2} + y\sqrt{320x}$
$\quad = \sqrt{100y^2} \cdot \sqrt{5x} + y\sqrt{64}\sqrt{5x}$
$\quad = 10y\sqrt{5x} + 8y\sqrt{5x}$
$\quad = 18y\sqrt{5x}$

26. $5\sqrt{8} + 2\sqrt{50} - 3\sqrt{72}$
$\quad = 5\sqrt{4} \cdot \sqrt{2} + 2\sqrt{25} \cdot \sqrt{2} - 3\sqrt{36} \cdot \sqrt{2}$
$\quad = 5(2\sqrt{2}) + 2(5\sqrt{2}) - 3(6\sqrt{2})$
$\quad = 10\sqrt{2} + 10\sqrt{2} - 18\sqrt{2}$
$\quad = 2\sqrt{2}$

27. $2\sqrt{5x} - 3\sqrt{20x} - 4\sqrt{45x}$
$\quad = 2\sqrt{5x} - 3\sqrt{4} \cdot \sqrt{5x} - 4\sqrt{9} \cdot \sqrt{5x}$
$\quad = 2\sqrt{5x} - 3\left(2\sqrt{5x}\right) - 4\left(3\sqrt{5x}\right)$
$\quad = 2\sqrt{5x} - 6\sqrt{5x} - 12\sqrt{5x}$
$\quad = -16\sqrt{5x}$

28. $3\sqrt{27c^2} - 2\sqrt{108c^2} - \sqrt{48c^2}$
$\quad = 3\sqrt{9c^2} \cdot \sqrt{3} - 2\sqrt{36c^2} \cdot \sqrt{3} - \sqrt{16c^2} \cdot \sqrt{3}$
$\quad = 3(3c\sqrt{3}) - 2(6c\sqrt{3}) - 4c\sqrt{3}$
$\quad = 9c\sqrt{3} - 12c\sqrt{3} - 4c\sqrt{3}$
$\quad = -7c\sqrt{3}$

29. $3\sqrt{50a^2} - 3\sqrt{72a^2} - 8a\sqrt{18}$
$\quad = 3\sqrt{25a^2} \cdot \sqrt{2} - 3\sqrt{36a^2} \cdot \sqrt{2} - 8a\sqrt{9} \cdot \sqrt{2}$
$\quad = 3\left(5a\sqrt{2}\right) - 3\left(6a\sqrt{2}\right) - 8a\left(3\sqrt{2}\right)$
$\quad = 15a\sqrt{2} - 18a\sqrt{2} - 24a\sqrt{2}$
$\quad = -27a\sqrt{2}$

30. $4\sqrt[3]{5} - 5\sqrt[3]{40} = 4\sqrt[3]{5} - 5\sqrt[3]{8}\cdot\sqrt[3]{5}$

$\qquad\qquad = 4\sqrt[3]{5} - 5\left(2\sqrt[3]{5}\right)$

$\qquad\qquad = 4\sqrt[3]{5} - 10\sqrt[3]{5}$

$\qquad\qquad = -6\sqrt[3]{5}$

31. $\sqrt[3]{108} + \sqrt[3]{32} = \sqrt[3]{27}\cdot\sqrt[3]{4} + \sqrt[3]{8}\cdot\sqrt[3]{4}$

$\qquad\qquad = 3\sqrt[3]{4} + 2\sqrt[3]{4}$

$\qquad\qquad = 5\sqrt[3]{4}$

32. $3\sqrt[3]{16} + \sqrt[3]{54} = 3\left(\sqrt[3]{8}\cdot\sqrt[3]{2}\right) + \sqrt[3]{27}\cdot\sqrt[3]{2}$

$\qquad\qquad = 3\left(2\sqrt[3]{2}\right) + 3\sqrt[3]{2}$

$\qquad\qquad = 6\sqrt[3]{2} + 3\sqrt[3]{2}$

$\qquad\qquad = 9\sqrt[3]{2}$

33. $\sqrt[3]{27} - 5\sqrt[3]{8} = 3 - 5\cdot 2 = 3 - 10 = -7$

34. $3\sqrt{45x^3} + \sqrt{5x} = 3\sqrt{9x^2}\cdot\sqrt{5x} + \sqrt{5x}$

$\qquad\qquad = 3\left(3x\sqrt{5x}\right) + \sqrt{5x}$

$\qquad\qquad = 9x\sqrt{5x} + \sqrt{5x}$

$\qquad\qquad = (9x+1)\sqrt{5x}$

35. $2\sqrt[3]{a^4b^2} + 4a\sqrt[3]{ab^2} = 2\sqrt[3]{a^3}\cdot\sqrt[3]{ab^2} + 4a\sqrt[3]{ab^2}$

$\qquad\qquad = 2a\sqrt[3]{ab^2} + 4a\sqrt[3]{ab^2}$

$\qquad\qquad = 6a\sqrt[3]{ab^2}$

36. $5y\sqrt[4]{48x^5} - x\sqrt[4]{3x^5y^4}$

$\qquad = 5y\sqrt[4]{16x^4}\cdot\sqrt[4]{3x} - x\sqrt[4]{x^4y^4}\cdot\sqrt[4]{3x}$

$\qquad = 5y\left(2x\sqrt[4]{3x}\right) - x(xy)\sqrt[4]{3x}$

$\qquad = 10xy\sqrt[4]{3x} - x^2y\sqrt[4]{3x}$

$\qquad = (10xy - x^2y)\sqrt[4]{3x}$

37. $\sqrt{4r^7s^5} + 3r^2\sqrt{r^3s^5} - 2rs\sqrt{r^5s^3}$

$\qquad = \sqrt{4r^6s^4}\cdot\sqrt{rs} + 3r^2\sqrt{r^2s^4}\cdot\sqrt{rs} - 2rs\sqrt{r^4s^2}\cdot\sqrt{rs}$

$\qquad = 2r^3s^2\sqrt{rs} + 3r^2\left(rs^2\sqrt{rs}\right) - 2rs(r^2s\sqrt{rs})$

$\qquad = 2r^3s^2\sqrt{rs} + 3r^3s^2\sqrt{rs} - 2r^3s^2\sqrt{rs}$

$\qquad = 3r^3s^2\sqrt{rs}$

38. $x\sqrt[3]{27x^5y^2} - x^2\sqrt[3]{x^2y^2} + 4\sqrt[3]{x^8y^2}$

$\qquad = x\sqrt[3]{27x^3}\cdot\sqrt[3]{x^2y^2} - x^2\sqrt[3]{x^2y^2} + 4\sqrt[3]{x^6}\cdot\sqrt[3]{x^2y^2}$

$\qquad = x\left(3x\sqrt[3]{x^2y^2}\right) - x^2\sqrt[3]{x^2y^2} + 4x^2\sqrt[3]{x^2y^2}$

$\qquad = 3x^2\sqrt[3]{x^2y^2} - x^2\sqrt[3]{x^2y^2} + 4x^2\sqrt[3]{x^2y^2}$

$\qquad = 6x^2\sqrt[3]{x^2y^2}$

39. $\sqrt[3]{128x^8y^{10}} - 2x^2y\sqrt[3]{16x^2y^7}$

$\qquad = \sqrt[3]{64x^8y^9}\sqrt[3]{2y} - 2x^2y\sqrt[3]{8x^2y^6}\sqrt[3]{2y}$

$\qquad = 4x^2y^3\sqrt[3]{2x^2y} - 2x^2y\left(2y^2\sqrt[3]{2x^2y}\right)$

$\qquad = 4x^2y^3\sqrt[3]{2x^2y} - 4x^2y^3\sqrt[3]{2x^2y}$

$\qquad = 0$

40. $5\sqrt[3]{320x^5y^8} + 3x\sqrt[3]{135x^2y^8}$

$\qquad = 5\sqrt[3]{64x^3y^6}\sqrt[3]{5x^2y^2} + 3x\sqrt[3]{27y^6}\sqrt[3]{5x^2y^2}$

$\qquad = 5(4xy^2\sqrt[3]{5x^2y^2}) + 3x(3y^2\sqrt[3]{5x^2y^2})$

$\qquad = 20xy^2\sqrt[3]{5x^2y^2} + 9xy^2\sqrt[3]{5x^2y^2}$

$\qquad = 29xy^2\sqrt[3]{5x^2y^2}$

41. $\sqrt{3}\sqrt{27} = \sqrt{3\cdot 27} = \sqrt{81} = 9$

42. $\sqrt[3]{2}\sqrt[3]{4} = \sqrt[3]{8} = 2$

43. $\sqrt[3]{4}\sqrt[3]{14} = \sqrt[3]{56} = \sqrt[3]{8\cdot 7} = 2\sqrt[3]{7}$

44. $\sqrt[3]{3}\sqrt[3]{54} = \sqrt[3]{162} = \sqrt[3]{27\cdot 6} = \sqrt[3]{27}\sqrt[3]{6} = 3\sqrt[3]{6}$

45. $\sqrt{9m^3n^7}\sqrt{3mn^4} = \sqrt{9m^3n^7\cdot 3mn^4}$

$\qquad\qquad = \sqrt{27m^4n^{11}}$

$\qquad\qquad = \sqrt{9\cdot 3\cdot m^4\cdot n^{10}\cdot n}$

$\qquad\qquad = \sqrt{9m^4n^{10}\cdot 3n}$

$\qquad\qquad = \sqrt{9m^4n^{10}}\sqrt{3n}$

$\qquad\qquad = 3m^2n^5\sqrt{3n}$

633

46. $\sqrt[3]{5ab^2}\sqrt[3]{25a^4b^{12}} = \sqrt[3]{5ab^2 \cdot 25a^4b^{12}}$

$= \sqrt[3]{125a^5b^{14}}$

$= \sqrt[3]{125 \cdot a^3 \cdot a^2 \cdot b^{12} \cdot b^2}$

$= \sqrt[3]{125a^3b^{12} \cdot a^2b^2}$

$= \sqrt[3]{125a^3b^{12}}\sqrt[3]{a^2b^2}$

$= 5ab^4\sqrt[3]{a^2b^2}$

47. $\sqrt[3]{9x^7y^{10}}\sqrt[3]{6x^4y^3} = \sqrt[3]{9x^7y^{10} \cdot 6x^4y^3}$

$= \sqrt[3]{54x^{11}y^{13}}$

$= \sqrt[3]{27 \cdot 2 \cdot x^9 \cdot x^2 \cdot y^{12} \cdot y}$

$= \sqrt[3]{27x^9y^{12} \cdot 2x^2y}$

$= \sqrt[3]{27x^9y^{12}}\sqrt[3]{2x^2y}$

$= 3x^3y^4\sqrt[3]{2x^2y}$

48. $\sqrt[4]{3x^9y^{12}}\sqrt[4]{54x^4y^7} = \sqrt[4]{3x^9y^{12} \cdot 54x^4y^7}$

$= \sqrt[4]{162x^{13}y^{19}}$

$= \sqrt[4]{81 \cdot 2 \cdot x^{12} \cdot x \cdot y^{16} \cdot y^3}$

$= \sqrt[4]{81x^{12}y^{16} \cdot 2xy^3}$

$= \sqrt[4]{81x^{12}y^{16}}\sqrt[4]{2xy^3}$

$= 3x^3y^4\sqrt[4]{2xy^3}$

49. $\sqrt[5]{x^{24}y^{30}z^9}\sqrt[5]{x^{13}y^8z^7}$

$= \sqrt[5]{x^{24}y^{30}z^9 \cdot x^{13}y^8z^7}$

$= \sqrt[5]{x^{37}y^{38}z^{16}}$

$= \sqrt[5]{x^{35} \cdot x^2 \cdot y^{35} \cdot y^3 \cdot z^{15} \cdot z}$

$= \sqrt[5]{x^{35}y^{35}z^{15} \cdot x^2y^3z}$

$= \sqrt[5]{x^{35}y^{35}z^{15}}\sqrt[5]{x^2y^3z}$

$= x^7y^7z^3\sqrt[5]{x^2y^3z}$

50. $\sqrt[4]{8x^4yz^3}\sqrt[4]{2x^2y^3z^7}$

$= \sqrt[4]{8x^4yz^3 \cdot 2x^2y^3z^7}$

$= \sqrt[4]{16x^6y^4z^{10}}$

$= \sqrt[4]{16 \cdot x^4 \cdot x^2 \cdot y^4 \cdot z^8 \cdot z^2}$

$= \sqrt[4]{16x^4y^4z^8 \cdot x^2z^2}$

$= \sqrt[4]{16x^4y^4z^8} \cdot \sqrt[4]{x^2z^2}$

$= 2xyz^2\sqrt[4]{x^2z^2}$

51. $\left(\sqrt[3]{2x^3y^4}\right)^2 = \sqrt[3]{(2x^3y^4)^2}$

$= \sqrt[3]{4x^6y^8}$

$= \sqrt[3]{4 \cdot x^6 \cdot y^6 \cdot y^2}$

$= \sqrt[3]{x^6y^6 \cdot 4y^2}$

$= \sqrt[3]{x^6y^6}\sqrt[3]{4y^2}$

$= x^2y^2\sqrt[3]{4y^2}$

52. $\sqrt{2}\left(\sqrt{6} + \sqrt{18}\right) = \left(\sqrt{2}\right)\left(\sqrt{6}\right) + \left(\sqrt{2}\right)\left(\sqrt{18}\right)$

$= \sqrt{12} + \sqrt{36}$

$= \sqrt{4}\sqrt{3} + 6$

$= 2\sqrt{3} + 6$

53. $\sqrt{5}\left(\sqrt{5} - \sqrt{3}\right) = \left(\sqrt{5}\right)\left(\sqrt{5}\right) - \left(\sqrt{5}\right)\left(\sqrt{3}\right)$

$= \sqrt{25} - \sqrt{15}$

$= 5 - \sqrt{15}$

54. $\sqrt{3}\left(\sqrt{12} + \sqrt{8}\right)$

$= \left(\sqrt{3}\right)\left(\sqrt{12}\right) + \left(\sqrt{3}\right)\left(\sqrt{8}\right)$

$= \sqrt{36} + \sqrt{24}$

$= 6 + \sqrt{4}\sqrt{6}$

$= 6 + 2\sqrt{6}$

55. $\sqrt[3]{y}\left(2\sqrt[3]{y}-\sqrt[3]{y^8}\right)$

$$=\left(\sqrt[3]{y}\right)\left(2\sqrt[3]{y}\right)-\left(\sqrt[3]{y}\right)\left(\sqrt[3]{y^8}\right)$$

$$=2\sqrt[3]{y^2}-\sqrt[3]{y^9}$$

$$=2\sqrt[3]{y^2}-y^3$$

56. $\sqrt{3y}\left(\sqrt{27y^2}-\sqrt{y}\right)$

$$=\left(\sqrt{3y}\right)\left(\sqrt{27y^2}\right)-\left(\sqrt{3y}\right)\left(\sqrt{y}\right)$$

$$=\sqrt{81y^3}-\sqrt{3y^2}$$

$$=\sqrt{81y^2}\sqrt{y}-\sqrt{y^2}\sqrt{3}$$

$$=9y\sqrt{y}-y\sqrt{3}$$

57. $2\sqrt[3]{x^4y^5}\left(\sqrt[3]{8x^{12}y^4}+\sqrt[3]{16xy^9}\right)$

$$=\left(2\sqrt[3]{x^4y^5}\right)\left(\sqrt[3]{8x^{12}y^4}\right)+\left(2\sqrt[3]{x^4y^5}\right)\left(\sqrt[3]{16xy^9}\right)$$

$$=2\sqrt[3]{8x^{16}y^9}+2\sqrt[3]{16x^5y^{14}}$$

$$=2\sqrt[3]{8x^{15}y^9}\sqrt[3]{x}+2\sqrt[3]{8x^3y^{12}}\sqrt[3]{2x^2y^2}$$

$$=2\cdot2x^5y^3\sqrt[3]{x}+2\cdot2xy^4\sqrt[3]{2x^2y^2}$$

$$=4x^5y^3\sqrt[3]{x}+4xy^4\sqrt[3]{2x^2y^2}$$

58. $\sqrt[5]{16x^7y^6}\left(\sqrt[5]{2x^6y^9}-\sqrt[5]{10x^3y^7}\right)$

$$=\left(\sqrt[5]{16x^7y^6}\right)\left(\sqrt[5]{2x^6y^9}\right)-\left(\sqrt[5]{16x^7y^6}\right)\left(\sqrt[5]{10x^3y^7}\right)$$

$$=\sqrt[5]{32x^{13}y^{15}}-\sqrt[5]{160x^{10}y^{13}}$$

$$=\sqrt[5]{32x^{10}y^{15}}\sqrt[5]{x^3}-\sqrt[5]{32x^{10}y^{10}}\sqrt[5]{5y^3}$$

$$=2x^2y^3\sqrt[5]{x^3}-2x^2y^2\sqrt[5]{5y^3}$$

59. $(8+\sqrt{5})(8-\sqrt{5})=8^2-(\sqrt{5})^2$

$$=64-5$$

$$=59$$

60. $\left(9-\sqrt{5}\right)\left(9+\sqrt{5}\right)=9^2-(\sqrt{5})^2$

$$=81-5$$

$$=76$$

61. $\left(\sqrt{6}+x\right)\left(\sqrt{6}-x\right)=\left(\sqrt{6}\right)^2-x^2$

$$=6-x^2$$

62. $\left(\sqrt{x}+y\right)\left(\sqrt{x}-y\right)=\left(\sqrt{x}\right)^2-y^2$

$$=x-y^2$$

63. $\left(\sqrt{7}-\sqrt{z}\right)\left(\sqrt{7}+\sqrt{z}\right)=\left(\sqrt{7}\right)^2-\left(\sqrt{z}\right)^2$

$$=7-z$$

64. $\left(3\sqrt{a}-5\sqrt{b}\right)\left(3\sqrt{a}+5\sqrt{b}\right)=\left(3\sqrt{a}\right)^2-\left(5\sqrt{b}\right)^2$

$$=9a-25b$$

65. $\left(\sqrt{3}+4\right)\left(\sqrt{3}+5\right)=\sqrt{9}+5\sqrt{3}+4\sqrt{3}+20$

$$=3+9\sqrt{3}+20$$

$$=23+9\sqrt{3}$$

66. $\left(1+\sqrt{5}\right)\left(8+\sqrt{5}\right)=8+\sqrt{5}+8\sqrt{5}+(\sqrt{5})^2$

$$=8+9\sqrt{5}+5$$

$$=13+9\sqrt{5}$$

67. $\left(3-\sqrt{2}\right)\left(4-\sqrt{8}\right)=12-3\sqrt{8}-4\sqrt{2}+\sqrt{16}$

$$=12-3\cdot2\sqrt{2}-4\sqrt{2}+4$$

$$=12-6\sqrt{2}-4\sqrt{2}+4$$

$$=16-10\sqrt{2}$$

68. $\left(5\sqrt{6}+3\right)\left(4\sqrt{6}-1\right)$

$$=5\sqrt{6}\left(4\sqrt{6}\right)-5\sqrt{6}+12\sqrt{6}-3$$

$$=20(6)-5\sqrt{6}+12\sqrt{6}-3$$

$$=120-3+7\sqrt{6}$$

$$=117+7\sqrt{6}$$

69. $\left(4\sqrt{3}+\sqrt{2}\right)\left(\sqrt{3}-\sqrt{2}\right)$

$$=4\sqrt{9}-4\sqrt{6}+\sqrt{6}-\sqrt{4}$$

$$=4\cdot3-3\sqrt{6}-2$$

$$=12-3\sqrt{6}-2$$

$$=10-3\sqrt{6}$$

70. $\left(\sqrt{3}+7\right)^2 = \left(\sqrt{3}+7\right)\left(\sqrt{3}+7\right)$

$\qquad = \sqrt{9} + 7\sqrt{3} + 7\sqrt{3} + 49$

$\qquad = 3 + 14\sqrt{3} + 49$

$\qquad = 52 + 14\sqrt{3}$

71. $\left(2\sqrt{5}-3\right)^2 = \left(2\sqrt{5}-3\right)\left(2\sqrt{5}-3\right)$

$\qquad = 4\sqrt{25} - 6\sqrt{5} - 6\sqrt{5} + 9$

$\qquad = 4 \cdot 5 - 12\sqrt{5} + 9$

$\qquad = 20 + 9 - 12\sqrt{5}$

$\qquad = 29 - 12\sqrt{5}$

72. $\left(\sqrt{y}+\sqrt{6z}\right)\left(\sqrt{2z}-\sqrt{8y}\right)$

$\qquad = \sqrt{y}\sqrt{2z} - \sqrt{y}\sqrt{8y} + \sqrt{6z}\sqrt{2z} - \sqrt{6z}\sqrt{8y}$

$\qquad = \sqrt{2yz} - \sqrt{8y^2} + \sqrt{12z^2} - \sqrt{48yz}$

$\qquad = \sqrt{2yz} - \sqrt{4y^2}\sqrt{2} + \sqrt{4z^2}\sqrt{3} - \sqrt{16}\sqrt{3yz}$

$\qquad = \sqrt{2yz} - 2y\sqrt{2} + 2z\sqrt{3} - 4\sqrt{3yz}$

73. $\left(2\sqrt{3x}-\sqrt{y}\right)\left(3\sqrt{3x}+\sqrt{y}\right)$

$\qquad = 6\left(\sqrt{3x}\right)^2 + 2\sqrt{3x}\sqrt{y} - 3\sqrt{3x}\sqrt{y} - \left(\sqrt{y}\right)^2$

$\qquad = 6(3x) + 2\sqrt{3xy} - 3\sqrt{3xy} - y$

$\qquad = 18x - \sqrt{3xy} - y$

74. $\left(\sqrt[3]{9}+\sqrt[3]{2}\right)\left(\sqrt[3]{3}+\sqrt[3]{4}\right)$

$\qquad = \sqrt[3]{27} + \sqrt[3]{36} + \sqrt[3]{6} + \sqrt[3]{8}$

$\qquad = 3 + \sqrt[3]{36} + \sqrt[3]{6} + 2$

$\qquad = 5 + \sqrt[3]{36} + \sqrt[3]{6}$

75. $\left(\sqrt[3]{4}-\sqrt[3]{6}\right)\left(\sqrt[3]{2}-\sqrt[3]{36}\right)$

$\qquad = \sqrt[3]{4}\sqrt[3]{2} - \sqrt[3]{4}\sqrt[3]{36} - \sqrt[3]{6}\sqrt[3]{2} + \sqrt[3]{6}\sqrt[3]{36}$

$\qquad = \sqrt[3]{8} - \sqrt[3]{144} - \sqrt[3]{12} + \sqrt[3]{216}$

$\qquad = 2 - 2\sqrt[3]{18} - \sqrt[3]{12} + 6$

$\qquad = 8 - 2\sqrt[3]{18} - \sqrt[3]{12}$

76. $\left(\sqrt[3]{4x}-\sqrt[3]{2y}\right)\left(\sqrt[3]{4x}+\sqrt[3]{10}\right)$

$\qquad = \sqrt[3]{4x}\sqrt[3]{4x} + \sqrt[3]{4x}\sqrt[3]{10} - \sqrt[3]{2y}\sqrt[3]{4x} - \sqrt[3]{2y}\sqrt[3]{10}$

$\qquad = \sqrt[3]{16x^2} + \sqrt[3]{40x} - \sqrt[3]{8xy} - \sqrt[3]{20y}$

$\qquad = \sqrt[3]{8}\sqrt[3]{2x^2} + \sqrt[3]{8}\sqrt[3]{5x} - \sqrt[3]{8}\sqrt[3]{xy} - \sqrt[3]{20y}$

$\qquad = 2\sqrt[3]{2x^2} + 2\sqrt[3]{5x} - 2\sqrt[3]{xy} - \sqrt[3]{20y}$

77. $(f \cdot g)(x) = f(x) \cdot g(x)$

$\qquad = \sqrt{2x}\left(\sqrt{8x} - \sqrt{32}\right)$

$\qquad = \sqrt{2x} \cdot \sqrt{8x} - \sqrt{2x} \cdot \sqrt{32}$

$\qquad = \sqrt{16x^2} - \sqrt{64x}$

$\qquad = 4x - 8\sqrt{x}$

78. $(f \cdot g)(x) = f(x) \cdot g(x)$

$\qquad = \sqrt{6x} \cdot \left(\sqrt{6x} - \sqrt{10x}\right)$

$\qquad = \sqrt{6x}\sqrt{6x} - \sqrt{6x}\sqrt{10x}$

$\qquad = \sqrt{36x^2} - \sqrt{60x^2}$

$\qquad = 6x - \sqrt{4x^2}\sqrt{15}$

$\qquad = 6x - 2x\sqrt{15}$

79. $(f \cdot g)(x) = f(x) \cdot g(x)$

$\qquad = \sqrt[3]{x}\left(\sqrt[3]{x^5} + \sqrt[3]{x^4}\right)$

$\qquad = \sqrt[3]{x}\sqrt[3]{x^5} + \sqrt[3]{x}\sqrt[3]{x^4}$

$\qquad = \sqrt[3]{x^6} + \sqrt[3]{x^5}$

$\qquad = \sqrt[3]{x^6} + \sqrt[3]{x^3 \cdot x^2}$

$\qquad = x^2 + x\sqrt[3]{x^2}$

80. $(f \cdot g)(x) = f(x) \cdot g(x)$

$\qquad = \sqrt[3]{2x^2}\left(\sqrt[3]{4x} + \sqrt[3]{32x^2}\right)$

$\qquad = \sqrt[3]{2x^2}\sqrt[3]{4x} + \sqrt[3]{2x^2}\sqrt[3]{32x^2}$

$\qquad = \sqrt[3]{8x^3} + \sqrt[3]{64x^4}$

$\qquad = \sqrt[3]{8x^3} + \sqrt[3]{64x^3 \cdot x}$

$\qquad = 2x + 4x\sqrt[3]{x}$

81. $(f \cdot g)(x) = f(x) \cdot g(x)$

$= \sqrt[4]{3x^2}\left(\sqrt[4]{9x^4} - \sqrt[4]{x^7}\right)$

$= \sqrt[4]{3x^2}\sqrt[4]{9x^4} - \sqrt[4]{3x^2}\sqrt[4]{x^7}$

$= \sqrt[4]{27x^6} - \sqrt[4]{3x^9}$

$= \sqrt[4]{x^4}\sqrt[4]{27x^2} - \sqrt[4]{x^8}\sqrt[4]{3x}$

$= x\sqrt[4]{27x^2} - x^2\sqrt[4]{3x}$

82. $(f \cdot g)(x) = f(x) \cdot g(x)$

$= \sqrt[4]{2x^3}\left(\sqrt[4]{8x^5} - \sqrt[4]{5x^6}\right)$

$= \sqrt[4]{2x^3}\sqrt[4]{8x^5} - \sqrt[4]{2x^3}\sqrt[4]{5x^6}$

$= \sqrt[4]{16x^8} - \sqrt[4]{10x^9}$

$= \sqrt[4]{16x^8} - \sqrt[4]{x^8}\sqrt[4]{10x}$

$= 2x^2 - x^2\sqrt[4]{10x}$

83. $\sqrt{24} = \sqrt{4 \cdot 6} = 2\sqrt{6}$

84. $\sqrt{300} = \sqrt{100 \cdot 3} = 10\sqrt{3}$

85. $\sqrt{125} - \sqrt{20} = \sqrt{25 \cdot 5} - \sqrt{4 \cdot 5}$

$= 5\sqrt{5} - 2\sqrt{5}$

$= 3\sqrt{5}$

86. $4\sqrt{7} + 2\sqrt{63} - 2\sqrt{28} = 4\sqrt{7} + 2\sqrt{9 \cdot 7} - 2\sqrt{4 \cdot 7}$

$= 4\sqrt{7} + 2 \cdot 3\sqrt{7} - 2 \cdot 2\sqrt{7}$

$= 4\sqrt{7} + 6\sqrt{7} - 4\sqrt{7}$

$= 6\sqrt{7}$

87. $\left(3\sqrt{2} - 4\right)\left(\sqrt{2} + 5\right)$

$= 3\left(\sqrt{2}\right)^2 + 15\sqrt{2} - 4\sqrt{2} - 20$

$= 6 + 11\sqrt{2} - 20$

$= -14 + 11\sqrt{2}$

88. $\left(\sqrt{5} + \sqrt{2}\right)\left(\sqrt{2} + \sqrt{20}\right)$

$= \sqrt{10} + \sqrt{100} + \sqrt{4} + \sqrt{40}$

$= \sqrt{10} + 10 + 2 + \sqrt{4}\sqrt{10}$

$= \sqrt{10} + 12 + 2\sqrt{10}$

$= 12 + 3\sqrt{10}$

89. $\sqrt{6}\left(5 - \sqrt{2}\right) = \sqrt{6} \cdot 5 - \sqrt{6} \cdot \sqrt{2}$

$= 5\sqrt{6} - \sqrt{12}$

$= 5\sqrt{6} - 2\sqrt{3}$

90. $3\sqrt[3]{81} + 4\sqrt[3]{24} = 3\sqrt[3]{27 \cdot 3} + 4\sqrt[3]{8 \cdot 3}$

$= 9\sqrt[3]{3} + 8\sqrt[3]{3}$

$= 17\sqrt[3]{3}$

91. $\sqrt{150}\sqrt{3} = \sqrt{450} = \sqrt{225 \cdot 2} = 15\sqrt{2}$

92. $\sqrt[4]{2}\sqrt[4]{40} = \sqrt[4]{80} = \sqrt[4]{16 \cdot 5} = 2\sqrt[4]{5}$

93. $\sqrt[3]{80x^{11}} = \sqrt[3]{8x^9 \cdot 10x^2} = 2x^3\sqrt[3]{10x^2}$

94. $\sqrt[3]{x^9 y^{11} z} = \sqrt[3]{x^9 y^9 \cdot y^2 z} = x^3 y^3 \sqrt[3]{y^2 z}$

95. $\sqrt[6]{128ab^{17}c^9} = \sqrt[6]{64b^{12}c^6 \cdot 2ab^5c^3}$

$= 2b^2 c \sqrt[6]{2ab^5c^3}$

96. $\sqrt[5]{14x^4 y^2}\sqrt[5]{3x^4 y^3} = \sqrt[5]{42x^8 y^5}$

$= \sqrt[5]{x^5 y^5 \cdot 42x^3}$

$= xy\sqrt[5]{42x^3}$

97. $2b\sqrt[4]{a^4 b} + ab\sqrt[4]{16b} = 2b\sqrt[4]{a^4} \cdot \sqrt[4]{b} + ab\sqrt[4]{16} \cdot \sqrt[4]{b}$

$= 2b\left(a\sqrt[4]{b}\right) + ab\left(2\sqrt[4]{b}\right)$

$= 2ab\sqrt[4]{b} + 2ab\sqrt[4]{b}$

$= 4ab\sqrt[4]{b}$

98. $2\sqrt[3]{24a^3 y^4} + 4a\sqrt[3]{81y^4}$

$= 2\sqrt[3]{8a^3 y^3} \cdot \sqrt[3]{3y} + 4a\sqrt[3]{27y^3} \cdot \sqrt[3]{3y}$

$= 2\left(2ay\sqrt[3]{3y}\right) + 4a\left(3y\sqrt[3]{3y}\right)$

$= 4ay\sqrt[3]{3y} + 12ay\sqrt[3]{3y}$

$= 16ay\sqrt[3]{3y}$

99. $\left(\sqrt[3]{x^2} - \sqrt[3]{y}\right)\left(\sqrt[3]{x} - 2\sqrt[3]{y^2}\right)$

$= \sqrt[3]{x^2}\sqrt[3]{x} - 2\sqrt[3]{x^2}\sqrt[3]{y^2} - \sqrt[3]{y}\sqrt[3]{x} + 2\sqrt[3]{y}\sqrt[3]{y^2}$

$= \sqrt[3]{x^3} - 2\sqrt[3]{x^2 y^2} - \sqrt[3]{xy} + 2\sqrt[3]{y^3}$

$= x - 2\sqrt[3]{x^2 y^2} - \sqrt[3]{xy} + 2y$

100. $\left(\sqrt[3]{a} + 5\right)\left(\sqrt[3]{a^2} - 6\right)$

$= \sqrt[3]{a}\sqrt[3]{a^2} - 6\sqrt[3]{a} + 5\sqrt[3]{a^2} - 30$

$= \sqrt[3]{a^3} - 6\sqrt[3]{a} + 5\sqrt[3]{a^2} - 30$

$= a - 6\sqrt[3]{a} + 5\sqrt[3]{a^2} - 30$

101. $\sqrt[3]{3ab^2}\left(\sqrt[3]{4a^4 b^3} - \sqrt[3]{8a^5 b^4}\right)$

$= \left(\sqrt[3]{3ab^2}\right)\left(\sqrt[3]{4a^4 b^3}\right) - \left(\sqrt[3]{3ab^2}\right)\left(\sqrt[3]{8a^5 b^4}\right)$

$= \sqrt[3]{12a^5 b^5} - \sqrt[3]{24a^6 b^6}$

$= \sqrt[3]{a^3 b^3 \cdot 12a^2 b^2} - \sqrt[3]{8a^6 b^6 \cdot 3}$

$= ab\sqrt[3]{12a^2 b^2} - 2a^2 b^2 \sqrt[3]{3}$

102. $\sqrt[4]{4st^2}\left(\sqrt[4]{2s^5 t^6} + \sqrt[4]{5s^9 t^2}\right)$

$= \left(\sqrt[4]{4st^2}\right)\left(\sqrt[4]{2s^5 t^6}\right) + \left(\sqrt[4]{4st^2}\right)\left(\sqrt[4]{5s^9 t^2}\right)$

$= \sqrt[4]{8s^6 t^8} + \sqrt[4]{20s^{10} t^4}$

$= \sqrt[4]{s^4 t^8 \cdot 8s^2} + \sqrt[4]{s^8 t^4 \cdot 20s^2}$

$= st^2 \sqrt[4]{8s^2} + s^2 t \sqrt[4]{20s^2}$

103. $f(x) = \sqrt{2x-5}\sqrt{2x-5} = 2x - 5$

No absolute value needed since $x \geq \dfrac{5}{2}$.

104. $g(a) = \sqrt{3a+7}\sqrt{3a+7} = 3a + 7$

No absolute value needed since $a \geq -\dfrac{7}{3}$.

105. $h(r) = \sqrt{4r^2 - 32r + 64}$

$= \sqrt{4\left(r^2 - 8r + 16\right)}$

$= \sqrt{4\left(r - 4\right)^2}$

$= 2|r - 4|$

106. $f(b) = \sqrt{20b^2 + 60b + 45}$

$= \sqrt{5\left(4b^2 + 12b + 9\right)}$

$= \sqrt{5\left(2b + 3\right)^2}$

$= \sqrt{5}\,|2b + 3|$

107. Perimeter $= \sqrt{45} + \sqrt{45} + \sqrt{80} + \sqrt{80}$

$= 2\sqrt{45} + 2\sqrt{80}$

$= 2\sqrt{9}\sqrt{5} + 2\sqrt{16}\sqrt{5}$

$= 2\left(3\sqrt{5}\right) + 2\left(4\sqrt{5}\right)$

$= 6\sqrt{5} + 8\sqrt{5}$

$= 14\sqrt{5}$

Area $= \sqrt{45}\sqrt{80}$

$= 3\sqrt{5} \cdot 4\sqrt{5}$

$= 12\left(\sqrt{5}\right)^2$

$= 12 \cdot 5$

$= 60$

108. Perimeter $= \sqrt{54} + \sqrt{96} + \sqrt{150}$

$= \sqrt{9}\sqrt{6} + \sqrt{16}\sqrt{6} + \sqrt{25}\sqrt{6}$

$= 3\sqrt{6} + 4\sqrt{6} + 5\sqrt{6}$

$= 12\sqrt{6}$

Area $= \dfrac{1}{2}\sqrt{24}\sqrt{150}$

$= \dfrac{1}{2} \cdot \sqrt{4}\sqrt{6} \cdot \sqrt{25}\sqrt{6}$

$= \dfrac{1}{2} \cdot 2\sqrt{6} \cdot 5\sqrt{6}$

$= \dfrac{1}{2}\left[10\left(\sqrt{6}\right)^2\right]$

$= 5 \cdot 6$

$= 30$

109. Perimeter $= \sqrt{245} + \sqrt{180} + \sqrt{80}$
$$= \sqrt{49}\sqrt{5} + \sqrt{36}\sqrt{5} + \sqrt{16}\sqrt{5}$$
$$= 7\sqrt{5} + 6\sqrt{5} + 4\sqrt{5}$$
$$= 17\sqrt{5}$$

Area $= \dfrac{1}{2}\sqrt{245}\sqrt{45}$
$$= \dfrac{1}{2}\sqrt{49}\sqrt{5}\sqrt{9}\sqrt{5}$$
$$= \dfrac{1}{2} \cdot 7 \cdot 3 \left(\sqrt{5}\right)^2$$
$$= \dfrac{21}{2} \cdot 5$$
$$= 52.5$$

110. Perimeter $= \sqrt{18} + \sqrt{40} + \sqrt{18} + \sqrt{160}$
$$= \sqrt{9}\sqrt{2} + \sqrt{4}\sqrt{10} + \sqrt{9}\sqrt{2} + \sqrt{16}\sqrt{10}$$
$$= 3\sqrt{2} + 2\sqrt{10} + 3\sqrt{2} + 4\sqrt{10}$$
$$= 6\sqrt{2} + 6\sqrt{10}$$

Area $= \dfrac{1}{2}h(b_1 + b_2)$
$$= \dfrac{1}{2}\sqrt{8}\left(\sqrt{40} + \sqrt{160}\right)$$
$$= \dfrac{\sqrt{8}}{2}\left(2\sqrt{10} + 4\sqrt{10}\right)$$
$$= \dfrac{2\sqrt{2}}{2}\left(6\sqrt{10}\right)$$
$$= \sqrt{2}\left(6\sqrt{10}\right)$$
$$= 6\sqrt{20}$$
$$= 12\sqrt{5} \approx 26.83$$

111. No, for example $-\sqrt{2} + \sqrt{2} = 0$

112. No, for example $\sqrt{2} - \sqrt{2} = 0$

113. **a.** $s = \sqrt{30FB}$
$$s = \sqrt{30(0.85)(80)} \approx 45.17$$
The car's speed was about 45.17 mph.

b. $s = \sqrt{30FB}$
$$s = \sqrt{30(0.52)(80)} \approx 35.33$$
The car's speed was about 35.33 mph.

114. $R = 28d^2\sqrt{P}$
$$R = 28(2.5)^2\sqrt{80}$$
$$R \approx 1565.25$$
The flow rate is about 1565.25 gallons per minute.

115. $f(t) = 3\sqrt{t} + 19$

a. $f(36) = 3\sqrt{36} + 19$
$$= 3(6) + 19$$
$$= 18 + 19$$
$$= 37$$
The length at 36 months is 37 inches.

b. $f(40) = 3\sqrt{40} + 19$
$$= 3\sqrt{4}\sqrt{10} + 19$$
$$= 3 \cdot 2\sqrt{10} + 19$$
$$= 6\sqrt{10} + 19$$
$$\approx 37.97$$
The length at 40 months is about 37.97 inches.

116. $\sigma = \sqrt{npq}$
$$\sigma = \sqrt{600(0.93)(0.07)}$$
$$\sigma = 6.25$$
In this case, the standard deviation is about 6.25.

117. **a.** $f(x) = \sqrt{x}$
$$g(x) = 2$$
$$(f+g)(x) = f(x) + g(x) = \sqrt{x} + 2$$

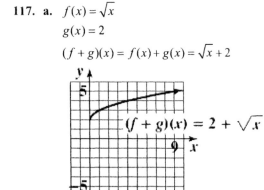

b. It raises the graph 2 units.

118. a.
$$f(x) = -\sqrt{x}$$
$$g(x) = 3$$
$$(f+g)(x) = f(x) + g(x)$$
$$= -\sqrt{x} + 3 \text{ or } 3 - \sqrt{x}$$

b. It raises the graph 3 units.

119. a.
$$(f-g)(x) = f(x) - g(x)$$
$$= \sqrt{x} - \left(\sqrt{x} - 2\right)$$
$$= \sqrt{x} - \sqrt{x} + 2$$
$$= 2$$

b. $\sqrt{x} \geq 0$, so $x \geq 0$

The domain is $\{x \mid x \geq 0\}$.

120. a.
$$(f+g)(x) = f(x) + g(x)$$
$$= \sqrt{x} + \left(-\sqrt{x} - 3\right)$$
$$= \sqrt{x} - \sqrt{x} - 3$$
$$= -3$$

b. $\sqrt{x} \geq 0$, so $x \geq 0$

The domain is $\{x \mid x \geq 0\}$.

121. $f(x) = \sqrt{x^2}$

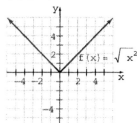

122. $f(x) = \sqrt{x^2} - 4$

123. A rational number is a quotient of two integers with a nonzero denominator.

124. A real number is a number that can represented on a real number line.

125. An irrational number is a real number that cannot be expressed as the quotient of two integers.

126. $|a| = \begin{cases} a, & a \geq 0 \\ -a, & a < 0 \end{cases}$

127. $E = \frac{1}{2}mv^2$
$$2E = 2\left(\frac{1}{2}mv^2\right)$$
$$2E = mv^2$$
$$\frac{2E}{v^2} = m \text{ or } m = \frac{2E}{v^2}$$

128. a.
$$-4 < 2x - 3 \leq 7$$
$$-4 + 3 < 2x - 3 + 3 \leq 7 + 3$$
$$-1 < 2x \leq 10$$
$$-\frac{1}{2} < x \leq 5$$

b. $\left(-\frac{1}{2}, 5\right]$

c. $\left\{x \mid -\frac{1}{2} < x \leq 5\right\}$

1. $\sqrt{121} = \sqrt{(11)^2} = 11$

2. $\sqrt[3]{-\dfrac{27}{64}} = \sqrt[3]{-\left(\dfrac{3}{4}\right)^3} = -\dfrac{3}{4}$

3. $\sqrt{(-16.3)^2} = |-16.3| = 16.3$

4. $\sqrt{\left(3a^2 - 4b^3\right)^2} = |3a^2 - 4b^3|$

5. $g(x) = \dfrac{x}{8} + \sqrt{4x - 7}$

$\quad g(16) = \dfrac{16}{8} + \sqrt{4(16) - 7}$

$\qquad\quad = 2 + \sqrt{64} - 7$

$\qquad\quad = 2 + 8 - 7$

$\qquad\quad = 3$

6. $\sqrt[5]{7a^4 b^3} = \left(7a^4 b^3\right)^{1/5}$

7. $-49^{1/2} + 81^{3/4} = -\sqrt{49} + \left(\sqrt[4]{81}\right)^3$

$\qquad\qquad\qquad\quad = -7 + (3)^3$

$\qquad\qquad\qquad\quad = -7 + 27$

$\qquad\qquad\qquad\quad = 20$

8. $\left(\sqrt[4]{a^2 b^3 c}\right)^{20} = \left[\left(a^2 b^3 c\right)^{1/4}\right]^{20} = \left(a^2 b^3 c\right)^{(1/4)\cdot 20}$

$\qquad\qquad\quad = \left(a^2 b^3 c\right)^5 = a^{2\cdot5} b^{3\cdot5} c^{1\cdot5}$

$\qquad\qquad\quad = a^{10} b^{15} c^5$

9. $7x^{-5/2} \cdot 2x^{3/2} = 7 \cdot 2 \cdot x^{-5/2} \cdot x^{3/2}$

$\qquad\qquad\quad = 14 x^{-5/2 + 3/2}$

$\qquad\qquad\quad = 14 x^{-2/2}$

$\qquad\qquad\quad = 14 x^{-1}$

$\qquad\qquad\quad = \dfrac{14}{x}$

10. $8x^{-2}\left(x^3 + 2x^{-1/2}\right)$

$\quad = 8x^{-2}\left(x^3\right) + 8x^{-2}\left(2x^{-1/2}\right)$

$\quad = 8x^{-2+3} + 16x^{-2+(-1/2)}$

$\quad = 8x^1 + 16x^{-5/2}$

$\quad = 8x + \dfrac{16}{x^{5/2}}$

11. $\sqrt{32x^4 y^9} = \sqrt{16x^4 y^8} \cdot \sqrt{2y}$

$\qquad\qquad = 4x^2 y^4 \sqrt{2y}$

12. $\sqrt[6]{64a^{13} b^{23} c^{15}} = \sqrt[6]{64a^{12} b^{18} c^{12}} \cdot \sqrt[6]{ab^5 c^3}$

$\qquad\qquad\qquad = 2a^2 b^3 c^2 \sqrt[6]{ab^5 c^3}$

13. $\dfrac{\sqrt[3]{3}}{\sqrt[3]{81}} = \sqrt[3]{\dfrac{3}{81}} = \sqrt[3]{\dfrac{1}{27}} = \dfrac{1}{3}$

14. $\dfrac{\sqrt{20x^5 y^{12}}}{\sqrt{180x^{15} y^7}} = \sqrt{\dfrac{20x^5 y^{12}}{180x^{15} y^7}} = \sqrt{\dfrac{y^5}{9x^{10}}}$

$\qquad\qquad = \dfrac{\sqrt{y^4} \cdot \sqrt{y}}{\sqrt{9x^{10}}} = \dfrac{y^2 \sqrt{y}}{3x^5}$

15. $2\sqrt{x} - 3\sqrt{y} + 9\sqrt{x} + 15\sqrt{y}$

$\quad = 2\sqrt{x} + 9\sqrt{x} - 3\sqrt{y} + 15\sqrt{y}$

$\quad = 11\sqrt{x} + 12\sqrt{y}$

16. $2\sqrt{90x^2 y} + 3x\sqrt{490y}$

$\quad = 2\sqrt{9x^2} \cdot \sqrt{10y} + 3x\sqrt{49} \cdot \sqrt{10y}$

$\quad = 2(3x)\sqrt{10y} + 3x(7)\sqrt{10y}$

$\quad = 6x\sqrt{10y} + 21x\sqrt{10y}$

$\quad = 27x\sqrt{10y} \quad \text{(assuming } x \geq 0)$

17. $\left(x + \sqrt{5}\right)\left(2x - 3\sqrt{5}\right)$

$\quad = x(2x) - x\left(3\sqrt{5}\right) + \sqrt{5}(2x) - \left(\sqrt{5}\right)\left(3\sqrt{5}\right)$

$\quad = 2x^2 - 3x\sqrt{5} + 2x\sqrt{5} - 3(5)$

$\quad = 2x^2 - x\sqrt{5} - 15$

18. $2\sqrt{3a}\left(\sqrt{27a^2}-5\sqrt{4a}\right)$

$$= 2\sqrt{3a}\cdot\sqrt{27a^2}-2\sqrt{3a}\cdot 5\sqrt{4a}$$

$$= 2\sqrt{81a^3}-10\sqrt{12a^2}$$

$$= 2\sqrt{81a^2}\cdot\sqrt{a}-10\sqrt{4a^2}\cdot\sqrt{3}$$

$$= 2(9a)\sqrt{a}-10(2a)\sqrt{3}$$

$$= 18a\sqrt{a}-20a\sqrt{3}$$

19. $3b\sqrt[4]{a^5b}+2ab\sqrt[4]{16ab}$

$$= 3b\sqrt[4]{a^4}\cdot\sqrt[4]{ab}+2ab\sqrt[4]{16}\cdot\sqrt[4]{ab}$$

$$= 3b(a)\sqrt[4]{ab}+2ab(2)\sqrt[4]{ab}$$

$$= 3ab\sqrt[4]{ab}+4ab\sqrt[4]{ab}$$

$$= 7ab\sqrt[4]{ab}\quad\text{(assuming }a\ge 0\text{)}$$

20. a. $\sqrt{(x-3)^2}=|x-3|$

The absolute value is needed here because we do not know the domain for x. Since the expression $x-3$ is negative for $x<3$, the absolute value is required.

b. $\sqrt{64x^2}=\sqrt{(8x)^2}=8x$

Since $x\ge 0$, we know that $8x\ge 0$. Since $8x$ is never negative, the absolute value is not needed.

Exercise Set 11.5

1. a. The conjugate of a binomial is a binomial with the same two terms as the original but the sign of the second term is changed. The conjugate of $a+b$ is $a-b$. Also, the conjugate of $a-b$ is $a+b$.

b. The conjugate of $x-\sqrt{3}$ is $x+\sqrt{3}$.

2. Rationalizing a denominator means to remove radicals from a denominator.

3. a. Answers will vary. Possible answer: Multiply the numerator and denominator by a quantity that will result in no radicals in the denominator.

b. $\dfrac{4}{\sqrt{3y}}=\dfrac{4}{\sqrt{3y}}\cdot\dfrac{\sqrt{3y}}{\sqrt{3y}}=\dfrac{4\sqrt{3y}}{\sqrt{9y^2}}=\dfrac{4\sqrt{3y}}{3y}$

4. a. Answers will vary. Possible answer: Multiply the numerator and denominator by the conjugate of the denominator.

b. $\dfrac{\sqrt{2}+\sqrt{5}}{\sqrt{2}-\sqrt{5}}=\dfrac{\sqrt{2}+\sqrt{5}}{\sqrt{2}-\sqrt{5}}\cdot\dfrac{\left(\sqrt{2}+\sqrt{5}\right)}{\left(\sqrt{2}+\sqrt{5}\right)}$

$$=\dfrac{\sqrt{4}+2\left(\sqrt{2}\right)\left(\sqrt{5}\right)+\sqrt{25}}{\left(\sqrt{2}\right)^2-\left(\sqrt{5}\right)^2}$$

$$=\dfrac{2+2\sqrt{10}+5}{2-5}$$

$$=\dfrac{7+2\sqrt{10}}{-3}=-\dfrac{7+2\sqrt{10}}{3}$$

5. (1) No perfect powers are factors of any radicand.

(2) No radicand contains fractions.

(3) No radicals are in any denominator.

6. a. The radicand, x^5, which can be written as $x^4\cdot x$, contains a perfect square factor, x^4.

b. The radicand contains a fraction.

c. There is a radical in the denominator.

7. $\dfrac{1}{\sqrt{3}}=\dfrac{1}{\sqrt{3}}\cdot\dfrac{\sqrt{3}}{\sqrt{3}}=\dfrac{\sqrt{3}}{3}$

8. $\dfrac{1}{\sqrt{6}}=\dfrac{1}{\sqrt{6}}\cdot\dfrac{\sqrt{6}}{\sqrt{6}}=\dfrac{\sqrt{6}}{6}$

9. $\dfrac{4}{\sqrt{5}}=\dfrac{4}{\sqrt{5}}\cdot\dfrac{\sqrt{5}}{\sqrt{5}}=\dfrac{4\sqrt{5}}{5}$

10. $\dfrac{3}{\sqrt{7}}=\dfrac{3}{\sqrt{7}}\cdot\dfrac{\sqrt{7}}{\sqrt{7}}=\dfrac{3\sqrt{7}}{7}$

11. $\dfrac{6}{\sqrt{6}}=\dfrac{6}{\sqrt{6}}\cdot\dfrac{\sqrt{6}}{\sqrt{6}}=\dfrac{6\sqrt{6}}{6}=\sqrt{6}$

12. $\dfrac{17}{\sqrt{17}}=\dfrac{17}{\sqrt{17}}\cdot\dfrac{\sqrt{17}}{\sqrt{17}}=\dfrac{17\sqrt{17}}{17}=\sqrt{17}$

13. $\dfrac{1}{\sqrt{z}}=\dfrac{1}{\sqrt{z}}\cdot\dfrac{\sqrt{z}}{\sqrt{z}}=\dfrac{\sqrt{z}}{z}$

14. $\dfrac{y}{\sqrt{y}} = \dfrac{y}{\sqrt{y}} \cdot \dfrac{\sqrt{y}}{\sqrt{y}} = \dfrac{y\sqrt{y}}{y} = \sqrt{y}$

15. $\dfrac{p}{\sqrt{2}} = \dfrac{p}{\sqrt{2}} \cdot \dfrac{\sqrt{2}}{\sqrt{2}} = \dfrac{p\sqrt{2}}{2}$

16. $\dfrac{m}{\sqrt{13}} = \dfrac{m}{\sqrt{13}} \cdot \dfrac{\sqrt{13}}{\sqrt{13}} = \dfrac{m\sqrt{13}}{13}$

17. $\dfrac{\sqrt{y}}{\sqrt{7}} = \dfrac{\sqrt{y}}{\sqrt{7}} \cdot \dfrac{\sqrt{7}}{\sqrt{7}} = \dfrac{\sqrt{7y}}{7}$

18. $\dfrac{\sqrt{19}}{\sqrt{q}} = \dfrac{\sqrt{19}}{\sqrt{q}} \cdot \dfrac{\sqrt{q}}{\sqrt{q}} = \dfrac{\sqrt{19q}}{q}$

19. $\dfrac{6\sqrt{3}}{\sqrt{6}} = \dfrac{6\sqrt{3}}{\sqrt{6}} \cdot \dfrac{\sqrt{6}}{\sqrt{6}} = \dfrac{6\sqrt{18}}{6} = \dfrac{6 \cdot 3\sqrt{2}}{6} = 3\sqrt{2}$

20. $\dfrac{15x}{\sqrt{x}} = \dfrac{15x}{\sqrt{x}} \cdot \dfrac{\sqrt{x}}{\sqrt{x}} = \dfrac{15x\sqrt{x}}{x} = 15\sqrt{x}$

21. $\dfrac{\sqrt{x}}{\sqrt{y}} = \dfrac{\sqrt{x}}{\sqrt{y}} \cdot \dfrac{\sqrt{y}}{\sqrt{y}} = \dfrac{\sqrt{xy}}{y}$

22. $\dfrac{2\sqrt{3}}{\sqrt{a}} = \dfrac{2\sqrt{3}}{\sqrt{a}} \cdot \dfrac{\sqrt{a}}{\sqrt{a}} = \dfrac{2\sqrt{3a}}{a}$

23. $\sqrt{\dfrac{5m}{8}} = \dfrac{\sqrt{5m}}{\sqrt{8}}$

$= \dfrac{\sqrt{5m}}{2\sqrt{2}}$

$= \dfrac{\sqrt{5m}}{2\sqrt{2}} \cdot \dfrac{\sqrt{2}}{\sqrt{2}}$

$= \dfrac{\sqrt{10m}}{2 \cdot 2} = \dfrac{\sqrt{10m}}{4}$

24. $\dfrac{9\sqrt{3}}{\sqrt{y^3}} = \dfrac{9\sqrt{3}}{y\sqrt{y}}$

$= \dfrac{9\sqrt{3}}{y\sqrt{y}} \cdot \dfrac{\sqrt{y}}{\sqrt{y}}$

$= \dfrac{9\sqrt{3y}}{y \cdot y}$

$= \dfrac{9\sqrt{3y}}{y^2}$

25. $\dfrac{2n}{\sqrt{18n}} = \dfrac{2n}{\sqrt{9}\sqrt{2n}}$

$= \dfrac{2n}{3\sqrt{2n}}$

$= \dfrac{2n}{3\sqrt{2n}} \cdot \dfrac{\sqrt{2n}}{\sqrt{2n}}$

$= \dfrac{2n\sqrt{2n}}{3 \cdot 2n} = \dfrac{\sqrt{2n}}{3}$

26. $\sqrt{\dfrac{120x}{4y^3}} = \sqrt{\dfrac{30x}{y^3}}$

$= \dfrac{\sqrt{30x}}{\sqrt{y^3}}$

$= \dfrac{\sqrt{30x}}{y\sqrt{y}}$

$= \dfrac{\sqrt{30x}}{y\sqrt{y}} \cdot \dfrac{\sqrt{y}}{\sqrt{y}}$

$= \dfrac{\sqrt{30xy}}{y \cdot y}$

$= \dfrac{\sqrt{30xy}}{y^2}$

27. $\sqrt{\dfrac{18x^4y^3}{2z^3}} = \sqrt{\dfrac{9x^4y^3}{z^3}} = \dfrac{\sqrt{9x^4y^3}}{\sqrt{z^2 \cdot z}}$

$= \dfrac{\sqrt{9x^4y^2}\sqrt{y}}{\sqrt{z^2}\sqrt{z}} = \dfrac{3x^2y\sqrt{y}}{z\sqrt{z}}$

$= \dfrac{3x^2y\sqrt{y}}{z\sqrt{z}} \cdot \dfrac{\sqrt{z}}{\sqrt{z}}$

$= \dfrac{3x^2y\sqrt{yz}}{z^2}$

28.
$$\sqrt{\frac{7pq^4}{2r}} = \frac{\sqrt{7pq^4}}{\sqrt{2r}}$$
$$= \frac{\sqrt{q^4}\sqrt{7p}}{\sqrt{2r}} = \frac{q^2\sqrt{7p}}{\sqrt{2r}}$$
$$= \frac{q^2\sqrt{7p}}{\sqrt{2r}} \cdot \frac{\sqrt{2r}}{\sqrt{2r}} = \frac{q^2\sqrt{14pr}}{\sqrt{4r^2}}$$
$$= \frac{q^2\sqrt{14pr}}{2r}$$

29.
$$\sqrt{\frac{20y^4z^3}{3xy^{-4}}} = \sqrt{\frac{20y^8z^3}{3x}} = \frac{\sqrt{20y^8z^3}}{\sqrt{3x}}$$
$$= \frac{\sqrt{4y^8z^2}\sqrt{5z}}{\sqrt{3x}} = \frac{2y^4z\sqrt{5z}}{\sqrt{3x}}$$
$$= \frac{2y^4z\sqrt{5z}}{\sqrt{3x}} \cdot \frac{\sqrt{3x}}{\sqrt{3x}}$$
$$= \frac{2y^4z\sqrt{15xz}}{3x}$$

30.
$$\sqrt{\frac{5xy^6}{3z}} = \frac{\sqrt{5xy^6}}{\sqrt{3z}} = \frac{\sqrt{y^6}\sqrt{5x}}{\sqrt{3z}}$$
$$= \frac{y^3\sqrt{5x}}{\sqrt{3z}} = \frac{y^3\sqrt{5x}}{\sqrt{3z}} \cdot \frac{\sqrt{3z}}{\sqrt{3z}}$$
$$= \frac{y^3\sqrt{15xz}}{3z}$$

31.
$$\sqrt{\frac{48x^6y^5}{3z^3}} = \sqrt{\frac{16x^6y^5}{z^3}} = \frac{\sqrt{16x^6y^5}}{\sqrt{z^2 \cdot z}}$$
$$= \frac{\sqrt{16x^6y^4}\sqrt{y}}{\sqrt{z^2}\sqrt{z}} = \frac{4x^3y^2\sqrt{y}}{z\sqrt{z}}$$
$$= \frac{4x^3y^2\sqrt{y}}{z\sqrt{z}} \cdot \frac{\sqrt{z}}{\sqrt{z}}$$
$$= \frac{4x^3y^2\sqrt{yz}}{z^2}$$

32.
$$\sqrt{\frac{45y^{12}z^{10}}{2x}} = \frac{\sqrt{45y^{12}z^{10}}}{\sqrt{2x}}$$
$$= \frac{\sqrt{9y^{12}z^{10}}\sqrt{5}}{\sqrt{2x}}$$
$$= \frac{3y^6z^5\sqrt{5}}{\sqrt{2x}}$$
$$= \frac{3y^6z^5\sqrt{5}}{\sqrt{2x}} \cdot \frac{\sqrt{2x}}{\sqrt{2x}}$$
$$= \frac{3y^6z^5\sqrt{10x}}{2x}$$

33. $\dfrac{1}{\sqrt[3]{2}} = \dfrac{1}{\sqrt[3]{2}} \cdot \dfrac{\sqrt[3]{4}}{\sqrt[3]{4}} = \dfrac{\sqrt[3]{4}}{\sqrt[3]{8}} = \dfrac{\sqrt[3]{4}}{2}$

34. $\dfrac{1}{\sqrt[3]{4}} = \dfrac{1}{\sqrt[3]{4}} \cdot \dfrac{\sqrt[3]{2}}{\sqrt[3]{2}} = \dfrac{\sqrt[3]{2}}{\sqrt[3]{8}} = \dfrac{\sqrt[3]{2}}{2}$

35. $\dfrac{8}{\sqrt[3]{y}} = \dfrac{8}{\sqrt[3]{y}} \cdot \dfrac{\sqrt[3]{y^2}}{\sqrt[3]{y^2}} = \dfrac{8\sqrt[3]{y^2}}{y}$

36. $\dfrac{2}{\sqrt[3]{a^2}} = \dfrac{2}{\sqrt[3]{a^2}} \cdot \dfrac{\sqrt[3]{a}}{\sqrt[3]{a}} = \dfrac{2\sqrt[3]{a}}{a}$

37. $\dfrac{1}{\sqrt[4]{3}} = \dfrac{1}{\sqrt[4]{3}} \cdot \dfrac{\sqrt[4]{27}}{\sqrt[4]{27}} = \dfrac{\sqrt[4]{27}}{\sqrt[4]{27}} = \dfrac{\sqrt[4]{27}}{3}$

38. $\dfrac{z}{\sqrt[4]{4}} = \dfrac{z}{\sqrt[4]{4}} \cdot \dfrac{\sqrt[4]{4}}{\sqrt[4]{4}} = \dfrac{z\sqrt[4]{4}}{\sqrt[4]{16}} = \dfrac{z\sqrt[4]{4}}{2}$

39. $\dfrac{a}{\sqrt[4]{8}} = \dfrac{a}{\sqrt[4]{8}} \cdot \dfrac{\sqrt[4]{2}}{\sqrt[4]{2}} = \dfrac{a\sqrt[4]{2}}{\sqrt[4]{16}} = \dfrac{a\sqrt[4]{2}}{2}$

40. $\dfrac{8}{\sqrt[4]{z}} = \dfrac{8}{\sqrt[4]{z}} \cdot \dfrac{\sqrt[4]{z^3}}{\sqrt[4]{z^3}} = \dfrac{8\sqrt[4]{z^3}}{\sqrt[4]{z^4}} = \dfrac{8\sqrt[4]{z^3}}{z}$

41. $\dfrac{5}{\sqrt[4]{z^2}} = \dfrac{5}{\sqrt[4]{z^2}} \cdot \dfrac{\sqrt[4]{z^2}}{\sqrt[4]{z^2}} = \dfrac{5\sqrt[4]{z^2}}{\sqrt[4]{z^4}} = \dfrac{5\sqrt[4]{z^2}}{z}$

42. $\dfrac{13}{\sqrt[4]{z^3}} = \dfrac{13}{\sqrt[4]{z^3}} \cdot \dfrac{\sqrt[4]{z}}{\sqrt[4]{z}} = \dfrac{13\sqrt[4]{z}}{\sqrt[4]{z^4}} = \dfrac{13\sqrt[4]{z}}{z}$

43. $\dfrac{10}{\sqrt[5]{y^3}} = \dfrac{10}{\sqrt[5]{y^3}} \cdot \dfrac{\sqrt[5]{y^2}}{\sqrt[5]{y^2}} = \dfrac{10\sqrt[5]{y^2}}{\sqrt[5]{y^5}} = \dfrac{10\sqrt[5]{y^2}}{y}$

44. $\dfrac{x}{\sqrt[5]{y^4}} = \dfrac{x}{\sqrt[5]{y^4}} \cdot \dfrac{\sqrt[5]{y}}{\sqrt[5]{y}} = \dfrac{x\sqrt[5]{y}}{\sqrt[5]{y^5}} = \dfrac{x\sqrt[5]{y}}{y}$

45. $\dfrac{2}{\sqrt[7]{a^4}} = \dfrac{2}{\sqrt[7]{a^4}} \cdot \dfrac{\sqrt[7]{a^3}}{\sqrt[7]{a^3}} = \dfrac{2\sqrt[7]{a^3}}{\sqrt[7]{a^7}} = \dfrac{2\sqrt[7]{a^3}}{a}$

46. $\sqrt[3]{\dfrac{4x}{y}} = \dfrac{\sqrt[3]{4x}}{\sqrt[3]{y}} = \dfrac{\sqrt[3]{4x}}{\sqrt[3]{y}} \cdot \dfrac{\sqrt[3]{y^2}}{\sqrt[3]{y^2}} = \dfrac{\sqrt[3]{4xy^2}}{y}$

47. $\sqrt[3]{\dfrac{1}{2x}} = \dfrac{\sqrt[3]{1}}{\sqrt[3]{2x}} = \dfrac{1}{\sqrt[3]{2x}} \cdot \dfrac{\sqrt[3]{4x^2}}{\sqrt[3]{4x^2}} = \dfrac{\sqrt[3]{4x^2}}{2x}$

48. $\sqrt[3]{\dfrac{7c}{9y^2}} = \dfrac{\sqrt[3]{7c}}{\sqrt[3]{3^2 y^2}} \cdot \dfrac{\sqrt[3]{3y}}{\sqrt[3]{3y}} = \dfrac{\sqrt[3]{21cy}}{3y}$

49. $\dfrac{5m}{\sqrt[4]{2}} = \dfrac{5m}{\sqrt[4]{2}} \cdot \dfrac{\sqrt[4]{2^3}}{\sqrt[4]{2^3}} = \dfrac{5m\sqrt[4]{8}}{2}$

50. $\dfrac{3}{\sqrt[4]{a}} = \dfrac{3}{\sqrt[4]{a}} \cdot \dfrac{\sqrt[4]{a^3}}{\sqrt[4]{a^3}} = \dfrac{3\sqrt[4]{a^3}}{a}$

51. $\sqrt[4]{\dfrac{5}{3x^3}} = \dfrac{\sqrt[4]{5}}{\sqrt[4]{3x^3}} \cdot \dfrac{\sqrt[4]{3^3 x}}{\sqrt[4]{3^3 x}} = \dfrac{\sqrt[4]{135x}}{3x}$

52. $\sqrt[4]{\dfrac{2x^3}{4y^2}} = \sqrt[4]{\dfrac{x^3}{2y^2}} = \dfrac{\sqrt[4]{x^3}}{\sqrt[4]{2y^2}}$

$= \dfrac{\sqrt[4]{x^3}}{\sqrt[4]{2y^2}} \cdot \dfrac{\sqrt[4]{8y^2}}{\sqrt[4]{8y^2}}$

$= \dfrac{\sqrt[4]{8x^3 y^2}}{2y}$

53. $\sqrt[3]{\dfrac{3x^2}{2y^2}} = \dfrac{\sqrt[3]{3x^2}}{\sqrt[3]{2y^2}} \cdot \dfrac{\sqrt[3]{4y}}{\sqrt[3]{4y}} = \dfrac{\sqrt[3]{12x^2 y}}{2y}$

54. $\sqrt[3]{\dfrac{15x^6 y^7}{2z^2}} = \dfrac{\sqrt[3]{15x^6 y^7}}{\sqrt[3]{2z^2}}$

$= \dfrac{\sqrt[3]{x^6 y^6}\,\sqrt[3]{15y}}{\sqrt[3]{2z^2}}$

$= \dfrac{x^2 y^2 \sqrt[3]{15y}}{\sqrt[3]{2z^2}} \cdot \dfrac{\sqrt[3]{2^2 z}}{\sqrt[3]{2^2 z}}$

$= \dfrac{x^2 y^2 \sqrt[3]{60yz}}{2z}$

55. $\sqrt[3]{\dfrac{14xy^2}{2z^2}} = \sqrt[3]{\dfrac{7xy^2}{z^2}}$

$= \dfrac{\sqrt[3]{7xy^2}}{\sqrt[3]{z^2}}$

$= \dfrac{\sqrt[3]{7xy^2}}{\sqrt[3]{z^2}} \cdot \dfrac{\sqrt[3]{z}}{\sqrt[3]{z}}$

$= \dfrac{\sqrt[3]{7xy^2 z}}{z}$

56. $\sqrt[6]{\dfrac{r^4 s^9}{2r^5}} = \sqrt[6]{\dfrac{s^9}{2r}}$

$= \dfrac{\sqrt[6]{s^9}}{\sqrt[6]{2r}}$

$= \dfrac{s\sqrt[6]{s^3}}{\sqrt[6]{2r}} \cdot \dfrac{\sqrt[6]{32r^5}}{32r^5}$

$= \dfrac{s\sqrt[6]{32r^5 s^3}}{2r}$

57. $\left(5 - \sqrt{6}\right)\left(5 + \sqrt{6}\right) = 5^2 - \left(\sqrt{6}\right)^2$

$= 25 - 6$

$= 19$

58. $\left(7 + \sqrt{3}\right)\left(7 - \sqrt{3}\right) = 7^2 - \left(\sqrt{3}\right)^2 = 49 - 3 = 46$

59. $\left(8 + \sqrt{2}\right)\left(8 - \sqrt{2}\right) = 8^2 - \left(\sqrt{2}\right)^2 = 64 - 2 = 62$

60. $\left(6 - \sqrt{7}\right)\left(6 + \sqrt{7}\right) = 6^2 - \left(\sqrt{7}\right)^2 = 36 - 7 = 29$

61. $\left(2 - \sqrt{10}\right)\left(2 + \sqrt{10}\right) = 2^2 - \left(\sqrt{10}\right)^2 = 4 - 10 = -6$

62. $\left(3+\sqrt{17}\right)\left(3-\sqrt{17}\right) = 3^2 - \left(\sqrt{17}\right)^2 = 9 - 17 = -8$

63. $\left(\sqrt{a}-\sqrt{b}\right)\left(\sqrt{a}+\sqrt{b}\right) = \left(\sqrt{a}\right)^2 - \left(\sqrt{b}\right)^2 = a - b$

64. $\left(\sqrt{x}-\sqrt{y}\right)\left(\sqrt{x}+\sqrt{y}\right) = \left(\sqrt{x}\right)^2 - \left(\sqrt{y}\right)^2 = x - y$

65. $\left(2\sqrt{x}-3\sqrt{y}\right)\left(2\sqrt{x}+3\sqrt{y}\right) = \left(2\sqrt{x}\right)^2 - \left(3\sqrt{y}\right)^2$
$$= 4x - 9y$$

66. $\left(5\sqrt{c}-4\sqrt{d}\right)\left(5\sqrt{c}+4\sqrt{d}\right) = \left(5\sqrt{c}\right)^2 - \left(4\sqrt{d}\right)^2$
$$= 25c - 16d$$

67. $\dfrac{2}{\sqrt{3}+1} = \dfrac{2}{\sqrt{3}+1} \cdot \dfrac{\left(\sqrt{3}-1\right)}{\left(\sqrt{3}-1\right)}$

$$= \dfrac{2\left(\sqrt{3}-1\right)}{\left(\sqrt{3}\right)^2 - 1^2}$$

$$= \dfrac{2\left(\sqrt{3}-1\right)}{3-1}$$

$$= \dfrac{2\left(\sqrt{3}-1\right)}{2}$$

$$= \sqrt{3}-1$$

68. $\dfrac{4}{\sqrt{2}+1} = \dfrac{4}{\sqrt{2}+1} \cdot \dfrac{\left(\sqrt{2}-1\right)}{\left(\sqrt{2}-1\right)}$

$$= \dfrac{4\sqrt{2}-4}{\left(\sqrt{2}\right)^2 - 1^2}$$

$$= \dfrac{4\sqrt{2}-4}{2-1}$$

$$= \dfrac{4\sqrt{2}-4}{1}$$

$$= 4\sqrt{2}-4$$

69. $\dfrac{1}{2+\sqrt{3}} = \dfrac{1}{2+\sqrt{3}} \cdot \dfrac{\left(2-\sqrt{3}\right)}{\left(2-\sqrt{3}\right)}$

$$= \dfrac{2-\sqrt{3}}{2^2 - (\sqrt{3})^2}$$

$$= \dfrac{2-\sqrt{3}}{4-3}$$

$$= \dfrac{2-\sqrt{3}}{1}$$

$$= 2-\sqrt{3}$$

70. $\dfrac{3}{5-\sqrt{7}} = \dfrac{3}{5-\sqrt{7}} \cdot \dfrac{\left(5-\sqrt{7}\right)}{\left(5+\sqrt{7}\right)}$

$$= \dfrac{15+3\sqrt{7}}{25-\left(\sqrt{7}\right)^2}$$

$$= \dfrac{15+3\sqrt{7}}{25-7}$$

$$= \dfrac{15+3\sqrt{7}}{18}$$

$$= \dfrac{5+\sqrt{7}}{6}$$

71. $\dfrac{5}{\sqrt{2}-7} = \dfrac{5}{\sqrt{2}-7} \cdot \dfrac{\left(\sqrt{2}+7\right)}{\left(\sqrt{2}+7\right)}$

$$= \dfrac{5\sqrt{2}+35}{2-49}$$

$$= \dfrac{5\sqrt{2}+35}{-47}$$

$$= \dfrac{-5\sqrt{2}-35}{47}$$

72. $\dfrac{6}{\sqrt{2}+\sqrt{3}} = \dfrac{6}{\sqrt{2}+\sqrt{3}} \cdot \dfrac{\left(\sqrt{2}-\sqrt{3}\right)}{\left(\sqrt{2}-\sqrt{3}\right)}$

$= \dfrac{6\left(\sqrt{2}-\sqrt{3}\right)}{2-3}$

$= \dfrac{6\left(\sqrt{2}-\sqrt{3}\right)}{-1}$

$= -6\left(\sqrt{2}-\sqrt{3}\right)$

$= -6\sqrt{2}+6\sqrt{3}$

$= 6\sqrt{3}-6\sqrt{2}$

73. $\dfrac{\sqrt{5}}{2\sqrt{5}-\sqrt{6}} = \dfrac{\sqrt{5}}{2\sqrt{5}-\sqrt{6}} \cdot \dfrac{\left(2\sqrt{5}+\sqrt{6}\right)}{\left(2\sqrt{5}+\sqrt{6}\right)}$

$= \dfrac{10+\sqrt{30}}{20-6}$

$= \dfrac{10+\sqrt{30}}{14}$

74. $\dfrac{1}{\sqrt{17}-\sqrt{8}} = \dfrac{1}{\sqrt{17}-\sqrt{8}} \cdot \dfrac{\left(\sqrt{17}+\sqrt{8}\right)}{\left(\sqrt{17}+\sqrt{8}\right)}$

$= \dfrac{\sqrt{17}+\sqrt{8}}{17-8}$

$= \dfrac{\sqrt{17}+\sqrt{4}\sqrt{2}}{9}$

$= \dfrac{\sqrt{17}+2\sqrt{2}}{9}$

75. $\dfrac{3}{6+\sqrt{x}} = \dfrac{3}{6+\sqrt{x}} \cdot \dfrac{\left(6-\sqrt{x}\right)}{\left(6-\sqrt{x}\right)} = \dfrac{18-3\sqrt{x}}{36-x}$

76. $\dfrac{4\sqrt{5}}{\sqrt{a}-3} = \dfrac{4\sqrt{5}}{\sqrt{a}-3} \cdot \dfrac{\left(\sqrt{a}+3\right)}{\left(\sqrt{a}+3\right)} = \dfrac{4\sqrt{5a}+12\sqrt{5}}{a-9}$

77. $\dfrac{4\sqrt{x}}{\sqrt{x}-y} = \dfrac{4\sqrt{x}}{\sqrt{x}-y} \cdot \dfrac{\left(\sqrt{x}+y\right)}{\left(\sqrt{x}+y\right)} = \dfrac{4x+4y\sqrt{x}}{x-y^{2}}$

78. $\dfrac{\sqrt{8x}}{x+\sqrt{y}} = \dfrac{\sqrt{8x}}{x+\sqrt{y}} \cdot \dfrac{\left(x-\sqrt{y}\right)}{\left(x-\sqrt{y}\right)}$

$= \dfrac{2\sqrt{2x}\left(x-\sqrt{y}\right)}{x^{2}-y}$

$= \dfrac{2x\sqrt{2x}-2\sqrt{2xy}}{x^{2}-y}$

79. $\dfrac{\sqrt{2}-2\sqrt{3}}{\sqrt{2}+4\sqrt{3}} = \dfrac{\sqrt{2}-2\sqrt{3}}{\sqrt{2}+4\sqrt{3}} \cdot \dfrac{\left(\sqrt{2}-4\sqrt{3}\right)}{\left(\sqrt{2}-4\sqrt{3}\right)}$

$= \dfrac{2-4\sqrt{6}-2\sqrt{6}+8\cdot3}{2-16\cdot3}$

$= \dfrac{26-6\sqrt{6}}{-46}$

$= \dfrac{-13+3\sqrt{6}}{23}$

80. $\dfrac{\sqrt{c}-\sqrt{2d}}{\sqrt{c}-\sqrt{d}}$

$= \dfrac{\sqrt{c}-\sqrt{2d}}{\sqrt{c}-\sqrt{d}} \cdot \dfrac{\left(\sqrt{c}+\sqrt{d}\right)}{\left(\sqrt{c}+\sqrt{d}\right)}$

$= \dfrac{\left(\sqrt{c}\right)^{2}+\sqrt{c}\sqrt{d}-\sqrt{2d}\sqrt{c}-\sqrt{2d}\sqrt{d}}{\left(\sqrt{c}\right)^{2}-\left(\sqrt{d}\right)^{2}}$

$= \dfrac{c+\sqrt{cd}-\sqrt{2cd}-d\sqrt{2}}{c-d}$

81. $\dfrac{\sqrt{a^{3}}+\sqrt{a^{7}}}{\sqrt{a}} = \dfrac{\sqrt{a^{3}}+\sqrt{a^{7}}}{\sqrt{a}} \cdot \dfrac{\left(\sqrt{a}\right)}{\left(\sqrt{a}\right)}$

$= \dfrac{\sqrt{a^{4}}+\sqrt{a^{8}}}{a}$

$= \dfrac{a^{2}+a^{4}}{a}$

$= a+a^{3}$

82.

$$\frac{2\sqrt{xy} - \sqrt{xy}}{\sqrt{x} + \sqrt{y}} = \frac{\sqrt{xy}}{\sqrt{x} + \sqrt{y}}$$

$$= \frac{\sqrt{xy}}{\sqrt{x} + \sqrt{y}} \cdot \frac{\sqrt{x} - \sqrt{y}}{\sqrt{x} - \sqrt{y}}$$

$$= \frac{\sqrt{xy}\left(\sqrt{x} - \sqrt{y}\right)}{\left(\sqrt{x}\right)^2 - \left(\sqrt{y}\right)^2}$$

$$= \frac{\sqrt{x^2 y} - \sqrt{xy^2}}{x - y}$$

$$= \frac{x\sqrt{y} - y\sqrt{x}}{x - y}$$

83.

$$\frac{4}{\sqrt{x+2} - 3} = \frac{4}{\sqrt{x+2} - 3} \cdot \frac{\left(\sqrt{x+2} + 3\right)}{\left(\sqrt{x+2} + 3\right)}$$

$$= \frac{4\sqrt{x+2} + 12}{\left(\sqrt{x+2}\right)^2 - 3^2}$$

$$= \frac{4\sqrt{x+2} + 12}{x + 2 - 9}$$

$$= \frac{4\sqrt{x+2} + 12}{x - 7}$$

84.

$$\frac{8}{\sqrt{y-3} + 6} = \frac{8}{\sqrt{y-3} + 6} \cdot \frac{\left(\sqrt{y-3} - 6\right)}{\left(\sqrt{y-3} - 6\right)}$$

$$= \frac{8\sqrt{y-3} - 48}{\left(\sqrt{y-3} + 6\right)\left(\sqrt{y-3} - 6\right)}$$

$$= \frac{8\sqrt{y-3} - 48}{\left(\sqrt{y-3}\right)^2 - (6)^2}$$

$$= \frac{8\sqrt{y-3} - 48}{y - 3 - 36}$$

$$= \frac{8\sqrt{y-3} - 48}{y - 39}$$

85. $\sqrt{\dfrac{x}{16}} = \dfrac{\sqrt{x}}{\sqrt{16}} = \dfrac{\sqrt{x}}{4}$

86. $\sqrt[4]{\dfrac{x^4}{16}} = \dfrac{\sqrt[4]{x^4}}{\sqrt[4]{16}} = \dfrac{x}{2}$

87. $\sqrt{\dfrac{2}{9}} = \dfrac{\sqrt{2}}{\sqrt{9}} = \dfrac{\sqrt{2}}{3}$

88. $\sqrt{\dfrac{a}{b}} = \dfrac{\sqrt{a}}{\sqrt{b}} = \dfrac{\sqrt{a}}{\sqrt{b}} \cdot \dfrac{\sqrt{b}}{\sqrt{b}} = \dfrac{\sqrt{ab}}{b}$

89. $\left(\sqrt{7} + \sqrt{6}\right)\left(\sqrt{7} - \sqrt{6}\right) = \left(\sqrt{7}\right)^2 - \left(\sqrt{6}\right)^2$

$$= 7 - 6$$

$$= 1$$

90. $\sqrt[3]{\dfrac{1}{16}} = \dfrac{\sqrt[3]{1}}{\sqrt[3]{16}} = \dfrac{1}{\sqrt[3]{16}} \cdot \dfrac{\sqrt[3]{4}}{\sqrt[3]{4}} = \dfrac{\sqrt[3]{4}}{4}$

91.

$$\sqrt{\frac{24x^3 y^6}{5z}} = \frac{\sqrt{24x^3 y^6}}{\sqrt{5z}}$$

$$= \frac{\sqrt{4x^2 y^6}\,\sqrt{6x}}{\sqrt{5z}}$$

$$= \frac{2xy^3 \sqrt{6x}}{\sqrt{5z}} \cdot \frac{\sqrt{5z}}{\sqrt{5z}}$$

$$= \frac{2xy^3 \sqrt{30xz}}{5z}$$

92. $\dfrac{5}{4 - \sqrt{y}} = \dfrac{5}{4 - \sqrt{y}} \cdot \dfrac{\left(4 + \sqrt{y}\right)}{\left(4 + \sqrt{y}\right)} = \dfrac{20 + 5\sqrt{y}}{16 - y}$

93. $\sqrt{\dfrac{28xy^4}{2x^3 y^4}} = \sqrt{\dfrac{14}{x^2}} = \dfrac{\sqrt{14}}{\sqrt{x^2}} = \dfrac{\sqrt{14}}{x}$

94. $\dfrac{8x}{\sqrt[3]{5y}} = \dfrac{8x}{\sqrt[3]{5y}} \cdot \dfrac{\sqrt[3]{5^2 y^2}}{\sqrt[3]{5^2 y^2}} = \dfrac{8x\,\sqrt[3]{5^2 y^2}}{5y} = \dfrac{8x\,\sqrt[3]{25y^2}}{5y}$

95.

$$\frac{1}{\sqrt{a} + 7} = \frac{1}{\sqrt{a} + 7} \cdot \frac{\sqrt{a} - 7}{\sqrt{a} - 7}$$

$$= \frac{\sqrt{a} - 7}{\left(\sqrt{a} + 7\right)\left(\sqrt{a} - 7\right)}$$

$$= \frac{\sqrt{a} - 7}{\left(\sqrt{a}\right)^2 - (7)^2}$$

$$= \frac{\sqrt{a} - 7}{a - 49}$$

96. $\dfrac{\sqrt{x}}{\sqrt{x}+6\sqrt{y}} = \dfrac{\sqrt{x}}{\sqrt{x}+6\sqrt{y}} \cdot \dfrac{\sqrt{x}-6\sqrt{y}}{\sqrt{x}-6\sqrt{y}}$

$$= \dfrac{\sqrt{x}\left(\sqrt{x}-6\sqrt{y}\right)}{\left(\sqrt{x}+6\sqrt{y}\right)\left(\sqrt{x}-6\sqrt{y}\right)}$$

$$= \dfrac{x-6\sqrt{xy}}{\left(\sqrt{x}\right)^2 - \left(6\sqrt{y}\right)^2}$$

$$= \dfrac{x-6\sqrt{xy}}{x-36y}$$

97. $-\dfrac{7\sqrt{x}}{\sqrt{98}} = -\dfrac{7\sqrt{x}}{7\sqrt{2}}$

$$= -\dfrac{\sqrt{x}}{\sqrt{2}} \cdot \dfrac{\sqrt{2}}{\sqrt{2}}$$

$$= -\dfrac{\sqrt{2x}}{\sqrt{4}}$$

$$= -\dfrac{\sqrt{2x}}{2}$$

98. $\sqrt{\dfrac{2xy^4}{50xy^2}} = \sqrt{\dfrac{y^2}{25}} = \dfrac{\sqrt{y^2}}{\sqrt{25}} = \dfrac{y}{5}$

99. $\sqrt[4]{\dfrac{3y^2}{2x}} = \dfrac{\sqrt[4]{3y^2}}{\sqrt[4]{2x}} \cdot \dfrac{\sqrt[4]{8x^3}}{\sqrt[4]{8x^3}} = \dfrac{\sqrt[4]{24x^3y^2}}{\sqrt[4]{16x^4}} = \dfrac{\sqrt[4]{24x^3y^2}}{2x}$

100. $\sqrt{\dfrac{49x^2y^5}{3z}} = \dfrac{\sqrt{49x^2y^5}}{\sqrt{3z}}$

$$= \dfrac{\sqrt{49x^2y^4}\sqrt{y}}{\sqrt{3z}}$$

$$= \dfrac{7xy^2\sqrt{y}}{\sqrt{3z}}$$

$$= \dfrac{7xy^2\sqrt{y}}{\sqrt{3z}} \cdot \dfrac{\sqrt{3z}}{\sqrt{3z}}$$

$$= \dfrac{7xy^2\sqrt{3yz}}{3z}$$

101. $\sqrt[3]{\dfrac{32y^{12}z^{10}}{2x}} = \sqrt[3]{\dfrac{16y^{12}z^{10}}{x}}$

$$= \dfrac{\sqrt[3]{16y^{12}z^{10}}}{\sqrt[3]{x}}$$

$$= \dfrac{\sqrt[3]{8y^{12}z^9}\,\sqrt[3]{2z}}{\sqrt[3]{x}}$$

$$= \dfrac{2y^4z^3\sqrt[3]{2z}}{\sqrt[3]{x}} \cdot \dfrac{\sqrt[3]{x^2}}{\sqrt[3]{x^2}}$$

$$= \dfrac{2y^4z^3\sqrt[3]{2x^2z}}{\sqrt[3]{x^3}}$$

$$= \dfrac{2y^4z^3\sqrt[3]{2x^2z}}{x}$$

102. $\dfrac{\sqrt{3}+2}{\sqrt{2}+\sqrt{3}} = \dfrac{\sqrt{3}+2}{\sqrt{2}+\sqrt{3}}$

$$= \dfrac{\sqrt{3}+2}{\sqrt{2}+\sqrt{3}} \cdot \dfrac{\left(\sqrt{2}-\sqrt{3}\right)}{\left(\sqrt{2}-\sqrt{3}\right)}$$

$$= \dfrac{\sqrt{6}-3+2\sqrt{2}-2\sqrt{3}}{\left(\sqrt{2}\right)^2-\left(\sqrt{3}\right)^2}$$

$$= \dfrac{\sqrt{6}-3+2\sqrt{2}-2\sqrt{3}}{-1}$$

$$= -\sqrt{6}+3-2\sqrt{2}+2\sqrt{3}$$

103. $\dfrac{\sqrt{ar}}{\sqrt{a}-2\sqrt{r}} \cdot \dfrac{\left(\sqrt{a}+2\sqrt{r}\right)}{\left(\sqrt{a}+2\sqrt{r}\right)} = \dfrac{\sqrt{ar}\left(\sqrt{a}+2\sqrt{r}\right)}{\left(\sqrt{a}\right)^2-\left(2\sqrt{r}\right)^2}$

$$= \dfrac{a\sqrt{r}+2r\sqrt{a}}{a-4r}$$

104. $\sqrt[4]{\dfrac{2}{9x}} = \dfrac{\sqrt[4]{2}}{\sqrt[4]{9x}} \cdot \dfrac{\sqrt[4]{9x^3}}{\sqrt[4]{9x^3}} = \dfrac{\sqrt[4]{18x^3}}{\sqrt[4]{81x^4}} = \dfrac{\sqrt[4]{18x^3}}{3x}$

105. $\dfrac{\sqrt[3]{6x}}{\sqrt[3]{5xy}} = \sqrt[3]{\dfrac{6x}{5xy}}$

$= \sqrt[3]{\dfrac{6}{5y}}$

$= \dfrac{\sqrt[3]{6}}{\sqrt[3]{5y}} \cdot \dfrac{\sqrt[3]{25y^2}}{\sqrt[3]{25y^2}}$

$= \dfrac{\sqrt[3]{150y^2}}{5y}$

106. $\dfrac{\sqrt[3]{16m^2n}}{\sqrt[3]{2mn^2}} = \sqrt[3]{\dfrac{16m^2n}{2mn^2}}$

$= \sqrt[3]{\dfrac{8m}{n}}$

$= \dfrac{\sqrt[3]{8m}}{\sqrt[3]{n}} \cdot \dfrac{\sqrt[3]{n^2}}{\sqrt[3]{n^2}}$

$= \dfrac{2\sqrt[3]{mn^2}}{n}$

107. $\sqrt[4]{\dfrac{2x^7y^{12}z^4}{3x^9}} = \sqrt[4]{\dfrac{2y^{12}z^4}{3x^2}}$

$= \dfrac{\sqrt[4]{2y^{12}z^4}}{\sqrt[4]{3x^2}}$

$= \dfrac{\sqrt[4]{y^{12}z^4}\sqrt[4]{2}}{\sqrt[4]{3x^2}}$

$= \dfrac{y^3z\sqrt[4]{2}}{\sqrt[4]{3x^2}} \cdot \dfrac{\sqrt[4]{27x^2}}{\sqrt[4]{27x^2}}$

$= \dfrac{y^3z\sqrt[4]{54x^2}}{\sqrt[4]{81x^4}}$

$= \dfrac{y^3z\sqrt[4]{54x^2}}{3x}$

108. $\dfrac{9}{\sqrt{y+9}-\sqrt{y}} = \dfrac{9}{\sqrt{y+9}-\sqrt{y}} \cdot \dfrac{\left(\sqrt{y+9}+\sqrt{y}\right)}{\left(\sqrt{y+9}+\sqrt{y}\right)}$

$= \dfrac{9\left(\sqrt{y+9}+\sqrt{y}\right)}{\left(\sqrt{y+9}\right)^2-\left(\sqrt{y}\right)^2}$

$= \dfrac{9\left(\sqrt{y+9}+\sqrt{y}\right)}{y+9-y}$

$= \dfrac{9\left(\sqrt{y+9}+\sqrt{y}\right)}{9}$

$= \sqrt{y+9}+\sqrt{y}$

109. $\dfrac{1}{\sqrt{2}} + \dfrac{\sqrt{2}}{2} = \dfrac{1}{\sqrt{2}} \cdot \dfrac{\sqrt{2}}{\sqrt{2}} + \dfrac{\sqrt{2}}{2}$

$= \dfrac{\sqrt{2}}{\sqrt{4}} + \dfrac{\sqrt{2}}{2}$

$= \dfrac{\sqrt{2}}{2} + \dfrac{\sqrt{2}}{2}$

$= \dfrac{2\sqrt{2}}{2} = \sqrt{2}$

110. $\dfrac{1}{\sqrt{3}} + \dfrac{\sqrt{3}}{3} = \dfrac{1}{\sqrt{3}} \cdot \dfrac{\sqrt{3}}{\sqrt{3}} + \dfrac{\sqrt{3}}{3}$

$= \dfrac{\sqrt{3}}{\sqrt{9}} + \dfrac{\sqrt{3}}{3}$

$= \dfrac{\sqrt{3}}{3} + \dfrac{\sqrt{3}}{3}$

$= \dfrac{2\sqrt{3}}{3}$

111. $\sqrt{5} - \dfrac{2}{\sqrt{5}} = \sqrt{5} - \dfrac{2}{\sqrt{5}} \cdot \dfrac{\sqrt{5}}{\sqrt{5}}$

$= \sqrt{5} - \dfrac{2\sqrt{5}}{5}$

$= \dfrac{5\sqrt{5}}{5} - \dfrac{2\sqrt{5}}{5}$

$= \dfrac{5\sqrt{5}-2\sqrt{5}}{5}$

$= \dfrac{3\sqrt{5}}{5}$

112. $\dfrac{\sqrt{6}}{2} - \dfrac{2}{\sqrt{6}} = \dfrac{\sqrt{6}}{2} - \dfrac{2}{\sqrt{6}} \cdot \dfrac{\sqrt{6}}{\sqrt{6}}$

$= \dfrac{\sqrt{6}}{2} - \dfrac{2\sqrt{6}}{6}$

$= \dfrac{3\sqrt{6}}{6} - \dfrac{2\sqrt{6}}{6}$

$= \dfrac{\sqrt{6}}{6}$

113. $4\sqrt{\dfrac{1}{6}} + \sqrt{24} = \dfrac{4}{\sqrt{6}} + 2\sqrt{6}$

$= \dfrac{4}{\sqrt{6}} \cdot \dfrac{\sqrt{6}}{\sqrt{6}} + 2\sqrt{6}$

$= \dfrac{4\sqrt{6}}{6} + 2\sqrt{6}$

$= \dfrac{2\sqrt{6}}{3} + \dfrac{\left(2\sqrt{6}\right)3}{3}$

$= \dfrac{2\sqrt{6}}{3} + \dfrac{6\sqrt{6}}{3}$

$= \dfrac{8\sqrt{6}}{3}$

114. $5\sqrt{3} - \dfrac{3}{\sqrt{3}} + 2\sqrt{18} = 5\sqrt{3} - \dfrac{3}{\sqrt{3}}\left(\dfrac{\sqrt{3}}{\sqrt{3}}\right) + 2\sqrt{9 \cdot 2}$

$= 5\sqrt{3} - \dfrac{3\sqrt{3}}{3} + 6\sqrt{2}$

$= 5\sqrt{3} - \sqrt{3} + 6\sqrt{2}$

$= 4\sqrt{3} + 6\sqrt{2}$

115. $5\sqrt{2} - \dfrac{2}{\sqrt{8}} + \sqrt{50} = 5\sqrt{2} - \dfrac{2}{\sqrt{8}} \cdot \dfrac{\sqrt{8}}{\sqrt{8}} + \sqrt{25}\sqrt{2}$

$= 3\sqrt{2} - \dfrac{2\sqrt{4}\sqrt{2}}{\sqrt{64}} + 5\sqrt{2}$

$= \dfrac{5\sqrt{2}}{1} - \dfrac{4\sqrt{2}}{8} + \dfrac{5\sqrt{2}}{1}$

$= \dfrac{10\sqrt{2}}{2} - \dfrac{\sqrt{2}}{2} + \dfrac{10\sqrt{2}}{2}$

$= \dfrac{(10 - 1 + 10)\sqrt{2}}{2}$

$= \dfrac{19\sqrt{2}}{2}$

116. $\dfrac{2}{3} + \dfrac{1}{\sqrt{3}} + \sqrt{75} = \dfrac{2}{3} + \dfrac{1}{\sqrt{3}} \cdot \dfrac{\sqrt{3}}{\sqrt{3}} + \sqrt{25}\sqrt{3}$

$= \dfrac{2}{3} + \dfrac{\sqrt{3}}{3} + 5\sqrt{3}$

$= \dfrac{2}{3} + \dfrac{\sqrt{3}}{3} + 5\sqrt{3} \cdot \dfrac{3}{3}$

$= \dfrac{2}{3} + \dfrac{\sqrt{3}}{3} + \dfrac{15\sqrt{3}}{3}$

$= \dfrac{2 + 16\sqrt{3}}{3}$

117. $\sqrt{\dfrac{1}{2}} + 7\sqrt{2} + \sqrt{18} = \dfrac{\sqrt{1}}{\sqrt{2}} \cdot \dfrac{\sqrt{2}}{\sqrt{2}} + 7\sqrt{2} + \sqrt{9} \cdot \sqrt{2}$

$= \dfrac{\sqrt{2}}{\sqrt{4}} + 7\sqrt{2} + 3\sqrt{2}$

$= \dfrac{\sqrt{2}}{2} + 10\sqrt{2}$

$= \dfrac{\sqrt{2}}{2} + \dfrac{20\sqrt{2}}{2}$

$= \dfrac{21\sqrt{2}}{2}$

118. $\dfrac{1}{2}\sqrt{18} - \dfrac{3}{\sqrt{2}} - 9\sqrt{50} = \dfrac{1}{2}\left(3\sqrt{2}\right) - \dfrac{3}{\sqrt{2}} - 9\left(5\sqrt{2}\right)$

$= \dfrac{3\sqrt{2}}{2} - \dfrac{3}{\sqrt{2}} \cdot \dfrac{\sqrt{2}}{\sqrt{2}} - 45\sqrt{2}$

$= \dfrac{3\sqrt{2}}{2} - \dfrac{3\sqrt{2}}{2} - 45\sqrt{2}$

$= 0 - 45\sqrt{2}$

$= -45\sqrt{2}$

119. $\dfrac{2}{\sqrt{50}} - 3\sqrt{50} - \dfrac{1}{\sqrt{8}}$

$= \dfrac{2}{5\sqrt{2}} - 3\left(5\sqrt{2}\right) - \dfrac{1}{2\sqrt{2}}$

$= \dfrac{2}{5\sqrt{2}} \cdot \dfrac{\sqrt{2}}{\sqrt{2}} - 15\sqrt{2} - \dfrac{1}{2\sqrt{2}} \cdot \dfrac{\sqrt{2}}{\sqrt{2}}$

$= \dfrac{2\sqrt{2}}{10} - 15\sqrt{2} - \dfrac{\sqrt{2}}{4}$

$= \dfrac{\sqrt{2}}{5} - 15\sqrt{2} - \dfrac{\sqrt{2}}{4}$

$= \dfrac{4\sqrt{2}}{20} - \dfrac{300\sqrt{2}}{20} - \dfrac{5\sqrt{2}}{20}$

$= -\dfrac{301\sqrt{2}}{20}$

120. $\dfrac{\sqrt{3}}{3} + \dfrac{5}{\sqrt{3}} + \sqrt{12} = \dfrac{\sqrt{3}}{3} + \dfrac{5}{\sqrt{3}} \cdot \dfrac{\sqrt{3}}{\sqrt{3}} + 2\sqrt{3}$

$= \dfrac{\sqrt{3}}{3} + \dfrac{5\sqrt{3}}{3} + 2\sqrt{3} \cdot \dfrac{3}{3}$

$= \dfrac{\sqrt{3}}{3} + \dfrac{5\sqrt{3}}{3} + \dfrac{6\sqrt{3}}{3}$

$= \dfrac{12\sqrt{3}}{3}$

$= 4\sqrt{3}$

121. $\sqrt{\dfrac{3}{8}} + \sqrt{\dfrac{3}{2}} = \dfrac{\sqrt{3}}{\sqrt{8}} + \dfrac{\sqrt{3}}{\sqrt{2}}$

$= \dfrac{\sqrt{3}}{2\sqrt{2}} + \dfrac{\sqrt{3}}{\sqrt{2}}$

$= \dfrac{\sqrt{3}}{2\sqrt{2}} \cdot \dfrac{\sqrt{2}}{\sqrt{2}} + \dfrac{\sqrt{3}}{\sqrt{2}} \cdot \dfrac{2\sqrt{2}}{2\sqrt{2}}$

$= \dfrac{\sqrt{6}}{4} + \dfrac{2\sqrt{6}}{4}$

$= \dfrac{3\sqrt{6}}{4}$

122. $2\sqrt{\dfrac{8}{3}} - 4\sqrt{\dfrac{100}{6}} = 2\sqrt{\dfrac{8}{3}} - 4\sqrt{\dfrac{50}{3}}$

$= 2\dfrac{\sqrt{8}}{\sqrt{3}} - 4\dfrac{\sqrt{50}}{\sqrt{3}}$

$= \dfrac{2\sqrt{4}\sqrt{2}}{\sqrt{3}} - \dfrac{4\sqrt{25}\sqrt{2}}{\sqrt{3}}$

$= \dfrac{2\left(2\sqrt{2}\right)}{\sqrt{3}} - \dfrac{4\left(5\sqrt{2}\right)}{\sqrt{3}}$

$= \dfrac{4\sqrt{2}}{\sqrt{3}} - \dfrac{20\sqrt{2}}{\sqrt{3}}$

$= \dfrac{-16\sqrt{2}}{\sqrt{3}} \cdot \dfrac{\sqrt{3}}{\sqrt{3}}$

$= -\dfrac{16\sqrt{6}}{3}$

123. $-2\sqrt{\dfrac{x}{y}} + 3\sqrt{\dfrac{y}{x}} = -2\dfrac{\sqrt{x}}{\sqrt{y}} + 3\dfrac{\sqrt{y}}{\sqrt{x}}$

$= -2\dfrac{\sqrt{x}}{\sqrt{y}} \cdot \dfrac{\sqrt{y}}{\sqrt{y}} + 3\dfrac{\sqrt{y}}{\sqrt{x}} \cdot \dfrac{\sqrt{x}}{\sqrt{x}}$

$= -2\dfrac{\sqrt{xy}}{y} + 3\dfrac{\sqrt{xy}}{x}$

$= \left(-\dfrac{2}{y} + \dfrac{3}{x}\right)\sqrt{xy}$

124. $-5x\sqrt{\dfrac{y}{y^2}} + 9x\sqrt{\dfrac{1}{y}} = -5x\sqrt{\dfrac{1}{y}} + 9x\sqrt{\dfrac{1}{y}}$

$= -5x\dfrac{1}{\sqrt{y}} + 9x\dfrac{1}{\sqrt{y}}$

$= \dfrac{-5x}{\sqrt{y}} + \dfrac{9x}{\sqrt{y}}$

$= \dfrac{4x}{\sqrt{y}}$

$= \dfrac{4x}{\sqrt{y}} \cdot \dfrac{\sqrt{y}}{\sqrt{y}}$

$= \dfrac{4x\sqrt{y}}{y}$

125. $\dfrac{3}{\sqrt{a}} - \sqrt{\dfrac{9}{a}} + 2\sqrt{a} = \dfrac{3}{\sqrt{a}} - \dfrac{\sqrt{9}}{\sqrt{a}} + 2\sqrt{a}$

$\qquad\qquad\qquad\qquad = \dfrac{3}{\sqrt{a}}\left(\dfrac{\sqrt{a}}{\sqrt{a}}\right) - \dfrac{\sqrt{9}}{\sqrt{a}}\left(\dfrac{\sqrt{a}}{\sqrt{a}}\right) + 2\sqrt{a}$

$\qquad\qquad\qquad\qquad = \dfrac{3\sqrt{a}}{a} - \dfrac{3\sqrt{a}}{a} + 2\sqrt{a}$

$\qquad\qquad\qquad\qquad = 2\sqrt{a}$

126. $6\sqrt{x} + \dfrac{1}{\sqrt{x}} + \sqrt{\dfrac{1}{x}} = 6\sqrt{x} + \dfrac{1}{\sqrt{x}}\cdot\dfrac{\sqrt{x}}{\sqrt{x}} + \dfrac{\sqrt{1}}{\sqrt{x}}\cdot\dfrac{\sqrt{x}}{\sqrt{x}}$

$\qquad\qquad\qquad\qquad = 6\sqrt{x} + \dfrac{\sqrt{x}}{\sqrt{x^2}} + \dfrac{\sqrt{x}}{\sqrt{x^2}}$

$\qquad\qquad\qquad\qquad = 6\sqrt{x} + \dfrac{\sqrt{x}}{x} + \dfrac{\sqrt{x}}{x}$

$\qquad\qquad\qquad\qquad = 6\sqrt{x} + \dfrac{2\sqrt{x}}{x}$

$\qquad\qquad\qquad\qquad = 2\sqrt{x}\left(3 + \dfrac{1}{x}\right)$

127. $\dfrac{\sqrt{(a+b)^4}}{\sqrt[3]{a+b}} = \dfrac{(a+b)^{4/2}}{(a+b)^{1/3}}$

$\qquad\qquad\quad = (a+b)^{6/3-1/3}$

$\qquad\qquad\quad = (a+b)^{5/3}$

$\qquad\qquad\quad = \sqrt[3]{(a+b)^5}$

128. $\dfrac{\sqrt[3]{c+2}}{\sqrt[4]{(c+2)^3}} = \dfrac{(c+2)^{1/3}}{(c+2)^{3/4}}$

$\qquad\qquad\quad = (c+2)^{1/3-3/4}$

$\qquad\qquad\quad = (c+2)^{-5/12}$

$\qquad\qquad\quad = \dfrac{1}{\sqrt[12]{(c+2)^5}}$

129. $\dfrac{\sqrt[5]{(a+2b)^4}}{\sqrt[3]{(a+2b)^2}} = \dfrac{(a+2b)^{4/5}}{(a+2b)^{2/3}}$

$\qquad\qquad\qquad = (a+2b)^{4/5-2/3}$

$\qquad\qquad\qquad = (a+2b)^{2/15}$

$\qquad\qquad\qquad = \sqrt[15]{(a+2b)^2}$

130. $\dfrac{\sqrt[6]{(r+3)^5}}{\sqrt[3]{(r+3)^5}} = \dfrac{(r+3)^{5/6}}{(r+3)^{5/3}}$

$\qquad\qquad\quad = (r+3)^{5/6-5/3}$

$\qquad\qquad\quad = (r+3)^{-5/6}$

$\qquad\qquad\quad = \dfrac{1}{\sqrt[6]{(r+3)^5}}$

131. $\dfrac{\sqrt[3]{r^2 s^4}}{\sqrt{rs}} = \dfrac{(r^2 s^4)^{1/3}}{(rs)^{1/2}}$

$\qquad\qquad = \dfrac{r^{2/3} s^{4/3}}{r^{1/2} s^{1/2}}$

$\qquad\qquad = r^{2/3-1/2} s^{4/3-1/2}$

$\qquad\qquad = r^{1/6} s^{5/6}$

$\qquad\qquad = (rs^5)^{1/6}$

$\qquad\qquad = \sqrt[6]{rs^5}$

132. $\dfrac{\sqrt{a^2 b^4}}{\sqrt[3]{ab^2}} = \dfrac{(a^2 b^4)^{1/2}}{(ab^2)^{1/3}}$

$\qquad\qquad = \dfrac{a^1 b^2}{a^{1/3} b^{2/3}}$

$\qquad\qquad = a^{1-1/3} b^{2-2/3}$

$\qquad\qquad = a^{2/3} b^{4/3}$

$\qquad\qquad = (a^2 b^4)^{1/3}$

$\qquad\qquad = \sqrt[3]{a^2 b^4}$

$\qquad\qquad = b\sqrt[3]{a^2 b}$

133. $\dfrac{\sqrt[5]{x^4 y^6}}{\sqrt[3]{(xy)^2}} = \dfrac{(x^4 y^6)^{1/5}}{(xy)^{2/3}}$

$\qquad\qquad = \dfrac{x^{4/5} y^{6/5}}{x^{2/3} y^{2/3}}$

$\qquad\qquad = x^{4/5-2/3} y^{6/5-2/3}$

$\qquad\qquad = x^{2/15} y^{8/15}$

$\qquad\qquad = (x^2 y^8)^{1/15}$

$\qquad\qquad = \sqrt[15]{x^2 y^8}$

134. $\dfrac{\sqrt[6]{4m^8 n^4}}{\sqrt[4]{m^4 n^2}} = \dfrac{(4m^8 n^4)^{1/6}}{(m^4 n^2)^{1/4}}$

$= \dfrac{4^{1/6} m^{8/6} n^{4/6}}{m^{4/4} n^{2/4}}$

$= 4^{1/6} m^{4/3-1} n^{2/3-1/2}$

$= 4^{1/6} m^{1/3} n^{1/6}$

$= 4^{1/6} m^{2/6} n^{1/6}$

$= (4m^2 n)^{1/6}$

$= \sqrt[6]{4m^2 n}$

135. $d = \sqrt{\dfrac{72}{I}}$

$d = \sqrt{\dfrac{72}{5.3}} \approx 3.69$

The person is about 3.69 m from the light source.

136. $T = \sqrt{\dfrac{0.05\ LB}{M}}$

$T = \sqrt{\dfrac{0.05(36)(800)}{2560}} = 0.75$

The thickness of the board is 0.75 inch.

137. $r = \sqrt[3]{\dfrac{3V}{4\pi}}$

$r = \sqrt[3]{\dfrac{3(7238.23)}{4\pi}} = 12$

The radius of the tank is 12 inches.

138. $\sigma = \sqrt{\dfrac{n^2 - 1}{12}}$

$\sigma = \sqrt{\dfrac{100^2 - 1}{12}} \approx 28.87$

139. $N(t) = \dfrac{6.21}{\sqrt[4]{t}}$

a. $t = 1960 - 1959 = 1$

$N(1) = \dfrac{6.21}{\sqrt[4]{1}} = 6.21$

The number of farms in 1960 was 6.21 million.

b. $t = 2008 - 1959 = 49$

$N(49) = \dfrac{6.21}{\sqrt[4]{49}} \approx 2.35$

The number of farms in 2008 will be about 2.35 million.

140. $N(t) = \dfrac{28.46}{\sqrt[3]{t^2}}$

a. $t = 1970 - 1969 = 1$

$N(1) = \dfrac{28.46}{\sqrt[3]{1^2}} = 28.46$

The infant mortality rate in 1970 was 28.46 per 1000 live births.

b. $t = 2006 - 1969 = 37$

$N(37) = \dfrac{28.46}{\sqrt[3]{37^2}} \approx 2.56$

The infant mortality rate in 2006 was about 2.56 per 1000 live births.

141. $\dfrac{2}{\sqrt{2}} = \dfrac{2}{\sqrt{2}} \cdot \dfrac{\sqrt{2}}{\sqrt{2}} = \dfrac{2\sqrt{2}}{\sqrt{4}} = \dfrac{2\sqrt{2}}{2} = \sqrt{2}$

$\dfrac{3}{\sqrt{3}} = \dfrac{3}{\sqrt{3}} \cdot \dfrac{\sqrt{3}}{\sqrt{3}} = \dfrac{3\sqrt{3}}{\sqrt{9}} = \dfrac{3\sqrt{3}}{3} = \sqrt{3}$

Since $3 > 2$, then $\sqrt{3} > \sqrt{2}$ and we conclude that $\dfrac{3}{\sqrt{3}} > \dfrac{2}{\sqrt{2}}$.

142. $\dfrac{\sqrt{3}}{2} = \dfrac{1}{2}\sqrt{3}$

$\dfrac{2}{\sqrt{3}} = \dfrac{2}{\sqrt{3}} \cdot \dfrac{\sqrt{3}}{\sqrt{3}} = \dfrac{2\sqrt{3}}{3} = \dfrac{2}{3}\sqrt{3}$

$\dfrac{2}{3}\sqrt{3} > \dfrac{1}{2}\sqrt{3}$ because $\dfrac{2}{3} > \dfrac{1}{2}$

Therefore, $\dfrac{2}{\sqrt{3}} > \dfrac{\sqrt{3}}{2}$.

143. $\dfrac{1}{\sqrt{3}+2} = \dfrac{1}{\sqrt{3}+2}\cdot\dfrac{\sqrt{3}-2}{\sqrt{3}-2}$

$= \dfrac{\sqrt{3}-2}{\left(\sqrt{3}\right)^2-2^2}$

$= \dfrac{\sqrt{3}-2}{3-4}$

$= \dfrac{\sqrt{3}-2}{-1}$

$= -\sqrt{3}+2$

$= 2-\sqrt{3}$

$2+\sqrt{3} > 2-\sqrt{3}$

Therefore, $2+\sqrt{3} > \dfrac{1}{\sqrt{3}+2}$.

144. $\dfrac{2}{\sqrt{12}}+\sqrt{48}+2\sqrt{3} = \dfrac{2}{2\sqrt{3}}+4\sqrt{3}+2\sqrt{3}$

$= \dfrac{2}{2\sqrt{3}}+6\sqrt{3}$

$= \dfrac{1}{\sqrt{3}}+6\sqrt{3}$

$= \dfrac{1}{\sqrt{3}}\cdot\dfrac{\sqrt{3}}{\sqrt{3}}+6\sqrt{3}$

$= \dfrac{\sqrt{3}}{3}+6\sqrt{3}$

$= \left(\dfrac{1}{3}+6\right)\sqrt{3}$

$= \dfrac{19}{3}\sqrt{3}$

$\dfrac{1}{\sqrt{3}}+\sqrt{75} = \dfrac{1}{\sqrt{3}}+5\sqrt{3}$

$= \dfrac{1}{\sqrt{3}}\cdot\dfrac{\sqrt{3}}{\sqrt{3}}+5\sqrt{3}$

$= \dfrac{\sqrt{3}}{3}+5\sqrt{3}$

$= \left(\dfrac{1}{3}+5\right)\sqrt{3}$

$= \dfrac{16}{3}\sqrt{3}$

Since $\dfrac{19}{3}\sqrt{3} > \dfrac{16}{3}\sqrt{3}$, we see that

$\dfrac{2}{\sqrt{12}}+\sqrt{48}+2\sqrt{3}$ is the greater quantity.

145. $f(x)=x^{a/2}$, $g(x)=x^{b/3}$

a. $x^{4/2}=x^2$

$x^{12/2}=x^6$

$x^{8/2}=x^4$

Therefore $x^{a/2}$ is a perfect square when $a=4,8,12$.

b. $x^{9/3}=x^3$

$x^{18/3}=x^6$

$x^{27/3}=x^9$

Therefore, $x^{b/3}$ is a perfect cube when $b=9,18,27$.

c. $(f\cdot g)(x)=f(x)\cdot g(x)$

$= x^{a/2}\cdot x^{b/3}$

$= x^{a/2+b/3}$

$= x^{3a/6+2b/6}$

$= x^{(3a+2b)/6}$

d. $\left(\dfrac{f}{g}\right)(x)=\dfrac{f(x)}{g(x)}$

$= \dfrac{x^{a/2}}{x^{b/3}}$

$= x^{a/2-b/3}$

$= x^{3a/6-2b/6}$

$= x^{(3a-2b)/6}$

146. $\dfrac{1}{\sqrt{a+b}} = \dfrac{1}{\sqrt{a+b}}\cdot\dfrac{\sqrt{a+b}}{\sqrt{a+b}} = \dfrac{\sqrt{a+b}}{a+b}$

147. $\dfrac{3}{\sqrt{2a-3b}} = \dfrac{3}{\sqrt{2a-3b}}\cdot\dfrac{\sqrt{2a-3b}}{\sqrt{2a-3b}} = \dfrac{3\sqrt{2a-3b}}{2a-3b}$

148. $\dfrac{\sqrt{7}}{3} = \dfrac{\sqrt{7}}{3}\cdot\dfrac{\sqrt{7}}{\sqrt{7}} = \dfrac{\sqrt{49}}{3\sqrt{7}} = \dfrac{7}{3\sqrt{7}}$

149. $\dfrac{5-\sqrt{5}}{6} = \dfrac{5-\sqrt{5}}{6}\cdot\dfrac{5+\sqrt{5}}{5+\sqrt{5}}$

$= \dfrac{25-5}{30+6\sqrt{5}} = \dfrac{20}{2(15+3\sqrt{5})}$

$= \dfrac{10}{15+3\sqrt{5}}$

150.
$$\frac{6\sqrt{x}-\sqrt{3}}{x} = \frac{6\sqrt{x}-\sqrt{3}}{x} \cdot \frac{6\sqrt{x}+\sqrt{3}}{6\sqrt{x}+\sqrt{3}}$$

$$= \frac{36x-3}{x\left(6\sqrt{x}+\sqrt{3}\right)}$$

$$= \frac{36x-3}{6x\sqrt{x}+x\sqrt{3}}$$

151.
$$\frac{\sqrt{x+h}-\sqrt{x}}{h} = \frac{\sqrt{x+h}-\sqrt{x}}{h} \cdot \frac{\sqrt{x+h}+\sqrt{x}}{\sqrt{x+h}+\sqrt{x}}$$

$$= \frac{x+h-x}{h\left(\sqrt{x+h}+\sqrt{x}\right)}$$

$$= \frac{h}{h\left(\sqrt{x+h}+\sqrt{x}\right)}$$

$$= \frac{1}{\sqrt{x+h}+\sqrt{x}}$$

152.
$$\frac{x}{1+\sqrt{3}} = \frac{5+\sqrt{3}}{\sqrt{12}}$$

$$x\sqrt{12} = \left(1+\sqrt{3}\right)\left(5+\sqrt{3}\right)$$

$$x \cdot 2\sqrt{3} = 5+\sqrt{3}+5\sqrt{3}+3$$

$$x \cdot 2\sqrt{3} = 8+6\sqrt{3}$$

$$x = \frac{8+6\sqrt{3}}{2\sqrt{3}}$$

$$= \frac{4+3\sqrt{3}}{\sqrt{3}} \cdot \frac{\sqrt{3}}{\sqrt{3}}$$

$$= \frac{4\sqrt{3}+9}{3}$$

153.
$$\frac{x}{2+2\sqrt{5}} = \frac{6+2\sqrt{5}}{\sqrt{80}}$$

$$x\sqrt{80} = \left(2+2\sqrt{5}\right)\left(6+2\sqrt{5}\right)$$

$$x \cdot 4\sqrt{5} = 12+4\sqrt{5}+12\sqrt{5}+20$$

$$x \cdot 4\sqrt{5} = 32+16\sqrt{5}$$

$$x = \frac{32+16\sqrt{5}}{4\sqrt{5}}$$

$$= \frac{8+4\sqrt{5}}{\sqrt{5}} \cdot \frac{\sqrt{5}}{\sqrt{5}}$$

$$= \frac{8\sqrt{5}+20}{5}$$

154.
$$A = \frac{1}{2}h(b_1+b_2)$$

$$2A = h(b_1+b_2)$$

$$\frac{2A}{h} = b_1+b_2$$

$$\frac{2A}{h}-b_1 = b_2$$

$$b_2 = \frac{2A}{h}-b_1$$

155. Let r be the rate of the slower car and $r+10$ be the rate of the faster.
Distance the first traveled plus distance the second traveled is 270 miles.

$$3r+3(r+10) = 270$$

$$3r+3r+30 = 270$$

$$6r+30 = 270$$

$$6r = 240$$

$$r = 40$$

The rate of the slower car is 40 mph and the rate of the faster car is $r+10=50$ mph.

156.
$$
\begin{array}{r}
4x^2+9x-2 \\
\underline{ x-2} \\
-8x^2-18x+4 \\
\underline{4x^3+9x^2-2x} \\
4x^3+x^2-20x+4
\end{array}
$$

157.
$$\frac{x}{2}-\frac{4}{x} = -\frac{7}{2}$$

$$2x\left(\frac{x}{2}-\frac{4}{x}\right) = 2x\left(-\frac{7}{2}\right)$$

$$x^2-8 = -7x$$

$$x^2+7x-8 = 0$$

$$(x+8)(x-1) = 0$$

$$x = -8 \text{ or } 1$$

Exercise Set 11.6

1. a. Answers will vary.

b.
$$\sqrt{2x+26} - 2 = 4$$
$$\sqrt{2x+26} - 2 + 2 = 4 + 2$$
$$\sqrt{2x+26} = 6$$
$$\left(\sqrt{2x+26}\right)^2 = 6^2$$
$$2x + 26 = 36$$
$$2x = 10$$
$$x = \frac{10}{2}$$
$$x = 5$$

2. Answers will vary. Possible answer:
The equation $\sqrt{x+3} = -\sqrt{2x+1}$ can have no real solution because $\sqrt{x+3}$ cannot be equal to a negative number.

3. 0 is the only solution to the equation. For all other values, the left side of the equation is negative and the right side is positive.

4. 0 is the only solution to the equation. For all other values, the left side of the equation is positive and the right side is negative.

5. Answers will vary. Possible answer:
The equation has no solution since the left side is a positive number whereas the right side is 0. A positive number is never equal to 0.

Also, the equation can be written as $\sqrt{x-3} = -4$ for which the left side is positive and the right side is negative. It is impossible for $\sqrt{x-3}$ to equal a negative number.

6. They may be extraneous solutions.

7. One solution, $x = 25$. Note that the domain of x is all nonnegative numbers. Therefore we have
$$\left(\sqrt{x}\right)^2 = 5^2$$
$$x = 25$$

8. Two solutions, $x = 3$ or -3.
$$x^2 = 9$$
$$\sqrt{x^2} = \sqrt{9}$$
$$|x| = 3$$
$$x = 3 \text{ or } x = -3$$

9.
$$\sqrt{x} = 4$$
$$\left(\sqrt{x}\right)^2 = 4^2$$
$$x = 16$$

Check: $\sqrt{16} = 4$
$$4 = 4 \text{ True}$$

10.
$$\sqrt{x} = 13$$
$$\left(\sqrt{x}\right)^2 = 13^2$$
$$x = 169$$

Check: $\sqrt{169} = 13$
$$13 = 13 \text{ True}$$

11. $\sqrt{x} = -9$ No real solution. The principal square root is never negative.

12.
$$\sqrt[3]{x} = 4$$
$$\left(\sqrt[3]{x}\right)^3 = 4^3$$
$$x = 64$$

Check: $\sqrt[3]{64} = 4$
$$\sqrt[3]{4^3} = 4$$
$$4 = 4 \text{ True}$$

13.
$$\sqrt[3]{x} = -4$$
$$\left(\sqrt[3]{x}\right)^3 = (-4)^3$$
$$x = -64$$

Check: $\sqrt[3]{-64} = -4$
$$\sqrt[3]{(-4)^3} = -4$$
$$-4 = -4 \text{ True}$$

14.
$$\sqrt{a} + 5 = 0$$
$$\sqrt{a} = -5$$
No real solution. The principal square root is never negative.

15. $\sqrt{2x+3}=5$

$\left(\sqrt{2x+3}\right)^2=(5)^2$

$2x+3=25$

$2x=22$

$x=11$

Check: $\sqrt{2x+3}=5$

$\sqrt{2(11)+3}=5$

$\sqrt{22+3}=5$

$\sqrt{25}=5$

$5=5$ True

16. $\sqrt[3]{7x-6}=4$

$\left(\sqrt[3]{7x-6}\right)^3=4^3$

$7x-6=64$

$7x=70$

$x=10$

Check: $\sqrt[3]{7(10)-6}=4$

$\sqrt[3]{70-6}=4$

$\sqrt[3]{64}=4$

$4=4$ True

17. $\sqrt[3]{3x}+4=7$

$\sqrt[3]{3x}=3$

$\left(\sqrt[3]{3x}\right)^3=(3)^3$

$3x=27$

$x=9$

Check: $\sqrt[3]{3(9)}+4=7$

$\sqrt[3]{27}+4=7$

$3+4=7$

$7=7$ True

18. $2\sqrt{4x+5}=14$

$\left(2\sqrt{4x+5}\right)^2=14^2$

$4(4x+5)=196$

$16x+20=196$

$16x=176$

$x=11$

Check: $2\sqrt{4(11)+5}=14$

$2\sqrt{44+5}=14$

$2\sqrt{49}=14$

$2(7)=14$

$14=14$ True

19. $\sqrt[3]{2x+29}=3$

$\left(\sqrt[3]{2x+29}\right)^3=3^3$

$2x+29=27$

$2x=-2$

$x=-1$

Check: $\sqrt[3]{2(-1)+29}=3$

$\sqrt[3]{-2+29}=3$

$\sqrt[3]{27}=3$

$3=3$ True

20. $\sqrt[3]{6x+2}=-4$

$\left(\sqrt[3]{6x+2}\right)^3=(-4)^3$

$6x+2=-64$

$6x=-66$

$x=-11$

Check: $\sqrt[3]{6(-11)+2}=-4$

$\sqrt[3]{-66+2}=-4$

$\sqrt[3]{-64}=-4$

$-4=-4$ True

21. $\sqrt[4]{x}=3$

$\left(\sqrt[4]{x}\right)^4=3^4$

$x=81$

Check: $\sqrt[4]{81}=3$

$\sqrt[4]{3^4}=3$

$3=3$ True

22. $\sqrt[4]{x}=-3$; no real solution since an even root of a real number will never be negative.

23. $\sqrt[4]{x+10} = 3$

$\left(\sqrt[4]{x+10}\right)^4 = 3^4$

$x + 10 = 81$

$x = 71$

Check: $\sqrt[4]{71+10} = 3$

$\sqrt[4]{81} = 3$

$\sqrt[4]{3^4} = 3$

$3 = 3$ True

24. $\sqrt[4]{3x-2} = 2$

$\left(\sqrt[4]{3x-2}\right)^4 = 2^4$

$3x - 2 = 16$

$3x = 18$

$x = 6$

Check: $\sqrt[4]{3(6)-2} = 2$

$\sqrt[4]{16} = 2$

$2 = 2$ True

25. $\sqrt[4]{2x+1} + 6 = 2$

$\sqrt[4]{2x+1} = -4$

No real solution exists because an even root of a real number is never negative.

26. $\sqrt{2x} + 7 = 13$

$\sqrt{2x} = 6$

$\left(\sqrt{2x}\right) = 6^2$

$2x = 36$

$x = 18$

A check will show that the solution is 18.

27. $\sqrt{x+8} = \sqrt{x-8}$

$\left(\sqrt{x+8}\right)^2 = \left(\sqrt{x-8}\right)^2$

$x + 8 = x - 8$

$8 = -8$ False

A contradiction results so the equation has no solution.

28. $\sqrt{r+5} + 7 = 10$

$\sqrt{r+5} = 3$

$\left(\sqrt{r+5}\right)^2 = (3)^2$

$r + 5 = 9$

$r = 4$

A check will show that the solution is 4.

29. $2\sqrt[3]{x-1} = \sqrt[3]{x^2+2x}$

$\left(2\sqrt[3]{x-1}\right)^3 = \left(\sqrt[3]{x^2+2x}\right)^3$

$8(x-1) = x^2 + 2x$

$8x - 8 = x^2 + 2x$

$x^2 - 6x + 8 = 0$

$(x-4)(x-2) = 0$

$x = 4$ or $x = 2$

A check will show that both 2 and 4 are solutions to the equation.

30. $\sqrt[3]{6t-1} = \sqrt[3]{2t+3}$

$\left(\sqrt[3]{6t-1}\right)^3 = \left(\sqrt[3]{2t+3}\right)^3$

$6t - 1 = 2t + 3$

$4t = 4$

$t = 1$

A check will show that the solution is 1.

31. $\sqrt[4]{x+8} = \sqrt[4]{2x}$

$\left(\sqrt[4]{x+8}\right)^4 = \left(\sqrt[4]{2x}\right)^4$

$x + 8 = 2x$

$x = 8$

A check will show that the solution is 8.

32. $\sqrt[4]{3x-1} + 4 = 0$

$\sqrt[4]{3x-1} = -4$

No real solution exists because an even root of a real number is never negative.

33. $\sqrt{5x+1} - 6 = 0$

$\sqrt{5x+1} = 6$

$\left(\sqrt[2]{5x+1}\right)^2 = (6)^2$

$5x + 1 = 36$

$5x = 35$

$x = 7$

A check will show that the solution is 7.

34.
$$\sqrt{x^2+12x+3} = -x$$
$$\left(\sqrt{x^2+12x+3}\right)^2 = (-x)^2$$
$$x^2+12x+3 = x^2$$
$$12x+3 = 0$$
$$12x = -3$$
$$x = \frac{-3}{12} = -\frac{1}{4}$$

Check:
$$\sqrt{x^2+12x+3} = -x$$
$$\sqrt{\left(-\frac{1}{4}\right)^2 + 12\left(-\frac{1}{4}\right) + 3} = -\left(-\frac{1}{4}\right)$$
$$\sqrt{\frac{1}{16} - 3 + 3} = \frac{1}{4}$$
$$\sqrt{\frac{1}{16}} = \frac{1}{4}$$
$$\frac{1}{4} = \frac{1}{4} \quad \text{True}$$

35.
$$\sqrt{m^2+6m-4} = m$$
$$\left(\sqrt{m^2+6m-4}\right)^2 = (m)^2$$
$$m^2+6m-4 = m^2$$
$$6m-4 = 0$$
$$6m = 4$$
$$m = \frac{2}{3}$$

Check:
$$\sqrt{\left(\frac{2}{3}\right)^2 + 6\left(\frac{2}{3}\right) - 4} = \frac{2}{3}$$
$$\sqrt{\frac{4}{9} + 4 - 4} = \frac{2}{3}$$
$$\sqrt{\frac{4}{9}} = \frac{2}{3}$$
$$\frac{2}{3} = \frac{2}{3} \quad \text{True}$$

36.
$$\sqrt{x^2+3x+12} = x$$
$$\left(\sqrt{x^2+3x+12}\right)^2 = x^2$$
$$x^2+3x+12 = x^2$$
$$3x+12 = 0$$
$$3x = -12$$
$$x = -4$$

Check:
$$\sqrt{x^2+3x+12} = x$$
$$\sqrt{(-4)^2 + 3(-4) + 12} = -4$$
$$\sqrt{16 - 12 + 12} = -4$$
$$\sqrt{16} = -4$$
$$4 = -4 \quad \text{False}$$

Thus, -3 is not a solution to this equation and we conclude that there is no real solution.

37.
$$\sqrt{5c+1} - 9 = 0$$
$$\sqrt{5c+1} = 9$$
$$\left(\sqrt{5c+1}\right)^2 = 9^2$$
$$5c+1 = 81$$
$$5c = 80$$
$$c = 16$$

A check will show that the solution is 16.

38.
$$\sqrt{b^2-2} = b+4$$
$$\left(\sqrt{b^2-2}\right)^2 = (b+4)^2$$
$$b^2-2 = b^2+8b+16$$
$$-2 = 8b+16$$
$$-18 = 8b$$
$$-\frac{18}{8} = b$$
$$-\frac{9}{4} = b$$

Check: $\sqrt{b^2 - 2} = b + 4$

$$\sqrt{\left(-\frac{9}{4}\right)^2 - 2} = -\frac{9}{4} + 4$$

$$\sqrt{\frac{81}{16} - 2} = \frac{7}{4}$$

$$\sqrt{\frac{49}{16}} = \frac{7}{4}$$

$$\frac{7}{4} = \frac{7}{4} \quad \text{True}$$

39. $\sqrt{z^2 + 5} = z + 1$

$$\left(\sqrt{z^2 + 5}\right)^2 = (z + 1)^2$$

$$z^2 + 5 = z^2 + 2z + 1$$

$$5 = 2z + 1$$

$$4 = 2z$$

$$2 = z$$

A check will show that the solution is 2.

40. $\sqrt{x} + 6x = 1$

$$\sqrt{x} = 1 - 6x$$

$$\left(\sqrt{x}\right)^2 = (1 - 6x)^2$$

$$x = 36x^2 - 12x + 1$$

$$0 = 36x^2 - 13x + 1$$

$$0 = (9x - 1)(4x - 1)$$

$$9x - 1 = 0 \quad \text{or} \quad 4x - 1 = 0$$

$$9x = 1 \qquad\qquad 4x = 1$$

$$x = \frac{1}{9} \qquad\qquad x = \frac{1}{4}$$

Check:

$$\sqrt{\frac{1}{9}} + 6\left(\frac{1}{9}\right) = 1 \qquad \sqrt{\frac{1}{4}} + 6\left(\frac{1}{4}\right) = 1$$

$$\frac{1}{3} + \frac{2}{3} = 1 \qquad\qquad \frac{1}{2} + \frac{3}{2} = 1$$

$$1 = 1 \quad \text{True} \qquad\qquad 2 = 1 \quad \text{False}$$

This check shows that only $\frac{1}{9}$ is a solution.

41. $\sqrt{2y + 5} + 5 - y = 0$

$$\sqrt{2y + 5} = y - 5$$

$$\left(\sqrt{2y + 5}\right)^2 = (y - 5)^2$$

$$2y + 5 = y^2 - 10y + 25$$

$$0 = y^2 - 12y + 20$$

$$0 = (y - 10)(y - 2)$$

$$y = 10 \quad \text{or} \quad y = 2$$

Check: $\sqrt{2y + 5} + 5 - y = 0$

$$\sqrt{2(10) + 5} + 5 - (10) = 0$$

$$\sqrt{25} - 5 = 0$$

$$0 = 0 \quad \text{True}$$

$$\sqrt{2y + 5} + 5 - y = 0$$

$$\sqrt{2(2) + 5} + 5 - (2) = 0$$

$$\sqrt{9} + 3 = 0$$

$$6 = 0 \quad \text{False}$$

This check shows that 10 is the only solution to this equation.

42. $\sqrt{4x + 1} = \frac{1}{2}x + 2$

$$\left(\sqrt{4x + 1}\right)^2 = \left(\frac{1}{2}x + 2\right)^2$$

$$4x + 1 = \frac{1}{4}x^2 + 2x + 4$$

$$0 = \frac{1}{4}x^2 - 2x + 3$$

$$4(0) = 4\left(\frac{1}{4}x^2 - 2x + 3\right)$$

$$0 = x^2 - 8x + 12$$

$$0 = (x - 6)(x - 2)$$

$$x = 6 \quad \text{or} \quad x = 2$$

Check:

$$\sqrt{4x + 1} = \frac{1}{2}x + 2 \qquad \sqrt{4x + 1} = \frac{1}{2}x + 2$$

$$\sqrt{4(6) + 1} = \frac{1}{2}(6) + 2 \qquad \sqrt{4(2) + 1} = \frac{1}{2}(2) + 2$$

$$\sqrt{25} = 3 + 2 \qquad\qquad \sqrt{9} = 1 + 2$$

$$5 = 5 \quad \text{True} \qquad\qquad 3 = 3 \quad \text{True}$$

This check shows that 6 and 2 are both solutions to this equation.

43. $\sqrt{5x+6} = 2x-6$

$\left(\sqrt{5x+6}\right)^2 = (2x-6)^2$

$5x+6 = 4x^2 - 24x + 36$

$0 = 4x^2 - 29x + 30$

$0 = (4x-5)(x-6)$

$x = \dfrac{5}{4}$ or $x = 6$

Check:

$\sqrt{5x+6} = 2x-6$ $\sqrt{5x+6} = 2x-6$

$\sqrt{5\left(\dfrac{5}{4}\right)+6} = 2\left(\dfrac{5}{4}\right)-6$ $\sqrt{5(6)+6} = 2(6)-6$

$\sqrt{\dfrac{49}{4}} = -\dfrac{14}{4}$ $\sqrt{36} = 12-6$

$\dfrac{7}{2} = -\dfrac{7}{2}$ False $6 = 6$ True

This check shows that 6 is the only solution to this equation.

44. $\sqrt{4b+5} + b = 10$

$\sqrt{4b+5} = 10-b$

$\left(\sqrt{4b+5}\right)^2 = (10-b)^2$

$4b+5 = 100 - 20b + b^2$

$b^2 - 24b + 95 = 0$

$(b-5)(b-19) = 0$

$b-5=0$ or $b-19=0$

$b=5$ $b=19$

Check:

$\sqrt{4b+5} + b = 10$ $\sqrt{4b+5} + b = 10$

$\sqrt{4(5)+5} + 5 = 10$ $\sqrt{4(19)+5} + 19 = 10$

$\sqrt{25} + 5 = 10$ $\sqrt{81} + 19 = 10$

$5+5 = 10$ $9+19 = 10$

$10 = 10$ True $28 = 10$ False

This check shows that 5 is the only solution to the equation.

45. $(2a+9)^{1/2} - a + 3 = 0$

$(2a+9)^{1/2} = a-3$

$[(2a+9)^{1/2}]^2 = (a-3)^2$

$2a+9 = a^2 - 6a + 9$

$0 = a^2 - 8a$

$0 = a(a-8)$

$a = 0$ or $a = 8$

Check: $(2a+9)^{1/2} - a + 3 = 0$

$(2 \cdot 0 + 9)^{1/2} - 0 + 3 = 0$

$3 + 3 = 0$

$6 = 0$ False

Check: $(2a+9)^{1/2} - a + 3 = 0$

$(2 \cdot 8 + 9)^{1/2} - 8 + 3 = 0$

$5 - 8 + 3 = 0$

$0 = 0$ True

This check shows that 8 is the only solution to the equation.

46. $(3x+4)^{1/2} - x = -2$

$(3x+4)^{1/2} = x-2$

$\left((3x+4)^{1/2}\right)^2 = (x-2)^2$

$3x+4 = x^2 - 4x + 4$

$0 = x^2 - 7x$

$0 = x(x-7)$

$x-7=0$ or $x=0$

$x = 7$

Check: $(3x+4)^{1/2} = x-2$

$(3(7)+4)^{1/2} = 7-2$

$25^{1/2} = 5$

$5 = 5$ True

Check: $(3x+4)^{1/2} = x-2$

$(3(0)+4)^{1/2} = 0-2$

$4^{1/2} = -2$

$2 = -2$ False

This check shows that 7 is the only solution to the equation.

47. $(2x^2 + 4x + 9)^{1/2} = \sqrt{2x^2 + 9}$

$$[(2x^2 + 4x + 9)^{1/2}]^2 = \left(\sqrt{2x^2 + 9}\right)^2$$

$$2x^2 + 4x + 9 = 2x^2 + 9$$

$$4x = 0$$

$$x = 0$$

Check: $\left(2(0)^2 + 4(0) + 9\right)^{1/2} = \sqrt{2(0)^2 + 9}$

$$(9)^{1/2} = \sqrt{9}$$

$$3 = 3 \quad \text{True}$$

48. $(2x+1)^{1/2} + 7 = x$

$$(2x+1)^{1/2} = x - 7$$

$$\left((2x+1)^{1/2}\right)^2 = (x-7)^2$$

$$2x + 1 = x^2 - 14x + 49$$

$$0 = x^2 - 16x + 48$$

$$0 = (x-12)(x-4)$$

$$x = 12 \text{ or } x = 4$$

Check:

$$(2x+1)^{1/2} + 7 = x$$

$$(2(12)+1)^{1/2} + 7 = (12)$$

$$\sqrt{25} + 7 = 12$$

$$12 = 12 \quad \text{True}$$

Check:

$$(2x+1)^{1/2} + 7 = x$$

$$(2(4)+1)^{1/2} + 7 = (4)$$

$$\sqrt{9} + 7 = 4$$

$$10 = 4 \quad \text{False}$$

This check shows that 12 is the only solution to this equation.

49. $(r+4)^{1/3} = (3r+10)^{1/3}$

$$[(r+4)^{1/3}]^3 = [(3r+10)^{1/3}]^3$$

$$r + 4 = 3r + 10$$

$$4 = 2r + 10$$

$$-6 = 2r$$

$$-3 = r$$

Check: $(-3+4)^{1/3} = [3(-3)+10]^{1/3}$

$$(1)^{1/3} = (1)^{1/3}$$

$$1 = 1 \quad \text{True}$$

50. $(7x+6)^{1/3} + 4 = 0$

$$(7x+6)^{1/3} = -4$$

$$[(7x+6)^{1/3}]^3 = (-4)^3$$

$$7x + 6 = -64$$

$$7x = -70$$

$$x = -10$$

Check: $(7x+6)^{1/3} + 4 = 0$

$$[7(-10)+6]^{1/3} + 4 = 0$$

$$(-64)^{1/3} + 4 = 0$$

$$-4 + 4 = 0$$

$$0 = 0 \quad \text{True}$$

51. $(5x+7)^{1/4} = (9x+1)^{1/4}$

$$[(5x+7)^{1/4}]^4 = [(9x+1)^{1/4}]^4$$

$$5x + 7 = 9x + 1$$

$$7 = 4x + 1$$

$$6 = 4x$$

$$\frac{3}{2} = x$$

Check: $(5x+7)^{1/4} = (9x+1)^{1/4}$

$$\left(5\cdot\frac{3}{2}+7\right)^{1/4} = \left(9\cdot\frac{3}{2}+1\right)^{1/4}$$

$$\left(\frac{15}{2}+7\right)^{1/4} = \left(\frac{27}{2}+1\right)^{1/4}$$

$$\left(\frac{29}{2}\right)^{1/4} = \left(\frac{29}{2}\right)^{1/4} \quad \text{True}$$

52. $(5b+3)^{1/4} = (2b+17)^{1/4}$

$$[(5b+3)^{1/4}]^4 = [(2b+17)^{1/4}]^4$$

$$5b + 3 = 2b + 17$$

$$3b + 3 = 17$$

$$3b = 14$$

$$b = \frac{14}{3}$$

Check: $\left(5\left(\frac{14}{3}\right)+3\right)^{1/4} = \left(2\left(\frac{14}{3}\right)+17\right)^{1/4}$

$\left(\frac{70}{3}+3\right)^{1/4} = \left(\frac{28}{3}+17\right)^{1/4}$

$\left(\frac{79}{3}\right)^{1/4} = \left(\frac{79}{3}\right)^{1/4}$ True

53. $\sqrt[4]{x+5} = -2$

$\left(\sqrt[4]{x+5}\right)^4 = (-2)^4$

$x+5 = 16$

$x = 11$

Check: $\sqrt[4]{x+5} = -2$

$\sqrt[4]{11+5} = -2$

$\sqrt[4]{16} = -2$

$2 = -2$ False

Thus, 11 is not a solution to this equation and we conclude that there is no real solution.

Note: We could have determined that there was no real solution immediately by noting that an even root of a real number is never negative.

54. $\sqrt{x^2+x-1} = -\sqrt{x+3}$

$\left(\sqrt{x^2+x-1}\right)^2 = \left(-\sqrt{x+3}\right)^2$

$x^2+x-1 = x+3$

$x^2-4 = 0$

$(x+2)(x-2) = 0$

$x = -2$ or $x = 2$

Check: $\sqrt{x^2+x-1} = -\sqrt{x+3}$

$\sqrt{(2)^2+(2)-1} = -\sqrt{(2)+3}$

$\sqrt{5} = -\sqrt{5}$ False

Check: $\sqrt{x^2+x-1} = -\sqrt{x+3}$

$\sqrt{(-2)^2+(-2)-1} = -\sqrt{(-2)+3}$

$\sqrt{1} = -\sqrt{1}$ False

This check shows that there is no real solution to this equation.

55. $\sqrt{4x+1} = \sqrt{2x}+1$

$\left(\sqrt{4x+1}\right)^2 = \left(\sqrt{2x}+1\right)^2$

$4x+1 = \left(\sqrt{2x}\right)^2 + 2\cdot 1\cdot \sqrt{2x}+1^2$

$4x+1 = 2x+2\sqrt{2x}+1$

$2x = 2\sqrt{2x}$

$x = \sqrt{2x}$

$x^2 = \left(\sqrt{2x}\right)^2$

$x^2 = 2x$

$x^2-2x = 0$

$x(x-2) = 0$

$x = 0$ or $x-2 = 0$

$x = 2$

A check will show that both 0 and 2 are solutions to the equation.

56. $3\sqrt{b}-1 = \sqrt{b+21}$

$\left(3\sqrt{b}-1\right)^2 = \left(\sqrt{b+21}\right)^2$

$\left(3\sqrt{b}\right)^2 - 2\cdot 1\cdot 3\sqrt{b}+1^2 = b+21$

$9b-6\sqrt{b}+1 = b+21$

$8b-20 = 6\sqrt{b}$

$4b-10 = 3\sqrt{b}$

$\left(4b-10\right)^2 = \left(3\sqrt{b}\right)^2$

$16b^2-80b+100 = 9b$

$16b^2-89b+100 = 0$

$(16b-25)(b-4) = 0$

$b = \frac{25}{16}$ or $b = 4$

Check: $3\sqrt{\frac{25}{16}}-1 = \sqrt{\frac{25}{16}+21}$

$3\left(\frac{5}{4}\right)-1 = \sqrt{\frac{361}{16}}$

$\frac{11}{4} = \frac{19}{4}$ False

Check: $3\sqrt{4}-1 = \sqrt{4+21}$

$3(2)-1 = \sqrt{25}$

$5 = 5$ True

The check shows that 4 is the only solution to the equation.

57.
$$\sqrt{3a+1} = \sqrt{a-4} + 3$$
$$\left(\sqrt{3a+1}\right)^2 = \left(\sqrt{a-4} + 3\right)^2$$
$$3a+1 = \left(\sqrt{a-4}\right)^2 + 2 \cdot 3\sqrt{a-4} + 3^2$$
$$3a+1 = a-4 + 6\sqrt{a-4} + 9$$
$$2a-4 = 6\sqrt{a-4}$$
$$\left(2a-4\right)^2 = \left(6\sqrt{a-4}\right)^2$$
$$4a^2 - 16a + 16 = 36(a-4)$$
$$4a^2 - 52a + 160 = 0$$
$$4\left(a^2 - 13a + 40\right) = 0$$
$$4(a-8)(a-5) = 0$$
$$a = 8 \text{ or } a = 5$$
A check will show that both 5 and 8 are solutions to the equation.

58.
$$\sqrt{x+1} = 2 - \sqrt{x}$$
$$\left(\sqrt{x+1}\right)^2 = \left(2 - \sqrt{x}\right)^2$$
$$x+1 = 4 - 4\sqrt{x} + x$$
$$-3 = -4\sqrt{x}$$
$$(-3)^2 = \left(-4\sqrt{x}\right)^2$$
$$9 = 16x$$
$$\frac{9}{16} = x$$

A check will show that the solution is $\frac{9}{16}$.

59.
$$\sqrt{x+3} = \sqrt{x} - 3$$
$$\left(\sqrt{x+3}\right)^2 = \left(\sqrt{x} - 3\right)^2$$
$$x+3 = x - 6\sqrt{x} + 9$$
$$-6 = -6\sqrt{x}$$
$$1 = \sqrt{x}$$
$$(1)^2 = \left(\sqrt{x}\right)^2$$
$$1 = x$$

Check: $\sqrt{x+3} = \sqrt{x} - 3$
$$\sqrt{1+3} = \sqrt{1} - 3$$
$$\sqrt{4} = 1 - 3$$
$$2 = -2 \quad \text{False}$$
Thus, 1 is not a solution to this equation and we conclude that there is no real solution.

60.
$$\sqrt{y+1} = 2 + \sqrt{y-7}$$
$$\left(\sqrt{y+1}\right)^2 = \left(2 + \sqrt{y-7}\right)^2$$
$$y+1 = 4 + 4\sqrt{y-7} + y - 7$$
$$4 = 4\sqrt{y-7}$$
$$1 = \sqrt{y-7}$$
$$(1)^2 = \left(\sqrt{y-7}\right)^2$$
$$1 = y - 7$$
$$8 = y$$
A check will show that the solution is 8.

61.
$$\sqrt{x+7} = 6 - \sqrt{x-5}$$
$$\left(\sqrt{x+7}\right)^2 = \left(6 - \sqrt{x-5}\right)^2$$
$$x+7 = 36 - 12\sqrt{x-5} + x - 5$$
$$12\sqrt{x-5} = 24$$
$$\sqrt{x-5} = 2$$
$$x - 5 = 4$$
$$x = 9$$
A check will show that the solution is 9.

62.
$$\sqrt{b-3} = 4 - \sqrt{b+5}$$
$$\left(\sqrt{b-3}\right)^2 = \left(4 - \sqrt{b+5}\right)^2$$
$$b-3 = 16 - 8\sqrt{b+5} + b + 5$$
$$8\sqrt{b+5} = 24$$
$$\sqrt{b+5} = 3$$
$$\left(\sqrt{b+5}\right)^2 = 3^2$$
$$b+5 = 9$$
$$b = 4$$
A check will show that the solution is 4.

63.

$$\sqrt{4x-3} = 2 + \sqrt{2x-5}$$

$$\left(\sqrt{4x-3}\right)^2 = \left(2+\sqrt{2x-5}\right)^2$$

$$4x-3 = 4 + 4\sqrt{2x-5} + 2x-5$$

$$2x-2 = 4\sqrt{2x-5}$$

$$x-1 = 2\sqrt{2x-5}$$

$$(x-1)^2 = \left(2\sqrt{2x-5}\right)^2$$

$$x^2 - 2x+1 = 4(2x-5)$$

$$x^2 - 2x+1 = 8x-20$$

$$x^2 - 10x+21 = 0$$

$$(x-7)(x-3) = 0$$

$$x-7=0 \quad \text{or} \quad x-3=0$$

$$x=7 \qquad\qquad x=3$$

A check will show that both 3 and 7 are solutions to the equation.

64. $\sqrt{r+10} + 2 + \sqrt{r-5} = 0$

Note that $\sqrt{r+10} \geq 0$, $2>0$, and $\sqrt{r-5} \geq 0$. Therefore, the left side must always be positive. Without going any further, it is clear that there is no solution to this problem since the left side must be positive and the right side is 0.

65.

$$\sqrt{y+1} = \sqrt{y+10} - 3$$

$$\left(\sqrt{y+1}\right)^2 = \left(\sqrt{y+10}-3\right)^2$$

$$y+1 = \left(\sqrt{y+10}\right)^2 - 6\sqrt{y+10} + 9$$

$$y+1 = y+10 - 6\sqrt{y+10} + 9$$

$$6\sqrt{y+10} = 18$$

$$\sqrt{y+10} = 3$$

$$\left(\sqrt{y+10}\right)^2 = 3^2$$

$$y+10 = 9$$

$$y = -1$$

A check will show that the solution is -1.

66.

$$3 + \sqrt{x+1} = \sqrt{3x+12}$$

$$\left(3+\sqrt{x+1}\right)^2 = \left(\sqrt{3x+12}\right)^2$$

$$9 + 6\sqrt{x+1} + x+1 = 3x+12$$

$$6\sqrt{x+1} = 2x+2$$

$$\left(6\sqrt{x+1}\right)^2 = (2x+2)^2$$

$$36(x+1) = 4x^2 + 8x+4$$

$$4x^2 - 28x-32 = 0$$

$$4(x-8)(x+1) = 0$$

$$x=8 \quad \text{or} \quad x=-1$$

A check will show that both 8 and -1 are solutions to the equation.

67.

$$f(x) = g(x)$$

$$\sqrt{x+8} = \sqrt{2x+1}$$

$$\left(\sqrt{x+8}\right)^2 = \left(\sqrt{2x+1}\right)^2$$

$$x+8 = 2x+1$$

$$7 = x$$

A check will show that $x=7$ is the solution to the equation $f(x) = g(x)$.

68.

$$f(x) = g(x)$$

$$\sqrt{x^2 - 6x+10} = \sqrt{x-2}$$

$$x^2 - 6x+10 = x-2$$

$$x^2 - 7x+12 = 0$$

$$(x-3)(x-4) = 0$$

$$x-3=0 \quad \text{or} \quad x-4=0$$

$$x=3 \qquad\qquad x=4$$

A check will show that $x=3$ and $x=4$ are both solutions to the equation $f(x) = g(x)$.

69.

$$f(x) = g(x)$$

$$\sqrt[3]{5x-19} = \sqrt[3]{6x-23}$$

$$\left(\sqrt[3]{5x-19}\right)^3 = \left(\sqrt[3]{6x-23}\right)^3$$

$$5x-19 = 6x-23$$

$$x=4$$

A check will show that $x=4$ is the solution to the equation $f(x) = g(x)$.

70.
$$f(x) = g(x)$$
$$(14x - 8)^{1/2} = 2(3x + 2)^{1/2}$$
$$[(14x - 8)^{1/2}]^2 = [2(3x + 2)^{1/2}]^2$$
$$14x - 8 = 4(3x + 2)$$
$$14x - 8 = 12x + 8$$
$$2x = 16$$
$$x = 8$$

A check will show that $x = 8$ is the solution to the equation $f(x) = g(x)$.

71.
$$f(x) = g(x)$$
$$2(8x + 24)^{1/3} = 4(2x - 2)^{1/3}$$
$$[2(8x + 24)^{1/3}]^3 = [4(2x - 2)^{1/3}]^3$$
$$8(8x + 24) = 64(2x - 2)$$
$$64x + 192 = 128x - 128$$
$$64x = 320$$
$$x = 5$$

A check will show that $x = 5$ is the solution to the equation $f(x) = g(x)$.

72.
$$f(x) = g(x)$$
$$2\sqrt{x + 2} = 8 - \sqrt{x + 14}$$
$$\left(2\sqrt{x + 2}\right)^2 = \left(8 - \sqrt{x + 14}\right)^2$$
$$4(x + 2) = 64 - 16\sqrt{x + 14} + (x + 14)$$
$$4x + 8 = 78 + x - 16\sqrt{x + 14}$$
$$3x - 70 = -16\sqrt{x + 14}$$
$$(3x - 70)^2 = \left(-16\sqrt{x + 14}\right)^2$$
$$9x^2 - 420x + 4900 = 256(x + 14)$$
$$9x^2 - 420x + 4900 = 256x + 3584$$
$$9x^2 - 676x + 1316 = 0$$
$$(9x - 658)(x - 2) = 0$$
$$9x - 658 = 0 \quad \text{or} \quad x - 2 = 0$$
$$9x = 658 \qquad\qquad x = 2$$
$$x = \frac{658}{9}$$

Check:
$$2\sqrt{x + 2} = 8 - \sqrt{x + 14}$$
$$2\sqrt{\frac{658}{9} + 2} = 8 - \sqrt{\frac{658}{9} + 14}$$
$$\frac{52}{3} = -\frac{4}{3} \quad \text{False}$$

$$2\sqrt{x + 2} = 8 - \sqrt{x + 14}$$
$$2\sqrt{2 + 2} = 8 - \sqrt{2 + 14}$$
$$2(2) = 8 - 4$$
$$4 = 4 \quad \text{True}$$

This check shows that 2 is the only solution to the equation $f(x) = g(x)$.

73.
$$p = \sqrt{2v}$$
$$p^2 = \left(\sqrt{2v}\right)^2$$
$$p^2 = 2v$$
$$\frac{p^2}{2} = v \quad \text{or} \quad v = \frac{p^2}{2}$$

74.
$$l = \sqrt{4r}$$
$$l^2 = \left(\sqrt{4r}\right)^2$$
$$l^2 = 4r$$
$$r = \frac{l^2}{4}$$

75.
$$v = \sqrt{2gh}$$
$$v^2 = \left(\sqrt{2gh}\right)^2$$
$$v^2 = 2gh$$
$$g = \frac{v^2}{2h}$$

76.
$$v = \sqrt{\frac{2E}{m}}$$
$$v^2 = \left(\sqrt{\frac{2E}{m}}\right)^2$$
$$v^2 = \frac{2E}{m}$$
$$mv^2 = 2E$$
$$E = \frac{mv^2}{2}$$

77. $v = \sqrt{\dfrac{FR}{M}}$

$v^2 = \left(\sqrt{\dfrac{FR}{M}}\right)^2$

$v^2 = \dfrac{FR}{M}$

$Mv^2 = FR$

$F = \dfrac{Mv^2}{R}$

78. $\omega = \sqrt{\dfrac{a_0}{b_0}}$

$\omega^2 = \dfrac{a_0}{b_0}$

$b_0 \omega^2 = a_0$

$b_0 = \dfrac{a_0}{\omega^2}$

79. $x = \sqrt{\dfrac{m}{k}} V_0$

$x^2 = \left(\sqrt{\dfrac{m}{k}} V_0\right)^2$

$x^2 = \dfrac{mV_0^2}{k}$

$x^2 k = mV_0^2$

$m = \dfrac{x^2 k}{V_0^2}$

80. $T = 2\pi \sqrt{\dfrac{L}{32}}$

$T^2 = \left(2\pi \sqrt{\dfrac{L}{32}}\right)^2$

$T^2 = 4\pi^2 \left(\dfrac{L}{32}\right)$

$T^2 = \dfrac{\pi^2 L}{8}$

$8T^2 = \pi^2 L$

$L = \dfrac{8T^2}{\pi^2}$

81. $r = \sqrt{\dfrac{A}{\pi}}$

$r^2 = \left(\sqrt{\dfrac{A}{\pi}}\right)^2$

$r^2 = \dfrac{A}{\pi}$

$\pi r^2 = A$ or $A = \pi r^2$

82. $r = \sqrt[3]{\dfrac{3V}{4\pi}}$

$r^3 = \left(\sqrt[3]{\dfrac{3V}{4\pi}}\right)^3$

$r^3 = \dfrac{3V}{4\pi}$

$4\pi r^3 = 3V$

$\dfrac{4\pi r^3}{3} = V$ or $V = \dfrac{4}{3}\pi r^3$

83. $a^2 + b^2 = c^2$

$\left(\sqrt{6}\right)^2 + 9^2 = x^2$

$6 + 81 = x^2$

$87 = x^2 \ \Rightarrow \ x = \sqrt{87}$

84. $a^2 + b^2 = c^2$

$\left(\sqrt{10}\right)^2 + x^2 = \left(\sqrt{70}\right)^2$

$10 + x^2 = 70$

$x^2 = 60$

$x = \sqrt{60} \ \Rightarrow \ x = 2\sqrt{15}$

85. $a^2 + b^2 = c^2$

$x^2 + 5^2 = \left(\sqrt{65}\right)^2$

$x^2 + 25 = 65$

$x^2 = 40$

$x = \sqrt{40} \ \Rightarrow \ x = 2\sqrt{10}$

86. $a^2 + b^2 = c^2$

$4^2 + 6^2 = x^2$

$16 + 36 = x^2$

$52 = x^2$

$x = \sqrt{52} \Rightarrow x = 2\sqrt{13}$

87.
$$\sqrt{x+5} - \sqrt{x} = \sqrt{x-3}$$

$$\left(\sqrt{x+5} - \sqrt{x}\right)^2 = \left(\sqrt{x-3}\right)^2$$

$$x + 5 - 2\sqrt{x(x+5)} + x = x - 3$$

$$x + 8 = 2\sqrt{x^2 + 5x}$$

$$(x+8)^2 = \left(2\sqrt{x^2+5x}\right)^2$$

$$x^2 + 16x + 64 = 4\left(x^2 + 5x\right)$$

$$x^2 + 16x + 64 = 4x^2 + 20x$$

$$3x^2 + 4x - 64 = 0$$

$$(3x+16)(x-4) = 0 \Rightarrow x = -\frac{16}{3} \text{ or } x = 4$$

A check will show that $-\dfrac{16}{3}$ is an extraneous solution. The solution to the equation is 4.

88.
$$\sqrt{2x} - \sqrt{x-4} = \sqrt{12-x}$$

$$\left(\sqrt{2x} - \sqrt{x-4}\right)^2 = \left(\sqrt{12-x}\right)^2$$

$$2x - 2\sqrt{2x(x-4)} + x - 4 = 12 - x$$

$$4x - 16 = 2\sqrt{2x^2 - 8x}$$

$$(4x-16)^2 = \left(2\sqrt{2x^2 - 8x}\right)^2$$

$$16x^2 - 128x + 256 = 4\left(2x^2 - 8x\right)$$

$$16x^2 - 128x + 256 = 8x^2 - 32x$$

$$8x^2 - 96x + 256 = 0$$

$$8(x-8)(x-4) = 0 \Rightarrow x = 8 \text{ or } x = 4$$

A check will show that both 4 and 8 are solutions to the equation.

89.
$$\sqrt{4y+6} + \sqrt{y+5} = \sqrt{y+1}$$

$$\left(\sqrt{4y+6} + \sqrt{y+5}\right)^2 = \left(\sqrt{y+1}\right)^2$$

$$4y + 6 + 2\sqrt{(4y+6)(y+5)} + y + 5 = y + 1$$

$$2\sqrt{(4y+6)(y+5)} = -4y - 10$$

$$\left(2\sqrt{4y^2 + 26y + 30}\right)^2 = (-4y-10)^2$$

$$4\left(4y^2 + 26y + 30\right) = 16y^2 + 80y + 100$$

$$16y^2 + 104y + 120 = 16y^2 + 80y + 100$$

$$24y = -20 \Rightarrow y = -\frac{5}{6}$$

Upon checking, this value does not satisfy the equation. There is no solution.

90.
$$\sqrt{2b-2} + \sqrt{b-5} = \sqrt{4b}$$

$$\left(\sqrt{2b-2} + \sqrt{b-5}\right)^2 = \left(\sqrt{4b}\right)^2$$

$$2b - 2 + 2\sqrt{(2b-2)(b-5)} + b - 5 = 4b$$

$$2\sqrt{(2b-2)(b-5)} = b + 7$$

$$\left(2\sqrt{2b^2 - 12b + 10}\right)^2 = (b+7)^2$$

$$4\left(2b^2 - 12b + 10\right) = b^2 + 14b + 49$$

$$8b^2 - 48b + 40 = b^2 + 14b + 49$$

$$7b^2 - 62b - 9 = 0$$

$$(7b+1)(b-9) = 0 \Rightarrow b = -\frac{1}{7} \text{ or } b = 9$$

A check will show that $-\dfrac{1}{7}$ is an extraneous solution. The solution to the equation is 9.

91. $\sqrt{c+1} + \sqrt{c-2} = \sqrt{3c}$

$\left(\sqrt{c+1} + \sqrt{c-2}\right)^2 = \left(\sqrt{3c}\right)^2$

$c + 1 + 2\sqrt{(c+1)(c-2)} + c - 2 = 3c$

$2\sqrt{(c+1)(c-2)} = c + 1$

$\left(2\sqrt{c^2 - c - 2}\right)^2 = (c+1)^2$

$4\left(c^2 - c - 2\right) = c^2 + 2c + 1$

$4c^2 - 4c - 8 = c^2 + 2c + 1$

$3c^2 - 6c - 9 = 0$

$3(c+1)(c-3) = 0 \implies c = -1 \text{ or } c = 3$

Upon checking, only $c = 3$ satisfies the equation.

92. $\sqrt{2t-1} + \sqrt{t-4} = \sqrt{3t+1}$

$\left(\sqrt{2t-1} + \sqrt{t-4}\right)^2 = \left(\sqrt{3t+1}\right)^2$

$2t - 1 + 2\sqrt{(2t-1)(t-4)} + t - 4 = 3t + 1$

$2\sqrt{(2t-1)(t-4)} = 6$

$\left(2\sqrt{2t^2 - 9t + 4}\right)^2 = (6)^2$

$4\left(2t^2 - 9t + 4\right) = 36$

$8t^2 - 36t + 16 = 36$

$8t^2 - 36t - 20 = 0$

$4(2t+1)(t-5) = 0 \implies t = -\dfrac{1}{2} \text{ or } t = 5$

Upon checking, only $t = 5$ satisfies the equation.

93. $\sqrt{a+2} - \sqrt{a-3} = \sqrt{a-6}$

$\left(\sqrt{a+2} - \sqrt{a-3}\right)^2 = \left(\sqrt{a-6}\right)^2$

$a + 2 - 2\sqrt{(a+2)(a-3)} + a - 3 = a - 6$

$a + 5 = 2\sqrt{(a+2)(a-3)}$

$(a+5)^2 = \left(2\sqrt{a^2 - a - 6}\right)^2$

$a^2 + 10a + 25 = 4\left(a^2 - a - 6\right)$

$a^2 + 10a + 25 = 4a^2 - 4a - 24$

$3a^2 - 14a - 49 = 0$

$(3a+7)(a-7) = 0 \implies a = -\dfrac{7}{3} \text{ or } a = 7$

Upon checking, only $a = 7$ satisfies the equation.

94. $\sqrt{r-1} - \sqrt{r+6} = \sqrt{r-9}$

$\left(\sqrt{r-1} - \sqrt{r+6}\right)^2 = \left(\sqrt{r-9}\right)^2$

$r - 1 - 2\sqrt{(r-1)(r+6)} + r + 6 = r - 9$

$r + 14 = 2\sqrt{(r-1)(r+6)}$

$(r+14)^2 = \left(2\sqrt{r^2 + 5r - 6}\right)^2$

$r^2 + 28r + 196 = 4\left(r^2 + 5r - 6\right)$

$r^2 + 28r + 196 = 4r^2 + 20r - 24$

$3r^2 - 8r - 220 = 0$

$(3r+22)(r-10) = 0 \implies r = -\dfrac{22}{3} \text{ or } r = 10$

Upon checking, neither value satisfies the equation. There is no solution

95. $\sqrt{2-\sqrt{x}} = \sqrt{x}$

$\left(\sqrt{2-\sqrt{x}}\right)^2 = \left(\sqrt{x}\right)^2$

$2-\sqrt{x} = x$

$2-x = \sqrt{x}$

$(2-x)^2 = \left(\sqrt{x}\right)^2$

$4-4x+x^2 = x$

$x^2-5x+4 = 0$

$(x-4)(x-1) = 0 \implies x = 4 \ \text{or}\ x = 1$

Upon checking, only $x = 1$ satisfies the equation.

96. $\sqrt{6+\sqrt{x+4}} = \sqrt{2x-1}$

$\left(\sqrt{6+\sqrt{x+4}}\right)^2 = \left(\sqrt{2x-1}\right)^2$

$6+\sqrt{x+4} = 2x-1$

$\sqrt{x+4} = 2x-7$

$\left(\sqrt{x+4}\right)^2 = (2x-7)^2$

$x+4 = 4x^2-28x+49$

$4x^2-29x+45 = 0$

$(4x-9)(x-5) = 0 \implies x = \dfrac{9}{4} \ \text{or}\ x = 5$

Upon checking, only $x = 5$ satisfies the equation.

97. $\sqrt{2+\sqrt{x+1}} = \sqrt{7-x}$

$\left(\sqrt{2+\sqrt{x+1}}\right)^2 = \left(\sqrt{7-x}\right)^2$

$2+\sqrt{x+1} = 7-x$

$\sqrt{x+1} = 5-x$

$\left(\sqrt{x+1}\right)^2 = (5-x)^2$

$x+1 = 25-10x+x^2$

$x^2-11x+24 = 0$

$(x-8)(x-3) = 0 \implies x = 8 \ \text{or}\ x = 3$

Upon checking, only $x = 3$ satisfies the equation.

98. $\sqrt{1+\sqrt{x-1}} = \sqrt{x-6}$

$\left(\sqrt{1+\sqrt{x-1}}\right)^2 = \left(\sqrt{x-6}\right)^2$

$1+\sqrt{x-1} = x-6$

$\sqrt{x-1} = x-7$

$\left(\sqrt{x-1}\right)^2 = (x-7)^2$

$x-1 = x^2-14x+49$

$x^2-15x+50 = 0$

$(x-5)(x-10) = 0 \implies x = 5 \ \text{or}\ x = 10$

Upon checking, only $x = 10$ satisfies the equation.

99. $c = \sqrt{90^2+90^2} = \sqrt{2(90)^2} = 90\sqrt{2} \approx 127.28$

Second base is about 127.28 feet from home plate.

100. $l = \sqrt{20^2+40^2}$

$l = \sqrt{400+1600}$

$ = \sqrt{2000}$

$ \approx 44.7 \text{ ft}$

101. $s = \sqrt{A}$

$s = \sqrt{169}$

$ = 13 \text{ feet}$

102. a. $r = \sqrt{\dfrac{A}{\pi}}$

$r = \sqrt{\dfrac{254.47}{\pi}}$

$ \approx 9 \text{ inches}$

b. $d = 9$ in. for basketball

$r = 4.5$ in. for basketball

9 in. for hoop $-$ 4.5 in. for basketball

$= 4.5$ inches

103. $T = 2\pi\sqrt{\dfrac{l}{32}}$

    a. Let $l = 8$

$$T = 2\pi\sqrt{\frac{l}{32}}$$

$$= 2\pi\sqrt{\frac{8}{32}} = 2\pi\sqrt{\frac{1}{4}}$$

$$= 2\pi\frac{1}{2} = \pi$$

$$\approx 3.14 \text{ seconds}$$

    b. Replace l with $2l$:

$$T_D = 2\pi\sqrt{\frac{2l}{32}}$$

$$= 2\pi\sqrt{2}\sqrt{\frac{l}{32}}$$

$$= \sqrt{2}\left(2\pi\sqrt{\frac{l}{32}}\right)$$

$$= \sqrt{2}\cdot T$$

    c. This part must be solved in two phases. First, we need to find the length of the pendulum:

$$T = 2\pi\sqrt{\frac{l}{g}}$$

$$2 = 2\pi\sqrt{\frac{l}{32}}$$

$$\frac{1}{\pi} = \sqrt{\frac{l}{32}}$$

$$\left(\frac{1}{\pi}\right)^2 = \frac{l}{32}$$

$$l = \frac{32}{\pi^2}$$

Now, find T using $g = \dfrac{32}{6}$ and $l = \dfrac{32}{\pi^2}$

$$T = 2\pi\sqrt{\frac{l}{g}}$$

$$= 2\pi\sqrt{\frac{\frac{32}{\pi^2}}{\frac{32}{6}}} = 2\pi\sqrt{\frac{6}{\pi^2}}$$

$$= 2\pi\frac{\sqrt{6}}{\pi} = 2\sqrt{6}$$

$$\approx 4.90 \text{ seconds}$$

104.   **a.** $d = \sqrt{L^2 + W^2 + H^2}$

$$d = \sqrt{(22)^2 + (15)^2 + (12)^2}$$

$$= \sqrt{484 + 225 + 144}$$

$$= \sqrt{853}$$

$$\approx 29.2 \text{ in.}$$

    b. $d = \sqrt{(2L)^2 + (2W)^2 + (2H^2)}$

$$= \sqrt{4L^2 + 4W^2 + 4H^2}$$

$$= \sqrt{4}\sqrt{L^2 + W^2 + H^2}$$

$$= 2\sqrt{L^2 + W^2 + H^2}$$

Thus, the diagonal is doubled.

    c. $d = \sqrt{L^2 + W^2 + H^2}$

$$d^2 = L^2 + W^2 + H^2$$

$$d^2 - L^2 - H^2 = W^2$$

$$W = \sqrt{d^2 - L^2 - H^2}$$

105. $r = \sqrt[4]{\dfrac{8\mu l}{\pi R}}$

$$r^4 = \left(\sqrt[4]{\frac{8\mu l}{\pi R}}\right)^4$$

$$r^4 = \frac{8\mu l}{\pi R^4}$$

$$\pi R r^4 = 8\mu l$$

$$R = \frac{8\mu l}{\pi r^4}$$

106. $t = \dfrac{\sqrt{19.6s}}{9.8}$

$$t = \frac{\sqrt{19.6(100)}}{9.8}$$

$$= \frac{\sqrt{1960}}{9.8}$$

$$\approx 4.52 \text{ seconds}$$

107. $N = 0.2\left(\sqrt{R}\right)^3$

$$N = 0.2\left(\sqrt{149.4}\right)^3$$

$$= 0.2(12.223)^3$$

$$= 0.2(1826.106)$$

$$\approx 365.2 \text{ days}$$

108. $N = 0.2\left(\sqrt{R}\right)^3$

$N = 0.2\left(\sqrt{58}\right)^3$

≈ 88.3 days

109. $R = \sqrt{F_1^2 + F_2^2}$

$R = \sqrt{60^2 + 80^2}$

$= \sqrt{10,000}$

$= 100$ lb

110. $v_e = \sqrt{2gR}$

$v_e = \sqrt{2(9.75)(6,370,000)}$

$= \sqrt{124,215,000}$

$\approx 11,145.18$ m/s

111. $c = \sqrt{gH} = \sqrt{32 \cdot 10} = \sqrt{320} \approx 17.89$ ft/sec

112. The diagonal and the two given sides form a right triangle. Use the Pythagorean formula to solve for the diagonal.

$a^2 + b^2 = c^2$

$32^2 + 20^2 = c^2$

$1024 + 400 = c^2$

$1424 = c^2 \quad\Rightarrow\quad c = \sqrt{1424} \approx 37.74$

The diagonal is about 37.74 inches in length.

113. The diagonal and the two given sides form a right triangle. Use the Pythagorean formula to solve for the diagonal.

$a^2 + b^2 = c^2$

$25^2 + 32^2 = c^2$

$625 + 1024 = c^2$

$1649 = c^2 \quad\Rightarrow\quad c = \sqrt{1649} \approx 40.61$

The diagonal is about 40.61 meters in length.

114. $v = 331.3\sqrt{1 + \dfrac{t}{273}}$

$v = 331.3\sqrt{1 + \dfrac{20}{273}}$

$\approx 331.3\sqrt{1.073260073}$

≈ 343.22 m/s

115. $x = \dfrac{-b \pm \sqrt{b^2 - 4ac}}{2a}$

$x = \dfrac{-0 \pm \sqrt{0^2 - 4(1)(-4)}}{2(1)} = \dfrac{\pm\sqrt{16}}{2} = \dfrac{\pm 4}{2} = \pm 2$

Now, $x = 2$ or $x = -2$.

116. $x = \dfrac{-b \pm \sqrt{b^2 - 4ac}}{2a}$

$x = \dfrac{-1 \pm \sqrt{1^2 - 4(1)(-12)}}{2(1)} = \dfrac{-1 \pm \sqrt{49}}{2} = \dfrac{-1 \pm 7}{2}$

Now, $x = \dfrac{-1 + 7}{2} = \dfrac{6}{2} = 3$ or

$x = \dfrac{-1 - 7}{2} = \dfrac{-8}{2} = -4$

117. $x = \dfrac{-b \pm \sqrt{b^2 - 4ac}}{2a}$

$x = \dfrac{-4 \pm \sqrt{4^2 - 4(-1)(5)}}{2(-1)}$

$= \dfrac{-4 \pm \sqrt{36}}{-2}$

$= \dfrac{-4 \pm 6}{-2}$

Now, $x = \dfrac{-4 + 6}{-2} = \dfrac{2}{-2} = -1$ or

$x = \dfrac{-4 - 6}{-2} = \dfrac{-10}{-2} = 5$

118. $x = \dfrac{-b \pm \sqrt{b^2 - 4ac}}{2a}$

$x = \dfrac{-5 \pm \sqrt{5^2 - 4(2)(-12)}}{2(2)}$

$= \dfrac{-5 \pm \sqrt{121}}{4}$

$= \dfrac{-5 \pm 11}{4}$

Now, $x = \dfrac{-5 + 11}{4} = \dfrac{6}{4} = \dfrac{3}{2}$ or

$x = \dfrac{-5 - 11}{4} = \dfrac{-16}{4} = -4$

119. $f(x) = \sqrt{x-5}$

$5 = \sqrt{x-5}$

$5^2 = \left(\sqrt{x-5}\right)^2$

$25 = x-5$

$30 = x$

120. $f(x) = \sqrt[3]{2x+3}$

$3 = \sqrt[3]{2x+3}$

$(3)^3 = \left(\sqrt[3]{2x+3}\right)^3$

$27 = 2x+3$

$24 = 2x$

$12 = x$

121. $f(x) = \sqrt{3x^2-11}+7$

$15 = \sqrt{3x^2-11}+7$

$8 = \sqrt{3x^2-11}$

$8^2 = \left(\sqrt{3x^2-11}\right)^2$

$64 = 3x^2-11$

$75 = 3x^2$

$25 = x^2$

$\pm 5 = x$

122. $f(x) = 8 + \sqrt[3]{x^2+152}$

$14 = 8 + \sqrt[3]{x^2+152}$

$6 = \sqrt[3]{x^2+152}$

$6^3 = \left(\sqrt[3]{x^2+152}\right)^3$

$216 = x^2+152$

$64 = x^2$

$\pm 8 = x$

123. a. $y = \sqrt{4x-12}$, $y = x-3$

The points of intersection are $(3, 0)$ and $(7, 4)$. The x-values are 3 and 7.

b. $\sqrt{4x-12} = x-3$

For $x=3$:　　　　　For $x=7$:

$\sqrt{4 \cdot 3 - 12} = 3-3$　　$\sqrt{4x-12} = x-3$

$\sqrt{12-12} = 0$　　　$\sqrt{4 \cdot 7 - 12} = 7-3$

$\sqrt{0} = 0$　　　　$\sqrt{16} = 4$

$0 = 0$ True　　　$4 = 4$ True

Both values are solutions to the equation.

c.　　$\sqrt{4x-12} = x-3$

$\left(\sqrt{4x-12}\right)^2 = (x-3)^2$

$4x-12 = x^2 - 6x + 9$

$0 = x^2 - 10x + 21$

$0 = (x-3)(x-7)$

$x-3 = 0$　or　$x-7 = 0$

$x = 3$　　　　$x = 7$

The answers agree.

124. The x-coordinates of the x-intercepts are solutions to $f(x) = 0$. If there are no x-intercepts, then there are no values for x such that $f(x) = 0$.

125. At $x = 4$, $g(x) = 0$ or $y = 0$.
Therefore, the graph must have an x-intercept at 4.

126. a. Domain is $\{x | x \ge 3\}$.

b. There are no real solutions since the graph does not cross or touch the x-axis.

127. $L_1 = p - 1.96\sqrt{\dfrac{p(1-p)}{n}}$

$L_1 = 0.60 - 1.96\sqrt{\dfrac{0.60(1-0.60)}{36}}$

$\approx 0.60 - 0.16$

≈ 0.44

$L_2 = p + 1.96\sqrt{\dfrac{p(1-p)}{n}}$

$L_2 = 0.60 + 1.96\sqrt{\dfrac{0.60(1-0.60)}{36}}$

$= 0.60 + 0.16$

≈ 0.76

128. quadratic mean $= \sqrt{\dfrac{\sum x^2}{n}}$

$$= \sqrt{\dfrac{2^2 + 4^2 + 10^2}{3}}$$

$$= \sqrt{40}$$

$$\approx 6.32$$

129. $\sqrt{x^2 + 49} = (x^2 + 49)^{1/2}$

$$\left(\sqrt{x^2 + 49}\right)^2 = [(x^2 + 49)^{1/2}]^2$$

$$x^2 + 49 = x^2 + 49$$

$$49 = 49$$

All real numbers, x, satisfy this equation.

130. $\sqrt{x^2 - 16} = (x^2 - 16)^{1/2}$

This is satisfied when $x^2 - 16 \geq 0$

$(x + 4)(x - 4) \geq 0$

$$
\begin{array}{ccccc}
- & & + & & + \\
\hline
- & & - & & + \\
\hline
+ & & - & & + \\
\hline
& -4 & & 4 &
\end{array}
\begin{array}{l}
\; x + 4 \\
\; x - 4 \\
\; \text{Product}
\end{array}
$$

The solution is $x \leq -4$ or $x \geq 4$.

131. Graph:

$y_1 = \sqrt{x + 8}$

$y_2 = \sqrt{3x + 5}$

-10, 10, 1, -10, 10, 1

The graphs of the equations intersect when $x = 1.5$.

132. Graph:

$y = \sqrt{10x - 16} - 15$

0, 30, 5, -10, 10, 1

The graph of the equation crosses the x-axis at $x = 24.1$.

133. Graph:

$y = \sqrt[3]{5x^2 - 6} - 4$

The graph of the equation crosses the x-axis at $x \approx -3.7$ and $x \approx 3.7$.

134. Graph:

$y_1 = \sqrt[3]{5x^2 - 22}$

$y_2 = \sqrt[3]{4x + 83}$

Intersection X=-4.2 Y=4.045318   Intersection X=5 Y=4.6875481

The graphs of the equations intersect when $x = -4.2$ and $x = 5$.

135. $\sqrt{\sqrt{x + 25} - \sqrt{x}} = 5$

$$\left(\sqrt{\sqrt{x + 25} - \sqrt{x}}\right)^2 = 5^2$$

$$\sqrt{x + 25} - \sqrt{x} = 25$$

$$\sqrt{x + 25} = 25 + \sqrt{x}$$

$$\left(\sqrt{x + 25}\right)^2 = \left(25 + \sqrt{x}\right)^2$$

$$x + 25 = 625 + 50\sqrt{x} + x$$

$$-600 = 50\sqrt{x}$$

$$-12 = \sqrt{x}$$

$$(-12)^2 = \left(\sqrt{x}\right)^2$$

$$144 = x$$

Check:

$$\sqrt{\sqrt{x + 25} - \sqrt{x}} = 5$$

$$\sqrt{\sqrt{144 + 25} - \sqrt{144}} = 5$$

$$\sqrt{\sqrt{169} - \sqrt{144}} = 5$$

$$\sqrt{13 - 12} = 5$$

$$\sqrt{1} = 5$$

$$1 = 5 \quad \text{False}$$

Thus, 144 is not a solution and we conclude that there is no solution.

136.
$$\sqrt{\sqrt{x+9}+\sqrt{x}} = 3$$
$$\left(\sqrt{\sqrt{x+9}+\sqrt{x}}\right)^2 = 3^2$$
$$\sqrt{x+9}+\sqrt{x} = 9$$
$$\sqrt{x+9} = 9-\sqrt{x}$$
$$\left(\sqrt{x+9}\right)^2 = \left(9-\sqrt{x}\right)^2$$
$$x+9 = 81-18\sqrt{x}+x$$
$$-72 = -18\sqrt{x}$$
$$4 = \sqrt{x}$$
$$4^2 = \left(\sqrt{x}\right)^2$$
$$16 = x$$

Check:
$$\sqrt{\sqrt{x+9}+\sqrt{x}} = 3$$
$$\sqrt{\sqrt{16+9}+\sqrt{16}} = 3$$
$$\sqrt{\sqrt{25}+\sqrt{16}} = 3$$
$$\sqrt{5+4} = 3$$
$$\sqrt{9} = 3$$
$$3 = 3 \text{ True}$$

This check confirms that the solution is 16.

137.
$$z = \frac{\overline{x}-\mu}{\dfrac{\sigma}{\sqrt{n}}}$$
$$z\left(\frac{\sigma}{\sqrt{n}}\right) = \overline{x}-\mu$$
$$\left(z\frac{\sigma}{\sqrt{n}}\right)^2 = \left(\overline{x}-\mu\right)^2$$
$$\frac{z^2\sigma^2}{n} = \left(\overline{x}-\mu\right)^2$$
$$z^2\sigma^2 = n\left(\overline{x}-\mu\right)^2$$
$$\frac{z^2\sigma^2}{\left(\overline{x}-\mu\right)^2} = n \text{ or } n = \frac{z^2\sigma^2}{\left(\overline{x}-\mu\right)^2}$$

138.
$$z = \frac{p'-p}{\sqrt{\dfrac{pq}{n}}}$$
$$z\sqrt{\frac{pq}{n}} = p'-p$$
$$\left(z\sqrt{\frac{pq}{n}}\right)^2 = (p'-p)^2$$
$$\frac{z^2 pq}{n} = (p'-p)^2$$
$$z^2 pq = n(p'-p)^2$$
$$\frac{z^2 pq}{(p'-p)^2} = n \text{ or } n = \frac{z^2 pq}{(p'-p)^2}$$

139. a.
$$S = \frac{3+4+5}{2} = \frac{12}{2} = 6$$
$$A = \sqrt{6(6-3)(6-4)(6-5)}$$
$$= \sqrt{6(3)(2)(1)}$$
$$= \sqrt{36}$$
$$= 6$$

The area is 6 square inches.

b. Answers will vary.

c. Answers will vary.

140.
$$P_1 P_2 - P_1 P_3 = P_2 P_3 \quad \text{Solve for } P_2.$$
$$P_1 P_2 - P_1 P_2 - P_1 P_3 = P_2 P_3 - P_1 P_2$$
$$-P_1 P_3 = P_2 P_3 - P_1 P_2$$
$$-P_1 P_3 = P_2(P_3 - P_1)$$
$$\frac{-P_1 P_3}{P_3 - P_1} = \frac{P_2(P_3 - P_1)}{P_3 - P_1}$$
$$\frac{P_1 P_3}{P_1 - P_3} = P_2 \text{ or } P_2 = \frac{P_1 P_3}{P_1 - P_3}$$

141.
$$\frac{x(x-5)+x(x-2)}{2x-7} = \frac{x^2-5x+x^2-2x}{2x-7}$$
$$= \frac{2x^2-7x}{2x-7}$$
$$= \frac{x(2x-7)}{2x-7}$$
$$= x$$

142. $\dfrac{4a^2 - 9b^2}{4a^2 + 12ab + 9b^2} \cdot \dfrac{6a^2 b}{8a^2 b^2 - 12ab^3}$

$\qquad = \dfrac{(2a - 3b)(2a + 3b)}{(2a + 3b)(2a + 3b)} \cdot \dfrac{6a^2 b}{4ab^2(2a - 3b)}$

$\qquad = \dfrac{3a}{2b(2a + 3b)}$

143. $(t^2 - 2t - 15) \div \dfrac{t^2 - 9}{t^2 - 3t}$

$\qquad = (t^2 - 2t - 15) \cdot \dfrac{t^2 - 3t}{t^2 - 9}$

$\qquad = (t - 5)(t + 3) \cdot \dfrac{t(t - 3)}{(t + 3)(t - 3)}$

$\qquad = \dfrac{t(t - 3)(t - 5)(t + 3)}{(t + 3)(t - 3)}$

$\qquad = \dfrac{t\,\cancel{(t - 3)}\,(t - 5)\,\cancel{(t + 3)}}{\cancel{(t + 3)}\,\cancel{(t - 3)}}$

$\qquad = t(t - 5)$

144. $\dfrac{2}{x + 3} - \dfrac{1}{x - 3} + \dfrac{2x}{x^2 - 9}$

$\qquad = \dfrac{2}{x + 3} - \dfrac{1}{x - 3} + \dfrac{2x}{(x + 3)(x - 3)}$

$\qquad = \dfrac{2}{x + 3} \cdot \dfrac{x - 3}{x - 3} - \dfrac{1}{x - 3} \cdot \dfrac{x + 3}{x + 3} + \dfrac{2x}{(x + 3)(x - 3)}$

$\qquad = \dfrac{2(x - 3)}{(x + 3)(x - 3)} - \dfrac{x + 3}{(x + 3)(x - 3)} + \dfrac{2x}{(x + 3)(x - 3)}$

$\qquad = \dfrac{2x - 6}{(x + 3)(x - 3)} - \dfrac{x + 3}{(x + 3)(x - 3)} + \dfrac{2x}{(x + 3)(x - 3)}$

$\qquad = \dfrac{2x - 6 - (x + 3) + 2x}{(x + 3)(x - 3)}$

$\qquad = \dfrac{2x - 6 - x - 3 + 2x}{(x + 3)(x - 3)}$

$\qquad = \dfrac{3x - 9}{(x + 3)(x - 3)}$

$\qquad = \dfrac{3(x - 3)}{(x + 3)(x - 3)}$

$\qquad = \dfrac{3}{x + 3}$

145. $2 + \dfrac{3x}{x - 1} = \dfrac{8}{x - 1}$

$\qquad (x - 1)(2) + (x - 1)\left(\dfrac{3x}{x - 1}\right) = (x - 1)\left(\dfrac{8}{x - 1}\right)$

$\qquad\qquad 2(x - 1) + 3x = 8$

$\qquad\qquad 2x - 2 + 3x = 8$

$\qquad\qquad 5x - 2 = 8$

$\qquad\qquad 5x = 10$

$\qquad\qquad x = 2$

Exercise Set 11.7

1. a. $i = \sqrt{-1}$

   b. $i^2 = -1$

2. $\sqrt{-n} = \sqrt{-1(n)} = \sqrt{-1}\sqrt{n} = i\sqrt{n}$

3. Yes, all the numbers listed are complex numbers.

4. $i^4 = \left(i^2\right)^2 = \left(-1\right)^2 = 1$

5. Yes

6. No; the set of real numbers is a subset of the complex numbers. Every real number is complex, but not every complex number is real.

7. The conjugate of $a + bi$ is $a - bi$.

8. a. Yes: $i \cdot i = i^2 = -1$

   b. No: $i \cdot i \cdot i = \left(i \cdot i\right) \cdot i = i^2 \cdot i = -1 \cdot i = -i$

9. Answers will vary. Possible answers:
   a. $\sqrt{2}$ b. 1 c. $\sqrt{-3}$ or $2i$ d. 6
   e. Every number we have studied is a complex number.

10. Answers will vary.

11. $7 = 7 + 0i$

12. $3i = 0 + 3i$

13. $\sqrt{25} = 5 = 5 + 0i$

14. $\sqrt{-100} = 0 + \sqrt{100}\sqrt{-1}$
    $= 0 + 10i$

15. $21 - \sqrt{-36} = 21 - \sqrt{36}\sqrt{-1}$
    $= 21 - 6i$

16. $\sqrt{3} + \sqrt{-3} = \sqrt{3} + \sqrt{-1}\sqrt{3} = \sqrt{3} + i\sqrt{3}$

17. $\sqrt{-24} = \sqrt{4}\sqrt{-1}\sqrt{6} = 2i\sqrt{6} = 0 + 2i\sqrt{6}$

18. $\sqrt{49} - \sqrt{-49} = \sqrt{49} - \sqrt{49}\sqrt{-1} = 7 - 7i$

19. $8 - \sqrt{-12} = 8 - \sqrt{12}\sqrt{-1}$
    $= 8 - \sqrt{4}\sqrt{3}\sqrt{-1}$
    $= 8 - 2i\sqrt{3}$

20. $\sqrt{-9} + \sqrt{-81} = 0 + \sqrt{9}\sqrt{-1} + \sqrt{81}\sqrt{-1}$
    $= 0 + 3i + 9i$
    $= 0 + 12i$

21. $3 + \sqrt{-98} = 3 + \sqrt{98}\sqrt{-1}$
    $= 3 + \sqrt{49}\sqrt{2}\sqrt{-1}$
    $= 3 + 7i\sqrt{2}$

22. $\sqrt{-9} + 7i = 0 + \sqrt{9}\sqrt{-1} + 7i$
    $= 0 + 3i + 7i$
    $= 0 + 10i$

23. $12 - \sqrt{-25} = 12 - \sqrt{25}\sqrt{-1}$
    $= 12 - 5i$

24. $10 + \sqrt{-32} = 10 + \sqrt{32}\sqrt{-1}$
    $= 10 + \sqrt{16}\sqrt{2}\sqrt{-1}$
    $= 10 + 4i\sqrt{2}$

25. $7i - \sqrt{-45} = 0 + 7i - \sqrt{9}\sqrt{5}\sqrt{-1}$
    $= 0 + 7i - 3i\sqrt{5}$
    $= 0 + \left(7 - 3\sqrt{5}\right)i$

26. $\sqrt{144} + \sqrt{-96} = 12 + \sqrt{-1}\sqrt{16}\sqrt{6}$
    $= 12 + 4i\sqrt{6}$

27. $(19 - i) + (2 + 9i) = 19 - i + 2 + 9i$
    $= 21 + 8i$

28. $(22 + i) - 5(11 - 3i) + 4 = 22 + i - 55 + 15i + 4$
    $= -29 + 16i$

29. $\left(8 - 3i\right) + \left(-8 + 3i\right) = 8 - 3i - 8 + 3i$
    $= 0$

30. $\left(7 - \sqrt{-4}\right) - \left(-1 - \sqrt{-16}\right)$
    $= 7 - \sqrt{-4} + 1 + \sqrt{-16}$
    $= 7 - 2i + 1 + 4i$
    $= 8 + 2i$

31. $\left(1+\sqrt{-1}\right)+\left(-18-\sqrt{-169}\right)$

$=1+\sqrt{-1}-18-\sqrt{-169}$

$=1+i-18-13i$

$=-17-12i$

32. $\left(16-i\sqrt{3}\right)+\left(17-\sqrt{-3}\right)$

$=16-i\sqrt{3}+17-\sqrt{-3}$

$=33-i\sqrt{3}-i\sqrt{3}$

$=33-2i\sqrt{3}$

33. $\left(\sqrt{3}+\sqrt{2}\right)+\left(3\sqrt{2}-\sqrt{-8}\right)$

$=\sqrt{3}+\sqrt{2}+3\sqrt{2}-\sqrt{-8}$

$=\sqrt{3}+\sqrt{2}+3\sqrt{2}-\sqrt{-4\cdot 2}$

$=\sqrt{3}+\sqrt{2}+3\sqrt{2}-2i\sqrt{2}$

$=\sqrt{3}+4\sqrt{2}-2i\sqrt{2}$

$=\left(\sqrt{3}+4\sqrt{2}\right)-2i\sqrt{2}$

34. $\left(8-\sqrt{2}\right)-\left(5+\sqrt{-15}\right)=8-\sqrt{2}-5-\sqrt{-15}$

$=3-\sqrt{2}-i\sqrt{15}$

$=\left(3-\sqrt{2}\right)-i\sqrt{15}$

35. $\left(5-\sqrt{-72}\right)+\left(6+\sqrt{-8}\right)$

$=5-\sqrt{-72}+6+\sqrt{-8}$

$=5-\sqrt{36}\sqrt{2}\sqrt{-1}+6+\sqrt{4}\sqrt{2}\sqrt{-1}$

$=5-6i\sqrt{2}+6+2i\sqrt{2}$

$=11-4i\sqrt{2}$

36. $\left(29+\sqrt{-75}\right)+\left(\sqrt{-147}\right)$

$=29+\sqrt{-75}+\sqrt{-147}$

$=29+\sqrt{25}\sqrt{3}\sqrt{-1}+\sqrt{49}\sqrt{3}\sqrt{-1}$

$=29+5i\sqrt{3}+7i\sqrt{3}$

$=29+12i\sqrt{3}$

37. $\left(\sqrt{4}-\sqrt{-45}\right)+\left(-\sqrt{25}+\sqrt{-5}\right)$

$=\sqrt{4}-\sqrt{-45}-\sqrt{25}+\sqrt{-5}$

$=\sqrt{4}-\sqrt{9}\sqrt{5}\sqrt{-1}-\sqrt{25}+\sqrt{-1}\sqrt{5}$

$=2-3i\sqrt{5}-5+i\sqrt{5}$

$=-3-2i\sqrt{5}$

38. $\left(\sqrt{20}-\sqrt{-12}\right)+\left(2\sqrt{5}+\sqrt{-75}\right)$

$=\sqrt{20}-\sqrt{-12}+2\sqrt{5}+\sqrt{-75}$

$=\sqrt{4}\sqrt{5}-\sqrt{4}\sqrt{3}\sqrt{-1}+2\sqrt{5}+\sqrt{25}\sqrt{3}\sqrt{-1}$

$=2\sqrt{5}-2i\sqrt{3}+2\sqrt{5}+5i\sqrt{3}$

$4\sqrt{5}+3i\sqrt{3}$

39. $2\left(3-i\right)=6-2i$

40. $-7\left(5+3i\sqrt{5}\right)=-35-21i\sqrt{5}$

41. $i\left(4+9i\right)=4i+9i^2=4i+9\left(-1\right)=-9+4i$

42. $3i\left(6-i\right)=18i-3i^2$

$=18i-3\left(-1\right)$

$=18i+3$

$=3+18i$

43. $\sqrt{-9}\left(6+11i\right)=3i\left(6+11i\right)$

$=18i+33i^2$

$=18i+33\left(-1\right)$

$=-33+18i$

44. $\dfrac{1}{2}i\left(\dfrac{1}{3}-18i\right)=\dfrac{1}{6}i-9i^2$

$=\dfrac{1}{6}i-9\left(-1\right)$

$=\dfrac{1}{6}i+9$

$=9+\dfrac{1}{6}i$

45. $\sqrt{-16}\left(\sqrt{3}-7i\right)=4i\left(\sqrt{3}-7i\right)$

$=4i\sqrt{3}-28i^2$

$=4i\sqrt{3}-28\left(-1\right)$

$=4i\sqrt{3}+28$

$=28+4i\sqrt{3}$

46. $-\sqrt{-24}\left(\sqrt{6}-\sqrt{-3}\right)$

$=-\sqrt{-4}\sqrt{6}\left(\sqrt{6}-\sqrt{-3}\right)$

$=-2i\sqrt{6}\left(\sqrt{6}-i\sqrt{3}\right)$

$=-2i\cdot6+2i^2\sqrt{18}$

$=-12i+2i^2\sqrt{9}\sqrt{2}$

$=-12i+2(-1)3\sqrt{2}$

$=-6\sqrt{2}-12i$

47. $\sqrt{-27}\left(\sqrt{3}-\sqrt{-3}\right)=\sqrt{-9}\sqrt{3}\left(\sqrt{3}-\sqrt{-3}\right)$

$=3i\sqrt{3}\left(\sqrt{3}-i\sqrt{3}\right)$

$=3i\cdot3-3i^2\cdot3$

$=9i-3(-1)\cdot3$

$=9+9i$

48. $\sqrt{-32}\left(\sqrt{2}+\sqrt{-8}\right)$

$=\sqrt{-16}\sqrt{2}\left(\sqrt{2}+\sqrt{-4}\sqrt{2}\right)$

$=4i\sqrt{2}\left(\sqrt{2}+2i\sqrt{2}\right)$

$=4i\cdot2+8i^2\cdot2$

$=8i+16i^2$

$=8i+16(-1)$

$=-16+8i$

49. $(3+2i)(1+i)$

$=3(1)+3(i)+2i(1)+2i(i)$

$=3+3i+2i+2i^2$

$=3+3i+2i+2(-1)$

$=3+3i+2i-2$

$=1+5i$

50. $\left(6-2i\right)\left(3+i\right)=18+6i-6i-2i^2$

$=18+6i-6i-2(-1)$

$=18+2$

$=20$

51. $\left(10-3i\right)\left(10+3i\right)=100+30i-30i-9i^2$

$=100+30i-30i-9(-1)$

$=100+9$

$=109$

52. $\left(-4+3i\right)\left(2-5i\right)=-8+20i+6i-15i^2$

$=-8+20i+6i-15(-1)$

$=-8+20i+6i+15$

$=7+26i$

53. $\left(7+\sqrt{-2}\right)\left(5-\sqrt{-8}\right)$

$=\left(7+i\sqrt{2}\right)\left(5-2i\sqrt{2}\right)$

$=35-14i\sqrt{2}+5i\sqrt{2}-2i^2\cdot2$

$=35-14i\sqrt{2}+5i\sqrt{2}-2(-1)\cdot2$

$=35-14i\sqrt{2}+5i\sqrt{2}+4$

$=39-9i\sqrt{2}$

54. $(\sqrt{4}-3i)\left(4+\sqrt{-4}\right)=(2-3i)\left(4+\sqrt{4}\sqrt{-1}\right)$

$=(2-3i)(4+2i)$

$=2(4)+2(2i)-3i(4)-3i(2i)$

$=8+4i-12i-6i^2$

$=8+4i-12i-6(-1)$

$=8+4i-12i+6$

$=14-8i$

55. $\left(\dfrac{1}{2}-\dfrac{1}{3}i\right)\left(\dfrac{1}{4}+\dfrac{2}{3}i\right)$

$=\dfrac{1}{8}+\dfrac{1}{3}i-\dfrac{1}{12}i-\dfrac{2}{9}i^2$

$=\dfrac{1}{8}+\dfrac{1}{3}i-\dfrac{1}{12}i-\dfrac{2}{9}(-1)$

$=\dfrac{1}{8}+\dfrac{1}{3}i-\dfrac{1}{12}i+\dfrac{2}{9}$

$=\dfrac{1}{8}+\dfrac{2}{9}+\left(\dfrac{1}{3}-\dfrac{1}{12}\right)i$

$=\dfrac{25}{72}+\dfrac{1}{4}i$

56. $\left(\dfrac{3}{5}-\dfrac{1}{4}i\right)\left(\dfrac{2}{3}+\dfrac{2}{5}i\right)$

$=\dfrac{3}{5}\left(\dfrac{2}{3}\right)+\dfrac{3}{5}\left(\dfrac{2}{5}i\right)-\dfrac{1}{4}i\left(\dfrac{2}{3}\right)-\left(\dfrac{1}{4}i\right)\left(\dfrac{2}{5}i\right)$

$=\dfrac{2}{5}+\dfrac{6}{25}i-\dfrac{2}{12}i-\dfrac{1}{10}i^2$

$=\dfrac{2}{5}+\dfrac{6}{25}i-\dfrac{1}{6}i-\dfrac{1}{10}(-1)$

$=\dfrac{2}{5}+\dfrac{6}{25}i-\dfrac{1}{6}i+\dfrac{1}{10}$

$=\dfrac{4}{10}+\dfrac{1}{10}+\dfrac{36}{150}i-\dfrac{25}{150}i$

$=\dfrac{5}{10}+\dfrac{11}{150}i$

$=\dfrac{1}{2}+\dfrac{11}{150}i$

57. $\dfrac{8}{3i}=\dfrac{8}{3i}\cdot\dfrac{-i}{-i}=\dfrac{-8i}{-3i^2}=\dfrac{-8i}{-3(-1)}=-\dfrac{8i}{3}$

58. $\dfrac{5}{4i}=\dfrac{5}{4i}\cdot\dfrac{i}{i}=\dfrac{5i}{4i^2}=\dfrac{5i}{4(-1)}=-\dfrac{5}{4}i$

59. $\dfrac{2+3i}{2i}=\dfrac{2+3i}{2i}\cdot\dfrac{-i}{-i}$

$=\dfrac{(2+3i)(-i)}{-2i^2}$

$=\dfrac{-2i-3i^2}{-2i^2}$

$=\dfrac{-2i-3(-1)}{-2(-1)}$

$=\dfrac{-2i+3}{2}$

$=\dfrac{3-2i}{2}$

60. $\dfrac{7-3i}{2i}=\dfrac{7-3i}{2i}\cdot\dfrac{-i}{-i}$

$=\dfrac{-7i+3i^2}{-2i^2}$

$=\dfrac{-7i+3(-1)}{-2(-1)}$

$=-\dfrac{3+7i}{2}$

61. $\dfrac{6}{2-i}=\dfrac{6}{2-i}\cdot\dfrac{2+i}{2+i}$

$=\dfrac{6(2+i)}{(2-i)(2+i)}$

$=\dfrac{12+6i}{4+2i-2i-i^2}$

$=\dfrac{12+6i}{4+2i-2i-(-1)}$

$=\dfrac{12+6i}{5}$

62. $\dfrac{9}{5+i}=\dfrac{9}{5+i}\cdot\dfrac{5-i}{5-i}$

$=\dfrac{9(5-i)}{(5+i)(5-i)}$

$=\dfrac{45-9i}{25-5i+5i-i^2}$

$=\dfrac{45-9i}{25-5i+5i-(-1)}$

$=\dfrac{45-9i}{26}$

63. $\dfrac{3}{1-2i}=\dfrac{3}{1-2i}\cdot\dfrac{1+2i}{1+2i}$

$=\dfrac{3(1+2i)}{(1-2i)(1+2i)}$

$=\dfrac{3+6i}{1+2i-2i-4i^2}$

$=\dfrac{3+6i}{1+2i-2i-4(-1)}$

$=\dfrac{3+6i}{5}$

64. $\dfrac{13}{-3-4i}=\dfrac{13}{-3-4i}\cdot\dfrac{-3+4i}{-3+4i}$

$=\dfrac{13(-3+4i)}{(-3-4i)(-3+4i)}$

$=\dfrac{-39+52i}{9-12i+12i-16i^2}$

$=\dfrac{-39+52i}{9-12i+12i-16(-1)}$

$=\dfrac{-39+52i}{25}$

65. $\dfrac{6-3i}{4+2i} = \dfrac{6-3i}{4+2i} \cdot \dfrac{4-2i}{4-2i}$

$= \dfrac{(6-3i)(4-2i)}{16-4i^2}$

$= \dfrac{24-12i-12i+6i^2}{16-4i^2}$

$= \dfrac{24-12i-12i-6}{16+4}$

$= \dfrac{18-24i}{20}$

$= \dfrac{2(9-12i)}{20}$

$= \dfrac{9-12i}{10}$

66. $\dfrac{4-3i}{4+3i} = \dfrac{4-3i}{4+3i} \cdot \dfrac{4-3i}{4-3i}$

$= \dfrac{(4-3i)(4-3i)}{16-9i^2}$

$= \dfrac{16-12i-12i+9i^2}{16-9i^2}$

$= \dfrac{16-12i-12i+9(-1)}{16-9(-1)}$

$= \dfrac{16-12i-12i-9}{16+9}$

$= \dfrac{7-24i}{25}$

67. $\dfrac{4}{6-\sqrt{-4}} = \dfrac{4}{6-\sqrt{4}\sqrt{-1}}$

$= \dfrac{4}{6-2i} \cdot \dfrac{6+2i}{6+2i}$

$= \dfrac{4(6+2i)}{36-4i^2}$

$= \dfrac{24+8i}{36-4(-1)}$

$= \dfrac{24+8i}{36+4}$

$= \dfrac{8(3+i)}{40}$

$= \dfrac{3+i}{5}$

68. $\dfrac{2}{3+\sqrt{-5}} = \dfrac{2}{3+\sqrt{5}\sqrt{-1}}$

$= \dfrac{2}{3+i\sqrt{5}} \cdot \dfrac{3-i\sqrt{5}}{3-i\sqrt{5}}$

$= \dfrac{2\left(3-i\sqrt{5}\right)}{9-i^2\sqrt{5}^2}$

$= \dfrac{2\left(3-i\sqrt{5}\right)}{9-(-1)(5)}$

$= \dfrac{2\left(3-i\sqrt{5}\right)}{9+5}$

$= \dfrac{2\left(3-i\sqrt{5}\right)}{14}$

$= \dfrac{3-i\sqrt{5}}{7}$

69. $\dfrac{\sqrt{2}}{5+\sqrt{-12}} = \dfrac{\sqrt{2}}{5+\sqrt{4}\sqrt{3}\sqrt{-1}}$

$= \dfrac{\sqrt{2}}{5+2i\sqrt{3}} \cdot \dfrac{5-2i\sqrt{3}}{5-2i\sqrt{3}}$

$= \dfrac{\sqrt{2}\left(5-2i\sqrt{3}\right)}{25-4i^2\sqrt{3}^2}$

$= \dfrac{5\sqrt{2}-2i\sqrt{6}}{25-4(-1)(3)}$

$= \dfrac{5\sqrt{2}-2i\sqrt{6}}{25+12}$

$= \dfrac{5\sqrt{2}-2i\sqrt{6}}{37}$

70. $\dfrac{\sqrt{6}}{\sqrt{3}-\sqrt{-9}} = \dfrac{\sqrt{6}}{\sqrt{3}-\sqrt{9}\sqrt{-1}}$

$= \dfrac{\sqrt{6}}{\sqrt{3}-3i} \cdot \dfrac{\sqrt{3}+3i}{\sqrt{3}+3i}$

$= \dfrac{\sqrt{6}\left(\sqrt{3}+3i\right)}{\sqrt{9}-9i^2}$

$= \dfrac{\sqrt{18}+3i\sqrt{6}}{3-9(-1)}$

$= \dfrac{\sqrt{9}\sqrt{2}+3i\sqrt{6}}{3+9}$

$= \dfrac{3\sqrt{2}+3i\sqrt{6}}{12}$

$= \dfrac{3\left(\sqrt{2}+i\sqrt{6}\right)}{12}$

$= \dfrac{\sqrt{2}+i\sqrt{6}}{4}$

71. $\dfrac{\sqrt{10}+\sqrt{-3}}{5-\sqrt{-20}}$

$= \dfrac{\sqrt{10}+\sqrt{3}\sqrt{-1}}{5-\sqrt{4}\sqrt{5}\sqrt{-1}}$

$= \dfrac{\sqrt{10}+i\sqrt{3}}{5-2i\sqrt{5}} \cdot \dfrac{5+2i\sqrt{5}}{5+2i\sqrt{5}}$

$= \dfrac{(\sqrt{10}+i\sqrt{3})(5+2i\sqrt{5})}{5^2-4i^2\sqrt{5}^2}$

$= \dfrac{5\sqrt{10}+2i\sqrt{50}+5i\sqrt{3}+2i^2\sqrt{15}}{5^2-4(-1)(5)}$

$= \dfrac{5\sqrt{10}+2i\sqrt{25}\sqrt{2}+5i\sqrt{3}+2(-1)\sqrt{15}}{25+20}$

$= \dfrac{(5\sqrt{10}-2\sqrt{15})+(10\sqrt{2}+5\sqrt{3})i}{45}$

72. $\dfrac{12-\sqrt{-12}}{\sqrt{3}+\sqrt{-5}} = \dfrac{12-\sqrt{4}\sqrt{3}\sqrt{-1}}{\sqrt{3}+\sqrt{5}\sqrt{-1}}$

$= \dfrac{12-2i\sqrt{3}}{\sqrt{3}+i\sqrt{5}} \cdot \dfrac{\sqrt{3}-i\sqrt{5}}{\sqrt{3}-i\sqrt{5}}$

$= \dfrac{\left(12-2i\sqrt{3}\right)\left(\sqrt{3}-i\sqrt{5}\right)}{\left(\sqrt{3}\right)^2-i^2\sqrt{5}^2}$

$= \dfrac{12\sqrt{3}-12i\sqrt{5}-2i\sqrt{9}+2i^2\sqrt{15}}{\sqrt{3}^2-i^2\sqrt{5}^2}$

$= \dfrac{12\sqrt{3}-12i\sqrt{5}-2i(3)+2(-1)\sqrt{15}}{3-(-1)(5)}$

$= \dfrac{12\sqrt{3}-12i\sqrt{5}-6i-2\sqrt{15}}{3+5}$

$= \dfrac{2\left(6\sqrt{3}-\sqrt{15}-6i\sqrt{5}-3i\right)}{8}$

$= \dfrac{\left(6\sqrt{3}-\sqrt{15}\right)-\left(6\sqrt{5}+3\right)i}{4}$

73. $\dfrac{\sqrt{-75}}{\sqrt{-3}} = \dfrac{\sqrt{25}\sqrt{3}\sqrt{-1}}{\sqrt{3}\sqrt{-1}} = \dfrac{5i\sqrt{3}}{i\sqrt{3}} = 5$

74. $\dfrac{\sqrt{-30}}{\sqrt{-2}} = \dfrac{\sqrt{30}\sqrt{-1}}{\sqrt{2}\sqrt{-1}} = \dfrac{i\sqrt{30}}{i\sqrt{2}} = \sqrt{\dfrac{30}{2}} = \sqrt{15}$

75. $\dfrac{\sqrt{-32}}{\sqrt{-18}\sqrt{8}} = \dfrac{\sqrt{32}\sqrt{-1}}{\sqrt{144}\sqrt{-1}} = \dfrac{i\sqrt{16}\sqrt{2}}{i\sqrt{144}} = \dfrac{4i\sqrt{2}}{12i} = \dfrac{\sqrt{2}}{3}$

76. $\dfrac{\sqrt{-40}\sqrt{-20}}{\sqrt{-4}} = \dfrac{\sqrt{40}\sqrt{-1}\cdot\sqrt{20}\sqrt{-1}}{\sqrt{4}\sqrt{-1}}$

$= \dfrac{(i\sqrt{40})(i\sqrt{20})}{i\sqrt{4}}$

$= \dfrac{i\sqrt{40}\sqrt{20}}{2}$

$= \dfrac{i\sqrt{800}}{2}$

$= \dfrac{i\sqrt{400}\sqrt{2}}{2}$

$= \dfrac{i20\sqrt{2}}{2}$

$= 10i\sqrt{2}$

77. $(9-2i)+(3-5i) = 9+3-2i-5i = 12-7i$

78. $\left(\dfrac{1}{2}+2i\right)-\left(\dfrac{3}{5}-\dfrac{2}{3}i\right)=\dfrac{1}{2}+2i-\dfrac{3}{5}+\dfrac{2}{3}i$

$\qquad\qquad = \dfrac{5}{10}+\dfrac{6}{3}i-\dfrac{6}{10}+\dfrac{2}{3}i$

$\qquad\qquad = -\dfrac{1}{10}+\dfrac{8}{3}i$

79. $\left(\sqrt{50}-\sqrt{2}\right)-\left(\sqrt{-12}-\sqrt{-48}\right)$

$\quad = \left(5\sqrt{2}-\sqrt{2}\right)-\left(2i\sqrt{3}-4i\sqrt{3}\right)$

$\quad = 4\sqrt{2}-\left(-2i\sqrt{3}\right)$

$\quad = 4\sqrt{2}+2i\sqrt{3}$

80. $(8-\sqrt{-6})-(2-\sqrt{-24})$

$\quad = (8-i\sqrt{6})-(2-2i\sqrt{6})$

$\quad = 8-i\sqrt{6}-2+2i\sqrt{6}$

$\quad = 6+i\sqrt{6}$

81. $5.2(4-3.2i) = 5.2(4)-5.2(3.2i) = 20.8-16.64i$

82. $\sqrt{-6}\left(\sqrt{3}-\sqrt{-10}\right)$

$\quad = i\sqrt{6}\left(\sqrt{3}-i\sqrt{10}\right)$

$\quad = i\sqrt{6}\sqrt{3}-i^2\sqrt{6}\sqrt{10}$

$\quad = i\sqrt{18}-i^2\sqrt{60}$

$\quad = 3i\sqrt{2}-(-1)2\sqrt{15}$

$\quad = 3i\sqrt{2}+2\sqrt{15}$

$\quad = 2\sqrt{15}+3i\sqrt{2}$

83. $(9+2i)(3-5i)$

$\quad = 27-45i+6i-10i^2$

$\quad = 27-39i-10(-1)$

$\quad = 27+10-39i$

$\quad = 37-39i$

84. $(\sqrt{3}+2i)(\sqrt{6}-\sqrt{-8})$

$\quad = (\sqrt{3}+2i)(\sqrt{6}-2i\sqrt{2})$

$\quad = \sqrt{3}\sqrt{6}-2i\sqrt{3}\sqrt{2}+2i\sqrt{6}-2i(2i\sqrt{2})$

$\quad = \sqrt{18}-2i\sqrt{6}+2i\sqrt{6}-4i^2\sqrt{2}$

$\quad = 3\sqrt{2}-4(-1)\sqrt{2}$

$\quad = 3\sqrt{2}+4\sqrt{2}$

$\quad = 7\sqrt{2}$

85. $\dfrac{11+4i}{2i} = \dfrac{11+4i}{2i}\cdot\dfrac{-2i}{-2i}$

$\qquad = \dfrac{(11+4i)(-2i)}{-4i^2}$

$\qquad = \dfrac{-22i-8i^2}{-4i^2}$

$\qquad = \dfrac{-22i-8(-1)}{-4(-1)}$

$\qquad = \dfrac{8-22i}{4}$

$\qquad = \dfrac{4-11i}{2}$

86. $\dfrac{1}{4+3i} = \dfrac{1}{4+3i}\cdot\dfrac{4-3i}{4-3i} = \dfrac{4-3i}{16+9} = \dfrac{4-3i}{25}$

87. $\dfrac{6}{\sqrt{3}-\sqrt{-4}} = \dfrac{6}{\sqrt{3}-2i}$

$\qquad = \dfrac{6}{\sqrt{3}-2i}\cdot\dfrac{\sqrt{3}+2i}{\sqrt{3}+2i}$

$\qquad = \dfrac{6(\sqrt{3}+2i)}{(\sqrt{3})^2-(2i)^2}$

$\qquad = \dfrac{6\sqrt{3}+12i}{3-4i^2}$

$\qquad = \dfrac{6\sqrt{3}+12i}{3-4(-1)}$

$\qquad = \dfrac{6\sqrt{3}+12i}{7}$

88. $\dfrac{5-2i}{3+2i} = \dfrac{5-2i}{3+2i}\cdot\dfrac{3-2i}{3-2i}$

$\qquad = \dfrac{15-10i-6i+4i^2}{9+4}$

$\qquad = \dfrac{15-16i-4}{13}$

$\qquad = \dfrac{11-16i}{13}$

89. $\left(11-\dfrac{5}{9}i\right)-\left(4-\dfrac{3}{5}i\right)=11-\dfrac{5}{9}i-4+\dfrac{3}{5}i$

$\qquad\qquad = 7-\dfrac{5}{9}i+\dfrac{3}{5}i$

$\qquad\qquad = 7-\dfrac{25}{45}i+\dfrac{27}{45}i$

$\qquad\qquad = 7+\dfrac{2}{45}i$

90. $\dfrac{8}{7}\left(4-\dfrac{2}{5}i\right)=\dfrac{32}{7}-\dfrac{16}{35}i$

91. $\left(\dfrac{2}{3}-\dfrac{1}{5}i\right)\left(\dfrac{3}{5}-\dfrac{3}{4}i\right)$

$\qquad =\left(\dfrac{2}{3}\right)\left(\dfrac{3}{5}\right)-\dfrac{2}{3}\left(\dfrac{3}{4}i\right)-\left(\dfrac{1}{5}i\right)\left(\dfrac{3}{5}\right)+\left(\dfrac{1}{5}i\right)\left(\dfrac{3}{4}i\right)$

$\qquad =\dfrac{2}{5}-\dfrac{1}{2}i-\dfrac{3}{25}i+\dfrac{3}{20}i^2$

$\qquad =\dfrac{2}{5}-\dfrac{1}{2}i-\dfrac{3}{25}i+\dfrac{3}{20}(-1)$

$\qquad =\left(\dfrac{2}{5}-\dfrac{3}{20}\right)+\left(-\dfrac{1}{2}-\dfrac{3}{25}\right)i$

$\qquad =\left(\dfrac{8}{20}-\dfrac{3}{20}\right)+\left(-\dfrac{25}{50}-\dfrac{6}{50}\right)i$

$\qquad =\dfrac{5}{20}-\dfrac{31}{50}i$

$\qquad =\dfrac{1}{4}-\dfrac{31}{50}i$

92. $\sqrt{\dfrac{4}{9}}\left(\sqrt{\dfrac{25}{36}}-\sqrt{-\dfrac{4}{25}}\right)=\dfrac{2}{3}\left(\dfrac{5}{6}-\dfrac{2}{5}i\right)=\dfrac{5}{9}-\dfrac{4}{15}i$

93. $\dfrac{\sqrt{-48}}{\sqrt{-12}}=\dfrac{\sqrt{48}\sqrt{-1}}{\sqrt{12}\sqrt{-1}}$

$\qquad =\dfrac{i\sqrt{48}}{i\sqrt{12}}$

$\qquad =\dfrac{\sqrt{48}}{\sqrt{12}}$

$\qquad =\sqrt{\dfrac{48}{12}}$

$\qquad =\sqrt{4}$

$\qquad =2$

94. $\dfrac{-6-2i}{2+\sqrt{-5}}=\dfrac{-6-2i}{2+i\sqrt{5}}$

$\qquad =\dfrac{-6-2i}{2+i\sqrt{5}}\cdot\dfrac{2-i\sqrt{5}}{2-i\sqrt{5}}$

$\qquad =\dfrac{-12+6i\sqrt{5}-4i-2\sqrt{5}}{4+5}$

$\qquad =\dfrac{-12+6i\sqrt{5}-4i-2\sqrt{5}}{9}$

$\qquad =\dfrac{\left(-12-2\sqrt{5}\right)+\left(6\sqrt{5}-4\right)i}{9}$

95. $(5.23-6.41i)-(9.56+4.5i)$
$\qquad = 5.23-6.41i-9.56-4.5i$
$\qquad = -4.33-10.91i$

96. $\left(\sqrt{-6}+3\right)\left(\sqrt{-15}+5\right)$

$\qquad =\left(i\sqrt{6}+3\right)\left(i\sqrt{15}+5\right)$

$\qquad =i^2\sqrt{90}+5i\sqrt{6}+3i\sqrt{15}+15$

$\qquad =-1\left(3\sqrt{10}\right)+5i\sqrt{6}+3i\sqrt{15}+15$

$\qquad =\left(-3\sqrt{10}+15\right)+\left(5\sqrt{6}+3\sqrt{15}\right)i$

97. $i^6=i^4\cdot i^2=1\cdot(-1)=-1$

98. $i^{63}=i^{60}\cdot i^3=(i^4)^{15}\cdot i^3=1^{15}\cdot i^3=1\cdot(-i)=-i$

99. $i^{160}=(i^4)^{40}=1^{40}=1$

100. $i^{231}=i^{228}\cdot i^3$

$\qquad =(i^4)^{57}\cdot i^3$

$\qquad =1^{57}\cdot i^3$

$\qquad =1\cdot(i^3)$

$\qquad =i^3$

$\qquad =-i$

101. $i^{93}=i^{92}\cdot i^1=(i^4)^{23}i=1^{23}\cdot i=1(i)=i$

102. $i^{103} = i^{100}i^3$

$= (i^4)^{25}i^3$

$= 1^{25} \cdot i^3$

$= 1(i^3)$

$= i^3$

$= -i$

103. $i^{811} = i^{808} \cdot i^3$

$= (i^4)^{202} \cdot i^3$

$= 1^{202} \cdot i^3$

$= 1 \cdot (i^3)$

$= i^3$

$= -i$

104. $i^{1213} = i^{1212} \cdot i^1 = (i^4)^{303} \cdot i = 1^{303} \cdot i = 1 \cdot (i) = i$

105. a. The additive inverse of $2 + 3i$ is its opposite, $-2 - 3i$. Note that $(2 + 3i) + (-2 - 3i) = 0$.

b. The multiplicative inverse of $2 + 3i$ is its reciprocal, $\dfrac{1}{2 + 3i}$. To simplify this, multiply the numerator and denominator by the conjugate of the denominator.

$\dfrac{1}{2 + 3i} = \dfrac{1}{2 + 3i} \cdot \dfrac{2 - 3i}{2 - 3i}$

$= \dfrac{2 - 3i}{(2 + 3i)(2 - 3i)}$

$= \dfrac{2 - 3i}{4 - 6i + 6i - 9i^2}$

$= \dfrac{2 - 3i}{13}$

106. a. The additive inverse of $4 - 5i$ is its opposite, $-4 + 5i$. Note that $(4 - 5i) + (-4 + 5i) = 0$.

b. The multiplicative inverse of $4 - 5i$ is its reciprocal, $\dfrac{1}{4 - 5i}$. To simplify this, multiply the numerator and denominator by the conjugate of the denominator.

$\dfrac{1}{4 - 5i} = \dfrac{1}{4 - 5i} \cdot \dfrac{4 + 5i}{4 + 5i}$

$= \dfrac{4 + 5i}{(4 - 5i)(4 + 5i)}$

$= \dfrac{4 + 5i}{16 + 20i - 20i - 25i^2}$

$= \dfrac{4 + 5i}{41}$

107. True. The product of two pure imaginary numbers is always a real number. Consider two pure imaginary numbers bi and di where b, d are non-zero real numbers whose product

$(bi)(di) = bdi^2$

$= bd(-1)$

$= -bd$

which is a real number.

108. False. $2i + (-2i) = 0$ and 0 is not an imaginary number.

109. False. The product of two complex numbers is not always a real number. For example,

$(1 + i)(1 + i) = 1 + i + i + i^2$

$= 1 + 2i + (-1)$

$= 0 + 2i$

which is not a real number.

110. True

111. Even values of n will result in i^n being a real number. $i^2 = -1, i^{2n} = (i^2)^n = (-1)^n$

112. All values of n will result in i^{2n} being a real number. $i^{2n} = (i^2)^n = (-1)^n$

113. $f(x) = x^2$

$f(2i) = (2i)^2 = 4i^2 = 4(-1) = -4$

114. $f(x) = x^2$

$f(4i) = (4i)^2 = 16i^2 = 16(-1) = -16$

115. $f(x) = x^4 - 2x$

$f(2i) = (2i)^4 - 2(2i)$

$\quad = 2^4 i^4 - 4i$

$\quad = 16(1) - 4i$

$\quad = 16 - 4i$

116. $f(x) = x^3 - 4x^2$

$f(5i) = (5i)^3 - 4(5i)^2$

$\quad = 5^3 i^3 - 4(5^2 i^2)$

$\quad = 125(-i) - 4[25(-1)]$

$\quad = -125i + 100$

$\quad = 100 - 125i$

117. $f(x) = x^2 + 2x$

$f(3+i) = (3+i)^2 + 2(3+i)$

$\quad = 9 + 6i + i^2 + 6 + 2i$

$\quad = 9 + 6i - 1 + 6 + 2i$

$\quad = 14 + 8i$

118. $f(x) = \dfrac{x^2}{x-2}$

$f(4-i) = \dfrac{(4-i)^2}{4-i-2}$

$\quad = \dfrac{16 - 8i + i^2}{2-i}$

$\quad = \dfrac{16 - 8i - 1}{2-i}$

$\quad = \dfrac{15 - 8i}{2-i}$

$\quad = \dfrac{15-8i}{2-i} \cdot \dfrac{2+i}{2+i}$

$\quad = \dfrac{30 + 15i - 16i - 8i^2}{4 - i^2}$

$\quad = \dfrac{30 + 15i - 16i + 8}{4 + 1}$

$\quad = \dfrac{38 - i}{5}$

119. $x^2 - 2x + 5$

$= (1+2i)^2 - 2(1+2i) + 5$

$= 1^2 + 2(1)(2i) + (2i)^2 - 2 - 4i + 5$

$= 1 + 4i - 4 - 2 - 4i + 5$

$= 0$

120. $x^2 - 2x + 5$

$= (1-2i)^2 - 2(1-2i) + 5$

$= 1^2 - 2(1)(2i) + (2i)^2 - 2 + 4i + 5$

$= 1 - 4i - 4 - 2 + 4i + 5$

$= 0 + 0i$

$= 0$

121. $x^2 + 2x + 7$

$= (-1 + i\sqrt{5})^2 + 2(-1 + i\sqrt{5}) + 7$

$= (-1)^2 - 2(1)(i\sqrt{5}) + (i\sqrt{5})^2 - 2 + 2i\sqrt{5} + 7$

$= 1 - 2i\sqrt{5} - 5 - 2 + 2i\sqrt{5} + 7$

$= 1 + 0i$

$= 1$

122. $x^2 + 2x + 9$

$= \left(-1 - i\sqrt{5}\right)^2 + 2\left(-1 - i\sqrt{5}\right) + 9$

$= (-1)^2 + 2(-1)\left(-i\sqrt{5}\right) + \left(i\sqrt{5}\right)^2 - 2 - 2i\sqrt{5} + 9$

$= 1 + 2i\sqrt{5} - 5 - 2 - 2i\sqrt{5} + 9$

$= 3$

123.
$$x^2 - 4x + 5 = 0$$
$$(2-i)^2 - 4(2-i) + 5 = 0$$
$$2^2 - 2(2)(i) + (i)^2 - 8 + 4i + 5 = 0$$
$$4 - 4i - 1 - 8 + 4i + 5 = 0$$
$$0 + 0i = 0$$
$$0 = 0 \quad \text{True}$$

$2 - i$ is a solution .

124.
$$x^2 - 4x + 5 = 0$$
$$(2+i)^2 - 4(2+i) + 5 = 0$$
$$2^2 + 2(2)(i) + i^2 - 8 - 4i + 5 = 0$$
$$4 + 4i - 1 - 8 - 4i + 5 = 0$$
$$0 + 0i = 0$$
$$0 = 0 \quad \text{True}$$

$2 + i$ is a solution.

125.
$$x^2 - 6x + 11 = 0$$
$$(-3 + i\sqrt{3})^2 - 6(-3 + i\sqrt{3}) + 11 = 0$$
$$(-3)^2 - 2(3)(i\sqrt{3}) + (i\sqrt{3})^2 + 18 - 6i\sqrt{3} + 11 = 0$$
$$9 - 6i\sqrt{3} - 3 + 18 - 6i\sqrt{3} + 11 = 0$$
$$35 - 12i\sqrt{3} = 0$$

False, $-3 + i\sqrt{3}$ is not a solution.

126.
$$x^2 - 6x + 15 = 0$$
$$\left(3 - i\sqrt{3}\right)^2 - 6\left(3 - i\sqrt{3}\right) + 15 = 0$$
$$3^2 - 2(3)\left(i\sqrt{3}\right) + \left(i\sqrt{3}\right)^2 - 18 + 6i\sqrt{3} + 15 = 0$$
$$9 - 6i\sqrt{3} - 3 - 18 + 6i\sqrt{3} + 15 = 0$$
$$3 + 0i = 0$$
$$3 \neq 0$$

False, $3 - i\sqrt{3}$ is not a solution.

127. $Z = \dfrac{V}{I}$
$$Z = \frac{1.8 + 0.5i}{0.6i}$$
$$= \frac{1.8 + 0.5i}{0.6i} \cdot \frac{-0.6i}{-0.6i}$$
$$= \frac{-1.08i - 0.3i^2}{-0.36i^2}$$
$$= \frac{-1.08i - 0.3(-1)}{-0.36(-1)}$$
$$= \frac{0.3 - 1.08i}{0.36}$$
$$\approx 0.83 - 3i$$

128. $Z = \dfrac{2.4 - 0.6i}{-0.4i}$
$$= \frac{2.4 - 0.6i}{-0.4i} \cdot \frac{0.4i}{0.4i}$$
$$= \frac{0.96i - 0.24i^2}{-0.16i^2}$$
$$= \frac{0.96i - 0.24(-1)}{(-0.16)(-1)}$$
$$= \frac{0.24 + 0.96i}{0.16}$$
$$= 1.5 + 6i$$

129. $Z_T = \dfrac{Z_1 Z_2}{Z_1 + Z_2}$
$$= \frac{(2 - i)(4 + i)}{(2 - i) + (4 + i)}$$
$$= \frac{8 + 2i - 4i - i^2}{6}$$
$$= \frac{8 - 2i - (-1)}{6}$$
$$= \frac{9 - 2i}{6}$$
$$\approx 1.5 - 0.33i$$

130. $Z_T = \dfrac{Z_1 Z_2}{Z_1 + Z_2}$
$$= \frac{(3 - i)(5 + i)}{3 - i + 5 + i}$$
$$= \frac{15 - 2i - i^2}{8}$$
$$= \frac{15 - 2i + 1}{8}$$
$$= \frac{16 - 2i}{8}$$
$$= 2 - 0.25i$$

131. $i^{-1} = \dfrac{1}{i} = \dfrac{1}{i} \cdot \dfrac{i}{i} = \dfrac{i}{i^2} = \dfrac{i}{-1} = -i$

132. $i^{-5} = \dfrac{1}{i^5} = \dfrac{1}{\left(i^4\right)i} = \dfrac{1}{i} = \dfrac{1}{i} \cdot \dfrac{i}{i} = \dfrac{i}{i^2} = \dfrac{i}{-1} = -i$

133. $x^2 - 2x + 6 = 0$
$$a = 1, b = -2, c = 6$$
$$x = \frac{-(-2) \pm \sqrt{(-2)^2 - 4(1)(6)}}{2(1)}$$
$$= \frac{2 \pm \sqrt{4 - 24}}{2}$$
$$= \frac{2 \pm \sqrt{-20}}{2}$$
$$= \frac{2 \pm 2i\sqrt{5}}{2}$$
$$= \frac{2\left(1 \pm i\sqrt{5}\right)}{2}$$
$$= 1 \pm i\sqrt{5}$$

134. $x^2 - 4x + 6 = 0$

$a = 1, b = -4, c = 6$

$x = \dfrac{-(-4) \pm \sqrt{(-4)^2 - 4(1)(6)}}{2(1)}$

$= \dfrac{4 \pm \sqrt{16 - 24}}{2}$

$= \dfrac{4 \pm \sqrt{-8}}{2}$

$= \dfrac{4 \pm 2i\sqrt{2}}{2}$

$= \dfrac{2\left(2 \pm i\sqrt{2}\right)}{2}$

$= 2 \pm i\sqrt{2}$

135. $a + b = 5 + 2i\sqrt{3} + 1 + i\sqrt{3}$

$\qquad = 5 + 1 + 2i\sqrt{3} + i\sqrt{3}$

$\qquad = 6 + 3i\sqrt{3}$

136. $a - b = (5 + 2i\sqrt{3}) - (1 + i\sqrt{3})$

$\qquad = 5 + 2i\sqrt{3} - 1 - i\sqrt{3}$

$\qquad = 5 - 1 + 2i\sqrt{3} - i\sqrt{3}$

$\qquad = 4 + i\sqrt{3}$

137. $ab = (5 + 2i\sqrt{3})(1 + i\sqrt{3})$

$\qquad = 5(1) + (5)(i\sqrt{3}) + (2i\sqrt{3})(1) + (2i\sqrt{3})(i\sqrt{3})$

$\qquad = 5 + 5i\sqrt{3} + 2i\sqrt{3} + 2i^2(\sqrt{3})^2$

$\qquad = 5 + 5i\sqrt{3} + 2i\sqrt{3} - 6$

$\qquad = -1 + 7i\sqrt{3}$

138. $\dfrac{a}{b} = \dfrac{5 + 2i\sqrt{3}}{1 + i\sqrt{3}} \cdot \dfrac{1 - i\sqrt{3}}{1 - i\sqrt{3}}$

$\qquad = \dfrac{5 - 5i\sqrt{3} + 2i\sqrt{3} - i^2(2)(\sqrt{3})^2}{1^2 + (\sqrt{3})^2}$

$\qquad = \dfrac{5 - 5i\sqrt{3} + 2i\sqrt{3} + 6}{1 + 3}$

$\qquad = \dfrac{11 - 3i\sqrt{3}}{4}$

139.

$$\begin{array}{r} 2c - 3 \\ 4c + 9 \overline{\smash{)}\, 8c^2 + 6c - 35} \end{array}$$

$\qquad \underline{8c^2 + 18c} \quad \leftarrow 2c(4c + 9)$

$\qquad\qquad -12c - 35$

$\qquad\qquad \underline{-12c - 27} \quad \leftarrow -3(4c + 9)$

$\qquad\qquad\qquad -8 \quad \leftarrow \text{Remainder}$

Thus, $\dfrac{8c^2 + 6c - 35}{4c + 9} = 2c - 3 - \dfrac{8}{4c + 9}$

140. $\dfrac{b}{a - b} + \dfrac{a + b}{b} = \dfrac{b}{a - b} \cdot \dfrac{b}{b} + \dfrac{a + b}{b} \cdot \dfrac{a - b}{a - b}$

$\qquad = \dfrac{b^2}{b(a - b)} + \dfrac{(a + b)(a - b)}{b(a - b)}$

$\qquad = \dfrac{b^2 + (a + b)(a - b)}{b(a - b)}$

$\qquad = \dfrac{b^2 + a^2 - b^2}{b(a - b)}$

$\qquad = \dfrac{a^2}{b(a - b)}$

141. $\dfrac{x}{4} + \dfrac{1}{2} = \dfrac{x - 1}{2}$

$\qquad 4\left(\dfrac{x}{4} + \dfrac{1}{2}\right) = 4\left(\dfrac{x - 1}{2}\right)$

$\qquad\qquad x + 2 = 2(x - 1)$

$\qquad\qquad x + 2 = 2x - 2$

$\qquad\qquad\qquad x = 4$

142. This problem can be solved using a single variable. To do this, let x be the amount that is \$5.50 per pound. Then $40 - x$ is the amount that is \$6.30 per pound and the equation is

$\qquad 5.50(x) + 6.30(40 - x) = 6(40)$

$\qquad\qquad 5.5x + 252 - 6.3x = 240$

$\qquad\qquad\qquad 252 - 0.8x = 240$

$\qquad\qquad\qquad\quad -0.8x = -12$

$\qquad\qquad\qquad\qquad x = 15$

Thus, combine 15 lb of the \$5.50 per pound coffee with $40 - 15 = 25$ lb of the \$6.30 per pound coffee to obtain 40 lb of \$6.00 per pound coffee.

Chapter 11 Review Exercises

1. $\sqrt{100} = \sqrt{10^2} = 10$

2. $\sqrt[3]{-27} = \sqrt[3]{(-3)^3} = -3$

3. $\sqrt[3]{-125} = \sqrt[3]{(-5)^3} = -5$

4. $\sqrt[4]{256} = \sqrt[4]{4^4} = 4$

5. $\sqrt{(-8)^2} = |-8| = 8$

6. $\sqrt{(38.2)^2} = 38.2$

7. $\sqrt{x^2} = |x|$

8. $\sqrt{(x-3)^2} = |x-3|$

9. $\sqrt{(x-y)^2} = |x-y|$

10. $\sqrt{\left(x^2 - 4x + 12\right)^2} = |x^2 - 4x + 12|$

    (Note: absolute value would not actually be required because $x^2 - 4x + 12 > 0$ for all x.)

11. $f(x) = \sqrt{10x + 9}$

    $f(4) = \sqrt{10(4) + 9}$

    $\quad = \sqrt{40 + 9}$

    $\quad = \sqrt{49}$

    $\quad = 7$

12. $k(x) = 2x + \sqrt{\dfrac{x}{3}}$

    $k(27) = 2(27) + \sqrt{\dfrac{27}{3}}$

    $\quad = 54 + \sqrt{9}$

    $\quad = 54 + 3$

    $\quad = 57$

13. $g(x) = \sqrt[3]{2x + 3}$

    $g(4) = \sqrt[3]{2(4) + 3}$

    $\quad = \sqrt[3]{11}$

    $\quad \approx 2.2$

14. Area $= (\text{side})^2$

    $144 = s^2$

    $\pm 12 = s$

    Disregard the negative value since lengths must be positive. The length of each side is 12 m.

15. $\sqrt{x^7} = x^{7/2}$

16. $\sqrt[3]{x^5} = x^{5/3}$

17. $\left(\sqrt[4]{y}\right)^{13} = y^{13/4}$

18. $\sqrt[7]{6^{-2}} = 6^{-2/7}$

19. $x^{1/2} = \sqrt{x}$

20. $a^{4/5} = \sqrt[5]{a^4}$

21. $(8m^2 n)^{7/4} = \left(\sqrt[4]{8m^2 n}\right)^7$

22. $(x + y)^{-5/3} = \dfrac{1}{\left(\sqrt[3]{x+y}\right)^5}$

23. $\sqrt[3]{4^6} = 4^{6/3} = 4^2 = 16$

24. $\sqrt{x^{12}} = x^{12/2} = x^6$

25. $\left(\sqrt[4]{9}\right)^8 = 9^{8/4} = 9^2 = 81$

26. $\sqrt[20]{a^5} = a^{5/20} = a^{1/4} = \sqrt[4]{a}$

27. $-36^{1/2} = -\sqrt{36} = -6$

28. $(-36)^{1/2}$ is not a real number.

29. $\left(\dfrac{64}{27}\right)^{-1/3} = \left(\dfrac{27}{64}\right)^{1/3} = \sqrt[3]{\dfrac{27}{64}} = \dfrac{\sqrt[3]{27}}{\sqrt[3]{64}} = \dfrac{3}{4}$

30. $64^{-1/2} + 8^{-2/3} = \dfrac{1}{64^{1/2}} + \dfrac{1}{8^{2/3}}$

$= \dfrac{1}{\sqrt{64}} + \dfrac{1}{\left(\sqrt[3]{8}\right)^2}$

$= \dfrac{1}{8} + \dfrac{1}{2^2}$

$= \dfrac{1}{8} + \dfrac{1}{4}$

$= \dfrac{1}{8} + \dfrac{2}{8}$

$= \dfrac{3}{8}$

31. $x^{3/5} x^{-1/3} = x^{3/5 - 1/3} = x^{9/15 - 5/15} = x^{4/15}$

32. $\left(\dfrac{64}{y^9}\right)^{1/3} = \sqrt[3]{\dfrac{64}{y^9}} = \dfrac{\sqrt[3]{64}}{\sqrt[3]{y^9}} = \dfrac{4}{y^3}$

33. $\left(\dfrac{a^{-6/5}}{a^{2/5}}\right)^{2/3} = \dfrac{a^{-6/5 \cdot 2/3}}{a^{2/5 \cdot 2/3}}$

$= \dfrac{a^{-12/15}}{a^{4/15}}$

$= a^{-12/15 - (4/15)}$

$= a^{-16/15}$

$= \dfrac{1}{a^{16/15}}$

34. $\left(\dfrac{20x^5 y^{-3}}{4y^{1/2}}\right)^2 = \left(\dfrac{5x^5}{y^{7/2}}\right)^2$

$= \dfrac{5^2 x^{5\cdot 2}}{y^{(7/2)\cdot 2}}$

$= \dfrac{25x^{10}}{y^7}$

35. $a^{1/2}\left(5a^{3/2} - 3a^2\right) = a^{1/2}\left(5a^{3/2}\right) - a^{1/2}\left(3a^2\right)$

$= 5a^{1/2 + 3/2} - 3a^{1/2 + 2}$

$= 5a^{4/2} - 3a^{1/2 + 4/2}$

$= 5a^2 - 3a^{5/2}$

36. $4x^{-2/3}\left(x^{-1/2} + \dfrac{11}{4}x^{2/3}\right)$

$= 4x^{-2/3}\left(x^{-1/2}\right) + 4x^{-2/3}\left(\dfrac{11}{4}x^{2/3}\right)$

$= 4x^{-2/3 + (-1/2)} + 11x^{-2/3 + (2/3)}$

$= 4x^{-4/6 + (-3/6)} + 11x^{0/3}$

$= 4x^{-7/6} + 11x^0$

$= \dfrac{4}{x^{7/6}} + 11$

37. $x^{2/5} + x^{7/5} = x^{2/5} + x^{2/5} \cdot x^1$

$= x^{2/5}\left(1 + x\right)$

38. $a^{-1/2} + a^{3/2} = a^{-1/2} + a^{-1/2} \cdot a^{4/2}$

$= a^{-1/2}\left(1 + a^2\right)$

$= \dfrac{1 + a^2}{a^{1/2}}$

39. $f(x) = \sqrt{6x - 11}$

$f(6) = \sqrt{6(6) - 11}$

$= \sqrt{36 - 11}$

$= \sqrt{25}$

$= 5$

40. $g(x) = \sqrt[3]{9x - 17}$

$g(4) = \sqrt[3]{9(4) - 17}$

$= \sqrt[3]{36 - 17}$

$= \sqrt[3]{19}$

≈ 2.668

41. $f(x) = \sqrt{x}$

x	$f(x)$
0	0
1	1
4	2
9	3

42. $f(x) = \sqrt{x} - 4$

x	$f(x)$
0	-4
1	-3
4	-2
9	-1
1	0

43. $\sqrt{48} = \sqrt{16}\sqrt{3} = 4\sqrt{3}$

44. $\sqrt[3]{128} = \sqrt[3]{64}\sqrt[3]{2} = 4\sqrt[3]{2}$

45. $\sqrt{\dfrac{49}{9}} = \dfrac{\sqrt{49}}{\sqrt{9}} = \dfrac{7}{3}$

46. $\sqrt[3]{\dfrac{8}{125}} = \dfrac{\sqrt[3]{8}}{\sqrt[3]{125}} = \dfrac{2}{5}$

47. $-\sqrt{\dfrac{81}{49}} = -\dfrac{\sqrt{81}}{\sqrt{49}} = -\dfrac{9}{7}$

48. $\sqrt[3]{-\dfrac{27}{125}} = \dfrac{\sqrt[3]{-27}}{\sqrt[3]{125}} = \dfrac{-3}{5} = -\dfrac{3}{5}$

49. $\sqrt{32}\sqrt{2} = \sqrt{32 \cdot 2} = \sqrt{64} = 8$

50. $\sqrt[3]{32} \cdot \sqrt[3]{2} = \sqrt[3]{32 \cdot 2} = \sqrt[3]{64} = 4$

51. $\sqrt{18x^2 y^3 z^4} = \sqrt{9x^2 y^2 z^4}\sqrt{2y} = 3xyz^2\sqrt{2y}$

52. $\sqrt{75x^3 y^7} = \sqrt{25x^2 y^6}\sqrt{3xy} = 5xy^3\sqrt{3xy}$

53. $\sqrt[3]{54a^7 b^{10}} = \sqrt[3]{27a^6 b^9}\sqrt[3]{2ab} = 3a^2 b^3\sqrt[3]{2ab}$

54. $\sqrt[3]{125x^8 y^9 z^{16}} = \sqrt[3]{125x^6 y^9 z^{15}}\sqrt[3]{x^2 z}$
$$= 5x^2 y^3 z^5 \sqrt[3]{x^2 z}$$

55. $\left(\sqrt[6]{x^2 y^3 z^5}\right)^{42} = (x^2 y^3 z^5)^{42/6}$
$$= (x^2 y^3 z^5)^7$$
$$= x^{14} y^{21} z^{35}$$

56. $\left(\sqrt[5]{2ab^4 c^6}\right)^{15} = \left(2ab^4 c^6\right)^{15/5}$
$$= \left(2ab^4 c^6\right)^3$$
$$= 8a^3 b^{12} c^{18}$$

57. $\sqrt{5x}\sqrt{8x^5} = \sqrt{40x^6} = \sqrt{4x^6}\sqrt{10} = 2x^3\sqrt{10}$

58. $\sqrt[3]{2x^2 y}\sqrt[3]{4x^9 y^4} = \sqrt[3]{8x^{11} y^5} = 2x^3 y\sqrt[3]{x^2 y^2}$

59. $\sqrt[3]{2x^4 y^5}\sqrt[3]{16x^4 y^4} = \sqrt[3]{32x^8 y^9}$
$$= \sqrt[3]{8x^6 y^9}\sqrt[3]{4x^2}$$
$$= 2x^2 y^3\sqrt[3]{4x^2}$$

60. $\sqrt[4]{4x^4 y^7}\sqrt[4]{4x^5 y^9} = \sqrt[4]{16x^9 y^{16}}$
$$= \sqrt[4]{16x^8 y^{16}}\sqrt[4]{x}$$
$$= 2x^2 y^4\sqrt[4]{x}$$

61. $\sqrt{3x}(\sqrt{12x} - \sqrt{20}) = \sqrt{36x^2} - \sqrt{60x}$

$\qquad\qquad\qquad = \sqrt{36x^2} - \sqrt{4}\sqrt{15x}$

$\qquad\qquad\qquad = 6x - 2\sqrt{15x}$

62. $\sqrt[3]{2x^2 y}\left(\sqrt[3]{4x^4 y^7} + \sqrt[3]{9x}\right)$

$\qquad = \sqrt[3]{8x^6 y^8} + \sqrt[3]{18x^3 y}$

$\qquad = \sqrt[3]{8x^6 y^6}\sqrt[3]{y^2} + \sqrt[3]{x^3}\sqrt[3]{18y}$

$\qquad = 2x^2 y^2 \sqrt[3]{y^2} + x\sqrt[3]{18y}$

63. $\sqrt{\sqrt{a^3 b^2}} = \left(\sqrt{a^3 b^2}\right)^{1/2}$

$\qquad = \left[\left(a^3 b^2\right)^{1/2}\right]^{1/2}$

$\qquad = \left(a^3 b^2\right)^{1/4}$

$\qquad = \sqrt[4]{a^3 b^2}$

64. $\sqrt{\sqrt[3]{x^5 y^2}} = \left(\sqrt[3]{x^5 y^2}\right)^{1/2}$

$\qquad = \left[\left(x^5 y^2\right)^{1/3}\right]^{1/2}$

$\qquad = \left(x^5 y^2\right)^{1/6}$

$\qquad = \sqrt[6]{\left(x^5 y^2\right)}$

65. $\left(\dfrac{4r^2 p^{1/3}}{r^{1/2} p^{4/3}}\right)^3 = (4r^{2-1/2} p^{1/3-4/3})^3$

$\qquad = (4r^{3/2} p^{-1})^3$

$\qquad = 4^3 (r^{3/2})^3 (p^{-1})^3$

$\qquad = 64r^{9/2} p^{-3}$

$\qquad = \dfrac{64r^{9/2}}{p^3}$

66. $\left(\dfrac{6y^{2/5} z^{1/3}}{x^{-1} y^{3/5}}\right)^{-1} = \left(\dfrac{6y^{2/5-3/5} z^{1/3}}{x^{-1}}\right)^{-1}$

$\qquad = \left(\dfrac{6y^{-1/5} z^{1/3}}{x^{-1}}\right)^{-1}$

$\qquad = \left(\dfrac{6xz^{1/3}}{y^{1/5}}\right)^{-1}$

$\qquad = \dfrac{y^{1/5}}{6xz^{1/3}}$

67. $\sqrt{\dfrac{3}{5}} = \dfrac{\sqrt{3}}{\sqrt{5}} \cdot \dfrac{\sqrt{5}}{\sqrt{5}} = \dfrac{\sqrt{15}}{5}$

68. $\sqrt[3]{\dfrac{7}{9}} = \dfrac{\sqrt[3]{7}}{\sqrt[3]{9}} = \dfrac{\sqrt[3]{7}}{\sqrt[3]{9}} \cdot \dfrac{\sqrt[3]{3}}{\sqrt[3]{3}} = \dfrac{\sqrt[3]{21}}{\sqrt[3]{27}} = \dfrac{\sqrt[3]{21}}{3}$

69. $\sqrt[4]{\dfrac{5}{4}} = \dfrac{\sqrt[4]{5}}{\sqrt[4]{4}} = \dfrac{\sqrt[4]{5}}{\sqrt[4]{4}} \cdot \dfrac{\sqrt[4]{2^2}}{\sqrt[4]{2^2}} = \dfrac{\sqrt[4]{20}}{\sqrt[4]{2^4}} = \dfrac{\sqrt[4]{20}}{2}$

70. $\dfrac{x}{\sqrt{10}} = \dfrac{x}{\sqrt{10}} \cdot \dfrac{\sqrt{10}}{\sqrt{10}} = \dfrac{x\sqrt{10}}{10}$

71. $\dfrac{8}{\sqrt{x}} = \dfrac{8}{\sqrt{x}} \cdot \dfrac{\sqrt{x}}{\sqrt{x}} = \dfrac{8\sqrt{x}}{x}$

72. $\dfrac{m}{\sqrt[3]{25}} = \dfrac{m}{\sqrt[3]{5^2}} \cdot \dfrac{\sqrt[3]{5}}{\sqrt[3]{5}} = \dfrac{m\sqrt[3]{5}}{\sqrt[3]{5^3}} = \dfrac{m\sqrt[3]{5}}{5}$

73. $\dfrac{10}{\sqrt[3]{y^2}} = \dfrac{10}{\sqrt[3]{y^2}} \cdot \dfrac{\sqrt[3]{y}}{\sqrt[3]{y}} = \dfrac{10\sqrt[3]{y}}{\sqrt[3]{y^3}} = \dfrac{10\sqrt[3]{y}}{y}$

74. $\dfrac{9}{\sqrt[4]{z}} = \dfrac{9}{\sqrt[4]{z}} \cdot \dfrac{\sqrt[4]{z^3}}{\sqrt[4]{z^3}} = \dfrac{9\sqrt[4]{z^3}}{\sqrt[4]{z^4}} = \dfrac{9\sqrt[4]{z^3}}{z}$

75. $\sqrt[3]{\dfrac{x^3}{27}} = \dfrac{\sqrt[3]{x^3}}{\sqrt[3]{27}} = \dfrac{x}{3}$

76. $\dfrac{\sqrt[3]{2x^{10}}}{\sqrt[3]{16x^7}} = \sqrt[3]{\dfrac{2x^{10}}{16x^7}} = \sqrt[3]{\dfrac{x^3}{8}} = \dfrac{\sqrt[3]{x^3}}{\sqrt[3]{8}} = \dfrac{x}{2}$

77. $\sqrt{\dfrac{32x^2 y^5}{2x^8 y}} = \sqrt{\dfrac{16y^4}{x^6}} = \dfrac{\sqrt{16y^4}}{\sqrt{x^6}} = \dfrac{4y^2}{x^3}$

78. $\sqrt[4]{\dfrac{48x^9 y^{15}}{3xy^3}} = \sqrt[4]{16x^8 y^{12}} = 2x^2 y^3$

79. $\sqrt{\dfrac{6x^4}{y}} = \dfrac{\sqrt{6x^4}}{\sqrt{y}}$

$= \dfrac{\sqrt{x^4}\sqrt{6}}{\sqrt{y}}$

$= \dfrac{x^2\sqrt{6}}{\sqrt{y}} \cdot \dfrac{\sqrt{y}}{\sqrt{y}}$

$= \dfrac{x^2\sqrt{6y}}{y}$

80. $\sqrt{\dfrac{12a}{7b}} = \dfrac{\sqrt{12a}}{\sqrt{7b}}$

$= \dfrac{2\sqrt{3a}}{\sqrt{7b}}$

$= \dfrac{2\sqrt{3a}}{\sqrt{7b}} \cdot \dfrac{\sqrt{7b}}{\sqrt{7b}}$

$= \dfrac{2\sqrt{21ab}}{7b}$

81. $\sqrt{\dfrac{18x^4 y^5}{3z}} = \dfrac{\sqrt{18x^4 y^5}}{\sqrt{3z}}$

$= \dfrac{\sqrt{9x^4 y^4}\sqrt{2y}}{\sqrt{3z}}$

$= \dfrac{3x^2 y^2 \sqrt{2y}}{\sqrt{3z}}$

$= \dfrac{3x^2 y^2 \sqrt{2y}}{\sqrt{3z}} \cdot \dfrac{\sqrt{3z}}{\sqrt{3z}}$

$= \dfrac{3x^2 y^2 \sqrt{6yz}}{3z}$

$= \dfrac{x^2 y^2 \sqrt{6yz}}{z}$

82. $\sqrt{\dfrac{125x^2 y^5}{3z}} = \dfrac{\sqrt{125x^2 y^5}}{\sqrt{3z}}$

$= \dfrac{\sqrt{25x^2 y^4}\sqrt{5y}}{\sqrt{3z}}$

$= \dfrac{5xy^2 \sqrt{5y}}{\sqrt{3z}} \cdot \dfrac{\sqrt{3z}}{\sqrt{3z}}$

$= \dfrac{5xy^2 \sqrt{15yz}}{3z}$

83. $\sqrt[3]{\dfrac{108x^3 y^7}{2y^3}} = \sqrt[3]{54x^3 y^4} = 3xy\sqrt[3]{2y}$

84. $\sqrt[3]{\dfrac{3x}{5y}} = \dfrac{\sqrt[3]{3x}}{\sqrt[3]{5y}} \cdot \dfrac{\sqrt[3]{25y^2}}{\sqrt[3]{25y^2}} = \dfrac{\sqrt[3]{75xy^2}}{5y}$

85. $\sqrt[3]{\dfrac{9x^5 y^3}{x^6}} = \sqrt[3]{\dfrac{9y^3}{x}}$

$= \dfrac{\sqrt[3]{9y^3}}{\sqrt[3]{x}}$

$= \dfrac{\sqrt[3]{y^3}\sqrt[3]{9}}{\sqrt[3]{x}}$

$= \dfrac{y\sqrt[3]{9}}{\sqrt[3]{x}} \cdot \dfrac{\sqrt[3]{x^2}}{\sqrt[3]{x^2}}$

$= \dfrac{y\sqrt[3]{9x^2}}{x}$

86. $\sqrt[3]{\dfrac{y^6}{5x^2}} = \dfrac{\sqrt[3]{y^6}}{\sqrt[3]{5x^2}} = \dfrac{y^2}{\sqrt[3]{5x^2}} \cdot \dfrac{\sqrt[3]{25x}}{\sqrt[3]{25x}} = \dfrac{y^2 \sqrt[3]{25x}}{5x}$

87. $\sqrt[4]{\dfrac{2a^2 b^{11}}{a^5 b}} = \sqrt[4]{\dfrac{2b^{10}}{a^3}}$

$= \dfrac{\sqrt[4]{2b^{10}}}{\sqrt[4]{a^3}} \cdot \dfrac{\sqrt[4]{a}}{\sqrt[4]{a}}$

$= \dfrac{\sqrt[4]{2ab^{10}}}{\sqrt[4]{a^4}}$

$= \dfrac{b^2 \sqrt[4]{2ab^2}}{a}$

88. $\sqrt[4]{\dfrac{3x^2y^6}{8x^3}} = \sqrt[4]{\dfrac{3y^6}{8x}}$

$= \dfrac{\sqrt[4]{3y^6}}{\sqrt[4]{8x}}$

$= \dfrac{y\sqrt[4]{3y^2}}{\sqrt[4]{8x}}$

$= \dfrac{y\sqrt[4]{3y^2}}{\sqrt[4]{8x}} \cdot \dfrac{\sqrt[4]{2x^3}}{\sqrt[4]{2x^3}}$

$= \dfrac{y\sqrt[4]{6x^3y^2}}{2x}$

89. $\left(3 - \sqrt{2}\right)\left(3 + \sqrt{2}\right) = 3^2 - \left(\sqrt{2}\right)^2 = 9 - 2 = 7$

90. $\left(\sqrt{x} + y\right)\left(\sqrt{x} - y\right) = \left(\sqrt{x}\right)^2 - y^2 = x - y^2$

91. $\left(x - \sqrt{y}\right)\left(x + \sqrt{y}\right) = x^2 - \left(\sqrt{y}\right)^2 = x^2 - y$

92. $\left(\sqrt{3} + 2\right)^2 = \left(\sqrt{3}\right)^2 + 2(2)\left(\sqrt{3}\right) + 2^2$

$= 3 + 4\sqrt{3} + 4$

$= 7 + 4\sqrt{3}$

93. $\left(\sqrt{x} - \sqrt{3y}\right)\left(\sqrt{x} + \sqrt{5y}\right)$

$= \left(\sqrt{x}\right)^2 + \sqrt{x}\sqrt{5y} - \sqrt{x}\sqrt{3y} - \sqrt{3y}\sqrt{5y}$

$= x + \sqrt{5xy} - \sqrt{3xy} - \sqrt{15y^2}$

$= x + \sqrt{5xy} - \sqrt{3xy} - y\sqrt{15}$

94. $\left(\sqrt[3]{2x} - \sqrt[3]{3y}\right)\left(\sqrt[3]{3x} - \sqrt[3]{2y}\right)$

$= \sqrt[3]{2x}\left(\sqrt[3]{3x}\right) - \left(\sqrt[3]{2x}\right)\left(\sqrt[3]{2y}\right)$

$\quad - \sqrt[3]{3y}\left(\sqrt[3]{3x}\right) + \sqrt[3]{3y}\sqrt[3]{2y}$

$= \sqrt[3]{6x^2} - \sqrt[3]{4xy} - \sqrt[3]{9xy} + \sqrt[3]{6y^2}$

95. $\dfrac{6}{2 + \sqrt{5}} = \dfrac{6}{2 + \sqrt{5}} \cdot \dfrac{2 - \sqrt{5}}{2 - \sqrt{5}}$

$= \dfrac{6\left(2 - \sqrt{5}\right)}{2^2 - \left(\sqrt{5}\right)^2}$

$= \dfrac{12 - 6\sqrt{5}}{4 - 5}$

$= \dfrac{12 - 6\sqrt{5}}{-1}$

$= -12 + 6\sqrt{5}$

96. $\dfrac{x}{4 + \sqrt{x}} = \dfrac{x}{4 + \sqrt{x}} \cdot \dfrac{4 - \sqrt{x}}{4 - \sqrt{x}}$

$= \dfrac{x\left(4 - \sqrt{x}\right)}{4^2 - \left(\sqrt{x}\right)^2}$

$= \dfrac{4x - x\sqrt{x}}{16 - x}$

97. $\dfrac{a}{4 - \sqrt{b}} = \dfrac{a}{4 - \sqrt{b}} \cdot \dfrac{4 + \sqrt{b}}{4 + \sqrt{b}}$

$= \dfrac{a\left(4 + \sqrt{b}\right)}{\left(4 - \sqrt{b}\right)\left(4 + \sqrt{b}\right)}$

$= \dfrac{4a + a\sqrt{b}}{16 + 4\sqrt{b} - 4\sqrt{b} - b}$

$= \dfrac{4a + a\sqrt{b}}{16 - b}$

98. $\dfrac{x}{\sqrt{y} - 7} = \dfrac{x}{\sqrt{y} - 7} \cdot \dfrac{\sqrt{y} + 7}{\sqrt{y} + 7}$

$= \dfrac{x\left(\sqrt{y} + 7\right)}{\left(\sqrt{y} - 7\right)\left(\sqrt{y} + 7\right)}$

$= \dfrac{x\sqrt{y} + 7x}{y + 7\sqrt{y} - 7\sqrt{y} - 49}$

$= \dfrac{x\sqrt{y} + 7x}{y - 49}$

99. $\dfrac{\sqrt{x}}{\sqrt{x}+\sqrt{y}} = \dfrac{\sqrt{x}}{\sqrt{x}+\sqrt{y}} \cdot \dfrac{\sqrt{x}-\sqrt{y}}{\sqrt{x}-\sqrt{y}}$

$= \dfrac{\sqrt{x}\left(\sqrt{x}-\sqrt{y}\right)}{\left(\sqrt{x}\right)^2 - \left(\sqrt{y}\right)^2}$

$= \dfrac{\sqrt{x^2}-\sqrt{xy}}{x-y}$

$= \dfrac{x-\sqrt{xy}}{x-y}$

100. $\dfrac{\sqrt{x}-3\sqrt{y}}{\sqrt{x}-\sqrt{y}} = \dfrac{\sqrt{x}-3\sqrt{y}}{\sqrt{x}-\sqrt{y}} \cdot \dfrac{\sqrt{x}+\sqrt{y}}{\sqrt{x}+\sqrt{y}}$

$= \dfrac{x+\sqrt{xy}-3\sqrt{xy}-3y}{\left(\sqrt{x}\right)^2 - \left(\sqrt{y}\right)^2}$

$= \dfrac{x-2\sqrt{xy}-3y}{x-y}$

101. $\dfrac{2}{\sqrt{a-1}-2} = \dfrac{2}{\sqrt{a-1}-2} \cdot \dfrac{\sqrt{a-1}+2}{\sqrt{a-1}+2}$

$= \dfrac{2\left(\sqrt{a-1}+2\right)}{\left(\sqrt{a-1}-2\right)\left(\sqrt{a-1}+2\right)}$

$= \dfrac{2\sqrt{a-1}+4}{a-1+2\sqrt{a-1}-2\sqrt{a-1}-4}$

$= \dfrac{2\sqrt{a-1}+4}{a-5}$

102. $\dfrac{5}{\sqrt{y+2}-3} = \dfrac{5}{\sqrt{y+2}-3} \cdot \dfrac{\sqrt{y+2}+3}{\sqrt{y+2}+3}$

$= \dfrac{5\sqrt{y+2}+15}{\left(\sqrt{y+2}\right)^2 - 3^2}$

$= \dfrac{5\sqrt{y+2}+15}{y+2-9}$

$= \dfrac{5\sqrt{y+2}+15}{y-7}$

103. $\sqrt[3]{x}+10\sqrt[3]{x}-2\sqrt[3]{x}=9\sqrt[3]{x}$

104. $\sqrt{3}+\sqrt{27}-\sqrt{192} = \sqrt{3}+3\sqrt{3}-\sqrt{64}\sqrt{3}$

$= \sqrt{3}+3\sqrt{3}-8\sqrt{3}$

$= -4\sqrt{3}$

105. $\sqrt[3]{16}-5\sqrt[3]{54}+3\sqrt[3]{64}$

$= \sqrt[3]{8}\sqrt[3]{2}-5\sqrt[3]{27}\sqrt[3]{2}+3\sqrt[3]{64}$

$= 2\sqrt[3]{2}-5\left(3\sqrt[3]{2}\right)+3(4)$

$= 2\sqrt[3]{2}-15\sqrt[3]{2}+12$

$= 12-13\sqrt[3]{2}$

106. $\sqrt{2}-\dfrac{3}{\sqrt{32}}+\sqrt{50}$

$= \sqrt{2}-\dfrac{3}{4\sqrt{2}}+5\sqrt{2}$

$= \sqrt{2}-\dfrac{3}{4\sqrt{2}}\cdot\dfrac{\sqrt{2}}{\sqrt{2}}+5\sqrt{2}$

$= \sqrt{2}-\dfrac{3\sqrt{2}}{8}+5\sqrt{2}$

$= \dfrac{8}{8}\left(\sqrt{2}\right)-\dfrac{3\sqrt{2}}{8}+\left(\dfrac{8}{8}\right)5\sqrt{2}$

$= \dfrac{8\sqrt{2}}{8}-\dfrac{3\sqrt{2}}{8}+\dfrac{40\sqrt{2}}{8}$

$= \dfrac{45\sqrt{2}}{8}$

107. $9\sqrt{x^5 y^6}-\sqrt{16x^7 y^8}$

$= 9\sqrt{x^4 y^6}\sqrt{x}-\sqrt{16x^6 y^8}\sqrt{x}$

$= 9x^2 y^3\sqrt{x}-4x^3 y^4\sqrt{x}$

$= \left(9x^2 y^3 - 4x^3 y^4\right)\sqrt{x}$

108. $8\sqrt[3]{x^7 y^8}-\sqrt[3]{x^4 y^2}+3\sqrt[3]{x^{10} y^2}$

$= 8\sqrt[3]{x^6 y^6}\sqrt[3]{xy^2}-\sqrt[3]{x^3}\sqrt[3]{xy^2}+3\sqrt[3]{x^9}\sqrt[3]{xy^2}$

$= 8x^2 y^2\sqrt[3]{xy^2}-x\sqrt[3]{xy^2}+3x^3\sqrt[3]{xy^2}$

$= (8x^2 y^2 - x + 3x^3)\sqrt[3]{xy^2}$

109. $(f \cdot g)(x) = f(x) \cdot g(x)$

$= \sqrt{3x} \cdot \left(\sqrt{6x} - \sqrt{15} \right)$

$= \sqrt{3x} \sqrt{6x} - \sqrt{3x} \sqrt{15}$

$= \sqrt{18x^2} - \sqrt{45x}$

$= \sqrt{9x^2} \sqrt{2} - \sqrt{9} \sqrt{5x}$

$= 3x\sqrt{2} - 3\sqrt{5x}$

110. $(f \cdot g)(x) = f(x) \cdot g(x)$

$= \sqrt[3]{2x^2} \left(\sqrt[3]{4x^4} + \sqrt[3]{16x^5} \right)$

$= \sqrt[3]{2x^2} \sqrt[3]{4x^4} + \sqrt[3]{2x^2} \sqrt[3]{16x^5}$

$= \sqrt[3]{8x^6} + \sqrt[3]{32x^7}$

$= \sqrt[3]{8x^6} + \sqrt[3]{8x^6} \sqrt[3]{4x}$

$= 2x^2 + 2x^2 \sqrt[3]{4x}$

111. $f(x) = \sqrt{2x+7} \sqrt{2x+7}, \quad x \geq -\dfrac{7}{2}$

$= \sqrt{(2x+7)^2}$

$= |2x+7|$

$= 2x+7 \quad \text{since } x \geq -\dfrac{7}{2}$

112. $g(a) = \sqrt{20a^2 + 100a + 125}$

$= \sqrt{5(4a^2 + 20a + 25)}$

$= \sqrt{5(2a+5)^2}$

$= \sqrt{5} |2a+5|$

113. $\dfrac{\sqrt[3]{(x+5)^5}}{\sqrt{(x+5)^3}} = \dfrac{(x+5)^{5/3}}{(x+5)^{3/2}}$

$= (x+5)^{5/3 - 3/2}$

$= (x+5)^{1/6}$

$= \sqrt[6]{x+5}$

114. $\dfrac{\sqrt[3]{a^3 b^2}}{\sqrt[4]{a^4 b}} = \dfrac{a\sqrt[3]{b^2}}{a\sqrt[4]{b}}$

$= \dfrac{\sqrt[3]{b^2}}{\sqrt[4]{b}}$

$= \dfrac{b^{2/3}}{b^{1/4}}$

$= b^{2/3 - 1/4}$

$= b^{5/12}$

$= \sqrt[12]{b^5}$

115. a. $P = 2l + 2w$

$P = 2\sqrt{48} + 2\sqrt{12}$

$= 2\sqrt{16 \cdot 3} + 2\sqrt{4 \cdot 3}$

$= 8\sqrt{3} + 4\sqrt{3}$

$= 12\sqrt{3}$

b. $A = lw$

$A = \left(\sqrt{48} \right) \left(\sqrt{12} \right)$

$= \sqrt{576}$

$= 24$

116. a. $P = s_1 + s_2 + s_3$

$P = \sqrt{125} + \sqrt{45} + \sqrt{130}$

$= 5\sqrt{5} + 3\sqrt{5} + \sqrt{130}$

$= 8\sqrt{5} + \sqrt{130}$

b. $A = \dfrac{1}{2} bh$

$A = \dfrac{1}{2} \left(\sqrt{130} \right) \left(\sqrt{40} \right)$

$= \dfrac{1}{2} \sqrt{5200}$

$= \dfrac{1}{2} \sqrt{400 \cdot 13}$

$= \dfrac{20}{2} \sqrt{13}$

$= 10\sqrt{13}$

117. **a.** $f(x) = \sqrt{x} + 2$

$g(x) = -3$

$(f+g)(x) = f(x) + g(x)$

$\qquad = \sqrt{x} + 2 - 3$

$\qquad = \sqrt{x} - 1$

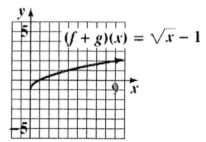

b. $\sqrt{x} \geq 0, x \geq 0$

The domain is $\left\{ x \mid x \geq 0 \right\}$.

118. **a.** $f(x) = -\sqrt{x}$

$g(x) = \sqrt{x} + 2$

$(f+g)(x) = f(x) + g(x)$

$\qquad = -\sqrt{x} + \sqrt{x} + 2$

$\qquad = 2$

b. $\sqrt{x} \geq 0, x \geq 0$

The domain is $\left\{ x \mid x \geq 0 \right\}$.

119. $\sqrt{x} = 9$

$\left(\sqrt{x} \right)^2 = 9^2$

$x = 81$

Check: $\sqrt{81} = 9$ True

81 is the solution.

120. $\sqrt{x} = -4$

$\left(\sqrt{x} \right)^2 = (-4)^2$

$x = 16$

Check: $\sqrt{16} = -4$

$\qquad\qquad 4 = -4$ False

no solution

121. $\sqrt[3]{x} = 4$

$\left(\sqrt[3]{x} \right)^3 = 4^3$

$x = 64$

Check: $\sqrt[3]{x} = 4$

$\qquad \sqrt[3]{64} = 4$

$\qquad\qquad 4 = 4$ True

The solution is 64.

122. $\sqrt[3]{x} = -5$

$\left(\sqrt[3]{x} \right)^3 = (-5)^3$

$x = -125$

Check: $\sqrt[3]{x} = -5$

$\qquad \sqrt[3]{-125} = -5$

$\qquad\qquad -5 = -5$ True

-125 is the solution.

123. $7 + \sqrt{x} = 10$

$\sqrt{x} = 3$

$\left(\sqrt{x} \right)^2 = 3^2$

$x = 9$

Check: $7 + \sqrt{x} = 10$

$\qquad 7 + \sqrt{9} = 10$

$\qquad 7 + 3 = 10$

$\qquad 10 = 10$ True

9 is the solution.

124. $7 + \sqrt[3]{x} = 12$

$\sqrt[3]{x} = 5$

$\left(\sqrt[3]{x}\right)^3 = 5^3$

$x = 125$

Check: $7 + \sqrt[3]{x} = 12$

$7 + \sqrt[3]{125} = 12$

$7 + 5 = 12$

$12 = 12$ True

125 is the solution.

125 $\sqrt{3x+4} = \sqrt{5x+14}$

$\left(\sqrt{3x+4}\right)^2 = \left(\sqrt{5x+14}\right)^2$

$3x + 4 = 5x + 14$

$-10 = 2x$

$-5 = x$

Check: $\sqrt{3x+4}$ becomes

$\sqrt{3(-5)+4} = \sqrt{-15+4} = \sqrt{-11}$

which is not a real number. -5 is not a solution so there is no real solution.

126. $\sqrt{x^2 + 2x - 8} = x$

$\left(\sqrt{x^2 + 2x - 8}\right)^2 = (x)^2$

$x^2 + 2x - 8 = x^2$

$2x - 8 = 0$

$2x = 8$

$x = 4$

Check: $\sqrt{2^2 + 2 \cdot 4 - 8} = 2$

$\sqrt{4 + 8 - 8} = 2$

$\sqrt{4} = 2$

$2 = 2$ True

4 is the solution.

127. $\sqrt[3]{x-9} = \sqrt[3]{5x+3}$

$\left(\sqrt[3]{x-9}\right)^3 = \left(\sqrt[3]{5x+3}\right)^3$

$x - 9 = 5x + 3$

$-4x = 12$

$x = -3$

Check: $\sqrt[3]{-3-9} = \sqrt[3]{5(-3)+3}$

$\sqrt[3]{-12} = \sqrt[3]{-15+3}$

$\sqrt[3]{-12} = \sqrt[3]{-12}$ True

-3 is the solution.

128. $(x^2 + 7)^{1/2} = x + 1$

$\left[(x^2 + 7)^{1/2}\right]^2 = (x+1)^2$

$x^2 + 7 = x^2 + 2x + 1$

$7 = 2x + 1$

$6 = 2x$

$x = 3$

Check: $(3^2 + 7)^{1/2} = 3 + 1$

$(9 + 7)^{1/2} = 4$

$16^{1/2} = 4$

$4 = 4$ True

3 is the solution.

129. $\sqrt{x} + 3 = \sqrt{3x+9}$

$\left(\sqrt{x}+3\right)^2 = \left(\sqrt{3x+9}\right)^2$

$\left(\sqrt{x}+3\right)\left(\sqrt{x}+3\right) = 3x + 9$

$x + 6\sqrt{x} + 9 = 3x + 9$

$6\sqrt{x} = 2x$

$\left(6\sqrt{x}\right)^2 = (2x)^2$

$36x = 4x^2$

$4x^2 - 36x = 0$

$4x(x - 9) = 0$

$4x = 0$ or $x - 9 = 0$

$x = 0$ $x = 9$

A check shows that 0 and 9 are both solutions.

130. $\sqrt{6x-5}-\sqrt{2x+6}-1=0$

$$\sqrt{6x-5}=\sqrt{2x+6}+1$$

$$\left(\sqrt{6x-5}\right)^2=\left(\sqrt{2x+6}+1\right)^2$$

$$6x-5=2x+6+2\sqrt{2x+6}+1$$

$$6x-5=2x+7+2\sqrt{2x+6}$$

$$4x-12=2\sqrt{2x+6}$$

$$\frac{4x}{2}-\frac{12}{2}=\frac{2}{2}\sqrt{2x+6}$$

$$2x-6=\sqrt{2x+6}$$

$$(2x-6)^2=\left(\sqrt{2x+6}\right)^2$$

$$4x^2-24x+36=2x+6$$

$$4x^2-26x+30=0$$

$$2x^2-13x+15=0$$

Express the middle term, $-13x$, as $-10x-3x$.

$$2x^2-10x-3x+15=0$$

$$2x(x-5)-3(x-5)=0$$

$$(2x-3)(x-5)=0$$

$$2x-3=0 \quad\text{or}\quad x-5=0$$

$$x=\frac{3}{2} \qquad x=5$$

The solution $x=5$ checks in the original equation but $x=\frac{3}{2}$ does not check. Therefore the only solution is $x=5$.

131. $f(x)=g(x)$

$$\sqrt{3x+4}=2\sqrt{2x-4}$$

$$\left(\sqrt{3x+4}\right)^2=\left(2\sqrt{2x-4}\right)^2$$

$$3x+4=4(2x-4)$$

$$3x+4=8x-16$$

$$20=5x$$

$$4=x$$

132. $f(x)=g(x)$

$$(4x+5)^{1/3}=(6x-7)^{1/3}$$

$$[(4x+5)^{1/3}]^3=[(6x-7)^{1/3}]^3$$

$$4x+5=6x-7$$

$$12=2x$$

$$6=x$$

133. $V=\sqrt{\dfrac{2L}{w}}$ Solve for L.

$$V^2=\frac{2L}{w}$$

$$V^2w=2L$$

$$\frac{V^2w}{2}=L \text{ or } L=\frac{V^2w}{2}$$

134. $r=\sqrt{\dfrac{A}{\pi}}$ Solve for A.

$$r^2=\left(\sqrt{\frac{A}{\pi}}\right)^2$$

$$r^2=\frac{A}{\pi}$$

$$\pi r^2=A \text{ or } A=\pi r^2$$

135. Pythagorean Theorem: $a^2+b^2=c^2$

$$\left(\sqrt{20}\right)^2+6^2=x^2$$

$$20+36=x^2$$

$$56=x^2$$

$$\sqrt{56}=x \text{ or } x=2\sqrt{14}$$

136. Pythagorean Theorem: $a^2+b^2=c^2$

$$\left(\sqrt{26}\right)^2+x^2=\left(\sqrt{101}\right)^2$$

$$26+x^2=101$$

$$x^2=75$$

$$x=\sqrt{75} \text{ or } x=5\sqrt{3}$$

137. $l=\sqrt{a^2+b^2}$

$$=\sqrt{5^2+2^2}$$

$$=\sqrt{29}$$

$$\approx 5.39 \text{ m}$$

138. $v=\sqrt{2gh}$

$$=\sqrt{2(32)(20)}$$

$$=\sqrt{1280}\approx 35.78 \text{ ft/sec}$$

139. $T = 2\pi\sqrt{\dfrac{L}{32}}$

$\quad = 2\pi\sqrt{\dfrac{64}{32}}$

$\quad = 2\pi\sqrt{2}$

$\quad \approx 8.89 \text{ sec}$

140. $V = \sqrt{\dfrac{2K}{m}}$

$\quad = \sqrt{\dfrac{2(45)}{0.145}}$

$\quad \approx 24.91 \text{ meters per second}$

141. $m = \dfrac{m_0}{\sqrt{1 - \dfrac{v^2}{c^2}}}$

$\quad = \dfrac{m_0}{\sqrt{1 - \dfrac{(0.98c)^2}{c^2}}}$

$\quad = \dfrac{m_0}{\sqrt{1 - \dfrac{0.9604c^2}{c^2}}}$

$\quad = \dfrac{m_0}{\sqrt{1 - 0.9604}}$

$\quad = \dfrac{m_0}{\sqrt{0.0396}}$

$\quad \approx 5m_0$

It is about 5 times its original mass.

142. $5 = 5 + 0i$

143. $-8 = -8 + 0i$

144. $7 - \sqrt{-256} = 7 - \sqrt{-1}\sqrt{256}$

$\quad\quad\quad\quad\quad = 7 - 16i$

145. $9 + \sqrt{-16} = 9 + \sqrt{16}\sqrt{-1}$

$\quad\quad\quad\quad\quad = 9 + 4i$

146. $(3 + 2i) + (10 - i) = 3 + 2i + 10 - i = 13 + i$

147. $(9 - 6i) - (3 - 4i) = 9 - 6i - 3 + 4i = 6 - 2i$

148. $\left(\sqrt{3} + \sqrt{-5}\right) + \left(11\sqrt{3} - \sqrt{-7}\right)$

$\quad = \sqrt{3} + \sqrt{5}\sqrt{-1} + 11\sqrt{3} - \sqrt{7}\sqrt{-1}$

$\quad = \sqrt{3} + i\sqrt{5} + 11\sqrt{3} - i\sqrt{7}$

$\quad = 12\sqrt{3} + \left(\sqrt{5} - \sqrt{7}\right)i$

149. $\sqrt{-6}\left(\sqrt{6} + \sqrt{-6}\right) = \sqrt{6}\sqrt{-1}\left(\sqrt{6} + \sqrt{6}\sqrt{-1}\right)$

$\quad = i\sqrt{6}\left(\sqrt{6} + i\sqrt{6}\right)$

$\quad = i\sqrt{36} + i^2\sqrt{36}$

$\quad = 6i + 6(-1) = -6 + 6i$

150. $(4 + 3i)(2 - 3i) = 8 - 12i + 6i - 9i^2$

$\quad\quad\quad\quad\quad\quad = 8 - 6i - 9(-1)$

$\quad\quad\quad\quad\quad\quad = 8 - 6i + 9$

$\quad\quad\quad\quad\quad\quad = 17 - 6i$

151. $\left(6 + \sqrt{-3}\right)\left(4 - \sqrt{-15}\right)$

$\quad = \left(6 + \sqrt{3}\sqrt{-1}\right)\left(4 - \sqrt{15}\sqrt{-1}\right)$

$\quad = \left(6 + i\sqrt{3}\right)\left(4 - i\sqrt{15}\right)$

$\quad = 24 - 6i\sqrt{15} + 4i\sqrt{3} - i^2\sqrt{45}$

$\quad = 24 - 6i\sqrt{15} + 4i\sqrt{3} - (-1)\sqrt{9}\sqrt{5}$

$\quad = \left(24 + 3\sqrt{5}\right) + \left(4\sqrt{3} - 6\sqrt{15}\right)i$

152. $\dfrac{8}{3i} = \dfrac{8}{3i} \cdot \dfrac{-3i}{-3i}$

$\quad = \dfrac{-24i}{-9i^2}$

$\quad = \dfrac{-24i}{-9(-1)}$

$\quad = -\dfrac{24i}{9}$

$\quad = -\dfrac{8i}{3}$

153. $\dfrac{2+\sqrt{3}}{2i} = \dfrac{2+\sqrt{3}}{2i} \cdot \dfrac{-2i}{-2i}$

$= \dfrac{-4i - 2i\sqrt{3}}{-4i^2}$

$= \dfrac{-4i - 2i\sqrt{3}}{-4(-1)}$

$= \dfrac{2\left(-2i - i\sqrt{3}\right)}{4}$

$= \dfrac{-2i - i\sqrt{3}}{2}$

$= \dfrac{\left(-2 - \sqrt{3}\right)i}{2}$

154. $\dfrac{4}{3+2i} = \dfrac{4}{3+2i} \cdot \dfrac{3-2i}{3-2i}$

$= \dfrac{4(3-2i)}{9-4i^2}$

$= \dfrac{12-8i}{9-4(-1)}$

$= \dfrac{12-8i}{9+4}$

$= \dfrac{12-8i}{13}$

155. $\dfrac{\sqrt{3}}{5-\sqrt{-6}} = \dfrac{\sqrt{3}}{5-i\sqrt{6}}$

$= \dfrac{\sqrt{3}}{\left(5-i\sqrt{6}\right)} \cdot \dfrac{5+i\sqrt{6}}{5+i\sqrt{6}}$

$= \dfrac{5\sqrt{3}+i\sqrt{18}}{(5)^2 - \left(i\sqrt{6}\right)^2}$

$= \dfrac{5\sqrt{3}+3i\sqrt{2}}{(5)^2 + \left(\sqrt{6}\right)^2}$

$= \dfrac{5\sqrt{3}+3i\sqrt{2}}{25+6}$

$= \dfrac{5\sqrt{3}+3i\sqrt{2}}{31}$

156. $x^2 - 2x + 9$

$= \left(1+2i\sqrt{2}\right)^2 - 2\left(1+2i\sqrt{2}\right) + 9$

$= 1^2 + 2(1)\left(2i\sqrt{2}\right) + \left(2i\sqrt{2}\right)^2 - 2 - 4i\sqrt{2} + 9$

$= 1 + 4i\sqrt{2} - 8 - 2 - 4i\sqrt{2} + 9$

$= 0 + 0i$

$= 0$

157. $x^2 - 2x + 12$

$= (1-2i)^2 - 2(1-2i) + 12$

$= 1^2 - 2(1)(2i) + (2i)^2 - 2 + 4i + 12$

$= 1 - 4i - 4 - 2 + 4i + 12$

$= 7 + 0i$

$= 7$

158. $i^{33} = i^{32}i = (i^4)^8 = 1^8 \cdot i = i$

159. $i^{59} = i^{56}i^3 = (i^4)^{14}i^3 = 1^{14} \cdot i^3 = 1(i^3) = i^3 = -i$

160. $i^{404} = (i^4)^{101} = 1^{101} = 1$

161. $i^{802} = i^{800}i^2$

$= (i^4)^{200}i^2$

$= 1^{200} \cdot i^2$

$= 1(i^2)$

$= i^2$

$= -1$

Chapter 11 Practice Test

1. $\sqrt{(5x-3)^2} = |5x-3|$

2. $\left(\dfrac{x^{2/5} \cdot x^{-1}}{x^{3/5}}\right)^2 = \left(x^{2/5-3/5-1}\right)^2$

$= \left(x^{2/5-3/5-5/5}\right)^2$

$= \left(x^{-6/5}\right)^2$

$= x^{-12/5}$

$= \dfrac{1}{x^{12/5}}$

3. $x^{-2/3} + x^{4/3} = x^{-2/3}\left(1\right) + x^{-2/3}\left(x^{6/3}\right)$

$\qquad\qquad = x^{-2/3}\left(1 + x^{6/3}\right)$

$\qquad\qquad = x^{-2/3}\left(1 + x^2\right)$

$\qquad\qquad = \dfrac{1 + x^2}{x^{2/3}}$

4. $g(x) = \sqrt{x} + 1$

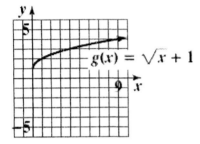

$g(x) = \sqrt{x} + 1$

5. $\sqrt{54x^7 y^{10}} = \sqrt{9x^6 y^{10}}\,\sqrt{6x}$

$\qquad\qquad = 3x^3 y^5 \sqrt{6x}$

6. $\sqrt[3]{25x^5 y^2}\,\sqrt[3]{10x^6 y^8} = \sqrt[3]{250x^{11} y^{10}}$

$\qquad\qquad\qquad = \sqrt[3]{125x^9 y^9}\cdot\sqrt[3]{2x^2 y}$

$\qquad\qquad\qquad = 5x^3 y^3 \sqrt[3]{2x^2 y}$

7. $\sqrt{\dfrac{7x^6 y^3}{8z}} = \dfrac{\sqrt{7x^6 y^3}}{\sqrt{8z}}$

$\qquad\qquad = \dfrac{\sqrt{x^6 y^2}\,\sqrt{7y}}{\sqrt{4}\,\sqrt{2z}}$

$\qquad\qquad = \dfrac{x^3 y \sqrt{7y}}{2\sqrt{2z}}\cdot\dfrac{\sqrt{2z}}{\sqrt{2z}}$

$\qquad\qquad = \dfrac{x^3 y \sqrt{14yz}}{2(2z)}$

$\qquad\qquad = \dfrac{x^3 y \sqrt{14yz}}{4z}$

8. $\dfrac{9}{\sqrt[3]{x}} = \dfrac{9}{\sqrt[3]{x}}\cdot\dfrac{\sqrt[3]{x^2}}{\sqrt[3]{x^2}} = \dfrac{9\sqrt[3]{x^2}}{x}$

9. $\dfrac{\sqrt{3}}{3+\sqrt{27}} = \dfrac{\sqrt{3}}{3+\sqrt{27}}\cdot\dfrac{3-\sqrt{27}}{3-\sqrt{27}}$

$\qquad\quad = \dfrac{\sqrt{3}\left(3-\sqrt{27}\right)}{\left(3+\sqrt{27}\right)\left(3-\sqrt{27}\right)}$

$\qquad\quad = \dfrac{3\sqrt{3}-\sqrt{81}}{9 - 3\sqrt{27} + 3\sqrt{27} - 27}$

$\qquad\quad = \dfrac{3\sqrt{3}-9}{-18}$

$\qquad\quad = \dfrac{\sqrt{3}-3}{-6}\ \text{ or }\ \dfrac{3-\sqrt{3}}{6}$

10. $2\sqrt{24} - 6\sqrt{6} + 3\sqrt{54}$

$\qquad = 2\sqrt{4}\,\sqrt{6} - 6\sqrt{6} + 3\sqrt{9}\,\sqrt{6}$

$\qquad = 4\sqrt{6} - 6\sqrt{6} + 9\sqrt{6}$

$\qquad = 7\sqrt{6}$

11. $\sqrt[3]{8x^3 y^5} + 4\sqrt[3]{x^6 y^8}$

$\qquad = \sqrt[3]{8x^3 y^3}\,\sqrt[3]{y^2} + 4\sqrt[3]{x^6 y^6}\,\sqrt[3]{y^2}$

$\qquad = 2xy\sqrt[3]{y^2} + 4x^2 y^2 \sqrt[3]{y^2}$

$\qquad = (2xy + 4x^2 y^2)\sqrt[3]{y^2}$

12. $\left(\sqrt{3}-2\right)\left(6-\sqrt{8}\right) = \sqrt{3}(6) - \sqrt{3}\sqrt{8} - 2(6) + 2\sqrt{8}$

$\qquad\qquad = 6\sqrt{3} - \sqrt{24} - 12 + 2\sqrt{8}$

$\qquad\qquad = 6\sqrt{3} - \sqrt{4\cdot 6} - 12 + 2\sqrt{4\cdot 2}$

$\qquad\qquad = 6\sqrt{3} - 2\sqrt{6} - 12 + 4\sqrt{2}$

13. $\sqrt[4]{\sqrt{x^5 y^3}} = \sqrt[4]{\left(x^5 y^3\right)^{1/2}}$

$\qquad\quad = \left[\left(x^5 y^3\right)^{1/2}\right]^{1/4}$

$\qquad\quad = \left(x^5 y^3\right)^{1/8}$

$\qquad\quad = \sqrt[8]{x^5 y^3}$

14. $\dfrac{\sqrt[4]{(7x+2)^5}}{\sqrt[3]{(7x+2)^2}} = \dfrac{(7x+2)^{5/4}}{(7x+2)^{2/3}}$

$\qquad\qquad = (7x+2)^{5/4-2/3}$

$\qquad\qquad = (7x+2)^{7/12}$

$\qquad\qquad = \sqrt[12]{(7x+2)^7}$

15. $\sqrt{2x+19} = 3$

$\qquad \left(\sqrt{2x+19}\right)^2 = 3^2$

$\qquad\qquad 2x+19 = 9$

$\qquad\qquad\quad 2x = -10$

$\qquad\qquad\quad\ \ x = -5$

Check: $\quad \sqrt{2x+19} = 3$

$\qquad\qquad \sqrt{2(-5)+19} = 3$

$\qquad\qquad\qquad\quad \sqrt{9} = 3$

$\qquad\qquad\qquad\quad 3 = 3 \quad$ True

This check confirms that -5 is the solution to the equation.

16. $\sqrt{x^2 - x - 12} = x + 3$

$\qquad \left(\sqrt{x^2 - x - 12}\right)^2 = (x+3)^2$

$\qquad\quad x^2 - x - 12 = x^2 + 6x + 9$

$\qquad\qquad\ -x - 12 = 6x + 9$

$\qquad\qquad\qquad -12 = 7x + 9$

$\qquad\qquad\qquad -21 = 7x$

$\qquad\qquad\qquad\quad\ x = -3$

Check:

$\sqrt{(-3)^2 - (-3) - 12} = -3 + 3$

$\qquad \sqrt{9 + 3 - 12} = -3 + 3$

$\qquad\qquad\quad \sqrt{0} = 0$

$\qquad\qquad\qquad 0 = 0$

This check confirms that -3 is the solution to the equation.

17. $\sqrt{a-8} = \sqrt{a} - 2$

$\qquad \left(\sqrt{a-8}\right)^2 = \left(\sqrt{a} - 2\right)^2$

$\qquad\qquad a - 8 = a - 4\sqrt{a} + 4$

$\qquad\qquad\ -12 = -4\sqrt{a}$

$\qquad\qquad\quad \sqrt{a} = 3$

$\qquad\qquad\qquad a = 3^2 = 9$

Check:

$\sqrt{a-8} = \sqrt{a} - 2$

$\sqrt{9-8} = \sqrt{9} - 2$

$\qquad \sqrt{1} = 3 - 2$

$\qquad\quad 1 = 1 \quad$ True

This check confirms that 9 is the solution.

18. $\qquad f(x) = g(x)$

$\qquad (9x+37)^{1/3} = 2(2x+2)^{1/3}$

$\qquad \left[(9x+37)^{1/3}\right]^3 = \left[2(2x+2)^{1/3}\right]^3$

$\qquad\qquad 9x + 37 = 8(2x+2)$

$\qquad\qquad 9x + 37 = 16x + 16$

$\qquad\qquad\qquad 21 = 7x$

$\qquad\qquad\qquad\ 3 = x$

19. $\qquad w = \dfrac{\sqrt{2gh}}{4} \quad$ Solve for g.

$\qquad\qquad 4w = \sqrt{2gh}$

$\qquad\qquad (4w)^2 = 2gh$

$\qquad\qquad \dfrac{16w^2}{2h} = \dfrac{2gh}{2h}$

$\qquad\qquad \dfrac{8w^2}{h} = g$

20. $V = \sqrt{64.4h}$

$\qquad V = \sqrt{64.4(200)}$

$\qquad\quad = \sqrt{12,880}$

$\qquad\quad \approx 113.49 \ \text{ft/sec}$

21. Let x be the length of the ladder.

$\qquad x = \sqrt{12^2 + 5^2}$

$\qquad\quad = 169$

$\qquad\quad = 13 \ \text{feet}$

22. $T = 2\pi\sqrt{\dfrac{m}{k}}$

$T = 2\pi\sqrt{\dfrac{1400}{65,000}}$

≈ 0.92 sec

23. $\left(6-\sqrt{-4}\right)\left(2+\sqrt{-16}\right) = (6-2i)(2+4i)$

$= 12 + 24i - 4i - 8i^2$

$= 12 + 20i - 8(-1)$

$= 12 + 20i + 8$

$= 20 + 20i$

24. $\dfrac{5-i}{7+2i} = \dfrac{5-i}{7+2i} \cdot \dfrac{7-2i}{7-2i}$

$= \dfrac{(5-i)(7-2i)}{(7+2i)(7-2i)}$

$= \dfrac{35 - 10i - 7i + 2i^2}{49 - 14i + 14i - 4i^2}$

$= \dfrac{35 - 17i + 2(-1)}{49 - 4(-1)}$

$= \dfrac{35 - 17i - 2}{49 + 4}$

$= \dfrac{33 - 17i}{53}$

25. $x^2 + 6x + 12$

$= (-3+i)^2 + 6(-3+i) + 12$

$= (-3)^2 - 2(3)(i) + (i)^2 - 18 + 6i + 12$

$= 9 - 6i - 1 - 18 + 6i + 12$

$= 2 + 0i$

$= 2$

Chapter 11 Cumulative Review Test

1. $\dfrac{1}{5}(x-3) = \dfrac{3}{4}(x+3) - x$

$20\left[\dfrac{1}{5}(x-3)\right] = 20\left[\dfrac{3}{4}(x+3)\right] - 20x$

$4(x-3) = 5(3)(x+3) - 20x$

$4x - 12 = 15x + 45 - 20x$

$4x - 12 = -5x + 45$

$9x - 12 = 45$

$9x = 57$

$x = \dfrac{57}{9}$

2. $3(x-4) = 6x - (4-5x)$

$3x - 12 = 6x - 4 + 5x$

$3x - 12 = 11x - 4$

$-8x = 8$

$x = -1$

3. Let x be the original price of the sweater.

$x - 60\%x = 16$

$x - 0.60x = 16$

$0.40x = 16$

$x = \dfrac{16}{0.40}$

$x = 40$

The original price of the sweater is \$40.

4. $y = \dfrac{3}{2}x - 3$

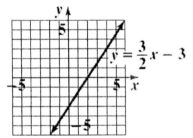

5. $\left(5xy - 3\right)\left(5xy + 3\right)$

$= 25x^2y^2 + 15xy - 15xy - 9$

$= 25x^2y^2 - 9$

6. $V = lwh$

$$6r^3 + 5r^2 + r = (3r+1)(w)(r)$$

$$\frac{6r^3 + 5r^2 + r}{(3r+1)(r)} = \frac{(3r+1)(w)(r)}{(3r+1)(r)}$$

$$\frac{r(6r^2 + 5r + 1)}{r(3r+1)} = w$$

$$\frac{r(3r+1)(2r+1)}{r(3r+1)} = w$$

$$w = 2r + 1$$

7. $4x^3 - 9x^2 + 5x = x(4x^2 - 9x + 5)$

$$= x(4x - 5)(x - 1)$$

8. $(x+1)^3 - 27 = (x+1)^3 - 3^3$

$$= (x + 1 - 3)\left((x+1)^2 + 3(x+1) + 3^2\right)$$

$$= (x - 2)(x^2 + 2x + 1 + 3x + 3 + 9)$$

$$= (x - 2)(x^2 + 5x + 13)$$

9. $8x^2 - 3 = -10x$

$$8x^2 + 10x - 3 = 0$$

$$(4x - 1)(2x + 3) = 0$$

$$4x - 1 = 0 \quad \text{or} \quad 2x + 3 = 0$$

$$4x = 1 \qquad\qquad 2x = -3$$

$$x = \frac{1}{4} \qquad\qquad x = -\frac{3}{2}$$

10. $\dfrac{4x + 4y}{x^2 y} \cdot \dfrac{y^3}{12x} = \dfrac{4(x+y)}{x^2 y} \cdot \dfrac{y^3}{12x}$

$$= \frac{x+y}{x^2} \cdot \frac{y^2}{3x}$$

$$= \frac{(x+y)y^2}{3x^3}$$

11. $\dfrac{x-4}{x-5} - \dfrac{3}{x+5} - \dfrac{10}{x^2 - 25}$

$$= \frac{x-4}{x-5} - \frac{3}{x+5} - \frac{10}{(x+5)(x-5)}$$

$$= \frac{x-4}{x-5} \cdot \frac{x+5}{x+5} - \frac{3}{x+5} \cdot \frac{x-5}{x-5} - \frac{10}{(x+5)(x-5)}$$

$$= \frac{(x-4)(x+5)}{(x+5)(x-5)} - \frac{3(x-5)}{(x+5)(x-5)} - \frac{10}{(x+5)(x-5)}$$

$$= \frac{(x-4)(x+5) - 3(x-5) - 10}{(x+5)(x-5)}$$

$$= \frac{x^2 + x - 20 - 3x + 15 - 10}{(x+5)(x-5)}$$

$$= \frac{x^2 - 2x - 15}{(x+5)(x-5)}$$

$$= \frac{(x-5)(x+3)}{(x+5)(x-5)}$$

$$= \frac{x+3}{x+5}$$

12. $\dfrac{4}{x} - \dfrac{1}{6} = \dfrac{1}{x}$

$$6x\left(\frac{4}{x} - \frac{1}{6} = \frac{1}{x}\right)$$

$$24 - x = 6$$

$$-x = -18$$

$$x = 18$$

Upon checking, this value satisfies the equation. The solution is 18.

13. $y = 3x - 8 \Rightarrow m_1 = 3$

$6y = 18x + 12 \Rightarrow y = 3x + 2 \Rightarrow m_2 = 3$

The slope of both lines is 3. Since the slopes of the two lines are the same, and the y-intercepts are different, the lines are parallel.

14. First find the slope of the given line.

$3x - 2y = 6$

$-2y = -3x + 6$

$y = \dfrac{3}{2}x - 3 \Rightarrow$ The slope is $\dfrac{3}{2}$.

The slope of any line perpendicular to this line must have an opposite reciprocal slope. Therefore, the slope of the line perpendicular to the given line is $-\dfrac{2}{3}$. Finally, use the point-slope formula to find the equation of the line.

$$y - y_1 = m(x - x_1) \text{ with } m = -\frac{2}{3} \text{ and } (1, -4)$$

$$y - (-4) = -\frac{2}{3}(x - 1)$$

$$y + 4 = -\frac{2}{3}x + \frac{2}{3}$$

$$y = -\frac{2}{3}x - \frac{10}{3}$$

15. $f(x) = x^2 - 3x + 4$ and $g(x) = 2x - 9$

$$(g - f)(x) = (2x - 9) - (x^2 - 3x + 4)$$

$$= 2x - 9 - x^2 + 3x - 4$$

$$= -x^2 + 5x - 13$$

16.
$$x + 2y = 12 \quad (1)$$
$$4x = 8 \quad (2)$$
$$3x - 4y + 5z = 20 \quad (3)$$

Using equation (2), solve for x.

$$4x = 8 \implies x = \frac{8}{4} \implies x = 2$$

Substitute 2 for x in equation (1) in order to solve for y.

$$2 + 2y = 12 \implies 2y = 10 \implies y = 5$$

Substitute 2 for x and 5 for y in equation (3) in order to solve for z.

$$3(2) - 4(5) + 5z = 20$$

$$6 - 20 + 5z = 20$$

$$-14 + 5z = 20$$

$$5z = 34$$

$$z = \frac{34}{5}$$

The solution is $\left(2, 5, \frac{34}{5}\right)$.

17. $\begin{vmatrix} 3 & -6 & -1 \\ 2 & 1 & -2 \\ 1 & 3 & 1 \end{vmatrix}$

$$= 3\begin{vmatrix} 1 & -2 \\ 3 & 1 \end{vmatrix} - (-6)\begin{vmatrix} 2 & -2 \\ 1 & 1 \end{vmatrix} + (-1)\begin{vmatrix} 2 & 1 \\ 1 & 3 \end{vmatrix}$$

$$= 3(1 - (-6)) + 6(2 - (-2)) - (6 - 1)$$

$$= 3(1 + 6) + 6(2 + 2) - (6 - 1)$$

$$= 3(7) + 6(4) - (5)$$

$$= 21 + 24 - 5$$

$$= 40$$

18.
$$|3 - 2x| < 5$$

$$-5 < 3 - 2x < 5$$

$$-5 - 3 < 3 - 2x - 3 < 5 - 3$$

$$-8 < -2x < 2$$

$$\frac{-8}{-2} > \frac{-2x}{-2} > \frac{2}{-2}$$

$$4 > x > -1 \text{ or } -1 < x < 4$$

The solution set is $\{x | -1 < x < 4\}$

19. $\sqrt{2x^2 + 7} + 3 = 8$

$$\sqrt{2x^2 + 7} = 5$$

$$\left(\sqrt{2x^2 + 7}\right)^2 = 5^2$$

$$2x^2 + 7 = 25$$

$$2x^2 = 18$$

$$x^2 = 9$$

$$x = 3 \text{ or } -3$$

Check:

$$\sqrt{2(3)^2 + 7} + 3 = 8 \quad \text{or} \quad \sqrt{2(-3)^2 + 7} + 3 = 8$$

$$\sqrt{25} = 5 \qquad\qquad \sqrt{25} = 5$$

$$5 = 5 \qquad\qquad\quad 5 = 5$$

Both values check. The solutions are 3 and –3.

20. $d = kt^2$

$$16 = k(1)^2 \implies k = 16$$

$$d = 16(5)^2$$

$$= 16 \cdot 25$$

$$= 400$$

The object will fall 400 feet in 5 seconds.

Chapter 12

Exercise Set 12.1

1. The two square roots of 36 are $\pm\sqrt{36} = \pm 6$.

2. The two square roots of 17 are $\pm\sqrt{17}$.

3. The square root property is: If $x^2 = a$, where a is a real number, then $x = \pm\sqrt{a}$.

4. The first step in completing the square for $ax^2 + bx + c = 0$ is to make $a = 1$.

5. A trinomial, $x^2 + bx + c$, is a perfect square trinomial if $\left(\dfrac{b}{2}\right)^2 = c$.

6. Answers will vary.

7. **a.** Yes, $x = 4$ is the solution to the equation. It is the only real number that satisfies the equation.

   b. No, $x = 2$ is not the solution. Both -2 and 2 satisfy the equation.

8. **a.** Yes, $x = -7$ is the solution to the equation. It is the only real number that satisfies the equation.

   b. No, $x = \pm\sqrt{7}$ is not the solution. The correct solution is $x = \pm i\sqrt{7}$.

9. Multiply the equation by $\dfrac{1}{2}$ to obtain a leading coefficient of 1.

10. Multiply the equation by 7 to obtain a leading coefficient of 1.

11. You should add the square of half the coefficient of the first degree term: $\left(\dfrac{-6}{2}\right)^2 = (-3)^2 = 9$.

12. You should add the square of half the coefficient of the first degree term: $\left(\dfrac{10}{2}\right)^2 = (5)^2 = 25$.

13. $x^2 - 25 = 0$
$$x^2 = 25$$
$$x = \pm\sqrt{25} = \pm 5$$

14. $x^2 - 49 = 0$
$$x^2 = 49$$
$$x = \pm\sqrt{49} = \pm 7$$

15. $x^2 + 49 = 0$
$$x^2 = -49$$
$$x = \pm\sqrt{-49} = \pm 7i$$

16. $y^2 - 24 = 0$
$$y^2 = 24$$
$$y = \pm\sqrt{24} = \pm 2\sqrt{6}$$

17. $y^2 + 24 = 0$
$$y^2 = -24$$
$$y = \pm\sqrt{-24} = \pm 2i\sqrt{6}$$

18. $y^2 - 10 = 51$
$$y^2 = 61$$
$$y = \pm\sqrt{61}$$

19. $y^2 + 10 = -51$
$$y^2 = -61$$
$$y = \pm\sqrt{-61} = \pm i\sqrt{61}$$

20. $(x-3)^2 = 49$
$$x - 3 = \pm\sqrt{49}$$
$$x - 3 = \pm\sqrt{49}$$
$$x = 3 \pm 7$$
$$x = 3 + 7 \quad \text{or} \quad x = 3 - 7$$
$$x = 10 \qquad\qquad x = -4$$

21. $(p-4)^2 = 16$
$$p - 4 = \pm\sqrt{16}$$
$$p - 4 = \pm 4$$
$$p = 4 \pm 4$$
$$p = 4 + 4 \quad \text{or} \quad p = 4 - 4$$
$$p = 8 \qquad\qquad p = 0$$

22. $(x+3)^2 = 49$

$$x+3 = \pm\sqrt{49}$$
$$x+3 = \pm\sqrt{49}$$
$$x = -3 \pm 7$$
$$x = -3+7 \quad \text{or} \quad x = -3-7$$
$$x = 4 \qquad\qquad x = -10$$

23. $(x+3)^2 + 25 = 0$

$$(x+3)^2 = -25$$
$$x+3 = \pm\sqrt{-25}$$
$$x+3 = \pm\sqrt{-25}$$
$$x = -3 \pm 5i$$

24. $(a-3)^2 = 45$

$$a-3 = \pm\sqrt{45}$$
$$a-3 = \pm 3\sqrt{5}$$
$$a = 3 \pm 3\sqrt{5}$$

25. $(a-2)^2 + 45 = 0$

$$(a-2)^2 = -45$$
$$a-2 = \pm\sqrt{-45}$$
$$a-2 = \pm 3i\sqrt{5}$$
$$a = 2 \pm 3i\sqrt{5}$$

26. $(a+2)^2 + 45 = 0$

$$(a+2)^2 = -45$$
$$a+2 = \pm\sqrt{-45}$$
$$a+2 = \pm 3i\sqrt{5}$$
$$a = -2 \pm 3i\sqrt{5}$$

27. $\left(b+\dfrac{1}{3}\right)^2 = \dfrac{4}{9}$

$$b+\frac{1}{3} = \pm\sqrt{\frac{4}{9}}$$
$$b+\frac{1}{3} = \pm\frac{2}{3}$$
$$b = -\frac{1}{3} \pm \frac{2}{3}$$
$$b = -\frac{1}{3}+\frac{2}{3} \quad \text{or} \quad b = -\frac{1}{3}-\frac{2}{3}$$
$$b = \frac{1}{3} \qquad\qquad b = -\frac{3}{3}$$
$$\qquad\qquad\qquad b = -1$$

28. $\left(b-\dfrac{1}{3}\right)^2 = \dfrac{4}{9}$

$$b-\frac{1}{3} = \pm\sqrt{\frac{4}{9}}$$
$$b-\frac{1}{3} = \pm\frac{2}{3}$$
$$b = \frac{1}{3} \pm \frac{2}{3}$$
$$b = \frac{1}{3}+\frac{2}{3} \quad \text{or} \quad b = \frac{1}{3}-\frac{2}{3}$$
$$b = \frac{3}{3} \qquad\qquad b = -\frac{1}{3}$$
$$b = 1$$

29. $\left(b-\dfrac{2}{3}\right)^2 + \dfrac{4}{9} = 0$

$$\left(b-\frac{2}{3}\right)^2 = -\frac{4}{9}$$
$$b-\frac{2}{3} = \pm\sqrt{-\frac{4}{9}}$$
$$b = \frac{2}{3} \pm \frac{2}{3}i \quad \text{or} \quad b = \frac{2 \pm 2i}{3}$$

30. $(x-0.2)^2 = 0.64$

$$x-0.2 = \pm\sqrt{0.64}$$
$$x-0.2 = \pm 0.8$$
$$x = 0.2 \pm 0.8$$
$$x = 0.2+0.8 \quad \text{or} \quad x = 0.2-0.8$$
$$x = 1.0 \qquad\qquad x = -0.6$$

31. $(x+0.8)^2 = 0.81$

$$x+0.8 = \pm\sqrt{0.81}$$
$$x+0.8 = \pm 0.9$$
$$x = -0.8 \pm 0.9$$
$$x = -0.8+0.9 \quad \text{or} \quad x = -0.8-0.9$$
$$x = 0.1 \qquad\qquad x = -1.7$$

32. $\left(x+\dfrac{1}{2}\right)^2=\dfrac{16}{9}$

$$x+\dfrac{1}{2}=\pm\sqrt{\dfrac{16}{9}}$$

$$x+\dfrac{1}{2}=\pm\dfrac{4}{3}$$

$$x=-\dfrac{1}{2}\pm\dfrac{4}{3}$$

$$x=-\dfrac{1}{2}+\dfrac{4}{3}\quad\text{or}\quad x=-\dfrac{1}{2}-\dfrac{4}{3}$$

$$x=\dfrac{5}{6}\qquad\qquad x=-\dfrac{11}{6}$$

33. $(2a-5)^2=18$

$$2a-5=\pm\sqrt{18}$$

$$2a-5=\pm3\sqrt{2}$$

$$2a=5\pm3\sqrt{2}$$

$$a=\dfrac{5\pm3\sqrt{3}}{2}$$

34. $(4y+1)^2=12$

$$4y+1=\pm\sqrt{12}$$

$$4y+1=\pm2\sqrt{3}$$

$$4y=-1\pm2\sqrt{3}$$

$$y=\dfrac{-1\pm2\sqrt{3}}{4}$$

35. $\left(2y+\dfrac{1}{2}\right)^2=\dfrac{4}{25}$

$$2y+\dfrac{1}{2}=\pm\sqrt{\dfrac{4}{25}}$$

$$2y+\dfrac{1}{2}=\pm\dfrac{2}{5}$$

$$2y+\dfrac{1}{2}=\dfrac{2}{5}\quad\text{or}\quad 2y+\dfrac{1}{2}=-\dfrac{2}{5}$$

$$2y=-\dfrac{1}{2}+\dfrac{2}{5}\qquad\qquad 2y=-\dfrac{1}{2}-\dfrac{2}{5}$$

$$2y=-\dfrac{1}{10}\qquad\qquad\quad 2y=-\dfrac{9}{10}$$

$$y=-\dfrac{1}{20}\qquad\qquad\quad y=-\dfrac{9}{20}$$

36. $\left(3x-\dfrac{1}{4}\right)^2=\dfrac{9}{25}$

$$3x-\dfrac{1}{4}=\pm\sqrt{\dfrac{9}{25}}$$

$$3x-\dfrac{1}{4}=\pm\dfrac{3}{5}$$

$$3x-\dfrac{1}{4}=\dfrac{3}{5}\quad\text{or}\quad 3x-\dfrac{1}{4}=-\dfrac{3}{5}$$

$$3x=\dfrac{1}{4}+\dfrac{3}{5}\qquad\qquad 3x=\dfrac{1}{4}-\dfrac{3}{5}$$

$$3x=\dfrac{17}{20}\qquad\qquad\quad 3x=-\dfrac{7}{20}$$

$$x=\dfrac{17}{60}\qquad\qquad\quad x=-\dfrac{7}{60}$$

37. $x^2+3x-4=0$

$$x^2+3x=4$$

$$x^2+3x+\dfrac{9}{4}=4+\dfrac{9}{4}$$

$$x^2+3x+\dfrac{9}{4}=\dfrac{16}{4}+\dfrac{9}{4}$$

$$\left(x+\dfrac{3}{2}\right)^2=\dfrac{25}{4}$$

$$x+\dfrac{3}{2}=\pm\sqrt{\dfrac{25}{4}}$$

$$x+\dfrac{3}{2}=\pm\dfrac{5}{2}$$

$$x=-\dfrac{3}{2}\pm\dfrac{5}{2}$$

$$x=-\dfrac{3}{2}+\dfrac{5}{2}\quad\text{or}\quad x=-\dfrac{3}{2}-\dfrac{5}{2}$$

$$x=\dfrac{2}{2}\qquad\qquad x=\dfrac{-8}{2}$$

$$x=1\qquad\qquad x=-4$$

38. $x^2 - 3x - 4 = 0$

$$x^2 - 3x = 4$$

$$x^2 - 3x + \frac{9}{4} = 4 + \frac{9}{4}$$

$$x^2 - 3x + \frac{9}{4} = \frac{16}{4} + \frac{9}{4}$$

$$\left(x - \frac{3}{2}\right)^2 = \frac{25}{4}$$

$$x - \frac{3}{2} = \pm\sqrt{\frac{25}{4}}$$

$$x - \frac{3}{2} = \pm\frac{5}{2}$$

$$x = \frac{3}{2} \pm \frac{5}{2}$$

$$x = \frac{3}{2} + \frac{5}{2} \quad \text{or} \quad x = \frac{3}{2} - \frac{5}{2}$$

$$x = \frac{8}{2} \qquad\qquad x = \frac{-2}{2}$$

$$x = 4 \qquad\qquad x = -1$$

39. $x^2 + 2x - 15 = 0$

$$x^2 + 2x = 15$$

$$x^2 + 2x + 1 = 15 + 1$$

$$(x + 1)^2 = 16$$

$$x + 1 = \pm\sqrt{16}$$

$$x + 1 = \pm 4$$

$$x = -1 \pm 4$$

$$x = -1 + 4 \quad \text{or} \quad x = -1 - 4$$

$$x = 3 \qquad\qquad x = -5$$

40. $x^2 - 8x + 15 = 0$

$$x^2 - 8x = -15$$

$$x^2 - 8x + 16 = -15 + 16$$

$$(x - 4)^2 = 1$$

$$x - 4 = \pm\sqrt{1}$$

$$x - 4 = \pm 1$$

$$x = 4 \pm 1$$

$$x = 4 + 1 \quad \text{or} \quad x = 4 - 1$$

$$x = 5 \qquad\qquad x = 3$$

41. $x^2 + 6x + 8 = 0$

$$x^2 + 6x = -8$$

$$x^2 + 6x + 9 = -8 + 9$$

$$x^2 + 6x + 9 = 1$$

$$(x + 3)^2 = 1$$

$$x + 3 = \pm\sqrt{1}$$

$$x + 3 = \pm 1$$

$$x = -3 \pm 1$$

$$x = -3 + 1 \quad \text{or} \quad x = -3 - 1$$

$$x = -2 \qquad\qquad x = -4$$

42. $x^2 - 6x + 8 = 0$

$$x^2 - 6x = -8$$

$$x^2 - 6x + 9 = -8 + 9$$

$$x^2 - 6x + 9 = 1$$

$$(x - 3)^2 = 1$$

$$x - 3 = \pm\sqrt{1}$$

$$x - 3 = \pm 1$$

$$x = 3 \pm 1$$

$$x = 3 + 1 \quad \text{or} \quad x = 3 - 1$$

$$x = 4 \qquad\qquad x = 2$$

43. $x^2 - 7x + 6 = 0$

$$x^2 - 7x = -6$$

$$x^2 - 7x + \frac{49}{4} = -6 + \frac{49}{4}$$

$$x^2 - 7x + \frac{49}{4} = -\frac{24}{4} + \frac{49}{4}$$

$$x^2 - 7x + \frac{49}{4} = \frac{25}{4}$$

$$\left(x - \frac{7}{2}\right)^2 = \frac{25}{4}$$

$$x - \frac{7}{2} = \pm\sqrt{\frac{25}{4}}$$

$$x - \frac{7}{2} = \pm\frac{5}{2}$$

$$x = \frac{7}{2} \pm \frac{5}{2}$$

$$x = \frac{7}{2} + \frac{5}{2} \quad \text{or} \quad x = \frac{7}{2} - \frac{5}{2}$$

$$x = \frac{12}{2} \qquad\qquad x = \frac{2}{2}$$

$$x = 6 \qquad\qquad x = 1$$

44.
$$x^2 + 9x + 18 = 0$$
$$x^2 + 9x = -18$$
$$x^2 + 9x + \frac{81}{4} = -18 + \frac{81}{4}$$
$$\left(x + \frac{9}{2}\right)^2 = \frac{-72}{4} + \frac{81}{4}$$
$$\left(x + \frac{9}{2}\right)^2 = \frac{9}{4}$$
$$x + \frac{9}{2} = \pm\sqrt{\frac{9}{4}}$$
$$x + \frac{9}{2} = \pm\frac{3}{2}$$
$$x = -\frac{9}{2} \pm \frac{3}{2}$$
$$x = -\frac{9}{2} + \frac{3}{2} \quad \text{or} \quad x = -\frac{9}{2} - \frac{3}{2}$$
$$x = -\frac{6}{2} \qquad\qquad x = -\frac{12}{2}$$
$$x = -3 \qquad\qquad x = -6$$

46.
$$3c^2 - 4c - 4 = 0$$
$$\frac{1}{3}\left(3c^2 - 4c - 4\right) = \frac{1}{3}(0)$$
$$c^2 - \frac{4}{3}c - \frac{4}{3} = 0$$
$$c^2 - \frac{4}{3}c = \frac{4}{3}$$
$$c^2 - \frac{4}{3}c + \frac{4}{9} = \frac{4}{3} + \frac{4}{9}$$
$$\left(c - \frac{2}{3}\right)^2 = \frac{16}{9}$$
$$c - \frac{2}{3} = \pm\frac{4}{3}$$
$$c = \frac{2}{3} \pm \frac{4}{3}$$
$$c = \frac{2}{3} + \frac{4}{3} \quad \text{or} \quad c = \frac{2}{3} - \frac{4}{3}$$
$$c = \frac{6}{3} \qquad\qquad c = -\frac{2}{3}$$
$$c = 2$$

45.
$$2x^2 + x - 1 = 0$$
$$\frac{1}{2}\left(2x^2 + x - 1\right) = \frac{1}{2}(0)$$
$$x^2 + \frac{1}{2}x - \frac{1}{2} = 0$$
$$x^2 + \frac{1}{2}x = \frac{1}{2}$$
$$x^2 + \frac{1}{2}x + \frac{1}{16} = \frac{1}{2} + \frac{1}{16}$$
$$\left(x + \frac{1}{4}\right)^2 = \frac{9}{16}$$
$$x + \frac{1}{4} = \pm\sqrt{\frac{9}{16}}$$
$$x + \frac{1}{4} = \pm\frac{3}{4}$$
$$x = -\frac{1}{4} \pm \frac{3}{4}$$
$$x = -\frac{1}{4} + \frac{3}{4} \quad \text{or} \quad x = -\frac{1}{4} - \frac{3}{4}$$
$$x = \frac{2}{4} \qquad\qquad x = -\frac{4}{4}$$
$$x = \frac{1}{2} \qquad\qquad x = -1$$

47.
$$2z^2 - 7z - 4 = 0$$
$$\frac{1}{2}\left(2z^2 - 7z - 4\right) = \frac{1}{2}(0)$$
$$z^2 - \frac{7}{2}z - 2 = 0$$
$$z^2 - \frac{7}{2}z = 2$$
$$z^2 - \frac{7}{2}z + \frac{49}{16} = 2 + \frac{49}{16}$$
$$\left(z - \frac{7}{4}\right)^2 = \frac{81}{16}$$
$$z - \frac{7}{4} = \pm\sqrt{\frac{81}{16}}$$
$$z - \frac{7}{4} = \pm\frac{9}{4}$$
$$z = \frac{7}{4} \pm \frac{9}{4}$$
$$z = \frac{7}{4} + \frac{9}{4} \quad \text{or} \quad z = \frac{7}{4} - \frac{9}{4}$$
$$z = \frac{16}{4} \qquad\qquad z = -\frac{2}{4}$$
$$z = 4 \qquad\qquad z = -\frac{1}{2}$$

48. $4a^2 + 9a = 9$

$$\frac{1}{4}\left(4a^2 + 9a\right) = \frac{1}{4}(9)$$

$$a^2 + \frac{9}{4}a = \frac{9}{4}$$

$$a^2 + \frac{9}{4}a + \frac{81}{64} = \frac{9}{4} + \frac{81}{64}$$

$$\left(a + \frac{9}{8}\right)^2 = \frac{225}{64}$$

$$a + \frac{9}{8} = \pm\sqrt{\frac{225}{64}}$$

$$a + \frac{9}{8} = \pm\frac{15}{8}$$

$$a = -\frac{9}{8} \pm \frac{15}{8}$$

$$a = -\frac{9}{8} + \frac{15}{8} \quad \text{or} \quad a = -\frac{9}{8} - \frac{15}{8}$$

$$a = \frac{6}{8} \qquad\qquad a = -\frac{24}{8}$$

$$a = \frac{3}{4} \qquad\qquad a = -3$$

49. $x^2 - 13x + 40 = 0$

$$x^2 - 13x = -40$$

$$x^2 - 13x + \frac{169}{4} = -40 + \frac{169}{4}$$

$$\left(x - \frac{13}{2}\right)^2 = \frac{9}{4}$$

$$x - \frac{13}{2} = \pm\sqrt{\frac{9}{4}}$$

$$x - \frac{13}{2} = \pm\frac{3}{2}$$

$$x = \frac{13}{2} \pm \frac{3}{2}$$

$$x = \frac{13}{2} + \frac{3}{2} \quad \text{or} \quad x = \frac{13}{2} - \frac{3}{2}$$

$$x = \frac{16}{2} \qquad\qquad x = \frac{10}{2}$$

$$x = 8 \qquad\qquad x = 5$$

50. $x^2 + x - 12 = 0$

$$x^2 + x = 12$$

$$x^2 + x + \frac{1}{4} = 12 + \frac{1}{4}$$

$$\left(x + \frac{1}{2}\right)^2 = \frac{48 + 1}{4}$$

$$\left(x + \frac{1}{2}\right)^2 = \frac{49}{4}$$

$$x + \frac{1}{2} = \pm\sqrt{\frac{49}{4}}$$

$$x + \frac{1}{2} = \pm\frac{7}{2}$$

$$x = -\frac{1}{2} \pm \frac{7}{2}$$

$$x = -\frac{1}{2} + \frac{7}{2} \quad \text{or} \quad x = -\frac{1}{2} - \frac{7}{2}$$

$$x = \frac{6}{2} \qquad\qquad x = -\frac{8}{2}$$

$$x = 3 \qquad\qquad x = -4$$

51. $-x^2 + 6x + 7 = 0$

$$-1\left(-x^2 + 6x + 7\right) = -1(0)$$

$$x^2 - 6x - 7 = 0$$

$$x^2 - 6x = 7$$

$$x^2 - 6x + 9 = 7 + 9$$

$$(x - 3)^2 = 16$$

$$x - 3 = \pm\sqrt{16}$$

$$x - 3 = \pm 4$$

$$x = 3 \pm 4$$

$$x = 3 + 4 \quad \text{or} \quad x = 3 - 4$$

$$x = 7 \qquad\qquad x = -1$$

52.
$$-a^2 - 5a + 14 = 0$$
$$-1(-a^2 - 5a + 14) = -1(0)$$
$$a^2 + 5a - 14 = 0$$
$$a^2 + 5a = 14$$
$$a^2 + 5a + \frac{25}{4} = 14 + \frac{25}{4}$$
$$\left(a + \frac{5}{2}\right)^2 = \frac{81}{4}$$
$$a + \frac{5}{2} = \pm\frac{9}{2}$$
$$a = -\frac{5}{2} \pm \frac{9}{2}$$
$$a = -\frac{5}{2} + \frac{9}{2} \quad \text{or} \quad a = -\frac{5}{2} - \frac{9}{2}$$
$$a = 2 \qquad\qquad a = -7$$

53.
$$-z^2 + 9z - 20 = 0$$
$$-1(-z^2 + 9z - 20) = -1(0)$$
$$z^2 - 9z + 20 = 0$$
$$z^2 - 9z = -20$$
$$z^2 - 9z + \frac{81}{4} = -20 + \frac{81}{4}$$
$$\left(z - \frac{9}{2}\right)^2 = \frac{1}{4}$$
$$z - \frac{9}{2} = \pm\sqrt{\frac{1}{4}}$$
$$z - \frac{9}{2} = \pm\frac{1}{2}$$
$$z = \frac{9}{2} \pm \frac{1}{2}$$
$$z = \frac{9}{2} + \frac{1}{2} \quad \text{or} \quad z = \frac{9}{2} - \frac{1}{2}$$
$$z = \frac{10}{2} \qquad\qquad z = \frac{8}{2}$$
$$z = 5 \qquad\qquad z = 4$$

54.
$$-z^2 - 4z + 12 = 0$$
$$-1(-z^2 - 4z + 12) = -1(0)$$
$$z^2 + 4z - 12 = 0$$
$$z^2 + 4z = 12$$
$$z^2 + 4z + 4 = 12 + 4$$
$$(z + 2)^2 = 16$$
$$z + 2 = \pm 4$$
$$z = -2 \pm 4$$
$$z = -2 + 4 \quad \text{or} \quad z = -2 - 4$$
$$z = 2 \qquad\qquad z = -6$$

55.
$$b^2 = 3b + 28$$
$$b^2 - 3b = 28$$
$$b^2 - 3b + \frac{9}{4} = \frac{112}{4} + \frac{9}{4}$$
$$\left(b - \frac{3}{2}\right)^2 = \frac{121}{4}$$
$$b - \frac{3}{2} = \pm\sqrt{\frac{121}{4}}$$
$$b - \frac{3}{2} = \pm\frac{11}{2}$$
$$b = \frac{3}{2} \pm \frac{11}{2}$$
$$b = \frac{3}{2} + \frac{11}{2} \quad \text{or} \quad b = \frac{3}{2} - \frac{11}{2}$$
$$b = \frac{14}{2} \qquad\qquad b = -\frac{8}{2}$$
$$b = 7 \qquad\qquad b = -4$$

56.
$$-x^2 = 6x - 27$$
$$-1(-x^2) = -1(6x - 27)$$
$$x^2 = -6x + 27$$
$$x^2 + 6x = 27$$
$$x^2 + 6x + 9 = 27 + 9$$
$$(x + 3)^2 = 36$$
$$x + 3 = \pm 6$$
$$x = -3 \pm 6$$
$$x = -3 + 6 \quad \text{or} \quad x = -3 - 6$$
$$x = 3 \qquad\qquad x = -9$$

57.
$$x^2 + 10x = 11$$
$$x^2 + 10x + 25 = 11 + 25$$
$$(x + 5)^2 = 36$$
$$x + 5 = \pm\sqrt{36}$$
$$x + 5 = \pm 6$$
$$x = -5 \pm 6$$
$$x = \frac{11}{2} - \frac{9}{2} \quad \text{or} \quad x = -\frac{11}{2} - \frac{9}{2}$$
$$x = \frac{2}{2} \qquad\qquad x = -\frac{20}{2}$$
$$x = 1 \qquad\qquad x = -10$$

58.
$$-x^2 + 40 = -3x$$
$$-1(-x^2 + 40) = -1(-3x)$$
$$x^2 - 40 = 3x$$
$$x^2 - 3x = 40$$
$$x^2 - 3x + \frac{9}{4} = 40 + \frac{9}{4}$$
$$\left(x - \frac{3}{2}\right)^2 = \frac{160}{4} + \frac{9}{4}$$
$$\left(x - \frac{3}{2}\right)^2 = \frac{169}{4}$$
$$x - \frac{3}{2} = \pm\frac{13}{2}$$
$$x = \frac{3}{2} \pm \frac{13}{2}$$
$$x = \frac{3}{2} + \frac{13}{2} \quad \text{or} \quad x = \frac{3}{2} - \frac{13}{2}$$
$$x = \frac{16}{2} \qquad\qquad x = -\frac{10}{2}$$
$$x = 8 \qquad\qquad x = -5$$

59.
$$x^2 - 4x - 10 = 0$$
$$x^2 - 4x = 10$$
$$x^2 - 4x + 4 = 10 + 4$$
$$(x - 2)^2 = 14$$
$$x - 2 = \pm\sqrt{14}$$
$$x = 2 \pm \sqrt{14}$$

60.
$$x^2 - 6x + 2 = 0$$
$$x^2 - 6x = -2$$
$$x^2 - 6x + 9 = -2 + 9$$
$$(x - 3)^2 = 7$$
$$x - 3 = \pm\sqrt{7}$$
$$x = 3 \pm \sqrt{7}$$

61.
$$r^2 + 8r + 5 = 0$$
$$r^2 + 8r = -5$$
$$r^2 + 8r + 16 = -5 + 16$$
$$(r + 4)^2 = 11$$
$$r + 4 = \pm\sqrt{11}$$
$$r = -4 \pm \sqrt{11}$$

62.
$$a^2 + 4a - 8 = 0$$
$$a^2 + 4a = 8$$
$$a^2 + 4a + 4 = 8 + 4$$
$$(a + 2)^2 = 12$$
$$a + 2 = \pm\sqrt{12}$$
$$a + 2 = \pm 2\sqrt{3}$$
$$a = -2 \pm 2\sqrt{3}$$

63.
$$c^2 - c - 3 = 0$$
$$c^2 - c = 3$$
$$c^2 - c + \frac{1}{4} = 3 + \frac{1}{4}$$
$$\left(c - \frac{1}{2}\right)^2 = \frac{13}{4}$$
$$c - \frac{1}{2} = \pm\sqrt{\frac{13}{4}}$$
$$c = \frac{1}{2} \pm \frac{\sqrt{13}}{2} = \frac{1 \pm \sqrt{13}}{2}$$

64.
$$p^2 - 5p = 4$$
$$p^2 - 5p + \frac{25}{4} = 4 + \frac{25}{4}$$
$$\left(p - \frac{5}{2}\right)^2 = \frac{41}{4}$$
$$p - \frac{5}{2} = \pm\frac{\sqrt{41}}{2}$$
$$p = \frac{5}{2} \pm \frac{\sqrt{41}}{2} = \frac{5 \pm \sqrt{41}}{2}$$

65.
$$x^2 + 3x + 6 = 0$$
$$x^2 + 3x = -6$$
$$x^2 + 3x + \frac{9}{4} = -6 + \frac{9}{4}$$
$$\left(x + \frac{3}{2}\right)^2 = \frac{-15}{4}$$
$$x + \frac{3}{2} = \pm\sqrt{\frac{-15}{4}}$$
$$x + \frac{3}{2} = \pm\frac{i\sqrt{15}}{2}$$
$$x = -\frac{3}{2} \pm \frac{i\sqrt{15}}{2} = \frac{-3 \pm i\sqrt{15}}{2}$$

66.
$$z^2 - 5z = -7$$
$$z^2 - 5z + 7 = 0$$
$$z^2 - 5z + \frac{25}{4} = -7 + \frac{25}{4}$$
$$\left(x - \frac{5}{2}\right)^2 = -\frac{3}{4}$$
$$x - \frac{5}{2} = \pm\sqrt{-\frac{3}{4}}$$
$$x - \frac{5}{2} = \pm\frac{i\sqrt{3}}{2}$$
$$x = \frac{5}{2} \pm \frac{i\sqrt{3}}{2} = \frac{5 \pm i\sqrt{3}}{2}$$

67.
$$9x^2 - 9x = 0$$
$$\frac{1}{9}(9x^2 - 9x) = \frac{1}{9}(0)$$
$$x^2 - x = 0$$
$$x^2 - x + \frac{1}{4} = \frac{1}{4}$$
$$\left(x - \frac{1}{2}\right)^2 = \frac{1}{4}$$
$$x - \frac{1}{2} = \pm\frac{1}{2}$$
$$x = \frac{1}{2} \pm \frac{1}{2}$$
$$x = \frac{1}{2} + \frac{1}{2} \quad \text{or} \quad x = \frac{1}{2} - \frac{1}{2}$$
$$x = 1 \qquad\qquad x = 0$$

68.
$$4y^2 + 12y = 0$$
$$\frac{1}{4}(4y^2 + 12y) = \frac{1}{4}(0)$$
$$y^2 + 3y = 0$$
$$y^2 + 3y + \frac{9}{4} = 0 + \frac{9}{4}$$
$$\left(x + \frac{3}{2}\right)^2 = \frac{9}{4}$$
$$x + \frac{3}{2} = \pm\sqrt{\frac{9}{4}}$$
$$x + \frac{3}{2} = \pm\frac{3}{2}$$
$$x = \frac{3}{2} \pm \frac{3}{2}$$
$$y = \frac{3}{2} + \frac{3}{2} \quad \text{or} \quad y = \frac{3}{2} - \frac{3}{2}$$
$$y = 3 \qquad\qquad y = 0$$

69.
$$-\frac{3}{4}b^2 - \frac{1}{2}b = 0$$
$$-\frac{4}{3}\left(-\frac{3}{4}b^2 - \frac{1}{2}b\right) = -\frac{4}{3}(0)$$
$$b^2 + \frac{2}{3}b = 0$$
$$b^2 + \frac{2}{3}b + \frac{1}{9} = 0 + \frac{1}{9}$$
$$\left(b + \frac{1}{3}\right)^2 = \frac{1}{9}$$
$$b + \frac{1}{3} = \pm\sqrt{\frac{1}{9}}$$
$$b + \frac{1}{3} = \pm\frac{1}{3}$$
$$b = -\frac{1}{3} \pm \frac{1}{3}$$
$$b = -\frac{1}{3} + \frac{1}{3} \quad \text{or} \quad b = -\frac{1}{3} - \frac{1}{3}$$
$$b = 0 \qquad\qquad b = -\frac{2}{3}$$

70.
$$\frac{1}{3}a^2 - \frac{5}{3}a = 0$$
$$3\left(\frac{1}{3}a^2 - \frac{5}{3}a\right) = 3(0)$$
$$a^2 - 5a = 0$$
$$a^2 - 5a + \frac{25}{4} = 0 + \frac{25}{4}$$
$$\left(a - \frac{5}{2}\right)^2 = \frac{25}{4}$$
$$a - \frac{5}{2} = \pm\sqrt{\frac{25}{4}}$$
$$a - \frac{5}{2} = \pm\frac{5}{2}$$
$$a = \frac{5}{2} \pm \frac{5}{2}$$
$$a = \frac{5}{2} + \frac{5}{2} \quad \text{or} \quad a = \frac{5}{2} - \frac{5}{2}$$
$$a = 5 \qquad\qquad a = 0$$

71.
$$36z^2 - 6z = 0$$
$$\frac{1}{36}\left(36z^2 - 6z\right) = \frac{1}{36}(0)$$
$$z^2 - \frac{1}{6}z = 0$$
$$z^2 - \frac{1}{6}z + \frac{1}{144} = 0 + \frac{1}{144}$$
$$\left(z - \frac{1}{12}\right)^2 = \frac{1}{144}$$
$$z - \frac{1}{12} = \pm\sqrt{\frac{1}{144}}$$
$$z - \frac{1}{12} = \pm\frac{1}{12}$$
$$z = \frac{1}{12} \pm \frac{1}{12}$$
$$z = \frac{1}{12} + \frac{1}{12} \quad \text{or} \quad z = \frac{1}{12} - \frac{1}{12}$$
$$z = \frac{2}{12} \qquad\qquad z = 0$$
$$z = \frac{1}{6}$$

72.
$$x^2 = \frac{9}{2}x$$
$$x^2 - \frac{9}{2}x = 0$$
$$x^2 - \frac{9}{2}x + \frac{81}{16} = 0 + \frac{81}{16}$$
$$\left(x - \frac{9}{4}\right)^2 = \frac{81}{16}$$
$$x - \frac{9}{4} = \pm\sqrt{\frac{81}{16}}$$
$$x - \frac{9}{4} = \pm\frac{9}{4}$$
$$x = \frac{9}{4} \pm \frac{9}{4}$$
$$x = \frac{9}{4} + \frac{9}{4} \quad \text{or} \quad x = \frac{9}{4} - \frac{9}{4}$$
$$x = \frac{18}{4} \qquad\qquad x = 0$$
$$x = \frac{9}{2}$$

73.
$$-\frac{1}{2}p^2 - p + \frac{3}{2} = 0$$
$$-2\left(-\frac{1}{2}p^2 - p + \frac{3}{2}\right) = -2(0)$$
$$p^2 + 2p - 3 = 0$$
$$p^2 + 2p = 3$$
$$p^2 + 2p + 1 = 3 + 1$$
$$(p+1)^2 = 4$$
$$p + 1 = \pm\sqrt{4}$$
$$p + 1 = \pm 2$$
$$p = -1 \pm 2$$
$$p = -1 + 2 \quad \text{or} \quad p = -1 - 2$$
$$p = 1 \qquad\qquad p = -3$$

74.
$$2x^2 + 6x = 20$$
$$\frac{1}{2}\left(2x^2 + 6x\right) = \frac{1}{2}(20)$$
$$x^2 + 3x = 10$$
$$x^2 + 3x + \frac{9}{4} = 10 + \frac{9}{4}$$
$$\left(x + \frac{3}{2}\right)^2 = \frac{49}{4}$$
$$x + \frac{3}{2} = \pm\frac{7}{2}$$
$$x = -\frac{3}{2} \pm \frac{7}{2}$$
$$x = -\frac{3}{2} + \frac{7}{2} \quad \text{or} \quad x = -\frac{3}{2} - \frac{7}{2}$$
$$x = \frac{4}{2} \qquad\qquad x = -\frac{10}{2}$$
$$x = 2 \qquad\qquad x = -5$$

75.
$$2x^2 = 8x + 64$$
$$\frac{1}{2}\left(2x^2\right) = \frac{1}{2}(8x + 64)$$
$$x^2 = 4x + 32$$
$$x^2 - 4x = 32$$
$$x^2 - 4x + 4 = 32 + 4$$
$$(x - 2)^2 = 36$$
$$x - 2 = \pm\sqrt{36}$$
$$x - 2 = \pm 6$$
$$x = 2 \pm 6$$
$$x = 2 + 6 \quad \text{or} \quad x = 2 - 6$$
$$x = 8 \qquad \text{or} \quad x = -4$$

76. $3x^2 + 33x + 72 = 0$

$$\frac{1}{3}\left(3x^2 + 33x + 72\right) = \frac{1}{3}(0)$$

$$x^2 + 11x + 24 = 0$$

$$x^2 + 11x = -24$$

$$x^2 + 11x + \frac{121}{4} = -24 + \frac{121}{4}$$

$$\left(x + \frac{11}{2}\right)^2 = -\frac{96}{4} + \frac{121}{4}$$

$$\left(x - \frac{11}{2}\right)^2 = \frac{25}{4}$$

$$x + \frac{11}{2} = \pm\frac{5}{2}$$

$$x = -\frac{11}{2} \pm \frac{5}{2}$$

$$x = -\frac{11}{2} + \frac{5}{2} \quad \text{or} \quad x = -\frac{11}{2} - \frac{5}{2}$$

$$x = -\frac{6}{2} \quad \text{or} \quad x = -\frac{16}{2}$$

$$x = -3 \quad \text{or} \quad x = -8$$

77. $2x^2 + 18x + 4 = 0$

$$\frac{1}{2}\left(2x^2 + 18x + 4\right) = \frac{1}{2}(0)$$

$$x^2 + 9x + 2 = 0$$

$$x^2 + 9x = -2$$

$$x^2 + 9x + \frac{81}{4} = -2 + \frac{81}{4}$$

$$\left(x + \frac{9}{2}\right)^2 = -\frac{8}{4} + \frac{81}{4}$$

$$\left(x + \frac{9}{2}\right)^2 = \frac{73}{4}$$

$$x + \frac{9}{2} = \pm\frac{\sqrt{73}}{2}$$

$$x = -\frac{9}{2} \pm \frac{\sqrt{73}}{2}$$

$$x = \frac{-9 \pm \sqrt{73}}{2}$$

78. $\frac{2}{3}x^2 + \frac{4}{3}x + 1 = 0$

$$\frac{3}{2}\left(\frac{2}{3}x^2 + \frac{4}{3}x + 1\right) = 0$$

$$x^2 + 2x + \frac{3}{2} = 0$$

$$x^2 + 2x = -\frac{3}{2}$$

$$x^2 + 2x + 1 = -\frac{3}{2} + 1$$

$$\left(x + 1\right)^2 = -\frac{1}{2}$$

$$x + 1 = \pm\sqrt{-\frac{1}{2}}$$

$$x + 1 = \pm\frac{i\sqrt{2}}{2}$$

$$x = -1 \pm \frac{i\sqrt{2}}{2}$$

$$x = \frac{-2 \pm i\sqrt{2}}{2}$$

79. $\frac{3}{4}w^2 + \frac{1}{2}w - \frac{1}{4} = 0$

$$\frac{4}{3}\left(\frac{3}{4}w^2 + \frac{1}{2}w - \frac{1}{4}\right) = \frac{4}{3}(0)$$

$$w^2 + \frac{2}{3}w - \frac{1}{3} = 0$$

$$w^2 + \frac{2}{3}w = \frac{1}{3}$$

$$w^2 + \frac{2}{3}w + \frac{1}{9} = \frac{1}{3} + \frac{1}{9}$$

$$\left(w + \frac{1}{3}\right)^2 = \frac{4}{9}$$

$$w + \frac{1}{3} = \pm\sqrt{\frac{4}{9}}$$

$$w + \frac{1}{3} = \pm\frac{2}{3}$$

$$w = -\frac{1}{3} \pm \frac{2}{3}$$

$$w = -\frac{1}{3} + \frac{2}{3} \quad \text{or} \quad w = -\frac{1}{3} - \frac{2}{3}$$

$$w = \frac{1}{3} \qquad\qquad w = -1$$

80. $\dfrac{3}{4}c^2 - 2c + 1 = 0$

$$\dfrac{4}{3}\left(\dfrac{3}{4}c^2 - 2c + 1\right) = \dfrac{4}{3}(0)$$

$$c^2 - \dfrac{8}{3}c + \dfrac{4}{3} = 0$$

$$c^2 - \dfrac{8}{3}c = -\dfrac{4}{3}$$

$$c^2 - \dfrac{8}{3}c + \dfrac{16}{9} = -\dfrac{4}{3} + \dfrac{16}{9}$$

$$\left(c - \dfrac{4}{3}\right)^2 = \dfrac{4}{9}$$

$$c - \dfrac{4}{3} = \pm\sqrt{\dfrac{4}{9}}$$

$$c - \dfrac{4}{3} = \pm\dfrac{2}{3}$$

$$c = \dfrac{4}{3} \pm \dfrac{2}{3}$$

$$c = \dfrac{4}{3} + \dfrac{2}{3} \quad \text{or} \quad c = \dfrac{4}{3} - \dfrac{2}{3}$$

$$c = \dfrac{6}{3} \qquad\qquad c = \dfrac{2}{3}$$

$$c = 2$$

81. $2x^2 - x = -5$

$$\dfrac{1}{2}\left(2x^2 - x\right) = \dfrac{1}{2}(-5)$$

$$x^2 - \dfrac{1}{2}x = -\dfrac{5}{2}$$

$$x^2 - \dfrac{1}{2}x + \dfrac{1}{16} = -\dfrac{40}{16} + \dfrac{1}{16}$$

$$\left(x - \dfrac{1}{4}\right)^2 = -\dfrac{39}{16}$$

$$x - \dfrac{1}{4} = \pm\dfrac{i\sqrt{39}}{4}$$

$$x = \dfrac{1}{4} \pm \dfrac{i\sqrt{39}}{4}$$

$$x = \dfrac{1 \pm i\sqrt{39}}{4}$$

82. $\dfrac{5}{2}x^2 + \dfrac{3}{2}x - \dfrac{5}{4} = 0$

$$\dfrac{2}{5}\left(\dfrac{5}{2}x^2 + \dfrac{3}{2}x - \dfrac{5}{4}\right) = \dfrac{2}{5}(0)$$

$$x^2 + \dfrac{3}{5}x - \dfrac{1}{2} = 0$$

$$x^2 + \dfrac{3}{5}x = \dfrac{1}{2}$$

$$x^2 + \dfrac{3}{5}x + \dfrac{9}{100} = \dfrac{1}{2} + \dfrac{9}{100}$$

$$\left(x + \dfrac{3}{10}\right)^2 = \dfrac{59}{100}$$

$$x + \dfrac{3}{10} = \pm\dfrac{\sqrt{59}}{10}$$

$$x = -\dfrac{3}{10} \pm \dfrac{\sqrt{59}}{10}$$

$$x = \dfrac{-3 \pm \sqrt{59}}{10}$$

83. $-3x^2 + 6x = 6$

$$-\dfrac{1}{3}\left(-3x^2 + 6x\right) = -\dfrac{1}{3}(6)$$

$$x^2 - 2x = -2$$

$$x^2 - 2x + 1 = -2 + 1$$

$$(x - 1)^2 = -1$$

$$x - 1 = \pm\sqrt{-1}$$

$$x - 1 = \pm i$$

$$x = 1 \pm i$$

84. $x^2 + 2x = -5$

$$x^2 + 2x + 1 = -5 + 1$$

$$(x + 1)^2 = -4$$

$$x + 1 = \pm\sqrt{-4}$$

$$x + 1 = \pm 2i$$

$$x = -1 \pm 2i$$

85. a. $21 = (x + 2)(x - 2)$

   b. $21 = (x + 2)(x - 2)$

$$21 = x^2 - 2x + 2x - 4$$

$$0 = x^2 - 25$$

$$0 = (x + 5)(x - 5)$$

$$x + 5 = 0 \quad \text{or} \quad x - 5 = 0$$

$$x = -5 \qquad\qquad x = 5$$

Disregard the negative answer since x represents a distance. $x = 5$.

86. a. $35 = (x+5)(x+3)$

b. $35 = (x+5)(x+3)$
$35 = x^2 + 3x + 5x + 15$
$0 = x^2 + 8x - 20$
$0 = (x+10)(x-2)$
$x+10 = 0 \quad$ or $\quad x-2 = 0$
$x = -10 \qquad\qquad x = 2$

Disregard the negative answer since x represents a distance. $x = 2$.

87. a. $18 = (x+4)(x+2)$

b. $18 = (x+4)(x+2)$
$18 = x^2 + 2x + 4x + 8$
$0 = x^2 + 6x - 10$
$x^2 + 6x = 10$
$x^2 + 6x + 9 = 10 + 9$
$(x+3)^2 = 19$
$x+3 = \pm\sqrt{19}$
$x = -3 \pm \sqrt{19}$

Disregard the negative answer since x represents a distance. $x = -3 + \sqrt{19}$.

88. a. $23 = (x-1)(x-3)$

b. $23 = (x-1)(x-3)$
$23 = x^2 - 3x - x + 3$
$0 = x^2 - 4x - 20$
$x^2 - 4x = 20$
$x^2 - 4x + 4 = 20 + 4$
$(x-2)^2 = 24$
$x-2 = \pm\sqrt{24}$
$x-2 = \pm 2\sqrt{6}$
$x = 2 \pm 2\sqrt{6}$

Disregard the negative answer since x represents a distance. $x = 2 + 2\sqrt{6}$.

89. $d = \frac{1}{6}x^2$
$150 = \frac{1}{6}x^2$
$6 \cdot 150 = x^2$
$900 = x^2$
$x = \pm\sqrt{900} = \pm 30$

Disregard the negative answer since speed must be positive. The car's speed was about 30 mph.

90. $d = \frac{1}{10}x^2$
$40 = \frac{1}{10}x^2$
$10 \cdot 40 = x^2$
$400 = x^2$
$x = \pm\sqrt{400} = \pm 20$

Disregard the negative answer since speed must be positive. The car's speed was about 20 mph.

91. Let x be the first integer. Then $x + 2$ is the next consecutive odd integer.
$x(x+2) = 35$
$x^2 + 2x = 35$
$x^2 + 2x + 1 = 35 + 1$
$(x+1)^2 = 36$
$x+1 = \pm\sqrt{36}$
$x+1 = \pm 6$
$x = -1 \pm 6$
$x = -1 + 6 \quad$ or $\quad x = -1 - 6$
$x = 5 \qquad\qquad x = -7$

Since it was given that the integers are positive, one integer is 5 and the other is $5 + 2 = 7$.

92. Let x be the smaller number. Then $2x + 2$ is the larger number.
$x(2x+2) = 12$
$2x^2 + 2x = 12$
$x^2 + x = 6$
$x^2 + x + \frac{1}{4} = \frac{24}{4} + \frac{1}{4}$
$\left(x + \frac{1}{2}\right)^2 = \frac{25}{4}$
$x + \frac{1}{2} = \pm\frac{5}{2}$
$x = \pm\frac{5}{2} - \frac{1}{2}$
$x = \frac{5}{2} - \frac{1}{2} \quad$ or $\quad x = -\frac{5}{2} - \frac{1}{2}$
$x = 2 \qquad\qquad x = -3$

If $x = 2$, then $2x + 2 = 2(2) + 2 = 6$ and
$2 \cdot 6 = 12$
If $x = -3$ then $2x + 2 = 2(-3) + 2 = -4$ but
$-4 < -3$ so we discard this solution. Therefore, the numbers are 2 and 6.

93. Let x be the width of the rectangle. Then $2x + 2$ is the length. Use length $\cdot$ width = area.

$$(2x + 2)x = 60$$

$$2x^2 + 2x = 60$$

$$x^2 + x = 30$$

$$x^2 + x + \frac{1}{4} = 30 + \frac{1}{4}$$

$$\left(x + \frac{1}{2}\right)^2 = \frac{120}{4} + \frac{1}{4}$$

$$\left(x + \frac{1}{2}\right)^2 = \frac{121}{4}$$

$$x + \frac{1}{2} = \pm\sqrt{\frac{121}{4}}$$

$$x + \frac{1}{2} = \pm\frac{11}{2}$$

$$x = -\frac{1}{2} \pm \frac{11}{2}$$

$$x = -\frac{1}{2} + \frac{11}{2} \quad \text{or} \quad x = -\frac{1}{2} - \frac{11}{2}$$

$$x = \frac{10}{2} \qquad\qquad x = -\frac{12}{2}$$

$$x = 5 \qquad\qquad x = -6$$

Since the width cannot be negative, the width is 5 ft.
Length $= 2(5) + 2 = 10 + 2 = 12$ ft.
The rectangle is 5 ft by 12 ft.

94. Let w be the width of the rectangle. Then $w + 18$ is the length (l). Use $A = lw$ to obtain

$$381.25 = (w + 18)w$$

$$381.25 = w^2 + 18w$$

$$381.25 + 81 = w^2 + 18w + 81$$

$$462.25 = (w + 9)^2$$

$$w + 9 = \pm\sqrt{462.25}$$

$$w + 9 = \pm 21.5$$

$$w = -9 + 21.5 \quad \text{or} \quad w = -9 - 21.5$$

$$w = 12.5 \qquad\qquad w = -30.5$$

Length is never negative. Thus, the width is 12.5 feet and the length is 12.5 + 18 = 30.5 feet.

95. Let s be the length of the side. Then $s + 6$ is the length of the diagonal (d). Use $s^2 + s^2 = d^2$.

$$2s^2 = (s + 6)^2$$

$$2s^2 = s^2 + 12s + 36$$

$$s^2 = 12s + 36$$

$$s^2 - 12s = 36$$

$$s^2 - 12s + 36 = 36 + 36$$

$$(s - 6)^2 = 72$$

$$s - 6 = \pm\sqrt{72}$$

$$s - 6 = \pm 6\sqrt{2}$$

$$s = 6 \pm 6\sqrt{2}$$

Length is never negative. Thus,
$s = 6 + 6\sqrt{2} \approx 14.49$.
The patio is about 14.49 ft by 14.49 ft.

96. Let s be the length of the side. Then $s + 7$ is the length of the diagonal (d). Use $s^2 + s^2 = d^2$.

$$2s^2 = (s + 7)^2$$

$$2s^2 = s^2 + 14s + 49$$

$$s^2 - 14s = 49$$

$$s^2 - 14s + 49 = 49 + 49$$

$$(s - 7)^2 = 98$$

$$s - 7 = \pm\sqrt{98}$$

$$s - 7 = \pm 7\sqrt{2}$$

$$s = 7 \pm 7\sqrt{2}$$

Length is never negative. Thus,
$s = 7 + 7\sqrt{2} \approx 16.90$.
The pool is about 16.90 ft by 16.90 ft.

97. Since the radius is 10 inches, the diameter (d) is 20 inches. Use the formula $s^2 + s^2 = d^2$ to find the length (s) of the other two sides.

$$s^2 + s^2 = d^2$$

$$2s^2 = 20^2$$

$$2s^2 = 400$$

$$s^2 = 200$$

$$s = \pm\sqrt{200} = \pm 10\sqrt{2}$$

Length is never negative.
Thus, $s = 10\sqrt{2} \approx 14.14$ inches.

98. Let x be the length of the third side.
$$x^2 + 6^2 = 12^2$$
$$x^2 + 36 = 144$$
$$x^2 = 108$$
$$x = \pm\sqrt{108} = \pm6\sqrt{3}$$
Length is never negative.
Thus, $x = 6\sqrt{3} \approx 10.39$ meters.

99. $A = \pi r^2$
$$24\pi = \pi r^2$$
$$24 = r^2$$
$$r = \pm\sqrt{24} = \pm2\sqrt{6}$$
Length is never negative.
Thus, $r = 2\sqrt{6} \approx 4.90$ feet .

100. $A = \pi r^2$
$$16.4\pi = \pi r^2$$
$$16.4 = r^2$$
$$r = \pm\sqrt{16.4}$$
Length is never negative.
Thus $r = \sqrt{16.4} \approx 4.05$ meters.

101. $A = P\left(1+\dfrac{r}{n}\right)^{nt}$
$$540.80 = 500\left(1+\frac{r}{1}\right)^{1(2)}$$
$$540.80 = 500\left(1+r\right)^2$$
$$1.0816 = \left(1+r\right)^2$$
$$1+r = \pm\sqrt{1.0816}$$
$$1+r = \pm1.04$$
$$r = -1\pm1.04$$
$$r = -1+1.04 \quad \text{or} \quad r = -1-1.04$$
$$r = 0.04 \qquad \text{or} \quad r = -2.04$$
An interest rate is never negative. Thus $r = 0.04 = 4\%$.

102. $A = P\left(1+\dfrac{r}{n}\right)^{nt}$
$$1102.50 = 1000\left(1+\frac{r}{1}\right)^{1(2)}$$
$$1102.50 = 1000(1+r)^2$$
$$1.1025 = (1+r)^2$$
$$1+r = \pm\sqrt{1.1025}$$
$$1+r = \pm1.05$$
$$r = -1\pm1.05$$
$$r = -1+1.05 \quad \text{or} \quad r = -1-1.05$$
$$r = 0.05 \qquad \text{or} \quad r = -2.05$$
An interest rate is never negative. Thus $r = 0.05 = 5\%$.

103. $A = P\left(1+\dfrac{r}{n}\right)^{nt}$
$$1432.86 = 1200\left(1+\frac{r}{2}\right)^{2(3)}$$
$$1432.86 = 1200\left(1+\frac{r}{2}\right)^6$$
$$1.19405 = \left(1+\frac{r}{2}\right)^6$$
$$1+\frac{r}{2} \approx \pm1.03$$
$$\frac{r}{2} \approx -1\pm1.03$$
$$r \approx -2\pm2.06$$
$$r \approx -2+2.06 \quad \text{or} \quad r \approx -2-2.06$$
$$r \approx 0.06 \qquad \text{or} \quad r \approx -4.06$$
An interest rate is never negative. Thus, Steve Rodi's annual interest rate is about 6%.

104. $A = P\left(1+\dfrac{r}{n}\right)^{nt}$
$$2052.85 = 1500\left(1+\frac{r}{2}\right)^{2(4)}$$
$$2052.85 = 1500\left(1+\frac{r}{2}\right)^8$$
$$1.3685666 \approx \left(1+\frac{r}{2}\right)^8$$
$$1+\frac{r}{2} \approx \pm1.04$$
$$r \approx -2\pm2.08$$
$$r \approx -2+2.08 \quad \text{or} \quad r \approx -2-2.08$$
$$r \approx 0.08 \qquad \text{or} \quad r \approx -4.08$$
An interest rate is never negative. Thus, the annual interest rate is about 8%.

105. a. To find the surface area, we must first determine the radius. Use $V = \pi r^2 h$ with $V = 160$ and $h = 10$ to get

$$160 = \pi r^2 (10)$$

$$16 = \pi r^2$$

$$\frac{16}{\pi} = r^2$$

$$r = \pm \frac{4}{\sqrt{\pi}}$$

The length cannot be negative, so $r = \dfrac{4}{\sqrt{\pi}}$.

Use the formula $S = 2\pi r^2 + 2\pi rh$ to calculate the surface area.

$$S = 2\pi \left(\frac{4}{\sqrt{\pi}} \right)^2 + 2\pi \left(\frac{4}{\sqrt{\pi}} \right)(10)$$

$$= 2\pi \left(\frac{16}{\pi} \right) + \frac{80\pi}{\sqrt{\pi}}$$

$$= 32 + 80\sqrt{\pi} \approx 173.80$$

The surface area is about 173.80 square inches.

b. Use $V = \pi r^2 h$ with $V = 160$ and $h = 10$ to obtain $160 = \pi r^2 (10)$. In part (a) this was solved for r to get

$$r = \frac{4}{\sqrt{\pi}} = \frac{4}{\sqrt{\pi}} \cdot \frac{\sqrt{\pi}}{\sqrt{\pi}} = \frac{4\sqrt{\pi}}{\pi} \approx 2.26$$

The radius is about 2.26 inches.

c. Use $S = 2\pi r^2 + 2\pi rh$ with $S = 160$ and $h = 10$.

$$160 = 2\pi r^2 + 2\pi r(10)$$

$$160 = 2\pi r^2 + 20\pi r$$

$$\frac{160}{2\pi} = \frac{2\pi r^2}{2\pi} + \frac{20\pi r}{2\pi}$$

$$\frac{80}{\pi} = r^2 + 10r$$

$$\frac{80}{\pi} + 25 = r^2 + 10r + 25$$

$$\frac{80 + 25\pi}{\pi} = (r+5)^2$$

$$r + 5 = \pm\sqrt{\frac{80 + 25\pi}{\pi}}$$

$$r = -5 \pm \sqrt{\frac{80 + 25\pi}{\pi}}$$

The radius is never negative so $r \approx 2.1$ in.

106. a. Answers will vary. One possibility is that the point must be this so that a right triangle will be formed.

b. $y_2 - y_1$

c. $x_2 - x_1$

d. $d^2 = (x_2 - x_1)^2 + (y_2 - y_1)^2$

$$d = \pm\sqrt{(x_2 - x_1)^2 + (y_2 - y_1)^2}$$

The distance must be positive, so

$$d = \sqrt{(x_2 - x_1)^2 + (y_2 - y_1)^2}$$

e. Let $(x_1, y_1) = (1, 4)$ and $(x_2, y_2) = (3, 7)$.

Then $d = \sqrt{(x_2 - x_1)^2 + (y_2 - y_1)^2}$

$$= \sqrt{(3-1)^2 + (7-4)^2}$$

$$= \sqrt{(2)^2 + (3)^2}$$

$$= \sqrt{4 + 9}$$

$$= \sqrt{13}$$

107. $-4(2z - 6) = -3(z - 4) + z$

$$-8z + 24 = -3z + 12 + z$$

$$-8z + 24 = -2z + 12$$

$$-6z = -12$$

$$z = 2$$

108. Let $x =$ the amount invested at 7%. Then the amount invested at $6\frac{1}{4}\%$ will be $10,000 - x$.

The interest earned at 7% will be $0.07x$. and the amount of interest earned at 6.25% will be $.0625(10,000 - x)$. The total interest earned is $656.50.

$$0.07x + 0.0625(10,000 - x) = 656.50$$

$$0.07x + 625 - 0.0625x = 656.50$$

$$0.0075x = 31.5$$

$$x = 4200$$

Thus, $4200 was invested at 7% and $10,000 - \$4200 = \$5800$ was invested at $6\frac{1}{4}\%$

109. $m = \dfrac{y_2 - y_1}{x_2 - x_1} = \dfrac{5-5}{0-(-2)} = \dfrac{0}{0+2} = \dfrac{0}{2} = 0$

110.
$$
\begin{array}{r}
4x^2 + 9x - 3 \\
x - 2 \\
\hline
-8x^2 - 18x + 6 \\
4x^3 + 9x^2 - 3x \\
\hline
4x^3 + x^2 - 21x + 6
\end{array}
$$

111. $|x+3| = |2x-7|$

$x + 3 = 2x - 7 \quad$ or $\quad x + 3 = -(2x - 7)$

$\quad -x = -10 \qquad\qquad x + 3 = -2x + 7$

$\qquad x = 10 \qquad\qquad\quad 3x = 4$

$\qquad\qquad\qquad\qquad\qquad x = \dfrac{4}{3}$

Exercise Set 12.2

1. For a quadratic equation in standard form, $ax^2 + bx + c = 0$, the quadratic formula is

$$x = \frac{-b \pm \sqrt{b^2 - 4ac}}{2a}.$$

2. $3x + 2x^2 - 9 = 0$

$2x^2 + 3x - 9 = 0$

$a = 2$, $b = 3$, and $c = -9$

3. $6x - 3x^2 + 8 = 0$

$-3x^2 + 6x + 8 = 0$

$a = -3$, $b = 6$, and $c = 8$

4. $4x^2 - 5x = 7$

$4x^2 - 5x - 7 = 0$

$a = 4$, $b = -5$, and $c = -7$

5. Yes, multiply both sides of the equation

$-6x^2 + \dfrac{1}{2}x - 5 = 0$ by -1 to obtain

$6x^2 - \dfrac{1}{2}x + 5 = 0$. The equations are equivalent

so they will have the same solutions.

6. a. Yes, the solutions will be the same since
since $12x^2 - 15x - 6 = 3(4x^2 - 5x - 2)$.

    b. $12x^2 - 15x - 6 = 0$. Use the quadratic

formula, $x = \dfrac{-b \pm \sqrt{b^2 - 4ac}}{2a}$, with

$a = 12$, $b = -15$, and $c = -6$.

$$x = \frac{15 \pm \sqrt{(-15)^2 - 4(12)(-6)}}{2(12)}$$

$$= \frac{15 \pm \sqrt{225 + 288}}{24}$$

$$= \frac{15 \pm \sqrt{513}}{24}$$

$$= \frac{15 \pm 3\sqrt{57}}{24}$$

$$= \frac{5 \pm \sqrt{57}}{8}$$

The solutions are $\dfrac{5 + \sqrt{57}}{8}$ and $\dfrac{5 - \sqrt{57}}{8}$.

    c. $3(4x^2 - 5x - 2) = 0$

$4x^2 - 5x - 2 = 0$

Use the quadratic formula,

$$x = \frac{-b \pm \sqrt{b^2 - 4ac}}{2a},$$

with $a = 4$, $b = -5$ and $c = -2$.

$$x = \frac{5 \pm \sqrt{(-5)^2 - 4(4)(-2)}}{2(4)}$$

$$= \frac{5 \pm \sqrt{25 + 32}}{8}$$

$$= \frac{5 \pm \sqrt{57}}{8}$$

The solutions are $\dfrac{5 + \sqrt{57}}{8}$ and $\dfrac{5 - \sqrt{57}}{8}$.

7. a. For a quadratic equation in standard form, $ax^2 + bx + c = 0$, the discriminant is the expression under the square root symbol in the quadratic formula, $b^2 - 4ac$.

    b. $3x^2 - 6x + 10 = 0$, $a = 3$, $b = -6$, and $c = 10$.

$b^2 - 4ac = (-6)^2 - 4(3)(10) = 36 - 120 = -84$

    c. If $b^2 - 4ac > 0$, then the quadratic equation will have two distinct real solutions. Since there is a positive number under the radical sign in the quadratic formula, the value of the radical will be real and there will be two real solutions. If $b^2 - 4ac = 0$, then the equation has the single real solution $\dfrac{-b}{2a}$. If $b^2 - 4ac < 0$, then the expression under the radical sign in the quadratic formula is negative. Thus, the equation will have no real solution.

8. The x-intercepts of a quadratic function, $f(x) = ax^2 + bx + c$, occur where $f(x) = 0$. If $b^2 - 4ac > 0$, there are two real solutions to the equation $f(x) = 0$. Thus the graph has two x-intercepts. If $b^2 - 4ac = 0$, there is one real solution to the equation $f(x) = 0$. Thus the graph has one x-intercept. If $b^2 - 4ac < 0$, there is no real solution to the equation $f(x) = 0$. The graph will have no x-intercept.

9. $x^2 + 3x + 1 = 0$
$$b^2 - 4ac = (3)^2 - 4(1)(1)$$
$$= 9 - 4$$
$$= 5$$
Since $5 > 0$, there are two real solutions.

10. $2x^2 + x + 3 = 0$
$$b^2 - 4ac = (1)^2 - 4(2)(3)$$
$$= 1 - 24$$
$$= -23$$
Since $-23 < 0$, there is no real solution.

11. $4z^2 + 6z + 5 = 0$
$$b^2 - 4ac = 6^2 - 4(4)(5)$$
$$= 36 - 80$$
$$= -44$$
Since $-44 < 0$, there is no real solution.

12. $-a^2 + 3a - 6 = 0$
$$b^2 - 4ac = 3^2 - 4(-1)(-6)$$
$$= 9 - 24$$
$$= -15$$
Since $-15 < 0$, there is no real solution.

13. $5p^2 + 3p - 7 = 0$
$$b^2 - 4ac = 3^2 - 4(5)(-7)$$
$$= 9 + 140$$
$$= 149$$
Since $149 > 0$, there are two real solutions.

14. $2x^2 = 16x - 32$
$$2x^2 - 16x + 32 = 0$$
$$b^2 - 4ac = (-16)^2 - 4(2)(32)$$
$$= 256 - 256$$
$$= 0$$
Since the discriminant is 0, there is one real solution.

15. $-5x^2 + 5x - 8 = 0$
$$b^2 - 4ac = 5^2 - 4(-5)(-8)$$
$$= 25 - 160$$
$$= -135$$
Since $-135 < 0$, there is no real solution.

16. $4.1x^2 - 3.1x - 2.8 = 0$
$$b^2 - 4ac = (-3.1)^2 - 4(4.1)(-2.8)$$
$$= 9.61 + 45.92$$
$$= 55.53$$
Since $55.53 > 0$ there are two real solutions.

17. $x^2 + 10.2x + 26.01 = 0$
$$b^2 - 4ac = (10.2)^2 - 4(1)(26.01)$$
$$= 104.04 - 104.04$$
$$= 0$$
Since the discriminant is 0, there is one real solution.

18. $\dfrac{1}{2}x^2 + \dfrac{2}{3}x + 10 = 0$
$$b^2 - 4ac = \left(\frac{2}{3}\right)^2 - 4\left(\frac{1}{2}\right)(10) = \frac{4}{9} - 20 = -\frac{176}{9}$$
Since $-\dfrac{176}{9} < 0$, there is no real solution.

19. $b^2 = -3b - \dfrac{9}{4}$
$$b^2 + 3b + \frac{9}{4} = 0$$
$$b^2 - 4ac = 3^2 - 4(1)\left(\frac{9}{4}\right) = 9 - 9 = 0$$
Since the discriminant is 0, there is one real solution.

20. $\dfrac{x^2}{3} = \dfrac{2x}{7}$
$$7x^2 = 6x$$
$$7x^2 - 6x = 0$$
$$b^2 - 4ac = (-6)^2 - 4(7)(0) = 36 - 0 = 36$$
Since $36 > 0$ there are two real solutions.

21. $x^2 - 9x + 18 = 0$

$$x = \frac{-(-9) \pm \sqrt{(-9)^2 - 4(1)(18)}}{2(1)}$$

$$= \frac{9 \pm \sqrt{81 - 72}}{2}$$

$$= \frac{9 \pm \sqrt{9}}{2}$$

$$= \frac{9 \pm 3}{2}$$

$$x = \frac{9+3}{2} \quad \text{or} \quad x = \frac{9-3}{2}$$

$$= \frac{12}{2} \qquad\qquad = \frac{6}{2}$$

$$= 6 \qquad\qquad\quad = 3$$

The solutions are 6 and 3.

22. $x^2 + 9x + 18 = 0$

$$x = \frac{-9 \pm \sqrt{9^2 - 4(1)(18)}}{2(1)}$$

$$= \frac{-9 \pm \sqrt{81 - 72}}{2}$$

$$= \frac{-9 \pm \sqrt{9}}{2}$$

$$= \frac{-9 \pm 3}{2}$$

$$x = \frac{-9+3}{2} \quad \text{or} \quad x = \frac{-9-3}{2}$$

$$= \frac{-6}{2} \qquad\qquad = \frac{-12}{2}$$

$$= -3 \qquad\qquad = -6$$

The solutions are −6 and −3.

23. $a^2 - 6a + 8 = 0$

$$a = \frac{-b \pm \sqrt{b^2 - 4ac}}{2a}$$

$$= \frac{6 \pm \sqrt{(-6)^2 - 4(1)(8)}}{2(1)}$$

$$= \frac{6 \pm \sqrt{36 - 32}}{2}$$

$$= \frac{6 \pm \sqrt{4}}{2}$$

$$= \frac{6 \pm 2}{2}$$

$$a = \frac{6-2}{2} \quad \text{or} \quad a = \frac{6+2}{2}$$

$$= \frac{4}{2} \qquad\qquad = \frac{8}{2}$$

$$= 2 \qquad\qquad = 4$$

The solutions are 2 and 4.

24. $a^2 + 6a + 8 = 0$

$$a = \frac{-b \pm \sqrt{b^2 - 4ac}}{2a}$$

$$= \frac{-6 \pm \sqrt{6^2 - 4(1)(8)}}{2(1)}$$

$$= \frac{-6 \pm \sqrt{36 - 32}}{2}$$

$$= \frac{-6 \pm \sqrt{4}}{2}$$

$$= \frac{-6 \pm 2}{2}$$

$$a = \frac{-6+2}{2} \quad \text{or} \quad a = \frac{-6-2}{2}$$

$$= \frac{-4}{2} \qquad\qquad = \frac{-8}{2}$$

$$= -2 \qquad\qquad = -4$$

The solutions are −2 and −4.

25. $$x^2 = -6x + 7$$

$$x^2 + 6x - 7 = 0$$

$$x = \frac{-6 \pm \sqrt{6^2 - 4(1)(-7)}}{2(1)}$$

$$= \frac{-6 \pm \sqrt{36 + 28}}{2}$$

$$= \frac{-6 \pm \sqrt{64}}{2}$$

$$= \frac{-6 \pm 8}{2}$$

$$x = \frac{-6+8}{2} \quad \text{or} \quad x = \frac{-6-8}{2}$$

$$= \frac{2}{2} \qquad\qquad = \frac{-14}{2}$$

$$= 1 \qquad\qquad = -7$$

The solutions are 1 and −7.

26. $-a^2 - 9a + 10 = 0$

$-1(-a^2 - 9a + 10) = -1(0)$

$a^2 + 9a - 10 = 0$

$a = \dfrac{-9 \pm \sqrt{9^2 - 4(1)(-10)}}{2(1)}$

$= \dfrac{-9 \pm \sqrt{81 + 40}}{2}$

$= \dfrac{-9 \pm \sqrt{121}}{2}$

$= \dfrac{-9 \pm 11}{2}$

$a = \dfrac{-9 + 11}{2}$ or $a = \dfrac{-9 - 11}{2}$

$= \dfrac{2}{2}$ $= \dfrac{-20}{2}$

$= 1$ $= -10$

The solutions are 1 and -10.

27. $-b^2 = 4b - 20$

$b^2 + 4b - 20 = 0$

$b = \dfrac{-4 \pm \sqrt{(4)^2 - 4(1)(-20)}}{2(1)}$

$= \dfrac{-4 \pm \sqrt{16 + 80}}{2}$

$= \dfrac{-4 \pm \sqrt{96}}{2}$

$= \dfrac{-4 \pm 4\sqrt{6}}{2}$

$= -2 \pm \sqrt{6}$

The solutions are $-2 + 2\sqrt{6}$ and $-2 - 2\sqrt{6}$.

28. $a^2 - 16 = 0$

$a = \dfrac{0 \pm \sqrt{0^2 - 4(1)(-16)}}{2(1)}$

$= \dfrac{\pm\sqrt{64}}{2}$

$= \pm\dfrac{8}{2}$

$= \pm 4$

The solutions are 4 and -4.

29. $b^2 - 64 = 0$

$b = \dfrac{0 \pm \sqrt{0^2 - 4(1)(-64)}}{2(1)}$

$= \dfrac{\pm\sqrt{256}}{2}$

$= \dfrac{\pm 16}{2}$

$= \pm 8$

The solutions are 8 and -8.

30. $2x^2 = 4x + 1$

$2x^2 - 4x - 1 = 0$

$x = \dfrac{-(-4) \pm \sqrt{(-4)^2 - 4(2)(-1)}}{2(2)}$

$= \dfrac{4 \pm \sqrt{16 + 8}}{4}$

$= \dfrac{4 \pm \sqrt{24}}{4}$

$= \dfrac{4 \pm 2\sqrt{6}}{4}$

$= \dfrac{2 \pm \sqrt{6}}{2}$

The solutions are $\dfrac{2 + \sqrt{6}}{2}$ and $\dfrac{2 - \sqrt{6}}{2}$.

31. $3w^2 - 4w + 5 = 0$

$w = \dfrac{-(-4) \pm \sqrt{(-4)^2 - 4(3)(5)}}{2(3)}$

$= \dfrac{4 \pm \sqrt{16 - 60}}{6}$

$= \dfrac{4 \pm \sqrt{-44}}{6}$

$= \dfrac{4 \pm 2i\sqrt{11}}{6}$

$= \dfrac{2\left(2 \pm i\sqrt{11}\right)}{6}$

$= \dfrac{2 \pm i\sqrt{11}}{3}$

The solutions are $\dfrac{2 - i\sqrt{11}}{3}$ and $\dfrac{2 + i\sqrt{11}}{3}$.

32. $x^2 - 6x = 0$

$$x = \frac{-(-6) \pm \sqrt{(-6)^2 - 4(1)(0)}}{2(1)}$$

$$= \frac{6 \pm \sqrt{36}}{2}$$

$$= \frac{6 \pm 6}{2}$$

$$x = \frac{6+6}{2} \quad \text{or} \quad x = \frac{6-6}{2}$$

$$= \frac{12}{2} \qquad\qquad = \frac{0}{2}$$

$$= 6 \qquad\qquad\quad = 0$$

The solutions are 6 and 0.

33. $c^2 - 5c = 0$

$$c = \frac{-(-5) \pm \sqrt{(-5)^2 - 4(1)(0)}}{2(1)}$$

$$= \frac{5 \pm \sqrt{25}}{2}$$

$$= \frac{5 \pm 5}{2}$$

$$c = \frac{5+5}{2} \quad \text{or} \quad c = \frac{5-5}{2}$$

$$= \frac{10}{2} \qquad\qquad = \frac{0}{2}$$

$$= 5 \qquad\qquad\quad = 0$$

The solutions are 5 and 0.

34. $-t^2 - t - 1 = 0$

$$-1(-t^2 - t - 1) = -1(0)$$

$$t^2 + t + 1 = 0$$

$$t = \frac{-1 \pm \sqrt{(1)^2 - 4(1)(1)}}{2(1)}$$

$$= \frac{-1 \pm \sqrt{1-4}}{2}$$

$$= \frac{-1 \pm \sqrt{-3}}{2}$$

$$= \frac{-1 \pm i\sqrt{3}}{2}$$

The solutions are $\dfrac{-1 + i\sqrt{3}}{2}$ and $\dfrac{-1 - i\sqrt{3}}{2}$.

35. $4s^2 - 8s + 6 = 0$

$$\frac{1}{2}(4s^2 - 8s + 6) = 0$$

$$2s^2 - 4s + 3 = 0$$

$$s = \frac{-(-4) \pm \sqrt{(-4)^2 - 4(2)(3)}}{2(2)}$$

$$= \frac{4 \pm \sqrt{16 - 24}}{4}$$

$$= \frac{4 \pm \sqrt{-8}}{4}$$

$$= \frac{4 \pm 2i\sqrt{2}}{4}$$

$$= \frac{2 \pm i\sqrt{2}}{2}$$

The solutions are $\dfrac{2 - i\sqrt{2}}{2}$ and $\dfrac{2 + i\sqrt{2}}{2}$.

36. $-3r^2 = 9r + 6$

$$-\frac{1}{3}(-3r^2) = -\frac{1}{3}(9r + 6)$$

$$r^2 = -3r - 2$$

$$r^2 + 3r + 2 = 0$$

$$r = \frac{-3 \pm \sqrt{3^2 - 4(1)(2)}}{2(1)}$$

$$= \frac{-3 \pm \sqrt{9 - 8}}{2}$$

$$= \frac{-3 \pm 1}{2}$$

$$r = \frac{-2}{2} \quad \text{or} \quad r = \frac{-4}{2}$$

$$= -1 \qquad\qquad = -2$$

The solutions are −1 and −2.

37. $a^2 + 2a + 1 = 0$

$$a = \frac{-2 \pm \sqrt{2^2 - 4(1)(1)}}{2(1)}$$

$$= \frac{-2 \pm \sqrt{4 - 4}}{2}$$

$$= \frac{-2 \pm \sqrt{0}}{2}$$

$$= \frac{-2}{2}$$

$$= -1$$

The solution is −1.

38. $y^2 + 16y + 64 = 0$

$$y = \frac{-16 \pm \sqrt{16^2 - 4(1)(64)}}{2(1)}$$

$$= \frac{-16 \pm \sqrt{256 - 256}}{2}$$

$$= \frac{-16 \pm \sqrt{0}}{2}$$

$$= \frac{-16}{2}$$

$$= -8$$

The solution is –3.

39. $16x^2 - 8x + 1 = 0$

$$x = \frac{-(-8) \pm \sqrt{(-8)^2 - 4(16)(1)}}{2(16)}$$

$$= \frac{8 \pm \sqrt{64 - 64}}{32}$$

$$= \frac{8 \pm \sqrt{0}}{32}$$

$$= \frac{8}{32}$$

$$= \frac{1}{4}$$

The solution is $\frac{1}{4}$.

40. $100m^2 + 20m + 1 = 0$

$$m = \frac{-20 \pm \sqrt{20^2 - 4(100)(1)}}{2(100)}$$

$$= \frac{-20 \pm \sqrt{400 - 400}}{200}$$

$$= \frac{-20 \pm \sqrt{0}}{200}$$

$$= \frac{-20}{200}$$

$$= -\frac{1}{10}$$

The solution is $-\frac{1}{10}$.

41. $x^2 - 2x - 1 = 0$

$$x = \frac{-(-2) \pm \sqrt{(-2)^2 - 4(1)(-1)}}{2(1)}$$

$$= \frac{2 \pm \sqrt{4 + 4}}{2}$$

$$= \frac{2 \pm \sqrt{8}}{2}$$

$$= \frac{2 \pm 2\sqrt{2}}{2}$$

$$= 1 \pm \sqrt{2}$$

The solutions are $1 - \sqrt{2}$ and $1 + \sqrt{2}$.

42. $2 - 3r^2 = -4r$

$$0 = 3r^2 - 4r - 2$$

$$r = \frac{-(-4) \pm \sqrt{(-4)^2 - 4(3)(-2)}}{2(3)}$$

$$= \frac{4 \pm \sqrt{16 + 24}}{6}$$

$$= \frac{4 \pm \sqrt{40}}{6}$$

$$= \frac{4 \pm 2\sqrt{10}}{6}$$

$$= \frac{2 \pm \sqrt{10}}{3}$$

The solutions are $\frac{2 + \sqrt{10}}{3}$ and $\frac{2 - \sqrt{10}}{3}$.

43. $-n^2 = 3n + 6$

$$0 = n^2 + 3n + 6$$

$$n = \frac{-3 \pm \sqrt{3^2 - 4(1)(6)}}{2(1)}$$

$$= \frac{-3 \pm \sqrt{9 - 24}}{2}$$

$$= \frac{-3 \pm \sqrt{-15}}{2}$$

$$= \frac{-3 \pm i\sqrt{15}}{2}$$

The solutions are $\frac{-3 + i\sqrt{15}}{2}$ and $\frac{-3 - i\sqrt{15}}{2}$.

44. $-9d - 3d^2 = 5$

$$0 = 3d^2 + 9d + 5$$

$$d = \frac{-9 \pm \sqrt{9^2 - 4(3)(5)}}{2(3)}$$

$$= \frac{-9 \pm \sqrt{81 - 60}}{6}$$

$$= \frac{-9 \pm \sqrt{21}}{6}$$

The solutions are $\dfrac{-9 + \sqrt{21}}{6}$ and $\dfrac{-9 - \sqrt{21}}{6}$.

45. $2x^2 + 5x - 3 = 0$

$$x = \frac{-5 \pm \sqrt{5^2 - 4(2)(-3)}}{2(2)}$$

$$= \frac{-5 \pm \sqrt{25 + 24}}{4}$$

$$= \frac{-5 \pm \sqrt{49}}{4}$$

$$= \frac{-5 \pm 7}{4}$$

$$x = \frac{-5 + 7}{4} \quad \text{or} \quad x = \frac{-5 - 7}{4}$$

$$= \frac{2}{4} \qquad\qquad = \frac{-12}{4}$$

$$= \frac{1}{2} \qquad\qquad = -3$$

The solutions are $\dfrac{1}{2}$ and -3.

46. $(r - 3)(3r + 4) = -10$

$$3r^2 - 5r - 12 = -10$$

$$3r^2 - 5r - 2 = 0$$

$$r = \frac{-(-5) \pm \sqrt{(-5)^2 - 4(3)(-2)}}{2(3)}$$

$$= \frac{5 \pm \sqrt{25 + 24}}{6}$$

$$= \frac{5 \pm \sqrt{49}}{6}$$

$$r = \frac{5 + 7}{6} \quad \text{or} \quad r = \frac{5 - 7}{6}$$

$$= \frac{12}{6} \qquad\qquad = \frac{-2}{6}$$

$$= 2 \qquad\qquad = -\frac{1}{3}$$

The solutions are 2 and $-\dfrac{1}{3}$.

47. $(2a + 3)(3a - 1) = 2$

$$6a^2 + 7a - 3 = 2$$

$$6a^2 + 7a - 5 = 0$$

$$a = \frac{-(7) \pm \sqrt{(7)^2 - 4(6)(-5)}}{2(6)}$$

$$= \frac{-7 \pm \sqrt{49 + 120}}{12}$$

$$= \frac{-7 \pm \sqrt{169}}{12}$$

$$= \frac{-7 \pm 13}{12}$$

$$a = \frac{-7 + 13}{12} \quad \text{or} \quad a = \frac{-7 - 13}{12}$$

$$= \frac{6}{12} \qquad\qquad = \frac{-20}{12}$$

$$= \frac{1}{2} \qquad\qquad = -\frac{5}{3}$$

The solutions are $\dfrac{1}{2}$ and $-\dfrac{5}{3}$.

48.

$$6x^2 = 21x + 27$$

$$6x^2 - 21x - 27 = 0$$

$$\frac{1}{3}\left(6x^2 - 21x - 27\right) = \frac{1}{3}(0)$$

$$2x^2 - 7x - 9 = 0$$

$$x = \frac{-(-7) \pm \sqrt{(-7^2) - 4(2)(-9)}}{2(2)}$$

$$= \frac{7 \pm \sqrt{49 + 72}}{4}$$

$$= \frac{7 \pm \sqrt{121}}{4}$$

$$= \frac{7 \pm 11}{4}$$

$$x = \frac{7 + 11}{4} \quad \text{or} \quad x = \frac{7 - 11}{4}$$

$$= \frac{18}{4} \qquad\qquad = \frac{-4}{4}$$

$$= \frac{9}{2} \qquad\qquad = -1$$

The solutions are $\dfrac{9}{2}$ or -1.

49. $\dfrac{1}{2}t^2 + t - 12 = 0$

$2\left(\dfrac{1}{2}t^2 + t - 12\right) = 2(0)$

$t^2 + 2t - 24 = 0$

$t = \dfrac{-(2) \pm \sqrt{(2)^2 - 4(1)(-24)}}{2(1)}$

$= \dfrac{-2 \pm \sqrt{4 + 96}}{2}$

$= \dfrac{-2 \pm \sqrt{100}}{2}$

$= \dfrac{-2 \pm 10}{2}$

$t = \dfrac{-2 + 10}{2}$ or $t = \dfrac{-2 - 10}{2}$

$= \dfrac{8}{2}$ $= \dfrac{-12}{2}$

$= 4$ $= -6$

The solutions are 4 and –6.

50. $\dfrac{2}{3}x^2 = 8x - 18$

$\dfrac{3}{2}\left(\dfrac{2}{3}x^2\right) = \dfrac{3}{2}(8x - 18)$

$x^2 = 12x - 27$

$x^2 - 12x + 27 = 0$

$x = \dfrac{-(-12) \pm \sqrt{(-12)^2 - 4(1)(27)}}{2(1)}$

$= \dfrac{12 \pm \sqrt{144 - 108}}{2}$

$= \dfrac{12 \pm \sqrt{36}}{2}$

$= \dfrac{12 \pm 6}{2}$

$x = \dfrac{12 + 6}{2}$ or $x = \dfrac{12 - 6}{2}$

$= 9$ $= 3$

The solutions are 9 and 3.

51. $9r^2 + 3r - 2 = 0$

$r = \dfrac{-3 \pm \sqrt{3^2 - 4(9)(-2)}}{2(9)}$

$= \dfrac{-3 \pm \sqrt{9 + 72}}{18}$

$= \dfrac{-3 \pm \sqrt{81}}{18}$

$= \dfrac{-3 \pm 9}{18}$

$r = \dfrac{-3 + 9}{18}$ or $r = \dfrac{-3 - 9}{18}$

$= \dfrac{6}{18}$ $= \dfrac{-12}{18}$

$= \dfrac{1}{3}$ $= -\dfrac{2}{3}$

The solutions are $\dfrac{1}{3}$ and $-\dfrac{2}{3}$.

52. $2x^2 - 4x - 2 = 0$

$\dfrac{1}{2}(2x^2 - 4x - 2) = \dfrac{1}{2}(0)$

$x^2 - 2x - 1 = 0$

$x = \dfrac{-(-2) \pm \sqrt{(-2)^2 - 4(1)(-1)}}{2(1)}$

$= \dfrac{2 \pm \sqrt{4 + 4}}{2}$

$= \dfrac{2 \pm \sqrt{8}}{2}$

$= \dfrac{2 \pm 2\sqrt{2}}{2}$

$= 1 \pm \sqrt{2}$

The solutions are $1 + \sqrt{2}$ and $1 - \sqrt{2}$.

53.

$$\frac{1}{2}x^2 + 2x + \frac{2}{3} = 0$$

$$6\left(\frac{1}{2}x^2 + 2x + \frac{2}{3}\right) = 6(0)$$

$$3x^2 + 12x + 4 = 0$$

$$x = \frac{-12 \pm \sqrt{(12)^2 - 4(3)(4)}}{2(3)}$$

$$= \frac{-12 \pm \sqrt{144 - 48}}{6}$$

$$= \frac{-12 \pm \sqrt{96}}{6}$$

$$= \frac{-12 \pm 4\sqrt{6}}{6}$$

$$= \frac{2(-6 \pm 2\sqrt{6})}{2(3)}$$

$$= \frac{-6 \pm 2\sqrt{6}}{3}$$

The solutions are $\dfrac{-6 + 2\sqrt{6}}{3}$ and $\dfrac{-6 - 2\sqrt{6}}{3}$.

54.

$$x^2 - \frac{11}{3}x = \frac{10}{3}$$

$$3\left(x^2 - \frac{11}{3}x - \frac{10}{3}\right) = 3(0)$$

$$3x^2 - 11x - 10 = 0$$

$$x = \frac{-(-11) \pm \sqrt{(-11)^2 - 4(3)(-10)}}{2(3)}$$

$$= \frac{11 \pm \sqrt{121 + 120}}{6}$$

$$= \frac{11 \pm \sqrt{241}}{6}$$

The solutions are $\dfrac{11 + \sqrt{241}}{6}$ and $\dfrac{11 - \sqrt{241}}{6}$.

55.

$$a^2 - \frac{a}{5} - \frac{1}{3} = 0$$

$$15\left(a^2 - \frac{a}{5} - \frac{1}{3}\right) = 15(0)$$

$$15a^2 - 3a - 5 = 0$$

$$a = \frac{-(-3) \pm \sqrt{(-3)^2 - 4(15)(-5)}}{2(15)}$$

$$= \frac{3 \pm \sqrt{9 + 300}}{30}$$

$$= \frac{3 \pm \sqrt{309}}{30}$$

The solutions are $\dfrac{3 - \sqrt{309}}{30}$ and $\dfrac{3 + \sqrt{309}}{30}$.

56.

$$b^2 = -\frac{b}{2} + \frac{2}{3}$$

$$6\left(b^2 + \frac{b}{2} - \frac{2}{3}\right) = 6(0)$$

$$6b^2 + 3b - 4 = 0$$

$$b = \frac{-3 \pm \sqrt{(3)^2 - 4(6)(-4)}}{2(6)}$$

$$= \frac{-3 \pm \sqrt{9 + 96}}{12}$$

$$= \frac{-3 \pm \sqrt{105}}{12}$$

The solutions are $\dfrac{-3 + \sqrt{105}}{12}$ and $\dfrac{-3 - \sqrt{105}}{12}$.

57.

$$c = \frac{c - 6}{4 - c}$$

$$c(4 - c) = c - 6$$

$$4c - c^2 = c - 6$$

$$0 = c^2 - 3c - 6$$

$$c = \frac{-(-3) \pm \sqrt{(-3)^2 - 4(1)(-6)}}{2(1)}$$

$$= \frac{3 \pm \sqrt{9 + 24}}{2}$$

$$= \frac{3 \pm \sqrt{33}}{2}$$

The solutions are $\dfrac{3 + \sqrt{33}}{2}$ and $\dfrac{3 - \sqrt{33}}{2}$.

58.

$$3y = \frac{5y+6}{2y+3}$$

$$3y(2y+3) = 5y+6$$

$$6y^2 + 9y = 5y + 6$$

$$6y^2 + 4y - 6 = 0$$

$$3y^2 + 2y - 3 = 0$$

$$y = \frac{-2 \pm \sqrt{2^2 - 4(3)(-3)}}{2(3)}$$

$$= \frac{-2 \pm \sqrt{4+36}}{6}$$

$$= \frac{-2 \pm \sqrt{40}}{6}$$

$$= \frac{-2 \pm 2\sqrt{10}}{6}$$

$$= \frac{2(-1 \pm \sqrt{10})}{2(3)}$$

$$= \frac{-1 \pm \sqrt{10}}{3}$$

The solutions are $\dfrac{-1+\sqrt{10}}{3}$ and $\dfrac{-1-\sqrt{-10}}{3}$.

59. $2x^2 - 4x + 5 = 0$

$$x = \frac{-(-4) \pm \sqrt{(-4)^2 - 4(2)(5)}}{2(2)}$$

$$= \frac{4 \pm \sqrt{16-40}}{4}$$

$$= \frac{4 \pm \sqrt{-24}}{4}$$

$$= \frac{4 \pm 2i\sqrt{6}}{4}$$

$$= \frac{2 \pm i\sqrt{6}}{2}$$

The solutions are $\dfrac{2+i\sqrt{6}}{2}$ and $\dfrac{2-i\sqrt{6}}{2}$.

60.

$$3a^2 - 4a = -5$$

$$3a^2 - 4a + 5 = 0$$

$$a = \frac{-(-4) \pm \sqrt{(-4)^2 - 4(3)(5)}}{2(3)}$$

$$= \frac{4 \pm \sqrt{16-60}}{6}$$

$$= \frac{4 \pm \sqrt{-44}}{6}$$

$$= \frac{4 \pm 2i\sqrt{11}}{6}$$

$$= \frac{2(2 \pm i\sqrt{11})}{6}$$

$$= \frac{2 \pm i\sqrt{11}}{3}$$

The solutions are $\dfrac{2-i\sqrt{11}}{3}$ and $\dfrac{2+i\sqrt{11}}{3}$.

61.

$$y^2 + \frac{y}{2} = -\frac{3}{2}$$

$$2\left(y^2 + \frac{y}{2}\right) = 2\left(-\frac{3}{2}\right)$$

$$2y^2 + y = -3$$

$$2y^2 + y + 3 = 0$$

$$y = \frac{-1 \pm \sqrt{(1)^2 - 4(2)(3)}}{2(2)}$$

$$= \frac{-1 \pm \sqrt{1-24}}{4}$$

$$= \frac{-1 \pm \sqrt{-23}}{4}$$

$$= \frac{-1 \pm i\sqrt{23}}{4}$$

The solutions are $\dfrac{-1+i\sqrt{23}}{4}$ and $\dfrac{-1-i\sqrt{23}}{4}$.

62. $2b^2 - \dfrac{7}{3}b + \dfrac{4}{3} = 0$

$3\left(2b^2 - \dfrac{7}{3}b + \dfrac{4}{3}\right) = 3(0)$

$6b^2 - 7b + 4 = 0$

$b = \dfrac{-(-7) \pm \sqrt{(-7)^2 - 4(6)(4)}}{2(6)}$

$= \dfrac{7 \pm \sqrt{49 - 96}}{12}$

$= \dfrac{7 \pm \sqrt{-47}}{12}$

$= \dfrac{7 \pm i\sqrt{47}}{12}$

The solutions are $\dfrac{7 - i\sqrt{47}}{12}$ and $\dfrac{7 + i\sqrt{47}}{12}$.

63. $0.1x^2 + 0.6x - 1.2 = 0$

$10(0.1x^2 + 0.6x - 1.2) = 10(0)$

$x^2 + 6x - 12 = 0$

$x = \dfrac{-6 \pm \sqrt{6^2 - 4(1)(-12)}}{2(1)}$

$= \dfrac{-6 \pm \sqrt{36 + 48}}{2}$

$= \dfrac{-6 \pm \sqrt{84}}{2}$

$= \dfrac{-6 \pm 2\sqrt{21}}{2}$

$= -3 \pm \sqrt{21}$

The solutions are $-3 + \sqrt{21}$ or $-3 - \sqrt{21}$.

64. $2.3x^2 - 5.6x - 0.4 = 0$

$10(2.3x^2 - 5.6x - 0.4) = 10(0)$

$23x^2 - 56x - 4 = 0$

$x = \dfrac{56 \pm \sqrt{(56)^2 - 4(23)(-4)}}{2(23)}$

$= \dfrac{56 \pm \sqrt{3136 + 368}}{46}$

$= \dfrac{56 \pm \sqrt{3504}}{46}$

$= \dfrac{56 \pm 4\sqrt{219}}{46} = \dfrac{28 \pm 2\sqrt{219}}{23}$

The solutions are $\dfrac{28 - 2\sqrt{219}}{23}$ and $\dfrac{28 + 2\sqrt{219}}{23}$.

65. $f(x) = x^2 - 2x + 5$, $f(x) = 5$

$x^2 - 2x + 5 = 5$

$x^2 - 2x = 0$

$x = \dfrac{2 \pm \sqrt{(-2)^2 - 4(1)(0)}}{2(1)}$

$= \dfrac{2 \pm \sqrt{4}}{2}$

$= \dfrac{2 \pm 2}{2}$

$x = \dfrac{2 + 2}{2}$ or $x = \dfrac{2 - 2}{2}$

$= \dfrac{4}{2}$ $\qquad = \dfrac{0}{2}$

$= 2$ $\qquad\quad = 0$

The values of x are 2 and 0.

66. $g(x) = x^2 + 3x + 8$, $g(x) = 8$

$x^2 + 3x + 8 = 8$

$x^2 + 3x = 0$

$x = \dfrac{-3 \pm \sqrt{(3)^2 - 4(1)(0)}}{2(1)}$

$= \dfrac{-3 \pm \sqrt{9}}{2}$

$= \dfrac{-3 \pm 3}{2}$

$x = \dfrac{-3 + 3}{2}$ or $x = \dfrac{-3 - 3}{2}$

$= \dfrac{0}{2}$ $\qquad\quad = \dfrac{-6}{2}$

$= 0$ $\qquad\qquad = -3$

The values of x are 0 and –3.

67. $k(x) = x^2 - x - 15$, $k(x) = 15$

$x^2 - x - 15 = 15$

$x^2 - x - 30 = 0$

$x = \dfrac{1 \pm \sqrt{(-1)^2 - 4(1)(-30)}}{2(1)}$

$= \dfrac{1 \pm \sqrt{1 + 120}}{2}$

$= \dfrac{1 \pm \sqrt{121}}{2}$

$= \dfrac{1 \pm 11}{2}$

$x = \dfrac{1 + 11}{2}$ or $x = \dfrac{1 - 11}{2}$

$= \dfrac{12}{2}$ $= \dfrac{-10}{2}$

$= 6$ $= -5$

The values of x are 6 and –5.

68. $p(r) = r^2 + 17r + 81$, $p(r) = 9$

$r^2 + 17r + 81 = 9$

$r^2 + 17r + 72 = 0$

$r = \dfrac{-17 \pm \sqrt{17^2 - 4(1)(72)}}{2(1)}$

$= \dfrac{-17 \pm \sqrt{289 - 288}}{2}$

$= \dfrac{-17 \pm \sqrt{1}}{2}$

$= \dfrac{-17 \pm 1}{2}$

$r = \dfrac{-17 + 1}{2}$ or $r = \dfrac{-17 - 1}{2}$

$= \dfrac{-16}{2}$ $= \dfrac{-18}{2}$

$= -8$ $= -9$

The values of r are –8 and –9.

69. $h(t) = 2t^2 - 7t + 6$, $h(t) = 2$

$2t^2 - 7t + 6 = 2$

$2t^2 - 7t + 4 = 0$

$t = \dfrac{7 \pm \sqrt{(-7)^2 - 4(2)(4)}}{2(2)}$

$= \dfrac{7 \pm \sqrt{49 - 32}}{4}$

$= \dfrac{7 \pm \sqrt{17}}{4}$

The values of t are $\dfrac{7 + \sqrt{17}}{4}$ and $\dfrac{7 - \sqrt{17}}{4}$.

70. $t(x) = x^2 + 5x - 4$, $t(x) = 3$

$x^2 + 5x - 4 = 3$

$x^2 + 5x - 7 = 0$

$x = \dfrac{-5 \pm \sqrt{5^2 - 4(1)(-7)}}{2(1)}$

$= \dfrac{-5 \pm \sqrt{25 + 28}}{2}$

$= \dfrac{-5 \pm \sqrt{53}}{2}$

The values of x are $\dfrac{-5 + \sqrt{53}}{2}$ and $\dfrac{-5 - \sqrt{53}}{2}$.

71. $g(a) = 2a^2 - 3a + 16$, $g(a) = 14$

$2a^2 - 3a + 16 = 14$

$2a^2 - 3a + 2 = 0$

$a = \dfrac{3 \pm \sqrt{(-3)^2 - 4(2)(2)}}{2(2)}$

$= \dfrac{3 \pm \sqrt{9 - 16}}{4}$

$= \dfrac{3 \pm \sqrt{-7}}{4}$

There are no real values of a for which $g(a) = 14$.

72. $h(x) = 6x^2 + 3x + 1, \quad h(x) = -7$

$6x^2 + 3x + 1 = -7$

$6x^2 + 3x + 8 = 0$

$x = \dfrac{-3 \pm \sqrt{3^2 - 4(6)(8)}}{2(6)}$

$= \dfrac{-3 \pm \sqrt{9 - 192}}{12}$

$= \dfrac{-3 \pm \sqrt{-183}}{12}$

There are no real values of x for which $h(x) = -7$.

73. $x = 2$ and $x = 5$

$x - 2 = 0$ and $x - 5 = 0$

$(x - 2)(x - 5) = 0$

$x^2 - 5x - 2x + 10 = 0$

$x^2 - 7x + 10 = 0$

74. $x = 3$ and $x = 4$

$x + 3 = 0$ and $x - 4 = 0$

$(x + 3)(x - 4) = 0$

$x^2 - 4x + 3x - 12 = 0$

$x^2 - x - 12 = 0$

75. $x = 1$ and $x = -9$

$x - 1 = 0$ and $x + 9 = 0$

$(x - 1)(x + 9) = 0$

$x^2 + 9x - x - 9 = 0$

$x^2 + 8x - 9 = 0$

76. $x = -2$ and $x = -6$

$x + 2 = 0$ and $x + 6 = 0$

$(x + 2)(x + 6) = 0$

$x^2 + 6x + 2x + 12 = 0$

$x^2 + 8x + 12 = 0$

77. $x = -\dfrac{3}{5}$ and $x = \dfrac{2}{3}$

$5x = -3$ and $3x = 2$

$5x + 3 = 0$ and $3x - 2 = 0$

$(5x + 3)(3x - 2) = 0$

$15x^2 - 10x + 9x - 6 = 0$

$15x^2 - x - 6 = 0$

78. $x = -\dfrac{1}{3}$ and $x = -\dfrac{3}{4}$

$3x = -1$ and $4x = -3$

$3x + 1 = 0$ and $4x + 3 = 0$

$(3x + 1)(4x + 3) = 0$

$12x^2 + 9x + 4x + 3 = 0$

$12x^2 + 13x + 3 = 0$

79. $x = \sqrt{2}$ and $x = -\sqrt{2}$

$x - \sqrt{2} = 0$ and $x + \sqrt{2} = 0$.

$\left(x - \sqrt{2}\right)\left(x + \sqrt{2}\right) = 0$

$x^2 + x\sqrt{2} - x\sqrt{2} - 2 = 0$

$x^2 - 2 = 0$

80. $x = \sqrt{5}$ and $x = -\sqrt{5}$

$x - \sqrt{5} = 0$ and $x + \sqrt{5} = 0$.

$\left(x - \sqrt{5}\right)\left(x + \sqrt{5}\right) = 0$

$x^2 + x\sqrt{5} - x\sqrt{5} - 2 = 0$

$x^2 - 5 = 0$

81. $x = 3i$ and $x = -3i$

$x - 3i = 0$ and $x + 3i = 0$.

$(x - 3i)(x + 3i) = 0$

$x^2 + 3ix - 3ix - 9i^2 = 0$

$x^2 - 9i^2 = 0$

$x^2 - 9(-1) = 0$

$x^2 + 9 = 0$

82. $x = 8i$ and $x = -8i$

$x - 8i = 0$ and $x + 8i = 0$.

$(x - 8i)(x + 8i) = 0$

$x^2 + 8ix - 8ix - 64i^2 = 0$

$x^2 - 64i^2 = 0$

$x^2 - 64(-1) = 0$

$x^2 + 64 = 0$

83. $x = 3 + \sqrt{2}$ and $x = 3 - \sqrt{2}$

$x - 3 - \sqrt{2} = 0$ and $x - 3 + \sqrt{2} = 0$

$\left(x - 3 - \sqrt{2}\right)\left(x - 3 + \sqrt{2}\right) = 0$

$\left[(x - 3) - \sqrt{2}\right]\left[(x - 3) + \sqrt{2}\right] = 0$

$\left(x - 3\right)^2 - \left(\sqrt{2}\right)^2 = 0$

$x^2 - 6x + 9 - 2 = 0$

$x^2 - 6x + 7 = 0$

84. $x = 5 - \sqrt{3}$ and $x = 5 + \sqrt{3}$

$x - 5 + \sqrt{3} = 0$ and $x - 5 - \sqrt{3} = 0$

$\left(x - 5 + \sqrt{3}\right)\left(x - 5 - \sqrt{3}\right) = 0$

$\left[(x - 5) + \sqrt{3}\right]\left[(x - 5) - \sqrt{3}\right] = 0$

$\left(x - 5\right)^2 - \left(\sqrt{3}\right)^2 = 0$

$x^2 - 10x + 25 - 3 = 0$

$x^2 - 10x + 22 = 0$

85. $x = 2 + 3i$ and $x = 2 - 3i$

$x - 2 - 3i = 0$ and $x - 2 + 3i = 0$

$(x - 2 - 3i)(x - 2 + 3i) = 0$

$[(x - 2) - 3i][(x - 2) + 3i] = 0$

$\left(x - 2\right)^2 - (3i)^2 = 0$

$x^2 - 4x + 4 - 9i^2 = 0$

$x^2 - 4x + 4 + 9 = 0$

$x^2 - 4x + 13 = 0$

86. $x = 5 - 4i$ and $x = 5 + 4i$

$x - 5 + 4i = 0$ and $x - 5 - 4i = 0$

$(x - 5 + 4i)(x - 5 - 4i) = 0$

$[(x - 5) + 4i][(x - 5) - 4i] = 0$

$\left(x - 5\right)^2 - (4i)^2 = 0$

$x^2 - 10x + 25 - 16i^2 = 0$

$x^2 - 10x + 25 + 16 = 0$

$x^2 - 10x + 41 = 0$

87. a. $n(10 - 0.02n) = 450$

b. $n(10 - 0.02n) = 450$

$10n - 0.02n^2 = 450$

$0.02n^2 - 10n + 450 = 0$

$$n = \frac{-(-10) \pm \sqrt{(-10)^2 - 4(0.02)(450)}}{2(0.02)}$$

$$n = \frac{10 \pm \sqrt{100 - 36}}{0.04}$$

$$n = \frac{10 \pm \sqrt{64}}{0.04}$$

$$n = \frac{10 \pm 8}{0.04}$$

$n = 450$ or $n = 50$

Since $n \le 65$, the number of lamps that must be sold is 50.

88. a. $n(25 - 0.1n) = 460$

b. $n(25 - 0.1n) = 460$

$25n - 0.1n^2 = 460$

$0.1n^2 - 25n + 460 = 0$

$$n = \frac{-(-25) \pm \sqrt{(-25)^2 - 4(0.1)(460)}}{2(0.1)}$$

$$n = \frac{25 \pm \sqrt{441}}{0.2}$$

$$n = \frac{25 \pm 21}{0.2}$$

$n = 230$ or $n = 20$

Since $n \le 26$, the number of batteries that must be sold is 20.

89. a. $n(50 - 0.2n) = 1680$

b. $n(50 - 0.4n) = 660$

$50n - 0.4n^2 = 660$

$0.4n^2 - 50n + 660 = 0$

$$n = \frac{-(-50) \pm \sqrt{(-50)^2 - 4(0.4)(660)}}{2(0.4)}$$

$$n = \frac{50 \pm \sqrt{2500 - 1056}}{0.8}$$

$$n = \frac{50 \pm \sqrt{1444}}{0.8}$$

$$n = \frac{50 \pm 38}{0.8}$$

$n = 110$ or $n = 15$

Since $n \le 50$, the number of chairs that must be sold is 15.

90. a. $n(30 - 0.15n) = 1260$

b.
$$n(30 - 0.15n) = 1260$$
$$30n - 0.15n^2 = 1260$$
$$0.15n^2 - 30n + 1260 = 0$$
$$n = \frac{-(-30) \pm \sqrt{(-30)^2 - 4(0.15)(1260)}}{2(0.15)}$$
$$n = \frac{30 \pm \sqrt{900 - 756}}{0.30}$$
$$n = \frac{30 \pm \sqrt{144}}{0.30}$$
$$n = \frac{30 \pm 12}{0.30}$$
$$n = 140 \text{ or } n = 60$$
Since $n \leq 75$, the number of watches that must be sold is 60.

91. Any quadratic equation for which the discriminant is a non-negative perfect square can be solved by factoring. Any quadratic equation for which the discriminant is a positive number but not a perfect square can be solved by the quadratic formula but not by factoring over the set of integers.

92. a. No. All quadratic equations can be solved by the quadratic formula or by completing the square.

b. Yes. Any quadratic equation for which the discriminant is not a perfect square can be solved by completing the square but not by factoring over the set of integers.

93. Yes. If the discriminant is a perfect square, the simplified expression will not contain a radical and the quadratic equation can be solved by factoring.

94. No. A quadratic equation can be solved by factoring only when the discriminant is a perfect square.

95. Let x be the number.
$$2x^2 + 3x = 27$$
$$2x^2 + 3x - 27 = 0$$
$$x = \frac{-3 \pm \sqrt{3^2 - 4(2)(-27)}}{2(2)}$$
$$x = \frac{-3 \pm \sqrt{9 + 112}}{4}$$
$$x = \frac{-3 \pm \sqrt{121}}{4}$$
$$x = \frac{-3 \pm 11}{4}$$
$$x = \frac{8}{4} \text{ or } x = \frac{-14}{4}$$
$$x = 2 \text{ or } x = -\frac{7}{2}$$
Since the number must be positive, it is 3.

96. Let x be the number.
$$3x^2 - 2x = 21$$
$$3x^2 - 2x - 21 = 0$$
$$x = \frac{-(-2) \pm \sqrt{(-2)^2 - 4(3)(-21)}}{2(3)}$$
$$x = \frac{2 \pm \sqrt{4 + 252}}{6}$$
$$x = \frac{2 \pm \sqrt{256}}{6}$$
$$x = \frac{2 \pm 16}{6}$$
$$x = \frac{18}{6} \text{ or } x = \frac{-14}{6}$$
$$x = 3 \text{ or } x = -\frac{7}{3}$$
Since the number must be positive, it is 3.

97. Let x be the width. Then $3x - 1$ is the length. Use $A = (\text{length})(\text{width})$.
$$24 = (3x - 1)(x)$$
$$24 = 3x^2 - x$$
$$0 = 3x^2 - x - 24$$
$$x = \frac{-(-1) \pm \sqrt{(-1)^2 - 4(3)(-24)}}{2(3)}$$
$$= \frac{1 \pm \sqrt{1 + 288}}{6}$$
$$= \frac{1 \pm \sqrt{289}}{6}$$
$$= \frac{1 \pm 17}{6}$$
Since width is positive, use
$$x = \frac{1 + 17}{6} = \frac{18}{6} = 3$$
$$3x - 1 = 3(3) - 1 = 9 - 1 = 8$$
The width is 3 feet and the length is 8 feet.

98. Let l be the length.
Then $w = P - 2l = 400 - 2l$.
The area is 15,000 sq ft.

$$l(400 - 2l) = 15,000$$
$$400l - 2l^2 = 15,000$$
$$400l - 2l^2 - 15,000 = 0$$
$$2l^2 - 400l + 15,000 = 0$$
$$l = \frac{-(-400) \pm \sqrt{(-400)^2 - 4(2)(15,000)}}{2(2)}$$
$$= \frac{400 \pm \sqrt{160,000 - 120,000}}{4}$$
$$= \frac{400 \pm \sqrt{40,000}}{4}$$
$$= \frac{400 \pm 200}{4}$$
$$l = \frac{400 - 200}{4} \quad \text{or} \quad l = \frac{400 + 200}{4}$$
$$= \frac{200}{4} \qquad\qquad = \frac{600}{4}$$
$$= 50 \qquad\qquad = 150$$

If $l = 50$, $w = 400 - 2(50) = 400 - 100 = 300$.
If $l = 150$, $w = 400 - 2(150) = 400 - 300 = 100$.
The region is either 50 ft by 300 ft or
150 ft by 100 ft.

99. Let x be the amount by which each side is to be reduced.
Then $6 - x$ is the new width
and $8 - x$ is the new length

new area $= \frac{1}{2}$ (old area) $= \frac{1}{2}(6 \cdot 8) = 24$

new area = (new width)(new length)
$$24 = (6 - x)(8 - x)$$
$$0 = 48 - 14x + x^2 - 24$$
$$0 = x^2 - 14x + 24$$
$$x = \frac{-(-14) \pm \sqrt{(-14)^2 - 4(1)(24)}}{2(1)}$$
$$= \frac{14 \pm \sqrt{196 - 96}}{2}$$
$$= \frac{14 \pm \sqrt{100}}{2}$$
$$= \frac{14 \pm 10}{2}$$

$$x = \frac{14 + 10}{2} \quad \text{or} \quad x = \frac{14 - 10}{2}$$
$$= \frac{24}{2} \qquad\qquad = \frac{4}{2}$$
$$= 12 \qquad\qquad = 2$$

We reject $x = 12$, since this would give negative values for width and length.
The only meaningful value is $x = 2$ inches since this gives positive values for the new width and length.

100. Let x be the width of the sidewalk. The dimensions of the resulting garden will be $(9 - 2x)$ by $(12 - 2x)$. The area of this must be half the area of the original garden.

$$(9 - 2x)(12 - 2x) = \frac{1}{2}(9)(12)$$
$$108 - 18x - 24x + 4x^2 = 54$$
$$4x^2 - 42x + 54 = 0$$
$$\frac{1}{2}(4x^2 - 42x + 54 = 0)$$
$$2x^2 - 21x + 27 = 0$$
$$(2x - 3)(x + 9) = 0$$
$$x = \frac{3}{2} \quad \text{or} \quad x = -9$$

Since the negative solution doesn't make sense, the width of the sidewalk must be $\frac{3}{2}$ or 1.5 meters.

101. Substitute $h = 0$ in the formula $h = -16t^2 + 308$.
$$0 = -16t^2 + 308$$
$$16t^2 = 308$$
$$t^2 = \frac{308}{16}$$
$$t^2 = \frac{77}{4}$$
$$t = \pm\sqrt{\frac{77}{7}} = \pm\frac{\sqrt{77}}{2}$$

Time must be positive, so $t = \frac{\sqrt{77}}{2} \approx 4.39$. It take approximately 4.39 seconds for the water to reach the bottom of the falls.

102. Substitute $h = 0$ in the formula $h = -16t^2 + 176$.

$$0 = -16t^2 + 176$$
$$16t^2 = 176$$
$$t^2 = \frac{176}{16}$$
$$t^2 = 11$$
$$t = \pm\sqrt{11}$$

Time must be positive, so $t = \sqrt{11} \approx 3.32$. It take approximately 3.32 seconds for the water to reach the bottom of the falls.

103. a. $h = \frac{1}{2}at^2 + v_0 t + h_0$

$$20 = \frac{1}{2}(-32)t^2 + 60t + 80$$
$$20 = -16t^2 + 60t + 80$$
$$0 = -16t^2 + 60t + 60$$
$$0 = 16t^2 - 60t - 60$$
$$t = \frac{-(-60) \pm \sqrt{(-60)^2 - 4(16)(-60)}}{2(16)}$$
$$t = \frac{60 \pm \sqrt{7440}}{32}$$

Since time must be positive, use

$$t = \frac{60 + \sqrt{7440}}{32} \approx 4.57$$

The horseshoe is 20 feet from the ground after about 4.57 seconds.

b. $0 = \frac{1}{2}(-32)t^2 + 60t + 80$

$$0 = -16t^2 + 60t + 80$$
$$t = \frac{-60 \pm \sqrt{60^2 - 4(-16)(80)}}{2(-16)}$$
$$t = \frac{-60 \pm \sqrt{8720}}{-32}$$
$$t = \frac{60 \pm \sqrt{8720}}{32}$$

Since time must be positive, use

$$t = \frac{60 + \sqrt{8720}}{32} \approx 4.79$$

The horseshoes strike the ground after about 4.79 seconds.

104. Since gravity is one-sixth that on Earth a in this context will equal $\frac{1}{6}(-32) = \frac{-16}{3}$.

$$0 = \frac{1}{2}\left(-\frac{16}{3}\right)t^2 + 40t + 60$$
$$0 = -\frac{8}{3}t^2 + 40t + 60$$
$$\frac{3}{4}\left(0 = -\frac{8}{3}t^2 + 40t + 60\right)$$
$$0 = -2t^2 + 30t + 45$$
$$t = \frac{-30 \pm \sqrt{30^2 - 4(-2)(45)}}{2(-2)}$$
$$t = \frac{-30 \pm \sqrt{1260}}{-4}$$
$$t = \frac{-30 + \sqrt{1260}}{-4} \quad \text{or} \quad t = \frac{-30 - \sqrt{1260}}{-4}$$
$$t \approx -1.37 \qquad\qquad t \approx 16.37$$

Neil Armstrong will land on the ground after about 16.37 sec.

105. $x^2 - \sqrt{5}x - 10 = 0, \ a = 1, b = -\sqrt{5}, c = -10$

$$x = \frac{-(-\sqrt{5}) \pm \sqrt{(-\sqrt{5})^2 - 4(1)(-10)}}{2(1)}$$
$$= \frac{\sqrt{5} \pm \sqrt{5 + 40}}{2}$$
$$= \frac{\sqrt{5} \pm \sqrt{45}}{2}$$
$$= \frac{\sqrt{5} \pm 3\sqrt{5}}{2}$$
$$x = \frac{\sqrt{5} + 3\sqrt{5}}{2} \quad \text{or} \quad x = \frac{\sqrt{5} - 3\sqrt{5}}{2}$$
$$= \frac{4\sqrt{5}}{2} \qquad\qquad = \frac{-2\sqrt{5}}{2}$$
$$= 2\sqrt{5} \qquad\qquad = -\sqrt{5}$$

The solutions are $2\sqrt{5}$ and $-\sqrt{5}$.

106. $x^2 + 5\sqrt{6}x + 36 = 0$, $a = 1$, $b = 5\sqrt{6}$, $c = 36$

$$x = \frac{-5\sqrt{6} \pm \sqrt{\left(5\sqrt{6}\right)^2 - 4(1)(36)}}{2(1)}$$

$$= \frac{-5\sqrt{6} \pm \sqrt{150 - 144}}{2}$$

$$= \frac{-5\sqrt{6} \pm \sqrt{6}}{2}$$

$$x = \frac{-5\sqrt{6} - \sqrt{6}}{2} \quad \text{or} \quad x = \frac{-5\sqrt{6} + \sqrt{6}}{2}$$

$$= \frac{-6\sqrt{6}}{2} \qquad\qquad = \frac{-4\sqrt{6}}{2}$$

$$= -3\sqrt{6} \qquad\qquad = -2\sqrt{6}$$

The solutions are $-3\sqrt{6}$ and $-2\sqrt{6}$.

107. Let s be the length of the side of the original cube. Then $s + 0.2$ is the length of the side of the expanded cube.

$$(s + 0.2)^3 = s^3 + 6$$

$$s^3 + 0.6s^2 + 0.12s + 0.008 = s^3 + 6$$

$$0.6s^2 + 0.12s + 0.008 = 6$$

$$0.6s^2 + 0.12s - 5.992 = 0$$

$$s = \frac{-0.12 \pm \sqrt{(0.12)^2 - 4(0.6)(-5.992)}}{2(0.6)}$$

$$= \frac{-0.12 \pm \sqrt{0.0144 + 14.3803}}{1.2}$$

$$= \frac{-0.12 \pm \sqrt{14.3952}}{1.2}$$

Use the positive value since a length cannot be negative.

$$s = \frac{-0.12 + \sqrt{14.3952}}{1.2}$$

$$\approx \frac{-0.12 + 3.7941}{1.2}$$

$$\approx 3.0618$$

The original side was about 3.0618 mm long.

108.
$$x^6 = 1$$
$$x^6 - 1 = 0$$
$$(x^3)^2 - 1^2 = 0$$
$$(x^3 - 1)(x^3 + 1) = 0$$
$$(x - 1)(x^2 + x + 1)(x + 1)(x^2 - x + 1) = 0$$

$$x - 1 = 0 \quad \Rightarrow \quad x = 1$$

$$x^2 + x + 1 = 0$$

$$x = \frac{-1 \pm \sqrt{1^2 - 4(1)(1)}}{2(1)} = \frac{-1 \pm \sqrt{-3}}{2} = \frac{-1 \pm i\sqrt{3}}{2}$$

$$x + 1 = 0 \quad \Rightarrow \quad x = -1$$

$$x^2 - x + 1 = 0$$

$$x = \frac{-(-1) \pm \sqrt{(-1)^2 - 4(1)(1)}}{2(1)} = \frac{1 \pm \sqrt{-3}}{2} = \frac{1 \pm i\sqrt{3}}{2}$$

The 6 solutions are ± 1, $\dfrac{-1 \pm i\sqrt{3}}{2}$, and $\dfrac{1 \pm i\sqrt{3}}{2}$.

109. a. $h = \dfrac{1}{2}at^2 + v_0 t + h_0$

$$0 = \frac{1}{2}(-32)t^2 + 0t + 60$$

$$0 = -16t^2 + 0t + 60$$

$$t = \frac{-(0) \pm \sqrt{0^2 - 4(-16)(60)}}{2(-16)}$$

$$t = \frac{0 \pm \sqrt{3840}}{-32}$$

$$t \approx -1.94 \text{ or } t \approx 1.94$$

Since time must be positive, use 1.94 sec.

b. $h = \dfrac{1}{2}at^2 + v_0 t + h_0$

$$0 = \frac{1}{2}(-32)t^2 + 0t + 120$$

$$0 = -16t^2 + 0t + 120$$

$$t = \frac{-(0) \pm \sqrt{0^2 - 4(-16)(120)}}{2(-16)}$$

$$t = \frac{0 \pm \sqrt{7680}}{-32}$$

$$t \approx -2.74 \text{ or } t \approx 2.74$$

Since time must be positive, use 2.74 sec.

c. The height of Travis' rock is given by $h(t) = -16t^2 + 100t + 60$. Set the height equal to 0 to determine the how long it will take Travis' rock to strike the ground.

$$-16t^2 + 100t + 60 = 0$$
$$4t^2 - 25t - 15 = 0$$
$$t = \frac{-(-25) \pm \sqrt{(-25)^2 - 4(4)(-15)}}{2(4)}$$
$$= \frac{25 \pm \sqrt{625 + 240}}{8}$$
$$= \frac{25 \pm \sqrt{865}}{8}$$
$$t \approx 6.80 \text{ or } t \approx -0.55$$

Time must be positive, so it will take about 6.80 seconds for Travis' rock to strike the ground.

The height of Courtney's rock is given by $h(t) = -16t^2 + 60t + 120$. Set the height equal to 0 to determine the how long it will take Courtney's rock to strike the ground.

$$-16t^2 + 60t + 120 = 0$$
$$4t^2 - 15t - 30 = 0$$
$$t = \frac{-(-15) \pm \sqrt{(-15)^2 - 4(4)(-30)}}{2(4)}$$
$$= \frac{15 \pm \sqrt{225 + 480}}{8}$$
$$= \frac{15 \pm \sqrt{705}}{8}$$
$$t \approx 5.19 \text{ or } t \approx -1.44$$

Time must be positive, so it will take about 5.19 seconds for Travis' rock to strike the ground.

Thus, Courtney's rock will strike the ground sooner than Travis'.

d. The height of Travis' rock is given by $h(t) = -16t^2 + 100t + 60$. The height of Courtney's rock is given by $h(t) = -16t^2 + 60t + 120$. We want to know when these will be equal.

$$-16t^2 + 100t + 60 = -16t^2 + 60t + 120$$
$$100t + 60 = 60t + 120$$
$$40t = 60$$
$$t = \frac{60}{40} = 1.5$$

The rocks will be the same distance above the ground after 1.5 seconds.

110. $$\frac{5.55 \times 10^3}{1.11 \times 10^1} = \frac{5.55}{1.11} \times \frac{10^3}{10^1} = 5 \times 10^2 \text{ or } 500$$

111. $$f(x) = x^2 + 2x - 8$$
$$f(3) = (3)^2 + 2(3) - 8$$
$$= 9 + 6 - 8$$
$$= 7$$

112. $$3x + 4y = 2$$
$$2x = -5y - 1$$

Rewrite the system in standard form.
$$3x + 4y = 2$$
$$2x + 5y = -1$$

To eliminate the x variable, multiply the first equation by 2 and the second equation by -3, and then add.

$$6x + 8y = 4$$
$$\underline{-6x - 15y = 3}$$
$$-7y = 7$$
$$y = -1$$

Substitute -1 for y in the first equation to find x.
$$3x + 4(-1) = 2$$
$$3x - 4 = 2$$
$$3x = 6$$
$$x = 2$$

The solution is $(2, -1)$.

113. $$\frac{x + \sqrt{y}}{x - \sqrt{y}} \cdot \frac{x + \sqrt{y}}{x + \sqrt{y}} = \frac{x^2 + x\sqrt{y} + x\sqrt{y} + (\sqrt{y})^2}{x^2 + x\sqrt{y} - x\sqrt{y} - (\sqrt{y})^2}$$
$$= \frac{x^2 + 2x\sqrt{y} + y}{x^2 - y}$$

114. $$\sqrt{x^2 - 6x - 4} = x$$
$$x^2 - 6x - 4 = x^2$$
$$-6x - 4 = 0$$
$$-6x = 4$$
$$x = \frac{4}{-6} = -\frac{2}{3}$$

Upon checking, this value does not satisfy the equation. There is no real solution.

Exercise Set 12.3

1. Answers will vary.

2. For ☺ to be a real number, $P \geq \square^2$.

3. $A = s^2$, for s.

$\sqrt{A} = s$

4. $A = (s+1)^2$, for s.

$\sqrt{A} = s + 1$

$\sqrt{A} - 1 = s$

5. $d = 4.9t^2$, for t

$\dfrac{d}{4.9} = t^2$

$\sqrt{\dfrac{d}{4.9}} = t$

6. $A = S^2 - s^2$, for S

$A + s^2 = S^2$

$\sqrt{A + s^2} = S$

7. $E = i^2 r$, for i

$\dfrac{E}{r} = i^2$

$\sqrt{\dfrac{E}{r}} = i$

8. $A = 4\pi r^2$, for r

$\dfrac{A}{4\pi} = r^2$

$\sqrt{\dfrac{A}{4\pi}} = r$

9. $d = 16t^2$, for t

$\dfrac{d}{16} = t^2$

$\sqrt{\dfrac{d}{16}} = t \implies t = \dfrac{\sqrt{d}}{4}$

10. $d = \dfrac{1}{9}x^2$, for x

$9d = x^2$

$\sqrt{9d} = x \implies x = 3\sqrt{d}$

11. $E = mc^2$, for c

$\dfrac{E}{m} = c^2$

$\sqrt{\dfrac{E}{m}} = c$

12. $V = \pi r^2 h$, for r

$\dfrac{V}{\pi h} = r^2$

$\sqrt{\dfrac{V}{\pi h}} = r$

13. $V = \dfrac{1}{3}\pi r^2 h$, for r

$3V = \pi r^2 h$

$\dfrac{3V}{\pi h} = r^2$

$\sqrt{\dfrac{3V}{\pi h}} = r$

14. $d = \sqrt{L^2 + W^2}$, for L

$d^2 = L^2 + W^2$

$d^2 - W^2 = L^2$

$\sqrt{d^2 - W^2} = L$

15. $d = \sqrt{L^2 + W^2}$, for W

$d^2 = L^2 + W^2$

$d^2 - L^2 = W^2$

$\sqrt{d^2 - L^2} = W$

16. $a^2 + b^2 = c^2$, for a

$a^2 = c^2 - b^2$

$a = \sqrt{c^2 - b^2}$

17. $a^2 + b^2 = c^2$, for b

$b^2 = c^2 - a^2$

$b = \sqrt{c^2 - a^2}$

18. $d = \sqrt{L^2 + W^2 + H^2}$, for L

$d^2 = L^2 + W^2 + H^2$

$d^2 - W^2 - H^2 = L^2$

$\sqrt{d^2 - W^2 - H^2} = L$

19. $d = \sqrt{L^2 + W^2 + H^2}$, for H

$$d^2 = L^2 + W^2 + H^2$$

$$d^2 - L^2 - W^2 = H^2$$

$$\sqrt{d^2 - L^2 - W^2} = H$$

20. $A = P(1+r)^2$, for r

$$\frac{A}{P} = (1+r)^2$$

$$\sqrt{\frac{A}{P}} = 1 + r$$

$$\sqrt{\frac{A}{P}} - 1 = r$$

21. $h = -16t^2 + s_0$, for t

$$16t^2 = s_0 - h$$

$$t^2 = \frac{s_0 - h}{16}$$

$$t = \sqrt{\frac{s_0 - h}{16}}$$

$$t = \frac{\sqrt{s_0 - h}}{4}$$

22. $h = -4.9t^2 + s_0$ for t

$$4.9t^2 = s_0 - h$$

$$t^2 = \frac{s_0 - h}{4.9}$$

$$t = \sqrt{\frac{s_0 - h}{4.9}}$$

23. $E = \frac{1}{2}mv^2$, for v

$$2E = mv^2$$

$$\frac{2E}{m} = v^2$$

$$\sqrt{\frac{2E}{m}} = v$$

24. $f_x^2 + f_y^2 = f^2$, for f_x

$$f_x^2 = f^2 - f_y^2$$

$$f_x = \sqrt{f^2 - f_y^2}$$

25. $a = \dfrac{v_2^2 - v_1^2}{2d}$, for v_1

$$2ad = v_2^2 - v_1^2$$

$$2ad + v_1^2 = v_2^2$$

$$v_1^2 = v_2^2 - 2ad$$

$$v_1 = \sqrt{v_2^2 - 2ad}$$

26. $A = 4\pi(R^2 - r^2)$, for R

$$\frac{A}{4\pi} = R^2 - r^2$$

$$\frac{A}{4\pi} + r^2 = R^2$$

$$\sqrt{\frac{A}{4\pi} + r^2} = R$$

27. $v' = \sqrt{c^2 - v^2}$, for c

$$(v')^2 = c^2 - v^2$$

$$(v')^2 + v^2 = c^2$$

$$\sqrt{(v')^2 + v^2} = c$$

28. $L = L_0\sqrt{1 - \dfrac{v^2}{c^2}}$, for v

$$\frac{L}{L_0} = \sqrt{1 - \frac{v^2}{c^2}}$$

$$\frac{L^2}{L_0^2} = 1 - \frac{v^2}{c^2}$$

$$\frac{L^2}{L_0^2} + \frac{v^2}{c^2} = 1$$

$$\frac{v^2}{c^2} = 1 - \frac{L^2}{L_0^2}$$

$$v^2 = c^2\left(1 - \frac{L^2}{L_0^2}\right)$$

$$v = \sqrt{c^2\left(1 - \frac{L^2}{L_0^2}\right)}$$

29. a. $P(n) = 2.7n^2 + 9n - 3$

$P(5) = 2.7(5)^2 + 9(5) - 3 = 109.5$

The profit would be $10,950.

b. $P(n) = 2.7n^2 + 9n - 3$

$200 = 2.7n^2 + 9n - 3$

$0 = 2.7n^2 + 9n - 203$

$x = \dfrac{-9 \pm \sqrt{9^2 - 4(2.7)(-203)}}{2(2.7)}$

$x = \dfrac{-9 \pm \sqrt{2273.4}}{5.4}$

$x \approx 7$ or $x \approx -10$

We disregard the negative answer. Thus 7 tractors must be sold.

30. a. $P(n) = 6.2n^2 + 6n - 3$

$P(7) = 6.2(7)^2 + 6(7) - 3 = 342.8$

The profit would be $342.80.

b. $P(n) = 6.2n^2 + 6n - 3$

$675 = 6.2n^2 + 6n - 3$

$0 = 6.2n^2 + 6n - 678$

$x = \dfrac{-6 \pm \sqrt{6^2 - 4(6.2)(-678)}}{2(6.2)}$

$x = \dfrac{-6 \pm \sqrt{16850.4}}{12.4}$

$x \approx 10$ or $x \approx -11$

We disregard the negative answer. Thus 10 refrigerators must be sold.

31. $T = 6.2t^2 + 12t + 32$

a. When the car is turned on, $t = 0$.

$T = 6.2(0)^2 + 12(0) + 32 = 32$

The temperature is $32°F$.

b. $T = 6.2(2)^2 + 12(2) + 32 = 80.8$

The temperature after 2 minutes is $80.8°F$.

c. $120 = 6.2t^2 + 12t + 32$

$0 = 6.2t^2 + 12t - 88$

$t = \dfrac{-12 \pm \sqrt{12^2 - 4(6.2)(-88)}}{2(6.2)}$

$t \approx \dfrac{-12 \pm 48.23}{12.4}$

$t \approx 2.92$ or $t \approx -4.86$

The radiator temperature will reach $120°F$ about 2.92 min. after the engine is started.

32. a. $N(t) = -0.043t^2 + 1.22t + 46.0$

In 1995, $t = 6$.

$N(6) = -0.043(6)^2 + 1.22(6) + 46.0 = 51.77$

Total enrollment in 1995 was approximately 51.77 million.

b. $N(t) = -0.043t^2 + 1.22t + 46.0$, $N(t) = 54$

$54 = -0.043t^2 + 1.22t + 46.0$

$0 = -0.043t^2 + 1.22t - 8$

$t = \dfrac{-1.22 \pm \sqrt{(1.22)^2 - 4(-0.043)(-8)}}{2(-0.043)}$

$= \dfrac{-1.22 \pm \sqrt{0.1124}}{-0.086}$

$\approx \dfrac{-1.22 \pm 0.335261}{-0.086}$

$t \approx \dfrac{-1.22 + 0.335261}{-0.086}$ or $t \approx \dfrac{-1.22 - 0.335261}{-0.086}$

$\approx \dfrac{-0.884739}{-0.086}$ $\qquad \approx \dfrac{-1.555261}{-0.086}$

≈ 10.29 $\qquad\qquad \approx 18.08$

The total enrollment will reach 54 million students 10.29 years after 1989 (which is 1999) and also 18.08 years after 1989 (which is 2007).

33. a. In 2006, $t = 4$.

$D(4) = 0.04(4)^2 - 0.03(4) + 0.01 = 0.53$

The number of downloads in 2006 was about 0.53 billion.

b. $D(t) = 0.04t^2 - 0.03t + 0.01$, $D(t) = 1$

$1 = 0.04t^2 - 0.03t + 0.01$

$0 = 0.04t^2 - 0.03t - 0.99$

$t = \dfrac{-(-0.03) \pm \sqrt{(-0.03)^2 - 4(0.04)(-0.99)}}{2(0.04)}$

$= \dfrac{0.03 \pm \sqrt{0.1593}}{0.08}$

$\approx \dfrac{0.03 \pm 0.3991}{0.08}$

$t \approx \dfrac{0.03 + 0.3991}{0.08}$ or $t \approx \dfrac{0.03 - 0.3991}{0.08}$

$\approx \dfrac{0.4291}{0.08}$ $\qquad \approx \dfrac{-0.3691}{0.08}$

≈ 5.36 $\qquad\qquad \approx -4.61$

We disregard the negative answer. The number of downloads will be 1 billion 5.36 years after 2002, which is the year 2007.

34. a. $G(0) = 0.01(0)^2 + 0.2(0) + 1.2 = 1.2$
The GPA is 1.2.

b. $G(3) = 0.01(3)^2 + 0.2(3) + 1.2 = 1.89$
The GPA is 1.89.

c. $3.2 = 0.01h^2 + 0.2h + 1.2$
$0 = 0.01h^2 + 0.2h - 2$
$$h = \frac{-0.2 \pm \sqrt{(0.2)^2 - 4(0.01)(-2)}}{2(0.01)}$$
$$= \frac{-0.2 \pm \sqrt{0.12}}{0.02}$$
$$h = \frac{-0.2 + \sqrt{0.12}}{0.02} \quad \text{or} \quad h = \frac{-0.2 - \sqrt{0.12}}{0.02}$$
$$\approx 7.3 \qquad\qquad\qquad \approx -27.3$$
We disregard the negative answer. Thus the average student must study 7.3 hours per week to achieve a GPA of 3.2.

35. a. In 2003, $t = 3$.
$Y(3) = 0.66(3)^2 - 2.49(3) + 12.93 = 11.4$
In 2003, the yield was about 11.4 tons per acre.

b. $0.66t^2 - 2.49t + 12.93 = 13$
$0.66t^2 - 2.49t - 0.07 = 0$
$$t = \frac{-(-2.49) \pm \sqrt{(-2.49)^2 - 4(0.66)(-0.07)}}{2(0.66)}$$
$$= \frac{2.49 \pm \sqrt{6.3849}}{2(0.66)}$$
$$= \frac{2.49 \pm 2.5268}{1.32}$$
$$t = \frac{2.49 + 2.5268}{1.32} \quad \text{or} \quad t = \frac{2.49 - 2.5268}{1.32}$$
$$= \frac{5.0168}{1.32} \qquad\qquad = \frac{-0.0368}{1.32}$$
$$\approx 3.80 \qquad\qquad\qquad \approx -0.03$$
We disregard the negative answer. Thus the yield will be 13 tons per acre about 3.8 years after 2000, which would be in the year 2003.

36. a. $f(a) = -2.32a^2 + 76.58a - 559.87$, $a = 14$
$f(14) = -2.32(14)^2 + 76.58(14) - 559.87$
$$= 57.53$$
Thus, about 57.53% of 14-year-olds say their school is not drug free.

b. $f(a) = -2.32a^2 + 76.58a - 559.87$, $f(a) = 70$
$-2.32a^2 + 76.58a - 559.87 = 70$
$-2.32a^2 + 76.58a - 629.87 = 0$
$$a = \frac{-76.58 \pm \sqrt{(76.58)^2 - 4(-2.32)(-629.87)}}{2(-2.32)}$$
$$= \frac{-76.58 \pm \sqrt{5864.4964 - 5845.1936}}{-4.64}$$
$$= \frac{-76.58 \pm \sqrt{19.3028}}{-4.64}$$
$$\approx \frac{-76.58 \pm 4.3934952}{-4.64}$$
$$a \approx \frac{-76.58 + 4.3935}{-4.64} \approx \frac{-72.1865}{-4.64} \approx 15.56$$
or
$$a \approx \frac{-76.58 - 4.3935}{-4.64} \approx \frac{-80.9735}{-4.64} \approx 17.45$$
Since $12 \le a \le 17$, the only solution is $a \approx 15.56$. At age about 15.56 years, 70% of the students say their school is not drug free.

37. a. $M = -0.00434t^2 + 0.142t + 0.315$
In 2007, $t = 10$.
$M(1) = -0.00434(10)^2 + 0.142(10) + 0.315$
$$= 1.301$$
In 2007, about 1.301 million motorcycles was sold in the United States.

b. $M = -0.00434t^2 + 0.142t + 0.315$, $M = 1.4$
$1.4 = -0.00434t^2 + 0.142t + 0.315$
$0.00434t^2 - 0.142t + 1.085 = 0$
$$t = \frac{-(-0.142) \pm \sqrt{(-0.142)^2 - 4(0.00434)(1.085)}}{2(0.00434)}$$
$$= \frac{0.142 \pm \sqrt{0.0013284}}{0.00868}$$
$$\approx \frac{0.142 \pm 0.036447}{0.00868}$$
$$t \approx \frac{0.142 + 0.036447}{0.00868} = \frac{0.178447}{0.00868} \approx 20.56$$
or
$$t \approx \frac{0.142 - 0.036447}{0.00868} = \frac{0.105553}{0.00868} \approx 12.16$$
The number of motorcycles sold in the U.S. will be 1.4 million 12.16 years after 1997, which is the year 2009, and 20.56 years after 1997, which is the year 2017.

38. a. $P = 0.2(3)^2 + 1.5(3) - 1.2 = 5.1$

The profit is 5.1 thousand dollars, or $5100.

b. $P = 0.2(5)^2 + 1.5(5) - 1.2 = 11.3$

The profit is 11.3 thousand dollars or $11,300.

c. $1.4 = 0.2t^2 + 1.5t - 1.2$

$14 = 2t^2 + 15t - 12$

$0 = 2t^2 + 15t - 26$

$t = \dfrac{-15 \pm \sqrt{15^2 - 4(2)(-26)}}{2(2)}$

$t = \dfrac{-15 \pm \sqrt{433}}{4}$

$t = \dfrac{-15 + \sqrt{433}}{4}$ or $t = \dfrac{-15 - \sqrt{433}}{4}$

$t \approx 1.45$ \qquad $t \approx -8.95$

We disregard the negative answer. Thus the company should charge $1.45 per tape.

39. Let x be the width of the playground. Then the length is given by $x + 10$.

Area = length × width

$600 = (x + 10)x$

$0 = x^2 + 10x - 600$

$0 = (x - 20)(x + 30)$

$x - 20 = 0$ or $x + 30 = 0$

$x = 20$ or $\qquad x = -30$

Disregard the negative value. The width of the playground is 20 meters and the length is 20 + 10 = 30 meters.

40. Use the relationship $\dfrac{\text{distance}}{\text{time}} = \text{time}$

Let r be the rate for the first part of the trip.

	distance	rate	time
In traffic	80	r	$\dfrac{80}{r}$
Highway	260	$r + 25$	$\dfrac{260}{r + 25}$

Time for both trips is 6 hours.

$\dfrac{80}{r} + \dfrac{260}{r + 25} = 6$

$r(r + 25)\left(\dfrac{80}{r} + \dfrac{260}{r + 25}\right) = r(r + 25)(6)$

$80(r + 25) + 260r = 6r(r + 25)$

$80r + 2000 + 260r = 6r^2 + 150r$

$6r^2 - 190r - 2000 = 0$

$r = \dfrac{-(-190) \pm \sqrt{(-190)^2 - 4(6)(-2000)}}{2(6)}$

$= \dfrac{190 \pm \sqrt{84,100}}{12}$

$= \dfrac{190 \pm 290}{12}$

$r = 4$ or ≈ -8.33

Disregard the negative answer. Thus, her speed in traffic was 40 mph while her speed on the highway was $r + 25$ or 65 mph.

41. Let r be the rate at which the present equipment drills.

	d	r	$t = \dfrac{d}{r}$
Present equipment	64	r	$\dfrac{64}{r}$
New equipment	64	$r + 1$	$\dfrac{64}{r + 1}$

They would have hit water in 3.2 hours less time with the new equipment.

$\dfrac{64}{r + 1} = \dfrac{64}{r} - 3.2$

$r(r + 1)\left(\dfrac{64}{r + 1}\right) = r(r + 1)\left(\dfrac{64}{r}\right) - r(r + 1)(3.2)$

$64r = 64(r + 1) - 3.2r(r + 1)$

$64r = 64r + 64 - 3.2r^2 - 3.2r$

$3.2r^2 + 3.2r - 64 = 0$

$r^2 + r - 20 = 0$

$(r + 5)(r - 4) = 0$

$r + 5 = 0$ or $r - 4 = 0$

$r = -5$ \qquad $r = 4$

Disregard the negative answer. Thus the present equipment drills at a rate of 4 ft/hr.

42. Use the relationship $\dfrac{\text{distance}}{\text{time}} = \text{time}$

Let r be the rate for the first part of the trip.

	distance	rate	time
Going	300	r	$\dfrac{300}{r}$
Return	300	$r + 10$	$\dfrac{300}{r+10}$

Time for both trip is 11 hours.

$$\frac{300}{r} + \frac{300}{r+10} = 11$$

$$r(r+10)\left(\frac{300}{r} + \frac{300}{r+10}\right) = r(r+10)(11)$$

$$300(r+10) + 300r = 11(r)(r+10)$$

$$300r + 3000 + 300r = 11r^2 + 110r$$

$$0 = 11r^2 - 490r - 3000$$

$$r = \frac{-(-490) \pm \sqrt{(-490)^2 - 4(11)(-3000)}}{2(11)}$$

$$= \frac{490 \pm \sqrt{372,100}}{22} = \frac{490 \pm 610}{22}$$

$r = 50$ or $r \approx -5.5$

Since the speed must be positive, the truck's speed going was 50 mph while return speed was $r + 10$ or 60 mph.

43. Let x be Latoya's rate going uphill so $x+2$ is her rate going downhill. Using $\dfrac{d}{r} = t$ gives

$$t_{\text{uphill}} + t_{\text{downhill}} = 1.75$$

$$\frac{6}{x} + \frac{6}{x+2} = 1.75$$

$$x(x+2)\left(\frac{6}{x}\right) + x(x+2)\left(\frac{6}{x+2}\right) = x(x+2)(1.75)$$

$$6(x+2) + 6x = 1.75x(x+2)$$

$$6x + 12 + 6x = 1.75x^2 + 3.5x$$

$$0 = 1.75x^2 - 8.5x - 12$$

$$x = \frac{-(-8.5) \pm \sqrt{(-8.5)^2 - 4(1.75)(-12)}}{2(1.75)}$$

$$= \frac{8.5 \pm \sqrt{156.25}}{3.5} = \frac{8.5 \pm 12.5}{3.5}$$

$x = 6$ or $x \approx -1.14$

Since the time must be positive, Latoya's uphill rate is 6 mph and her downhill rate is $x + 2 = 8$ mph.

44. Let r be Kathy's average speed.

	d	r	$t = \dfrac{d}{r}$
Actual trip	300	r	$\dfrac{300}{r}$
Faster trip	300	$r + 10$	$\dfrac{300}{r+10}$

Since Kathy would have decreased the time by 1 hour at the faster rate.

$$\frac{300}{r+10} = \frac{300}{r} - 1$$

$$r(r+10)\left(\frac{300}{r+10}\right) = r(r+10)\left(\frac{300}{r}\right) - r(r+10)(1)$$

$$300r = 300(r+10) - r(r+10)$$

$$300r = 300r + 3000 - r^2 - 10r$$

$$0 = 3000 - r^2 - 10r$$

$$r^2 + 10r - 3000 = 0$$

$$(r+60)(r-50) = 0$$

$r + 60 = 0$ or $r - 50 = 0$

$r = -60$ $r = 50$

Use the positive value. Kathy drove at an average speed of 50 mph.

45. Let x be the Bonita's time, then $x + 1$ is the Pamela's time.

$$\frac{6}{x} + \frac{6}{x+1} = 1$$

$$x(x+1)\left(\frac{6}{x}\right) + x(x+1)\left(\frac{6}{x+1}\right) = x(x+1)(1)$$

$$6(x+1) + 6x = x^2 + x$$

$$6x + 6 + 6x = x^2 + x$$

$$0 = x^2 - 11x - 6$$

$$x = \frac{-(-11) \pm \sqrt{(-11)^2 - 4(1)(-6)}}{2(1)}$$

$$= \frac{11 \pm \sqrt{121 + 24}}{2}$$

$$= \frac{11 \pm \sqrt{145}}{2}$$

$x = \dfrac{11 + \sqrt{145}}{2}$ or $x = \dfrac{11 - \sqrt{145}}{2}$

≈ 11.52 ≈ -0.52

Since the time must be positive, it takes Bonita about 11.52 hours and Pamela about 12.52 hours to rebuild the engine.

46. Let r be Ricky's average speed going. The distance each way is 15 miles.

	d	r	$t = \dfrac{d}{r}$
Going	15	r	$\dfrac{15}{r}$
Returning	15	$r + 5$	$\dfrac{15}{r+5}$

The time going and the time returning is 4.5 hours.

$$\frac{15}{r} + \frac{15}{r+5} = 4.5$$

$$r(r+5)\left(\frac{15}{r} + \frac{15}{r+5}\right) = r(r+5)4.5$$

$$15(r+5) + 15r = 4.5r(r+5)$$

$$15r + 75 + 15r = 4.5r^2 + 22.5r$$

$$4.5r^2 - 7.5r - 75 = 0$$

$$r = \frac{7.5 \pm \sqrt{(-7.5)^2 - 4(4.5)(-75)}}{2(4.5)}$$

$$= \frac{7.5 \pm \sqrt{1406.25}}{9} = \frac{7.5 \pm 37.5}{9}$$

$$r = 5 \text{ or } r = -\frac{10}{3}$$

Disregard the negative value. Ricky's average speed going 5 mph and his average speed returning was 5 + 5 = 10 mph.

47. Let r be the speed of the plane in still air.

	d	r	$t = \dfrac{d}{r}$
With wind	80	$r + 30$	$\dfrac{80}{r+30}$
Against wind	80	$r - 30$	$\dfrac{80}{r-30}$

The total time is 1.3 hours

$$\frac{80}{r+30} + \frac{80}{r-30} = 1.3$$

$$(r+30)(r-30)\left(\frac{80}{r+30} + \frac{80}{r-30} = 1.3\right)$$

$$80(r-3) + 80(r+30) = 1.3(r^2 - 900)$$

$$80r - 240 + 80r + 240 = 1.3r^2 - 1170$$

$$160r = 1.3r^2 - 1170$$

$$0 = 1.3r^2 - 160r - 1170$$

$$r = \frac{-(-160) \pm \sqrt{(-160)^2 - 4(1.3)(-1170)}}{2(1.3)}$$

$$= \frac{160 \pm \sqrt{25,600 + 6084}}{2.6}$$

$$= \frac{160 \pm \sqrt{31,684}}{2.6}$$

$$= \frac{160 \pm 178}{2.6}$$

$$r = \frac{160 + 178}{2.6} \quad \text{or} \quad r = \frac{160 - 178}{2.6}$$

$$= \frac{338}{2.6} \qquad\qquad\quad = \frac{-18}{2.6}$$

$$= 130 \qquad\qquad\qquad \approx -6.92$$

Since speed must be positive, the speed of the plane in still air is 130 mph.

48. Let t be the time of the newer ship.

$$\frac{8}{t} + \frac{8}{t+3} = 1$$

$$t(t+3)\left(\frac{8}{t}\right) + t(t+3)\left(\frac{8}{t+3}\right) = t(t+3)(1)$$

$$8(t+3) + 8t = t^2 + 3t$$

$$16t + 24 = t^2 + 3t$$

$$0 = t^2 - 13t - 24$$

$$t = \frac{-(-13) \pm \sqrt{(-13)^2 - 4(1)(-24)}}{2(1)}$$

$$= \frac{13 \pm \sqrt{169 + 96}}{2}$$

$$= \frac{13 \pm \sqrt{265}}{2}$$

$$t = \frac{13 + \sqrt{265}}{2} \quad \text{or} \quad t = \frac{13 - \sqrt{265}}{2}$$

$$\approx 14.64 \qquad\qquad\quad \approx -1.64$$

Since the time cannot be negative, the time for the newer ship is 14.64 hours.

49. Let t be the number of hours for Chris to clean alone. Then $t + 0.5$ is the number of hours for John to clean alone.

	Rate of work	Time worked	Part of Task completed
Chris	$\dfrac{1}{t}$	6	$\dfrac{6}{t}$
John	$\dfrac{1}{t+0.5}$	6	$\dfrac{6}{t+0.5}$

$$1 = \frac{6}{t} + \frac{6}{t+0.5}$$

$$t(t+0.5)(1) = t(t+0.5)\left(\frac{6}{t}\right) + t(t+0.5)\left(\frac{6}{t+0.5}\right)$$

$$t(t+0.5) = 6(t+0.5) + 6t$$

$$t^2 + 0.5t = 6t + 3 + 6t$$

$$t^2 + 0.5t = 12t + 3$$

$$t^2 - 11.5t - 3 = 0$$

$$t = \frac{11.5 \pm \sqrt{(-11.5)^2 - 4(1)(-3)}}{2(1)}$$

$$= \frac{11.5 \pm \sqrt{132.25 + 12}}{2}$$

$$= \frac{11.5 \pm \sqrt{144.25}}{2}$$

$$t = \frac{11.5 + \sqrt{144.25}}{2} \quad \text{or} \quad t = \frac{11.5 - \sqrt{144.25}}{2}$$

$$\approx 11.76 \qquad\qquad\qquad \approx -0.26$$

Since the time must be positive, it takes Chris about 11.76 hours and John about $11.76 + 0.5 = 12.26$ hours to clean alone

50. Let t be the time for the large heater to heat the garage. Then $t + 6$ is the time for the small heater to do the job.

	Rate of work	Time worked	Part of Task completed
Small heater	$\dfrac{1}{t+6}$	42	$\dfrac{42}{t+6}$
Large heater	$\dfrac{1}{t}$	42	$\dfrac{42}{t}$

$$\frac{42}{t+6} + \frac{42}{t} = 1$$

$$t(t+6)\left(\frac{42}{t+6}\right) + t(t+6)\left(\frac{42}{t}\right) = t(t+6)(1)$$

$$42t + 42(t+6) = t(t+6)$$

$$42t + 42t + 252 = t^2 + 6t$$

$$0 = t^2 - 78t - 252$$

$$t = \frac{-(-78) \pm \sqrt{(-78)^2 - 4(1)(-252)}}{2(1)}$$

$$= \frac{78 \pm \sqrt{7092}}{2}$$

$$t = \frac{78 \pm \sqrt{7092}}{2} \quad \text{or} \quad t = \frac{78 - \sqrt{7092}}{2}$$

$$\approx 81.1 \qquad\qquad\qquad \approx -3.1$$

The time must be positive, so it takes 81.1 minutes for the larger heater and $81.1 + 6 = 87.1$ minutes for the smaller heater to heat the garage.

51. Let x be the speed of the trip from Lubbock to Plainview. Then $x - 10$ is the speed from Plainview to Amarillo.

	d	r	t
First part	75	x	$\dfrac{75}{x}$
Second part	195	$x - 10$	$\dfrac{195}{x-10}$

Including the 2 hours she spent in Plainview, the entire trip took Lisa 6 hours.

$$\frac{75}{x} + 2 + \frac{195}{x-10} = 6$$

$$\frac{75}{x} + \frac{195}{x-10} = 4$$

$$x(x-10)\left(\frac{75}{x} + \frac{195}{x-10}\right) = x(x-10)4$$

$$75(x-10) + 195x = 4x^2 - 40x$$

$$75x - 750 + 195x = 4x^2 - 40x$$

$$270x - 750 = 4x^2 - 40x$$

$$0 = 4x^2 - 310x + 750$$

$$0 = 2(2x^2 - 155x + 375)$$

$$0 = 2(2x - 5)(x - 75)$$

$$2x - 5 = 0 \quad \text{or} \quad x - 75 = 0$$

$$x = \frac{5}{2} \qquad\qquad x = 75$$

We disregard $x = \dfrac{5}{2}$ since it would result in a negative speed for the second part of the trip. Shywanda's average speed from San Antonio to Austin was 75 mph.

52. Let r be the average speed of the car.

	d	r	$t = \dfrac{d}{r}$
Car	500	r	$\dfrac{500}{r}$
Train	800	$r + 20$	$\dfrac{800}{r+20}$

The train traveled $1\dfrac{2}{3}$ or $\dfrac{5}{3}$ hours longer.

$$\frac{800}{r+20} = \frac{500}{r} + \frac{5}{3}$$

$$3r(r+20)\left(\frac{800}{r+20}\right) = 3r(r+20)\left(\frac{500}{r} + \frac{5}{3}\right)$$

$$3r(800) = 3(r+20)(500) + 5r(r+20)$$

$$2400r = 1500r + 30,000 + 5r^2 + 100r$$

$$2400r = 5r^2 + 1600r + 30,000$$

$$0 = 5r^2 - 800r + 30,000$$

$$0 = r^2 - 160r + 6000$$

$$0 = (r-60)(r-100)$$

$$r - 60 = 0 \quad \text{or} \quad r - 100 = 0$$

$$r = 60 \qquad\qquad r = 100$$

A car traveling 100 mph is not reasonable. Thus the car's average rate was 60 mph and the train's average rate was 80 mph.

53. From the figure, $16x =$ the length and $9x =$ the height.

$$(16x)^2 + (9x)^2 = 40^2$$

$$256x^2 + 81x^2 = 1600$$

$$337x^2 = 1600$$

$$x^2 = \frac{1600}{337}$$

$$x = \pm\sqrt{\frac{1600}{337}} \approx \pm 2.179$$

Disregard the negative answer.
The length is $16(2.179) \approx 34.86$ inches and the height is $9(2.179) \approx 19.61$ inches.

54. Since the television screen aspect ratio is 4:3, let $4x =$ the length and $3x =$ the height.

$$(4x)^2 + (3x)^2 = 36^2$$

$$16x^2 + 9x^2 = 1296$$

$$25x^2 = 1296$$

$$x^2 = \frac{1296}{25}$$

$$x = \pm\sqrt{\frac{1296}{25}} = \pm 7.2$$

Disregard the negative answer.
The length is $4(7.2) = 28.8$ inches and the height is $3(7.2) = 21.6$ inches.

55 – 56. Answers will vary.

57. Let $l =$ original length and $w =$ original width. A system of equations that describes this situation is

$$l \cdot w = 18$$

$$(l+2)(w+3) = 48$$

Solve the first equation for l to obtain $l = \dfrac{18}{w}$.

Substitute $\dfrac{18}{w}$ for l in the second equation. The result is an equation in only one variable which can be solved.

$$(l+2)(w+3) = 48$$

$$\left(\frac{18}{w} + 2\right)(w+3) = 48$$

$$18 + \frac{54}{w} + 2w + 6 = 48$$

$$2w - 24 + \frac{54}{w} = 0$$

$$w\left(2w - 24 + \frac{54}{w}\right) = w(0)$$

$$2w^2 - 24w + 54 = 0$$

$$2(w-3)(w-9) = 0$$

$$w = 3 \quad \text{or} \quad w = 9$$

If $w = 3$, then $l = \dfrac{18}{3} = 6$. One possible set of dimensions for the original rectangle is 6 meters by 3 meters. If $w = 9$, then $l = \dfrac{18}{9} = 2$. Another possible set of dimensions for the original rectangle is 2 meters by 9 meters.

58. Let l = original length and w = original width. A system of equations that describes this situation is

$$l \cdot w = 35$$
$$(l-1)(w+1) = 36$$

Solve the first equation for l to obtain $l = \dfrac{35}{w}$.

Substitute $\dfrac{35}{w}$ for l in the second equation. The result is an equation in only one variable that can be solved.

$$(l-1)(w+1) = 36$$
$$\left(\frac{35}{w}-1\right)(w+1) = 36$$
$$35 + \frac{35}{w} - w - 1 = 36$$
$$-w - 2 + \frac{35}{w} = 0$$
$$-w\left(-w-2+\frac{35}{w}\right) = -w(0)$$
$$w^2 + 2w - 35 = 0$$
$$(w+7)(w-5) = 0$$
$$w = -7 \text{ or } w = 5$$

Disregard the negative value. If $w = 5$, then $l = \dfrac{35}{5} = 7$. The dimensions for the original rectangle are 5 inches by 7 inches.

59. $-\left[4(5-3)^3\right] + 2^4 = -\left[4(2)^3\right] + 2^4$

$$= -\left[4(8)\right] + 16$$
$$= -32 + 16$$
$$= -16$$

60. $IR + Ir = E$, for R

$$IR = E - Ir$$
$$R = \frac{E - Ir}{I}$$

61. $\dfrac{r}{r-4} - \dfrac{r}{r+4} + \dfrac{32}{r^2-16}$

$$= \frac{r}{r-4} \cdot \frac{r+4}{r+4} - \frac{r}{r+4} \cdot \frac{r-4}{r-4} + \frac{32}{(r+4)(r-4)}$$
$$= \frac{r(r+4) - r(r-4) + 32}{(r+4)(r-4)} = \frac{r^2 + 4r - r^2 + 4r + 32}{(r+4)(r-4)}$$
$$= \frac{8r + 32}{(r+4)(r-4)} = \frac{8(r+4)}{(r+4)(r-4)} = \frac{8}{r-4}$$

62. $\left(\dfrac{x^{3/4} y^{-2}}{x^{1/2} y^2}\right)^8 = \left(x^{(3/4)-(1/2)} y^{-2-2}\right)^8$

$$= \left(x^{1/4} y^{-4}\right)^8$$
$$= x^2 y^{-32}$$
$$= \frac{x^2}{y^{32}}$$

63. $\sqrt{x^2 + 3x + 12} = x$

$$x^2 + 3x + 12 = x^2$$
$$3x + 12 = 0$$
$$3x = -12$$
$$x = -4$$

Upon checking, this value does not satisfy the equation. There is no real solution.

Mid-Chapter Test: 12.1-12.3

1. $x^2 - 12 = 86$

$$x^2 = 98$$
$$x = \pm\sqrt{98} = \pm 7\sqrt{2}$$

2. $(a-3)^2 + 20 = 0$

$$(a-3)^2 = -20$$
$$a - 3 = \pm\sqrt{-20}$$
$$a - 3 = \pm 2i\sqrt{5}$$
$$a = 3 \pm 2i\sqrt{5}$$

3. $(2m+7)^2 = 36$

$$2m + 7 = \pm\sqrt{36}$$
$$2m + 7 = \pm 6$$
$$2m = -7 \pm 6$$
$$m = \frac{-7 \pm 6}{2}$$
$$m = \frac{-7+6}{2} \text{ or } m = \frac{-7-6}{2}$$
$$m = -\frac{1}{2} \qquad\qquad m = -\frac{13}{2}$$

4. $y^2 + 4y - 12 = 0$

$$y^2 + 4y = 12$$

$$y^2 + 4y + 4 = 12 + 4$$

$$(y+2)^2 = 16$$

$$y + 2 = \pm\sqrt{16}$$

$$y + 2 = \pm 4$$

$$y = -2 \pm 4$$

$y = -2 + 4$ or $y = -2 - 4$

$y = 2$ $\qquad\qquad y = -6$

5. $3a^2 - 12a - 30 = 0$

$$\frac{1}{3}(3a^2 - 12a - 30) = \frac{1}{3}(0)$$

$$a^2 - 4a - 10 = 0$$

$$a^2 - 4a = 10$$

$$a^2 - 4a + 4 = 10 + 4$$

$$(a-2)^2 = 14$$

$$a - 2 = \pm\sqrt{14}$$

$$y = 2 \pm \sqrt{14}$$

6. $\qquad 4c^2 + c = -9$

$$\frac{1}{4}\left(4c^2 + c\right) = \frac{1}{4}(-9)$$

$$c^2 + \frac{1}{4}c = -\frac{9}{4}$$

$$c^2 + \frac{1}{4}c + \frac{1}{64} = -\frac{9}{4} + \frac{1}{64}$$

$$\left(c + \frac{1}{8}\right)^2 = -\frac{143}{64}$$

$$\left(c + \frac{1}{8}\right)^2 = -\frac{143}{64}$$

$$c + \frac{1}{8} = \sqrt{-\frac{143}{64}}$$

$$c + \frac{1}{8} = \pm\frac{i\sqrt{143}}{8}$$

$$c = -\frac{1}{8} \pm \frac{i\sqrt{143}}{8}$$

$$c = \frac{-1 \pm i\sqrt{143}}{8}$$

7. Let x = the length of one side of the patio. Then $x + 6$ is the length of the diagonal.

$$x^2 + x^2 = (x+6)^2$$

$$2x^2 = x^2 + 12x + 36$$

$$x^2 - 12x = 36$$

$$x^2 - 12x + 36 = 36 + 36$$

$$(x-6)^2 = 72$$

$$x - 6 = \pm\sqrt{72}$$

$$x - 6 = \pm 6\sqrt{2}$$

$$x = 6 \pm 6\sqrt{2}$$

The length of one side is $\left(6 \pm 6\sqrt{2}\right)$ meters.

8. a. $b^2 - 4ac$

  b. If $b^2 - 4ac > 0$, then the quadratic equation will have two distinct real solutions. If $b^2 - 4ac = 0$, then the equation has the single real solution $\frac{-b}{2a}$. If $b^2 - 4ac < 0$, then the expression under the radical sign in the quadratic formula is negative. Thus, the equation will have no real solution.

9. $2b^2 - 6b - 11 = 0$

$b^2 - 4ac = (-6)^2 - 4(2)(-11) = 36 + 88 = 124$

Since the discriminant is positive, the equation will have two distinct real solutions.

10. $\qquad 6n^2 + n = 15$

$$6n^2 + n - 15 = 0$$

$$n = \frac{-b \pm \sqrt{b^2 - 4ac}}{2a}$$

$$= \frac{-1 \pm \sqrt{1^2 - 4(6)(-15)}}{2(6)}$$

$$= \frac{-1 \pm \sqrt{1 + 360}}{12}$$

$$= \frac{-1 \pm \sqrt{361}}{12}$$

$$= \frac{-1 \pm 19}{12}$$

$n = \dfrac{-1 + 19}{12}$ or $n = \dfrac{-1 - 19}{12}$

$\quad = \dfrac{18}{12} \qquad\qquad = \dfrac{-20}{12}$

$\quad = \dfrac{3}{2} \qquad\qquad = -\dfrac{5}{3}$

11.
$$p^2 = -4p + 8$$
$$p^2 + 4p - 8 = 0$$
$$p = \frac{-b \pm \sqrt{b^2 - 4ac}}{2a}$$
$$= \frac{-4 \pm \sqrt{4^2 - 4(1)(-8)}}{2(1)}$$
$$= \frac{-4 \pm \sqrt{16 + 32}}{2}$$
$$= \frac{-4 \pm \sqrt{48}}{2}$$
$$= \frac{-4 \pm 4\sqrt{3}}{2}$$
$$= -2 \pm 2\sqrt{3}$$

12. $3d^2 - 2d + 5 = 0$
$$d = \frac{-b \pm \sqrt{b^2 - 4ac}}{2a}$$
$$= \frac{-(-2) \pm \sqrt{(-2)^2 - 4(3)(5)}}{2(3)}$$
$$= \frac{2 \pm \sqrt{4 - 60}}{6}$$
$$= \frac{2 \pm \sqrt{-56}}{6}$$
$$= \frac{2 \pm 2i\sqrt{14}}{6}$$
$$= \frac{1 \pm i\sqrt{14}}{3}$$

13. $x = 7$ and $x = -2$
$$x - 7 = 0 \text{ and } x + 2 = 0$$
$$(x - 7)(x + 2) = 0$$
$$x^2 + 2x - 7x - 14 = 0$$
$$x^2 - 5x - 14 = 0$$

14. $x = 2 + \sqrt{5}$ and $x = 2 - \sqrt{5}$
$$x - 2 - \sqrt{5} = 0 \text{ and } x - 2 + \sqrt{5} = 0$$
$$\left(x - 2 - \sqrt{5}\right)\left(x - 2 + \sqrt{5}\right) = 0$$
$$\left[(x - 2) - \sqrt{5}\right]\left[(x - 2) + \sqrt{5}\right] = 0$$
$$(x - 2)^2 - \left(\sqrt{5}\right)^2 = 0$$
$$x^2 - 4x + 4 - 5 = 0$$
$$x^2 - 4x - 1 = 0$$

15. The revenue function is
$$R(n) = n(60 - 0.5n) = 60n - 0.5n^2$$
Let $R(n) = 550$.
$$550 = 60n - 0.5n^2$$
$$0.5n^2 - 60n + 550 = 0$$
$$2(0.5n^2 - 60n + 550) = 2(0)$$
$$n^2 - 120n + 1100 = 0$$
$$n = \frac{-b \pm \sqrt{b^2 - 4ac}}{2a}$$
$$= \frac{-(-120) \pm \sqrt{(-120)^2 - 4(1)(1100)}}{2(1)}$$
$$= \frac{120 \pm \sqrt{14,400 - 4400}}{2}$$
$$= \frac{120 \pm \sqrt{10,000}}{2}$$
$$= \frac{120 \pm 100}{2}$$

$$n = \frac{120 + 100}{2} \quad \text{or} \quad n = \frac{120 - 100}{2}$$
$$= \frac{220}{2} \qquad\qquad = \frac{20}{2}$$
$$= 110 \qquad\qquad\quad = 10$$

We have a restriction of $n \le 20$, so disregard 110. Thus 10 lamps must be sold.

16. $y = x^2 - r^2$, for r
$$r^2 = x^2 - y$$
$$r = \sqrt{x^2 - y}$$

17. $A = \dfrac{1}{3} kx^2$, for r
$$3(A) = 3\left(\frac{1}{3} kx^2\right)$$
$$3A = kx^2$$
$$\frac{3A}{k} = x^2$$
$$\sqrt{\frac{3A}{k}} = x$$

18. $D = \sqrt{x^2 + y^2}$, for y
$$D^2 = x^2 + y^2$$
$$D^2 - x^2 = y^2$$
$$\sqrt{D^2 - x^2} = y$$

19. Let w = the width of the rectangle. Then $2w + 2$ = the length.

$$w(2w + 2) = 60$$

$$2w^2 + 2w - 60 = 0$$

$$\frac{1}{2}(2w^2 + 2w - 60) = \frac{1}{2}(0)$$

$$w^2 + w - 30 = 0$$

$$w = \frac{-1 \pm \sqrt{1^2 - 4(1)(-30)}}{2(1)}$$

$$= \frac{-1 \pm \sqrt{1 + 120}}{2}$$

$$= \frac{-1 \pm \sqrt{121}}{2}$$

$$= \frac{-1 \pm 11}{2}$$

$$w = \frac{-1 + 11}{2} \quad \text{or} \quad w = \frac{-1 - 11}{2}$$

$$= \frac{10}{2} \qquad\qquad = \frac{-12}{2}$$

$$= 5 \qquad\qquad = -6$$

The width must be positive, so disregard the negative answer. The width is 5 feet and the length is $2(5) + 2 = 12$ feet.

20. Note: 2000 = 20 hundreds

$$p(n) = 2n^2 + n - 35; \quad p(n) = 20$$

$$20 = 2n^2 + n - 35$$

$$0 = 2n^2 + n - 55$$

$$0 = 2n^2 + n - 55$$

$$n = \frac{-1 \pm \sqrt{1^2 - 4(2)(-55)}}{2(2)}$$

$$= \frac{-1 \pm \sqrt{1 + 440}}{4}$$

$$= \frac{-1 \pm \sqrt{441}}{4}$$

$$= \frac{-1 \pm 21}{4}$$

$$n = \frac{-1 + 21}{4} \quad \text{or} \quad n = \frac{-1 - 21}{4}$$

$$= \frac{20}{4} \qquad\qquad = \frac{-22}{4}$$

$$= 5 \qquad\qquad = -\frac{11}{2}$$

Disregard the negative answer. Thus, 5 clocks must be sold.

Exercise Set 12.4

1. A given equation can be expressed as an equation in quadratic form if the equation can be written in the form $au^2 + bu + c = 0$.

2. It is essential to check for extraneous solutions when both sides of an equation are raised to a power since answers may not satisfy the original equation.

3. Let $u = x^2$. Then
$$3x^4 - 5x^2 + 1 = 0$$
$$3(x^2)^2 - 5x^2 + 1 = 0$$
$$3u^2 - 5u + 1 = 0$$

4. Let $u = y^{2/3}$. Then
$$2y^{4/3} + 9y^{2/3} - 7 = 0$$
$$2(y^{2/3})^2 + 9y^{2/3} - 7 = 0$$
$$2u^2 + 9u - 7 = 0$$

5. Let $u = z^{-1}$. Then
$$z^{-2} - z^{-1} = 56$$
$$(z^{-1})^2 - z^{-1} = 56$$
$$u^2 - u = 56$$

6. Let $u = \frac{x+2}{x+3}$. Then
$$3\left(\frac{x+2}{x+3}\right)^2 + \left(\frac{x+2}{x+3}\right) - 9 = 0$$
$$3u^2 + u - 9 = 0$$

7. Let $u = x^2$.
$$x^4 + x^2 - 6 = (x^2)^2 + x^2 - 6$$
$$= u^2 + u - 6$$
$$= (u + 3)(u - 2)$$
Back substitute x^2 for u.
$$= (x^2 + 3)(x^2 - 2)$$

8. Let $u = x^2$.
$$x^4 - 3x^2 - 10 = (x^2)^2 - 3x^2 - 10$$
$$= u^2 - 3u - 10$$
$$= (u + 2)(u - 5)$$
Back substitute x^2 for u.
$$= (x^2 + 2)(x^2 - 5)$$

9. Let $u = x^2$.

$$x^4 + 5x^2 + 6 = \left(x^2\right)^2 + 5x^2 + 6$$
$$= u^2 + 5u + 6$$
$$= (u+2)(u+3)$$

Back substitute x^2 for u.
$$= \left(x^2 + 2\right)\left(x^2 + 3\right)$$

10. Let $u = x^2$.

$$x^4 + 2x^2 - 35 = \left(x^2\right)^2 + 2x^2 - 35$$
$$= u^2 + 2u - 35$$
$$= (u+7)(u-5)$$

Back substitute x^2 for u.
$$= \left(x^2 + 7\right)\left(x^2 - 5\right)$$

11. Let $u = a^2$.

$$6a^4 + 5a^2 - 25 = 6\left(a^2\right)^2 + 5a^2 - 25$$
$$= 6u^2 + 5u - 25$$
$$= (2u+5)(3u-5)$$

Back substitute a^2 for u.
$$= \left(2a^2 + 5\right)\left(3a^2 - 5\right)$$

12. Let $u = 2x+1$.

$$(2x+1)^2 + 2(2x+1) - 15$$
$$= u^2 + 2u - 15$$
$$= (u+5)(u-3)$$

Back substitute $2x+1$ for u.
$$= [(2x+1)+5][(2x+1)-3]$$
$$= (2x+6)(2x-2)$$
$$= 2(x+3) \cdot 2(x-1)$$
$$= 4(x+3)(x-1)$$

13. Let $u = x+1$.

$$4(x+1)^2 + 8(x+1) + 3$$
$$= 4u^2 + 8u + 3$$
$$= (2u+3)(2u+1)$$

Back substitute $x+1$ for u.
$$= [2(x+1)+3][2(x+1)+1]$$
$$= (2x+2+3)(2x+2+1)$$
$$= (2x+5)(2x+3)$$

14. Let $u = 2x+3$.

$$(2x+3)^2 - (2x+3) - 6$$
$$= u^2 - u - 6$$
$$= (u-3)(u+2)$$

Back substitute $2x+3$ for u.
$$= [(2x+3)-3][(2x+3)+2]$$
$$= 2x(2x+5)$$

15. Let $u = a+2$.

$$6(a+2)^2 - 7(a+2) - 5$$
$$= 6u^2 - 7u - 5$$
$$= (2u+1)(3u-5)$$

Back substitute $a+2$ for u.
$$= [2(a+2)+1][3(a+2)-5]$$
$$= (2a+4+1)(3a+6-5)$$
$$= (2a+5)(3a+1)$$

16. Let $u = p-5$.

$$6(p-5)^2 + 11(p-5) + 3$$
$$= 6u^2 + 11u + 3$$
$$= (2u+3)(3u+1)$$

Back substitute $p-5$ for u.
$$= [2(p-5)+3][3(p-5)+1]$$
$$= (2p-10+3)(3p-15+1)$$
$$= (2p-7)(3p-14)$$

17. Let $u = ab$.

$$a^2b^2 + 8ab + 15 = (ab)^2 + 8ab + 15$$
$$= u^2 + 8u + 15$$
$$= (u+3)(u+5)$$

Back substitute ab for u.
$$= (ab+3)(ab+5)$$

18. Let $u = xy$.

$$x^2y^2 - 10xy + 24 = (xy)^2 - 10xy + 24$$
$$= u^2 - 10u + 24$$
$$= (u-6)(u-4)$$

Back substitute xy for u.
$$= (xy-6)(xy-4)$$

19. Let $u = xy$.

$$3x^2y^2 - 2xy - 5 = 3(xy)^2 - 2xy - 5$$
$$= 3u^2 - 2u - 5$$
$$= (3u-5)(u+1)$$

Back substitute xy for u.
$$= (3xy-5)(xy+1)$$

20. Let $u = pq$.

$$3p^2q^2 + 11pq + 6 = 3(pq)^2 + 11pq + 6$$
$$= 3u^2 + 11u + 6$$
$$= (3u + 2)(u + 3)$$

Back substitute pq for u.

$$= (3pq + 2)(pq + 3)$$

21. Factor out $(5 - a)$.

$$2a^2(5 - a) - 7a(5 - a) + 5(5 - a)$$
$$= (5 - a)(2a^2 - 7a + 5)$$
$$= (5 - a)(2a - 5)(a - 1)$$

22. Factor out $(y + 2)$.

$$2y^2(y + 2) + 13y(y + 2) + 15(y + 2)$$
$$= (y + 2)(2y^2 + 13y + 15)$$
$$= (y + 2)(2y + 3)(y + 5)$$

23. Factor out $(x - 3)$.

$$2x^2(x - 3) + 7x(x - 3) + 6(x - 3)$$
$$= (x - 3)(2x^2 + 7x + 6)$$
$$= (x - 3)(2x + 3)(x + 2)$$

24. Factor out $(x - 2)$.

$$3x^2(x - 2) + 5x(x - 2) - 2(x - 2)$$
$$= (x - 2)(3x^2 + 5x - 2)$$
$$= (x - 3)(3x - 1)(x + 2)$$

25. Let $u = y^2$.

$$y^4 + 13y^2 + 30 = (y^2)^2 + 13y^2 + 30$$
$$= u^2 + 13u + 30$$
$$= (u + 10)(u + 3)$$

Back substitute y^2 for u.

$$= (y^2 + 10)(y^2 + 3)$$

26. Let $u = z^2$.

$$3z^4 - 16z^2 + 5 = 3(z^2)^2 - 16z^2 + 5$$
$$= 3u^2 - 16u + 5$$
$$= (3u - 1)(u - 5)$$

Back substitute z^2 for u.

$$= (3z^2 - 1)(z^2 - 5)$$

27. Factor out $(x + 3)$.

$$x^2(x + 3) + 3x(x + 3) + 2(x + 3)$$
$$= (x + 3)(x^2 + 3x + 2)$$
$$= (x + 3)(x + 1)(x + 2)$$

28. Factor out $(x - 1)$.

$$x^2(x - 1) - x(x - 1) - 30(x - 1)$$
$$= (x - 1)(x^2 - x - 30)$$
$$= (x - 1)(x - 6)(x + 5)$$

29. Factor out a^3b^2.

$$5a^5b^2 - 8a^4b^3 + 3a^3b^4$$
$$= a^3b^2(5a^2 - 8ab + 3b^2)$$
$$= a^3b^2(5a - 3b)(a - b)$$

30. Factor out y^4.

$$2x^2y^6 + 3xy^5 - 9y^4$$
$$= y^4(2x^2y^2 + 3xy - 9)$$

Let $u = xy$.

$$= y^4\left[2(xy)^2 + 3(xy) - 9\right]$$
$$= y^4(2u^2 + 3u - 9)$$
$$= y^4(2u - 3)(u + 3)$$

Back substitute xy for u.

$$= y^4(2xy - 3)(xy + 3)$$

31.
$$x^4 - 10x^2 + 9 = 0$$
$$(x^2)^2 - 10x^2 + 9 = 0$$

Let $u = x^2$.

$$u^2 - 10u + 9 = 0$$
$$(u - 9)(u - 1) = 0$$
$$u - 9 = 0 \quad \text{or} \quad u - 1 = 0$$
$$u = 9 \qquad\qquad u = 1$$

Substitute x^2 for u.

$$x^2 = 9 \qquad \text{or} \quad x^2 = 1$$
$$x = \pm\sqrt{9} = \pm 3 \qquad x = \pm\sqrt{1} = \pm 1$$

The solutions are 3, –3, 1, and –1.

32. $x^4 - 37x^2 + 36 = 0$

$(x^2)^2 - 37x^2 + 36 = 0$

Let $u = x^2$.

$u^2 - 37u + 36 = 0$

$(u - 36)(u - 1) = 0$

$u - 36 = 0$ or $u - 1 = 0$

$u = 36$ $u = 1$

Substitute x^2 for u.

$x^2 = 36$ or $x^2 = 1$

$x = \pm\sqrt{36} = \pm 6$ $x = \pm\sqrt{1} = \pm 1$

The solutions are 6, –6, 1, and –1.

33. $x^4 + 17x^2 + 16 = 0$

$(x^2)^2 + 17x^2 + 16 = 0$

Let $u = x^2$.

$u^2 + 17u + 16 = 0$

$(u + 16)(u + 1) = 0$

$u + 16 = 0$ or $u + 1 = 0$

$u = -16$ $u = -1$

Substitute x^2 for u.

$x^2 = -16$ or $x^2 = -1$

$x = \pm\sqrt{-16} = \pm 4i$ $x = \pm\sqrt{-1} = \pm i$

The solutions are $4i$, $-4i$, i, and $-i$.

34. $x^4 + 50x^2 + 49 = 0$

$(x^2)^2 + 50x^2 + 49 = 0$

Let $u = x^2$.

$u^2 + 50u + 49 = 0$

$(u + 49)(u + 1) = 0$

$u + 49 = 0$ or $u + 1 = 0$

$u = -49$ $u = -1$

Substitute x^2 for u.

$x^2 = -49$ or $x^2 = -1$

$x = \pm\sqrt{-49} = \pm 7i$ $x = \pm\sqrt{-1} = \pm i$

The solutions are $7i$, $-7i$, i, and $-i$.

35. $x^4 - 13x^2 + 36 = 0$

$(x^2)^2 - 13x^2 + 36 = 0$

Let $u = x^2$.

$u^2 - 13u + 36 = 0$

$(u - 9)(u - 4) = 0$

$u - 9 = 0$ or $u - 4 = 0$

$u = 9$ $u = 4$

Substitute x^2 for u.

$x^2 = 9$ or $x^2 = 4$

$x = \pm\sqrt{9} = \pm 3$ $x = \pm\sqrt{4} = \pm 2$

The solutions are 3, –3, 2, and –2.

36. $x^4 + 13x^2 + 36 = 0$

$(x^2)^2 + 13x^2 + 36 = 0$

Let $u = x^2$.

$u^2 + 13u + 36 = 0$

$(u + 9)(u + 4) = 0$

$u + 9 = 0$ or $u + 4 = 0$

$u = -9$ $u = -4$

Substitute x^2 for u.

$x^2 = -9$ or $x^2 = -4$

$x = \pm\sqrt{-9} = \pm 3i$ $x = \pm\sqrt{-4} = \pm 2i$

The solutions are $3i$, $-3i$, $2i$, and $-2i$.

37. $a^4 - 7a^2 + 12 = 0$

$(a^2)^2 - 7a^2 + 12 = 0$

Let $u = a^2$.

$u^2 - 7u + 12 = 0$

$(u - 4)(u - 3) = 0$

$u - 4 = 0$ or $u - 3 = 0$

$u = 4$ $u = 3$

Substitute a^2 for u.

$a^2 = 4$ or $a^2 = 3$

$a = \pm\sqrt{4} = \pm 2$ $a = \pm\sqrt{3}$

The solutions are 2, –2, $\sqrt{3}$, and $-\sqrt{3}$.

38. $b^4 + 7b^2 + 12 = 0$

$(b^2)^2 + 7b^2 + 12 = 0$

Let $u = b^2$.

$u^2 + 7u + 12 = 0$

$(u + 4)(u + 3) = 0$

$u + 4 = 0$ or $u + 3 = 0$

$u = -4$ $u = -3$

Substitute b^2 for u.

$b^2 = -4$ or $b^2 = -3$

$b = \pm\sqrt{-4} = \pm 2i$ $b = \pm\sqrt{-3} = \pm i\sqrt{3}$

The solutions are $2i$, $-2i$, $i\sqrt{3}$, and $-i\sqrt{3}$.

39. $4x^4 - 17x^2 + 4 = 0$

$4(x^2)^2 - 17x^2 + 4 = 0$

Let $u = x^2$.

$4u^2 - 17u + 4 = 0$

$(4u - 1)(u - 4) = 0$

$4u - 1 = 0$ or $u - 4 = 0$

$u = \dfrac{1}{4}$ $u = 4$

Substitute x^2 for u.

$x^2 = \dfrac{1}{4}$ or $x^2 = 4$

$x = \pm\sqrt{\dfrac{1}{4}} = \pm\dfrac{1}{2}$ $x = \pm\sqrt{4} = \pm 4$

The solutions are $\dfrac{1}{2}$, $-\dfrac{1}{2}$, 2, and –2.

40. $9d^4 - 13d^2 + 4 = 0$

$9(d^2)^2 - 13d^2 + 4 = 0$

Let $u = d^2$.

$9u^2 - 13u + 4 = 0$

$(9u - 4)(u - 1) = 0$

$9u - 4 = 0$ or $u - 1 = 0$

$u = \dfrac{4}{9}$ $u = 1$

Substitute d^2 for u.

$d^2 = \dfrac{4}{9}$ or $d^2 = 1$

$d = \pm\sqrt{\dfrac{4}{9}} = \pm\dfrac{2}{3}$ $d = \pm\sqrt{1} = \pm 1$

The solutions are $\dfrac{2}{3}$, $-\dfrac{2}{3}$, 1, and –1.

41. $r^4 - 8r^2 = -15$

$r^4 - 8r^2 + 15 = 0$

$(r^2)^2 - 8r^2 + 15 = 0$

Let $u = r^2$.

$u^2 - 8u + 15 = 0$

$(u - 3)(u - 5) = 0$

$u - 3 = 0$ or $u - 5 = 0$

$u = 3$ $u = 5$

Substitute r^2 for u.

$r^2 = 3$ or $r^2 = 5$

$r = \pm\sqrt{3}$ $r = \pm\sqrt{5}$

The solutions are $\sqrt{3}, -\sqrt{3}, \sqrt{5}$, and $-\sqrt{5}$.

42. $p^4 - 8p^2 = -12$

$p^4 - 8p^2 + 12 = 0$

$(p^2)^2 - 8p^2 + 12 = 0$

Let $u = p$.

$u^2 - 8u + 12 = 0$

$(u - 6)(u - 2) = 0$

$u - 6 = 0$ or $u - 2 = 0$

$u = 6$ $u = 2$

Substitute p^2 for u.

$p^2 = 6$ or $p^2 = 2$

$p = \pm\sqrt{6}$ $p = \pm\sqrt{2}$

The solutions are $\sqrt{6}, -\sqrt{6}, \sqrt{2},$ and $-\sqrt{2}$.

43. $z^4 - 7z^2 = 18$

$z^4 - 7z^2 - 18 = 0$

$(z^2)^2 - 7z^2 - 18 = 0$

Let $u = z$.

$u^2 - 7u - 18 = 0$

$(u - 9)(u + 2) = 0$

$u - 9 = 0$ or $u + 2 = 0$

$u = 9$ $u = -2$

Substitute z^2 for u.

$z^2 = 9$ or $z^2 = -2$

$z = \pm 3$ $z = \pm\sqrt{-2} = \pm i\sqrt{2}$

The solutions are $3, -3, i\sqrt{2}$, and $-i\sqrt{2}$.

44. $a^4 + a^2 = 42$

$a^4 + a^2 - 42 = 0$

$(a^2)^2 + a^2 - 42 = 0$

Let $u = a$.

$u^2 + u - 42 = 0$

$(u + 7)(u - 6) = 0$

$u + 7 = 0$ or $u - 6 = 0$

$u = -7$ $u = 6$

Substitute a^2 for u.

$a^2 = -7$ or $a^2 = 6$

$a = \pm\sqrt{-7} = \pm i\sqrt{7}$ $a = \pm\sqrt{6}$

The solutions are $i\sqrt{7}, -i\sqrt{7}, \sqrt{6},$ and $-\sqrt{6}$.

45. $-c^4 = 4c^2 - 5$

$0 = c^4 + 4c^2 - 5$

$0 = \left(c^2\right)^2 + 4c^2 - 5$

Let $u = c$.

$u^2 + 4u - 5 = 0$

$(u-1)(u+5) = 0$

$u - 1 = 0$ or $u + 5 = 0$

$u = 1$ $\qquad$ $u = -5$

Substitute c^2 for u.

$c^2 = 1$ or $c^2 = -5$

$c = \pm 1$ $\qquad$ $c = \pm\sqrt{-5} = \pm i\sqrt{5}$

The solutions are $1, -1, i\sqrt{5}$, and $-i\sqrt{5}$.

46. $9b^4 = 57b^2 - 18$

$9b^4 - 57b^2 + 18 = 0$

$9\left(b^2\right)^2 - 57b^2 + 18 = 0$

Let $u = b$.

$9u^2 - 57u + 18 = 0$

$3(3u^2 - 19u + 6) = 0$

$3(3u - 1)(u - 6) = 0$

$3u - 1 = 0$ or $u - 6 = 0$

$u = \dfrac{1}{3}$ $\qquad$ $u = 6$

Substitute b^2 for u.

$b = \pm\sqrt{\dfrac{1}{3}} = \pm\dfrac{\sqrt{3}}{3}$ or $b = \pm\sqrt{6}$

The solutions are $\dfrac{\sqrt{3}}{3}, -\dfrac{\sqrt{3}}{3}, \sqrt{6}$, and $-\sqrt{6}$.

47. $\sqrt{x} = 2x - 6$

$0 = 2x - \sqrt{x} - 6$

$0 = 2\left(x^{1/2}\right)^2 - x^{1/2} - 6$

Let $u = x^{1/2}$.

$2u^2 - u - 6 = 0$

$(2u + 3)(u - 2) = 0$

$2u + 3 = 0$ or $u - 2 = 0$

$u = -\dfrac{3}{2}$ $\qquad$ $u = 2$

Substitute $x^{1/2}$ for u.

$x^{1/2} = -\dfrac{3}{2}$ or $x^{1/2} = 2$

Not real $\qquad$ $x = 2^2 = 4$

The solution is 4.

48. $x - 2\sqrt{x} = 8$

$x - 2\sqrt{x} - 8 = 0$

$\left(x^{1/2}\right)^2 - 2x^{1/2} - 8 = 0$

Let $u = x^{1/2}$.

$u^2 - 2u - 8 = 0$

$(u + 2)(u - 4) = 0$

$u + 2 = 0$ or $u - 4 = 0$

$u = -2$ $\qquad$ $u = 4$

Substitute $x^{1/2}$ for u.

$x^{1/2} = -2$ or $x^{1/2} = 4$

Not real $\qquad$ $x = 4^2 = 16$

The solution is 16.

49. $x - \sqrt{x} = 6$

$x - \sqrt{x} - 6 = 0$

$\left(x^{1/2}\right)^2 - x^{1/2} - 6 = 0$

Let $u = x^{1/2}$.

$u^2 - u - 6 = 0$

$(u + 2)(u - 3) = 0$

$u + 2 = 0$ or $u - 3 = 0$

$u = -2$ or $\qquad$ $u = 3$

Substitute $x^{1/2}$ for u.

$x^{1/2} = -2$ or $x^{1/2} = 3$

Not real $\qquad$ $x = 3^2 = 9$

The solution is 9.

50. $x - 4 = -3\sqrt{x}$

$x + 3\sqrt{x} - 4 = 0$

$\left(x^{1/2}\right)^2 + 3x^{1/2} - 4 = 0$

Let $u = x^{1/2}$.

$u^2 + 3u - 4 = 0$

$(u + 4)(u - 1) = 0$

$u + 4 = 0$ or $u - 1 = 0$

$u = -4$ or $\qquad$ $u = 1$

Substitute $x^{1/2}$ for u.

$x^{1/2} = -4$ or $x^{1/2} = 1$

Not real $\qquad$ $x = 1^2 = 1$

The solution is 1.

51.
$$9x + 3\sqrt{x} = 2$$
$$9x + 3\sqrt{x} - 2 = 0$$
$$9\left(x^{1/2}\right)^2 + 3x^{1/2} - 2 = 0$$
Let $u = x^{1/2}$.
$$9u^2 + 3u - 2 = 0$$
$$(3u + 2)(3u - 1) = 0$$
$$3u + 2 = 0 \quad \text{or} \quad 3u - 1 = 0$$
$$u = -\frac{2}{3} \qquad u = \frac{1}{3}$$
Substitute $x^{1/2}$ for u.
$$x^{1/2} = -\frac{2}{3} \quad \text{or} \quad x^{1/2} = \frac{1}{3}$$
Not real $\qquad x = \left(\frac{1}{3}\right)^2 = \frac{1}{9}$

The solution is $\frac{1}{9}$.

52.
$$8x + 2\sqrt{x} = 1$$
$$8x + 2\sqrt{x} - 1 = 0$$
$$8\left(x^{1/2}\right)^2 + 2x^{1/2} - 1 = 0$$
Let $u = x^{1/2}$.
$$8u^2 + 2u - 1 = 0$$
$$(2u + 1)(4u - 1) = 0$$
$$2u + 1 = 0 \quad \text{or} \quad 4u - 1 = 0$$
$$u = -\frac{1}{2} \qquad u = \frac{1}{4}$$
Substitute $x^{1/2}$ for u.
$$x^{1/2} = -\frac{1}{2} \quad \text{or} \quad x^{1/2} = \frac{1}{4}$$
Not real $\qquad x = \left(\frac{1}{4}\right)^2 = \frac{1}{16}$

The solution is $\frac{1}{16}$.

53.
$$(x+3)^2 + 2(x+3) = 24$$
$$(x+3)^2 + 2(x+3) - 24 = 0$$
Let $u = x + 3$.
$$u^2 + 2u - 24 = 0$$
$$(u - 4)(u + 6) = 0$$
$$u - 4 = 0 \quad \text{or} \quad u + 6 = 0$$
$$u = 4 \qquad u = -6$$
Substitute $x + 3$ for u.
$$x + 3 = 4 \quad \text{or} \quad x + 3 = -6$$
$$x = 1 \qquad x = -9$$
The solutions are 1 and –9.

54.
$$(x+1)^2 + 4(x+1) + 3 = 0$$
Let $u = x + 1$.
$$u^2 + 4u + 3 = 0$$
$$(u + 3)(u + 1) = 0$$
$$u + 3 = 0 \quad \text{or} \quad u + 1 = 0$$
$$u = -3 \qquad u = -1$$
Substitute $x + 1$ for u.
$$x + 1 = -3 \quad \text{or} \quad x + 1 = -1$$
$$x = -4 \qquad x = -2$$
The solutions are –4 and –2.

55.
$$6(a-2)^2 = -19(a-2) - 10$$
$$6(a-2)^2 + 19(a-2) + 10 = 0$$
Let $u = a - 2$.
$$6u^2 + 19u + 10 = 0$$
$$(3u + 2)(2u + 5) = 0$$
$$3u + 2 = 0 \quad \text{or} \quad 2u + 5 = 0$$
$$u = -\frac{2}{3} \qquad u = -\frac{5}{2}$$
Substitute $a - 2$ for u.
$$a - 2 = -\frac{2}{3} \quad \text{or} \quad a - 2 = -\frac{5}{2}$$
$$a = \frac{4}{3} \qquad a = -\frac{1}{2}$$
The solutions are $\frac{4}{3}$ and $-\frac{1}{2}$.

56.
$$10(z+2)^2 = 3(z+2) + 1$$
$$10(z+2)^2 - 3(z+2) - 1 = 0$$
Let $u = z + 2$.
$$10u^2 - 3u - 1 = 0$$
$$(2u - 1)(5u + 1) = 0$$
$$2u - 1 = 0 \quad \text{or} \quad 5u + 1 = 0$$
$$u = \frac{1}{2} \qquad u = -\frac{1}{5}$$
Substitute $z + 2$ for u.
$$z + 2 = \frac{1}{2} \quad \text{or} \quad z + 2 = -\frac{1}{5}$$
$$z = -\frac{3}{2} \qquad z = -\frac{11}{5}$$
The solutions are $-\frac{3}{2}$ and $-\frac{11}{5}$.

57. $(x^2 - 3)^2 - (x^2 - 3) - 6 = 0$

Let $u = x^2 - 3$.

$u^2 - u - 6 = 0$

$(u + 2)(u - 3) = 0$

$u + 2 = 0$ or $u - 3 = 0$

$u = -2$ $u = 3$

Substitute $x^2 - 1$ for u.

$x^2 - 3 = -2$ or $x^2 - 3 = 3$

$x^2 = 1$ $x^2 = 6$

$x = \pm\sqrt{1} = \pm 1$ $x = \pm\sqrt{6}$

The solutions are $1, -1, \sqrt{6}$, and $-\sqrt{6}$.

58. $(a^2 - 1)^2 - 5(a^2 - 1) - 14 = 0$

Let $u = a^2 - 1$.

$u^2 - 5u - 14 = 0$

$(u + 2)(u - 7) = 0$

$u + 2 = 0$ or $u - 7 = 0$

$u = -2$ $u = 7$

Substitute $a^2 - 1$ for u.

$a^2 - 1 = -2$ or $a^2 - 1 = 7$

$a^2 = -1$ $a^2 = 8$

$a = \sqrt{-1} = \pm i$ $a = \pm\sqrt{8} = \pm 2\sqrt{2}$

The solutions are $i, -i, 2\sqrt{2}$, and $-2\sqrt{2}$.

59. $2(b + 3)^2 + 5(b + 3) - 3 = 0$

Let $u = b + 3$.

$2u^2 + 5u - 3 = 0$

$(u + 3)(2u - 1) = 0$

$u + 3 = 0$ or $2u - 1 = 0$

$u = -3$ $u = \dfrac{1}{2}$

Substitute $b + 3$ for u.

$b + 3 = -3$ or $b + 3 = \dfrac{1}{2}$

$b = -6$ $b = -\dfrac{5}{2}$

The solutions are -6 and $-\dfrac{5}{2}$.

60. $(z^2 - 6)^2 + 2(z^2 - 6) - 24 = 0$

Let $u = z^2 - 6$.

$u^2 + 2u - 24 = 0$

$(u - 4)(u + 6) = 0$

$u - 4 = 0$ or $u + 6 = 0$

$u = 4$ $u = -6$

Substitute $z^2 - 6$ for u.

$z^2 - 6 = 4$ or $z^2 - 6 = -6$

$z^2 = 10$ $z^2 = 0$

$z = \pm\sqrt{10}$ $z = 0$

The solutions are $\sqrt{10}, -\sqrt{10}$, and 0.

61. $18(x^2 - 5)^2 + 27(x^2 - 5) + 10 = 0$

Let $u = x^2 - 5$.

$18u^2 + 27u + 10 = 0$

$(3u + 2)(6u + 5) = 0$

$3u + 2 = 0$ or $6u + 5 = 0$

$u = -\dfrac{2}{3}$ $u = -\dfrac{5}{6}$

Substitute $x^2 - 5$ for u.

or $x^2 - 5 = -\dfrac{5}{6}$

$x^2 - 5 = -\dfrac{2}{3}$ or $x^2 - 5 = -\dfrac{5}{6}$

$x^2 = \dfrac{13}{3}$ $x^2 = \dfrac{25}{6}$

$x = \pm\sqrt{\dfrac{13}{3}}$ $x = \pm\sqrt{\dfrac{25}{6}}$

$= \pm\dfrac{\sqrt{13}}{\sqrt{3}} \cdot \dfrac{\sqrt{3}}{\sqrt{3}}$ $= \pm\dfrac{5}{\sqrt{6}} \cdot \dfrac{\sqrt{6}}{\sqrt{6}}$

$= \pm\dfrac{\sqrt{39}}{3}$ $= \pm\dfrac{5\sqrt{6}}{6}$

The solutions are $\dfrac{\sqrt{39}}{3}, -\dfrac{\sqrt{39}}{3}, \dfrac{5\sqrt{6}}{6}$, and

$-\dfrac{5\sqrt{6}}{6}$.

62. $28(x^2-8)^2 - 23(x^2-8) - 15 = 0$

Let $u = x^2 - 8$.

$28u^2 - 23u - 15 = 0$

$(7u+3)(4u-5) = 0$

$7u+3 = 0$　or　$4u - 5 = 0$

$u = -\dfrac{3}{7}$　　　$u = \dfrac{5}{4}$

Substitute $x^2 - 8$ for u.

$x^2 - 8 = -\dfrac{3}{7}$　or　$x^2 - 8 = \dfrac{5}{4}$

$x^2 = \dfrac{53}{7}$　　　$x^2 = \dfrac{37}{4}$

$x = \pm\sqrt{\dfrac{53}{7}}$　　$x = \pm\sqrt{\dfrac{37}{4}}$

$= \pm\dfrac{\sqrt{53}}{\sqrt{7}}\cdot\dfrac{\sqrt{7}}{\sqrt{7}}$　$= \pm\dfrac{\sqrt{37}}{2}$

$= \pm\dfrac{\sqrt{371}}{7}$

The solutions are $\dfrac{\sqrt{371}}{7}, -\dfrac{\sqrt{371}}{7}, \dfrac{\sqrt{37}}{2}$, and

$-\dfrac{\sqrt{37}}{2}$.

63. $a^{-2} + 4a^{-1} + 4 = 0$

$(a^{-1})^2 + 4(a^{-1}) + 4 = 0$

Let $u = a^{-1}$.

$u^2 + 4u + 4 = 0$

$(u+2)^2 = 0$

$u + 2 = 0$

$u = -2$

Substitute a^{-1} for u.

$a^{-1} = -2$

$a = -\dfrac{1}{2}$

The solution is $-\dfrac{1}{2}$.

64. $x^{-2} + 10x^{-1} + 25 = 0$

$(x^{-1})^2 + 10(x^{-1}) + 25 = 0$

Let $u = x^{-1}$.

$u^2 + 10u + 25 = 0$

$(u+5)^2 = 0$

$u + 5 = 0$

$u = -5$

Substitute x^{-1} for u.

$x^{-1} = -5$

$x = -\dfrac{1}{5}$

The solution is $-\dfrac{1}{5}$.

65. $12b^{-2} - 7b^{-1} + 1 = 0$

$12(b^{-1})^2 - 7(b^{-1}) + 1 = 0$

Let $u = b^{-1}$.

$12u^2 - 7u + 1 = 0$

$(4u-1)(3u-1) = 0$

$4u - 1 = 0$　or　$3u - 1 = 0$

$u = \dfrac{1}{4}$　　　$u = \dfrac{1}{3}$

Substitute b^{-1} for u.

$b^{-1} = \dfrac{1}{4}$　or　$b^{-1} = \dfrac{1}{3}$

$b = 4$　　　$b = 3$

The solutions are 4 and 3.

66. $5x^{-2} + 4x^{-1} - 1 = 0$

$5(x^{-1})^2 + 4(x^{-1}) - 1 = 0$

Let $u = x^{-1}$.

$5u^2 + 4u - 1 = 0$

$(5u-1)(u+1) = 0$

$5u - 1 = 0$　or　$u + 1 = 0$

$u = \dfrac{1}{5}$　　　$u = -1$

Substitute x^{-1} for u.

$x^{-1} = \dfrac{1}{5}$　or　$x^{-1} = -1$

$x = 5$　　　$x = -1$

The solutions are 5 and -1.

67.
$$2b^{-2} = 7b^{-1} - 3$$
$$2b^{-2} - 7b^{-1} + 3 = 0$$
$$2(b^{-1})^2 - 7(b^{-1}) + 3 = 0$$
Let $u = b^{-1}$.
$$2u^2 - 7u + 3 = 0$$
$$(2u - 1)(u - 3) = 0$$
$$2u - 1 = 0 \quad \text{or} \quad u - 3 = 0$$
$$u = \frac{1}{2} \qquad u = 3$$
Substitute b^{-1} for u.
$$b^{-1} = \frac{1}{2} \quad \text{or} \quad b^{-1} = 3$$
$$b = 2 \qquad b = \frac{1}{3}$$
The solutions are 2 and $\frac{1}{3}$.

68.
$$10z^{-2} - 3z^{-1} - 1 = 0$$
$$10(z^{-1})^2 - 3(z^{-1}) - 1 = 0$$
Let $u = z^{-1}$.
$$10u^2 - 3u - 1 = 0$$
$$(5u + 1)(2u - 1) = 0$$
$$5u + 1 = 0 \quad \text{or} \quad 2u - 1 = 0$$
$$u = -\frac{1}{5} \qquad u = \frac{1}{2}$$
Substitute z^{-1} for u.
$$b^{-1} = -\frac{1}{5} \quad \text{or} \quad b^{-1} = \frac{1}{2}$$
$$b = -5 \qquad b = 2$$
The solutions are -5 and 2.

69.
$$x^{-2} + 9x^{-1} = 10$$
$$x^{-2} + 9x^{-1} - 10 = 0$$
$$(x^{-1})^2 + 9(x^{-1}) - 10 = 0$$
Let $u = x^{-1}$.
$$u^2 + 9u - 10 = 0$$
$$(u + 10)(u - 1) = 0$$
$$u + 10 = 0 \quad \text{or} \quad u - 1 = 0$$
$$u = -10 \qquad u = 1$$
Substitute x^{-1} for u.
$$x^{-1} = -10 \quad \text{or} \quad x^{-1} = 1$$
$$x = -\frac{1}{10} \qquad x = 1$$
The solutions are $-\frac{1}{10}$ and 1.

70.
$$6a^{-2} = a^{-1} + 12$$
$$6a^{-2} - a^{-1} - 12 = 0$$
$$6(a^{-1})^2 - (a^{-1}) - 12 = 0$$
Let $u = a^{-1}$.
$$6u^2 - u - 12 = 0$$
$$(2u - 3)(3u + 4) = 0$$
$$2u - 3 = 0 \quad \text{or} \quad 3u + 4 = 0$$
$$u = \frac{3}{2} \qquad u = -\frac{4}{3}$$
Substitute a^{-1} for u.
$$a^{-1} = \frac{3}{2} \quad \text{or} \quad a^{-1} = -\frac{4}{3}$$
$$a = \frac{2}{3} \qquad a = -\frac{3}{4}$$
The solutions are $\frac{2}{3}$ and $-\frac{3}{4}$.

71.
$$x^{-2} = 4x^{-1} + 12$$
$$x^{-2} - 4x^{-1} - 12 = 0$$
$$(x^{-1})^2 - 4(x^{-1}) - 12 = 0$$
Let $u = x^{-1}$.
$$u^2 - 4u - 12 = 0$$
$$(u + 2)(u - 6) = 0$$
$$u + 2 = 0 \quad \text{or} \quad u - 6 = 0$$
$$u = -2 \qquad u = 6$$
Substitute x^{-1} for u.
$$x^{-1} = -2 \quad \text{or} \quad x^{-1} = 6$$
$$x = -\frac{1}{2} \qquad x = \frac{1}{6}$$
The solutions are $-\frac{1}{2}$ and $\frac{1}{6}$.

72.
$$x^{2/3} - 5x^{1/3} + 6 = 0$$
$$(x^{1/3})^2 - 5x^{1/3} + 6 = 0$$
Let $u = x^{1/3}$.
$$u^2 - 5u + 6 = 0$$
$$(u - 3)(u - 2) = 0$$
$$u - 3 = 0 \quad \text{or} \quad u - 2 = 0$$
$$u = 3 \qquad u = 2$$
Substitute $x^{1/3}$ for u.
$$x^{1/3} = 3 \qquad \text{or} \quad x^{1/3} = 2$$
$$x = 3^3 = 27 \qquad x = 2^3 = 8$$
The solutions are 27 and 8.

73. $x^{2/3} - 4x^{1/3} = -3$

$\left(x^{1/3}\right)^2 - 4x^{1/3} + 3 = 0$

Let $u = x^{1/3}$.

$u^2 - 4u + 3 = 0$

$(u-1)(u-3) = 0$

$u - 1 = 0$ or $u - 3 = 0$

$u = 1$ $\qquad u = 3$

Substitute $x^{1/3}$ for u.

$x^{1/3} = 1$ or $x^{1/3} = 3$

$x = 1^3 = 1$ $\qquad x = 3^3 = 27$

The solutions are 1 and 27.

74. $x^{2/3} = 3x^{1/3} + 4$

$\left(x^{1/3}\right)^2 - 3x^{1/3} - 4 = 0$

Let $u = x^{1/3}$.

$u^2 - 3u - 4 = 0$

$(u+1)(u-4) = 0$

$u + 1 = 0$ or $u - 4 = 0$

$u = -1$ $\qquad u = 4$

Substitute $x^{1/3}$ for u.

$x^{1/3} = -1$ or $x^{1/3} = 4$

$x = (-1)^3 = -1$ $\qquad x = 4^3 = 64$

The solutions are -1 and 64.

75. $b^{2/3} - 9b^{1/3} + 18 = 0$

$\left(b^{1/3}\right)^2 - 9b^{1/3} + 18 = 0$

Let $u = b^{1/3}$.

$u^2 - 9u + 18 = 0$

$(u-6)(u-3) = 0$

$u - 6 = 0$ or $u - 3 = 0$

$u = 6$ $\qquad u = 3$

Substitute $b^{1/3}$ for u.

$b^{1/3} = 6$ or $b^{1/3} = 3$

$b = 6^3 = 216$ $\qquad b = 3^3 = 27$

The solutions are 216 and 27.

76. $c^{2/3} - 4 = 0$

$\left(c^{1/3}\right)^2 - 4 = 0$

Let $u = c^{1/3}$.

$u^2 - 4 = 0$

$(u+2)(u-2) = 0$

$u + 2 = 0$ or $u - 2 = 0$

$u = -2$ $\qquad u = 2$

Substitute $c^{1/3}$ for u.

$c^{1/3} = -2$ or $c^{1/3} = 2$

$c = (-2)^3 = -8$ $\qquad c = 2^3 = 8$

The solutions are -8 and 8.

77. $-2a - 5a^{1/2} + 3 = 0$

$-2\left(a^{1/2}\right)^2 - 5a^{1/2} + 3 = 0$

Let $u = a^{1/2}$.

$-2u^2 - 5u + 3 = 0$

$2u^2 + 5u - 3 = 0$

$(2u-1)(u+3) = 0$

$2u - 1 = 0$ or $u + 3 = 0$

$u = \dfrac{1}{2}$ $\qquad u = -3$

Substitute $a^{1/2}$ for u.

$a^{1/2} = 2$ or $a^{1/2} = -3$

$a = \left(\dfrac{1}{2}\right)^2 = \dfrac{1}{4}$ $\qquad$ not real

The solution is $\dfrac{1}{4}$.

78. $r^{2/3} - 7r^{1/3} + 10 = 0$

$\left(r^{1/3}\right)^2 - 7r^{1/3} + 10 = 0$

Let $u = r^{1/3}$.

$u^2 - 7u + 10 = 0$

$(u-5)(u-2) = 0$

$u - 5 = 0$ or $u - 2 = 0$

$u = 5$ $\qquad u = 2$

Substitute $r^{1/3}$ for u.

$r^{1/3} = 5$ or $r^{1/3} = 2$

$r = 5^3 = 125$ $\qquad r = 2^3 = 8$

The solutions are 8 and 125.

79. $c^{2/5} + 3c^{1/5} + 2 = 0$

$\left(c^{1/5}\right)^2 + 3c^{1/5} + 2 = 0$

Let $u = c^{1/5}$.

$u^2 + 3u + 2 = 0$

$(u+2)(u+1) = 0$

$u + 2 = 0$ or $u + 1 = 0$

     $u = -2$ $u = -1$

Substitute $c^{1/5}$ for u.

$c^{1/5} = -2$ or $c^{1/5} = -1$

   $c = (-2)^5 = -32$ $c = (-1)^5 = -1$

The solutions are -32 and -1.

80. $x^{2/5} - 5x^{1/5} + 6 = 0$

$\left(x^{1/5}\right)^2 - 5x^{1/5} + 6 = 0$

Let $u = x^{1/5}$.

$u^2 - 5u + 6 = 0$

$(u-3)(u-2) = 0$

$u - 3 = 0$ or $u - 2 = 0$

     $u = 3$ $u = 2$

Substitute $x^{1/3}$ for u.

$x^{1/5} = 3$ or $x^{1/5} = 2$

   $x = 3^5 = 243$ $x = 2^5 = 32$

The solutions are 32 and 243.

81. $f(x) = x - 5\sqrt{x} + 4$, $f(x) = 0$

$0 = \left(x^{1/2}\right)^2 - 5x^{1/2} + 4$

Let $u = x^{1/2}$.

$0 = u^2 - 5u + 4$

$0 = (u-1)(u-4)$

$u - 1 = 0$ or $u - 4 = 0$

     $u = 1$ $u = 4$

Substitute $x^{1/2}$ for u.

$x^{1/2} = 1$ or $x^{1/2} = 4$

   $x = 1^2 = 1$ $x = 4^2 = 16$

The x-intercepts are $(1, 0)$ and $(16, 0)$.

82. $g(x) = x - 15\sqrt{x} + 56$, $g(x) = 0$

$0 = \left(x^{1/2}\right)^2 - 15x^{1/2} + 56$

Let $u = x^{1/2}$.

$0 = u^2 - 15u + 56$

$0 = (u-8)(u-7)$

$u - 8 = 0$ or $u - 7 = 0$

     $u = 8$ $u = 7$

Substitute $x^{1/2}$ for u.

$x^{1/2} = 8$ or $x^{1/2} = 7$

   $x = 8^2 = 64$ $x = 7^2 = 49$

The x-intercepts are $(64, 0)$ and $(49, 0)$.

83. $h(x) = x + 14\sqrt{x} + 45$, $h(x) = 0$

$0 = \left(x^{1/2}\right)^2 + 14x^{1/2} + 45$

Let $u = x^{1/2}$.

$0 = u^2 + 14u + 45$

$0 = (u+9)(u+5)$

$u + 9 = 0$ or $u + 5 = 0$

     $u = -9$ $u = -5$

Substitute $x^{1/2}$ for u.

$x^{1/2} = -9$ or $x^{1/2} = -5$

There are no values of x for which $x^{1/2} = -9$ or $x^{1/2} = -5$. There are no x-intercepts.

84. $k(x) = x + 7\sqrt{x} + 12$, $k(x) = 0$

$0 = \left(x^{1/2}\right)^2 + 7x^{1/2} + 12$

Let $u = x^{1/2}$.

$0 = u^2 + 7u + 12$

$0 = (u+3)(u+4)$

$u + 3 = 0$ or $u + 4 = 0$

     $u = -3$ $u = -4$

Substitute $x^{1/2}$ for u.

$x^{1/2} = -3$ or $x^{1/2} = -4$

There are no values of x for which $x^{1/2} = -3$ or $x^{1/2} = -4$. There are no x-intercepts.

85. $p(x) = 4x^{-2} - 19x^{-1} - 5$, $p(x) = 0$

$0 = 4\left(x^{-1}\right)^2 - 19x^{-1} - 5$

Let $u = x^{-1}$.

$0 = 4u^2 - 19u - 5$

$0 = (4u+1)(u-5)$

$4u + 1 = 0$ or $u - 5 = 0$

     $u = -\dfrac{1}{4}$ $u = 5$

Substitute x^{-1} for u.

$x^{-1} = -\dfrac{1}{4}$ or $x^{-1} = 5$

   $x = -4$ $x = \dfrac{1}{5}$

The x-intercepts are $(-4, 0)$ and $\left(\dfrac{1}{5}, 0\right)$.

86. $g(x) = 4x^{-2} + 12x^{-1} + 9$, $g(x) = 0$

$0 = 4(x^{-1})^2 + 12x^{-1} + 9$

Let $u = x^{-1}$.

$0 = 4u^2 + 12u + 9$

$0 = (2u + 3)^2$

$0 = 2u + 3$

$u = -\dfrac{3}{2}$

Substitute x^{-1} for u.

$x^{-1} = -\dfrac{3}{2}$

$x = -\dfrac{2}{3}$

The x-intercept is $\left(-\dfrac{2}{3}, 0\right)$.

87. $f(x) = x^{2/3} - x^{1/3} - 6$, $f(x) = 0$

$0 = (x^{1/3})^2 - x^{1/3} - 6$

Let $u = x^{1/3}$.

$0 = u^2 - u - 6$

$0 = (u - 3)(u + 2)$

$u - 3 = 0$ or $u + 2 = 0$

$u = 3$ $\qquad\quad$ $u = -2$

Substitute $x^{1/3}$ for u.

$x^{1/3} = 3^3 = 27$ or $x^{1/3} = (-2)^3 = -8$

The x-intercepts are $(27, 0)$ and $(-8, 0)$.

88. $f(x) = x^{1/2} + 6x^{1/4} - 7$, $f(x) = 0$

$0 = (x^{1/4})^2 + 6x^{1/4} - 7$

Let $u = x^{1/4}$.

$0 = u^2 + 6u - 7$

$0 = (u + 7)(u - 1)$

$u + 7 = 0$ or $u - 1 = 0$

$u = -7$ $\qquad\quad$ $u = 1$

Substitute $x^{1/4}$ for u.

$x^{1/4} = -7$ or $x^{1/4} = 1$

Not real $\qquad\quad$ $x = 1^4 = 1$

There is no value of x for which $x^{1/4} = -5$, so the only x-intercept is $(1, 0)$.

89. $g(x) = (x^2 - 3x)^2 + 2(x^2 - 3x) - 24$, $g(x) = 0$

Let $u = x^2 - 3x$.

$0 = u^2 + 2u - 24$

$0 = (u + 6)(u - 4)$

$u + 6 = 0$ or $u - 4 = 0$

$u = -6$ $\qquad\quad$ $u = 4$

Substitute $(x^2 - 3x)$ for u.

$x^2 - 3x = -6$ or $\qquad$ $x^2 - 3x = 4$

$x^2 - 3x + 6 = 0$ $\qquad\quad$ $x^2 - 3x - 4 = 0$

$\qquad\qquad\qquad\qquad$ $(x - 4)(x + 1) = 0$

$\qquad\qquad\qquad\qquad\quad$ $x = 4$ or $x = -1$

There are no x-intercepts for $x^2 - 3x + 6 = 0$ since $b^2 - 4ac = (-3)^2 - 4(1)(6) = -15$ (that is, since the discriminant is negative). The x-intercepts are $(4, 0)$ or $(-1, 0)$.

90. $g(x) = (x^2 - 6x)^2 - 5(x^2 - 6x) - 24$, $g(x) = 0$

Let $u = x^2 - 6x$.

$0 = u^2 - 5u - 24$

$0 = (u - 8)(u + 3)$

$u = 8$ or $u = -3$

Substitute $(x^2 - 6x)$ for u.

$x^2 - 6x = 8$ $\qquad$ or $\qquad$ $x^2 - 6x = 3$

$x^2 - 6x - 8 = 0$ $\qquad\qquad$ $x^2 - 6x + 3 = 0$

$x = \dfrac{6 \pm \sqrt{(-6)^2 - 4(1)(-8)}}{2(1)}$ $\qquad$ $x = \dfrac{6 \pm \sqrt{(-6)^2 - 4(1)(3)}}{2(1)}$

$\qquad = \dfrac{6 \pm \sqrt{68}}{2}$ $\qquad\qquad\qquad = \dfrac{6 \pm \sqrt{24}}{2}$

$\qquad = \dfrac{6 \pm 2\sqrt{17}}{2}$ $\qquad\qquad\qquad = \dfrac{6 \pm 2\sqrt{6}}{2}$

$\qquad = 3 \pm \sqrt{17}$ $\qquad\qquad\qquad = 3 \pm \sqrt{6}$

The x-intercepts are $(3 + \sqrt{17}, 0)$, $(3 - \sqrt{17}, 0)$, $(3 + \sqrt{6}, 0)$, and $(3 - \sqrt{6}, 0)$.

91. $f(x) = x^4 - 29x + 100$, $f(x) = 0$

$0 = (x^2)^2 - 29x^2 + 100$

Let $u = x^2$.

$0 = u^2 - 29u + 100$

$0 = (u - 25)(u - 4)$

$u - 25 = 0$ or $u - 4 = 0$

$u = 25$ $\qquad\quad$ $u = 4$

Substitute x^2 for u.

$x^2 = 25$ $\qquad$ or $\qquad$ $x^2 = 4$

$x = \pm\sqrt{25} = \pm5$ $\qquad$ $x = \pm\sqrt{4} = \pm2$

The x-intercepts are $(5, 0)$, $(-5, 0)$, $(2, 0)$, and $(-2, 0)$.

92. $h(x) = x^4 - 4x + 3, \ h(x) = 0$

$0 = (x^2)^2 - 4x^2 + 3$

Let $u = x^2$.

$0 = u^2 - 4u + 3$

$0 = (u-3)(u-1)$

$u - 3 = 0 \quad \text{or} \quad u - 1 = 0$

$\quad u = 3 \qquad\qquad u = 1$

Substitute x^2 for u.

$x^2 = 3 \quad \text{or} \quad x^2 = 1$

$x = \pm\sqrt{3} \qquad x = \pm\sqrt{1} = \pm 1$

The x-intercepts are $\left(\sqrt{3}, \ 0\right)$, $\left(-\sqrt{3}, \ 0\right)$, $(1, 0)$, and $(-1, 0)$.

93. When solving an equation of the form $ax^4 + bx^2 + c = 0$, let $u = x^2$.

94. When solving an equation of the form $ax^{2n} + bx^n + c = 0$, let $u = x^n$.

95. When solving an equation of the form $ax^{-2} + bx^{-1} + c = 0$, let $u = x^{-1}$.

96. When solving an equation of the form $a(x-r)^2 + b(x-r) - c = 0$, let $u = x - r$.

97. If the solutions are ± 2 and ± 1, the factors must be $(x-2), (x+2), (x-1)$, and $(x+1)$.

$(x-2)(x+2)(x-1)(x+1) = 0$

$\left(x^2 - 4\right)\left(x^2 - 1\right) = 0$

$x^4 - 5x^2 + 4 = 0$

98. If the solutions are ± 3 and $\pm 2i$, the factors must be $(x-3), (x+3), (x-2i)$, and $(x+2i)$.

$(x-3)(x+3)(x-2i)(x+2i) = 0$

$\left(x^2 - 9\right)\left(x^2 + 4\right) = 0$

$x^4 - 5x^2 - 36 = 0$

99. If the solutions are $\pm\sqrt{2}$ and $\pm\sqrt{5}$, the factors must be $\left(x+\sqrt{2}\right), \left(x-\sqrt{2}\right), \left(x+\sqrt{5}\right), \left(x-\sqrt{5}\right)$.

$\left(x+\sqrt{2}\right)\left(x-\sqrt{2}\right)\left(x+\sqrt{5}\right)\left(x-\sqrt{5}\right) = 0$

$\left(x^2 - 2\right)\left(x^2 - 5\right) = 0$

$x^4 - 7x^2 + 10 = 0$

100. If the solutions are $\pm 2i$, and $\pm 5i$, the factors must be $(x+2i), (x-2i), (x+3i), (x-3i)$.

$(x+2i)(x-2i)(x+5i)(x-5i) = 0$

$\left(x^2 + 4\right)\left(x^2 + 25\right) = 0$

$x^4 + 29x^2 + 100 = 0$

101. No. An equation of the form $ax^4 + bx^2 + c = 0$ can have no imaginary solutions, two imaginary solutions, or four imaginary solutions.

102. No. An equation of the form $ax^4 + bx^2 + c = 0$ can have no real solutions, two real solutions, or four real solutions.

103. a.
$$\frac{3}{x^2} - \frac{3}{x} = 60 \quad \text{The LCD is } x^2$$

$$x^2\left(\frac{3}{x^2}\right) - x^2\left(\frac{3}{x}\right) = x^2(60)$$

$$3 - 3x = 60x^2$$

$$0 = 60x^2 + 3x - 3$$

$$0 = 3\left(20x^2 + x - 1\right)$$

$$0 = 3(5x - 1)(4x + 1)$$

$5x - 1 = 0 \quad \text{or} \quad 4x + 1 = 0$

$x = \dfrac{1}{5} \qquad\qquad x = -\dfrac{1}{4}$

The solutions are $\dfrac{1}{5}$ and $-\dfrac{1}{4}$.

b.
$$\frac{3}{x^2} - \frac{3}{x} = 60$$

$$3x^{-2} - 3x^{-1} = 60$$

$$3\left(x^{-1}\right)^2 - 3x^{-1} - 60 = 0$$

Let $u = x^{-1}$.

$$3u^2 - 3u - 60 = 0$$

$$3\left(u^2 - u - 20\right) = 0$$

$$3(u-5)(u+4) = 0$$

$u - 5 = 0 \quad \text{or} \quad u + 4 = 0$

$\quad u = 5 \qquad\qquad u = -4$

Substitute x^{-1} for u.

$x^{-1} = 5 \quad \text{or} \quad x^{-1} = -4$

$x = \dfrac{1}{5} \qquad\qquad x = -\dfrac{1}{4}$

The solutions are $\dfrac{1}{5}$ and $-\dfrac{1}{4}$.

104. a.
$$1 = \frac{2}{x} - \frac{2}{x^2} \quad \text{The LCD is } x^2$$

$$x^2(1) = x^2\left(\frac{2}{x}\right) - x^2\left(\frac{2}{x^2}\right)$$

$$x^2 = 2x - 2$$

$$x^2 - 2x + 2 = 0$$

$$x = \frac{2 \pm \sqrt{(-2)^2 - 4(1)(2)}}{2(1)}$$

$$= \frac{2 \pm \sqrt{4-8}}{2} = \frac{2 \pm \sqrt{-4}}{2} = \frac{2 \pm 2i}{2} = 1 \pm i$$

The solutions are $1 + i$ and $1 - i$.

b.
$$1 = \frac{2}{x} - \frac{2}{x^2}$$

$$1 = 2x^{-1} - 2x^{-2}$$

$$2x^{-2} - 2x^{-1} + 1 = 0$$

$$2\left(x^{-1}\right)^2 - 2x^{-1} + 1 = 0$$

Let $u = x^{-1}$.

$$2u^2 - 2u + 1 = 0$$

$$u = \frac{2 \pm \sqrt{(-2)^2 - 4(2)(1)}}{2(2)}$$

$$= \frac{2 \pm \sqrt{-4}}{4} = \frac{2 \pm 2i}{4} = \frac{1 \pm i}{2}$$

Substitute x^{-1} for u.

$$x^{-1} = \frac{1 \pm i}{2}$$

$$x = \frac{2}{1 \pm i}$$

$$x = \frac{2}{1+i} \quad \text{or} \quad x = \frac{2}{1-i}$$

$$= \frac{2}{1+i}\left(\frac{1-i}{1-i}\right) \qquad = \frac{2}{1-i}\left(\frac{1+i}{1+i}\right)$$

$$= \frac{2(1-i)}{1-i^2} \qquad = \frac{2(1+i)}{1-i^2}$$

$$= \frac{2(1-i)}{1+1} \qquad = \frac{2(1+i)}{1+1}$$

$$= \frac{2(1-i)}{2} \qquad = \frac{2(1+i)}{2}$$

$$= 1-i \qquad = 1+i$$

The solutions are $1 - i$ and $1 + i$.

105.
$$15(r+2) + 22 = -\frac{8}{r+2}$$

$$15(r+2)(r+2) + 22(r+2) = -\frac{8}{r+2}(r+2)$$

$$15(r+2)^2 + 22(r+2) = -8$$

$$15(r+2)^2 + 22(r+2) + 8 = 0$$

Let $u = r + 2$.

$$15u^2 + 22u + 8 = 0$$

$$(5u + 4)(3u + 2) = 0$$

$$5u + 4 = 0 \quad \text{or} \quad 3u + 2 = 0$$

$$u = -\frac{4}{5} \qquad\qquad u = -\frac{2}{3}$$

Substitute $r + 2$ for u.

$$r + 2 = -\frac{4}{5} \quad \text{or} \quad r + 2 = -\frac{2}{3}$$

$$r = -\frac{14}{5} \qquad\qquad r = -\frac{8}{3}$$

The solutions are $-\frac{14}{5}$ and $-\frac{8}{3}$.

106.
$$2(p+3) + 5 = \frac{3}{p+3}$$

$$2(p+3)(p+3) + 5(p+3) = \frac{3}{p+3}(p+3)$$

$$2(p+3)^2 + 5(p+3) = 3$$

$$2(p+3)^2 + 5(p+3) - 3 = 0$$

$$2u^2 + 5u - 3 = 0$$

Let $u = p + 3$.

$$u = \frac{-5 \pm \sqrt{5^2 - 4(2)(-3)}}{2(2)}$$

$$= \frac{-5 \pm \sqrt{49}}{4} = \frac{-5 \pm 7}{4}$$

$$u = \frac{-5 + 7}{4} \quad \text{or} \quad u = \frac{-5 - 7}{4}$$

$$= \frac{1}{2} \qquad\qquad = -3$$

Substitute $p + 3$ for u.

$$p + 3 = \frac{1}{2} \quad \text{or} \quad p + 3 = -3$$

$$p = -\frac{5}{2} \qquad\qquad p = -6$$

The solutions are $-\frac{5}{2}$ and -6.

107.
$$4-(x-1)^{-1}=3(x-1)^{-2}$$
$$3(x-1)^{-2}+(x-1)^{-1}-4=0$$
$$3\left[(x-1)^{-1}\right]^2+(x-1)^{-1}-4=0$$
Let $u=(x-1)^{-1}$
$$3u^2+u-4=0$$
$$(3u+4)(u-1)=0$$
$$3u+4=0 \quad \text{or} \quad u-1=0$$
$$u=-\frac{4}{3} \qquad u=1$$
Substitute $(x-1)^{-1}$ for u.
$$(x-1)^{-1}=-\frac{4}{3} \quad \text{or} \quad (x-1)^{-1}=1$$
$$x-1=-\frac{3}{4} \qquad x-1=1$$
$$x=\frac{1}{4} \qquad x=2$$
The solutions are $\dfrac{1}{4}$ and 2.

108.
$$3(x-4)^{-2}=16(x-4)^{-1}+12$$
$$3(x-4)^{-2}-16(x-4)^{-1}-12=0$$
$$3\left[(x-4)^{-1}\right]^2-16(x-4)^{-1}-12=0$$
Let $u=(x-4)^{-1}$.
$$3u^2-16u-12=0$$
$$(3u+2)(u-6)=0$$
$$3u+2=0 \quad \text{or} \quad u-6=0$$
$$u=-\frac{2}{3} \qquad u=6$$
Substitute $(x-4)^{-1}$ for u.
$$(x-4)^{-1}=-\frac{2}{3} \quad \text{or} \quad (x-4)^{-1}=6$$
$$x-4=-\frac{3}{2} \qquad x-4=\frac{1}{6}$$
$$x=\frac{5}{2} \qquad x=\frac{25}{6}$$
The solutions are $\dfrac{5}{2}$ and $\dfrac{25}{6}$.

109.
$$x^6-9x^3+8=0$$
$$\left(x^3\right)^2-9x^3+8=0$$
Let $u=x^3$.
$$u^2-9u+8=0$$
$$(u-8)(u-1)=0$$

$$u-8=0 \quad \text{or} \quad u-1=0$$
$$u=8 \qquad u=1$$
Substitute x^3 for u.
$$x^3=8 \qquad \text{or} \quad x^3=1$$
$$x=\sqrt[3]{8}=2 \qquad x=\sqrt[3]{1}=1$$
The solutions are 2 and 1.

110.
$$x^6-28x^3+27=0$$
$$\left(x^3\right)^2-28x^3+27=0$$
Let $u=x^3$.
$$u^2-28u+27=0$$
$$(u-27)(u-1)=0$$
$$u-27=0 \quad \text{or} \quad u-1=0$$
$$u=27 \qquad u=1$$
Substitute x^3 for u.
$$x^3=27 \qquad \text{or} \quad x^3=1$$
$$x=\sqrt[3]{27}=3 \qquad x=\sqrt[3]{1}=1$$
The solutions are 3 and 1.

111. $(x^2+2x-2)^2-7(x^2+2x-2)+6=0$
Let $u=x^2+2x-2$.
$$u^2-7u+6=0$$
$$(u-6)(u-1)=0$$
$$u=6 \quad \text{or} \quad u=1$$
Substitute x^2+2x-2 for u.
$$x^2+2x-2=6 \quad \text{or} \quad x^2+2x-2=1$$
$$x^2+2x-8=0 \qquad x^2+2x-3=0$$
$$(x+4)(x-2)=0 \qquad (x+3)(x-1)=0$$
$$x=-4 \quad \text{or} \quad x=2 \qquad x=-3 \quad \text{or} \quad x=1$$
The solutions are -4, 2, -3, and 1.

112. $\left(x^2+3x-2\right)^2-10\left(x^2+3x-2\right)+16=0$
Let $u=x^2+3x-2$.
$$u^2-10u+16=0$$
$$(u-8)(u-2)=0$$
$$u=8 \quad \text{or} \quad u=2$$
Substitute x^2+3x-2 for u.
$$x^2+3x-2=8 \quad \text{or} \quad x^2+3x-2=2$$
$$x^2+3x-10=0 \qquad x^2+3x-4=0$$
$$(x+5)(x-2)=0 \qquad (x+4)(x-1)=0$$
$$x=-5 \quad \text{or} \quad x=2 \qquad x=-4 \quad \text{or} \quad x=1$$
The solutions are -5, 2, -4, and 1.

113. $2n^4 - 6n^2 - 3 = 0$

$2\left(n^2\right)^2 - 6n^2 - 3 = 0$

Let $u = n^2$.

$2u^2 - 6u - 3 = 0$

$u = \dfrac{6 \pm \sqrt{(-6)^2 - 4(2)(-3)}}{2(2)}$

$= \dfrac{6 \pm \sqrt{60}}{4} = \dfrac{6 \pm 2\sqrt{15}}{4} = \dfrac{3 \pm \sqrt{15}}{2}$

Substitute n^2 for u.

$n^2 = \dfrac{3 \pm \sqrt{15}}{2}$

$n = \pm\sqrt{\dfrac{3 \pm \sqrt{15}}{2}}$

114. $3x^4 + 8x^2 - 1 = 0$

$3\left(x^2\right)^2 + 8x^2 - 1 = 0$

Let $u = x^2$.

$3u^2 + 8u - 1 = 0$

$u = \dfrac{-8 \pm \sqrt{8^2 - 4(3)(-1)}}{3(2)}$

$= \dfrac{-8 \pm \sqrt{76}}{6} = \dfrac{-8 \pm 2\sqrt{19}}{6} = \dfrac{-4 \pm \sqrt{19}}{3}$

Substitute x^2 for u.

$x^2 = \dfrac{-4 \pm \sqrt{19}}{3}$

$x = \pm\sqrt{\dfrac{-4 \pm \sqrt{19}}{3}}$

115. $\dfrac{4}{5} - \left(\dfrac{3}{4} - \dfrac{2}{3}\right) = \dfrac{4}{5} - \left(\dfrac{9}{12} - \dfrac{8}{12}\right)$

$= \dfrac{4}{5} - \dfrac{1}{12}$

$= \dfrac{48}{60} - \dfrac{5}{60}$

$= \dfrac{43}{60}$

116. $3(x + 2) - 2(3x + 3) = -3$

$3x + 6 - 6x - 6 = -3$

$-3x = -3$

$x = 1$

117. $y = (x - 3)^2$

Domain : $\mathbb{R}$

Range: $\{y \mid y \ge 0\}$

118. $\sqrt[3]{16x^3y^6} = \sqrt[3]{8 \cdot 2 \cdot x^3 \left(y^2\right)^3} = 2xy^2\sqrt[3]{2}$

119. $\sqrt{75} + \sqrt{48} = \sqrt{25 \cdot 3} + \sqrt{16 \cdot 3}$

$= 5\sqrt{3} + 4\sqrt{3}$

$= 9\sqrt{3}$

Exercise Set 12.5

1. The graph of a quadratic equation is called a parabola.

2. The vertex of a parabola is the highest or lowest point on the graph.

3. The axis of symmetry of a parabola is the line where, if the graph is folded, the two sides overlap.

4. For $f(x) = ax^2 + bx + c$, the equation of the axis of symmetry is $x = -\dfrac{b}{2a}$.

5. For $f(x) = ax^2 + bx + c$, the vertex of the graph is $\left(-\dfrac{b}{2a}, \dfrac{4ac - b^2}{4}\right)$.

6. **a.** If the discriminant < 0, a quadratic function will have no x-intercepts.

   b. If the discriminant = 0, a quadratic function will have one x-intercept.

   c. If the discriminant > 0, a quadratic function will have two x-intercepts.

7. **a.** For $f(x) = ax^2 + bx + c$, $f(x)$ will have a minimum if $a > 0$ since the graph opens upward.

   b. For $f(x) = ax^2 + bx + c$, $f(x)$ will have a maximum if $a < 0$ since the graph opens downward.

8. To find the x-intercepts of the graph of a quadratic function, set $y = 0$ and solve for x.

9. To find the *y*-intercepts of the graph of a quadratic function, set $x = 0$ and solve for *y*.

10. For the graph of $f(x) = ax^2$, as $|a|$ increases, the parabola becomes narrower, as $|a|$ decreases, the parabola becomes wider.

11. **a.** For $f(x) = ax^2$, the general shape of $f(x)$ if $a > 0$ is

   b. For $f(x) = ax^2$, the general shape of $f(x)$ if $a < 0$ is

12. Yes, the graph of $f(x) = ax^2$ and $g(x) = -ax^2$ will have the same vertex for any nonzero real number *a*. The vertex is the point (0, 0).

13. Since $a = 3$ is greater than 0, the graph opens upward, and therefore has a minimum value.

14. Since $a = -\frac{1}{2}$ is less than 0, the graph opens downward, and therefore has a maximum value.

15. $P(x) = x^2 - 6x + 4$
$$P(2) = (2)^2 - 6(2) + 4 = 4 - 12 + 4 = -8 + 4 = -4$$

16. $P(x) = 4x^2 - 6x + 22$
$$\begin{aligned}P(-1) &= 4(-1)^2 - 6(-1) + 22 \\ &= 4(1) - 6(-1) + 22 \\ &= 4 + 6 + 22 \\ &= 32\end{aligned}$$

17. $P(x) = 2x^2 - 3x - 6$
$$\begin{aligned}P\left(\frac{1}{2}\right) &= 2\left(\frac{1}{2}\right)^2 - 3\left(\frac{1}{2}\right) - 6 \\ &= 2\left(\frac{1}{4}\right) - 3\left(\frac{1}{2}\right) - 6 \\ &= \frac{1}{2} - \frac{3}{2} - \frac{12}{2} \\ &= -\frac{14}{2} \\ &= -7\end{aligned}$$

18. $P(x) = \frac{1}{2}x^3 - x^2 + 6$
$$\begin{aligned}P\left(\frac{1}{3}\right) &= \frac{1}{2}\left(\frac{1}{3}\right)^3 - \left(\frac{1}{3}\right)^2 + 6 \\ &= \frac{1}{2}\left(\frac{1}{27}\right) - \left(\frac{1}{9}\right) + 6 \\ &= \frac{1}{54} - \frac{1}{9} + 6 \\ &= \frac{1}{54} - \frac{6}{54} + \frac{324}{54} \\ &= \frac{319}{54}\end{aligned}$$

19. $P(x) = 0.2x^3 + 1.6x^2 - 2.3$
$$\begin{aligned}P(0.4) &= 0.2(0.4)^3 + 1.6(0.4)^2 - 2.3 \\ &= 0.2(0.064) + 1.6(0.16) - 2.3 \\ &= 0.0128 + 0.256 - 2.3 \\ &= 0.2688 - 2.3 \\ &= -2.0312\end{aligned}$$

20. $P(x) = -1.6x^3 - 4.6x^2 - 0.1x$
$$\begin{aligned}P(-1.2) &= -1.6(-1.2)^3 - 4.6(-1.2)^2 - 0.1(-1.2) \\ &= -1.6(-1.728) - 4.6(1.44) - 0.1(-1.2) \\ &= 2.7648 - 6.624 + 0.12 \\ &= -3.8592 + 0.12 \\ &= -3.7392\end{aligned}$$

21. $f(x) = x^2 + 8x + 15$

   a. Since $a = 1$, the parabola opens upward.

   b. $y = (0)^2 + 8(0) + 15 = 15$
   The *y*-intercept is (0, 15).

   c. $x = -\dfrac{b}{2a} = -\dfrac{8}{2(1)} = -\dfrac{8}{2} = -4$
$$\begin{aligned}y &= \frac{4ac - b^2}{4a} \\ &= \frac{4(1)(15) - 8^2}{4(1)} \\ &= \frac{60 - 64}{4} \\ &= \frac{-4}{4} \\ &= -1\end{aligned}$$
   The vertex is (−4, −1).

d. $x^2 + 8x + 15 = 0$

$(x+5)(x+3) = 0$

$x + 5 = 0$ or $x + 3 = 0$

$x = -5$ $\qquad x = -3$

The *x*-intercepts are $(-5, 0)$ and $(-3, 0)$.

e.

$f(x) = x^2 + 8x + 15$

22. $g(x) = x^2 + 2x - 3$

a. Since $a = 1$ the parabola opens upward.

b. $y = 0^2 + 2(0) - 3 = -3$

The *y*-intercept is $(0, -3)$.

c. $x = -\dfrac{b}{2a} = -\dfrac{2}{2(1)} = -\dfrac{2}{2} = -1$

$y = \dfrac{4ac - b^2}{4a} = \dfrac{4(1)(-3) - (2)^2}{4(1)} = -4$

The vertex is $(-1, -4)$.

d. $x^2 + 2x - 3 = 0$

$(x-1)(x+3) = 0$

$x = 1$ or $x = -3$

The *x*-intercepts are $(1, 0)$ and $(-3, 0)$.

e.

$g(x) = x^2 + 2x - 3$

23. $f(x) = x^2 - 4x + 3$

a. Since $a = 1$, the parabola opens upward.

b. $y = 0^2 - 4(0) + 3 = 3$

The *y*-intercept is $(0, 3)$.

c. $x = -\dfrac{b}{2a} = -\dfrac{-4}{2(1)} = \dfrac{4}{2} = 2$

$y = \dfrac{4ac - b^2}{4a}$

$= \dfrac{4(1)(3) - (-4)^2}{4(1)}$

$= \dfrac{12 - 16}{4}$

$= \dfrac{-4}{4}$

$= -1$

The vertex is $(2, -1)$.

d. $x^2 - 4x + 3 = 0$

$(x-3)(x-1) = 0$

$x - 3 = 0$ or $x - 1 = 0$

$x = 3$ $\qquad x = 1$

The *x*-intercepts are $(3, 0)$ and $(1, 0)$.

e.

$f(x) = x^2 - 4x + 3$

24. $h(x) = x^2 - 2x - 8$

a. Since $a = 1$, the parabola opens upward.

b. $y = 0^2 - 2(0) - 8 = -8$

The *y*-intercept is $(0, -8)$.

c. $x = -\dfrac{b}{2a} = -\dfrac{-2}{2(1)} = \dfrac{2}{2} = 1$

$y = \dfrac{4ac - b^2}{4a}$

$= \dfrac{4(1)(-8) - (-2)^2}{4(1)}$

$= \dfrac{-32 - 4}{4}$

$= \dfrac{-36}{4}$

$= -9$

The vertex is $(1, -9)$.

d. $x^2 - 2x - 8 = 0$

$(x-4)(x+2) = 0$

$x - 4 = 0$ or $x + 2 = 0$

$x = 4$ $\qquad$ $x = -2$

The x-intercepts are (4, 0) and (–2, 0).

e.

$h(x) = x^2 - 2x - 8$

25. $f(x) = -x^2 - 2x + 8$

a. Since $a = -1$, the parabola opens downward.

b. $y = -(0)^2 - 2(0) + 8 = 8$

The y-intercept is (0, 8).

c. $x = -\dfrac{b}{2a} = -\dfrac{-2}{2(-1)} = -\dfrac{2}{2} = -1$

$y = \dfrac{4ac - b^2}{4a}$

$= \dfrac{4(-1)(8) - (-2)^2}{4(-1)}$

$= \dfrac{-32 - 4}{-4} = \dfrac{-36}{-4} = 9$

The vertex is $(-1, 9)$.

d. $-x^2 - 2x + 8 = 0$

$x^2 + 2x - 8 = 0$

$(x+4)(x-2) = 0$

$x + 4 = 0$ or $x - 2 = 0$

$x = -4$ $\qquad$ $x = 2$

The x-intercepts are (–4, 0) and (2, 0).

e.

$f(x) = -x^2 - 2x + 8$

26. $p(x) = -x^2 + 8x - 15$

a. Since $a = -1$, the parabola opens downward.

b. $y = -(0)^2 + 8(0) - 15 = -15$

The y-intercept is (0, –15).

c. $x = -\dfrac{b}{2a} = -\dfrac{8}{2(-1)} = \dfrac{8}{2} = 4$

$y = \dfrac{4ac - b^2}{4a} = \dfrac{4(-1)(-15) - (8)^2}{4(-1)}$

$= \dfrac{60 - 64}{-4} = \dfrac{-4}{-4} = 1$

The vertex is (4, 1).

d. $-x^2 + 8x - 15 = 0$

$x^2 - 8x + 15 = 0$

$(x-5)(x-3) = 0$

$x - 5 = 0$ or $x - 3 = 0$

$x = 5$ $\qquad$ $x = 3$

The x-intercepts are (5, 0) and (3, 0).

e.

$f(x) = -x^2 + 8x - 15$

27. $g(x) = -x^2 + 4x + 5$

a. Since $a = -1$, the parabola opens downward.

b. $y = -(0)^2 + 4(0) + 5 = 8$

The y-intercept is (0, 5).

c. $x = -\dfrac{b}{2a} = -\dfrac{4}{2(-1)} = \dfrac{4}{2} = 2$

$y = \dfrac{4ac - b^2}{4a}$

$= \dfrac{4(-1)(5) - (4)^2}{4(-1)}$

$= \dfrac{-20 - 16}{-4} = \dfrac{-36}{-4} = 9$

The vertex is (2, 9).

d. $-x^2 + 4x + 5 = 0$

$x^2 - 4x - 5 = 0$

$(x-5)(x+1) = 0$

$x - 5 = 0$ or $x + 1 = 0$

$x = 5$ $x = -1$

The x-intercepts are $(5, 0)$ and $(-1, 0)$.

e.

$f(x) = -x^2 + 4x + 5$

28. $n(x) = -x^2 - 2x + 24$

a. Since $a = -1$, the parabola opens downward.

b. $y = -(0)^2 - 2(0) + 24 = 24$

The y-intercept is $(0, 24)$.

c. $x = -\dfrac{b}{2a} = -\dfrac{-2}{2(-1)} = -\dfrac{2}{2} = -1$

$y = \dfrac{4ac - b^2}{4a}$

$= \dfrac{4(-1)(24) - (-2)^2}{4(-1)}$

$= \dfrac{-96 - 4}{-4} = \dfrac{-100}{-4} = 25$

The vertex is $(-1, 25)$.

d. $-x^2 - 2x + 24 = 0$

$x^2 + 2x - 24 = 0$

$(x-4)(x+6) = 0$

$x - 4 = 0$ or $x + 6 = 0$

$x = 4$ $x = -6$

The x-intercepts are $(4, 0)$ and $(-6, 0)$.

e.

$n(x) = -x^2 - 2x + 24$

29. $t(x) = -x^2 + 4x - 5$

a. Since $a = -1$, the parabola opens downward.

b. $y = -0^2 + 4(0) - 5 = -5$; The y-intercept is $(0, -5)$.

c. $x = -\dfrac{b}{2a} = -\dfrac{4}{2(-1)} = -\dfrac{4}{-2} = 2$

$y = \dfrac{4ac - b^2}{4a} = \dfrac{4(-1)(-5) - (4)^2}{4(-1)}$

$= \dfrac{20 - 16}{-4} = \dfrac{4}{-4} = -1$

The vertex is $(2, -1)$.

d. $0 = -x^2 + 4x - 5$

Since this is not factorable, check the discriminant.

$b^2 - 4ac = 4^2 - 4(-1)(-5) = 16 - 20 = -4$

Since $-4 < 0$ there are no real roots. Thus, there are no x-intercepts.

e.

$t(x) = -x^2 + 4x - 5$

30. $g(x) = x^2 + 6x + 13$

a. Since $a = 1$, the parabola opens upward.

b. $y = 0^2 + 6(0) + 13 = 13$

The y-intercept is $(0, 13)$.

c. $x = -\dfrac{b}{2a} = -\dfrac{6}{2(1)} = -\dfrac{6}{2} = -3$

$y = \dfrac{4ac - b^2}{4a} = \dfrac{4(1)(13) - (6)^2}{4(1)}$

$= \dfrac{52 - 36}{4} = \dfrac{16}{4} = 4$

The vertex is $(-3, 4)$.

d. $0 = x^2 + 6x + 13$

Since this is not factorable, check the discriminant.

$b^2 - 4ac = 6^2 - 4(1)(13) = 36 - 52 = -16$

Since $-16 < 0$ there are no real roots. Thus, there are no x-intercepts.

e.

$g(x) = x^2 + 6x + 13$

31. $f(x) = x^2 - 4x + 4$

a. Since $a = 1$, the parabola opens upward.

b. $y = 0^2 - 4(0) + 4 = 4$

The y-intercept is $(0, 4)$.

c. $x = -\dfrac{b}{2a} = -\dfrac{-4}{2(1)} = \dfrac{4}{2} = 2$

$y = \dfrac{4ac - b^2}{4a} = \dfrac{4(1)(4) - (-4)^2}{4(1)}$

$= \dfrac{16 - 16}{4} = \dfrac{0}{4} = 0$

The vertex is $(2, 0)$.

d. $x^2 - 4x + 4 = 0$

$(x - 2)^2 = 0$

$x - 2 = 0$

$x = 2$

The x-intercept $(2, 0)$.

e.

$f(x) = x^2 - 4x + 4$

32. $r(x) = -x^2 + 10x - 25$

a. Since $a = -1$, the parabola opens downward.

b. $y = -(0)^2 + 10(0) - 25 = -25$

The y-intercept is $(0, -25)$.

c. $x = -\dfrac{b}{2a} = -\dfrac{10}{2(-1)} = \dfrac{10}{2} = 5$

$y = \dfrac{4ac - b^2}{4a} = \dfrac{4(-1)(-25) - (10)^2}{4(-1)}$

$= \dfrac{100 - 100}{-4} = \dfrac{0}{-4} = 0$

The vertex is $(5, 0)$.

d. $-x^2 + 10x - 25 = 0$

$x^2 - 10x + 25 = 0$

$(x - 5)^2 = 0$

$x - 5 = 0$

$x = 5$

The x-intercept is $(5, 0)$.

e.

$r(x) = -x^2 + 10x - 25$

33. $r(x) = x^2 + 2$

a. Since $a = 1$ the parabola opens upward.

b. $y = 0^2 + 2 = 2$

The y-intercept is $(0, 2)$.

c. $x = -\dfrac{b}{2a} = -\dfrac{0}{2(1)} = \dfrac{0}{2} = 0$

$y = \dfrac{4ac - b^2}{4a} = \dfrac{4(1)(2) - 0^2}{4(1)} = \dfrac{8}{4} = 2$

The vertex is $(0, 2)$.

d. $0 = x^2 + 2$

Since this is not factorable, check the discriminant.

$b^2 - 4ac = 0 - 4(1)2 = -8$

There are no real roots. Thus, there are no x-intercepts.

e.
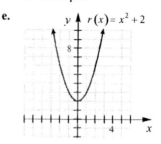

$r(x) = x^2 + 2$

34. $f(x) = x^2 + 4x$

    a. Since $a = 1$ the parabola opens upward.

    b. $y = 0^2 + 4(0) = 0$

        The y-intercept is $(0, 0)$.

    c. $x = -\dfrac{b}{2a} = -\dfrac{4}{2(1)} = -\dfrac{4}{2} = -2$

        $y = \dfrac{4ac - b^2}{4a} = \dfrac{4(1)(0) - 4^2}{4(1)} = \dfrac{-16}{4} = -4$

        The vertex is $(-2, -4)$.

    d. $x^2 + 4x = 0$

        $x(x + 4) = 0$

        $x = 0$ or $x + 4 = 0$

        $x = 0$ $x = -4$

        The x-intercepts are $(0, 0)$ and $(-4, 0)$.

    e.

$y = x^2 + 4x$

35. $l(x) = -x^2 + 5$

    a. Since $a = -1$, the parabola opens downward.

    b. $y = -(0)^2 + 5 = 5$

        The y-intercept is $(0, 5)$.

    c. $x = -\dfrac{b}{2a} = -\dfrac{0}{2(-1)} = \dfrac{0}{2} = 0$

        $y = \dfrac{4ac - b^2}{4a} = \dfrac{4(-1)(5) - (0)^2}{4(-1)}$

        $= \dfrac{-20 - 0}{-4} = \dfrac{-20}{-4} = 5$

        The vertex is $(0, 5)$.

    d. $-x^2 + 5 = 0$

        $-x^2 = -5$

        $x^2 = 5$

        $x = \pm\sqrt{5}$

        The x-intercepts are $\left(\sqrt{5}, 0\right)$ and $\left(-\sqrt{5}, 0\right)$.

    e.

$l(x) = -x^2 + 5$

36. $g(x) = -x^2 + 6x$

    a. Since $a = -1$ the parabola opens downward.

    b. $y = -0^2 + 6(0) = 0$

        The y-intercept is $(0, 0)$.

    c. $x = -\dfrac{b}{2a} = -\dfrac{6}{2(-1)} = -\dfrac{6}{-2} = 3$

        $y = \dfrac{4ac - b^2}{4a} = \dfrac{4(-1)(0) - 6^2}{4(-1)}$

        $= \dfrac{0 - 36}{-4} = \dfrac{-36}{-4} = 9$

        The vertex is $(3, 9)$.

    d. $-x^2 + 6x = 0$

        $-x(x - 6) = 0$

        $-x = 0$ or $x - 6 = 0$

        $x = 0$ $x = 6$

        The x-intercepts are $(0, 0)$ and $(6, 0)$.

    e.

$g(x) = -x^2 + 6x$

37. $y = -2x^2 + 4x - 8$

    a. Since $a = -2$ the parabola opens downward.

    b. $y = -2(0)^2 + 4(0) - 8 = -8$

        The y-intercept is $(0, -8)$.

c. $x = -\dfrac{b}{2a} = -\dfrac{4}{2(-2)} = -\dfrac{4}{-4} = 1$

$y = \dfrac{4ac - b^2}{4a} = \dfrac{4(-2)(-8) - (4)^2}{4(-2)}$

$= \dfrac{64 - 16}{-8} = \dfrac{48}{-8} = -6$

The vertex is $(1, -6)$.

d. $-2x^2 + 4x - 8 = 0$

$-2(x^2 - 2x + 4) = 0$

Since this is not factorable, check the discriminant.

$b^2 - 4ac = 4^2 - 4(-2)(-8) = 16 - 64 = -48$

Since $-48 < 0$, there are no real roots. Thus, there are no x-intercepts.

e.

$f(x) = -2x^2 + 4x - 8$

38. $g(x) = -2x^2 - 6x + 4$

a. Since $a = -2$ the parabola opens downward.

b. $y = -2(0)^2 - 6(0) + 4 = 4$

The y-intercept is $(0, 4)$.

c. $x = -\dfrac{b}{2a} = -\dfrac{(-6)}{2(-2)} = \dfrac{6}{-4} = -\dfrac{3}{2}$

$y = \dfrac{4ac - b^2}{4a} = \dfrac{4(-2)(4) - (-6)^2}{4(-2)}$

$= \dfrac{-32 - 36}{-8} = \dfrac{-68}{-8} = \dfrac{17}{2}$

The vertex is $\left(-\dfrac{3}{2}, \dfrac{17}{2}\right)$.

d. $-2x^2 - 6x + 4 = 0$

$-2(x^2 + 3x - 2) = 0$

Since this is not factorable, check the discriminant.

$b^2 - 4ac = (-6)^2 - 4(-2)(4) = 36 + 32 = 68$

There are two real roots.

$x = \dfrac{-b \pm \sqrt{b^2 - 4ac}}{2a} = \dfrac{-(-6) \pm \sqrt{68}}{2(-2)}$

$= \dfrac{6 \pm 2\sqrt{17}}{-4} = \dfrac{3 \pm \sqrt{17}}{-2} = \dfrac{-3 \pm \sqrt{17}}{2}$

The x-intercepts are

$\left(\dfrac{-3 + \sqrt{17}}{2}, 0\right)$ and $\left(\dfrac{-3 - \sqrt{17}}{2}, 0\right)$.

e.

$g(x) = -2x^2 - 6x + 4$

39. $m(x) = 3x^2 + 4x + 3$

a. Since $a = 3$ the parabola opens upward.

b. $y = 3(0) + 4(0) + 3 = 3$

The y-intercept is $(0, 3)$.

c. $x = -\dfrac{b}{2a} = -\dfrac{4}{2(3)} = -\dfrac{4}{6} = -\dfrac{2}{3}$

$y = \dfrac{4ac - b^2}{4a} = \dfrac{4(3)(3) - 4^2}{4(3)}$

$= \dfrac{36 - 16}{12} = \dfrac{20}{12} = \dfrac{5}{3}$

The vertex is $\left(-\dfrac{2}{3}, \dfrac{5}{3}\right)$.

d. $0 = 3x^2 + 4x + 3$

Since this is not factorable, check the discriminant.

$b^2 - 4ac = 4^2 - 4(3)(3) = 16 - 36 = -20$

Since $-20 < 0$ there are no real roots. Thus, there are no x-intercepts.

e.

$y = 3x^2 + 4x + 3$

40. $p(x) = -2x^2 + 5x + 4$

a. Since $a = -2$ the parabola opens downward.

b. $y = -2(0)^2 + 5(0) + 4 = 4$
The y-intercept is $(0, 4)$.

c. $x = -\dfrac{b}{2a} = -\dfrac{5}{2(-2)} = -\dfrac{5}{-4} = \dfrac{5}{4}$

$y = \dfrac{4ac - b^2}{4a} = \dfrac{4(-2)(4) - 5^2}{4(-2)}$

$= \dfrac{-32 - 25}{-8} = \dfrac{-57}{-8} = \dfrac{57}{8}$

The vertex is $\left(\dfrac{5}{4}, \dfrac{57}{8}\right)$.

d. $0 = -2x^2 + 5x + 4$
Since this is not factorable, check the discriminant.
$b^2 - 4ac = 5^2 - 4(-2)(4) = 25 + 32 = 57$
Since $57 > 0$ there are 2 real roots.

$x = \dfrac{-b \pm \sqrt{b^2 - 4ac}}{2a} = \dfrac{-5 \pm \sqrt{25 - 4(-2)(4)}}{2(-2)}$

$= \dfrac{-5 \pm \sqrt{57}}{-4} = \dfrac{5 \pm \sqrt{57}}{4}$

The x-intercepts are
$\left(\dfrac{5 + \sqrt{57}}{4}, 0\right)$ and $\left(\dfrac{5 - \sqrt{57}}{4}, 0\right)$.

e.

$f(x) = -2x^2 + 5x + 4$

41. $y = 3x^2 + 4x - 6$

a. Since $a = 3$ the parabola opens upward.

b. $y = 3(0)^2 + 4(0) - 6 = -6$
The y-intercept is $(0, -6)$.

c. $x = -\dfrac{b}{2a} = -\dfrac{4}{2(3)} = -\dfrac{4}{6} = -\dfrac{2}{3}$

$y = \dfrac{4ac - b^2}{4a} = \dfrac{4(3)(-6) - 4^2}{4(3)}$

$= \dfrac{-72 - 16}{12} = -\dfrac{22}{3}$

The vertex is $\left(-\dfrac{2}{3}, -\dfrac{22}{3}\right)$.

d. $0 = 3x^2 + 4x - 6$
Since this is not factorable, check the discriminant.
$b^2 - 4ac = 4^2 - 4(3)(-6) = 88$
Since $88 > 0$ there are two real roots.

$x = \dfrac{-b \pm \sqrt{b^2 - 4ac}}{2a} = \dfrac{-4 \pm \sqrt{88}}{2(3)}$

$= \dfrac{-4 \pm 2\sqrt{22}}{6} = \dfrac{-2 \pm \sqrt{22}}{3}$

The x-intercepts are
$\left(\dfrac{-2 + \sqrt{22}}{3}, 0\right)$ and $\left(\dfrac{-2 - \sqrt{22}}{3}, 0\right)$.

e.

$y = 3x^2 + 4x - 6$

42. $y = x^2 - 6x + 4$

a. Since $a = 1$ the parabola opens upward.

b. $y = 0^2 - 6(0) + 4 = 4$
The y-intercept is $(0, 4)$.

c. $x = -\dfrac{b}{2a} = -\dfrac{-6}{2(1)} = \dfrac{6}{2} = 3$

$y = \dfrac{4ac - b^2}{4a} = \dfrac{4(1)(4) - (-6)^2}{4(1)}$

$= \dfrac{16 - 36}{4} = \dfrac{-20}{4} = -5$

The vertex is $(3, -5)$.

d. $0 = x^2 - 6x + 4$

Since this is not factorable check the discriminant.

$b^2 - 4ac = (-6)^2 - 4(1)(4) = 36 - 16 = 20$

Since $20 > 0$ there are two real roots.

$$x = \frac{-b \pm \sqrt{b^2 - 4ac}}{2a} = \frac{-(-6) \pm \sqrt{20}}{2(1)}$$

$$= \frac{6 \pm 2\sqrt{5}}{2} = 3 \pm \sqrt{5}$$

The x-intercepts are

$\left(3 + \sqrt{5}, 0\right)$ and $\left(3 - \sqrt{5}, 0\right)$.

e.

43. $y = 2x^2 - x - 6$

a. Since $a = 2$ the parabola opens upward.

b. $y = 2(0)^2 - 0 - 6 = -6$

The y-intercept is $(0, -6)$.

c. $x = -\dfrac{b}{2a} = -\dfrac{-1}{2(2)} = \dfrac{1}{4}$

$$y = \frac{4ac - b^2}{4a} = \frac{4(2)(-6) - (-1)^2}{4(2)}$$

$$= \frac{-48 - 1}{8} = -\frac{49}{8}$$

The vertex is $\left(\dfrac{1}{4}, -\dfrac{49}{8}\right)$.

d. $2x^2 - x - 6 = 0$

$(2x + 3)(x - 2) = 0$

$2x + 3 = 0$ or $x - 2 = 0$

$x = -\dfrac{3}{2}$ $\qquad x = 2$

The x-intercepts are $\left(-\dfrac{3}{2}, 0\right)$ and $(2, 0)$.

e.

44. $g(x) = -4x^2 + 6x - 9$

a. Since $a = -4$ the parabola opens downward.

b. $y = -4(0)^2 + 6(0) - 9 = -9$

The y-intercept is $(0, -9)$.

c. $x = -\dfrac{b}{2a} = -\dfrac{6}{2(-4)} = -\dfrac{6}{-8} = \dfrac{3}{4}$

$$y = \frac{4ac - b^2}{4a} = \frac{4(-4)(-9) - 6^2}{4(-4)}$$

$$= \frac{144 - 36}{-16} = \frac{108}{-16} = -\frac{27}{4}$$

The vertex is $\left(\dfrac{3}{4}, -\dfrac{27}{4}\right)$.

d. $0 = -4x^2 + 6x - 9$

Since this is not factorable, check the discriminant.

$b^2 - 4ac = 6^2 - 4(-4)(-9) = 36 - 144 = -108$

Since $-108 < 0$ there are no real roots. There are no x-intercepts.

e.

45. $f(x) = -x^2 + 3x - 5$

a. Since $a = -1$ the parabola opens downward.

b. $y = -0^2 + 3(0) - 5 = -5$

The y-intercept is $(0, -5)$.

c. $x = -\dfrac{b}{2a} = -\dfrac{3}{2(-1)} = -\dfrac{3}{-2} = \dfrac{3}{2}$

$$y = \frac{4ac - b^2}{4a} = \frac{4(-1)(-5) - 3^2}{4(-1)} = -\frac{11}{4}$$

The vertex is $\left(\dfrac{3}{2}, -\dfrac{11}{4}\right)$.

d. $0 = -x^2 + 3x - 5$

Since this is not factorable, check the discriminant.

$b^2 - 4ac = 3^2 - 4(-1)(-5) = 9 - 20 = -11$

Since $-11 < 0$ there are no real roots. Thus, there are no x-intercepts.

e.

46. $h(x) = -2x^2 + 4x - 5$

a. Since $a = -2$ the parabola opens downward.

b. $y = -2(0)^2 + 4(0) - 5 = -5$

The y-intercept is $(0, -5)$.

c. $x = -\dfrac{b}{2a} = -\dfrac{4}{2(-2)} = -\dfrac{4}{-4} = 1$

$y = \dfrac{4ac - b^2}{4a} = \dfrac{4(-2)(-5) - (4)^2}{4(-2)}$

$= \dfrac{40 - 16}{-8} = -3$

The vertex is $(1, -3)$.

d. $0 = -2x^2 + 4x - 5$

Since this is not factorable, check the discriminant.

$b^2 - 4ac = 4^2 - 4(-2)(-5) = 16 - 40 = -24$

Since $-24 < 0$, there are no real roots. Thus, there are no x-intercepts.

e.

$h(x) = -2x^2 + 4x - 5$

47. In the function $f(x) = (x-3)^2$, h has a value of 3. The graph of $f(x)$ is the graph of $g(x) = x^2$ shifted 3 units to the right.

48. In the function $f(x) = (x-4)^2$, h has a value of 4. The graph of $f(x)$ is the graph of $g(x) = x^2$ shifted 4 units to the right.

49. In the function $f(x) = (x+1)^2$, h has a value of -1. The graph of $f(x)$ is the graph of $g(x) = x^2$ shifted 1 unit to the left.

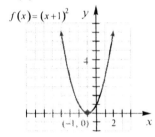

50. In the function $f(x) = (x+2)^2$, h has a value of -2. The graph of $f(x)$ is the graph of $g(x) = x^2$ shifted 2 units to the left.

51. In the function $f(x) = x^2 + 3$, k has a value of 3. The graph $f(x)$ will be the graph of $g(x) = x^2$ shifted 3 units up.

52. In the function $f(x) = x^2 + 5$, k has a value of 5. The graph $f(x)$ will be the graph of $g(x) = x^2$ shifted 5 units up.

53. In the function $f(x) = x^2 - 1$, k has a value of -1. The graph $f(x)$ will be the graph of $g(x) = x^2$ shifted 1 units down.

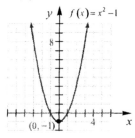

54. In the function $f(x) = x^2 - 4$, k has a value of -4. The graph of $f(x)$ will be the graph of $g(x) = x^2$ shifted 4 units down.

55. In the function $f(x) = (x-2)^2 + 3$, h has a value of 2 and k has a value of 3. The graph of $f(x)$ will be the graph of $g(x) = x^2$ shifted 2 units to the right and 3 units up.

56. In the function $f(x) = (x-3)^2 - 4$, h has a value of 3 and k has a value of -4. The graph of $f(x)$ will be the graph of $g(x) = x^2$ shifted 3 units to the right and 4 units down.

57. In the function $f(x) = (x+4)^2 + 4$, h has a value of -4 and k has a value of 4. The graph of $f(x)$ will be the graph of $g(x) = x^2$ shifted 4 units to the left and 4 units up.

58. In the function $h(x) = (x+4)^2 - 1$, h has a value of -4 and k has a value of -1. The graph of $h(x)$ is the graph of $f(x) = x^2$ shifted 4 units to the left and 1 unit down.

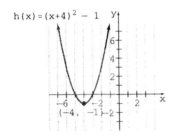

59. In the function $g(x) = -(x+3)^2 - 2$, a has the value -1, h has the value -3, and k has the value -2. Since $a < 0$, the parabola opens downward. The graph of $g(x)$ will be the graph of $f(x) = -x^2$ shifted 3 units to the left and 2 units down.

60. In the function $g(x) = (x-1)^2 + 4$, h has a value of 1 and k has a value of 4. The graph of $g(x)$ will be the graph of $f(x) = x^2$ shifted 1 unit to the right and 4 units up.

61. In the function $y = -2(x-2)^2 + 2$, a has a value of -2, h has a value of 2, and k has a value of 2. The graph of y will be the graph of $g(x) = -2x^2$ shifted 2 units to the right and 2 units up.

62. In the function $y = -2(x-3)^2 + 1$, a has a value of -2, h has a value of 3, and k has a value of 1. The graph of y will be the graph of $f(x) = -2x^2$ shifted 3 units to the right and 1 unit up.

63. In the function $h(x) = -2(x+1)^2 - 3$, a has a value of -2, h has a value of -1, and k has a value of -3. Since $a < 0$, the parabola opens downward. The graph of $h(x)$ will be the graph of $f(x) = -2x^2$ shifted 1 unit left and 3 units down.

64. In the function $f(x) = -(x-5)^2 + 2$, a has a value of -1, h has a value of 5, and k has a value of 2. The graph of $f(x)$ will be the graph of $g(x) = -x^2$ shifted 5 units to the right and 2 units up.

f (x) = -(x-5)²+2

65. a. $f(x) = x^2 - 6x + 8$
$$f(x) = (x^2 - 6x + 9) + 8 - 9$$
$$f(x) = (x-3)^2 - 1$$

b. Since $h = 3$ and $k = -1$, the vertex is $(3, -1)$

66. a. $g(x) = x^2 + 6x + 2$
$$g(x) = (x^2 + 6x + 9) + 2 - 9$$
$$g(x) = (x+3)^2 - 7$$

b. Since $h = -3$ and $k = -7$, the vertex is $(-3, -7)$.

67. a. $g(x) = x^2 - x - 3$
$$g(x) = \left(x^2 - x + \frac{1}{4}\right) - 3 - \frac{1}{4}$$
$$g(x) = \left(x - \frac{1}{2}\right)^2 - \frac{13}{4}$$

b. Since $h = \frac{1}{2}$ and $k = -\frac{13}{4}$, the vertex is $\left(\frac{1}{2}, -\frac{13}{4}\right)$.

68. a. $f(x) = x^2 - x + 1$
$$f(x) = \left(x^2 - x + \frac{1}{4}\right) + 1 - \frac{1}{4}$$
$$f(x) = \left(x - \frac{1}{2}\right)^2 + \frac{3}{4}$$

b. Since $h = \frac{1}{2}$ and $k = \frac{3}{4}$, the vertex is $\left(\frac{1}{2}, \frac{3}{4}\right)$.

69. a. $f(x) = -x^2 - 4x - 6$
$$f(x) = -(x^2 + 4x) - 6$$
$$f(x) = -(x^2 + 4x + 4) - 6 - (-4)$$
$$f(x) = -(x+2)^2 - 2$$

b. Since $h = -2$ and $k = -2$, the vertex is $(-2, -2)$. Since $a < 0$, the parabola opens downward.

f (x) = x² -4x-6

784

70. a. $h(x) = -x^2 + 6x + 1$

$h(x) = -(x^2 - 6x) + 1$

$h(x) = -(x^2 - 6x + 9) + 1 - (-9)$

$h(x) = -(x - 3)^2 + 10$

b. Since $h = 3$ and $k = 10$, the vertex is $(3, 10)$. Since $a < 0$, the parabola opens downward.

71. a. $g(x) = x^2 - 4x - 1$

$g(x) = (x^2 - 4x + 4) - 1 - 4$

$g(x) = (x - 2)^2 - 5$

b. Since $h = 2$ and $k = -5$, the vertex is $(2, -5)$.

72. a. $p(x) = x^2 - 2x - 6$

$p(x) = (x^2 - 2x + 1) - 6 - 1$

$p(x) = (x - 1)^2 - 7$

b. Since $h = 1$ and $k = -7$, the vertex is $(1, -7)$.

73. a. $f(x) = 2x^2 + 5x - 3$

$f(x) = 2\left(x^2 + \frac{5}{2}x\right) - 3$

$f(x) = 2\left(x^2 + \frac{5}{2}x + \frac{25}{16}\right) - 3 - 2\left(\frac{25}{16}\right)$

$f(x) = 2\left(x^2 + \frac{5}{2}x + \frac{25}{16}\right) - 3 - \frac{25}{8}$

$f(x) = 2\left(x + \frac{5}{4}\right)^2 - \frac{49}{8}$

b. Since $h = -\frac{5}{4}$ and $k = -\frac{49}{8}$, the vertex is $\left(-\frac{5}{4}, -\frac{49}{8}\right)$. The graph of $f(x)$ will be the graph of $g(x) = 2x^2$ shifted $\frac{5}{4}$ units left and $\frac{49}{8}$ units down.

74. a. $k(x) = 2x^2 + 7x - 4$

$k(x) = 2\left(x^2 + \frac{7}{2}x\right) - 4$

$k(x) = 2\left(x^2 + \frac{7}{2}x + \frac{49}{16}\right) - 4 - 2\left(\frac{49}{16}\right)$

$k(x) = 2\left(x^2 + \frac{7}{2}x + \frac{49}{16}\right) - 4 - \frac{49}{8}$

$k(x) = 2\left(x + \frac{7}{4}\right)^2 - \frac{81}{8}$

b. Since $h = -\frac{7}{4}$ and $k = -\frac{81}{8}$, the vertex is $\left(-\frac{7}{4}, -\frac{81}{8}\right)$ the graph of $f(x)$ will be the graph of $k(x) = 2x^2$ shifted $\frac{7}{4}$ units left and $\frac{81}{8}$ units down.

$$k(x) = 2x^2 + 7x - 4$$

75. $y = x^2 + 3x - 4$

$$x = -\frac{b}{2a} = -\frac{3}{2}$$

The parabola opens up and the x-coordinate of

the vertex is $-\dfrac{3}{2}$. The graph is (c).

76. $y = x^3 + 2x^2 - 4$

The leading coefficient is positive. The function will increase as x increases. The y-intercept is $(0, -4)$. The graph is (b).

77. $y = -x^3 + 2x^2 - 6$

The leading coefficient is negative. The function will decrease as x increases. The y-intercept is $(0, -6)$. The graph is (c).

78. $y = x^3 + 4x^2 - 5$

The leading coefficient is positive. The function will increase as x increases. The y-intercept is $(0, -5)$. The graph is (b).

79. a. $y_1 = x^3$

$\qquad$ $y_2 = x^3 - 3x^2 - 3$

b. As x increases the functions increase.

c. Answers will vary.

d. As x decreases, the functions decrease.

e. Answers will vary.

80. a. $y_1 = x^4$

$\qquad$ $y_2 = x^4 - 6x^2$

b. As x increases the functions increase.

c. Answers will vary.

d. As x decreases, the functions increase.

e. Answers will vary.

81. $f(x) = 2(x+3)^2 - 1$. The vertex is $(h, k) = (-3, -1)$. Since $a > 0$, the parabola opens up. The graph is (d).

82. $f(x) = -2(x+3)^2 - 1$. The vertex is $(h, k) = (-3, -1)$. Since $a < 0$, the parabola opens down. The graph is (a).

83. $f(x) = 2(x-1)^2 + 3$ The vertex is $(h, k) = (1, 3)$. Since $a > 0$, the parabola opens up. The graph is (b).

84. $f(x) = -2(x-1)^2 + 3$. The vertex is $(h, k) = (1, 3)$. Since $a < 0$, the parabola opens down. The graph is (c).

85. a. $f(x) = (x+4)(18-x)$

$\qquad\qquad = 18x - x^2 + 72 - 4x$

$\qquad\qquad = -x^2 + 14x + 72$

Since $a = -1$, the graph of this function is a parabola that opens downward and thus has a maximum value at its vertex.

$$x = -\frac{b}{2a} = -\frac{14}{2(-1)} = 7$$

b. $y = \dfrac{4ac - b^2}{4a} = \dfrac{4(-1)(72) - (14)^2}{4(-1)}$

$\qquad = \dfrac{-288 - 196}{-4} = \dfrac{-484}{-4} = 121$

The maximum area is 121 square units.

86. a. $f(x) = (x+7)(19-x)$

$$= 19x - x^2 + 133 - 7x$$

$$= -x^2 + 12x + 133$$

Since $a = -1$, the graph of this function is a parabola that opens downward and thus has a maximum value at its vertex.

$$x = -\frac{b}{2a} = -\frac{12}{2(-1)} = 6$$

b. $y = \dfrac{4ac - b^2}{4a} = \dfrac{4(-1)(133) - (12)^2}{4(-1)}$

$$= \frac{-532 - 144}{-4} = \frac{-676}{-4} = 169$$

The maximum area is 169 square units.

87. a. $f(x) = (x+5)(26-x)$

$$= 26x - x^2 + 130 - 5x$$

$$= -x^2 + 21x + 130$$

Since $a = -1$, the graph of this function is a parabola that opens downward and thus has a maximum value at its vertex.

$$x = -\frac{b}{2a} = -\frac{21}{2(-1)} = 10.5$$

b. $y = \dfrac{4ac - b^2}{4a} = \dfrac{4(-1)(130) - (21)^2}{4(-1)}$

$$= \frac{-520 - 441}{-4} = 240.25$$

The maximum area is 240.25 square units.

88. a. $f(x) = (x+2)(19-x)$

$$= 19x - x^2 + 38 - 2x$$

$$= -x^2 + 17x + 38$$

Since $a = -1$, the graph of this function is a parabola that opens downward and thus has a maximum value at its vertex.

$$x = -\frac{b}{2a} = -\frac{17}{2(-1)} = 8.5$$

b. $y = \dfrac{4ac - b^2}{4a} = \dfrac{4(-1)(38) - (17)^2}{4(-1)}$

$$= \frac{-152 - 289}{-4} = \frac{-441}{-4} = 110.25$$

The maximum area is 110.25 square units.

89. a. $R(n) = -0.02n^2 + 8n$

Since $a = -0.02$, the graph of this function is a parabola that opens downward and thus has a maximum value at its vertex.

$$x = -\frac{b}{2a} = -\frac{8}{2(-0.02)} = 200$$

The maximum revenue will be achieved when 200 batteries are sold.

b. $y = \dfrac{4ac - b^2}{4a} = \dfrac{4(-0.02)(0) - (8)^2}{4(-0.02)}$

$$= \frac{0 - 64}{-0.08} = \frac{-64}{-0.08} = 800$$

The maximum revenue is \$800.

90. a. $R(n) = -0.1n^2 + 25n$

Since $a = -0.1$, the graph of this function is a parabola that opens downward and thus has a maximum value at its vertex.

$$x = -\frac{b}{2a} = -\frac{25}{2(-0.1)} = 125$$

The maximum revenue will be achieved when 125 watches are sold.

b. $y = \dfrac{4ac - b^2}{4a} = \dfrac{4(-0.1)(0) - (25)^2}{4(-0.1)}$

$$= \frac{0 - 625}{-0.4} = \frac{-625}{-0.4} = 1562.5$$

The maximum revenue is \$1562.50.

91. $N(t) = -0.043t^2 + 1.82t + 46.0$

Since $a = -0.043$, the graph of this function is a parabola that opens downward and thus has a maximum value at its vertex.

$$x = -\frac{b}{2a} = -\frac{1.82}{2(-0.043)} \approx 21.2$$

The maximum enrollment will be obtained about 21 years after 1989 which is the year 2010.

92. $f(a) = -2.32a^2 + 76.58a - 559.87$

Since $a = -2.32$, the graph of this function is a parabola that opens downward and thus has a maximum value at its vertex.

$$x = -\frac{b}{2a} = -\frac{76.58}{2(-2.32)} \approx 16.5$$

The age that has the highest percent of students who say their school is not drug free is 16.5 years.

93. For $f(x) = (x-2)^2 + \dfrac{5}{2}$, the vertex is $\left(2, \dfrac{5}{2}\right)$.

For $g(x) = (x-2)^2 - \dfrac{3}{2}$, the vertex is $\left(2, -\dfrac{3}{2}\right)$.

These points are on the vertical line $x = 2$. The distance between the two points is

$\dfrac{5}{2} - \left(-\dfrac{3}{2}\right) = \dfrac{5}{2} + \dfrac{3}{2} = \dfrac{8}{2} = 4$ units.

94. For $f(x) = 2(x-4)^2 - 3$, the vertex is $(4, -3)$.

For $g(x) = -3(x-4)^2 + 2$, the vertex is $(4, 2)$.

These points are on the vertical line $x = 4$. The distance between the two points is
$2 - (-3) = 2 + 3 = 5$ units.

95. For $f(x) = 2(x+4)^2 - 3$, the vertex is $(-4, -3)$.

For $g(x) = -(x+1)^2 - 3$, the vertex is $(-1, -3)$.

These points are on the horizontal line $y = -3$. The distance between the two points is
$-1 - (-4) = -1 + 4 = 3$ units.

96. For $f(x) = -\dfrac{1}{3}(x-3)^2 - 2$, the vertex is $(3, -2)$.

For $g(x) = 2(x+5)^2 - 2$, the vertex is $(-5, -2)$.

These points are on the horizontal line $y = -2$. The distance between the two points is
$3 - (-5) = 3 + 5 = 8$ units.

97. A function that has the shape of $f(x) = 2x^2$ will have the form $f(x) = 2(x-h)^2 + k$. If $(h, k) = (3, -2)$, the function is

$f(x) = 2(x-3)^2 - 2$.

98. A function that has the shape of $f(x) = -\dfrac{1}{2}x^2$

will have the form $f(x) = -\dfrac{1}{2}(x-h)^2 + k$. If

$(h, k) = \left(\dfrac{2}{3}, -5\right)$, the function is

$f(x) = -\dfrac{1}{2}\left(x - \dfrac{2}{3}\right)^2 - 5$.

99. A function that has the shape of $f(x) = -4x^2$

will have the form $f(x) = -4(x-h)^2 + k$. If

$(h, k) = \left(-\dfrac{3}{5}, -\sqrt{2}\right)$, the function is

$f(x) = -4\left(x + \dfrac{3}{5}\right)^2 - \sqrt{2}$.

100. A function that has the shape of $f(x) = \dfrac{3}{5}x^2$

will have the form $f(x) = \dfrac{3}{5}(x-h)^2 + k$. If

$(h, k) = \left(-\sqrt{3}, \sqrt{5}\right)$, the function is

$f(x) = \dfrac{3}{5}\left(x + \sqrt{3}\right)^2 + \sqrt{5}$.

101. a. The graphs will have the same x-intercepts but $f(x) = x^2 - 8x + 12$ will open up and $g(x) = -x^2 + 8x - 12$ will open down.

b. Yes, because the x-intercepts are located by setting $x^2 - 8x + 12$ and $-x^2 + 8x - 12$ equal to zero. They have the same solution set, therefore the x-intercepts are equal. The x-intercepts for both are $(6, 0)$, and $(2, 0)$.

c. No. The vertex for $f(x) = x^2 - 8x + 12$ is $(4, -4)$ and the vertex for $g(x) = -x^2 + 8x - 12$ is $(4, 4)$.

d.

$g(x) = -x^2 + 8x - 12$

102. For $f(x) = ax^2 + bx + c = a(x-h)^2 + k$, the parabola will have:

No *x*-intercepts if
i) $a > 0, k > 0$ or   ii) $a < 0, k < 0$

One *x*-intercept if $k = 0$

Two *x*-intercepts if
i) $a > 0, k < 0$ or   ii) $a < 0, k > 0$

103. a. The vertex $x = -\dfrac{b}{2a} = -\dfrac{24}{2(-1)} = 12$

$$I = -(12)^2 + 24(12) - 44$$
$$= -144 + 288 - 44$$
$$= 100$$

The vertex is at (12, 100). To find the roots set $I = 0$.

$$0 = -x^2 + 24x - 44$$
$$= -1(x^2 - 24x + 44)$$
$$= -1(x-2)(x-22)$$
$$x - 2 = 0 \quad \text{or} \quad x - 22 = 0$$
$$x = 2 \qquad\qquad x = 22$$

The roots are 2 and 22.

$I = -x^2 + 24x - 44, \ 0 \le x \le 24$

b. The minimum cost will be $2 since the smaller root is 2.

c. The maximum cost is $22 since the larger root is 22.

d. The maximum value will occur at the vertex of the parabola, (12, 100). Therefore, they should charge $12.

e. The maximum value will occur at the vertex of the parabola, (12, 100). Since *I* is in hundreds of dollars the maximum income is $100(\$100) = \$10,000$.

104. a. $d = -16t^2 + 192t$

Let $t = 3$:

$$d = -16t^2 + 192t$$
$$= -16(3)^2 + 192(3)$$
$$= -16(9) + 192(3)$$
$$= -144 + 576$$
$$= 432$$

After 3 seconds, the object is 432 feet above the ground.

b. $t = -\dfrac{b}{2a} = -\dfrac{192}{-2(16)} = 6$

When $t = 6$,

$$d = -16(6)^2 + 192(6) = -576 + 1152 = 576$$

The vertex is (6, 576). To find the roots, set $d = 0$.

$$0 = -16t^2 + 192t$$
$$0 = -16t(t - 12)$$
$$-16t = 0 \quad \text{or} \quad t - 12 = 0$$
$$t = 0 \quad \text{or} \qquad t = 12$$

The roots are 0 and 12. These are the *x*-intercepts.

c. The object will reach a maximum height of 576 ft.

d. It will reach its maximum height after 6 seconds.

e. The object strikes after 12 seconds.

105. a. The number of bird feeders sold for the maximum profit will be the x-coordinate of the vertex.

$$f(x) = -0.4x^2 + 80x - 200$$

$$x = -\frac{b}{2a} = -\frac{80}{2(-0.4)} = -\frac{80}{-0.8} = 100$$

The company must sell 100 bird feeders for maximum profit.

b. The maximum profit will be the y-coordinate of the vertex, $y = f(100)$.

$$f(100) = -0.4(100)^2 + 80(100) - 200$$

$$= -0.4(10,000) + 8000 - 200$$

$$= -4000 + 8000 - 200$$

$$= 3800$$

The maximum profit will be $3800.

106. a. The number of rocking chairs sold for maximum profit will be the x-coordinate of the vertex,

$$f(x) = -1.2x^2 + 180x - 280$$

$$x = -\frac{b}{2a} = -\frac{180}{2(-1.2)} = -\frac{180}{-2.4} = 75$$

The company must sell 75 rocking chairs for maximum profit.

b. The maximum profit will be the y-coordinate of the vertex, $y = f(75)$.

$$f(75) = -1.2(75)^2 + 180(75) - 280$$

$$= -1.2(5265) + 13,500 - 280$$

$$= -6750 + 13,500 - 280$$

$$= 6470$$

The maximum profit will be $6470.

107. a. The maximum height is h, the y-coordinate of the vertex.

$$h(t) = -4.9t^2 + 24.5t + 9.8$$

$$h = \frac{4ac - b^2}{4a} = \frac{4(-4.9)(9.8) - (24.5)^2}{4(-4.9)}$$

$$= \frac{-192.08 - 600.25}{-19.6} = \frac{-792.33}{-19.6} = 40.425$$

The maximum height obtained by the cannonball is 40.425 meters.

b. The time the cannonball reaches the maximum height is t, the x-coordinate of the vertex,. $t = -\dfrac{b}{2a} = -\dfrac{24.5}{2(-4.9)} = 2.5$

The cannonball will reach the maximum height after 2.5 seconds.

c. $f(x) = 0$ when the cannonball hits the ground.

$$h(t) = -4.9t^2 + 24.5t + 9.8$$

$$0 = -4.9t^2 + 24.5t + 9.8$$

$$t = \frac{-24.5 \pm \sqrt{(24.5)^2 - 4(-4.9)(9.8)}}{2(-4.9)}$$

$$= \frac{-24.5 \pm \sqrt{792.33}}{-9.8}$$

$$\approx \frac{-24.5 \pm 28.14836}{-9.8}$$

$$t \approx -0.37 \text{ or } t \approx 5.37$$

Disregard the negative value. The cannonball will hit the ground after about 5.37 seconds.

108. The time the ball reaches the maximum height is t, the x-coordinate of the vertex, and the maximum height is h, the y-coordinate.

$$h = 96t - 16t^2 = -16t^2 + 96t$$

$$t = -\frac{b}{2a} = -\frac{96}{2(-16)} = -\frac{96}{-32} = 3$$

The ball will reach the maximum height after 3 seconds.

$$h(3) = 96(3) - 16(3)^2 = 288 - 144 = 144$$

The maximum height is 144 feet.

109. a. The year 2007 is represented by $t = 13$.

$$r(t) = -2.723t^2 + 35.273t + 579$$

$$r(13) = -2.723(13)^2 + 35.273(13) + 579 \approx 577$$

The average monthly rent should be about $577.

b. The function will reach a maximum at it's vertex: $t = -\dfrac{b}{2a} = -\dfrac{35.273}{2(-2.723)} \approx 6.5$

The monthly rent for an apartment reached a maximum about 6.5 years after 1994, which was during the year 2000.

110. a. February 22, 2008 is represented by $t = 8$.

$$C(t) = 0.019t^2 - 0.074t + 0.702$$

$$C(8) = 0.019(8)^2 - 0.074(8) + 0.702 \approx 1.33$$

On February 22, 2008, the value of the Canadian dollar should be about $1.33.

b. The function will reach a minimum at it's vertex: $t = -\dfrac{b}{2a} = -\dfrac{-0.074}{2(0.019)} \approx 2$

The Canadian dollar, in U.S. dollars, will reached a minimum about 2 years after 2000, which was about the year 2002.

111. If the perimeter of the room is 8 ft., then
$80 = 2l + 2w$, where l is the length and w is the
width. Then $80 = 2(l + w)$ and $40 = l + w$.

Therefore, $l = 40 - w$. The area of the room is
$A = lw = (40 - w)w = 40w - w^2 = -w^2 + 40w$. The
maximum area is the y-coordinate of the vertex.
$$A = \frac{4ac - b^2}{4a} = \frac{4(-1)(0) - 40^2}{4(-1)}$$
$$= \frac{0 - 1600}{-4} = \frac{-1600}{-4} = 400$$
The maximum area is 400 square feet.

112. If the perimeter of the garden is 70 ft. then
$70 = 2l + 2w$, when l is the length and w is the
width, then $70 = 2(l + w)$ and $35 = l + w$.

Therefore, $l = 35 - w$. The area of the garden is
$A = lw - (35 - w)w$
$= 35w - w^2$
$= -w^2 + 35w$
The maximum area is the y-coordinate of the
vertex.
$$A = \frac{4ac - b^2}{4a} = \frac{4(-1)(0) - 35^2}{4(-1)} = \frac{0 - 1225}{-4}$$
$$= 306.25$$
The maximum area is 306.25 square feet.

113. If two numbers differ by 8 and x is one of the
numbers, then $x + 8$ is the other number. The
product is $f(x) = x(x + 8) = x^2 + 8x$. The
maximum product is the y-coordinate of the
vertex.
$$x = -\frac{b}{2a} = -\frac{8}{2(1)} = -4$$
$$y = f(-4) = (-4)^2 + 8(-4) = -16$$
The maximum product is −16. The numbers are
−4 and −4 + 8 = 4.

114. If two numbers differ by 10 and x is one of the
numbers, then $x + 10$ is the other number. The
product is $f(x) = x(x + 10) = x^2 + 10x$. The
minimum product is the y-coordinate of the
vertex.
$$x = -\frac{b}{2a} = -\frac{10}{2(1)} = -5$$
$$y = f(-5) = (-5)^2 + 10(-5) = 25 - 50 = -25$$
The minimum product is −25. The numbers are
−5 and −5 + 10 = 5.

115. If two numbers add to 60 and x is one of the
numbers, then $60 - x$ is the other number. The
product is
$f(x) = x(60 - x) = 60x - x^2 = -x^2 + 60x$.
The maximum product is the y-coordinate of the
vertex.
$$x = -\frac{b}{2a} = -\frac{60}{2(-1)} = -\frac{60}{-2} = 30$$
$$y = f(30) = -30^2 + 60(30) = -900 + 1800 = 900$$
The maximum product is 900. The numbers are
30 and 60 − 30 = 30.

116. If two numbers add to 5 and x is one of the
numbers, then $5 - x$ is the other number. The
product is $f(x) = x(5 - x) = 5x - x^2 = -x^2 + 5x$.
The maximum product is the y-coordinate of the
vertex.
$$x = -\frac{b}{2a} = -\frac{5}{2(-1)} = -\frac{5}{-2} = \frac{5}{2}$$
$$y = f\left(\frac{5}{2}\right) = -\left(\frac{5}{2}\right)^2 + 5\left(\frac{5}{2}\right) = -\frac{25}{4} + \frac{25}{2} = \frac{25}{4}$$
The maximum product is $\frac{25}{4}$. The numbers are
$\frac{5}{2}$ and $5 - \frac{5}{2} = \frac{5}{2}$.

117. $C(x) = 2000 + 40x,\ R(x) = 800x - x^2$
$P(x) = R(x) - C(x)$
$P(x) = (800x - x^2) - (2000 + 40x)$
$= 800x - x^2 - 2000 - 40x$
$= -x^2 + 760x - 2000$
The maximum profit is $P(x)$, the y-coordinate
of the vertex. The number of items that must be
produced and sold to obtain maximum profit is
the x coordinate of the vertex.
$$x = -\frac{b}{2a} = -\frac{760}{2(-1)} = 380$$

a. $P(380) = -380^2 + 760(380) - 2000$
$= -144,400 + 288800 - 2000$
$= 142,400$
The maximum profit is $142,400.

b. The number of items that must be produced
and sold to obtain maximum profit is 380.

118. $C(x) = 5000 + 12x$, $R(x) = 2000x - x^2$

$P(x) = R(x) - C(x)$

$P(x) = (2000x - x^2) - (5000 + 12x)$

$\qquad = 2000x - x^2 - 5000 - 12x$

$\qquad = -x^2 + 1988x - 5000$

The maximum profit is $P(x)$, the y-coordinate of the vertex. The number of items that must be produced and sold to obtain maximum profit is the x-coordinate of the vertex.

$x = -\dfrac{b}{2a} = -\dfrac{1988}{2(-1)} = 994$

a. $P(994) = -994^2 + 1988(994) - 5000$

$\qquad = -988,036 + 1,976,072 - 5000$

$\qquad = 983,036$

The maximum profit is \$983,036.

b. The number of items that must be produced and sold to obtain maximum profit is 994.

119. The y-intercept is $(0, -5)$. As x increases, the function decreases because of the leading coefficient. The graph is (b).

120. The y-intercept is $(0, -5)$. As x increases, the function decreases because of the leading coefficient. Also, as x decreases, the function increases. The graph is (c).

121. a. $f(t) = -16t^2 + 52t + 3$

$\qquad = -16(t^2 - 3.25t) + 3$

$\qquad = -16\left[t^2 - 3.25t + \left(\dfrac{3.25}{2}\right)^2 \right] + 3 + 16\left(\dfrac{3.25}{2}\right)^2$

$\qquad = -16(t - 1.625)^2 + 3 + 42.25$

$\qquad = -16(t - 1.625)^2 + 45.25$

b. The maximum height was 45.25 feet obtained at 1.625 seconds.

c. It is the same answer.

122. The leading coefficient is $3x^3$. As x decreases, the function decreases. The graph is (c).

123. The leading coefficient is $-2x^4$. As x decreases, the function decreases, and as x increases, the function decreases. The graph could be (a) or (b).

124. Answers will vary.

125. The radius of the outer circle is $r = 15$ ft. The area $A = \pi r^2 = \pi(15^2) = 225\pi$ ft^2. The radius of the inner circle is $r = 5$ ft. The area is $A = \pi r^2 = \pi(5^2) = 25\pi$ ft^2. The blue shaded area is 225π ft^2 − 25π ft^2 = 200π ft^2.

126. $(x-3) \div \dfrac{x^2 + 3x - 18}{x} = \dfrac{x-3}{1} \cdot \dfrac{x}{x^2 + 3x - 18}$

$\qquad\qquad = \dfrac{x-3}{1} \cdot \dfrac{x}{(x+6)(x-3)}$

$\qquad\qquad = \dfrac{x}{x+6}$

127. $\quad x - y \quad\; = -5 \quad (1)$

$\quad 2x + 2y - z = \;\; 0 \quad (2)$

$\quad x + \;\; y + z = \;\; 3 \quad (3)$

First eliminate the variable z from equations (2) and (3) by adding these equations.

$\quad 2x + 2y - z = 0$

$\underline{\quad x + \;\; y + z = 3\quad}$

$\quad 3x + 3y \quad\;\; = 3 \qquad (4)$

Equations (1) and (4) form a system of equations in two variables. Multiply equation (1) by 3 and add the result to equation (4) to eliminate the variable y.

$3(x - y) = 3(-5) \;\Rightarrow\; 3x - 3y = -15$

$3x + 3y = 3 \qquad\quad \Rightarrow \;\; \underline{3x + 3y = \quad 3\quad}$

$\qquad\qquad\qquad\qquad\qquad 6x \qquad = -12$

$\qquad\qquad\qquad\qquad\qquad\quad x = -2$

Substitute −2 for x in equation (1) to find y.

$(-2) - y = -5$

$\qquad -y = -3$

$\qquad\;\; y = 3$

Substitute −2 for x and 3 for y in equation (3) to find z.

$(-2) + (3) + z = 3$

$\qquad\quad 1 + z = 3$

$\qquad\qquad\;\; z = 2$

The solution is $(-2, 3, 2)$.

128. $\begin{vmatrix} \frac{1}{2} & 3 \\ 2 & -4 \end{vmatrix} = \left(\dfrac{1}{2}\right)(-4) - (2)(3) = -2 - 6 = -8$

129. $y \le \dfrac{2}{3}x + 3$

Exercise Set 12.6

1. a. For $f(x) = x^2 - 7x + 10$, $f(x) > 0$ when the graph is above the *x*-axis. The solution is $x < 2$ or $x > 5$.

b. For $f(x) = x^2 - 7x + 10$ $f(x) < 0$ when the graph is below the *x*-axis. The solution is $2 < x < 5$.

2. a. For $f(x) = -x^2 - 4x + 5$, $f(x) \ge 0$ when the graph is on or above the *x*-axis.. The solution is $-5 \le x \le 1$.

b. For $f(x) = -x^2 - 4x + 5$, $f(x) \le 0$ when the graph is on or below the *x*-axis. The solution is $x \le -5$ or $x \ge 1$.

3. Yes. The boundary values 5 and –3 are included in the solution set since this is a greater than *or equal to* inequality. These values make the expression equal to zero.

4. No. The boundary values 2 and –4 are not included in the solution set since this is a strictly less than inequality. These values make the expression equal to zero.

5. The boundary values –2 and 1 are included in the solution set since this is a less than *or equal to* inequality. These values make the expression equal to zero. However, the boundary value –1 is not included in the solution set since it would result in a zero in the denominator, which is undefined.

6. The boundary value –3 is included in the solution set since this is a greater than *or equal to* inequality. This value makes the expression equal to zero. However, the boundary values –4 and 2 are not included in the solution set since either would result in a zero in the denominator, which is undefined.

7. $x^2 - 2x - 8 \ge 0$

$(x+2)(x-4) \ge 0$

8. $x^2 - 2x - 8 < 0$

$(x+2)(x-4) < 0$

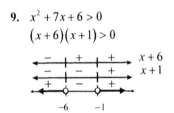

9. $x^2 + 7x + 6 > 0$

$(x+6)(x+1) > 0$

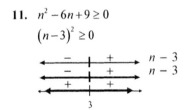

10. $x^2 + 8x + 7 < 0$

$(x+7)(x+1) < 0$

11. $n^2 - 6n + 9 \ge 0$

$(n-3)^2 \ge 0$

12. $x^2 - 8x \ge 0$

$x(x-8) \ge 0$

13. $x^2 - 16 < 0$

$(x+4)(x-4) < 0$

14. $r^2 - 5r < 0$

$r(r-5) < 0$

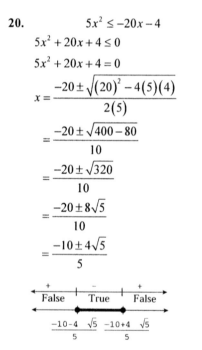

15. $2x^2 + 5x - 3 \geq 0$

$(2x-1)(x+3) \geq 0$

16. $3n^2 - 7n \leq 6$

$3n^2 - 7n - 6 \leq 0$

$(3n+2)(n-3) \leq 0$

17. $5x^2 + 6x \leq 8$

$5x^2 + 6x - 8 \leq 0$

$(x+2)(5x-4) \leq 0$

18. $3x^2 + 5x - 3 \leq 0$

$3x^2 + 5x - 3 = 0$

$x = \dfrac{-5 \pm \sqrt{5^2 - 4(3)(-3)}}{2(3)}$

$= \dfrac{-5 \pm \sqrt{25 + 36}}{6}$

$= \dfrac{-5 \pm \sqrt{61}}{6}$

19. $2x^2 - 12x + 9 \leq 0$

$2x^2 - 12x + 9 = 0$

$x = \dfrac{-(-12) \pm \sqrt{(-12)^2 - 4(2)(9)}}{2(2)}$

$= \dfrac{12 \pm \sqrt{144 - 72}}{4}$

$= \dfrac{12 \pm \sqrt{72}}{4} = \dfrac{12 \pm 6\sqrt{2}}{4} = \dfrac{6 \pm 3\sqrt{2}}{2}$

20. $5x^2 \leq -20x - 4$

$5x^2 + 20x + 4 \leq 0$

$5x^2 + 20x + 4 = 0$

$x = \dfrac{-20 \pm \sqrt{(20)^2 - 4(5)(4)}}{2(5)}$

$= \dfrac{-20 \pm \sqrt{400 - 80}}{10}$

$= \dfrac{-20 \pm \sqrt{320}}{10}$

$= \dfrac{-20 \pm 8\sqrt{5}}{10}$

$= \dfrac{-10 \pm 4\sqrt{5}}{5}$

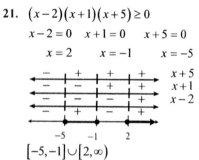

21. $(x-2)(x+1)(x+5) \geq 0$

$x - 2 = 0 \quad x + 1 = 0 \quad x + 5 = 0$

$x = 2 \qquad x = -1 \qquad x = -5$

$[-5, -1] \cup [2, \infty)$

22. $(x-2)(x+2)(x+5) \leq 0$

$x-2=0 \quad x+2=0 \quad x+5=0$

$x=2 \qquad x=-2 \qquad x=-5$

$(-\infty, -5] \cup [-2, 2]$

23. $(a-3)(a+2)(a+4) < 0$

$a-3=0 \quad a+2=0 \quad a+4=0$

$a=3 \qquad a=-2 \qquad a=-4$

$(-\infty, -4) \cup (-2, 3)$

24. $(r-1)(r+2)(r+7) < 0$

$r-1=0 \quad r+2=0 \quad r+7=0$

$r=1 \qquad r=-2 \qquad r=-7$

$(-\infty, -7) \cup (-2, 1)$

25. $(2c+5)(3c-6)(c+6) > 0$

$2c+5=0 \qquad 3c-6=0 \quad c+6=0$

$2c=-5 \qquad 3c=6 \qquad c=-6$

$c=-\dfrac{5}{2} \qquad c=2$

$\left(-6, -\dfrac{5}{2}\right) \cup (2, \infty)$

26. $(a-4)(a-2)(a+8) > 0$

$a-4=0 \quad a-2=0 \quad a+8=0$

$a=4 \qquad a=2 \qquad a=-8$

$(-8, 2) \cup (4, \infty)$

27. $(3x+5)(x-3)(x+1) > 0$

$3x+5=0 \qquad x-3=0 \quad x+1=0$

$3x=-5 \qquad x=3 \qquad x=-1$

$x=-\dfrac{5}{3}$

$\left(-\dfrac{5}{3}, -1\right) \cup (3, \infty)$

28. $(3c-1)(c+4)(3c+6) \leq 0$

$3c-1=0 \quad c+4=0 \qquad 3c+6=0$

$3c=1 \qquad c=-4 \qquad 3c=-6$

$c=\dfrac{1}{3} \qquad\qquad c=-2$

$(-\infty, -4] \cup \left[-2, \dfrac{1}{3}\right]$

29. $(x+2)(x+2)(3x-8) \geq 0$

$x+2=0 \qquad 3x-8=0$

$x=-2 \qquad x=\dfrac{8}{3}$

$\{-2\} \cup \left[\dfrac{8}{3}, \infty\right)$

30. $(x+3)^2 (4x-7) \le 0$

$x+3=0 \qquad 4x-7=0$

$x=-3 \qquad x=\dfrac{7}{4}$

$\left(-\infty, \dfrac{7}{4}\right]$

31. $x^3 - 6x^2 + 9x < 0$

$x(x^2 - 6x + 9) < 0$

$x(x-3)^2 < 0$

$x=0 \quad x-3=0$

$x=3$

$(-\infty, 0)$

32. $x^3 + 3x^2 - 40x > 0$

$x(x^2 + 3x - 40) > 0$

$x(x+8)(x-5) > 0$

$x=0 \quad x+8=0 \quad x-5=0$

$x=-8 \qquad x=5$

33. $f(x) = x^2 - 6x, \ f(x) \ge 0$

$x^2 - 6x \ge 0$

$x(x-6) \ge 0$

$x=0 \quad x-6=0$

$x=6$

34. $f(x) = x^2 - 7x, \ f(x) > 0$

$x^2 - 7x > 0$

$x(x-7) > 0$

$x=0 \quad x-7=0$

$x=7$

35. $f(x) = x^2 + 4x, \ f(x) > 0$

$x^2 + 4x > 0$

$x(x+4) > 0$

$x=0 \quad x+4=0$

$x=-4$

36. $f(x) = x^2 + 8x, \ f(x) \le 0$

$x^2 + 8x \le 0$

$x(x+8) \le 0$

$x=0 \quad x+8=0$

$x=-8$

37. $f(x) = x^2 - 14x + 48, \ f(x) < 0$

$x^2 - 14x + 48 < 0$

$(x-6)(x-8) < 0$

$x-6=0 \quad x-8=0$

$x=6 \qquad x=8$

38. $f(x) = x^2 - 2x - 15,\ f(x) < 0$

$x^2 - 2x - 15 < 0$

$(x+3)(x-5) < 0$

$x+3 = 0 \qquad x-5 = 0$

$\quad x = -3 \qquad\quad x = 5$

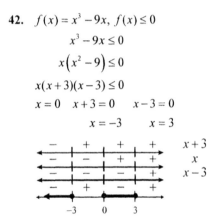

39. $f(x) = 2x^2 + 9x - 1,\ f(x) \le 5$

$2x^2 + 9x - 1 \le 5$

$2x^2 + 9x - 6 \le 0$

$x = \dfrac{-9 \pm \sqrt{9^2 - 4(2)(-6)}}{2(2)}$

$\quad = \dfrac{-9 \pm \sqrt{129}}{4}$

$x = \dfrac{-9 - \sqrt{129}}{4} \quad x = \dfrac{-98 + \sqrt{129}}{4}$

40. $f(x) = x^2 + 5x - 3,\ f(x) \le 4$

$x^2 + 5x - 3 \le 4$

$x^2 + 5x - 7 \le 0$

$x = \dfrac{-5 \pm \sqrt{5^2 - 4(1)(-7)}}{2(1)}$

$\quad = \dfrac{-5 \pm \sqrt{53}}{2}$

$x = \dfrac{-5 - \sqrt{53}}{2} \quad x = \dfrac{-5 + \sqrt{53}}{2}$

41. $f(x) = 2x^3 + 9x^2 - 35x,\ f(x) \ge 0$

$2x^3 + 9x^2 - 35x \ge 0$

$x(2x^2 + 9x - 35) \ge 0$

$x(2x - 5)(x + 7) \ge 0$

$x = 0 \quad 2x - 5 = 0 \quad x + 7 = 0$

$\qquad\qquad x = \dfrac{5}{2} \qquad\quad x = -7$

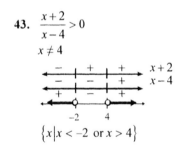

42. $f(x) = x^3 - 9x,\ f(x) \le 0$

$x^3 - 9x \le 0$

$x(x^2 - 9) \le 0$

$x(x + 3)(x - 3) \le 0$

$x = 0 \quad x + 3 = 0 \qquad x - 3 = 0$

$\qquad\qquad x = -3 \qquad\quad x = 3$

43. $\dfrac{x+2}{x-4} > 0$

$x \ne 4$

$\{x \mid x < -2 \text{ or } x > 4\}$

44. $\dfrac{x+2}{x-4} \ge 0$

$x \ne 4$

$\{x \mid x \le -2 \text{ or } x > 4\}$

45. $\dfrac{x-1}{x+5} < 0$

$x \neq -5$

$\{x \mid -5 < x < 1\}$

46. $\dfrac{x-1}{x+5} \leq 0$

$x \neq -5$

$\{x \mid -5 < x \leq 1\}$

47. $\dfrac{x+3}{x-2} \geq 0$

$x \neq 2$

$\{x \mid x \leq -3 \text{ or } x > 2\}$

48. $\dfrac{x-4}{x+6} > 0$

$x \neq -6$

$\{x \mid x < -6 \text{ or } x > 4\}$

49. $\dfrac{a-9}{a+5} < 0$

$a \neq -5$

$\{a \mid -5 < a < 9\}$

50. $\dfrac{b+7}{b+1} \leq 0$

$b \neq -1$

$\{b \mid -7 \leq b < -1\}$

51. $\dfrac{c-10}{c-4} > 0$

$c \neq 4$

$\{c \mid c < 4 \text{ or } c > 10\}$

52. $\dfrac{2d-6}{d-1} < 0$

$d \neq 1,$
$2d-6 = 0 \;\Rightarrow\; d = 3$

$\{d \mid 1 < d < 3\}$

53. $\dfrac{3y+6}{y+4} \leq 0$

$y \neq -4,$
$3y+6 = 0 \;\Rightarrow\; y = -2$

$\{y \mid -4 < y \leq -2\}$

54. $\dfrac{4z-8}{z-9} \geq 0$

$z \neq 9,$
$4z-8 = 0 \;\Rightarrow\; z = 2$

$\{z \mid z \leq 2 \text{ or } z > 9\}$

55. $\dfrac{5a+10}{3a-1} \geq 0$

$a \neq \dfrac{1}{3}$,

$5a+10 = 0 \;\Rightarrow\; a = -2$

$$\left\{a \,\middle|\, a \leq -2 \text{ or } a > \dfrac{1}{3}\right\}$$

56. $\dfrac{x+4}{x-4} \leq 0$

$x \neq 4$

$$\left\{x \,\middle|\, -4 \leq x < 4\right\}$$

57. $\dfrac{3x+4}{2x-1} < 0$

$x \neq \dfrac{1}{2}$

$$\left\{x \,\middle|\, -\dfrac{4}{3} < x < \dfrac{1}{2}\right\}$$

58. $\dfrac{k+3}{k} \geq 0$

$k \neq 0$

$$\left\{k \,\middle|\, k \leq -3 \text{ or } k > 0\right\}$$

59. $\dfrac{3x+8}{x-2} \leq 0$

$x \neq 2$

$$\left\{x \,\middle|\, -\dfrac{8}{3} \leq x < 2\right\}$$

60. $\dfrac{4x-2}{2x-8} > 0$

$x \neq 4$

$$\left\{x \,\middle|\, x < \dfrac{1}{2} \text{ or } x > 4\right\}$$

61. $\dfrac{(x+1)(x-6)}{x+3} < 0$

$x \neq -3$

$$(-\infty, -3) \cup (-1, 6)$$

62. $\dfrac{(x+1)(x-6)}{x+3} \leq 0$

$x \neq -3$

$$(-\infty, -3) \cup [-1, 6]$$

63. $\dfrac{(x-2)(x+3)}{x-5} > 0$

$x \neq 5$

$$(-3, 2) \cup (5\;\infty)$$

64. $\dfrac{(x-2)(x+3)}{x-5} \ge 0$

$x \ne 5$

$$\begin{array}{ccccc} - & | & + & | & + & | & + \\ - & | & - & | & + & | & + \\ - & | & - & | & - & | & + \\ - & | & + & | & - & | & + \end{array} \quad \begin{array}{c} x+3 \\ x-2 \\ x-5 \end{array}$$

$\underset{-3}{\bullet} \quad \underset{2}{\bullet} \quad \underset{5}{\circ}$

$[-3, 2] \cup (5, \infty)$

65. $\dfrac{(a-1)(a-7)}{a+2} \ge 0$

$a \ne -2$

$$\begin{array}{ccccc} - & | & + & | & + & | & + \\ - & | & - & | & + & | & + \\ - & | & - & | & - & | & + \\ - & | & + & | & - & | & + \end{array} \quad \begin{array}{c} a+2 \\ a-1 \\ a-7 \end{array}$$

$\underset{-2}{\circ} \quad \underset{1}{\bullet} \quad \underset{7}{\bullet}$

$(-2, 1] \cup [7, \infty)$

66. $\dfrac{(b-2)(b+4)}{b} < 0$

$b \ne 0$

$$\begin{array}{ccccc} - & | & + & | & + & | & + \\ - & | & - & | & + & | & + \\ - & | & - & | & - & | & + \\ - & | & + & | & - & | & + \end{array} \quad \begin{array}{c} b+4 \\ b \\ b-2 \end{array}$$

$\underset{-4}{\circ} \quad \underset{0}{\circ} \quad \underset{2}{\circ}$

$(-\infty, -4) \cup (0, 2)$

67. $\dfrac{c}{(c-3)(c+8)} \le 0$

$c \ne 3, \ c \ne -8$

$$\begin{array}{ccccc} - & | & + & | & + & | & + \\ - & | & - & | & + & | & + \\ - & | & - & | & - & | & + \\ - & | & + & | & - & | & + \end{array} \quad \begin{array}{c} c+8 \\ c \\ c-3 \end{array}$$

$\underset{-8}{\circ} \quad \underset{0}{\bullet} \quad \underset{3}{\circ}$

$(-\infty, -8) \cup [0, 3)$

68. $\dfrac{z-5}{(z+6)(z-9)} \ge 0$

$z \ne -6, z \ne 9$

$$\begin{array}{ccccc} - & | & + & | & + & | & + \\ - & | & - & | & + & | & + \\ - & | & - & | & - & | & + \\ - & | & + & | & - & | & + \end{array} \quad \begin{array}{c} z+6 \\ z-5 \\ z-9 \end{array}$$

$\underset{-6}{\circ} \quad \underset{5}{\bullet} \quad \underset{9}{\circ}$

$(-6, 5] \cup (9, \infty)$

69. $\dfrac{x-6}{(x+4)(x-1)} \le 0$

$x \ne -4, x \ne 1$

$$\begin{array}{ccccc} - & | & + & | & + & | & + \\ - & | & - & | & + & | & + \\ - & | & - & | & - & | & + \\ - & | & + & | & - & | & + \end{array} \quad \begin{array}{c} x+4 \\ x-1 \\ x-6 \end{array}$$

$\underset{-4}{\circ} \quad \underset{1}{\circ} \quad \underset{6}{\bullet}$

$(-\infty, -4) \cup (1, 6]$

70. $\dfrac{x+9}{(x-2)(x+4)} > 0$

$x \ne -4, x \ne 2$

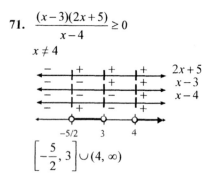

$\underset{-9}{\circ} \quad \underset{-4}{\circ} \quad \underset{2}{}$

$(-9, -4) \cup (2, \infty)$

71. $\dfrac{(x-3)(2x+5)}{x-4} \ge 0$

$x \ne 4$

$$\begin{array}{ccccc} - & | & + & | & + & | & + \\ - & | & - & | & + & | & + \\ - & | & - & | & - & | & + \\ - & | & + & | & - & | & + \end{array} \quad \begin{array}{c} 2x+5 \\ x-3 \\ x-4 \end{array}$$

$\underset{-5/2}{\circ} \quad \underset{3}{\circ} \quad \underset{4}{\circ}$

$\left[-\dfrac{5}{2}, 3\right] \cup (4, \infty)$

72. $\dfrac{r(r-8)}{2r+6} < 0$

$r \ne -3$

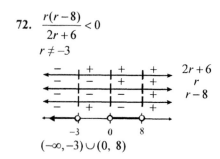

$\underset{-3}{\circ} \quad \underset{0}{\bullet} \quad \underset{8}{}$

$(-\infty, -3) \cup (0, 8)$

73.
$$\frac{2}{x-4} \geq 1$$
$$\frac{2}{x-4} - 1 \geq 0$$
$$\frac{2}{x-4} + \frac{-1(x-4)}{x-4} \geq 0$$
$$\frac{2-x+4}{x-4} \geq 0$$
$$\frac{6-x}{x-4} \geq 0$$
$$x \neq 4$$

74.
$$\frac{2}{x-4} > 1$$
$$\frac{2}{x-4} - 1 > 0$$
$$\frac{2}{x-4} + \frac{-1(x-4)}{x-4} > 0$$
$$\frac{2-x+4}{x-4} > 0$$
$$\frac{6-x}{x-4} > 0$$
$$x \neq 4$$

75.
$$\frac{3}{x-1} > -1$$
$$\frac{3}{x-1} + 1 > 0$$
$$\frac{3}{x-1} + \frac{1(x-1)}{x-1} > 0$$
$$\frac{3+x-1}{x-1} > 0$$
$$\frac{x+2}{x-1} > 0$$
$$x \neq 1$$

76.
$$\frac{3}{x+1} \geq -1$$
$$\frac{3}{x+1} + 1 \geq 0$$
$$\frac{3}{x+1} + \frac{1(x+1)}{x+1} \geq 0$$
$$\frac{3+x+1}{x+1} \geq 0$$
$$\frac{x+4}{x+1} \geq 0$$
$$x \neq -1$$

77.
$$\frac{5}{x+2} \leq 1$$
$$\frac{5}{x+2} - 1 \leq 0$$
$$\frac{5}{x+2} + \frac{-1(x+2)}{x+2} \leq 0$$
$$\frac{5-x-2}{x+2} \leq 0$$
$$\frac{3-x}{x+2} \leq 0$$
$$x \neq -2$$

78.
$$\frac{5}{x+2} < 1$$
$$\frac{5}{x+2} - 1 < 0$$
$$\frac{5}{x+2} + \frac{-1(x+2)}{x+2} < 0$$
$$\frac{5-x-2}{x+2} < 0$$
$$\frac{3-x}{x+2} < 0, \quad x \neq -2$$

79.
$$\frac{2p-5}{p-4} \le 1$$
$$\frac{2p-5}{p-4} - 1 \le 0$$
$$\frac{2p-5}{p-4} - \frac{1(p-4)}{p-4} \le 0$$
$$\frac{2p-5-p+4}{p-4} \le 0$$
$$\frac{p-1}{p-4} \le 0, \quad p \ne 4$$

80.
$$\frac{2}{2a-1} > 2$$
$$\frac{2}{2a-1} - 2 > 0$$
$$\frac{2}{2a-1} - \frac{2(2a-1)}{2a-1} > 0$$
$$\frac{2-4a+2}{2a-1} > 0$$
$$\frac{4-4a}{2a-1} > 0$$
$$\frac{4(1-a)}{2a-1} > 0 \qquad a \ne \frac{1}{2}$$

81.
$$\frac{4}{x+2} \ge 2$$
$$\frac{4}{x+2} - 2 \ge 0$$
$$\frac{4}{x+2} - \frac{2(x+2)}{x+2} \ge 0$$
$$\frac{4-2x-4}{x+2} \ge 0$$
$$\frac{-2x}{x+2} \ge 0, \quad x \ne -2$$

82.
$$\frac{x+6}{x+2} > 1$$
$$\frac{x+6}{x+2} - 1 > 0$$
$$\frac{x+6}{x+2} - \frac{1(x+2)}{x+2} > 0$$
$$\frac{x+6-x-2}{x+2} > 0$$
$$\frac{8}{x+2} > 0$$
$$x \ne -2$$

83.
$$\frac{w}{3w-2} > -2$$
$$\frac{w}{3w-2} + 2 > 0$$
$$\frac{w}{3w-2} + \frac{2(3w-2)}{3w-2} > 0$$
$$\frac{w+6w-4}{3w-2} > 0$$
$$\frac{7w-4}{3w-2} > 0$$
$$w \ne \frac{2}{3}$$

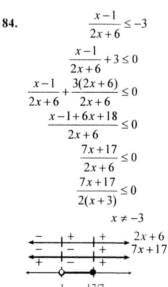

84.
$$\frac{x-1}{2x+6} \le -3$$
$$\frac{x-1}{2x+6} + 3 \le 0$$
$$\frac{x-1}{2x+6} + \frac{3(2x+6)}{2x+6} \le 0$$
$$\frac{x-1+6x+18}{2x+6} \le 0$$
$$\frac{7x+17}{2x+6} \le 0$$
$$\frac{7x+17}{2(x+3)} \le 0$$
$$x \ne -3$$

85. a. $y = \dfrac{x^2 - 4x + 4}{x - 4} > 0$ where the graph of y is above the x-axis, on the interval $(4, \infty)$.

   b. $y = \dfrac{x^2 - 4x + 4}{x - 4} < 0$ where the graph of y is below the x-axis, on the interval $(-\infty, 2) \cup (2, 4)$.

86. a. $y = \dfrac{x^2 + x - 6}{x - 4} \geq 0$ where the graph of y is on or above the x-axis, on the interval $[-3, 2] \cup (4, \infty)$.

   b. $y = \dfrac{x^2 + x - 6}{x - 4} < 0$ where the graph of y is below the x-axis, on the interval $(-\infty, -3) \cup (2, 4)$.

87. A quadratic inequality with the union of the two outer regions of the number line as its solution, not including the boundary values, will be of the form $ax^2 + bx + c > 0$ with $a > 0$. Since the boundary values are $x = -4$ and $x = 2$, the factors are $x + 4$ and $x - 2$. Therefore one quadratic inequality is $(x + 4)(x - 2) > 0$ or $x^2 + 2x - 8 > 0$.

88. A quadratic inequality with the middle region of the number line as its solution, including the boundary values, will be of the form $ax^2 + bx + c \leq 0$, with $a > 0$. Since the boundary values are $x = -3$ and $x = 5$, the factors are $x + 3$ and $x - 5$. Therefore the quadratic inequality is $(x + 3)(x - 5) \leq 0$ or $x^2 - 2x - 15 \leq 0$.

89. Since the solution set is $x \leq -3$ and $x > 4$, the factors are $x + 3$ and $x - 4$. Because -3 is included in the solution set, $x + 3$ is the numerator. Since 4 is not included in the solution set, $x - 4$ is the denominator. The inequality symbol will be $\geq$ because the union of the outer regions of number line is the solution set.

   Therefore, the rational inequality is $\dfrac{x + 3}{x - 4} \geq 0$.

90. Since the solution set is $-6 < x \leq -1$ or $x > -6$ and $x \leq -1$, the factors are $x + 6$ and $x + 1$. Because -6 is not included in the solution set, $x + 6$ is the denominator and $x + 1$ is the numerator. The inequality symbol will be $\leq$ because the middle region of the number line is

the solution set. Therefore, the rational inequality is $\dfrac{x + 1}{x + 6} \leq 0$.

91. $(x + 3)^2 (x - 1)^2 \geq 0$

The solution is all real numbers since any nonzero number squared is positive and zero squared is zero.

92. $x^2 (x - 3)^2 (x + 4)^2 < 0$

There is no real solution to this inequality since any nonzero real number squared is positive and zero squared is zero. Therefore, for any real number x:

$x^2 (x - 3)^2 (x + 4)^2 \geq 0$

93. $\dfrac{x^2}{(x + 2)^2} \geq 0$

This solution is all real numbers, except -2, since any nonzero number squared is negative. It is undefined when $x = -2$. Therefore, -2 is not a solution.

94. $\dfrac{x^2}{(x - 3)^2} > 0$

The solution is all real numbers, except 0 and 3, since $x = 0$ gives us $0 > 0$, which is false, and $x = 3$ gives us a zero in the denominator, which is undefined.

95. If $f(x) = ax^2 + bx + c$ and $a > 0$, the graph of $f(x)$ opens upward. If the discriminant is negative, the graph of $f(x)$ has no x-intercepts. Therefore, the graph lies above the x-axis and $f(x) < 0$ has no solution.

96. If $f(x) = ax^2 + bx + c$ and $a < 0$, the graph of $f(x)$ opens downward. If the discriminant is negative, the graph of $f(x)$ has no x-intercepts. Therefore, the graph lies below the x-axis and $f(x) > 2$ has no solution.

97. $(x + 1)(x - 3)(x + 5)(x + 8) \geq 0$

98. $\dfrac{(x-4)(x+2)}{x(x+9)} \geq 0$

$x \neq 0 \quad x \neq -9$

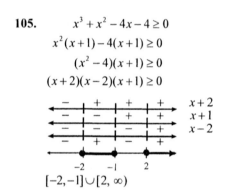

99. One possible answer is: Use a parabola that opens upward and has x-intercepts of $(0, 0)$ and $(3, 0)$. The x-values for which the parabola lies above the x-axis are $(-\infty, 0) \cup (3, \infty)$.

$x^2 - 3x > 0$

100. One possible answer is: Use a parabola that opens upward and has exactly one x-intercept at $(2, 0)$. The x-value for which the parabola lies on or below the x-axis is 2.

$x^2 - 4x + 4 \leq 0$

101. One possible answer is: Use a parabola that opens upward and has its vertex on or above the x-axis. Then there are no x-values for which the parabola lies below the x-axis.

$x^2 < 0$

102. One possible answer is: Use a parabola that opens upward and has its vertex on or above the x-axis. Then the x-values for which the parabola lies on or above the x-axis are all real numbers.

$x^2 \geq 0$

103. $x^4 - 10x^2 + 9 > 0$

$(x^2)^2 - 10x^2 + 9 > 0$

Let $u = x^2$.

$u^2 - 10u + 9 > 0$

$(u-9)(u-1) > 0$

Substitute x^2 for u.

$$(x^2 - 9)(x^2 - 1) > 0$$

$(x+3)(x-3)(x+1)(x-1) > 0$

$(-\infty, -3) \cup (-1, 1) \cup (3, \infty)$

104. $x^4 - 26x^2 + 25 \leq 0$

$(x^2)^2 - 26x^2 + 25 \leq 0$

Let $u = x^2$.

$u^2 - 26u + 25 \leq 0$

$(u - 25)(u - 1) \leq 0$

Substitute x^2 for u.

$$(x^2 - 25)(x^2 - 1) \leq 0$$

$(x+5)(x-5)(x+1)(x-1) \leq 0$

$[-5, -1] \cup [1, 5]$

105. $x^3 + x^2 - 4x - 4 \geq 0$

$x^2(x+1) - 4(x+1) \geq 0$

$(x^2 - 4)(x+1) \geq 0$

$(x+2)(x-2)(x+1) \geq 0$

$[-2, -1] \cup [2, \infty)$

106. $2x^3 + x^2 - 32x - 16 < 0$

$x^2(2x+1) - 16(2x+1) < 0$

$(x^2 - 16)(2x+1) < 0$

$(x+4)(x-4)(2x+1) < 0$

$(-\infty, -4) \cup \left(-\dfrac{1}{2}, 4\right)$

107. Given the locations of a, b, and c on the number line, results in the following table of positive and negative values.

804

a. Intervals 2 and 4 will satisfy the inequality $(x-a)(x-b)(x-c) > 0$.

b. Intervals 1 and 3 will satisfy the inequality $(x-a)(x-b)(x-c) < 0$.

108. Given the locations of a, b, c, and d on the number line, results in the following table of positive and negative values.

a. Intervals 1, 3 and 5 will satisfy the inequality $(x-a)(x-b)(x-c)(x-d) > 0$.

b. Intervals 2 and 4 will satisfy the inequality $(x-a)(x-b)(x-c)(x-d) < 0$.

109. Let x = the number of quarts of 100% antifreeze added. The equation below describes the situation.

$$100\%(x) + 20\%(10) = 50\%(x+10)$$
$$x + 0.2(10) = 0.5(x+10)$$
$$x + 2 = 0.5x + 5$$
$$0.5x = 3$$
$$x = 6$$

Paul should add 6 quarts of 100% antifreeze.

110. $\left(6r + 5s - t\right) + \left(-3r - 2s - 8t\right)$
$= 6r + 5s - t - 3r - 2s - 8t$
$= 3r + 3s - 9t$

111. $\dfrac{1 + \dfrac{x}{x+1}}{\dfrac{2x+1}{x-3}} = \dfrac{\dfrac{1}{1} \cdot \dfrac{x+1}{x+1} + \dfrac{x}{x+1}}{\dfrac{2x+1}{x-3}}$

$= \dfrac{\dfrac{2x+1}{x+1}}{\dfrac{2x+1}{x-3}}$

$= \dfrac{2x+1}{x+1} \cdot \dfrac{x-3}{2x+1}$

$= \dfrac{x-3}{x+1}$

112. $h(x) = \dfrac{x^2 + 4x}{x+9}$

$h(-3) = \dfrac{(-3)^2 + 4(-3)}{(-3)+9} = \dfrac{9-12}{6} = \dfrac{-3}{6} = -\dfrac{1}{2}$

113. $(3 - 4i)(6 + 5i) = 18 + 15i - 24i - 20i^2$
$= 18 - 9i - 20(-1)$
$= 18 - 9i + 20$
$= 38 - 9i$

Chapter 12 Review Exercises

1. $(x-5)^2 = 24$

$x - 5 = \pm\sqrt{24}$

$x - 5 = \pm 2\sqrt{6}$

$x = 5 \pm 2\sqrt{6}$

$x = 5 + 2\sqrt{6}$ or $x = 5 - 2\sqrt{6}$

2. $(2x + 1)^2 = 60$

$2x + 1 = \pm\sqrt{60}$

$2x + 1 = \pm 2\sqrt{15}$

$2x = -1 \pm 2\sqrt{15}$

$x = \dfrac{-1 \pm 2\sqrt{15}}{2}$

$x = \dfrac{-1 + 2\sqrt{15}}{2}$ or $x = \dfrac{-1 - 2\sqrt{15}}{2}$

3. $\left(x - \dfrac{1}{3}\right)^2 = \dfrac{4}{9}$

$x - \dfrac{1}{3} = \pm\sqrt{\dfrac{4}{9}}$

$x - \dfrac{1}{3} = \pm\dfrac{2}{3}$

$x = \dfrac{1}{3} \pm \dfrac{2}{3}$

$x = \dfrac{1}{3} + \dfrac{2}{3}$ or $x = \dfrac{1}{3} - \dfrac{2}{3}$

$\quad = \dfrac{3}{3} \qquad\qquad = -\dfrac{1}{3}$

$\quad = 1$

$x = 1$ or $x = -\dfrac{1}{3}$

4. $\left(2x-\dfrac{1}{2}\right)^2 = 4$

$$2x-\dfrac{1}{2} = \pm\sqrt{4}$$

$$2x-\dfrac{1}{2} = \pm 2$$

$$2x = \dfrac{1}{2}\pm 2$$

$$2x = \dfrac{1\pm 4}{2}$$

$$x = \dfrac{1\pm 4}{4}$$

$$x = \dfrac{1+4}{4} \quad \text{or} \quad x = \dfrac{1-4}{4}$$

$$= \dfrac{5}{4} \qquad\qquad = -\dfrac{3}{4}$$

5. $x^2 - 7x + 12 = 0$

$$x^2 - 7x = -12$$

$$x^2 - 7x + \dfrac{49}{4} = -\dfrac{48}{4} + \dfrac{49}{4}$$

$$x^2 - 7x + \dfrac{49}{4} = \dfrac{1}{4}$$

$$\left(x - \dfrac{7}{2}\right)^2 = \dfrac{1}{4}$$

$$x - \dfrac{7}{2} = \pm\dfrac{1}{2}$$

$$x = \dfrac{7}{2}\pm\dfrac{1}{2}$$

$$x = \dfrac{7}{2}+\dfrac{1}{2} \quad \text{or} \quad x = \dfrac{7}{2}-\dfrac{1}{2}$$

$$= 4 \qquad\qquad = 3$$

6. $x^2 + 4x - 32 = 0$

$$x^2 + 4x = 32$$

$$x^2 + 4x + 4 = 32 + 4$$

$$\left(x+2\right)^2 = 36$$

$$x + 2 = \pm\sqrt{36}$$

$$x + 2 = \pm 6$$

$$x = -2 \pm 6$$

$$x = 4 \ \text{ or } \ x = -8$$

7. $a^2 + 2a - 9 = 0$

$$a^2 + 2a = 9$$

$$a^2 + 2a + 1 = 9 + 1$$

$$\left(a+1\right)^2 = 10$$

$$a + 1 = \pm\sqrt{10}$$

$$a = -1 \pm\sqrt{10}$$

$$a = -1 + \sqrt{10} \quad \text{or} \quad a = -1 - \sqrt{10}$$

8. $z^2 + 6z = 12$

$$z^2 + 6z + 9 = 12 + 9$$

$$\left(z+3\right)^2 = 21$$

$$z + 3 = \pm\sqrt{21}$$

$$z = -3 \pm\sqrt{21}$$

$$z = -3 + \sqrt{21} \quad \text{or} \quad z = -3 - \sqrt{21}$$

9. $x^2 - 2x + 10 = 0$

$$x^2 - 2x = -10$$

$$x^2 - 2x + 1 = -10 + 1$$

$$\left(x-1\right)^2 = -9$$

$$\left(x-1\right)^2 = \sqrt{-9}$$

$$x - 1 = \pm 3i$$

$$x = 1 \pm 3i$$

$$x = 1 + 3i \quad \text{or} \quad x = 1 - 3i$$

10. $2r^2 - 8r = -64$

$$r^2 - 4r = -32$$

$$r^2 - 4r + 4 = -32 + 4$$

$$\left(r-2\right)^2 = -28$$

$$r - 2 = \pm\sqrt{-28}$$

$$r = 2 \pm\sqrt{4}\sqrt{7}\sqrt{-1}$$

$$r = 2 \pm 2i\sqrt{7}$$

$$r = 2 + 2i\sqrt{7} \quad \text{or} \quad r = 2 - 2i\sqrt{7}$$

11. a. $\quad$ Area $=$ length $\times$ width

$$32 = (x+5)(x+1)$$

b. $\quad 32 = (x+5)(x+1)$

$$32 = x^2 + x + 5x + 5$$

$$0 = x^2 + 6x - 27$$

$$0 = (x-3)(x+9)$$

$$x = 3 \quad \text{or} \quad x = -9$$

Disregard the negative value. $x = 3$.

12. a. Area = length × width
$$63 = (x+2)(x+4)$$

b. $63 = (x+2)(x+4)$
$$63 = x^2 + 4x + 2x + 8$$
$$0 = x^2 + 6x - 55$$
$$0 = (x-5)(x+11)$$
$$x = 5 \quad \text{or} \quad x = -11$$

Disregard the negative value. $x = 5$.

13. Let x = the smaller integer. The larger will then be $x + 1$. Their product is 42.
$$x(x+1) = 42$$
$$x^2 + x = 42$$
$$x^2 + x - 42 = 0$$
$$(x+7)(x-6) = 0$$
$$x + 7 = 0 \quad \text{or} \quad x - 6 = 0$$
$$x = -7 \qquad\qquad x = 6$$

Since the integers must be positive, disregard the negative value. The smaller integer is 6 and the larger is 7.

14. Let x = the length of side of the square room. The diagonal can then be described by $x + 7$. Two of the adjacent sides and the diagonal make up a right triangle. Use the Pythagorean theorem to solve the problem.
$$a^2 + b^2 = c^2$$
$$x^2 + x^2 = (x+7)^2$$
$$2x^2 = x^2 + 14x + 49$$
$$x^2 - 14x - 49 = 0$$
$$x = \frac{-(-14) \pm \sqrt{(-14)^2 - 4(1)(-49)}}{2(1)} = \frac{14 \pm \sqrt{392}}{2}$$
$$x \approx 16.90 \quad \text{or} \quad x \approx -2.90$$

Disregard the negative value. The room is about 16.90 feet by 16.90 feet.

15. $2x^2 - 5x - 1 = 0$
$$a = 2, b = -5, c = -1$$
$$b^2 - 4ac = (-5)^2 - 4(2)(-1) = 25 + 8 = 33$$

Since the discriminant is positive, this equation has two distinct real solutions.

16. $3x^2 + 2x = -6$
$$3x^2 + 2x + 6 = 0$$
$$a = 3, b = 2, c = 6$$
$$b^2 - 4ac = (2)^2 - 4(3)(6) = 4 - 72 = -68$$

Since the discriminant is negative, this equation has no real solutions.

17. $r^2 + 16r = -64$
$$r^2 + 16r + 64 = 0$$
$$a = 1, b = 16, c = 64$$
$$b^2 - 4ac = (16)^2 - 4(1)(64) = 256 - 256 = 0$$

Since the discriminant is 0, the equation has one real solution.

18. $5x^2 - x + 2 = 0$
$$a = 5, b = -1, c = 2$$
$$b^2 - 4ac = (-1)^2 - 4(5)(2) = 1 - 40 = -39$$

Since the discriminant is negative, this equation has no real solutions.

19. $a^2 - 14n = -49$
$$a^2 - 14n + 49 = 0$$
$$a = 1, b = -14, c = 49$$
$$b^2 - 4ac = (-14)^2 - 4(1)(49) = 196 - 196 = 0$$

Since the discriminant is 0, the equation has one real solution.

20. $\dfrac{1}{2}x^2 - 3x = 8$
$$\frac{1}{2}x^2 - 3x - 8 = 0$$
$$a = \frac{1}{2}, b = -3, c = -8$$
$$b^2 - 4ac = (-3)^2 - 4\left(\frac{1}{2}\right)(-8) = 9 + 16 = 25$$

Since the discriminant is positive, this equation has two real solutions.

21. $3x^2 + 4x = 0$
$$a = 3, b = 4, c = 0$$
$$x = \frac{-b \pm \sqrt{b^2 - 4ac}}{2a}$$
$$x = \frac{-4 \pm \sqrt{4^2 - 4(3)(0)}}{2(3)}$$
$$= \frac{-4 \pm \sqrt{16}}{6}$$
$$= \frac{-4 \pm 4}{6}$$
$$x = \frac{-4 + 4}{6} \quad \text{or} \quad x = \frac{-4 - 4}{6}$$
$$x = \frac{0}{6} \qquad\qquad x = \frac{-8}{6}$$
$$x = 0 \qquad\qquad x = -\frac{4}{3}$$

22. $x^2 - 11x = -18$

$x^2 - 11x + 18 = 0$

$a = 1, b = -11, c = 18$

$x = \dfrac{-b \pm \sqrt{b^2 - 4ac}}{2a}$

$x = \dfrac{-(-11) \pm \sqrt{(-11)^2 - 4(1)(18)}}{2(1)}$

$= \dfrac{11 \pm \sqrt{121 - 72}}{2}$

$= \dfrac{11 \pm \sqrt{49}}{2}$

$= \dfrac{11 \pm 7}{2}$

$x = \dfrac{11 + 7}{2}$ or $x = \dfrac{11 - 7}{2}$

$\quad = \dfrac{18}{2} \qquad\qquad = \dfrac{4}{2}$

$\quad = 9 \qquad\qquad\quad = 2$

23. $r^2 = 3r + 40$

$r^2 - 3r - 40 = 0$

$a = 1, b = -3, c = -40$

$r = \dfrac{-b \pm \sqrt{b^2 - 4ac}}{2a}$

$r = \dfrac{-(-3) \pm \sqrt{(-3)^2 - 4(1)(-40)}}{2(1)}$

$= \dfrac{3 \pm \sqrt{9 + 160}}{2}$

$= \dfrac{3 \pm \sqrt{169}}{2}$

$= \dfrac{3 \pm 13}{2}$

$r = \dfrac{3 + 13}{2}$ or $r = \dfrac{3 - 13}{2}$

$\quad = \dfrac{16}{2} \qquad\qquad = \dfrac{-10}{2}$

$\quad = 8 \qquad\qquad\quad = -5$

24. $7x^2 = 9x$

$7x^2 - 9x = 0$

$a = 7, b = -9, c = 0$

$x = \dfrac{-b \pm \sqrt{b^2 - 4ac}}{2a}$

$x = \dfrac{-(-9) \pm \sqrt{(-9)^2 - 4(7)(0)}}{2(7)}$

$= \dfrac{9 \pm \sqrt{81 - 0}}{14}$

$= \dfrac{9 \pm \sqrt{81}}{14}$

$= \dfrac{9 \pm 9}{14}$

$x = \dfrac{9 + 9}{14}$ or $x = \dfrac{9 - 9}{14}$

$\quad = \dfrac{18}{14} \qquad\qquad = \dfrac{0}{14}$

$\quad = \dfrac{9}{7} \qquad\qquad\quad = 0$

25. $6a^2 + a - 15 = 0$

$a = 6, b = 1, c = -15$

$a = \dfrac{-b \pm \sqrt{b^2 - 4ac}}{2a}$

$a = \dfrac{-1 \pm \sqrt{1^2 - 4(6)(-15)}}{2(6)}$

$= \dfrac{-1 \pm \sqrt{1 + 360}}{12}$

$= \dfrac{-1 \pm \sqrt{361}}{12}$

$= \dfrac{-1 \pm 19}{12}$

$a = \dfrac{-1 + 19}{12}$ or $a = \dfrac{-1 - 19}{12}$

$\quad = \dfrac{18}{12} \qquad\qquad = \dfrac{-20}{12}$

$\quad = \dfrac{3}{2} \qquad\qquad\quad = -\dfrac{5}{3}$

26.
$$4x^2 + 11x = 3$$
$$4x^2 + 11x - 3 = 0$$
$$a = 4, b = 11, c = -3$$
$$x = \frac{-b \pm \sqrt{b^2 - 4ac}}{2a}$$
$$x = \frac{-(11) \pm \sqrt{(11)^2 - 4(4)(-3)}}{2(4)}$$
$$= \frac{-11 \pm \sqrt{121 + 48}}{8}$$
$$= \frac{-11 \pm \sqrt{169}}{8}$$
$$= \frac{-11 \pm 13}{8}$$
$$x = \frac{-11 + 13}{8} \quad \text{or} \quad x = \frac{-11 - 13}{8}$$
$$= \frac{2}{8} \qquad\qquad = \frac{-24}{8}$$
$$= \frac{1}{4} \qquad\qquad = -3$$

27.
$$x^2 + 8x + 5 = 0$$
$$a = 1, b = 8, c = 5$$
$$x = \frac{-b \pm \sqrt{b^2 - 4ac}}{2a}$$
$$x = \frac{-8 \pm \sqrt{8^2 - 4(1)(5)}}{2(1)}$$
$$= \frac{-8 \pm \sqrt{64 - 20}}{2}$$
$$= \frac{-8 \pm \sqrt{44}}{2}$$
$$= \frac{-8 \pm 2\sqrt{11}}{2}$$
$$= -4 \pm \sqrt{11}$$
$$x = -4 + \sqrt{11} \quad \text{or} \quad x = -4 - \sqrt{11}$$

28.
$$b^2 + 4b = 8$$
$$b^2 + 4b - 8 = 0$$
$$a = 1, b = 4, c = -8$$
$$b = \frac{-b \pm \sqrt{b^2 - 4ac}}{2a}$$
$$b = \frac{-(4) \pm \sqrt{(4)^2 - 4(1)(-8)}}{2(1)}$$
$$= \frac{-4 \pm \sqrt{16 + 32}}{2}$$
$$= \frac{-4 \pm \sqrt{48}}{2}$$
$$= \frac{-4 \pm 4\sqrt{3}}{2}$$
$$= -2 \pm 2\sqrt{3}$$
$$x = -2 + 2\sqrt{3} \quad \text{or} \quad x = -2 - 2\sqrt{3}$$

29.
$$2x^2 + 4x - 3 = 0$$
$$a = 2, b = 4, c = -3$$
$$x = \frac{-b \pm \sqrt{b^2 - 4ac}}{2a}$$
$$x = \frac{-4 \pm \sqrt{4^2 - 4(2)(-3)}}{2(2)}$$
$$= \frac{-4 \pm \sqrt{16 + 24}}{4}$$
$$= \frac{-4 \pm \sqrt{40}}{4}$$
$$= \frac{-4 \pm 2\sqrt{10}}{4}$$
$$= \frac{2\left(-2 \pm \sqrt{10}\right)}{2(2)}$$
$$= \frac{-2 \pm \sqrt{10}}{2}$$
$$x = \frac{-2 + \sqrt{10}}{2} \quad \text{or} \quad x = \frac{-2 - \sqrt{10}}{2}$$

30.

$$3y^2 - 6y = 8$$

$$3y^2 - 6y - 8 = 0$$

$$a = 3, b = -6, c = -8$$

$$y = \frac{-b \pm \sqrt{b^2 - 4ac}}{2a}$$

$$y = \frac{-(-6) \pm \sqrt{(-6)^2 - 4(3)(-8)}}{2(3)}$$

$$= \frac{6 \pm \sqrt{36 + 96}}{6}$$

$$= \frac{6 \pm \sqrt{132}}{6}$$

$$= \frac{6 \pm 2\sqrt{33}}{6}$$

$$= \frac{2(3 \pm \sqrt{33})}{6}$$

$$= \frac{3 \pm \sqrt{33}}{3}$$

$$y = \frac{3 + \sqrt{33}}{3} \quad \text{or} \quad y = \frac{3 - \sqrt{33}}{3}$$

31.

$$x^2 - x + 13 = 0$$

$$a = 1, b = -1, c = 13$$

$$x = \frac{-b \pm \sqrt{b^2 - 4ac}}{2a}$$

$$x = \frac{-(-1) \pm \sqrt{(-1)^2 - 4(1)(13)}}{2(1)}$$

$$= \frac{1 \pm \sqrt{1 - 52}}{2}$$

$$= \frac{1 \pm \sqrt{-51}}{2}$$

$$= \frac{1 \pm i\sqrt{51}}{2}$$

$$x = \frac{1 + i\sqrt{51}}{2} \quad \text{or} \quad x = \frac{1 - i\sqrt{51}}{2}$$

32.

$$x^2 - 2x + 11 = 0$$

$$a = 1, b = -2, c = 11$$

$$x = \frac{-b \pm \sqrt{b^2 - 4ac}}{2a}$$

$$x = \frac{-(-2) \pm \sqrt{(-2)^2 - 4(1)(11)}}{2(1)}$$

$$= \frac{2 \pm \sqrt{4 - 44}}{2}$$

$$= \frac{2 \pm \sqrt{-40}}{2}$$

$$= \frac{2 \pm 2i\sqrt{10}}{2}$$

$$= 1 \pm i\sqrt{10}$$

$$x = 1 + i\sqrt{10} \quad \text{or} \quad x = 1 - i\sqrt{10}$$

33.

$$2x^2 - \frac{5}{3}x = \frac{25}{3}$$

$$3\left(2x^2 - \frac{5}{3}x\right) = 3\left(\frac{25}{3}\right)$$

$$6x^2 - 5x = 25$$

$$6x^2 - 5x - 25 = 0$$

$$a = 6, b = -5, c = -25$$

$$x = \frac{-b \pm \sqrt{b^2 - 4ac}}{2a}$$

$$x = \frac{-(-5) \pm \sqrt{(-5)^2 - 4(6)(-25)}}{2(6)}$$

$$x = \frac{5 \pm \sqrt{25 + 600}}{12}$$

$$= \frac{5 \pm \sqrt{625}}{12}$$

$$= \frac{5 \pm 25}{12}$$

$$x = \frac{5 + 25}{12} \quad \text{or} \quad x = \frac{5 - 25}{12}$$

$$= \frac{30}{12} \qquad\qquad = \frac{-20}{12}$$

$$= \frac{5}{2} \qquad\qquad = -\frac{5}{3}$$

34. $4x^2 + 5x - \dfrac{3}{2} = 0$

$2\left(4x^2 + 5x - \dfrac{3}{2}\right) = 2(0)$

$8x^2 + 10x - 3 = 0$
$a = 8, b = 10, c = -3$

$x = \dfrac{-b \pm \sqrt{b^2 - 4ac}}{2a}$

$= \dfrac{-10 \pm \sqrt{10^2 - 4(8)(-3)}}{2(8)}$

$= \dfrac{-10 \pm \sqrt{100 + 96}}{16}$

$= \dfrac{-10 \pm \sqrt{196}}{16}$

$= \dfrac{-10 \pm 14}{16}$

$x = \dfrac{-10 + 14}{16}$ or $x = \dfrac{-10 - 14}{16}$

$= \dfrac{1}{4}$ $\qquad = -\dfrac{3}{2}$

35. $f(x) = x^2 - 4x - 35$, $f(x) = 25$

$x^2 - 4x - 35 = 25$
$x^2 - 4x - 60 = 0$
$(x - 10)(x + 6) = 0$
$x - 10 = 0$ or $x + 6 = 0$
$x = 10$ $\qquad x = -6$
The solutions are 10 and –6.

36. $g(x) = 6x^2 + 5x$, $g(x) = 6$

$6x^2 + 5x = 6$
$6x^2 + 5x - 6 = 0$
$(2x + 3)(3x - 2) = 0$
$2x + 3 = 0$ or $3x - 2 = 0$
$x = -\dfrac{3}{2}$ $\qquad x = \dfrac{2}{3}$
The solutions are $-\dfrac{3}{2}$ and $\dfrac{2}{3}$.

37. $h(r) = 5r^2 - 7r - 10$, $h(r) = -8$

$5r^2 - 7r - 10 = -8$
$5r^2 - 7r - 2 = 0$

$r = \dfrac{7 \pm \sqrt{(-7)^2 - 4(5)(-2)}}{2(5)}$

$= \dfrac{7 \pm \sqrt{49 + 40}}{10}$

$= \dfrac{7 \pm \sqrt{89}}{10}$

The solutions are $\dfrac{7 + \sqrt{89}}{10}$ and $\dfrac{7 - \sqrt{89}}{10}$.

38. $f(x) = -2x^2 + 6x + 7$, $f(x) = -2$

$-2x^2 + 6x + 7 = -2$
$-2x^2 + 6x + 9 = 0$

$x = \dfrac{-6 \pm \sqrt{6^2 - 4(-2)(9)}}{2(-2)}$

$= \dfrac{-6 \pm \sqrt{36 + 72}}{-4}$

$= \dfrac{-6 \pm \sqrt{108}}{-4}$

$= \dfrac{-6 \pm 6\sqrt{3}}{-4}$

$= \dfrac{3 \pm 3\sqrt{3}}{2}$

The solutions are $\dfrac{3 + 3\sqrt{3}}{2}$ and $\dfrac{3 - 3\sqrt{3}}{2}$.

39. Solutions are $x = 3$ and $x = -1$.
$x - 3 = 0$ and $x + 1 = 0$.
$(x - 3)(x + 1) = 0$
$x^2 - 2x - 3 = 0$

40. Solutions are $x = \dfrac{2}{3}$ and $x = -2$.
$3x = 2$ and $x + 2 = 0$
$3x - 2 = 0$
$(3x - 2)(x + 2) = 0$
$3x^2 + 4x - 4 = 0$

41. Solutions are $x = -\sqrt{11}$ and $x = \sqrt{11}$.
$x + \sqrt{11} = 0$ and $x - \sqrt{11} = 0$.
$(x+\sqrt{11})(x-\sqrt{11}) = 0$
$x^2 - 11 = 0$

42. Solutions are $x = 3 - 2i$ and $x = 3 + 2i$.
$x - (3-2i) = 0$ and $x - (3+2i) = 0$
$x - 3 + 2i = 0 \qquad x - 3 - 2i = 0$
$(x-3+2i)(x-3-2i) = 0$
$[(x-3)+2i][(x-3)-2i] = 0$
$(x-3)^2 - (2i)^2 = 0$
$x^2 - 6x + 9 - 4i^2 = 0$
$x^2 - 6x + 9 + 4 = 0$
$x^2 - 6x + 13 = 0$

43. Let x = the width of the garden. Then the length is $x + 4$.
Area = length × width
$96 = (x+4)x$
$96 = x^2 + 4x$
$0 = x^2 + 4x - 96$
$0 = (x+12)(x-8)$
$x + 12 = 0 \qquad$ or $\quad x - 8 = 0$
$x = -12 \qquad\qquad x = 8$
Disregard the negative value. The width is 8 feet and the length is 8 + 4 = 12 feet.

44. Using the Pythagorean Theorem, $a^2 + b^2 = c^2$
$8^2 + 8^2 = x^2$
$64 + 64 = x^2$
$128 = x^2$
$\sqrt{128} = x$
$x = 8\sqrt{2} \approx 11.31$

45. $A = P\left(1 + \dfrac{r}{n}\right)^{nt}$
$1081.60 = 1000\left(1 + \dfrac{r}{1}\right)^{1(2)}$
$1081.60 = 1000(1+r)^2$
$1.08160 = (1+r)^2$
$\pm 1.04 = 1 + r$
$r = -1 \pm 1.04$
The rate must be positive, so
$r = -1 + 1.04 = 0.04$.
The annual interest is 4%.

46. Let x be the smaller positive number. Then $x + 4$ is the larger positive number.
$x(x+4) = 77$
$x^2 + 4x - 77 = 0$
$(x+11)(x-7) = 0$
$x = -11 \quad$ or $\quad x = 7$
Since x must be positive, $x = 7$ and $7 + 2 = 9$.

47. Let x be the width. Then $2x - 4$ is the length and the equation is $A = lw$.
$96 = (2x-4)(x)$
$96 = 2x^2 - 4x$
$0 = 2x^2 - 4x - 96$
$0 = (2x+12)(x-8)$
$0 = 2x+12 \quad$ or $\quad 0 = x-8$
$-12 = 2x \qquad\qquad 8 = x$
$-6 = x$
Since the width must be positive, $x = 8$.
The width is 8 inches and the length $2x - 4$ is $2(8) - 4 = 16 - 4 = 12$ inches.

48. $V = 12d - 0.05d^2$, $d = 60$
$V = 12(60) - 0.05(60)^2 = 720 - 180 = 540$
The value is $540.

49. a. Note that 2004 is represented by $t = 3$.
$E(t) = 7t^2 - 7.8t + 82.2$
$E(3) = 7(3)^2 - 7.8(3) + 82.2 = 121.8$
The expenditure of oil companies in 2004 was about $121.8 billion.

b. $E(t) = 579$
$579 = 7t^2 - 7.8t + 82.2$
$0 = 7t^2 - 7.8t - 496.8$
$0 = 7t^2 - 7.8t - 496.8$
$t = \dfrac{-(-7.8) \pm \sqrt{(-7.8)^2 - 4(7)(-496.8)}}{2(7)}$
$= \dfrac{7.8 \pm \sqrt{13,971.24}}{14} = \dfrac{7.8 \pm 118.2}{14}$
$t = \dfrac{7.8 + 118.2}{14} \quad$ or $\quad t = \dfrac{7.8 - 118.2}{14}$
$= \dfrac{126}{14} = 9 \qquad\qquad = -\dfrac{110.4}{14}$
Since the time must be positive, $t = 9$, which represents the year 2010. If the trend continues, the expenditure by oil companies will be $579 billion in the year 2010.

50. $d = -16t^2 + 784$

a. $d = -16(2)^2 + 784 = -64 + 784 = 720$

The object is 720 feet from the ground 2 seconds after being dropped.

b. $0 = -16t^2 + 784$

$16t^2 = 784$

$t^2 = 49$

$t = \pm\sqrt{49} = \pm 7$

Since the time must be positive, $t = 7$ seconds.

51. a. $L(t) = 0.0004t^2 + 0.16t + 20$

$L(100) = 0.0004(100)^2 + 0.16(100) + 20 = 40$

40 milliliters will leak out at 100°C.

b. $53 = 0.0004t^2 + 0.16t + 20$

$0 = 0.0004t^2 + 0.16t - 33$

$t = \dfrac{-0.16 \pm \sqrt{(0.16)^2 - 4(0.0004)(-33)}}{2(0.0004)}$

$= \dfrac{-0.16 \pm \sqrt{0.0784}}{0.0008}$

$= \dfrac{-0.16 \pm 0.28}{0.0008}$

$t = \dfrac{-0.16 + 0.28}{0.0008}$ or $t = \dfrac{-0.16 - 0.28}{0.0008}$

$= 150$ $= -550$

Since the temperature must be positive, $t = 150$. The operating temperature is 150°C.

52. Let x be the time in which the smaller machine can do the job then $x - 1$ is the time for the larger machine.

$$\frac{12}{x} + \frac{12}{x-1} = 1$$

$$x(x-1)\left(\frac{12}{x}\right) + x(x-1)\left(\frac{12}{x-1}\right) = x(x-1)$$

$$12(x-1) + 12x = x^2 - x$$

$$12x - 12 + 12x = x^2 - x$$

$$-12 + 24x = x^2 - x$$

$$0 = x^2 - 25x + 12$$

$$x = \frac{-(-25) \pm \sqrt{(-25)^2 - 4(1)(12)}}{2(1)} = \frac{25 \pm \sqrt{577}}{2}$$

$$x = \frac{25 + \sqrt{577}}{2} \approx 24.51 \text{ or } x = \frac{25 - \sqrt{577}}{2} \approx 0.49$$

x cannot equal 0.49 since this would mean the smaller machine could do the work in 0.49 hours and the larger can do the work in $x - 1$ or -0.51 hours. Therefore the smaller machine does the work in 24.51 hours and the larger machine does the work in 23.51 hours.

53. Let x be the speed (in miles per hour) for the first 25 miles. Then, the speed for the next 65 miles is $x + 15$. The time for the first 20 miles is $\dfrac{d}{r} = \dfrac{25}{x}$ and the time for the next 30 miles is $\dfrac{d}{r} = \dfrac{65}{x+15}$.

The total time is 1.5 hours.

$$\frac{25}{x} + \frac{65}{x+15} = 1.5$$

$$x(x+15)\left(\frac{25}{x} + \frac{65}{x+15}\right) = x(x+15)(1.5)$$

$$25(x+15) + x(65) = (x^2 + 15x)(1.5)$$

$$90x + 375 = 1.5x^2 + 22.5x$$

$$0 = 1.5x^2 - 67.5x - 375$$

$$0 = 3x^2 - 135x - 750$$

$$0 = 3(x - 50)(x + 5)$$

$$x - 50 = 0 \quad \text{or} \quad x + 5 = 0$$

$$x = 50 \quad \text{or} \qquad x = -5$$

Since the speed must be positive, $x = 50$. Thus, the speed was 50 mph.

54. Let r be the speed (in miles per hour) of the canoe in still water. For the trip downstream, the rate is $r + 0.4$ and the distance 3 miles so that the time is $t = \dfrac{3}{r + 0.4}$. For the trip upstream the rate is $r - 0.4$ and the distance is 3 miles so that the time is $t = \dfrac{3}{r - 0.4}$. The total time is 4 hours.

$$\frac{3}{r+0.4} + \frac{3}{r-0.4} = 4$$

$$(r+0.4)(r-0.4)\left[\frac{3}{r+0.4} + \frac{3}{r-0.4} = 4\right]$$

$$3(r-0.4) + 3(r+0.4) = 4(r+0.4)(r-0.4)$$

$$3r - 1.2 + 3r + 1.2 = 4(r^2 - 0.16)$$

$$6r = 4r^2 - 0.64$$

$$0 = 4r^2 - 6r - 0.64$$

$$0 = 2r^2 - 3r - 0.32$$

$$r = \frac{-(-3)\pm\sqrt{(-3)^2 - 4(2)(-0.32)}}{2(2)}$$

$$= \frac{3\pm\sqrt{9+2.56}}{4}$$

$$= \frac{3\pm\sqrt{11.56}}{4}$$

$$= \frac{3\pm3.4}{4}$$

$$r = \frac{3+3.4}{4} \quad \text{or} \quad r = \frac{3-3.4}{4}$$

$$= \frac{6.4}{4} \qquad\qquad = \frac{-0.4}{4}$$

$$= 1.6 \qquad\qquad = -0.1$$

Since the rate must be positive, $r = 1.6$. Rachel canoes 1.6 miles per hour in still water.

55. Let x be the length. The width is $x - 2$.
Area = length × width

$$80 = x(x-2)$$

$$80 = x^2 - 2x$$

$$0 = x^2 - 2x - 80$$

$$x = \frac{-(-2)\pm\sqrt{(-2)^2 - 4(1)(-80)}}{2(1)}$$

$$= \frac{2\pm\sqrt{324}}{2} = \frac{2\pm18}{2}$$

$$x = \frac{20}{2} = 10 \quad \text{or} \quad x = \frac{-16}{2} = -8$$

Since the width must be positive, $x = 10$. The length is 10 units and the width is $10 - 2 = 8$ units.

56. If the business sells n tables at a price of $(60 - 0.3n)$ dollars per table, then the revenue is given by $R(n) = n(60 - 0.3n)$ with n ≤ 40. Set this equal to 1080 and solve for n.

$$R(n) = n(60-0.3n)$$

$$1080 = n(60-0.3n)$$

$$1080 = 60n - 0.3n^2$$

$$0.3n^2 - 60n + 1080 = 0$$

$$n^2 - 200n + 3600 = 0$$

$$(n-20)(n-180) = 0$$

$$n = 20 \quad \text{or} \quad n = 180$$

Disregard $n = 180$ since $n \le 40$. The business must sell 20 tables.

57.
$$a^2 + b^2 = c^2$$

$$a^2 = c^2 - b^2$$

$$\sqrt{a^2} = \pm\sqrt{c^2 - b^2}$$

$$a = \pm\sqrt{c^2 - b^2}$$

Since a refers to a length, it cannot be negative. Therefore disregard the negative sign.

$$a = \sqrt{c^2 - b^2}$$

58.
$$h = -4.9t^2 + c$$

$$h - c = -4.9t^2$$

$$\frac{h-c}{-4.9} = \frac{-4.9t^2}{-4.9}$$

$$\frac{h-c}{-4.9} = t^2$$

$$\pm\sqrt{\frac{h-c}{-4.9}} = t \quad \text{or} \quad t = \pm\sqrt{\frac{c-h}{4.9}}$$

Disregard the negative value for time:

$$t = \sqrt{\frac{c-h}{4.9}}$$

59. $v_x^2 + v_y^2 = v^2$ for v_y

$$v_y^2 = v^2 - v_x^2$$

$$v_y = \sqrt{v^2 - v_x^2}$$

60. $a = \dfrac{v_2^2 - v_1^2}{2d}$ for v_2

$$2ad = v_2^2 - v_1^2$$

$$2ad + v_1^2 = v_2^2$$

$$v_2 = \sqrt{v_1^2 + 2ad}$$

61. Let $u = x^2$.

$$x^4 - x^2 - 20 = (x^2)^2 - x^2 - 20$$

$$= u^2 - u - 20$$

$$= (u+4)(u-5)$$

Back substitute x^2 for u.

$$= (x^2 + 4)(x^2 - 5)$$

62. Let $u = x^2$.

$$4x^4 + 4x^2 - 3 = 4(x^2)^2 + 4x^2 - 3$$

$$= 4u^2 + 4u - 3$$

$$= (2u - 1)(2u + 3)$$

Back substitute x^2 for u.

$$= (2x^2 - 1)(2x^2 + 3)$$

63. Let $u = x + 5$.

$(x+5)^2 + 10(x+5) + 24$

$= u^2 + 10u + 24$

$= (u+4)(u+6)$

Back substitute $x+5$ for u.

$= [(x+5)+4][(x+5)+6]$

$= (x+9)(x+11)$

64. Let $u = 2x + 3$.

$4(2x+3)^2 - 12(2x+3) + 5$

$= 4u^2 - 12u + 5$

$= (2u-5)(2u-1)$

Back substitute $2x+3$ for u.

$= [2(2x+3)-5][2(2x+3)-1]$

$= (4x+6-5)(4x+6-1)$

$= (4x+1)(4x+5)$

65. $x^4 - 13x^2 + 36 = 0$

$(x^2)^2 - 13x^2 + 36 = 0$

Let $u = x^2$

$u^2 - 13u + 36 = 0$

$(u-9)(u-4) = 0$

$u-9 = 0$ or $u-4 = 0$

$u = 9$ $\qquad u = 4$

Substitute x^2 for u.

$x^2 = 9$ or $x^2 = 4$

$x = \pm 3$ $\qquad x = \pm 2$

The solutions are ± 3 and ± 2.

66. $x^4 - 21x^2 + 80 = 0$

$(x^2)^2 - 21x^2 + 80 = 0$

Let $u = x^2$

$u^2 - 21u + 80 = 0$

$(u-16)(u-5) = 0$

$u-16 = 0$ or $u-5 = 0$

$u = 16$ $\qquad u = 5$

Substitute x^2 for u.

$x^2 = 16$ or $x^2 = 5$

$x = \pm 4$ $\qquad x = \pm\sqrt{5}$

The solutions are ± 4 and $\pm\sqrt{5}$.

67. $\qquad a^4 = 5a^2 + 24$

$a^4 - 5a^2 - 24 = 0$

$(a^2)^2 - 5a^2 - 24 = 0$

Let $u = a^2$

$u^2 - 5u - 24 = 0$

$(u-8)(u+3) = 0$

$u-8 = 0$ or $u+3 = 0$

$u = 8$ $\qquad u = -3$

Substitute a^2 for u.

$a^2 = 8$ $\qquad$ or $\qquad a^2 = -3$

$a = \pm\sqrt{8}$ $\qquad a = \pm\sqrt{-3}$

$= \pm 2\sqrt{2}$ $\qquad = \pm i\sqrt{3}$

The solutions are $\pm 2\sqrt{2}$ and $\pm i\sqrt{3}$.

68. $\qquad 3y^{-2} + 16y^{-1} = 12$

$3(y^{-1})^2 + 16(y^{-1}) - 12 = 0$

Let $u = y^{-1}$.

$3u^2 + 16u - 12 = 0$

$(3u-2)(u+6) = 0$

$3u-2 = 0$ or $u+6 = 0$

$u = \dfrac{2}{3}$ $\qquad u = -6$

Substitute y^{-1} for u.

$y^{-1} = \dfrac{2}{3}$ or $y^{-1} = -6$

$y = \dfrac{3}{2}$ $\qquad y = -\dfrac{1}{6}$

The solutions are $\dfrac{3}{2}$ and $-\dfrac{1}{6}$.

69.

$$3r + 11\sqrt{r} - 4 = 0$$

$$3\left(r^{1/2}\right)^2 + 11r^{1/2} - 4 = 0$$

Let $u = r^{1/2}$

$$3u^2 + 11u - 4 = 0$$

$$(3u - 1)(u + 4) = 0$$

$$3u - 1 = 0 \quad \text{or} \quad u + 4 = 0$$

$$u = \frac{1}{3} \qquad\qquad u = -4$$

Substitute $r^{1/2}$ for u.

$$r^{1/2} = \frac{1}{3} \qquad \text{or} \qquad r^{1/2} = -6$$

$$\qquad\qquad\qquad\qquad\qquad \text{not real}$$

$$r = \left(\frac{1}{3}\right)^2 = \frac{1}{9}$$

There are no solutions for $r^{1/2} = -6$ since there is no real number x for which $r^{1/2} = -6$.

The solution is $\frac{1}{9}$.

70.

$$2p^{2/3} - 7p^{1/3} + 6 = 0$$

$$2\left(p^{1/3}\right)^2 - 7p^{1/3} + 6 = 0$$

Let $u = p^{1/3}$

$$2u^2 - 7u + 6 = 0$$

$$(2u - 3)(u - 2) = 0$$

$$2u - 3 = 0 \quad \text{or} \quad u - 2 = 0$$

$$u = \frac{3}{2} \qquad\qquad u = 2$$

Substitute $p^{1/3}$ for u.

$$p^{1/3} = \frac{3}{2} \qquad p^{1/3} = 2$$

$$p = \left(\frac{3}{2}\right)^3 \qquad p = 2^3$$

$$= \frac{27}{8} \qquad\qquad = 8$$

The solutions are $\frac{27}{8}$ and 8.

71.

$$6(x-2)^{-2} = -13(x-2)^{-1} + 8$$

$$6\left[(x-2)^{-1}\right]^2 + 13(x-2)^{-1} - 8 = 0$$

Let $u = (x-2)^{-1}$

$$6u^2 + 13u - 8 = 0$$

$$(2u - 1)(3u + 8) = 0$$

$$2u - 1 = 0 \quad \text{or} \quad 3u + 8 = 0$$

$$u = \frac{1}{2} \qquad\qquad u = -\frac{8}{3}$$

Substitute $(x-2)^{-1}$ for u.

$$(x-2)^{-1} = \frac{1}{2} \quad \text{or} \quad (x-2)^{-1} = -\frac{8}{3}$$

$$x - 2 = 2 \qquad\qquad x - 2 = -\frac{3}{8}$$

$$x = 4 \qquad\qquad\qquad x = \frac{13}{8}$$

The solutions are 4 and $\frac{13}{8}$.

72.

$$10(r+1) = \frac{12}{r+1} - 7$$

$$(r+1)\left[10(r+1)\right] = (r+1)\left[\frac{12}{r+1} - 7\right]$$

$$10(r+1)^2 + 7(r+1) = 12$$

$$10(r+1)^2 + 7(r+1) - 12 = 0$$

Let $u = r + 1$.

$$10u^2 + 7u - 12 = 0$$

$$(5u - 4)(2u + 3) = 0$$

$$5u - 4 = 0 \quad \text{or} \quad 2u + 3 = 0$$

$$u = \frac{4}{5} \qquad\qquad u = -\frac{3}{2}$$

Substitute $(r+1)$ for u.

$$r + 1 = \frac{4}{5} \quad \text{or} \quad r + 1 = -\frac{3}{2}$$

$$r = -\frac{1}{5} \qquad\qquad r = -\frac{5}{2}$$

The solutions are $-\frac{1}{5}$ and $-\frac{5}{2}$.

73. $f(x) = x^4 - 82x^2 + 81$

To find the x-intercepts, set $f(x) = 0$.

$0 = x^4 - 82x^2 + 81$

$0 = \left(x^2\right)^2 - 82x^2 + 81$

Let $u = x^2$.

$0 = u^2 - 82u + 81$

$0 = (u - 81)(u - 1)$

$u - 81 = 0 \quad$ or $\quad u - 1 = 0$

$\quad u = 81 \qquad\qquad u = 1$

Substitute x^2 for u.

$x^2 = 81 \quad$ or $\quad x^2 = 1$

$x = \pm 9 \qquad\qquad x = \pm 1$

The x-intercepts are $(9, 0)$, $(-9, 0)$, $(1, 0)$, and $(-1, 0)$.

74. $f(x) = 30x + 13\sqrt{x} - 10$

To find the x-intercepts, set $f(x) = 0$.

$0 = 30x + 13\sqrt{x} - 10$

$0 = 30\left(\sqrt{x}\right)^2 + 13\sqrt{x} - 10$

Let $u = \sqrt{x}$.

$0 = 30u^2 + 13u - 10$

$0 = (6u + 5)(5u - 2)$

$6u + 5 = 0 \quad$ or $\quad 5u - 2 = 0$

$\quad u = -\dfrac{5}{6} \qquad\qquad u = \dfrac{2}{5}$

Substitute $\sqrt{x}$ for u.

$\sqrt{x} = -\dfrac{5}{6} \quad$ or $\quad \sqrt{x} = \dfrac{2}{5}$

$\quad$ not real $\qquad\qquad x = \dfrac{4}{25}$

Since $\sqrt{x}$ cannot be negative, the solution is $\dfrac{4}{25}$. The only x-intercept is $\left(\dfrac{4}{25}, 0\right)$.

75. $f(x) = x - 6\sqrt{x} + 12$

To find the x-intercepts, set $f(x) = 0$.

$0 = x - 6\sqrt{x} + 12$

$0 = \left(\sqrt{x}\right)^2 - 6\sqrt{x} + 12$

Let $u = \sqrt{x}$.

$0 = u^2 - 6u + 12$

$u = \dfrac{-(-6) \pm \sqrt{(-6)^2 - 4(1)(10)}}{2(1)}$

$\quad = \dfrac{6 \pm \sqrt{-4}}{2} = \dfrac{6 \pm 2i}{2} = 3 \pm i$

Substitute $\sqrt{x}$ for u.

$\sqrt{x} = 3 \pm i$

Since x-intercepts must be real numbers, this function has no x-intercepts.

76. $g(x) = \left(x^2 - 6x\right)^2 - 5\left(x^2 - 6x\right) - 24$

To find the x-intercepts, set $g(x) = 0$.

$0 = \left(x^2 - 6x\right)^2 - 5\left(x^2 - 6x\right) - 24$

Let $u = x^2 - 6x$.

$0 = u^2 - 5u - 24$

$0 = (u + 3)(u - 8)$

$u + 3 = 0 \quad$ or $\quad u - 8 = 0$

$\quad u = -3 \qquad\qquad u = 8$

Substitute $\left(x^2 - 6x\right)$ for u.

$x^2 - 6x = -3 \quad$ or $\quad x^2 - 6x = 8$

$x^2 - 6x + 3 = 0 \qquad x^2 - 6x - 8 = 0$

$\dfrac{6 \pm \sqrt{(-6)^2 - 4(1)(3)}}{2(1)} \quad \dfrac{6 \pm \sqrt{(-6)^2 - 4(1)(-8)}}{2(1)}$

$\dfrac{6 \pm \sqrt{24}}{2} \qquad\qquad \dfrac{6 \pm \sqrt{68}}{2}$

$\dfrac{6 \pm 2\sqrt{6}}{2} \qquad\qquad \dfrac{6 \pm 2\sqrt{17}}{2}$

$3 \pm \sqrt{6} \qquad\qquad 3 \pm \sqrt{17}$

The x-intercepts are $\left(3 + \sqrt{6}, 0\right), \left(3 - \sqrt{6}, 0\right),$ $\left(3 + \sqrt{17}, 0\right)$ and $\left(3 - \sqrt{17}, 0\right)$.

77. $f(x) = x^2 + 5x$

   a. Since $a = 1$ the parabola opens upward.

   b. $y = f(0) = 0^2 + 5(0) = 0$

      The y-intercept is $(0, 0)$.

   c. $x = -\dfrac{b}{2a} = -\dfrac{5}{2(1)} = -\dfrac{5}{2}$

      $y = \dfrac{4ac - b^2}{4a} = \dfrac{4(1)(0) - 5^2}{4(1)} = -\dfrac{25}{4}$

      The vertex is $\left(-\dfrac{5}{2}, -\dfrac{25}{4}\right)$.

   d. $0 = x^2 + 5x$

      $0 = x(x + 5)$

      $0 = x$ or $0 = x + 5$

      $x = 0$ $x = -5$

      The x-intercepts are $(0, 0)$ and $(-5, 0)$.

   e.

78. $f(x) = x^2 - 2x - 8$

   a. Since $a = 1$ the parabola opens upward.

   b. $y = f(0) = (0)^2 - 2(0) - 8 = -8$

      The y-intercept is $(0, -8)$.

   c. $x = -\dfrac{b}{2a} = -\dfrac{-2}{2(1)} = \dfrac{2}{2} = 1$

      $y = \dfrac{4ac - b^2}{4a} = \dfrac{4(1)(-8) - (-2)^2}{4(1)} = \dfrac{-36}{4} = -9$

      The vertex is $(1, -9)$.

   d. $0 = x^2 - 2x - 8$

      $0 = (x - 4)(x + 2)$

      $0 = x - 4$ or $0 = x + 2$

      $4 = x$ or $-2 = x$

      The x-intercepts are $(4, 0)$ and $(-2, 0)$.

   e.

79. $g(x) = -x^2 - 2$

   a. Since $a = -1$ the parabola opens downward.

   b. $y = g(0) = -(0)^2 - 2 = -2$

      The y-intercept is $(0, -2)$.

   c. $x = -\dfrac{b}{2a} = -\dfrac{0}{2(-1)} = -\dfrac{0}{-2} = 0$

      $y = \dfrac{4ac - b^2}{4a} = \dfrac{4(-1)(-2) - 0^2}{4(-1)} = \dfrac{8}{-4} = -2$

      The vertex is $(0, -2)$.

   d. $0 = -x^2 - 2$

      $x^2 = -2$

      $x = \pm\sqrt{-2} = \pm i\sqrt{2}$

      There are no real roots. Thus, there are no x-intercepts.

   e.

80. $g(x) = -2x^2 - x + 15$

   a. Since $a = -2$ the parabola opens downward.

   b. $y = -2(0)^2 - 0 + 15 = 15$

      The y-intercept is $(0, 15)$.

   c. $x = -\dfrac{b}{2a} = -\dfrac{-1}{2(-2)} = \dfrac{1}{-4} = -\dfrac{1}{4}$

      $y = \dfrac{4ac - b^2}{4a} = \dfrac{4(-2)(15) - (-1)^2}{4(-2)} = \dfrac{121}{8}$

      The vertex is $\left(-\dfrac{1}{4}, \dfrac{121}{8}\right)$.

d. $0 = -1\left(2x^2 + x - 15\right)$

$0 = -1\left(2x - 5\right)\left(x + 3\right)$

$0 = \left(2x - 5\right) \quad$ or $\quad 0 = x + 3$

$5 = 2x$

$\dfrac{5}{2} = x \qquad\qquad -3 = x$

The x-intercepts are $(-3, 0)$ and $\left(\dfrac{5}{2}, 0\right)$.

e.

$y = -2x^2 - x + 15$

81. a. $I = -x^2 + 22x - 45$, $2 \le x \le 20$

The x-coordinate of the vertex will be the cost per ticket to maximize profit.

$x = -\dfrac{b}{2a} = -\dfrac{22}{2(-1)} = 11$

They should charge $11 per ticket.

b. The maximum profit in hundreds is the y-coordinate of the vertex.

$I(11) = -11^2 + 22(11) - 45$

$= -121 + 242 - 45$

$= 76$

The maximum profit is $76 hundred or $7600.

82. a. $s(t) = -16t^2 + 80t + 75$

The ball will attain maximum height at the x-coordinate of the vertex.

$t = -\dfrac{b}{2a} = -\dfrac{80}{2(-16)} = -\dfrac{80}{-32} = 2.5$

The ball will attain maximum height 2.5 seconds after being thrown.

b. The maximum height is the y-coordinate of the vertex.

$s(2.5) = -16(2.5)^2 + 80(2.5) + 74$

$= -100 + 200 + 75$

$= 175$

The maximum height is 175 feet.

83. The graph of $f(x) = (x - 3)^2$ has vertex $(3, 0)$. The graph will be $g(x) = x^2$ shifted right 3 units.

84. The graph of $f(x) = -(x + 2)^2 - 3$ has vertex $(-2, -3)$. Since $a < 0$, the parabola opens downward. The graph will be $g(x) = -x^2$ shifted left 2 units and down 3 units.

85. The graph of $g(x) = -2(x + 4)^2 - 1$ has vertex $(-4, -1)$. Since $a < 0$, the parabola opens downward. The graph will be $f(x) = -2x^2$ shifted left 4 units and down 1 unit.

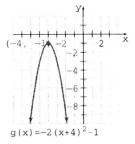

86. The graph of $h(x) = \dfrac{1}{2}(x-1)^2 + 3$ has vertex

$(1, 3)$. The graph will be $f(x) = \dfrac{1}{2}x^2$ shifted

right 1 unit and up 3 units.

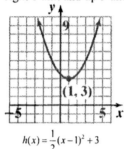

$$h(x) = \tfrac{1}{2}(x-1)^2 + 3$$

87. $x^2 + 4x + 3 \geq 0$
$(x+1)(x+3) \geq 0$

88. $x^2 + 3x - 10 \leq 0$
$(x+5)(x-2) \leq 0$

89. $x^2 \leq 11x - 20$
$x^2 - 11x + 20 \leq 0$
$x^2 - 11x + 20 = 0$
$$x = \frac{-(-11) \pm \sqrt{(-11)^2 - 4(1)(20)}}{2(1)}$$
$$= \frac{11 \pm \sqrt{121 - 80}}{2}$$
$$= \frac{11 \pm \sqrt{41}}{2}$$

$$\frac{11 - \sqrt{41}}{2} \qquad \frac{11 + \sqrt{41}}{2}$$

90. $3x^2 + 8x > 16$
$3x^2 + 8x - 16 > 0$
$(3x - 4)(x + 4) > 0$
$3x - 4 = 0 \quad$ or $\quad x + 4 = 0$
$$x = \frac{4}{3} \qquad\qquad x = -4$$

91. $4x^2 - 9 \leq 0$
$(2x - 3)(2x + 3) \leq 0$
$2x - 3 = 0 \quad$ or $\quad 2x + 3 = 0$
$$x = \frac{3}{2} \qquad\qquad x = -\frac{3}{2}$$

92.
$$6x^2 - 30 > 0$$
$$6(x^2 - 5) > 0$$
$$6(x + \sqrt{5})(x - \sqrt{5}) > 0$$
$$x + \sqrt{5} = 0 \qquad \text{or} \qquad x - \sqrt{5} = 0$$
$$x = -\sqrt{5} \qquad\qquad x = \sqrt{5}$$

93. $\dfrac{x+1}{x-5} > 0$
$x \neq 5$

$$\{x \mid x < -1 \text{ or } x > 5\}$$

94. $\dfrac{x-3}{x+2} \le 0$

$x = -2$

$$\{x \mid -2 < x \le 3\}$$

95. $\dfrac{2x-4}{x+3} \ge 0$

$\dfrac{2(x-2)}{x+3} \ge 0$

$x \ne -3$

$$\{x \mid x < -3 \text{ or } x \ge 2\}$$

96. $\dfrac{3x+5}{x-6} < 0$

$x \ne 6$

$$\left\{x \mid -\dfrac{5}{3} < x < 6\right\}$$

97. $(x+4)(x+1)(x-2) > 0$

$$\{x \mid -4 < x < -1 \text{ or } x > 2\}$$

98. $x(x-3)(x-6) \le 0$

$$\{x \mid x \le 0 \text{ or } 3 \le x \le 6\}$$

99. $(3x+4)(x-1)(x-3) \ge 0$

$$\left[-\dfrac{4}{3}, 1\right] \cup [3, \infty)$$

100. $2x(x+2)(x+4) < 0$

$$(-\infty, -4) \cup (-2, 0)$$

101. $\dfrac{x(x-4)}{x+2} > 0$

$x \ne -2$

$$(-2, 0) \cup (4, \infty)$$

102. $\dfrac{(x-2)(x-8)}{x+3} < 0$

$x \ne -3$

$$(-\infty, -3) \cup (2, 8)$$

103. $\dfrac{x-3}{(x+2)(x-7)} \ge 0$

$x \ne -2, x \ne 7$

$$(-2, 3] \cup (7, \infty)$$

104. $\dfrac{x(x-6)}{x+3} \le 0$

$x \ne -3$

$(-\infty, -3) \cup [0, 6]$

105. $\dfrac{5}{x+4} \ge -1$

$\dfrac{5}{x+4} + 1 \ge 0$

$\dfrac{5+1(x+4)}{x+4} \ge 0$

$\dfrac{5+x+4}{x+4} \ge 0$

$\dfrac{x+9}{x+4} \ge 0$

$x \ne -4$

106. $\dfrac{2x}{x-2} \le 1$

$\dfrac{2x}{x-2} - 1 \le 0$

$\dfrac{2x}{x-2} - \dfrac{1(x-2)}{x-2} \le 0$

$\dfrac{2x-x+2}{x-2} \le 0$

$\dfrac{x+2}{x-2} \le 0$

$x \ne 2$

107. $\dfrac{2x+3}{3x-5} < 4$

$\dfrac{2x+3}{3x-5} - 4 < 0$

$\dfrac{2x+3-4(3x-5)}{3x-5} < 0$

$\dfrac{2x+3-12x+20}{3x-5} < 0$

$\dfrac{-10x+23}{3x-5} < 0$

Chapter 12 Practice Test

1. $x^2 + 2x - 15 = 0$

$x^2 + 2x = 15$

$x^2 + 2x + 1 = 15 + 1$

$(x+1)^2 = 16$

$x+1 = \pm 4$

$x = -1 \pm 4$

$x = 3 \text{ or } x = -5$

2. $a^2 + 7 = 6a$

$a^2 - 6a = -7$

$a^2 - 6a + 9 = -7 + 9$

$(a-3)^2 = 2$

$a-3 = \pm\sqrt{2}$

$a = 3 \pm \sqrt{2}$

$a = 3 + \sqrt{2} \text{ or } a = 3 - \sqrt{2}$

3. $x^2 - 6x - 16 = 0$, $a = 1$, $b = -6$, $c = -16$

$$x = \frac{-b \pm \sqrt{b^2 - 4ac}}{2a}$$

$$x = \frac{-(-6) \pm \sqrt{(-6)^2 - 4(1)(-16)}}{2(1)}$$

$$= \frac{6 \pm \sqrt{36 + 64}}{2}$$

$$= \frac{6 \pm \sqrt{100}}{2}$$

$$= \frac{6 \pm 10}{2}$$

$$x = \frac{6 + 10}{2} \quad \text{or} \quad x = \frac{6 - 10}{2}$$

$$= \frac{16}{2} \qquad\qquad = \frac{-4}{2}$$

$$= 8 \qquad\qquad\quad = -2$$

4. $x^2 - 4x = -11$

$x^2 - 4x + 11 = 0$

$a = 1$, $b = -4$, $c = 11$

$$x = \frac{-b \pm \sqrt{b^2 - 4ac}}{2a}$$

$$x = \frac{-(-4) \pm \sqrt{(-4)^2 - 4(1)(11)}}{2(1)}$$

$$= \frac{4 \pm \sqrt{16 - 44}}{2}$$

$$= \frac{4 \pm \sqrt{-28}}{2}$$

$$= \frac{4 \pm 2i\sqrt{7}}{2} = 2 \pm i\sqrt{7}$$

$$x = 2 + i\sqrt{7} \quad \text{or} \quad x = 2 - i\sqrt{7}$$

5. $3r^2 + r = 2$

$3r^2 + r - 2 = 0$

$(3r - 2)(r + 1) = 0$

$3r - 2 = 0 \quad \text{or} \quad r + 1 = 0$

$\quad 3r = 2 \qquad\qquad r = -1$

$$r = \frac{2}{3}$$

6. $p^2 + 4 = -7p$

$p^2 + 7p + 4 = 0$

$$p = \frac{-7 \pm \sqrt{(7)^2 - 4(1)(4)}}{2(1)}$$

$$= \frac{-7 \pm \sqrt{49 - 16}}{2}$$

$$= \frac{-7 \pm \sqrt{33}}{2}$$

$$p = \frac{-7 + \sqrt{33}}{2} \quad \text{or} \quad p = \frac{-7 - \sqrt{33}}{2}$$

7. $x = 4$ and $x = -\dfrac{2}{5}$

$x - 4 = 0$ and $5x + 2 = 0$

$(x - 4)(5x + 2) = 0$

$5x^2 - 18x - 8 = 0$

8. $K = \dfrac{1}{2}mv^2$ for v

$2K = mv^2$

$\dfrac{2K}{m} = v^2$

$v = \sqrt{\dfrac{2K}{m}}$

9. a. $c(s) = -0.01s^2 + 78s + 22,000$

$c(1600) = -0.01(1600)^2 + 78(1600) + 22,000$

$\qquad\qquad = -25,600 + 124,800 + 22,000$

$\qquad\qquad = 121,200$

The cost is about \$121,200.

b. $160,000 = -0.01s^2 + 78s + 22,000$

$0 = -0.01s^2 + 78s - 138,000$

$$s = \frac{-78 \pm \sqrt{78^2 - 4(-0.01)(-138,000)}}{2(-0.01)}$$

$$= \frac{-78 \pm \sqrt{564}}{-0.02}$$

$$s = \frac{-78 + \sqrt{564}}{-0.02} \approx 2712.57$$

$$s = \frac{-78 - \sqrt{564}}{-0.02} \approx 5087.43$$

Since $1300 \le s \le 3900$, the house should have about 2712.57 square feet.

10. The formula $d = rt$ can be written $t = \dfrac{d}{r}$.

Let r = his actual rate.

	distance	rate	time $= \dfrac{d}{r}$
Actual trip	520	r	$\dfrac{520}{r}$
Faster trip	520	$r + 15$	$\dfrac{520}{r+15}$

The faster trip would have taken 2.4 hours less time than the actual trip.

$$\frac{520}{r+15} = \frac{520}{r} - 2.4$$

$$r(r+15)\left(\frac{520}{r+15}\right) = r(r+15)\left(\frac{520}{r} - 2.4\right)$$

$$520r = 520(r+15) - 2.4r(r+15)$$

$$520r = 520r + 7800 - 2.4r^2 - 36r$$

$$0 = -2.4r^2 - 36r + 7800$$

$$0 = r^2 + 15r - 3250$$

$$0 = (r+65)(r-50)$$

$$r + 65 = 0 \qquad r - 50 = 0$$

$$r = -65 \qquad r = 50$$

Since speed is never negative, Tom drove an average speed of 50 mph.

11. $\quad 2x^4 + 15x^2 - 50 = 0$

$$2\left(x^2\right)^2 + 15x^2 - 50 = 0$$

Let $u = x^2$.

$$2u^2 + 15u - 50 = 0$$

$$(u+10)(2u-5) = 0$$

$$u + 10 = 0 \quad \text{or} \quad 2u - 5 = 0$$

$$u = -10 \qquad\qquad u = \frac{5}{2}$$

Substitute x^2 for u.

$$x^2 = -10 \quad \text{or} \quad x^2 = \frac{5}{2}$$

$$x = \pm\sqrt{-10} \qquad x = \pm\sqrt{\frac{5}{2}}$$

$$= \pm i\sqrt{10} \qquad = \pm \frac{\sqrt{5}}{\sqrt{2}} \cdot \frac{\sqrt{2}}{\sqrt{2}}$$

$$= \pm \frac{\sqrt{10}}{2}$$

12. $\quad 3r^{2/3} + 11r^{1/3} - 42 = 0$

$$3\left(r^{1/3}\right)^2 + 11r^{1/3} - 42 = 0$$

Let $u = r^{1/3}$.

$$3u^2 + 11u - 42 = 0$$

$$(3u - 7)(u + 6) = 0$$

$$3u - 7 = 0 \quad \text{or} \quad u + 6 = 0$$

$$u = \frac{7}{3} \qquad\qquad u = -6$$

$$r^{1/3} = \frac{7}{3} \quad \text{or} \quad r^{1/3} = -6$$

$$r = \left(\frac{7}{3}\right)^3 \qquad r = (-6)^3$$

$$= \frac{343}{27} \qquad\qquad r = -216$$

13. $\quad f(x) = 16x - 24\sqrt{x} + 9$

$$0 = 16\left(\sqrt{x}\right)^2 - 24\sqrt{x} + 9$$

Let $u = \sqrt{x}$.

$$0 = 16u^2 - 24u + 9$$

$$0 = (4u - 3)^2$$

$$4u - 3 = 0$$

$$u = \frac{3}{4}$$

Substitute $\sqrt{x}$ for u.

$$\sqrt{x} = \frac{3}{4}$$

$$x = \left(\frac{3}{4}\right)^2 = \frac{9}{16}$$

The x-intercept is $\left(\dfrac{9}{16}, 0\right)$.

14. $\quad f(x) = (x-3)^2 + 2$

The vertex is (3, 2). The graph will be the graph of $g(x) = x^2$ shifted right 3 units and up 2 units.

15. $h(x) = -\frac{1}{2}(x-2)^2 - 2$

The vertex is $(2, -2)$. The graph will be the

graph of $g(x) = -\frac{1}{2}x^2$ shifted right 2 units and

down 2 units.

$h(x) = -\frac{1}{2}(x-2)^2 - 2$

16. $\qquad 6x^2 = 2x + 3$

$6x^2 - 2x - 3 = 0$
$a = 6, b = -2, c = -3$
The discriminant is
$b^2 - 4ac = (-2)^2 - 4(6)(-3) = 4 + 72 = 76$
Since the discriminant is greater than 0, the
quadratic equation has two distinct real solutions.

17. $y = x^2 + 2x - 8$

a. Since $a = 1$ the parabola opens upward.

b. Let $x = 0$: $y = 0^2 + 2(0) - 8 = -8$
The y-intercept is $(0, -8)$.

c. $x = -\frac{b}{2a} = -\frac{2}{2(1)} = -1$

$y = (-1)^2 + 2(-1) - 8 = -9$
The vertex is $(-1, -9)$.

d. The x-intercepts occur when $y = 0$.
$0 = x^2 + 2x - 8$
$0 = (x+4)(x-2)$
$x + 4 = 0 \quad$ or $\quad x - 2 = 0$
$\quad x = -4 \qquad\qquad x = 2$
The x-intercepts are $(2, 0)$ and $(-4, 0)$.

e.

18. $x = -7$ and $x = \frac{1}{2}$

$x + 7 = 0$ and $2x - 1 = 0$
$(x + 7)(2x - 1) = 0$
$2x^2 + 13x - 7 = 0$

19. $\qquad x^2 - x \geq 42$

$x^2 - x - 42 \geq 0$
$(x - 7)(x + 6) \geq 0$
$x - 7 = 0 \quad$ or $\quad x + 6 = 0$
$\quad x = 7 \qquad\qquad x = -6$

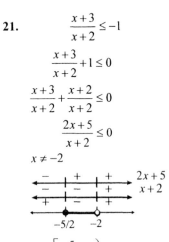

20. $\dfrac{(x+5)(x-4)}{x+1} \geq 0$

$x \neq -1$
$x + 5 = 0 \quad$ or $\quad x - 4 = 0 \quad$ or $\quad x + 1 = 0$
$\quad x = -5 \qquad\qquad x = 4 \qquad\qquad x = -1$

21. $\qquad \dfrac{x+3}{x+2} \leq -1$

$\dfrac{x+3}{x+2} + 1 \leq 0$

$\dfrac{x+3}{x+2} + \dfrac{x+2}{x+2} \leq 0$

$\dfrac{2x+5}{x+2} \leq 0$

$x \neq -2$

a. $\left[-\dfrac{5}{2}, -2\right)$

b. $\left\{ x \,\middle|\, -\dfrac{5}{2} \leq x < -2 \right\}$

22. Let x be the width of the carpet. Then $2x + 3$ is the length $A = lw$.

$$65 = x(2x+3)$$
$$65 = 2x^2 + 3x$$
$$0 = 2x^2 + 3x - 65$$
$$0 = (2x+13)(x-5)$$

$$2x+13 = 0 \quad \text{or} \quad x-5 = 0$$
$$x = -\frac{13}{2} \qquad\qquad x = 5$$

Disregard the negative answer. The width is 5 feet and the length is $2 \cdot 5 + 3 = 10 + 3 = 13$ feet.

23. $d = -16t^2 + 80t + 96$

$d = 0$ when the ball strikes the ground.

$$0 = -16t^2 + 80t + 96$$
$$0 = -16(t^2 - 5t - 6)$$
$$0 = -16(t-6)(t+1)$$

$$t-6 = 0 \quad \text{or} \quad t+1 = 0$$
$$t = 6 \qquad\qquad t = -1$$

The time must be positive, so $t = 6$.
Thus, the ball strikes the ground in 6 seconds.

24. a. $f(x) = -1.4x^2 + 56x - 70$

$$x = -\frac{b}{2a} = -\frac{56}{2(-1.4)} = -\frac{56}{-2.8} = 20$$

The company must sell 20 carvings.

b. $f(20) = -1.4(20)^2 + 56(20) - 70$
$$= -560 + 1120 - 70$$
$$= 490$$

The maximum weekly profit is $490.

25. If the business sells n brooms at a price of $(10 - 0.1n)$ dollars per broom, then the revenue is given by $R(n) = n(10-0.1n)$ with $n \le 32$. Set this equal to 160 and solve for n.

$$R(n) = n(10-0.1n)$$
$$210 = n(10-0.1n)$$
$$210 = 10n - 0.1n^2$$
$$0.1n^2 - 10n + 210 = 0$$
$$n^2 - 100n + 2100 = 0$$
$$(n-30)(n-70) = 0$$

$n = 30$ or $n = 70$

Disregard $n = 70$ since $n \le 32$. The business must sell 30 brooms.

Chapter 12 Cumulative Review Test

1. $-4 \div (-2) + 18 - \sqrt{49} = -4 \div (-2) + 18 - 7$
$$= 2 + 18 - 7$$
$$= 20 - 7$$
$$= 13$$

2. Evaluate $2x^2 + 3x + 4$ when $x = 2$.
$$2(2)^2 + 3(2) + 4 = 8 + 6 + 4 = 18$$

3. $6x - \{3 - [2(x-2) - 5x]\}$
$$= 6x - \{3 - [2x - 4 - 5x]\}$$
$$= 6x - \{3 - [-4 - 3x]\}$$
$$= 6x - \{3 + 4 + 3x\}$$
$$= 6x - \{7 + 3x\}$$
$$= 6x - 7 - 3x$$
$$= 3x - 7$$

4. $-\frac{1}{2}(4x-6) = \frac{1}{3}(3-6x) + 2$
$$-2x + 3 = 1 - 2x + 2$$
$$-2x + 3 = -2x + 3$$
This is an identity. The solution is all real numbers.

5. a. $x = -4$ is a vertical line.

b. $y = 2$ is a horizontal line.

6. $m = \dfrac{y_2 - y_1}{x_2 - x_1} = \dfrac{3-5}{4-6} = \dfrac{-2}{-2} = 1$

$y - y_1 = m(x - x_1)$

$y - 3 = 1(x - 4)$

$y - 3 = x - 4$

$y = x - 1$

7. $2{,}540{,}000 = 2.54 \times 10^6$

8. $\dfrac{x+2}{x^2 - x - 6} + \dfrac{x-3}{x^2 - 8x + 15}$

$= \dfrac{x+2}{(x-3)(x+2)} + \dfrac{x-3}{(x-5)(x-3)}$

$= \dfrac{1}{(x-3)} + \dfrac{1}{(x-5)}$

$= \dfrac{1}{x-3} \cdot \dfrac{x-5}{x-5} + \dfrac{1}{x-5} \cdot \dfrac{x-3}{x-3}$

$= \dfrac{x-5+x-3}{(x-3)(x-5)}$

$= \dfrac{2x-8}{(x-3)(x-5)}$ or $\dfrac{2(x-4)}{(x-3)(x-5)}$

9.

$\dfrac{1}{a-2} = \dfrac{4a-1}{a^2+5a-14} + \dfrac{2}{a+7}$

$\dfrac{1}{a-2} = \dfrac{4a-1}{(a+7)(a-2)} + \dfrac{2}{a+7}$

$(a+7)(a-2)\left[\dfrac{1}{a-2} = \dfrac{4a-1}{(a+7)(a-2)} + \dfrac{2}{a+7} \right]$

$a+7 = 4a-1+2(a-2)$

$a+7 = 4a-1+2a-4$

$a+7 = 6a-5$

$-5a+7 = -5$

$-5a = -12$

$a = \dfrac{12}{5}$

10. $w = kI^2 R$, $w = 12$, $I = 2$, $R = 100$

$12 = k(2)^2(100)$

$12 = 400k$

$k = \dfrac{12}{400} = \dfrac{3}{100}$

$w = \dfrac{3}{100} I^2 R$, $I = 0.8$, $R = 600$

$w = \dfrac{3}{100}(0.8)^2(600) = 11.52$

The wattage is 11.52 watts.

11. $N(x) = -0.2x^2 + 40x$

$N(50) = -0.2(50)^2 + 40(50)$

$= -500 + 2000$

$= 1500$

50 trees would produce about 1500 baskets of apples.

12. a. No, the graph is not a function since each x-value does not have a unique y-value.

b. The domain is the set of x-values,

Domain : $\{x \mid x \geq -2\}$.

The range is the set of y-values,

Range: $\mathbb{R}$.

13. $4x - 3y = 10$ (1)

$2x + y = 5$ (2)

To eliminate the y variable, multiply equation (2) by 3 and add the result to equation (1).

$4x - 3y = 10 \qquad\qquad 4x - 3y = 10$

$3(2x + y = 5) \quad \Rightarrow \quad \dfrac{6x + 3y = 15}{10x = 25}$

$x = \dfrac{5}{2}$

Substitute $\dfrac{5}{2}$ for x in equation (2) and then solve for y.

$2\left(\dfrac{5}{2}\right) + y = 5$

$5 + y = 5$

$y = 0$

The solution is $\left(\dfrac{5}{2}, 0\right)$.

14. $\begin{vmatrix} 4 & 0 & -2 \\ 3 & 5 & 1 \\ 1 & -1 & 7 \end{vmatrix} = 4\begin{vmatrix} 5 & 1 \\ -1 & 7 \end{vmatrix} - 0\begin{vmatrix} 3 & 1 \\ 1 & 7 \end{vmatrix} + (-2)\begin{vmatrix} 3 & 5 \\ 1 & -1 \end{vmatrix}$

$= 4(35+1) - 0(21-1) - 2(-3-5)$

$= 4(36) - 0(20) - 2(-8)$

$= 144 - 0 + 16$

$= 160$

15. $-4 < \dfrac{x+4}{2} < 6$

$-8 < x + 4 < 12$

$-12 < x < 8$

In interval notation the solution is $(-12, 8)$.

16. $|4 - 2x| = 5$

$4 - 2x = 5$ or $4 - 2x = -5$

$-2x = 1$ $\qquad -2x = -9$

$x = -\dfrac{1}{2}$ $\qquad x = \dfrac{9}{2}$

The solution set is $\left\{ -\dfrac{1}{2}, \dfrac{9}{2} \right\}$

17. $\dfrac{3 - 4i}{2 + 5i} = \left(\dfrac{3 - 4i}{2 + 5i} \right) \left(\dfrac{2 - 5i}{2 - 5i} \right)$

$= \dfrac{6 - 23i + 20i^2}{4 - 25i^2}$

$= \dfrac{6 - 23i - 20}{4 + 25}$

$= \dfrac{-14 - 23i}{29}$

18. $4x^2 = -3x - 12$

$4x^2 + 3x + 12 = 0$

Using the quadratic formula, $a = 4$, $b = 3$, $c = 12$.

$x = \dfrac{-b \pm \sqrt{b^2 - 4ac}}{2a}$

$= \dfrac{-(3) \pm \sqrt{(3)^2 - 4(4)(12)}}{2(4)}$

$= \dfrac{-3 \pm \sqrt{9 - 192}}{8}$

$= \dfrac{-3 \pm \sqrt{-183}}{8}$

$= \dfrac{-3 \pm i\sqrt{183}}{8}$

19. $V = \dfrac{1}{3} \pi r^2 h$

$3(V) = 3\left(\dfrac{1}{3} \pi r^2 h \right)$

$3V = \pi r^2 h$

$\dfrac{3V}{\pi h} = \dfrac{\pi r^2 h}{\pi h}$

$\dfrac{3V}{\pi h} = r^2$

$\sqrt{\dfrac{3V}{\pi h}} = \sqrt{r^2}$

$\sqrt{\dfrac{3V}{\pi h}} = r$

20. $(x + 3)^2 + 10(x + 3) + 24$

$= [(x + 3) + 4][(x + 3) + 6]$

$= (x + 7)(x + 9)$

Chapter 13

1. To find $(f \circ g)(x)$, substitute $g(x)$ for x in $f(x)$.

2. To find $(g \circ f)(x)$, substitute $f(x)$ for x in $g(x)$.

3. a. Each y has a unique x in a one-to-one function.

    b. Use the horizontal line test to determine whether a graph is one-to-one.

4. No; only one-to-one functions have inverse functions.

5. a. Yes; each first coordinate is paired with only one second coordinate.

    b. Yes; each second coordinate is paired with only one first coordinate.

    c. $\{(5, 3), (2, 4), (3, -1), (-2, 0)\}$
    Reverse each ordered pair.

6. a. $(f \circ g)(x) = x$

    b. $(g \circ f)(x) = x$

7. The domain of f is the range of f^{-1} and the range of f is the domain of f^{-1}.

8. Since $(f \circ f^{-1})(x) = x$, then $(f \circ f^{-1})(6) = 6$.

9. $f(x) = x^2 + 1$, $g(x) = x + 2$

    a. $(f \circ g)(x) = (x+2)^2 + 1$
$$= x^2 + 4x + 4 + 1$$
$$= x^2 + 4x + 5$$

    b. $(f \circ g)(4) = 4^2 + 4(4) + 5 = 37$

    c. $(g \circ f)(x) = (x^2 + 1) + 2 = x^2 + 3$

    d. $(g \circ f)(4) = 4^2 + 3 = 19$

10. $f(x) = x^2 - 3$, $g(x) = x + 6$

    a. $(f \circ g)(x) = (x+6)^2 - 3$
$$= x^2 + 12x + 36 - 3$$
$$= x^2 + 12x + 33$$

    b. $(f \circ g)(4) = 4^2 + 12(4) + 33 = 97$

    c. $(g \circ f)(x) = (x^2 - 3) + 6 = x^2 + 3$

    d. $(g \circ f)(4) = 4^2 + 3 = 19$

11. $f(x) = x + 3$, $g(x) = x^2 + x - 4$

    a. $(f \circ g)(x) = (x^2 + x - 4) + 3 = x^2 + x - 1$

    b. $(f \circ g)(4) = 4^2 + 4 - 1 = 19$

    c. $(g \circ f)(x) = (x+3)^2 + (x+3) - 4$
$$= x^2 + 6x + 9 + x + 3 - 4$$
$$= x^2 + 7x + 8$$

    d. $(g \circ f)(4) = 4^2 + 7(4) + 8 = 52$

12. $f(x) = x + 2$, $g(x) = x^2 + 4x - 2$

    a. $(f \circ g)(x) = (x^2 + 4x - 2) + 2 = x^2 + 4x$

    b. $(f \circ g)(4) = 4^2 + 4(4) = 32$

    c. $(g \circ f)(x) = (x+2)^2 + 4(x+2) - 2$
$$= x^2 + 4x + 4 + 4x + 8 - 2$$
$$= x^2 + 8x + 10$$

    d. $(g \circ f)(4) = 4^2 + 8(4) + 10 = 58$

13. $f(x) = \dfrac{1}{x}$, $g(x) = 2x + 3$

    a. $(f \circ g)(x) = \dfrac{1}{2x+3}$

b. $(f \circ g)(4) = \dfrac{1}{2(4)+3} = \dfrac{1}{11}$

c. $(g \circ f)(x) = 2\left(\dfrac{1}{x}\right) + 3 = \dfrac{2}{x} + 3$

d. $(g \circ f)(4) = \dfrac{2}{4} + 3 = 3\dfrac{1}{2}$

14. $f(x) = \dfrac{2}{x}, g(x) = x^2 + 1$

    a. $(f \circ g)(x) = \dfrac{2}{x^2 + 1}$

    b. $(f \circ g)(4) = \dfrac{2}{4^2 + 1} = \dfrac{2}{17}$

    c. $(g \circ f)(x) = \left(\dfrac{2}{x}\right)^2 + 1 = \dfrac{4}{x^2} + 1$

    d. $(g \circ f)(4) = \dfrac{4}{4^2} + 1 = 1\dfrac{1}{4}$

15. $f(x) = 3x + 1, \ g(x) = \dfrac{3}{x}$

    a. $(f \circ g)(x) = 3\left(\dfrac{3}{x}\right) + 1 = \dfrac{9}{x} + 1$

    b. $(f \circ g)(4) = \dfrac{9}{4} + 1 = 3\dfrac{1}{4}$

    c. $(g \circ f)(x) = \dfrac{3}{3x + 1}$

    d. $(g \circ f)(4) = \dfrac{3}{3(4) + 1} = \dfrac{3}{13}$

16. $f(x) = x^2 - 5, \ g(x) = \dfrac{4}{x}$

    a. $(f \circ g)(x) = \left(\dfrac{4}{x}\right)^2 - 5 = \dfrac{16}{x^2} - 5$

    b. $(f \circ g)(4) = \dfrac{16}{(4)^2} - 5 = 1 - 5 = -4$

c. $(g \circ f)(x) = \dfrac{4}{x^2 - 5}$

d. $(g \circ f)(4) = \dfrac{4}{(4)^2 - 5} = \dfrac{4}{16 - 5} = \dfrac{4}{11}$

17. $f(x) = x^2 + 1, g(x) = x^2 + 5$

    a. $(f \circ g)(x) = (x^2 + 5)^2 + 1$
            $= x^4 + 10x^2 + 25 + 1$
            $= x^4 + 10x^2 + 26$

    b. $(f \circ g)(4) = 4^4 + 10(4)^2 + 26 = 442$

    c. $(g \circ f)(x) = (x^2 + 1)^2 + 5$
            $= x^4 + 2x^2 + 1 + 5$
            $= x^4 + 2x^2 + 6$

    d. $(g \circ f)(4) = 4^4 + 2(4)^2 + 6 = 294$

18. $f(x) = x^2 - 4, g(x) = x^2 + 3$

    a. $(f \circ g)(x) = (x^2 + 3)^2 - 4$
            $= x^4 + 6x^2 + 9 - 4$
            $= x^4 + 6x^2 + 5$

    b. $(f \circ g)(4) = 4^4 + 6(4)^2 + 5 = 357$

    c. $(g \circ f)(x) = (x^2 - 4)^2 + 3$
            $= x^4 - 8x^2 + 16 + 3$
            $= x^4 - 8x^2 + 19$

    d. $(g \circ f)(4) = 4^4 - 8(4)^2 + 19 = 147$

19. $f(x) = x - 4, \ g(x) = \sqrt{x + 5}, x \geq -5$

    a. $(f \circ g)(x) = \sqrt{x + 5} - 4$

    b. $(f \circ g)(4) = \sqrt{4 + 5} - 4$
            $= \sqrt{9} - 4$
            $= 3 - 4$
            $= -1$

c. $(g \circ f)(x) = \sqrt{(x-4)+5} = \sqrt{x+1}$

d. $(g \circ f)(4) = \sqrt{4+1} = \sqrt{5}$

20. $f(x) = \sqrt{x+6}$, $x \geq -6$, $g(x) = x + 7$

   a. $(f \circ g)(x) = \sqrt{(x+7)+6} = \sqrt{x+13}$

   b. $(f \circ g)(4) = \sqrt{4+13} = \sqrt{17}$

   c. $(g \circ f)(x) = \sqrt{x+6} + 7$

   d. $(g \circ f)(4) = \sqrt{4+6} + 7 = \sqrt{10} + 7$

21. This function is not a one-to-one function since it does not pass the horizontal line test.

22. This function is a one-to-one function since it passes the horizontal line test.

23. This function is a one-to-one function since it passes the horizontal line test.

24. This function is not a one-to-one function since it does not pass the horizontal line test.

25. Yes, the ordered pairs represent a one-to-one function. For each value of x there is a unique value for y and each y-value has a unique x-value.

26. Yes, the ordered pairs represent a one-to-one function. For each value of x there is a unique value for y and each y-value has a unique x-value.

27. No, the ordered pairs do not represent a one-to-one function. For each value of x there is a unique y, but for each y-value there is not a unique x since $(-4, 2)$ and $(0, 2)$ are ordered pairs in the given set.

28. No, the ordered pairs do not represent a one-to-one function. For each value of x there is a unique y, but for each y-value there is not a unique x since $(0, 5)$ and $(-3, 5)$ are ordered pairs in the given set.

29. $y = 2x + 5$ is a line with a slope of 2 and having a y-intercept of 5. It is a one-to-one function since it passes both the vertical line test and the horizontal line test.

30. $y = 3x - 8$ is a line with slope 3 and having a y-intercept of -8. It is a one-to-one function since it passes both the vertical line test and the horizontal line test.

31. $y = x^2 - 1$ is a parabola with vertex at $(0, -1)$. It is not a one-to-one function since it does not pass the horizontal line test. Horizontal lines above $y = -1$ intersect the graph at 2 different points.

32. $y = -x^2 + 3$ is a parabola with vertex at $(0, 3)$. It is not a one-to-one function since it does not pass the horizontal line test. Horizontal lines below $y = 3$ intersect the graph at 2 different points.

33. $y = x^2 - 2x + 5$ is a parabola with vertex at $(1, 4)$. It is not a one-to-one function since it does not pass the horizontal line test. Horizontal lines above $y = 4$ intersect the graph at two different points.

34. $y = x^2 - 2x + 6$, $x \geq 1$ is the right side of a parabola. It is a one-to-one function since it passes both the vertical line test and the horizontal line test.

35. $y = x^2 - 9$, $x \geq 0$ is the right side of a parabola. It is a one-to-one function since it passes both the vertical line test and the horizontal line test.

36. $y = x^2 - 9$, $x \leq 0$ is the left side of the parabola from Exercise 35. It is a one-to-one function since it passes both the vertical line test and the horizontal line test.

37. $y = \sqrt{x}$ is a one-to-one function since it passes both the vertical line test and the horizontal line test.

38. $y = -\sqrt{x}$ is a one-to-one function since it passes both the vertical line test and the horizontal line test.

39. $y = |x|$ is not a one-to-one function since it does not pass the vertical line test and the horizontal line test. Horizontal lines above $y = 0$ intersect the graph at two different points.

40. $y = -|x|$ is not a one-to-one function since it does not pass the vertical line test and the horizontal line test. Horizontal lines below $y = 0$ intersect the graph at two different points.

41. $y = \sqrt[3]{x}$ is a one-to-one function since it passes both the vertical line test and the horizontal line test.

42. $y = x^3$ is a one-to-one function since it passes both the vertical line test and the horizontal line test.

43. For $f(x)$: Domain: $\{-2, -1, 2, 4, 8\}$
Range: $\{0, 4, 6, 7, 9\}$
For $f^{-1}(x)$: Domain: $\{0, 4, 6, 7, 9\}$
Range: $\{-2, -1, 2, 4, 8\}$

44. For $f(x)$: Domain: $\{-4, -2, 2, 5, 6\}$
Range: $\left\{-3, 0, \dfrac{1}{2}, 2, 3\right\}$
For $f^{-1}(x)$: Domain: $\left\{-3, 0, \dfrac{1}{2}, 2, 3\right\}$
Range: $\{-4, -2, 2, 5, 6\}$

45. For $f(x)$: Domain: $\{-1, 1, 2, 4\}$
Range: $\{-3, -1, 0, 2\}$
For $f^{-1}(x)$: Domain: $\{-3, -1, 0, 2\}$
Range: $\{-1, 1, 2, 4\}$

46. For $f(x)$: Domain: $\{0, 1, 2, 4\}$
Range: $\{-2, 0, 1, 4\}$
For $f^{-1}(x)$: Domain: $\{-2, 0, 1, 4\}$
Range: $\{0, 1, 2, 4\}$

47. For $f(x)$: Domain: $\{x | x \geq 2\}$
Range: $\{y | y \geq 0\}$
For $f^{-1}(x)$: Domain: $\{x | x \geq 0\}$
Range: $\{y | y \geq 2\}$

48. For $f(x)$: Domain: $\mathbb{R}$
Range: $\mathbb{R}$
For $f^{-1}(x)$: Domain: $\mathbb{R}$
Range: $\mathbb{R}$

49. a. Yes, $f(x) = x - 2$ is a one-to-one function.

b.
$$y = x - 2$$
$$x = y - 2$$
$$x + 2 = y$$
$$y = x + 2$$
$$f^{-1}(x) = x + 2$$

50. a. Yes, $g(x) = x + 5$ is a one-to-one function.

b.
$$y = x + 5$$
$$x = y + 5$$
$$x - 5 = y$$
$$y = x - 5$$
$$g^{-1}(x) = x - 5$$

51. a. Yes, $h(x) = 4x$ is a one-to-one function.

b.
$$y = 4x$$
$$x = 4y$$
$$y = \frac{x}{4}$$
$$h^{-1}(x) = \frac{x}{4}$$

52. a. Yes, $k(x) = 2x - 7$ is a one-to-one function.

b.
$$y = 2x - 7$$
$$x = 2y - 7$$
$$x + 7 = 2y$$
$$\frac{x + 7}{2} = y$$
$$k^{-1}(x) = \frac{x + 7}{2}$$

53. a. No, $p(x) = 3x^2$ is not a one-to-one function.

b. Does not exist

54. a. No, $r(x) = |x|$ is not a one-to-one function

b. Does not exist

55. a. No; $t(x) = x^2 + 3$ is not a one-to-one function.

b. Does not exist

56. a. No; $m(x) = -x^2 + x + 8$ is not a one-to-one function.

    b. Does not exist

57. a. Yes; $g(x) = \dfrac{1}{x}$ is a one-to-one function.

    b.
$$y = \frac{1}{x}$$
$$x = \frac{1}{y}$$
$$y = \frac{1}{x}$$
$$g^{-1}(x) = \frac{1}{x}$$

58. a. Yes; $h(x) = \dfrac{5}{x}$ is a one-to-one function.

    b.
$$y = \frac{5}{x}$$
$$x = \frac{5}{y}$$
$$y = \frac{5}{x}$$
$$h^{-1}(x) = \frac{5}{x}$$

59. a. No; $f(x) = x^2 + 10$ is not a one-to-one function.

    b. Does not exist

60. a. Yes, $g(x) = x^3 + 9$ is a one-to-one function.

    b.
$$y = x^3 + 9$$
$$x = y^3 + 9$$
$$x - 9 = y^3$$
$$\sqrt[3]{x - 9} = y$$
$$g^{-1}(x) = \sqrt[3]{x - 9}$$

61. a. Yes, $g(x) = x^3 - 6$ is a one-to-one function.

    b.
$$y = x^3 - 6$$
$$x = y^3 - 6$$
$$x + 6 = y^3$$
$$\sqrt[3]{x + 6} = y$$
$$g^{-1}(x) = \sqrt[3]{x + 6}$$

62. a. Yes, $f(x) = \sqrt{x}, x \geq 0$ is a one-to-one function.

    b.
$$y = \sqrt{x}$$
$$x = \sqrt{y}$$
$$x^2 = y$$
$$f^{-1}(x) = x^2, x \geq 0$$

63. a. Yes, $g(x) = \sqrt{x + 2}$, $x \geq -2$ is a one-to-one function.

    b.
$$y = \sqrt{x + 2}$$
$$x = \sqrt{y + 2}$$
$$x^2 = y + 2$$
$$x^2 - 2 = y$$
$$g^{-1}(x) = x^2 - 2, x \geq 0$$

64. a. Yes, $f(x) = x^2 - 3$, $x \geq 0$ is one-to-one.

    b.
$$y = x^2 - 3$$
$$x = y^2 - 3$$
$$x + 3 = y^2$$
$$y = \sqrt{x + 3}$$
$$f^{-1}(x) = \sqrt{x + 3}, x \geq -3$$

65. a. Yes, $h(x) = x^2 - 4, x \geq 0$ is one-to-one.

    b.
$$y = x^2 - 4$$
$$x = y^2 - 4$$
$$x + 4 = y^2$$
$$y = \sqrt{x + 4}$$
$$h^{-1}(x) = \sqrt{x + 4}, x \geq -4$$

66. a. No, $h(x) = |x|$ is not a one-to-one function

   b. Does not exist

67. $f(x) = 2x + 8$

   a. $y = 2x + 8$
   $$x = 2y + 8$$
   $$x - 8 = 2y$$
   $$\frac{x-8}{2} = y$$
   $$f^{-1}(x) = \frac{x-8}{2}$$

   b.

x	$f(x)$
0	8
−4	0

x	$f^{-1}(x)$
0	−4
8	0

68. $f(x) = -3x + 6$

   a. $y = -3x + 6$
   $$x = -3y + 6$$
   $$x - 6 = -3y$$
   $$\frac{x-6}{-3} = y$$
   $$-\frac{1}{3}x + 2 = y$$
   $$f^{-1}(x) = -\frac{1}{3}x + 2$$

   b.

x	$f(x)$
0	6
2	0

x	$f^{-1}(x)$
6	0
0	2

69. $f(x) = \sqrt{x}$, $x \geq 0$

   a. $y = \sqrt{x}$
   $$x = \sqrt{y}$$
   $$x^2 = \left(\sqrt{y}\right)^2$$
   $$x^2 = y$$
   $$f^{-1}(x) = x^2 \text{ for } x \geq 0$$

   b.

x	$f(x)$
0	0
1	1
4	2

x	$f^{-1}(x)$
0	0
1	1
2	4

70. $f(x) = -\sqrt{x}$, $x \geq 0$

   a. $y = -\sqrt{x}$
   $$x = -\sqrt{y}$$
   $$x^2 = \left(-\sqrt{y}\right)^2$$
   $$x^2 = y$$
   $$f^{-1}(x) = x^2 \text{ for } x \leq 0$$

   b.

x	$f(x)$
0	0
1	−1
4	−2

x	$f^{-1}(x)$
0	0
−1	1
−2	4

71. $f(x) = \sqrt{x-1}, x \geq 1$

   a. $y = \sqrt{x-1}$

              $x = \sqrt{y-1}$

              $x^2 = \left(\sqrt{y-1}\right)^2$

              $x^2 = y - 1$

            $x^2 + 1 = y$

        $f^{-1}(x) = x^2 + 1$ for $x \geq 0$

   b.

x	$f(x)$
1	0
2	1
5	2

x	$f^{-1}(x)$
0	1
1	2
2	5

72. $f(x) = \sqrt{x+4}, x \geq -4$

   a. $y = \sqrt{x+4}$

              $x = \sqrt{y+4}$

             $x^2 = \left(\sqrt{y+4}\right)^2$

             $x^2 = y + 4$

           $x^2 - 4 = y$

        $f^{-1}(x) = x^2 - 4$ for $x \geq 0$

   b.

x	$f(x)$
-4	0
-3	1
0	2

x	$f^{-1}(x)$
0	-4
1	-3
2	0

73. $f(x) = \sqrt[3]{x}$

   a. $y = \sqrt[3]{x}$

          $x = \sqrt[3]{y}$

         $x^3 = \left(\sqrt[3]{y}\right)^3$

         $x^3 = y$

       $f^{-1}(x) = x^3$

   b.

x	$f(x)$
-8	-2
-1	-1
0	0
1	1
8	2

x	$f^{-1}(x)$
-2	-8
-1	-1
0	0
1	1
2	8

74. $f(x) = \sqrt[3]{x+3}$

   a. $y = \sqrt[3]{x+3}$

            $x = \sqrt[3]{y+3}$

           $x^3 = \left(\sqrt[3]{y+3}\right)^3$

           $x^3 = y + 3$

        $x^3 - 3 = y$

       $f^{-1}(x) = x^3 - 3$

b.

x	$f(x)$
-11	-2
-4	-1
-3	0
-2	1
5	2

x	$f^{-1}(x)$
-2	-11
-1	-4
0	-3
1	-2
2	5

75. $f(x) = \dfrac{1}{x}, x > 0$

a. $y = \dfrac{1}{x}$

$x = \dfrac{1}{y}$

$xy = 1$

$y = \dfrac{1}{x}$

$f^{-1}(x) = \dfrac{1}{x}, x > 0$

b.

x	$f(x)$
$\dfrac{1}{2}$	2
1	1
3	$\dfrac{1}{3}$

x	$f^{-1}(x)$
2	$\dfrac{1}{2}$
1	1
$\dfrac{1}{3}$	3

76. $f(x) = \dfrac{1}{x}$

a. $y = \dfrac{1}{x}$

$xy = 1$

$y = \dfrac{1}{x}$

$f^{-1}(x) = \dfrac{1}{x}$

b.

77. $(f \circ f^{-1})(x) = (x+8) - 8 = x$

$(f^{-1} \circ f)(x) = (x-8) + 8 = x$

78. $(f \circ f^{-1})(x) = 7\left(\dfrac{x-3}{7}\right) + 3$

$= x - 3 + 3$

$= x$

$(f^{-1} \circ f)(x) = \dfrac{(7x+3)-3}{7} = \dfrac{7x}{7} = x$

79. $(f \circ f^{-1})(x) = \dfrac{1}{2}(2x-6) + 3$

$= x - 3 + 3$

$= x$

$(f^{-1} \circ f)(x) = 2\left(\dfrac{1}{2}x + 3\right) - 6$

$= x + 6 - 6$

$= x$

80. $(f \circ f^{-1})(x) = -\dfrac{1}{3}(-3x+6)+2$

$\qquad = x - 2 + 2$

$\qquad = x$

$(f^{-1} \circ f)(x) = -3\left(-\dfrac{1}{3}x+2\right)+6$

$\qquad = x - 6 + 6$

$\qquad = x$

81. $(f \circ f^{-1})(x) = \sqrt[3]{(x^3+2)-2}$

$\qquad = \sqrt[3]{x^3}$

$\qquad = x$

$(f^{-1} \circ f)(x) = \left(\sqrt[3]{x-2}\right)^3 + 2$

$\qquad = x - 2 + 2$

$\qquad = x$

82. $(f \circ f^{-1})(x) = \sqrt[3]{(x^3-9)+9}$

$\qquad = \sqrt[3]{x^3}$

$\qquad = x$

$(f^{-1} \circ f)(x) = \left(\sqrt[3]{x+9}\right)^3 - 9$

$\qquad = x + 9 - 9$

$\qquad = x$

83. $(f \circ f^{-1})(x) = \dfrac{3}{\frac{3}{x}} = 3 \cdot \dfrac{x}{3} = x$

$(f^{-1} \circ f)(x) = \dfrac{3}{\frac{3}{x}} = 3 \cdot \dfrac{x}{3} = x$

84. $(f \circ f^{-1})(x) = \sqrt{(x^2-5)+5} = \sqrt{x^2} = x$

$(f^{-1} \circ f)(x) = \left(\sqrt{x+5}\right)^2 - 5 = x+5-5 = x$

85. No, composition of functions is not commutative.

Let $f(x) = x^2$ and $g(x) = x+1$.

Then $(f \circ g)(x) = (x+1)^2 = x^2 + 2x + 1$ while

$(g \circ f)(x) = x^2 + 1$.

86. a. $(f \circ g)(x) = \sqrt{(x^2-5)+5}$

$\qquad = \sqrt{x^2}$

$\qquad = x$

$(g \circ f)(x) = \left(\sqrt{x+5}\right)^2 - 5$

$\qquad = x + 5 - 5$

$\qquad = x$

b. Since values of $x < 0$ are not in the domain of $g(x)$, values of $x < 0$ are not in the domain of $(f \circ g)(x)$.

87. a. $(f \circ g)(x) = f[g(x)]$

$\qquad = \left(\sqrt[3]{x-2}\right)^3 + 2$

$\qquad = x - 2 + 2$

$\qquad = x$

$(g \circ f)(x) = g[f(x)]$

$\qquad = \sqrt[3]{\left(x^3+2\right)-2}$

$\qquad = \sqrt[3]{x^3}$

$\qquad = x$

b. The domain of f is all real numbers and the domain of g is all real numbers. The domains of $(f \circ g)(x)$ and $(g \circ f)(x)$ are also all real numbers.

88. The range of $f^{-1}(x)$ is the domain of $f(x)$.

89. The range of $f^{-1}(x)$ is the domain of $f(x)$.

90. $f(x) = 12x$ where x is feet and y is inches.

$y = 12x$

$x = 12y$

$\dfrac{x}{12} = y$

$f^{-1}(x) = \dfrac{x}{12}$

Here x is inches and $f^{-1}(x)$ is feet. The inverse function converts inches to feet.

91. $f(x) = 3x$ converts yards, x, into feet, y.

$$y = 3x$$

$$x = 3y$$

$$\frac{x}{3} = y$$

$$f^{-1}(x) = \frac{x}{3}$$

Here, x is feet and $f^{-1}(x)$ is yards. The inverse function converts feet to yards.

92. $f(x) = \frac{22}{15}x$ where x is miles per hour and y is feet per second.

$$y = \frac{22}{15}x$$

$$x = \frac{22}{15}y$$

$$\frac{15}{22}x = y$$

$$f^{-1}(x) = \frac{15}{22}x$$

Here, x is feet per second and $f^{-1}(x)$ is miles per hour. The inverse function converts feet per second to miles per hour.

93. $f(x) = \frac{5}{9}(x - 32)$ where x is degrees Fahrenheit and $f(x)$ is degrees Celsius.

$$y = \frac{5}{9}(x - 32)$$

$$x = \frac{5}{9}(y - 32)$$

$$\frac{9}{5}x = \frac{9}{5}\left[\frac{5}{9}(y - 32)\right]$$

$$\frac{9}{5}x = y - 32$$

$$\frac{9}{5}x + 32 = y$$

$$f^{-1}(x) = \frac{9}{5}x + 32$$

Here, x is degrees Celsius and $f^{-1}(x)$ is degrees Fahrenheit. The inverse function converts Celsius to Fahrenheit.

94. a. $f(x) = |x|$ does not have an inverse function since it does not pass the horizontal line test. Horizontal lines above $y = 0$ intersect the graph in two points. Thus, it is not a one-to-one function.

b. Yes, if $x \geq 0$ then $f(x) = |x|$ becomes $f(x) = x$ and it has an inverse since this function is one-to-one.

c. $f(x) = x, x \geq 0$

$$y = x$$

$$x = y$$

$$f^{-1}(x) = x, x \geq 0$$

95. $f(x) = 16x$; $g(x) = 28.35x$

$(f \circ g)(x) = 16(28.35x) = 453.6x$

In this composition, x represents pounds and $(f \circ g)(x)$ represents grams. The composition converts pounds to grams.

96. $f(x) = 2000x$; $g(x) = 16x$

$(f \circ g)(x) = 2000(16x) = 32,000x$

In this composition, x represents tons and $(f \circ g)(x)$ represents ounces. The composition converts tons to ounces.

97. $f(x) = 3x$; $g(x) = 0.305x$

$(f \circ g)(x) = 3(0.305x) = 0.915x$

In this composition, x represents yards and $(f \circ g)(x)$ represents meters. The composition converts yards to meters.

98. $f(x) = 1760x$; $g(x) = 0.915x$

$(f \circ g)(x) = 1760(0.915x) = 1610.4x$

In this composition, x represents miles and $(f \circ g)(x)$ represents meters. The composition converts miles to meters.

99.

-4.7, 4.7, 1, -3.1, 3.1, 1

Yes, the functions are inverses.

100.

-4.7, 4.7, 1, -3.1, 3.1, 1

No, the functions are not inverses.

101.

-28.2, 28.2, 4, -18.6, 18.6, 4

Yes, the functions are inverses.

102.

-14.1, 14.1, 2, -9.3, 9.3, 1

Yes, the functions are inverses.

103. a. $r(3) = 2(3) = 6$
The radius is 6 feet.

   b. $A = \pi r^2$
$A = \pi(6)^2$
$A = 36\pi \approx 113.10$
The surface area is $36\pi \approx 113.10$ square feet.

   c. $(A \circ r)(t) = \pi(2t)^2 = \pi(4t^2) = 4\pi t^2$

   d. $4\pi(3)^2 = 4\pi(9) = 36\pi$

   e. The answers should agree.

104. a. $r(2) = 1.2(2) = 2.4$
The radius is 2.4 inches

   b. $S(r) = 4\pi r^2$
$S(2.4) = 4\pi(2.4)^2$
$= 4\pi(5.76)$
$= 23.04\pi$
≈ 72.38
The surface area is $23.04\pi \approx 72.38$ square inches.

   c. $(S \circ r)(t) = 4\pi(1.2t)^2$
$= 4\pi(1.44t^2)$
$= 5.76\pi t^2$

   d. $(S \circ r)(2) = 5.76\pi(2)^2 = 23.04\pi \approx 72.38$
The surface area is about 72.38 square inches.

   e. The answers should agree.

105. a. $f(x) = 2^x$

x	$f(x) = 2^x$
-2	$f(-2) = 2^{-2} = \dfrac{1}{2^2} = \dfrac{1}{4}$
-1	$f(-1) = 2^{-1} = \dfrac{1}{2}$
0	$f(0) = 2^0 = 1$
1	$f(1) = 2^1 = 2$
2	$f(2) = 2^2 = 4$

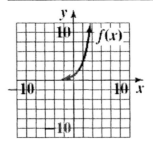

   b. The graph indicates the function is one-to-one. Therefore, it should have an inverse.

c.

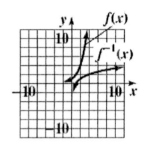

d. Answers will vary. Since the domain of f is the range of f^{-1} and the range of f is the domain of f^{-1}, we could obtain points on the graph of f^{-1} by switching the coordinates of the points we found when graphing f.

Point on graph of f		Point on graph of f^{-1}
$\left(-2,\dfrac{1}{4}\right)$		$\left(\dfrac{1}{4},-2\right)$
$\left(-1,\dfrac{1}{2}\right)$	$\rightarrow$	$\left(\dfrac{1}{2},-1\right)$
$(0,1)$		$(1,0)$
$(1,2)$		$(2,1)$
$(2,4)$		$(4,2)$

106. First find the slope of the given line.
$2x+3y-9=0$

$3y=-2x+9$

$y=-\dfrac{2}{3}x+3 \;\Rightarrow\; m=-\dfrac{2}{3}$

Now use this slope together with the given point $\left(\dfrac{1}{2},3\right)$ to find the equation.

point-slope form:

$y-y_1 = m\left(x-x_1\right)$

$y-3=-\dfrac{2}{3}\left(x-\dfrac{1}{2}\right)$

$y-3=-\dfrac{2}{3}x+\dfrac{1}{3}$

$3\left(y-3=-\dfrac{2}{3}x+\dfrac{1}{3}\right)$

$3y-9=-2x+1$

$2x+3y=10$

107. $x+2=x-(-2) \rightarrow c=-2$

$$
\begin{array}{r|rrrr}
-2 & 1 & 6 & 6 & -8 \\
 & & -2 & -8 & 4 \\
\hline
 & 1 & 4 & -2 & -4
\end{array}
$$

$\dfrac{x^3+6x^2+6x-8}{x+2}=x^2+4x-2-\dfrac{4}{x+2}$

108. $\dfrac{\dfrac{3}{x^2}-\dfrac{2}{x}}{\dfrac{x}{6}}=\dfrac{6x^2\left(\dfrac{3}{x^2}-\dfrac{2}{x}\right)}{6x^2\left(\dfrac{x}{6}\right)}=\dfrac{18-12x}{x^3}$

109. $\sqrt{\dfrac{24x^3y^2}{3xy^3}}=\sqrt{\dfrac{8x^2y}{y^2}}=\dfrac{\sqrt{8x^2y}}{\sqrt{y^2}}$

$=\dfrac{\sqrt{4x^2\cdot 2y}}{\sqrt{y^2}}=\dfrac{2x\sqrt{2y}}{y}$

110. $x^2+2x-6=0$

$x^2+2x=6$

$x^2+2x+1=6+1$

$(x+1)^2=7$

$x+1=\pm\sqrt{7}$

$x=-1\pm\sqrt{7}$

Exercise Set 13.2

1. Exponential functions are functions of the form $f(x) = a^x, a > 0, a \neq 1$.

2. **a.** $y = 2^x$; as x increases, y increases.

   b. No, y can never be zero because 2^x can never be 0.

   c. No, y can never be negative because 2^x is never negative.

3. **a.** $y = \left(\dfrac{1}{2}\right)^x$; as x increases, y decreases.

   b. No, y can never be zero because $\left(\dfrac{1}{2}\right)^x$ can never be 0.

   c. No, y can never be negative because $\left(\dfrac{1}{2}\right)^x$ is never negative.

4. $y = 2^{-x}$ or $y = 2^{-x}$

   $y = 2^{-1(x)}$ $y = (2^x)^{-1}$

   $y = \left(\frac{1}{2}\right)^x$ or $y = \dfrac{1}{2^x}$

5. $y = 2^x$ and $y = 3^x$

   a. Let $x = 0$
   $y = 2^0 \quad y = 3^0$
   $y = 1 \quad y = 1$
   They have the same y-intercept at $(0, 1)$.

   b. $y = 3^x$ will be steeper than $y = 2^x$ for $x > 0$ because it has a larger base.

6. $y = \left(\dfrac{1}{2}\right)^x$ and $y = \left(\dfrac{1}{3}\right)^x$

   a. Let $x = 0$
   $$y = \left(\frac{1}{2}\right)^0 \quad y = \left(\frac{1}{3}\right)^0$$
   $y = 1 \qquad y = 1$
   They have the same y-intercept at $(0, 1)$.

   b. $y = \left(\dfrac{1}{3}\right)^x$ will be steeper than $y = \left(\dfrac{1}{2}\right)^x$ for $x < 0$ because it has a larger base.

7. $y = 2^x$

x	-2	-1	0	1	2
y	$\frac{1}{4}$	$\frac{1}{2}$	1	2	4

   Domain: $\mathbb{R}$; Range: $\{y \mid y > 0\}$

8. $y = 3^x$

x	-2	-1	0	1	2
y	$\frac{1}{9}$	$\frac{1}{3}$	1	3	9

   Domain: $\mathbb{R}$; Range: $\{y \mid y > 0\}$

9. $y = \left(\dfrac{1}{2}\right)^x$

x	-2	-1	0	1	2
y	4	2	1	$\frac{1}{2}$	$\frac{1}{4}$

Domain: $\mathbb{R}$; Range: $\left\{y \mid y > 0\right\}$

10. $y = \left(\dfrac{1}{3}\right)^x$

x	-2	-1	0	1	2
y	9	3	1	$\frac{1}{3}$	$\frac{1}{9}$

Domain: $\mathbb{R}$; Range: $\left\{y \mid y > 0\right\}$

11. $y = 4^x$

x	-2	-1	0	1	2
y	$\frac{1}{16}$	$\frac{1}{4}$	1	4	16

Domain: $\mathbb{R}$; Range: $\left\{y \mid y > 0\right\}$

12. $y = 5^x$

x	-2	-1	0	1	2
y	$\frac{1}{25}$	$\frac{1}{5}$	1	5	25

Domain: $\mathbb{R}$; Range: $\left\{y \mid y > 0\right\}$

13. $y = \left(\dfrac{1}{4}\right)^x$

x	-2	-1	0	1	2
y	16	4	1	$\frac{1}{4}$	$\frac{1}{16}$

Domain: $\mathbb{R}$; Range: $\left\{y \mid y > 0\right\}$

14. $y = \left(\dfrac{1}{5}\right)^x$

x	-2	-1	0	1	2
y	25	5	1	$\frac{1}{5}$	$\frac{1}{25}$

Domain: $\mathbb{R}$; Range: $\left\{y \mid y > 0\right\}$

15. $y = 3^{-x} = \dfrac{1}{3^x} = \left(\dfrac{1}{3}\right)^x$

x	-2	-1	0	1	2
y	9	3	1	$\frac{1}{3}$	$\frac{1}{9}$

Domain: $\mathbb{R}$; Range: $\{y \mid y > 0\}$

18. $y = \left(\dfrac{1}{4}\right)^{-x} = 4^x$

x	-2	-1	0	1	2
y	$\frac{1}{16}$	$\frac{1}{4}$	1	4	16

Domain: $\mathbb{R}$; Range: $\{y \mid y > 0\}$

16. $y = 4^{-x} = \dfrac{1}{4^x} = \left(\dfrac{1}{4}\right)^x$

x	-2	-1	0	1	2
y	16	4	1	$\frac{1}{4}$	$\frac{1}{16}$

Domain: $\mathbb{R}$; Range: $\{y \mid y > 0\}$

19. $y = 2^{x-1}$

x	-2	0	2	4	6
y	$\frac{1}{8}$	$\frac{1}{2}$	2	8	32

Domain: $\mathbb{R}$; Range: $\{y \mid y > 0\}$

17. $y = \left(\dfrac{1}{3}\right)^{-x} = 3^x$

x	-2	-1	0	1	2
y	$\frac{1}{9}$	$\frac{1}{3}$	1	3	9

Domain: $\mathbb{R}$; Range: $\{y \mid y > 0\}$

20. $y = 2^{x+1}$

x	-4	-2	0	2	4
y	$\frac{1}{8}$	$\frac{1}{2}$	2	8	32

Domain: $\mathbb{R}$; Range: $\{y \mid y > 0\}$

843

21. $y = \left(\dfrac{1}{3}\right)^{x+1}$

x	-3	-2	-1	0	1
y	9	3	1	$\frac{1}{3}$	$\frac{1}{9}$

Domain: $\mathbb{R}$; Range: $\left\{y \mid y > 0\right\}$

22. $y = \left(\dfrac{1}{3}\right)^{x-1}$

x	-1	0	1	2	3
y	9	3	1	$\frac{1}{3}$	$\frac{1}{9}$

Domain: $\mathbb{R}$; Range: $\left\{y \mid y > 0\right\}$

23. $y = 2^x + 1$

x	-2	-1	0	1	2	3
y	$\frac{5}{4}$	$\frac{3}{2}$	2	3	5	9

Domain: $\mathbb{R}$; Range: $\left\{y \mid y > 1\right\}$

24. $y = 2^x - 1$

x	-2	-1	0	1	2	3
y	$-\frac{3}{4}$	$-\frac{1}{2}$	0	1	3	7

Domain: $\mathbb{R}$; Range: $\left\{y \mid y > -1\right\}$

25. $y = 3^x - 1$

x	-2	-1	0	1	2
y	$-\frac{8}{9}$	$-\frac{2}{3}$	0	2	8

Domain: $\mathbb{R}$; Range: $\left\{y \mid y > -1\right\}$

26. $y = 3^x + 2$

x	-2	-1	0	1	2
y	$\frac{19}{9}$	$\frac{7}{3}$	3	5	11

Domain: $\mathbb{R}$; Range: $\left\{y \mid y > 2\right\}$

844

27. **a.** The graph is the horizontal line through $y = 1$.

    b. Yes. A horizontal line will pass the vertical line test.

    c. No. $f(x)$ is not one-to-one and therefore does not have an inverse function.

28. The graph of $y = a^x + k$ will have the same basic shape as the graph of $y = a^x$. However, the graph of $y = a^x + k$ will be k units higher than that of $y = a^x$.

29. The graph of $y = a^x - k$ will have the same basic shape as the graph of $y = a^x$. However, the graph of $y = a^x - k$ will be k units lower than that of $y = a^x$.

30. The graph of $y = a^{x+1}$ is the graph of $y = a^x$ shifted 1 unit to the left.

31. The graph of $y = a^{x+2}$ is the graph of $y = a^x$ shifted 2 units to the left.

32. **a.** No, $y = x^{\pi}$ is not an exponential function since there is no variable in the exponent.

    b. Yes, $y = \pi^x$ is an exponential function since the variable is in the exponent.

33. **a.** For 2060 we have $t = 2060 - 1960 = 100$.
    $$f(100) = 0.592(1.042)^{100} \approx 36.232$$
    The function estimates that in 2060 there will be 36.232 million people in the U.S. aged 85 or older.

    b. For 2100 we have $t = 2100 - 1960 = 140$.
    $$f(140) = 0.592(1.042)^{140} \approx 187.846$$
    The function estimates that in 2100 there will be 187.846 million people in the U.S. aged 85 or older.

34. **a.** For 2010 we have $t = 2010 - 1650 = 360$.
    $$f(360) = \frac{1}{2}(2.718)^{0.0072(360)} \approx 6.68$$
    The function estimates that in 2010 the world population will be about 6.68 billion.

    b. For 2015 we have $t = 2015 - 1650 = 365$.
    $$f(365) = \frac{1}{2}(2.718)^{0.0072(365)} \approx 6.92$$
    The function estimates that in 2015 the world population will be about 6.92 billion.

35. The amount each day is given by the function $A(d) = 2^d$ where d is the number of days.
    $$A(9) = 2^9 = 512$$
    After 9 days, the amount would be $512.

36. The amount each day is given by the function $A(d) = 2^d$ where d is the number of days.
    $$A(12) = 2^{12} = 4096$$
    After 12 days, the amount would be $4096.

37. **a.** About 14 years

    b. About 10 years

    c. From the graph, the difference is about $25. Using the formulas given, we get:
    $$A = 100(1.07)^{10} = 196.72 \text{ (exponential)}$$
    $$A = 100 + 100(.07)(10) = 170 \text{ (linear)}$$
    The difference is $26.72.

    d. For daily compounding we would get
    $$A = 100\left(1 + \frac{0.07}{365}\right)^{(365\cdot10)} = 201.36$$
    This is about a $5 increase over compounding annually. Daily compounding increases the amount.

38. **a.** For 2007 we have $t = 2007 - 2001 = 6$.
    $$f(6) = 1.841(1.045)^6 \approx 2.397$$
    The function estimates that the outstanding consumer credit will be about $2.397 trillion in 2007.

    b. For 2011 we have $t = 2011 - 2001 = 10$.
    $$f(10) = 1.841(1.045)^{10} \approx 2.859$$
    The function estimates that the outstanding consumer credit will be about $2.859 trillion in 2011.

39. $N(t) = 5(3)^t, t = 2$

$N(2) = 5(3)^2 = 5 \cdot 9 = 45$

There will be 45 bacteria in the petri dish after two days.

40. $N(t) = 5(3)^t, t = 6$

$N(6) = 5(3)^6 = 5 \cdot 729 = 3,645$

There will be 3,645 bacteria in the petri dish after six days.

41. $A = p\left(1 + \dfrac{r}{n}\right)^{nt}$.

Use $p = 5000$,

$r = 6\% = 0.06$ and $n = 4$ and $t = 4$.

$A = 5000\left(1 + \dfrac{0.06}{4}\right)^{4 \cdot 4}$

$A = 5000(1 + 0.015)^{16}$

$A = 5000(1.015)^{16}$

$A \approx 5000(1.2689855)$

$A \approx 6344.93$

He has \$6344.93 after 4 years.

42. $A = p\left(1 + \dfrac{r}{n}\right)^{nt}$

Use $p = 8000$, $r = 4\% = 0.08$, $n = 4$, and $t = 5$.

$A = 8000\left(1 + \dfrac{0.04}{4}\right)^{4 \cdot 5}$

$A = 8000(1 + 0.01)^{20}$

$A = 8000(1.01)^{20}$

$A \approx 8000(1.22019)$

$A \approx 9761.52$

He has \$9761.52 after 5 years.

43. $A = A_0 2^{-t/5600}$

Use $A_0 = 12$ and $t = 1000$.

$A = 12(2^{-1000/5600})$

$A \approx 12(2^{-0.18})$

$A \approx 12(0.88)$

$A \approx 10.6$ grams

There are about 10.6 grams left.

44. $A = A_0 \cdot 2^{-t/5600}$

Use $A_0 = 60$ and $t = 10,000$.

$A = 60(2^{-10,000/5600})$

$A \approx 60(2^{-1.8})$

$A \approx 60(0.29)$

$A \approx 17.4$

There will be about 17.4 grams left.

45. $y = 80(2)^{-0.4t}$

a. $t = 10$

$y = 80(2)^{-0.4(10)}$

$y = 80(2)^{-4} = 80\left(\dfrac{1}{16}\right) = 5$

After 10 years, 5 grams remain.

b. $t = 100$

$y = 80(2)^{-0.4(100)}$

$y = 80(2)^{-40}$

$y \approx 80(9.094947 \times 10^{-13})$

$y \approx 7.28 \times 10^{-11}$

After 100 years, about 7.28×10^{-11} grams are left.

46. $y = 20(3)^{-0.6t}, t = 4$

$y = 20(3)^{-0.6(4)}$

$y = 20(3)^{-2.4} \approx 1.432$

After 4 years, about 1.432 grams remain.

47. $y = 2000(1.2)^{0.1t}$

a. $t = 10$

$y = 2000(1.2)^{0.1(10)}$

$y = 2000(1.2)^1$

$y = 2400$

In 10 years, the population is expected to be 2400.

b. $t = 50$

$y = 2000(1.2)^{0.1(50)}$

$y = 2000(1.2)^5$

$y = 2000(2.48832)$

$y \approx 4977$

In 50 years, the population is expected to be about 4,977.

48. $y = 6800(1.4)^{-0.2t}$, $t = 30$

$y = 6800(1.4)^{-0.3(20)}$

$y = 6800(1.4)^{-6} \approx 903.11$

After 30 years, the population will be about 903.

49. $V(t) = 24,000(0.82)^t$, $t = 4$

$V(t) = 24,000(0.82)^4 \approx 10,850.92$

The SUV will be worth about $10,850.92 in 4 years.

50. $V(t) = 6200(0.85)^t$, $t = 10$

$V(t) = 6200(0.85)^{10} \approx 1220.62$

The ATV will be worth about $1220.62 in 10 years.

51. a. Answers will vary. One possible answer is: Since the amount is reduced by 5%, the consumption is 95% of the previous year, or 0.95. Thus, $A(t) = 580,000(0.95)^t$.

b. $t = 2009 - 2005 = 4$

$A(4) = 580,000(0.95)^4$

$\approx 472,414$

The expected average use in 2009 is about 472,414 gallons.

52. a. Answers will vary. One possible answer is:

Since $\frac{2}{3}$ are being recycled, then the previous year's amount is multiplied by $\frac{2}{3}$.

b. $n = 2011 - 2004 = 7$

$A(7) = 190,000,000\left(\frac{2}{3}\right)^7$

$= 190,000,000\left(\frac{128}{2187}\right)$

≈ 11.1

In 2011, about 11.1 million cans are expected to be made from recycled 2004 cans.

53. $A = 41.97(0.996)^x$

$A(389) = 41.97(0.996)^{389}$

$A \approx 8.83$

The altitude at the top of Mt. Everest is about 8.83 kilometers.

54. a. $f(t) = 71.24(1.045)^t$

$t = 2060 - 1995 = 65$

$f(t) = 71.24(1.045)^{65}$

≈ 1245.325

There will be about 1,245,325 centenarians in the year 2060.

b. $f(t) = 71.24(1.045)^t$

$t = 2070 - 1995 = 75$

$f(t) = 71.24(1.045)^{75}$

≈ 1933.952

There will be about 1,933,952 centenarians in the year 2070.

55. a. $A = p\left(1 + \dfrac{r}{n}\right)^{nt}$

$A = 100\left(1 + \dfrac{0.07}{365}\right)^{365 \cdot 10}$

$A \approx 100(1.0001918)^{3650}$

$A = 201.36$

The amount is $201.36.

b. For simple interest,

$A = 100 + 100(0.07)t$

$A = 100 + 100(0.07)(10)$

$A = 100 + 70$

$A = 170$

$201.36 - $170 = $31.36

56. $y_1 = 2x$ and $y_2 = 3^x$

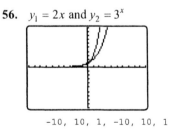

-10, 10, 1, -10, 10, 1

847

57. a. $y_1 = 3^{x-5}$

-10, 10, 1, -10, 10, 1

b. $4 = 3^{x-5}$ when $x \approx 6.26$.

58. a. $y_1 = \left(\dfrac{1}{2}\right)^{2x+3}$

-10, 10, 1, -10, 10, 1

b. Since $\left(\dfrac{1}{2}\right)^{2x+3} > 0$ for all x, there is no

x-value for which $-3 = \left(\dfrac{1}{2}\right)^{2x+3}$.

59. a. Day 15: $2^{15-1} = 2^{14} = \$16,384$

b. Day 20: $2^{20-1} = 2^{19} = \$524,288$

c. nth Day: 2^{n-1}

d. Day 30: $2^{30-1} = \$2^{29} = \$536,870,912$

e. $2^0 + 2^1 + 2^2 + \cdots + 2^{29}$

60. a. Answers will vary.

b. Answers will vary.

c. Answers will vary.

61. a. $2.3x^4 y - 6.2x^6 y^2 + 9.2x^5 y^2$
$= -6.2x^6 y^2 + 9.2x^5 y^2 + 2.3x^4 y$

b. $-6.2x^6 y^2$ is the leading term.
$6 + 2 = 8$ is the degree of the polynomial.

c. $-6.2x^6 y^2$ is the leading term, so -6.2 is the leading coefficient.

62. $(f \cdot g)(x) = f(x) \cdot g(x)$
$= (x+5)(x^2 - 2x + 4)$
$= x^3 - 2x^2 + 4x + 5x^2 - 10x + 20$
$= x^3 + 3x^2 - 6x + 20$

63. $\sqrt{a^2 - 8a + 16} = \sqrt{(a-4)^2} = |a - 4|$

64. $\sqrt[4]{\dfrac{32x^5 y^9}{2y^3 z}} = \sqrt[4]{\dfrac{16x^5 y^6}{z}}$

$= \dfrac{\sqrt[4]{16x^5 y^6}}{\sqrt[4]{z}}$

$= \dfrac{\sqrt[4]{16x^4 y^4 \cdot xy^2}}{\sqrt[4]{z}}$

$= \dfrac{2xy \sqrt[4]{xy^2}}{\sqrt[4]{z}} \cdot \dfrac{\sqrt[4]{z^3}}{\sqrt[4]{z^3}}$

$= \dfrac{2xy \sqrt[4]{xy^2 z^3}}{\sqrt[4]{z^4}}$

$= \dfrac{2xy \sqrt[4]{xy^2 z^3}}{z}$

Exercise Set 13.3

1. $y = \log_a x$

a. The base a must be positive and must not be equal to one.

b. The argument x represents a number that is greater than 0. Thus, the domain is $\{x \mid x > 0\}$.

c. $\mathbb{R}$

2. $y = \log_a x \Leftrightarrow a^y = x$

3. The functions $f(x) = a^x$ and $g(x) = \log_a x$ are inverse functions. Therefore, some of the points on the function are $g(x) = \log_a x$ are

$\left(\dfrac{1}{27}, -3\right)\left(\dfrac{1}{9}, -2\right), \left(\dfrac{1}{3}, -1\right)(1, 0), (3, 1), (9, 2),$

and $(27, 3)$. These points were obtained by switching the coordinates of the given points for the graph of $f(x) = a^x$.

4. For the logarithmic function $y = \log_a(x-3)$, the argument, $x-3$, represents a number greater than 0, therefore, x must be greater than 3.

5. The functions $y = a^x$ and $y = \log_a x$ for $a \neq 1$ are inverses of each other, thus the graphs are symmetric with respect to the line $y = x$. For each ordered pair (x, y) on the graph of $y = a^x$, the ordered pair (y, x) is on the graph of $y = \log_a x$.

6. $y = \log_a x$ or $a^y = x$
Set $y = 0$ and solve for y.
$a^0 = x$
$1 = x$
The x-intercept is $(1, 0)$.

7. $y = \log_2 x$
Convert to exponential form.
$2^y = x$

x	$\frac{1}{4}$	$\frac{1}{2}$	1	2	4
y	-2	-1	0	1	2

Domain: $\left\{x \mid x > 0\right\}$
Range: $\mathbb{R}$

8. $y = \log_3 x$
Convert to exponential form.
$x = 3^y$

x	$\frac{1}{9}$	$\frac{1}{3}$	1	3	9
y	-2	-1	0	1	2

Domain: $\{x \mid x > 0\}$
Range: $\mathbb{R}$

9. $y = \log_{1/2} x$
Convert to exponential form.

$x = \left(\dfrac{1}{2}\right)^y$

x	4	2	1	$\frac{1}{2}$	$\frac{1}{4}$
y	-2	-1	0	1	2

Domain: $\{x \mid x > 0\}$
Range: $\mathbb{R}$

10. $y = \log_{1/3} x$
Convert to exponential form.

$x = \left(\dfrac{1}{3}\right)^y$

x	9	3	1	$\frac{1}{3}$	$\frac{1}{9}$
y	-2	-1	0	1	2

Domain: $\{x \mid x > 0\}$
Range: $\mathbb{R}$

11. $y = \log_5 x$

Convert to the exponential form.

$x = 5^y$

x	$\frac{1}{25}$	$\frac{1}{5}$	1	5	25
y	-2	-1	0	1	2

Domain: $\{x \mid x > 0\}$

Range: $\mathbb{R}$

12. $y = \log_4 x$

Convert to the exponential form.

$x = 4^y$

x	$\frac{1}{16}$	$\frac{1}{4}$	1	4	16
y	-2	-1	0	1	2

Domain: $\{x \mid x > 0\}$

Range: $\mathbb{R}$

13. $y = \log_{1/5} x$ Convert to exponential form.

$x = \left(\dfrac{1}{5}\right)^y$

x	25	5	1	$\frac{1}{5}$	$\frac{1}{25}$
y	-2	-1	0	1	2

Domain: $\{x \mid x > 0\}$

Range: $\mathbb{R}$

14. $y = \log_{1/4} x$ Convert to exponential form.

$x = \left(\dfrac{1}{4}\right)^y$

x	16	4	1	$\frac{1}{4}$	$\frac{1}{16}$
y	-2	-1	0	1	2

Domain: $\{x \mid x > 0\}$

Range: $\mathbb{R}$

15. $y = 2^x$

x	-2	-1	0	1	2
y	$\frac{1}{4}$	$\frac{1}{2}$	1	2	4

$y = \log_{1/2} x$

Convert to exponential form.

$x = \left(\dfrac{1}{2}\right)^y$

x	4	2	1	$\frac{1}{2}$	$\frac{1}{4}$
y	-2	-1	0	1	2

16. $y = \left(\dfrac{1}{2}\right)^x$

x	-2	-1	0	1	2
y	4	2	1	$\frac{1}{2}$	$\frac{1}{4}$

$y = \log_2 x$

Convert to exponential form.

$x = 2^y$

x	$\frac{1}{4}$	$\frac{1}{2}$	1	2	4
y	-2	-1	0	1	2

17. $y = 2^x$

x	-2	-1	0	1	2
y	$\frac{1}{4}$	$\frac{1}{2}$	1	2	4

$y = \log_2 x$

Convert to exponential form.

$x = 2^y$

18. $y = \left(\dfrac{1}{2}\right)^x$

x	-2	-1	0	1	2
y	4	2	1	$\frac{1}{2}$	$\frac{1}{4}$

$y = \log_{1/2} x$

Convert to exponential form.

$x = \left(\dfrac{1}{2}\right)^y$

x	4	2	1	$\frac{1}{2}$	$\frac{1}{4}$
y	-2	-1	0	1	2

19. $2^3 = 8$

$\log_2 8 = 3$

20. $3^5 = 243$

$\log_3 243 = 5$

21. $3^2 = 9$

$\log_3 9 = 2$

22. $2^6 = 64$

$\log_2 64 = 6$

23. $16^{1/2} = 4$

$\log_{16} 4 = \dfrac{1}{2}$

24. $49^{1/2} = 7$

$\log_{49} 7 = \dfrac{1}{2}$

25. $8^{1/3} = 2$

$\log_8 2 = \dfrac{1}{3}$

26. $16^{1/4} = 2$

$\log_{16} 2 = \dfrac{1}{4}$

27. $\left(\dfrac{1}{2}\right)^5 = \dfrac{1}{32}$

$\log_{1/2}\left(\dfrac{1}{32}\right) = 5$

28. $\left(\dfrac{1}{3}\right)^4 = \dfrac{1}{81}$

$\log_{1/3}\left(\dfrac{1}{81}\right) = 4$

29. $2^{-3} = \dfrac{1}{8}$

$\log_2 \dfrac{1}{8} = -3$

30. $6^{-3} = \dfrac{1}{216}$

$\log_6 \dfrac{1}{216} = -3$

31. $4^{-3} = \dfrac{1}{64}$

$\log_4 \dfrac{1}{64} = -3$

32. $81^{1/2} = 9$

$\log_{81} 9 = \dfrac{1}{2}$

33. $64^{1/3} = 4$

$\log_{64} 4 = \dfrac{1}{3}$

34. $5^{-4} = \dfrac{1}{625}$

$\log_5 \dfrac{1}{625} = -4$

35. $8^{-1/3} = \dfrac{1}{2}$

$\log_8 \dfrac{1}{2} = -\dfrac{1}{3}$

36. $16^{-1/2} = \dfrac{1}{4}$

$\log_{16} \dfrac{1}{4} = -\dfrac{1}{2}$

37. $81^{-1/4} = \dfrac{1}{3}$

$\log_{81} \dfrac{1}{3} = -\dfrac{1}{4}$

38. $32^{-1/5} = \dfrac{1}{2}$

$\log_{32} \dfrac{1}{2} = -\dfrac{1}{5}$

39. $10^{0.8451} = 7$

$\log_{10} 7 = 0.8451$

40. $10^{1.0792} = 12$

$\log_{10} 12 = 1.0792$

41. $e^2 = 7.3891$

$\log_e 7.3891 = 2$

42. $e^{-1/2} = 0.6065$

$\log_e 0.6065 = -\dfrac{1}{2}$

43. $a^n = b$

$\log_a b = n$

44. $c^b = w$

$\log_c w = b$

45. $\log_2 8 = 3$

$2^3 = 8$

46. $\log_5 125 = 3$

$5^3 = 125$

47. $\log_{1/3} \dfrac{1}{27} = 3$

$\left(\dfrac{1}{3}\right)^3 = \dfrac{1}{27}$

48. $\log_{1/2} \dfrac{1}{64} = 6$

$\left(\dfrac{1}{2}\right)^6 = \dfrac{1}{64}$

49. $\log_5 \dfrac{1}{25} = -2$

$5^{-2} = \dfrac{1}{25}$

50. $\log_5 \dfrac{1}{625} = -4$

$5^{-4} = \dfrac{1}{625}$

51. $\log_{49} 7 = \dfrac{1}{2}$

$49^{1/2} = 7$

52. $\log_{64} 4 = \dfrac{1}{3}$

$64^{1/3} = 4$

53. $\log_9 \dfrac{1}{81} = -2$

$9^{-2} = \dfrac{1}{81}$

54. $\log_{10} \dfrac{1}{100} = -2$

$10^{-2} = \dfrac{1}{100}$

55. $\log_{10} \dfrac{1}{1000} = -3$

$10^{-3} = \dfrac{1}{1000}$

56. $\log_{10} 1000 = 3$

$10^3 = 1000$

57. $\log_6 216 = 3$

$6^3 = 216$

58. $\log_4 1024 = 5$

$4^5 = 1024$

59. $\log_{10} 0.62 = -0.2076$

$10^{-0.2076} = 0.62$

60. $\log_{10} 8 = 0.9031$

$10^{0.9031} = 8$

61. $\log_e 6.52 = 1.8749$

$e^{1.8749} = 6.52$

62. $\log_e 30 = 3.4012$

$e^{3.4012} = 30$

63. $\log_w s = -p$

$w^{-p} = s$

64. $\log_r c = -a$

$r^{-a} = c$

65. $\log_4 64 = y$

$4^y = 64$

$4^y = 4^3$

$y = 3$

66. $\log_5 25 = y$

$5^y = 25$

$5^y = 5^2$

$y = 2$

67. $\log_a 125 = 3$

$a^3 = 125$

$a^3 = 5^3$

$a = 5$

68. $\log_a 81 = 4$

$a^4 = 81$

$a^4 = 3^4$

$a = 3$

69. $\log_3 x = 3$

$3^3 = x$

$27 = x$

70. $\log_2 x = 5$

$2^5 = x$

$32 = x$

71. $\log_2 \dfrac{1}{16} = y$

$2^y = \dfrac{1}{16}$

$2^y = 2^{-4}$

$y = -4$

72. $\log_8 \dfrac{1}{64} = y$

$8^y = \dfrac{1}{64}$

$8^y = 8^{-2}$

$y = -2$

73. $\log_{1/2} x = 6$

$\left(\dfrac{1}{2}\right)^6 = x$

$\dfrac{1}{64} = x$

74. $\log_{1/3} x = 4$

$\left(\dfrac{1}{3}\right)^4 = x$

$\dfrac{1}{81} = x$

75. $\log_a \dfrac{1}{27} = -3$

$a^{-3} = \dfrac{1}{27}$

$a^{-3} = 3^{-3}$

$a = 3$

76. $\log_9 \dfrac{1}{81} = y$

$9^y = \dfrac{1}{81}$

$9^y = 9^{-2}$

$y = -2$

77. $\log_{10} 1 = 0$ because $10^0 = 1$

78. $\log_{10} 10 = 1$ because $10^1 = 10$

79. $\log_{10} 100 = 2$ because $10^2 = 100$

80. $\log_{10} 1000 = 3$ because $10^3 = 1000$

81. $\log_{10} \dfrac{1}{100} = -2$ because $10^{-2} = \dfrac{1}{10^2} = \dfrac{1}{100}$

82. $\log_{10} \dfrac{1}{1000} = -3$ because $10^{-3} = \dfrac{1}{10^3} = \dfrac{1}{1000}$

83. $\log_{10} 10,000 = 4$ because $10^4 = 10,000$

84. $\log_{10} 100,000 = 5$ because $10^5 = 100,000$

85. $\log_4 256 = 4$ because $4^4 = 256$

86. $\log_{13} 169 = 2$ because $13^2 = 169$

87. $\log_3 \dfrac{1}{81} = -4$ because $3^{-4} = \dfrac{1}{3^4} = \dfrac{1}{81}$

88. $\log_5 \dfrac{1}{125} = -3$ because $5^{-3} = \dfrac{1}{5^3} = \dfrac{1}{125}$

89. $\log_8 \dfrac{1}{64} = -2$ because $8^{-2} = \dfrac{1}{8^2} = \dfrac{1}{64}$

90. $\log_{14} \dfrac{1}{14} = -1$ because $14^{-1} = \dfrac{1}{14^1} = \dfrac{1}{14}$

91. $\log_9 1 = 0$ because $9^0 = 1$

92. $\log_{15} 1 = 0$ because $15^0 = 1$

93. $\log_9 9 = 1$ because $9^1 = 9$

94. $\log_{12} 12 = 1$ because $12^1 = 12$

95. $\log_4 1024 = 5$ because $4^5 = 1024$

96. $\log_2 128 = 7$ because $2^7 = 128$

97. If $f(x) = 5^x$, then $f^{-1}(x) = \log_5 x$.

98. If $f(x) = \log_6 x$, then $f^{-1}(x) = 6^x$.

99. $\log_3 62$ lies between 3 and 4 since 62 lies between $3^3 = 27$ and $3^4 = 81$.

100. $\log_{10} 0.672$ lies between -1 and 0 since 0.672 lies between $10^{-1} = 0.1$ and $10^0 = 1$.

101. $\log_{10} 425$ lies between 2 and 3 since 425 lies between $10^2 = 100$ and $10^3 = 1000$.

102. $\log_5 0.3256$ lies between -1 and 0 since 0.3256 lies between $5^{-1} = 0.2$ and $5^0 = 1$.

103. For $x > 1$, 2^x will grow faster than $\log_{10} x$. Note that when $x = 10$, $2^x = 1024$ while $\log_{10} x = 1$.

104. For $x > 1$, x will grow faster than $\log_{10} x$. Note that when $x = 100$, $\log_{10} x = 2$.

105. $x = \log_{10} 10^6$

$10^x = 10^6$

$x = 6$

106. $x = \log_7 7^9$

$7^x = 7^9$

$x = 9$

107. $x = \log_b b^8$

$b^x = b^8$

$x = 8$

108. $x = \log_e e^5$

$e^x = e^5$

$x = 5$

109. $x = 10^{\log_{10} 3}$

$\log_{10} x = \log_{10} 3$

$x = 3$

110. $x = 6^{\log_6 5}$

$\log_6 x = \log_6 5$

$x = 5$

111. $x = b^{\log_b 9}$

$\log_b x = \log_b 9$

$x = 9$

112. $x = c^{\log_c 2}$

$\log_c x = \log_c 2$

$x = 2$

113. $R = \log_{10} I$

$7 = \log_{10} I$

$10^7 = I$

$I = 10,000,000$

The earthquake is 10,000,000 times more intense than the smallest measurable activity.

114. $R = \log_{10} I$

$5 = \log_{10} I$

$10^5 = I$

$I = 100,000$

The earthquake is 100,000 times more intense than the smallest measurable activity.

115.

$$R = \log_{10} I \qquad R = \log_{10} I$$
$$6 = \log_{10} I \qquad 2 = \log_{10} I$$
$$10^6 = I \qquad\quad 10^2 = I$$
$$1,000,000 = I \qquad 100 = I$$

$$\frac{1,000,000}{100} = 10,000$$

An earthquake that measures 6 is 10,000 times more intense than one that measures 2.

116.

$$R = \log_{10} I \qquad R = \log_{10} I$$
$$1 = \log_{10} I \qquad 4 = \log_{10} I$$
$$10^1 = I \qquad\quad 10^4 = I$$
$$10 = I \qquad\quad 10,000 = I$$

$$\frac{10,000}{10} = 1000$$

An earthquake that measures 4 is 1000 times more intense than one that measures 1.

117. $y = \log_2 (x-1)$ or $2^y = x - 1$

x	$1\frac{1}{4}$	$1\frac{1}{2}$	2	3	5
y	-2	-1	0	1	2

118. $y = \log_3 (x-2)$ or $3^y = x - 2$

x	$2\frac{1}{9}$	$2\frac{1}{3}$	3	5	11
y	-2	-1	0	1	2

119. $2x^3 - 6x^2 - 36x = 2x\left(x^2 - 3x - 18\right)$
$$= 2x(x+3)(x-6)$$

120. $x^4 - 16 = \left(x^2 - 4\right)\left(x^2 + 4\right)$
$$= (x-2)(x+2)\left(x^2 + 4\right)$$

121. $40x^2 + 52x - 12 = 4\left(10x^2 + 13x - 3\right)$
$$= 4(2x+3)(5x-1)$$

122. $6r^2 s^2 + rs - 1 = (3rs - 1)(2rs + 1)$

Exercise Set 13.4

1. Answers will vary.

2. Answers will vary.

3. Answers will vary.

4. x and y are positive real numbers because logarithms of negative numbers do not exist.

5. Yes. This is true because of the product rule for logarithms.

6. No. There is no special rule for the logarithm of a sum.

7. $\log_4 (3 \cdot 10) = \log_4 3 + \log_4 10$

8. $\log_5 (4 \cdot 7) = \log_5 4 + \log_5 7$

9. $\log_8 7(x+3) = \log_8 7 + \log_8 (x+3)$

10. $\log_9 x(x+2) = \log_9 x + \log_9 (x+2)$

11. $\log_2 \dfrac{27}{11} = \log_2 27 - \log_2 11$

12. $\log_5 (41 \cdot 9) = \log_5 41 + \log_5 9$

13. $\log_{10} \dfrac{\sqrt{x}}{x-9} = \log_{10} \dfrac{x^{1/2}}{x-9}$

$\qquad = \log_{10} x^{1/2} - \log_{10}(x-9)$

$\qquad = \dfrac{1}{2}\log_{10} x - \log_{10}(x-9)$

14. $\log_5 3^8 = 8\log_5 3$

15. $\log_6 x^7 = 7\log_6 x$

16. $\log_9 12(4)^6 = \log_9 12 + \log_9 4^6$

$\qquad = \log_9 12 + 6\log_9 4$

17. $\log_4 (r+7)^5 = 5\log_4 (r+7)$

18. $\log_8 b^3(b-2) = \log_8 b^3 + \log_8(b-2)$

$\qquad = 3\log_8 b + \log_8(b-2)$

19. $\log_4 \sqrt{\dfrac{a^3}{a+2}} = \log_4 \left(\dfrac{a^3}{a+2}\right)^{1/2}$

$\qquad = \dfrac{1}{2}\log_4 \dfrac{a^3}{a+2}$

$\qquad = \dfrac{1}{2}[\log_4 a^3 - \log_4(a+2)]$

$\qquad = \dfrac{1}{2}[3\log_4 a - \log_4(a+2)]$

$\qquad = \dfrac{3}{2}\log_4 a - \dfrac{1}{2}\log_4(a+2)$

20. $\log_9 (x-6)^3 x^2 = \log_9 (x-6)^3 + \log_9 x^2$

$\qquad = 3\log_9 (x-6) + 2\log_9 x$

21. $\log_3 \dfrac{d^6}{(a-8)^4} = \log_3 d^6 - \log_3(a-8)^4$

$\qquad = 6\log_3 d - 4\log_3(a-8)$

22. $\log_7 x^2(x-13) = \log_7 x^2 + \log_7(x-13)$

$\qquad = 2\log_7 x + \log_7(x-13)$

23. $\log_8 \dfrac{y(y+4)}{y^3} = \log_8 y + \log_8(y+4) - \log_8 y^3$

$\qquad = \log_8 y + \log_8(y+4) - 3\log_8 y$

$\qquad = \log_8 (y+4) - 2\log_8 y$

24. $\log_{10} \left(\dfrac{z}{6}\right)^2 = 2\log_{10}\dfrac{z}{6}$

$\qquad = 2(\log_{10} z - \log_{10} 6)$

$\qquad = 2\log_{10} z - 2\log_{10} 6$

25. $\log_{10} \dfrac{9m}{8n} = \log_{10} 9m - \log_{10} 8n$

$\qquad = \log_{10} 9 + \log_{10} m - (\log_{10} 8 + \log_{10} n)$

$\qquad = \log_{10} 9 + \log_{10} m - \log_{10} 8 - \log_{10} n$

26. $\log_5 \dfrac{\sqrt{a}\,\sqrt[3]{b}}{\sqrt[4]{c}} = \log_5 \sqrt{a}\,\sqrt[3]{b} - \log_5 \sqrt[4]{c}$

$\qquad = \log_5 a^{1/2} + \log_5 b^{1/3} - \log_5 c^{1/4}$

$\qquad = \dfrac{1}{2}\log_5 a + \dfrac{1}{3}\log_5 b - \dfrac{1}{4}\log_5 c$

27. $\log_5 2 + \log_5 8 = \log_5 (2\cdot 8) = \log_5 16$

28. $\log_3 4 + \log_3 11 = \log_3 (4\cdot 11) = \log_3 44$

29. $\log_2 9 - \log_2 5 = \log_2 \dfrac{9}{5}$

30. $\log_7 17 - \log_7 3 = \log_7 \dfrac{17}{3}$

31. $6\log_4 2 = \log_4 2^6 = \log_4 64$

32. $\dfrac{1}{3}\log_8 7 = \log_8 7^{1/3} = \log_8 \sqrt[3]{7}$

33. $\log_{10} x + \log_{10}(x+3) = \log_{10} x(x+3)$

34. $\log_5 (a+1) - \log_5(a+10) = \log_5 \dfrac{a+1}{a+10}$

35. $2\log_9 z - \log_9(z-2) = \log_9 z^2 - \log_9(z-2)$

$\qquad = \log_9 \dfrac{z^2}{z-2}$

36. $3\log_8 y + 2\log_8(y-9)$

$\qquad = \log_8 y^3 + \log_8(y-9)^2$

$\qquad = \log_8 y^3(y-9)^2$

37. $4(\log_5 p - \log_5 3) = 4\log_5 \dfrac{p}{3}$

$$= \log_5\left(\dfrac{p}{3}\right)^4$$

38. $\dfrac{1}{2}\left[\log_6(r-1) - \log_6 r\right] = \dfrac{1}{2}\log_6 \dfrac{r-1}{r}$

$$= \log_6\left[\dfrac{r-1}{r}\right]^{1/2}$$

$$= \log_6 \sqrt{\dfrac{r-1}{r}}$$

39. $\log_2 n + \log_2(n+4) - \log_2(n-3)$

$\log_2 n(n+4) - \log_2(n-3)$

$\log_2 \dfrac{n(n+4)}{n-3}$

40. $2\log_5 t + 5\log_5(t-6) + \log_5(3t+7)$

$\log_5 t^2 + \log_5(t-6)^5 + \log_5(3t+7)$

$\log_5 t^2(t-6)^5(3t+7)$

41. $\dfrac{1}{2}\left[\log_5(x-8) - \log_5 x\right] = \dfrac{1}{2}\log_5 \dfrac{x-8}{x}$

$$= \log_5\left[\dfrac{x-8}{x}\right]^{1/2}$$

$$= \log_5 \sqrt{\dfrac{x-8}{x}}$$

42. $6\log_7(a+3) + 2\log_7(a-1) - \dfrac{1}{2}\log_7 a$

$= \log_7(a+3)^6 + \log_7(a-1)^2 - \log_7 a^{1/2}$

$= \log_7(a+3)^6(a-1)^2 - \log_7 a^{1/2}$

$= \log_7 \dfrac{(a+3)^6(a-1)^2}{a^{1/2}}$

$= \log_7 \dfrac{(a+3)^6(a-1)^2}{\sqrt{a}}$

43. $2\log_9 4 + \dfrac{1}{3}\log_9(r-6) - \dfrac{1}{2}\log_9 r$

$= \log_9 4^2 + \log_9(r-6)^{1/3} - \log_9 r^{1/2}$

$= \log_9 16 + \log_9 \sqrt[3]{r-6} - \log_9 \sqrt{r}$

$= \log_9 16\sqrt[3]{r-6} - \log_9 \sqrt{r}$

$= \log_9 \dfrac{16\sqrt[3]{r-6}}{\sqrt{r}}$

44. $5\log_6(x+3) - [2\log_6(7x+1) + 3\log_6 x]$

$= \log_6(x+3)^5 - [\log_6(7x+1)^2 + \log_6 x^3]$

$= \log_6(x+3)^5 - [\log_6(7x+1)^2 x^3]$

$= \log_6 \dfrac{(x+3)^5}{(7x+1)^2 x^3}$

45. $4\log_6 3 - [2\log_6(x+3) + 4\log_6 x]$

$= \log_6 3^4 - [\log_6(x+3)^2 + \log_6 x^4]$

$= \log_6 81 - \log_6(x+3)^2 x^4$

$= \log_6 \dfrac{81}{(x+3)^2 x^4}$

46. $2\log_7(m-4) + 3\log_7(m+3)$

$\qquad\qquad - [5\log_7 2 + 3\log_7(m-2)]$

$= \log_7(m-4)^2 + \log_7(m+3)^3$

$\qquad\qquad - [\log_7 2^5 + \log_7(m-2)^3]$

$= \log_7(m-4)^2(m+3)^3 - \log_7 2^5(m-2)^3$

$= \log_7 \dfrac{(m-4)^2(m+3)^3}{2^5(m-2)^3}$

$= \log_7 \dfrac{(m-4)^2(m+3)^3}{32(m-2)^3}$

47. $\log_a 10 = \log_a(2)(5)$

$\qquad\quad = \log_a 2 + \log_a(5)$

$\qquad\quad = 0.3010 + 0.6990$

$\qquad\quad = 1$

48. $\log_a 2.5 = \log_a \dfrac{5}{2}$

$\qquad\quad = \log_a 5 - \log_a 2$

$\qquad\quad = 0.6990 - 0.3010$

$\qquad\quad = 0.3980$

49. $\log_a 0.4 = \log_a \dfrac{2}{5}$

$\qquad = \log_a 2 - \log_a 5$

$\qquad = 0.3010 - 0.6990$

$\qquad = -0.3980$

50. $\log_a \dfrac{1}{8} = \log_a 1 - \log_a 8$

$\qquad = \log_a 1 - \log 2^3$

$\qquad = \log_a 1 - 3\log_a 2$

$\qquad = 0 - 3(0.3010)$

$\qquad = -0.9030$

51. $\log_a 25 = \log_a 5^2$

$\qquad = 2(\log_a 5)$

$\qquad = 2(0.6990)$

$\qquad = 1.3980$

52. $\log_a \sqrt[3]{5} = \log_a 5^{1/3}$

$\qquad = \dfrac{1}{3}\log_a 5$

$\qquad = \dfrac{1}{3}(0.6990)$

$\qquad = 0.2330$

53. $5^{\log_5 10} = 10$

54. $\log_3 3 = \log_3 3^1 = 1$

55. $(2^3)^{\log_8 7} = 8^{\log_8 7} = 7$

56. $\log_8 64 = \log_8 8^2 = 2$

57. $\log_3 27 = \log_3 3^3 = 3$

58. $2\log_9 \sqrt{9} = 2\log_9 9^{1/2} = 2\left(\dfrac{1}{2}\right) = 1$

59. $5\left(\sqrt[3]{27}\right)^{\log_3 5} = 5(3)^{\log_3 5}$

$\qquad = 5(5)$

$\qquad = 25$

60. $\dfrac{1}{2}\log_6 \sqrt[3]{6} = \dfrac{1}{2}\log_6 6^{1/3}$

$\qquad = \dfrac{1}{2} \cdot \dfrac{1}{3}$

$\qquad = \dfrac{1}{6}$

61. Yes

62. Yes

63. $\log_a \dfrac{x}{y} = \log_a xy^{-1}$

$\qquad = \log_a x + \log_a y^{-1}$

$\qquad = \log_a x + \log_a \dfrac{1}{y}$

64. a. $\log_a \dfrac{3}{xy} = \log_a 3 - (\log_a xy)$

b. $\log_a \dfrac{3}{xy} = \log_a 3 - \log_a (xy)$

$\qquad = \log_a 3 - \left(\log_a x + \log_a y\right)$

$\qquad = \log_a 3 - \log_a x - \log_a y$

65. $\log_a (x^2 - 4) - \log_a (x + 2) = \log_a \dfrac{x^2 - 4}{x + 2}$

$\qquad = \log_a \dfrac{(x+2)(x-2)}{x+2}$

$\qquad = \log_a (x - 2)$

66. $\log_a (x - 3) - \log_a (x^2 + 5x - 24)$

$\qquad = \log_a \dfrac{x - 3}{x^2 + 5x - 24}$

$\qquad = \log_a \dfrac{x - 3}{(x + 8)(x - 3)}$

$\qquad = \log_a \dfrac{1}{x + 8}$

67. Yes, assuming $x + 4 > 0$.

$\qquad \log_a (x^2 + 8x + 16) = \log_a (x + 4)^2$

$\qquad\qquad = 2\log_a (x + 4)$

68. Yes, assuming $2x - 5 > 0$.

$\qquad \log_a (4x^2 - 20x + 25) = \log_a (2x - 5)^2$

$\qquad\qquad = 2\log_a (2x - 5)$

69. $\log_{10} x^2 = 2\log_{10} x$
$= 2(0.4320)$
$= 0.8640$

70. $\log_{10} \sqrt[3]{x} = \log_{10} x^{1/3}$
$= \dfrac{1}{3}\log_{10} x$
$= \dfrac{1}{3}(0.4320) = 0.1440$

71. $\log_{10} \sqrt[4]{x} = \log_{10} x^{1/4}$
$= \dfrac{1}{4}\log_{10} x$
$= \dfrac{1}{4}(0.4320) = 0.1080$

72. $\log_{10} x^{11} = 11\log_{10} x$
$= 11(0.4320)$
$= 4.7520$

73. $\log_{10} xy = \log_{10} x + \log_{10} y$
$= 0.5000 + 0.2000$
$= 0.7000$

74. $\log_{10}\left(\dfrac{x}{y}\right) = \log_{10} x - \log_{10} y$
$= 0.5000 - 0.2000$
$= 0.3000$

75. No; answers will vary. There is no simplification rule for the log of a sum.

76. No, the domain of $y = \log_b x^2$ is all real numbers except 0 whereas the domain of $y = 2\log_b x$ is $\{x \mid x > 0\}$.

77.
$\log_2 \dfrac{\sqrt[4]{xy}\ \sqrt[3]{a}}{\sqrt[5]{a-b}} = \log_2 \sqrt[4]{xy}\ \sqrt[3]{a} - \log_2 \sqrt[5]{a-b}$

$= \log_2 (xy)^{1/4} + \log_2 a^{1/3} - \log_2 (a-b)^{1/5}$

$= \dfrac{1}{4}\log_2 xy + \dfrac{1}{3}\log_2 a - \dfrac{1}{5}\log_2(a-b)$

$= \dfrac{1}{4}\log_2 x + \dfrac{1}{4}\log_2 y + \dfrac{1}{3}\log_2 a - \dfrac{1}{5}\log_2(a-b)$

78. $\log_3\left[\dfrac{(a^2+b^2)(c^2)}{(a-b)(b+c)(c+d)}\right]^2$

$= 2\log_3 \dfrac{(a^2+b^2)(c^2)}{(a-b)(b+c)(c+d)}$

$= 2[\log_3 (a^2+b^2)(c^2) - \log_3 (a-b)(b+c)(c+d)]$

$= 2[\log_3 (a^2+b^2) + 2\log_3 c - \log_3 (a-b) - \log_3 (b+c) - \log_3 (c+d)]$

$= 2\log_3 (a^2+b^2) + 4\log_3 c - 2\log_3 (a-b) - 2\log_3 (b+c) - 2\log_3 (c+d)$

79. Let $\log_a x = m$ and $\log_a y = n$. Then
$a^m = x$ and $a^n = y$, so $\dfrac{x}{y} = \dfrac{a^m}{a^n} = a^{m-n}$.
Thus, $\log_a \dfrac{x}{y} = m - n = \log_a x - \log_a y$.

80. Let $\log_a x^n = p$ and $\log_a x = q$. Then
$a^p = x^n$ and $a^q = x$, so $a^p = x^n = (a^q)^n = a^{nq}$.
Thus, $p = nq$ or $\log_a x^n = n\log_a x$.

81. a. $\log_a \dfrac{\sqrt{x^4 y}}{\sqrt{xy^3}} = \log_a \sqrt{x^4 y} - \log_a \sqrt{xy^3}$

$= \dfrac{1}{2}\log_a x^4 y - \dfrac{1}{2}\log_a xy^3$

$= \dfrac{1}{2}\log_a x^4 + \dfrac{1}{2}\log_a y - \dfrac{1}{2}\log_a x - \dfrac{1}{2}\log_a y^3$

$= 2\log_a x + \dfrac{1}{2}\log_a y - \dfrac{1}{2}\log_a x - \dfrac{3}{2}\log_a y$

$= \dfrac{3}{2}\log_a x - \log_a y$

b. $\log_a \dfrac{\sqrt{x^4 y}}{\sqrt{xy^3}} = \log_a \left[\left(x^4 y\right)^{1/2} \cdot \left(xy^3\right)^{-1/2} \right]$

$= \log_a \left(x^4 y\right)^{1/2} + \log_a \left(xy^3\right)^{-1/2}$

$= \dfrac{1}{2}\log_a x^4 y - \dfrac{1}{2}\log_a xy^3$

$= \dfrac{1}{2}\log_a x^4 + \dfrac{1}{2}\log_a y - \dfrac{1}{2}\log_a x - \dfrac{1}{2}\log_a y^3$

$= 2\log_a x + \dfrac{1}{2}\log_a y - \dfrac{1}{2}\log_a x - \dfrac{3}{2}\log_a y$

$= \dfrac{3}{2}\log_a x - \log_a y$

c. $\log_a \dfrac{\sqrt{x^4 y}}{\sqrt{xy^3}} = \log_a \sqrt{\dfrac{x^4 y}{xy^3}}$

$= \log_a \sqrt{\dfrac{x^3}{y^2}} = \dfrac{1}{2}\log_a \dfrac{x^3}{y^2}$

$= \dfrac{1}{2}\log_a x^3 - \dfrac{1}{2}\log_a y^2$

$= \dfrac{3}{2}\log_a x - \log_a y$

d. Yes.

82. $\dfrac{2x+5}{x^2 - 7x + 12} \div \dfrac{x-4}{2x^2 - x - 15}$

$= \dfrac{2x+5}{(x-4)(x-3)} \div \dfrac{x-4}{(2x+5)(x-3)}$

$= \dfrac{(2x+5)}{(x-4)(x-3)} \cdot \dfrac{(2x+5)(x-3)}{(x-4)}$

$= \dfrac{(2x+5)^2}{(x-4)^2}$

83. $\dfrac{2x+5}{x^2 - 7x + 12} - \dfrac{x-4}{2x^2 - x - 15}$

$= \dfrac{2x+5}{(x-4)(x-3)} - \dfrac{x-4}{(2x+5)(x-3)}$

$= \dfrac{(2x+5)(2x+5)}{(x-4)(x-3)(2x+5)} - \dfrac{(x-4)(x-4)}{(x-4)(x-3)(2x+5)}$

$= \dfrac{(4x^2 + 20x + 25) - (x^2 - 8x + 16)}{(x-4)(x-3)(2x+5)}$

$= \dfrac{4x^2 + 20x + 25 - x^2 + 8x - 16}{(x-4)(x-3)(2x+5)}$

$= \dfrac{3x^2 + 28x + 9}{(x-4)(x-3)(2x+5)}$

$= \dfrac{(3x+1)(x+9)}{(x-4)(x-3)(2x+5)}$

84. $\dfrac{x}{4} + \dfrac{x}{5} = 1$

$5x + 4x = 20$

$9x = 20$

$x = \dfrac{20}{9} = 2\dfrac{2}{9}$

It will take them $2\dfrac{2}{9}$ days to paint the house together.

85. $\sqrt[3]{4x^4 y^7} \cdot \sqrt[3]{12x^7 y^{10}} = \sqrt[3]{4x^4 y^7 \cdot 12x^7 y^{10}}$

$= \sqrt[3]{48x^{11} y^{17}}$

$= \sqrt[3]{8x^9 y^{15} \cdot 6x^2 y^2}$

$= 2x^3 y^5 \sqrt[3]{6x^2 y^2}$

86. $2a - 7\sqrt{a} = 30$

$2a - 7\sqrt{a} - 30 = 0 \quad \rightarrow \quad \text{let } u = \sqrt{a}$

$2u^2 - 7u - 30 = 0$

$(2u + 5)(u - 6) = 0$

$2u + 5 = 0 \qquad\qquad \text{or} \qquad u - 6 = 0$

$2u = -5 \qquad\qquad\qquad\qquad u = 6$

$2\sqrt{a} = -5 \qquad\qquad\qquad\quad \sqrt{a} = 6$

$\quad$ not possible $\qquad\qquad\qquad a = 36$

The solution is $a = 36$.

Mid-Chapter Test: 13.1 – 13.4

1. a. In $f(x)$, replace x by $g(x)$.

   b. $f(x) = 3x + 3;\ g(x) = 2x + 5$

$$(f \circ g)(x) = 3(2x + 5) + 3$$
$$= 6x + 15 + 3$$
$$= 6x + 18$$

2. a. $(f \circ g)(x) = \left(\dfrac{6}{x}\right)^2 + 5$

$$= \dfrac{36}{x^2} + 5$$

   b. $(f \circ g)(3) = \dfrac{36}{3^2} + 5 = \dfrac{36}{9} + 5 = 4 + 5 = 9$

   c. $(g \circ f)(x) = \dfrac{6}{x^2 + 5}$

   d. $(g \circ f)(3) = \dfrac{6}{3^2 + 5} = \dfrac{6}{9 + 5} = \dfrac{6}{14} = \dfrac{3}{7}$

3. a. Answers will vary. A function is one-to-one if each input corresponds to exactly one output and each output corresponds to exactly one input.

   b. No, the function is not one-to-one because it fails the horizontal line test.

4. a. The function is one-to-one. Each value in the range corresponds to exactly one value in the domain.

   b. $\{(2, -3), (3, 2), (1, 5), (8, 6)\}$

5. a. The function is one-to-one. Each value in the range corresponds to exactly one value in the domain.

   b.
$$y = \dfrac{1}{3}x - 5$$
$$x = \dfrac{1}{3}y - 5$$
$$x + 5 = \dfrac{1}{3}y$$
$$3(x + 5) = y$$
$$3x + 15 = y \ \text{ or } \ p^{-1}(x) = 3x + 15$$

6. a. The function is one-to-one. Each value in the range corresponds to exactly one value in the domain.

   b.
$$y = \sqrt{x - 4}$$
$$x = \sqrt{y - 4}$$
$$x^2 = y - 4$$
$$x^2 + 4 = y \ \text{ or } \ k^{-1}(x) = x^2 + 4,\ x \ge 0$$

7. $m(x) = -2x + 4$
$$y = -2x + 4$$
$$x = -2y + 4$$
$$x - 4 = -2y$$
$$\dfrac{x - 4}{-2} = y$$
$$2 - \dfrac{1}{2}x = y \ \text{ or } \ m^{-1}(x) = -\dfrac{1}{2}x + 2$$

8. $y = 2^x$

9. $y = 3^{-x}$

10. $y = \log_2 x$

11. a. $N(t) = 5(2)^t$

$N(1) = 5(2)^1 = 5(2) = 10$

After 1 hour there are 10 bacteria in the dish.

b. $N(t) = 5(2)^t$

$N(6) = 5(2)^6 = 5(64) = 320$

After 6 hours there are 320 bacteria in the dish.

12. $27^{2/3} = 9 \iff \log_{27} 9 = \dfrac{2}{3}$

13. $\log_2 \dfrac{1}{64} = -6 \iff 2^{-6} = \dfrac{1}{64}$

14. $\log_5 125 = \log_5 5^3 = 3\log_5 5 = 3 \cdot 1 = 3$

15. $\log_{1/4} \dfrac{1}{16} = x$

$\log_{1/4} \left(\dfrac{1}{4}\right)^2 = x$

$2\log_{1/4} \dfrac{1}{4} = x$

$2 \cdot 1 = x$

$2 = x$

16. $\log_x 64 = 3$

Write the equivalent exponential equation and solve for x.

$x^3 = 64$

$x^3 = 4^3 \implies x = 4$

17. $\log_9 x^2(x-5) = \log_9 x^2 + \log_9 (x-5)$

$\qquad = 2\log_9 x + \log_9 (x-5)$

18. $\log_5 \dfrac{7m}{\sqrt{n}} = \log_5 (7m) - \log_5 \sqrt{n}$

$\qquad = \log_5 (7m) - \log_5 n^{1/2}$

$\qquad = \log_5 7 + \log_5 m - \dfrac{1}{2}\log_5 n$

19. $3\log_2 x + \log_2 (x+7) - 4\log_2 (x+1)$

$\qquad = \log_2 x^3 + \log_2 (x+7) - \log_2 (x+1)^4$

$\qquad = \log_2 x^3 (x+7) - \log_2 (x+1)^4$

$\qquad = \log_2 \dfrac{x^3(x+7)}{(x+1)^4}$

20. $\dfrac{1}{2}\left[\log_7 (x+2) - \log_7 x\right]$

$\qquad = \dfrac{1}{2}\left[\log_7 \dfrac{(x+2)}{x}\right]$

$\qquad = \log_7 \left[\dfrac{(x+2)}{x}\right]^{1/2}$

$\qquad = \log_7 \sqrt{\dfrac{x+2}{x}}$

Exercise Set 13.5

1. Common logarithms are logarithms with base 10.

2. $\log N = L \iff 10^L = N$

3. Antilogarithms are numbers obtained by taking the base of the logarithm and raising it to the power that the logarithm is equal to. They are the numbers *inside* the logarithm.

4. If $\log 793 = 2.8993$, then antilog $2.8993 = 793$.

5. $\log 86 = 1.9345$

6. log 352 = 2.5465

7. log 19,200 = 4.2833

8. log 1000 = 3.0000

9. log 0.0613 = −1.2125

10. log 941,000 = 5.9736

11. log 100 = 2.0000

12. log 0.000835 = −3.0783

13. log 3.75 = 0.5740

14. log 0.375 = −0.4260

15. log 0.0173 = −1.7620

16. log 0.00872 = −2.0595

17. antilog 0.2137 = 1.64

18. antilog 1.3845 = 24.2

19. antilog 4.6283 = 42,500

20. antilog 3.5527 = 3570

21. antilog (−1.7086) = 0.0196

22. antilog (−3.7431) = 0.000181

23. antilog 0.0000 = 1.00

24. antilog 5.5922 = 391,000

25. antilog 2.7625 = 579

26. antilog (−0.1543) = 0.701

27. antilog (−4.1390) = 0.0000726

28. antilog (−2.8139) = 0.00153

29. log N = 2.0000
    N = antilog 2.000
    N = 100

30. log N = 1.4612
    N = antilog 1.4612
    N = 28.9

31. log N = 3.3817
    N = antilog 3.3817
    N = 2410

32. log N = 1.9330
    N = antilog 1.9330
    N = 85.7

33. log N = 4.1409
    N = antilog 4.1409
    N = 13,800

34. log N = −2.103
    N = antilog (−2.103)
    N = 0.00789

35. log N = −1.06
    N = antilog (−1.06)
    N = 0.0871

36. log N = −3.1469
    N = antilog (−3.1469)
    N = 0.000713

37. log N = −0.6218
    N = antilog (−0.6218)
    N = 0.239

38. log N = 1.5177
    N = antilog 1.5177
    N = 32.9

39. log N = −0.1256
    N = antilog (−0.1256)
    N = 0.749

40. log N = −1.3206
    N = antilog (−1.3206)
    N = 0.0478

41. log 3560 = 3.5514
    Therefore, $10^{3.5514} \approx 3560$.

42. log 817,000 = 5.9122
    Therefore, $10^{5.9122} \approx 817,000$.

43. $\log 0.0727 = -1.1385$
Therefore, $10^{-1.1385} \approx 0.0727$.

44. $\log 0.00612 = -2.2132$
Therefore, $10^{-2.2132} \approx 0.00612$.

45. $\log 243 = 2.3856$
Therefore, $10^{2.3856} \approx 243$.

46. $\log 8.16 = 0.9117$
Therefore, $10^{0.9117} \approx 8.16$.

47. $\log 0.00592 = -2.2277$
Therefore, $10^{-2.2277} \approx 0.00592$.

48. $\log 73,700,000 = 7.8675$
Therefore, $10^{7.8675} \approx 73,700,000$.

49. $10^{2.8316} = 679$

50. $10^{3.2473} = 1770$

51. $10^{-0.5186} = 0.303$

52. $10^{-3.7081} = 0.000196$

53. $10^{-1.4802} = 0.0331$

54. $10^{4.5619} = 36,500$

55. $10^{1.3503} = 22.4$

56. $10^{-2.1918} = 0.00643$

57. $\log 1 = x$
$10^x = 1$
$10^x = 10^0$
$x = 0$
Therefore, $\log 1 = 0$.

58. $\log 100 = x$
$10^x = 100$
$10^x = 10^2$
$x = 2$
Therefore, $\log 100 = 2$.

59. $\log 0.1 = x$
$10^x = 0.1$
$10^x = \dfrac{1}{10}$
$10^x = 10^{-1}$
$x = -1$
Therefore, $\log 0.1 = -1$.

60. $\log 1000 = x$
$10^x = 1000$
$10^x = 10^3$
$x = 3$
Therefore, $\log 1000 = 3$.

61. $\log 0.01 = x$
$10^x = 0.01$
$10^x = \dfrac{1}{100}$
$10^x = 10^{-2}$
$x = -2$
Therefore, $\log 0.01 = -2$.

62. $\log 10 = x$
$10^x = 10$
$10^x = 10^1$
$x = 1$
Therefore, $\log 10 = 1$.

63. $\log 0.001 = x$
$10^x = 0.001$
$10^x = \dfrac{1}{1000}$
$10^x = 10^{-3}$
$x = -3$
Therefore, $\log 0.001 = -3$.

64. $\log 0.0001 = x$
$10^x = 0.0001$
$10^x = 10^{-4}$
$x = -4$
Therefore, $\log 0.0001 = -4$.

65. $\log 10^7 = 7$

66. $\log 10^{3.4} = 3.4$

67. $10^{\log 7} = 7$

68. $10^{\log 3.4} = 3.4$

69. $4 \log 10^{5.2} = 4(5.2) = 20.8$

70. $8 \log 10^{1.2} = 8(1.2) = 9.6$

71. $5(10^{\log 8.3}) = 5(8.3) = 41.5$

72. $2.3(10^{\log 5.2}) = (2.3)(5.2) = 11.96$

73. No; $10^2 = 100$ and since $462 > 100$,
log 462 must be greater than 2.

74. No; $10^3 = 1000$ and since $6250 > 1000$, log 6250
must be greater than 3.

75. No; $10^0 = 1$ and $10^{-1} = 0.1$ and since
$0.1 < 0.163 < 1$, log 0.163 must be between 0 and
-1.

76. No; the log of a negative number does not exist.

77. No;

$$\log \frac{y}{4x} = \log y - \log 4x$$
$$= \log y - (\log 4 + \log x)$$
$$= \log y - \log 4 - \log x$$

78. No;

$$\log \frac{5x^2}{3} = \log 5x^2 - \log 3$$
$$= \log 5 + \log x^2 - \log 3$$
$$= \log 5 + 2 \log x - \log 3$$

79. $\log 125 = \log(25 \cdot 5)$
$$= \log 25 + \log 5$$
$$= 1.3979 + 0.6990$$
$$= 2.0969$$

80. log 35 is not possible given this information.

81. $\log \dfrac{1}{5} = \log 5^{-1}$
$$= -\log 5$$
$$= -1(0.6990)$$
$$= -0.6990$$

82. $\log \dfrac{1}{25} = \log 25^{-1}$
$$= -\log 25$$
$$= -1(1.3979)$$
$$= -1.3979$$

83. $\log 625 = \log 25^2$
$$= 2 \log 25$$
$$= 2(1.3979)$$
$$= 2.7958$$

84. $\log \sqrt{5} = \log 5^{1/2}$
$$= \frac{1}{2} \log 5$$
$$= \frac{1}{2}(0.6990)$$
$$= 0.3495$$

85. $R = \log I, R = 3.4$
$$3.4 = \log I$$
$$I = \text{antilog}(3.4)$$
$$I \approx 2510$$
This earthquake is about 2,510 times more
intense than the smallest measurable activity.

86. $R = \log I, R = 4.9$
$$4.9 = \log I$$
$$I = \text{antilog}(4.9)$$
$$I \approx 79,400$$
This earthquake is about 79,400 times more
intense than the smallest measurable activity.

87. $R = \log I, R = 5.7$
$$5.7 = \log I$$
$$I = \text{antilog}(5.7)$$
$$I \approx 501,000$$
This earthquake is about 501,000 times more
intense than the smallest measurable activity.

88. $R = \log I, R = 8.1$
$$8.1 = \log I$$
$$I = \text{antilog}(8.1)$$
$$I \approx 126,000,000$$
This earthquake is about 126,000,000 times more
intense than the smallest measurable activity.

89. $\log d = 3.7 - 0.2g$

  a. $g = 11$

$\log d = 3.7 - 0.2(11)$

$= 3.7 - 2.2$

$= 1.5$

$d = $ antilog $1.5 = 31.62$

A planet with absolute magnitude of 11 has a diameter of 31.62 kilometers.

  b. $g = 20$

$\log d = 3.7 - 0.2(20)$

$= 3.7 - 4$

$= -0.3$

$d = $ antilog $(-0.3) = 0.50$

A planet with absolute magnitude of 20 has a diameter of 0.50 kilometers.

  c. $d = 5.8$

$\log 5.8 = 3.7 - 0.2g$

$\log 5.8 - 3.7 = -0.2g$

$0.76343 - 3.7 = -0.2g$

$-2.93657 = -0.2g$

$\dfrac{-2.93657}{-0.2} = g$

$14.68 = g$

A planet with diameter 5.8 kilometers has an absolute magnitude of 14.68.

90. $f(x) = \log 0.3x + 1.8$

  a. $f(15) = \log 0.3(15) + 1.8$

$= \log 4.5 + 1.8$

$\approx 0.6532 + 1.8$

≈ 2.45

The average score after 15 hours of studying is 2.45.

  b. $f(55) = \log 0.3(55) + 1.8$

$= \log 16.5 + 1.8$

$\approx 1.2175 + 1.8$

≈ 3.02

The average score after studying for 55 hours is 3.02.

91. $R(t) = 94 - 46.8\log(t+1)$

  a. $R(2) = 94 - 46.8\log(2+1)$

$= 94 - 46.8\log(3)$

≈ 72

After two months, Sammy will remember about 72% of the course material.

  b. $R(48) = 94 - 46.8\log(2+48)$

$= 94 - 46.8\log(50)$

≈ 15

After forty-eight months, Sammy will remember about 15% of the course material.

92. $R(t) = 85 - 41.9\log(t+1)$

  a. $R(10) = 85 - 41.9\log(10+1)$

$= 85 - 41.9\log(11)$

≈ 41

After ten months, Karen will remember about 41% of the course material.

  b. $R(25) = 85 - 41.9\log(25+1)$

$= 85 - 41.9\log(26)$

≈ 26

After twenty-five months, Karen will remember about 26% of the course material.

93. $R = \log I, R = 3.8$

$3.8 = \log I$

$I = $ anti log(3.8)

$I \approx 6310$

This earthquake is about 6310 times more intense than the smallest measurable activity.

94. $f(t) = 0.98 + 1.97\log(t+1)$

  a. $t = 2003 - 1992 = 11$

$f(11) = 0.98 + 1.97\log(11+1)$

$= 0.98 + 1.97\log(12)$

≈ 3.11

The number of SUV's to sold in 2003 is estimated to have been 3.11 million.

b. $t = 2008 - 1992 = 16$

$$f(16) = 0.98 + 1.97\log(16 + 1)$$
$$= 0.98 + 1.97\log(17)$$
$$\approx 3.40$$

The number of SUV's to be sold in 2008 is estimated to be 3.40 million.

95. $\log E = 11.8 + 1.5m_s$

a. $\log E = 11.8 + 1.5(6)$

$\log E = 20.8$

$10^{20.8} = E$

$E = 6.31 \times 10^{20}$

The energy released is 6.31×10^{20}.

b. $\log(1.2 \times 10^{15}) = 11.8 + 1.5m_s$

$15.07918125 = 11.8 + 1.5m_s$

$3.27918125 = 1.5m_s$

$m_s \approx 2.19$

The surface wave has magnitude 2.19.

96. $s_p = 20\log\left(\dfrac{p_r}{0.0002}\right)$

a. $s_p = 20\log\left(\dfrac{0.0036}{0.0002}\right)$

$= 20\log 18$

$= 20(1.2553)$

≈ 25.1

The sound pressure level is 25.1.

b. $10 = 20\log\left(\dfrac{p_r}{0.0002}\right)$

$0.5 = \log\left(\dfrac{p_r}{0.0002}\right)$

$10^{0.5} = \dfrac{p_r}{0.0002}$

$0.0002(10^{0.5}) = p_r$

$0.000632 \approx p_r$

The sound pressure is 0.000632 dynes/cm^2.

97. $M = \dfrac{\log E - 11.8}{1.5}$

$$M = \dfrac{\log(1.259 \times 10^{21}) - 11.8}{1.5}$$

$$= \dfrac{\log 1.259 + \log 10^{21} - 11.8}{1.5}$$

$$= \dfrac{\log 1.259 + 21 - 11.8}{1.5}$$

$$= \dfrac{\log 1.259 + 9.2}{1.5}$$

$$\approx \dfrac{0.1000 + 9.2}{1.5}$$

$$\approx 6.2$$

The magnitude is about 6.2.

98. $pH = -\log[H_3O^+]$

$pH = -\log[2.8 \times 10^{-3}]$

$= -\log[0.0028]$

$\approx -(-2.55)$

≈ 2.55

The pH is about 2.55.

99. $R = \log I$

$\text{antilog}(R) = \text{antilog}(\log I)$

$\text{antilog}(R) = I$

100. $\log E = 11.8 + 1.5m,\ \text{for } E$

$\text{antilog}(\log E) = \text{antilog}(11.8 + 1.5m)$

$E = \text{antilog}(11.8 + 1.5m)$

101. $R = 26 - 41.9\log(t + 1)$

$R - 26 = -41.9\log(t + 1)$

$\dfrac{R - 26}{-41.9} = \dfrac{-41.9\log(t + 1)}{-41.9}$

$\dfrac{26 - R}{41.9} = \log(t + 1)$

$\text{antilog}\left(\dfrac{26 - R}{41.9}\right) = \text{antilog}(\log(t + 1))$

$\text{antilog}\left(\dfrac{26 - R}{41.9}\right) = t + 1$

$\text{antilog}\left(\dfrac{26 - R}{41.9}\right) - 1 = t$

102. $f = 76 - \log x$

$\log x = 76 - f$

$\text{antilog}\left(\log x\right) = \text{antilog}\left(76 - f\right)$

$x = \text{antilog}\left(76 - f\right)$

103. a. $\log_3 45 = \dfrac{\log 45}{\log 3} \approx 3.4650$

b. $\log_5 30 = \dfrac{\log 30}{\log 5} \approx 2.1133$

c. $\log_6 40 = \dfrac{\log 40}{\log 6} \approx 2.0588$

d. $y = \log_2 x = \dfrac{\log x}{\log 2}$

104. $3r = -4s - 6 \quad \Rightarrow \quad 3r + 4s = -6 \quad (1)$

$3s = -5r + 1 \quad \Rightarrow \quad 5r + 3s = 1 \quad (2)$

To eliminate the variable r, multiply equation (1) by -5 and equation (2) by 3 then add.

$-5\left(3r + 4s = -6\right) \quad \Rightarrow -15r - 20s = 30$

$\underline{3\left(5r + 3s = 1\right) \quad \Rightarrow \quad 15r + 9s = 3}$

$\qquad\qquad\qquad\qquad -11s = 33$

$\qquad\qquad\qquad\qquad\qquad s = -3$

Substitute -3 for s in equation (1) and solve for r.

$3r + 4\left(-3\right) = -6$

$3r - 12 = -6$

$3r = 6$

$r = 2$

The solution is $(2, -3)$.

105. Let r equal the rate of car 2.

	d	r	t
Car 1	$4(r+5)$	$r+5$	4
Car 2	$4r$	r	4

The total distance was 420 miles.

$4\left(r + 5\right) + 4r = 420$

$4r + 20 + 4r = 420$

$8r + 20 = 420$

$8r = 400$

$r = 50$

The rate of car 2 is 50 mph and the rate of car 1 is $50 + 5 = 55$ mph.

106. $-3x^2 - 4x - 8 = 0$

$a = -3$, $b = -4$, $c = -8$

$x = \dfrac{-(-4) \pm \sqrt{(-4)^2 - 4(-3)(-8)}}{2(-3)}$

$= \dfrac{4 \pm \sqrt{16 - 96}}{-6} = \dfrac{-4 \pm \sqrt{-80}}{6}$

$= \dfrac{-4 \pm 4i\sqrt{5}}{6} = \dfrac{-2 \pm 2i\sqrt{5}}{3}$

107. Let $x =$ the speed of the boat in still water.

Direction	Distance	Rate	Time
downriver	15	$x+5$	$\dfrac{15}{x+5}$
upriver	15	$x-5$	$\dfrac{15}{x-5}$

$\dfrac{15}{x+5} + \dfrac{15}{x-5} = 4$

$15(x-5) + 15(x+5) = 4\left(x^2 - 25\right)$

$15x - 75 + 15x + 75 = 4x^2 - 100$

$4x^2 - 30x - 100 = 0$

$2x^2 - 15x - 50 = 0$

$\left(2x + 5\right)\left(x - 10\right) = 0$

$2x + 5 = 0 \quad$ or $\quad x - 10 = 0$

$2x = -5 \qquad\qquad\qquad x = 10$

$x = -\dfrac{5}{2}$

Speed is nonnegative so we discard the negative solution. The speed of the boat in still water is 10 miles per hour.

108. $y = (x-2)^2 + 1$

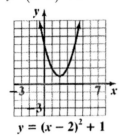

$$y = (x - 2)^2 + 1$$

109. $\dfrac{2x-3}{5x+10} < 0$

The numerator is 0 when $x = \dfrac{3}{2}$ and the denominator is 0 when $x = -2$. Therefore, our intervals are: $(-\infty, -2)$, $\left(-2, \dfrac{3}{2}\right)$, and $\left(\dfrac{3}{2}, \infty\right)$.

Interval A	Interval B	Interval C
$(-\infty, -2)$	$\left(-2, \dfrac{3}{2}\right)$	$\left(\dfrac{3}{2}, \infty\right)$
test value, -3	test value, 0	test value, 2

$$\frac{2x-3}{5x+10} < 0 \qquad \frac{2x-3}{5x+10} < 0 \qquad \frac{2x-3}{5x+10} < 0$$

$$\frac{2(-3)-3}{5(-3)+10} < 0 \qquad \frac{2(0)-3}{5(0)+10} < 0 \qquad \frac{2(2)-3}{5(2)+10} < 0$$

$$\frac{9}{5} < 0 \text{ false} \qquad -\frac{3}{10} < 0 \text{ true} \qquad \frac{1}{20} < 0 \text{ false}$$

Only interval B satisfies the inequality. The inequality is strict so we will not include any boundaries. The solution set is $\left\{ x \mid -2 < x < \dfrac{3}{2} \right\}$.

Exercise Set 13.6

1. $c = d$

2. $r = s$

3. Check for extraneous solutions.

4. Logarithms of negative numbers do not exist.

5. $\log(-2)$ is not a real number

6. No, $\log_3(-1)$ is not a real number.

7. $5^x = 125$
$5^x = 5^3$
$x = 3$

8. $2^x = 128$
$2^x = 2^7$
$x = 7$

9. $3^x = 81$
$3^x = 3^4$
$x = 4$

10. $4^x = 256$
$4^x = 4^4$
$x = 4$

11. $64^x = 8$
$(8^2)^x = 8^1$
$8^{2x} = 8^1$
$2x = 1$
$x = \dfrac{1}{2}$

12. $81^x = 3$
$(3^4)^x = 3^1$
$3^{4x} = 3^1$
$4x = 1$
$x = \dfrac{1}{4}$

13. $7^{-x} = \dfrac{1}{49}$
$7^{-x} = 7^{-2}$
$-x = -2$
$x = 2$

14. $6^{-x} = \dfrac{1}{216}$
$6^{-x} = 6^{-3}$
$-x = -3$
$x = 3$

15. $27^x = \dfrac{1}{3}$

$\left(3^3\right)^x = 3^{-1}$

$3^{3x} = 3^{-1}$

$3x = -1$

$x = -\dfrac{1}{3}$

16. $25^x = \dfrac{1}{5}$

$\left(5^2\right)^x = 5^{-1}$

$5^{2x} = 5^{-1}$

$2x = -1$

$x = -\dfrac{1}{2}$

17. $2^{x+2} = 64$

$2^{x+2} = 2^6$

$x + 2 = 6$

$x = 4$

18. $3^{x-6} = 81$

$3^{x-6} = 3^4$

$x - 6 = 4$

$x = 10$

19. $2^{3x-2} = 128$

$2^{3x-2} = 2^7$

$3x - 2 = 7$

$3x = 9$

$x = 3$

20. $64^x = 4^{4x+1}$

$\left(4^3\right)^x = 4^{4x+1}$

$4^{3x} = 4^{4x+1}$

$3x = 4x + 1$

$-x = 1$

$x = -1$

21. $27^x = 3^{2x+3}$

$3^{3x} = 3^{2x+3}$

$3x = 2x + 3$

$x = 3$

22. $\left(\dfrac{1}{2}\right)^x = 16$

$2^{-x} = 2^4$

$-x = 4$

$x = -4$

23. $7^x = 50$

$\log 7^x = \log 50$

$x \log 7 = \log 50$

$x = \dfrac{\log 50}{\log 7}$

$x \approx 2.01$

24. $1.05^x = 23$

$\log 1.05^x = \log 23$

$x \log 1.05 = \log 23$

$x = \dfrac{\log 23}{\log 1.05}$

$x \approx 64.26$

25. $4^{x-1} = 35$

$\log 4^{x-1} = \log 35$

$(x-1)\log 4 = \log 35$

$x - 1 = \dfrac{\log 35}{\log 4}$

$x = \dfrac{\log 35}{\log 4} + 1$

$x \approx 3.56$

26. $2.3^{x-1} = 26.2$

$\log 2.3^{x-1} = \log 26.2$

$(x-1)\log 2.3 = \log 26.2$

$x - 1 = \dfrac{\log 26.2}{\log 2.3}$

$x = \dfrac{\log 26.2}{\log 2.3} + 1$

$x \approx 4.92$

27.
$$1.63^{x+1} = 25$$
$$\log 1.63^{x+1} = \log 25$$
$$(x+1)\log 1.63 = \log 25$$
$$x+1 = \frac{\log 25}{\log 1.63}$$
$$x+1 \approx 6.59$$
$$x \approx 5.59$$

28.
$$4^x = 9^{x-2}$$
$$\log 4^x = \log 9^{x-2}$$
$$x\log 4 = (x-2)\log 9$$
$$x\log 4 = x\log 9 - 2\log 9$$
$$x\log 4 - x\log 9 = -2\log 9$$
$$x(\log 4 - \log 9) = -2\log 9$$
$$x = \frac{-2\log 9}{\log 4 - \log 9}$$
$$x \approx 5.42$$

29.
$$3^{x+4} = 6^x$$
$$\log 3^{x+4} = \log 6^x$$
$$(x+4)\log 3 = x\log 6$$
$$x\log 3 + 4\log 3 = x\log 6$$
$$4\log 3 = x\log 6 - x\log 3$$
$$4\log 3 = x(\log 6 - \log 3)$$
$$\frac{4\log 3}{\log 6 - \log 3} = x$$
$$6.34 \approx x$$

30.
$$5^x = 2^{x+5}$$
$$\log 5^x = \log 2^{x+5}$$
$$x\log 5 = (x+5)\log 2$$
$$x\log 5 = x\log 2 + 5\log 2$$
$$x\log 5 - x\log 2 = 5\log 2$$
$$gx(\log 5 - \log 2) = 5\log 2$$
$$x = \frac{5\log 2}{\log 5 - \log 2}$$
$$x \approx 3.78$$

31. $\log_{36} x = \frac{1}{2}$
$$36^{1/2} = x$$
$$\sqrt{36} = x$$
$$6 = x$$

32. $\log_{81} x = \frac{1}{2}$
$$81^{1/2} = x$$
$$\sqrt{81} = x$$
$$9 = x$$

33. $\log_{125} x = \frac{1}{3}$
$$125^{1/3} = x$$
$$\sqrt[3]{125} = x$$
$$5 = x$$

34. $\log_{81} x = \frac{1}{4}$
$$81^{1/4} = x$$
$$\sqrt[4]{81} = x$$
$$3 = x$$

35. $\log_2 x = -4$
$$2^{-4} = x$$
$$\frac{1}{2^4} = x$$
$$\frac{1}{16} = x$$

36. $\log_7 x = -2$
$$7^{-2} = x$$
$$\frac{1}{7^2} = x$$
$$\frac{1}{49} = x$$

37. $\log x = 2$
$$\log_{10} x = 2$$
$$10^2 = x$$
$$100 = x$$

38. $\log x = 4$
$$\log_{10} x = 4$$
$$10^4 = x$$
$$10,000 = x$$

39. $\log_2(5-3x)=3$

$$2^3=5-3x$$
$$8=5-3x$$
$$3x=-3$$
$$x=-1$$

40. $\log_4(3x+7)=3$

$$4^3=3x+7$$
$$64=3x+7$$
$$57=3x$$
$$19=x$$

41. $\log_5(x+1)^2=2$

$$(x+1)^2=5^2$$
$$(x+1)^2=25$$
$$x+1=\pm\sqrt{25}$$
$$x+1=\pm5$$
$$x+1=5 \quad\text{or}\quad x+1=-5$$
$$x=4 \qquad\qquad x=-6$$

Both values check. The solutions are 4 and –6.

42. $\log_3(a-2)^2=2$

$$(a-2)^2=3^2$$
$$a^2-4a+4=9$$
$$a^2-4a-5=0$$
$$(a-5)(a+1)=0$$
$$a-5=0 \quad\text{or}\quad a+1=0$$
$$a=5 \qquad\qquad a=-1$$

Both values check. The solutions are 5 and –1.

43. $\log_2(r+4)^2=4$

$$(r+4)^2=2^4$$
$$r^2+8r+16=16$$
$$r^2+8r=0$$
$$r(r+8)=0$$
$$r=0 \quad\text{or}\quad r+8=0$$
$$r=-8$$

Both values check. The solutions are 0 and –8.

44. $\log_2(p-3)^2=6$

$$(p-3)^2=2^6$$
$$(p-3)^2=64$$
$$p-3=\pm\sqrt{64}$$
$$p-3=\pm8$$
$$p-3=8 \quad\text{or}\quad p-3=-8$$
$$p=11 \qquad\qquad p=-5$$

Both values check. The solutions are 11 and –5.

45. $\log(x+8)=2$

$$\log_{10}(x+8)=2$$
$$10^2=x+8$$
$$100=x+8$$
$$x=92$$

46. $\log(3x-8)=1$

$$3x-8=10^1$$
$$3x-8=10$$
$$3x=18$$
$$x=6$$

47. $\log_2 x+\log_2 5=2$

$$\log_2 5x=2$$
$$5x=2^2$$
$$x=\frac{4}{5}$$

48. $\log_3 2x+\log_3 x=4$

$$\log_3 2x^2=4$$
$$2x^2=3^4$$
$$x^2=\frac{81}{2}=40.5$$
$$x=\pm\sqrt{40.5}$$

Note that in the original problem, we must have $x>0$. Therefore, we discard the negative value. The solution is $x=\sqrt{40.5}\approx6.36$.

49. $\log(r+2)=\log(3r-1)$

$$r+2=3r-1$$
$$3=2r$$
$$\frac{3}{2}=r$$

50. $\log 2a = \log(1-a)$

$2a = 1-a$

$3a = 1$

$a = \dfrac{1}{3}$

51. $\log(2x+1) + \log 4 = \log(7x+8)$

$\log(8x+4) = \log(7x+8)$

$8x+4 = 7x+8$

$x = 4$

52. $\log(x-5) + \log 3 = \log(2x)$

$\log\left[3(x-5)\right] = \log 2x$

$3(x-5) = 2x$

$3x - 15 = 2x$

$x - 15 = 0$

$x = 15$

53. $\log n + \log(3n-5) = \log 2$

$\log(3n^2 - 5n) = \log 2$

$3n^2 - 5n = 2$

$3n^2 - 5n - 2 = 0$

$(3n+1)(n-2) = 0$

$3n+1 = 0 \quad$ or $\quad n-2 = 0$

$3n = -1 \qquad\qquad n = 2$

$n = -\frac{1}{3}$

Check: $n = -\dfrac{1}{3}$

$\log n + \log(3n-5) = \log 2$

$\log\left(-\dfrac{1}{3}\right) + \log\left[3\left(\dfrac{-1}{3}\right) - 5\right] = \log 2$

Logarithms of negative numbers are not real numbers so $-\dfrac{1}{3}$ is an extraneous solution.

Check: $n = 2$

$\log n + \log(3n-5) = \log 2$

$\log 2 + \log[3(2) - 5] = \log 2$

$\log 2 + \log 1 = \log 2$

$\log(2 \cdot 1) = \log 2$

$\log 2 = \log 2$

2 is the only solution.

54. $\log(x+4) - \log x = \log(x+1)$

$\log\dfrac{x+4}{x} = \log(x+1)$

$\dfrac{x+4}{x} = x+1$

$x+4 = x^2 + x$

$0 = x^2 - 4$

$0 = (x+2)(x-2)$

$x+2 = 0 \quad$ or $\quad x-2 = 0$

$x = -2 \qquad\qquad x = 2$

Check: $x = -2$

$\log(x+4) - \log x = \log(x+1)$

$\log(-2+4) - \log(-2) = \log(-2+1)$

Logarithms of negative numbers are not real numbers so -2 is an extraneous solution.

Check: $x = 2$

$\log(x+4) - \log x = \log(x+1)$

$\log(2+4) - \log(2) = \log(2+1)$

$\log 6 - \log 2 = \log 3$

$\log\dfrac{6}{2} = \log 3$

$\log 3 = \log 3$

2 is the only solution.

55. $\log 6 + \log y = 0.72$

$\log 6y = 0.72$

$6y = \text{antilog}\, 0.72$

$y = \dfrac{\text{antilog}\, 0.72}{6}$

$y \approx 0.87$

56. $\log(x+4) - \log x = 1.22$

$\log\dfrac{x+4}{x} = 1.22$

$\dfrac{x+4}{x} = \text{antilog}\, 1.22$

$\dfrac{x+4}{x} \approx 16.6$

$x + 4 \approx 16.6x$

$4 \approx 15.6x$

$x \approx \dfrac{4}{15.6}$

$x \approx 0.26$

57. $2\log x - \log 9 = 2$

$\log x^2 - \log 9 = 2$

$\log\dfrac{x^2}{9} = 2$

$\dfrac{x^2}{9} = \text{antilog } 2$

$\dfrac{x^2}{9} = 100$

$x^2 = 900$

$x^2 - 900 = 0$

$(x+30)(x-30) = 0$

$x + 30 = 0 \quad$ or $\quad x - 30 = 0$

$\quad x = -30 \qquad\qquad x = 30$

Check: $x = -30$

$2\log x - \log 9 = 2$

$2\log(-30) - \log 9 = 2$

Logarithms of negative numbers are not real numbers so -30 is an extraneous solution.

Check: $x = 30$

$2\log x - \log 9 = 2$

$2\log 30 - \log 9 = 2$

$\log\dfrac{900}{9} = 2$

$\log 100 = 2$

$100 = \text{antilog } 2$

$100 = 100$

Thus, 30 is the only solution.

58. $\log 6000 - \log(x+2) = 3.15$

$\log\dfrac{6000}{x+2} = 3.15$

$\dfrac{6000}{x+2} = \text{antilog } 3.15$

$\dfrac{6000}{x+2} = 1412.54$

$6000 = 1412.54(x+2)$

$6000 = 1412.54x + 2825.08$

$3174.92 = 1412.54x$

$x = \dfrac{3174.92}{1412.54}$

$x \approx 2.25$

59. $\log x + \log(x-3) = 1$

$\log(x^2 - 3x) = 1$

$x^2 - 3x = \text{antilog } 1$

$x^2 - 3x = 10$

$x^2 - 3x - 10 = 0$

$(x-5)(x+2) = 0$

$x - 5 = 0 \quad$ or $\quad x + 2 = 0$

$\quad x = 5 \qquad\qquad x = -2$

A check shows that -2 is an extraneous solution so 5 is the only solution.

60. $2\log_2 x = 4$

$\log_2 x = 2$

$2^2 = x$

$x = 4$

61. $\log x = \dfrac{1}{3}\log 64$

$\log x = \log 64^{1/3}$

$\log x = \log 4$

$x = 4$

62. $\log_7 x = \dfrac{3}{2}\log_7 9$

$\log_7 x = \log_7 9^{3/2}$

$\log_7 x = \log_7 \left(\sqrt{9}\right)^3$

$\log_7 x = \log_7 (3)^3$

$\log_7 x = \log_7 27$

$x = 27$

63. $\log_8 x = 4\log_8 2 - \log_8 8$

$\log_8 x = \log_8 2^4 - \log_8 8$

$\log_8 x = \log_8 \dfrac{16}{8}$

$\log_8 x = \log_8 2$

$x = 2$

64. $\log_4 x + \log_4 (6x - 7) = \log_4 5$

$\log_4 (6x^2 - 7x) = \log_4 5$

$6x^2 - 7x = 5$

$6x^2 - 7x - 5 = 0$

$(2x + 1)(3x - 5) = 0$

$2x + 1 = 0 \quad$ or $\quad 3x - 5 = 0$

$x = -\frac{1}{2} \qquad\qquad x = \frac{5}{3}$

Since we cannot take the logarithm of a negative number, $-\dfrac{1}{2}$ is an extraneous solution.

Check: $x = \dfrac{5}{3}$

$\log_4 \left(\dfrac{5}{3}\right) + \log_4 \left(6\left(\dfrac{5}{3}\right) - 7\right) = \log_4 5$

$\log_4 \dfrac{5}{3} + \log_4 3 = \log_4 5$

$\log_4 \left(\dfrac{5}{3}\right)(3) = \log_4 5$

$\log_4 5 = \log_4 5$

Therefore, $\dfrac{5}{3}$ is the only solution.

65. $\log_5 (x + 3) + \log_5 (x - 2) = \log_5 6$

$\log_5 (x + 3)(x - 2) = \log_5 6$

$\log_5 (x^2 + x - 6) = \log_5 6$

$x^2 + x - 6 = 6$

$x^2 + x - 12 = 0$

$(x + 4)(x - 3) = 0$

$x + 4 = 0 \quad$ or $\quad x - 3 = 0$

$x = -4 \qquad\qquad x = 3$

Check $x = -4$:

$\log_5 \left(-4 + 3\right) + \log_5 \left(-4 - 2\right) = \log_5 6$

$\log_5 \left(-1\right) + \log_5 \left(-6\right) = \log_5 6$

Since we cannot take the logarithm of a negative number, -4 is an extraneous solution.

Check $x = 3$:

$\log_5 \left(3 + 3\right) + \log_5 \left(3 - 2\right) = \log_5 6$

$\log_5 \left(6\right) + \log_5 \left(1\right) = \log_5 6$

$\log_5 6 = \log_5 6$

Therefore, $x = 3$ is the only solution.

66. $\log_7 (x + 6) - \log_7 (x - 3) = \log_7 4$

$\log_7 \dfrac{x + 6}{x - 3} = \log_7 4$

$\dfrac{x + 6}{x - 3} = 4$

$x + 6 = 4x - 12$

$18 = 3x$

$6 = x$

67. $\log_2 (x + 3) - \log_2 (x - 6) = \log_2 4$

$\log_2 \dfrac{x + 3}{x - 6} = \log_2 4$

$\dfrac{x + 3}{x - 6} = 4$

$x + 3 = 4x - 24$

$27 = 3x$

$9 = x$

68. $\log(x - 7) - \log(x + 3) = \log 6$

$\log \dfrac{x - 7}{x + 3} = \log 6$

$\dfrac{x - 7}{x + 3} = 6$

$x - 7 = 6x + 18$

$-25 = 5x$

$-5 = x$

Disregard $x = -5$ since $\log(-5 - 7) = \log(-12)$ is not a real number. Therefore the equation has no solution.

69.
$$50,000 = 4500(2^t)$$

$$\dfrac{50,000}{4500} = 2^t$$

$$\log \dfrac{50,000}{4500} = \log 2^t$$

$$\log \dfrac{50,000}{4500} = t \log 2$$

$$\log 50,000 - \log 4500 = t \log 2$$

$$\dfrac{\log 50,000 - \log 4500}{\log 2} = t$$

$$3.47 \approx t$$

There are 50,000 bacteria after about 3.47 hours.

70. Let x be the number of bacteria present initially.

$$2224 = x \cdot 2^4$$
$$2224 = 16x$$
$$139 = x$$

There were 139 bacteria present initially.

71.
$$80 = 200(0.75)^t$$
$$0.4 = (0.75)^t$$
$$\log 0.4 = \log(0.75)^t$$
$$\log 0.4 = t \log 0.75$$
$$\frac{\log 0.4}{\log 0.75} = t$$
$$3.19 \approx t$$

80 grams remain after about 3.19 years.

72.
$$A(t) = 70(0.62)^t$$
$$10 = 70(0.62)^t$$
$$\frac{10}{70} = \frac{70(0.62)^t}{70}$$
$$\frac{1}{7} = (0.62)^t$$
$$\log\frac{1}{7} = \log(0.62)^t$$
$$\log\frac{1}{7} = t \log(0.62)$$
$$\frac{\log\dfrac{1}{7}}{\log(0.62)} = t \quad \Rightarrow \quad t \approx 4.07 \text{ years}$$

10 grams will be remaining in about 4.07 years.

73.
$$A = P\left(1 + \frac{r}{n}\right)^{nt}$$
$$4600 = 2000\left(1 + \frac{0.05}{1}\right)^{1 \cdot t}$$
$$4600 = 2000(1.05)^t$$
$$\frac{4600}{2000} = 1.05^t$$
$$2.3 = 1.05^t$$
$$\log 2.3 = \log 1.05^t$$
$$\log 2.3 = t \log 1.05$$
$$\frac{\log 2.3}{\log 1.05} = t \quad \Rightarrow \quad t \approx 17.07 \text{ years}$$

The \$2000 will grow to \$4600 in about 17.07 years.

74.
$$A = P\left(1 + \frac{r}{n}\right)^{nt}$$
$$1800 = 600\left(1 + \frac{0.06}{2}\right)^{2 \cdot t}$$
$$1800 = 600(1.03)^{2t}$$
$$3 = 1.03^{2t}$$
$$\log 3 = \log 1.03^{2t}$$
$$\log 3 = 2t \log 1.03$$
$$\frac{\log 3}{2 \log 1.03} = t \quad \Rightarrow \quad t \approx 18.58 \text{ years}$$

The \$600 will grow to \$1800 in about 18.58 years.

75. $f(t) = 26 - 12.1 \cdot \log(t+1)$

a. $x = 1990 - 1960 = 30$
$f(30) = 26 - 12.1 \log(30+1) = 7.95$
In 1990, the rate was about 7.95 deaths per 1000 live births.

b. $x = 2005 - 1960 = 45$
$f(45) = 26 - 12.1 \log(45+1) \approx 5.88$
In 2005, the rate was about 5.88 deaths per 1000 live births.

76. $f(t) = 1997 - 1576 \cdot \log(t+1)$
$$t = 2008 - 1993 = 15$$
$$f(15) = 1997 - 1576 \cdot \log(15+1)$$
$$= 1997 - 1576 \cdot \log(16)$$
$$\approx 99$$

The number of homicides in New York City in 2008 should be about 99.

77. $c = 50{,}000$, $n = 12$, $r = 0.15$.
$$S = c(1-r)^n$$
$$S = 50{,}000(1 - 0.15)^{12}$$
$$S = 50{,}000(0.85)^{12}$$
$$S \approx 7112.09$$

The scrap value is about \$7112.09.

78. $S = 100{,}000(1 - 0.08)^{15}$
$$= 100{,}000(0.92)^{15}$$
$$\approx 100{,}000(0.286297404)$$
$$\approx 28{,}629.74$$

The scrap value is about \$28,629.74.

79. $P_{out} = 12.6$ and $P_{in} = 0.146$

$$P = 10 \log \left(\frac{12.6}{0.146} \right)$$

$$P \approx 10 \log 86.30137$$

$$P \approx 10(1.936)$$

$$P \approx 19.36$$

The power gain is about 19.36 watts.

80. $R = \log I$

a. $8.25 = \log I$

$$10^{8.25} = I$$

$$I = 177,827,941$$

The 1906 San Francisco earthquake was 177,827,941 times more intense than the minimum level for comparison.

b. $8.3 = \log I$ $\qquad$ $4.7 = \log I$

$$10^{8.3} = I \qquad\qquad 10^{4.7} = I$$

$$\frac{10^{8.3}}{10^{4.7}} = 10^{3.6} \approx 3981$$

An earthquake registering 8.3 is about 3981 times more intense than one registering 4.7.

81. a. $d = 120$

$$d = 10 \log I$$

$$120 = 10 \log I$$

$$12 = \log I$$

$$I = \text{antilog } 12$$

$$I = 10^{12}$$

$$I = 1,000,000,000,000$$

The intensity is 1,000,000,000,000 times the minimum intensity of audible sound.

b. $d = 50$

$$d = 10 \log I$$

$$50 = 10 \log I$$

$$5 = \log I$$

$$I = \text{antilog } 5$$

$$I = 10^5$$

$$I = 100,000$$

$$\frac{1,000,000,000,000}{100,000} = 10,000,000$$

The sound of an airplane engine is 10,000,000 times more intense than the noise in a busy city street.

82. Observe that $\log(0.1)$ is less than 0, so you must change the direction of the inequality symbol in step 2.

83. $8^x = 16^{x-2}$

$$2^{3x} = 2^{4(x-2)}$$

$$3x = 4(x-2)$$

$$3x = 4x - 8$$

$$8 = x$$

84. $27^x = 81^{x-3}$

$$3^{3x} = 3^{4(x-3)}$$

$$3x = 4(x-3)$$

$$3x = 4x - 12$$

$$12 = x$$

85. $2^{2x} - 6(2^x) + 8 = 0$

$$(2^x)^2 - 6(2^x) + 8 = 0$$

$$y^2 - 6y + 8 = 0 \leftarrow \text{Replace } 2^x \text{ with } y$$

$$(y-4)(y-2) = 0$$

$$y - 4 = 0 \quad \text{or} \quad y - 2 = 0$$

$$y = 4 \qquad\qquad y = 2$$

$$2^x = 4 \qquad 2^x = 2 \leftarrow \text{Replace } y \text{ with } 2^x$$

$$2^x = 2^2 \qquad 2^x = 2^1$$

$$x = 2 \qquad\quad x = 1$$

The solutions are $x = 2$ and $x = 1$.

86. $2^{2x} - 18(2^x) + 32 = 0$

$$(2^x)^2 - 18(2^x) + 32 = 0$$

$$y^2 - 18y + 32 = 0 \leftarrow \text{Replace } 2^x \text{ with } y$$

$$(y-16)(y-2) = 0$$

$$y = 16 \quad \text{or} \quad y = 2$$

$$2^x = 16 \qquad\quad 2^x = 2 \leftarrow \text{Replace } y \text{ with } 2^x$$

$$2^x = 2^4 \qquad\quad 2^x = 2^1$$

$$x = 4 \qquad\qquad x = 1$$

The solutions are $x = 4$ and $x = 1$.

87. $2^x = 8^y$

$x + y = 4$

The first equation simplifies to

$2^x = (2^3)^y$

$2^x = 2^{3y}$

$x = 3y$

The system becomes

$x = 3y$

$x + y = 4$

Substitute $3y$ for x in the second equation.

$x + y = 4$

$3y + y = 4$

$4y = 4$

$y = 1$

Now, substitute 1 for y in the first equation.

$x = 3y$

$x = 3(1) = 3$

The solution is $(3, 1)$.

88. $3^{2x} = 9^{y+1}$

$x - 2y = -3$

The first equation simplifies to

$3^{2x} = 3^{2(y+1)}$

$2x = 2(y+1)$

$x = y + 1$

The system becomes

$x = y + 1$

$x - 2y = -3$

Substitute $y + 1$ for x in the second equation.

$x - 2y = -3$

$y + 1 - 2y = -3$

$-y + 1 = -3$

$-y = -4$

$y = 4$

Now, substitute 4 for y in the first equation.

$x = y + 1$

$x = 4 + 1$

$x = 5$

The solution is $(5, 4)$.

89. $\log(x + y) = 2$

$x - y = 8$

The first equation can be written as

$x + y = 10^2$

$x + y = 100$

The system becomes

$x + y = 100$

$x - y = 8$

Add: $\overline{2x = 108}$

$x = 54$

Substitute 54 for x in the first equation.

$54 + y = 100$

$y = 46$

The solution is $(54, 46)$.

90. $\log(x + y) = 3$

$2x - y = 5$

The first equation can be written as

$x + y = 10^3 \quad \Rightarrow \quad x + y = 1000$

The system becomes

$x + y = 1000$

$2x - y = 5$

Add: $\overline{3x = 1005}$

$x = 335$

Now, substitute 335 for x in the first equation.

$335 + y = 1000$

$y = 665$

The solution is $(335, 665)$.

91.

$-10, 30, 5, -10, 10, 1$

The solution is $x \approx 2.8$.

92.

$-10, 10, 1, -10, 10, 1$

The solution is $x \approx 3.3$.

93.

-10, 10, 1, -10, 10, 1

There is no real-number solution.

94.

0, 10, 1, -20, 20, 2

The solution is $x \approx 4.2$.

95. Volume of cylinder:

$$V_1 = \pi r^2 h = \pi \left(\frac{3}{2}\right)^2 \cdot 4 \approx 28.2743 \text{ cubic feet}$$

Volume of box:

$$V_2 = l \cdot w \cdot h = (3)(3)(4) = 36 \text{ cubic feet}$$

The box has the greater volume.
Difference in volumes:

$$V_2 - V_1 \approx 7.73 \text{ cubic feet}$$

96. $f(x) = x^2 - x, \ g(x) = x - 1$

$$(g - f)(x) = (x - 1) - (x^2 - x)$$
$$= x - 1 - x^2 + x$$
$$= -x^2 + 2x - 1$$
$$(g - f)(3) = -(3)^2 + 2(3) - 1$$
$$= -9 + 6 - 1$$
$$= -4$$

97. $3x - 4y \le 6$

$y > -x + 4$

For $3x - 4y \le 6$, graph the line $3x - 4y = 6$ using a solid line. For the check point, select (0, 0):

$$3x - 4y \le 6$$
$$3(0) - 4(0) \le 6$$
$$0 \le 6 \quad \text{True}$$

Since this is a true statement, shade the region which contains the point (0, 0). This is the region "above" the line.

For $y > -x + 4$, graph the line $y = -x + 4$ using a dashed line. For the check point, select (0, 0):

$$y > -x + 4$$
$$(0) > -(0) + 4$$
$$0 > 4 \quad \text{False}$$

Since this is a false statement, shade the region which does not contain the point (0, 0). This is the region "above" the line. To obtain the final region, take the intersection of the above two regions.

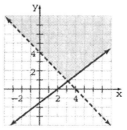

98. $\dfrac{2\sqrt{xy} - \sqrt{xy}}{\sqrt{x} + \sqrt{y}} = \dfrac{2\sqrt{xy} - \sqrt{xy}}{\sqrt{x} + \sqrt{y}} \cdot \dfrac{\sqrt{x} - \sqrt{y}}{\sqrt{x} - \sqrt{y}}$

$$= \frac{\left(2\sqrt{xy} - \sqrt{xy}\right) \cdot \left(\sqrt{x} - \sqrt{y}\right)}{\left(\sqrt{x} + \sqrt{y}\right) \cdot \left(\sqrt{x} - \sqrt{y}\right)}$$

$$= \frac{2\sqrt{x^2 y} - 2\sqrt{xy^2} - \sqrt{x^2 y} + \sqrt{xy^2}}{\sqrt{x^2} - \sqrt{xy} + \sqrt{xy} - \sqrt{y^2}}$$

$$= \frac{\sqrt{x^2 y} - \sqrt{xy^2}}{\sqrt{x^2} - \sqrt{y^2}}$$

$$= \frac{x\sqrt{y} - y\sqrt{x}}{x - y}$$

99. $E = mc^2$, for c

$$\frac{E}{m} = \frac{mc^2}{m}$$

$$\frac{E}{m} = c^2$$

$$\sqrt{\frac{E}{m}} = c$$

(Recall that when using the square root property to solve for a variable in a formula we only use the principal square root because we are generally solving for a variable that cannot be negative.)

100. Use $f(x) = a(x - h)^2 + k$, where $a = 2$ and $(h, k) = (3, -5)$.

$$f(x) = 2(x - 3)^2 - 5$$

Exercise Set 13.7

1. a. The base in the natural exponential function is e.

   b. The approximate value of e is 2.7183.

2. $\log_e x = \ln x$

3. The domain of $\ln x$ is $\{x \mid x > 0\}$.

4. $\ln x < 0$ for $0 < x < 1$.

5. $\log_a x = \dfrac{\log_b x}{\log_b a}$

6. Yes; $n \log_e x = n \ln x = \ln x^n$

7. $\ln e^x = x$

8. $e^{\ln x} = x$

9. The inverse of $\ln x$ is e^x.

10. P increases when t increases for $k > 0$.

11. P decreases when t increases for $k < 0$.

12. No, -3.52 is not in the domain of $\ln x$.

13. $\ln 62 \approx 4.1271$

14. $\ln 791 \approx 6.6733$

15. $\ln 0.813 \approx -0.2070$

16. $\ln 0.000568 \approx -7.4734$

17. $\ln N = 1.6$
$$e^{\ln N} = e^{1.6}$$
$$N = e^{1.6} \approx 4.95$$

18. $\ln N = 5.2$
$$e^{\ln N} = e^{5.2}$$
$$N = e^{5.2} \approx 181$$

19. $\ln N = -2.85$
$$e^{\ln N} = e^{-2.85}$$
$$N = e^{-2.85} \approx 0.0578$$

20. $\ln N = 0.543$
$$e^{\ln N} = e^{0.543}$$
$$N = e^{0.543} \approx 1.72$$

21. $\ln N = -0.0287$
$$e^{\ln N} = e^{-0.0287}$$
$$N = e^{-0.0287} \approx 0.972$$

22. $\ln N = -0.674$
$$e^{\ln N} = e^{-0.674}$$
$$N = e^{-0.674} \approx 0.510$$

23. $\log_3 56 = \dfrac{\log 56}{\log 3} \approx 3.6640$

24. $\log_3 198 = \dfrac{\log 198}{\log 3} \approx 4.8136$

25. $\log_2 21 = \dfrac{\log 21}{\log 2} \approx 4.3923$

26. $\log_2 89 = \dfrac{\log 89}{\log 2} \approx 6.4757$

27. $\log_4 11 = \dfrac{\log 11}{\log 4} \approx 1.7297$

28. $\log_4 316 = \dfrac{\log 316}{\log 4} \approx 4.1519$

29. $\log_5 82 = \dfrac{\log 82}{\log 5} \approx 2.7380$

30. $\log_5 1893 = \dfrac{\log 1893}{\log 5} \approx 4.6885$

31. $\log_6 185 = \dfrac{\log 185}{\log 6} \approx 2.9135$

32. $\log_6 806 = \dfrac{\log 806}{\log 6} \approx 3.7349$

33. $\ln 51 = \dfrac{\log 51}{\log e} \approx 3.9318$

34. $\ln 3294 = \dfrac{\log 3294}{\log e} \approx 8.0999$

35. $\log_5 0.463 = \dfrac{\log 0.463}{\log 5} \approx -0.4784$

36. $\log_3 0.0365 = \dfrac{\log 0.0365}{\log 3} \approx -3.0133$

37. $\ln x + \ln(x-1) = \ln 12$

$\ln x(x-1) = \ln 12$

$e^{\ln[x(x-1)]} = e^{\ln 12}$

$x(x-1) = 12$

$x^2 - x - 12 = 0$

$(x-4)(x+3) = 0$

$x - 4 = 0 \qquad x + 3 = 0$

$x = 4 \qquad x = -3$

Only $x = 4$ checks since $x = -3$ is an extraneous solution. Note that when $x = -3$ we would get $\ln(-3)$ and $\ln(-4)$ which are not real numbers.

38. $\ln(x+4) + \ln(x-2) = \ln 16$

$\ln(x+4)(x-2) = \ln 16$

$\ln(x^2 + 2x - 8) = \ln 16$

$e^{\ln(x^2+2x-8)} = e^{\ln 16}$

$x^2 + 2x - 8 = 16$

$x^2 + 2x - 24 = 0$

$(x-4)(x+6) = 0$

$x - 4 = 0 \quad \text{or} \quad x + 6 = 0$

$x = 4 \qquad x = -6$

Only $x = 4$ checks since $x = -6$ is an extraneous solution. Note that when $x = -6$ we would get $\ln(-2)$ and $\ln(-8)$ which are not real numbers.

39. $\ln x + \ln(x+4) = \ln 5$

$\ln x(x+4) = \ln 5$

$e^{\ln(x^2+4x)} = e^{\ln 5}$

$x^2 + 4x = 5$

$x^2 + 4x - 5 = 0$

$(x+5)(x-1) = 0$

$x + 5 = 0 \quad \text{or} \quad x - 1 = 0$

$x = -5 \qquad x = 1$

Only $x = 1$ checks since $x = -5$ is an extraneous solution. Note that when $x = -5$ we would get $\ln(-5)$ and $\ln(-1)$ which are not real numbers.

40. $\ln(x+3) + \ln(x-3) = \ln 40$

$\ln(x+3)(x-3) = \ln 40$

$\ln(x^2 - 9) = \ln 40$

$e^{\ln(x^2-9)} = e^{\ln 40}$

$x^2 - 9 = 40$

$x^2 - 49 = 0$

$(x-7)(x+7) = 0$

$x - 7 = 0 \quad \text{or} \quad x + 7 = 0$

$x = 7 \qquad x = -7$

Only $x = 7$ checks since $x = -7$ is an extraneous solution. Note that when $x = -7$ we would get $\ln(-4)$ and $\ln(-10)$ which are not real numbers.

41. $\ln x = 5\ln 2 - \ln 8$

$\ln x = \ln 2^5 - \ln 8$

$\ln x = \ln \dfrac{32}{8}$

$\ln x = \ln 4$

$e^{\ln x} = e^{\ln 4}$

$x = 4$

$x = 4$ checks.

42. $\ln x = \dfrac{3}{2}\ln 16$

$\ln x = \ln 16^{3/2}$

$e^{\ln x} = e^{\ln 16^{3/2}}$

$x = 16^{3/2}$

$x = \left(\sqrt{16}\right)^3$

$x = 4^3 = 64$

$x = 64$ checks.

43. $\ln(x^2 - 4) - \ln(x + 2) = \ln 4$

$\ln(x^2 - 4) - \ln(x + 2) = \ln 4$

$\ln\left(\dfrac{x^2 - 4}{x + 2}\right) = \ln 4$

$\ln\left(x - 2\right) = \ln 4$

$e^{\ln(x-2)} = e^{\ln(4)}$

$x - 2 = 4$

$x = 6$

$x = 6$ checks.

44. $\ln(x + 12) - \ln(x - 4) = \ln 5$

$\ln\dfrac{x + 12}{x - 4} = \ln 5$

$e^{\ln\frac{x+12}{x-4}} = e^{\ln 5}$

$\dfrac{x + 12}{x - 4} = 5$

$5\left(x - 4\right) = x + 12$

$5x - 20 = x + 12$

$4x = 32$

$x = 8$

$x = 8$ checks.

45. $P = 120e^{(2.3)(1.6)}$

$P = 120e^{3.68}$

$P \approx 4757.5673$

46. $900 = P_0 e^{0.4(3)}$

$900 = P_0 e^{1.2}$

$\dfrac{900}{e^{1.2}} = P_0$

$P_0 \approx 271.0748$

47. $50 = P_0 e^{-0.5(3)}$

$50 = P_0 e^{-1.5}$

$\dfrac{50}{e^{-1.5}} = P_0$

$P_0 \approx 224.0845$

48. $18 = 9e^{2t}$

$2 = e^{2t}$

$\ln 2 = \ln e^{2t}$

$\ln 2 = 2t$

$\dfrac{\ln 2}{2} = t$

$t \approx 0.3466$

49. $60 = 20e^{1.4t}$

$3 = e^{1.4t}$

$\ln 3 = \ln e^{1.4t}$

$\ln 3 = 1.4t$

$t = \dfrac{\ln 3}{1.4} \approx 0.7847$

50. $29 = 58e^{-0.5t}$

$0.5 = e^{-0.5t}$

$\ln 0.5 = \ln(e^{-0.5t})$

$\ln 0.5 = -0.5t$

$\dfrac{\ln 0.5}{-0.5} = t$

$t \approx 1.3863$

51. $86 = 43e^{k(3)}$

$2 = e^{3k}$

$\ln 2 = \ln e^{3k}$

$\ln 2 = 3k$

$k = \dfrac{\ln 2}{3} \approx 0.2310$

52.
$$15 = 75e^{k(4)}$$
$$0.2 = e^{4k}$$
$$\ln 0.2 = \ln e^{4k}$$
$$\ln 0.2 = 4k$$
$$\frac{\ln 0.2}{4} = k$$
$$k \approx -0.4024$$

53.
$$20 = 40e^{k(2.4)}$$
$$0.5 = e^{2.4k}$$
$$\ln 0.5 = \ln e^{2.4k}$$
$$\ln 0.5 = 2.4k$$
$$k = \frac{\ln 0.5}{2.4} \approx -0.2888$$

54.
$$100 = A_0 e^{-0.02(3)}$$
$$100 = A_0 e^{-0.06}$$
$$\frac{100}{e^{-0.06}} = A_0$$
$$A_0 \approx 106.1837$$

55.
$$A = 6000e^{-0.08(3)}$$
$$A = 6000e^{-0.24}$$
$$A \approx 4719.7672$$

56.
$$51 = 68e^{-0.04t}$$
$$0.75 = e^{-0.04t}$$
$$\ln 0.75 = \ln e^{-0.04t}$$
$$\ln 0.75 = -0.04t$$
$$\frac{\ln 0.75}{-0.04} = t$$
$$t \approx 7.1921$$

57. $V = V_0 e^{kt}$
$$\frac{V}{e^{kt}} = V_0 \text{ or } V_0 = \frac{V}{e^{kt}}$$

58. $P = P_0 e^{kt}$
$$\frac{P}{e^{kt}} = P_0 \text{ or } P_0 = \frac{P}{e^{kt}}$$

59.
$$P = 150e^{7t}$$
$$\frac{P}{150} = e^{7t}$$
$$\ln \frac{P}{150} = \ln e^{7t}$$
$$\ln \frac{P}{150} = 7t$$
$$\frac{\ln P - \ln 150}{7} = t \text{ or } t = \frac{\ln P - \ln 150}{7}$$

60.
$$361 = P_0 e^{kt}$$
$$\frac{361}{P_0} = e^{kt}$$
$$\ln \frac{361}{P_0} = \ln e^{kt}$$
$$\ln \frac{361}{P_0} = kt$$
$$\frac{\ln \frac{361}{P_0}}{k} = t \text{ or } t = \frac{\ln 361 - \ln P_0}{k}$$

61.
$$A = A_0 e^{kt}$$
$$\frac{A}{A_0} = e^{kt}$$
$$\ln \frac{A}{A_0} = \ln e^{kt}$$
$$\ln A - \ln A_0 = kt$$
$$\frac{\ln A - \ln A_0}{t} = k \text{ or } k = \frac{\ln A - \ln A_0}{t}$$

62.
$$167 = R_0 e^{kt}$$
$$\frac{167}{R_0} = e^{kt}$$
$$\ln \frac{167}{R_0} = \ln e^{kt}$$
$$\ln \frac{167}{R_0} = kt$$
$$\frac{\ln \frac{167}{R_0}}{t} = k \text{ or } \frac{\ln 167 - \ln R_0}{t}$$

63. $\ln y - \ln x = 2.3$

$$\ln \frac{y}{x} = 2.3$$

$$e^{\ln(y/x)} = e^{2.3}$$

$$\frac{y}{x} = e^{2.3}$$

$$y = xe^{2.3}$$

64. $\ln y + 9 \ln x = \ln 2$

$$\ln y + \ln x^9 = \ln 2$$

$$\ln yx^9 = \ln 2$$

$$e^{\ln yx^9} = e^{\ln 2}$$

$$yx^9 = 2$$

$$y = \frac{2}{x^9}$$

65. $\ln y - \ln(x + 6) = 5$

$$\ln \frac{y}{x+6} = 5$$

$$e^{\ln \frac{y}{x+6}} = e^5$$

$$\frac{y}{x+6} = e^5$$

$$y = (x+6)e^5$$

66. $\ln(x + 2) - \ln(y - 1) = \ln 5$

$$\ln(x+2) - \ln 5 = \ln(y-1)$$

$$\ln \frac{x+2}{5} = \ln(y-1)$$

$$e^{\ln \frac{x+2}{5}} = e^{\ln(y-1)}$$

$$\frac{x+2}{5} = y-1$$

$$\frac{x+2}{5} + 1 = y$$

$$\frac{x+2+5}{5} = y$$

$$\frac{x+7}{5} = y$$

67. $e^x = 12.183$

Take the natural logarithm of both sides of the equation.

$$\ln e^x = \ln 12.183$$

$$x = \ln 12.183 \approx 2.5000$$

68. $e^x = 184.93$

$$\ln e^x = \ln 184.93$$

$$x = \ln 184.93 \approx 5.2200$$

69. $P = P_0 e^{kt}$

a. $P = 5000e^{0.06(2)}$

$$= 5000e^{0.12}$$

$$\approx 5637.48$$

The amount will be \$5637.48.

b. If the amount in the account is to double, then $P = 2(5000) = 10,000$.

$$10,000 = 5000e^{0.06t}$$

$$2 = e^{0.06t}$$

$$\ln 2 = \ln e^{0.06t}$$

$$\ln 2 = 0.06t$$

$$\frac{\ln 2}{0.06} = t$$

$$11.55 \approx t$$

It would take about 11.55 years for the value to double.

70. $P = P_0 e^{kt}$

a. $P = 3000e^{0.03(30)}$

$$= 3000e^{0.9}$$

$$\approx 7378.81$$

The amount will be \$7378.81.

b. If the amount in the account is to double, then $P = 2(3000) = 6,000$.

$$6,000 = 3000e^{0.03t}$$

$$2 = e^{0.03t}$$

$$\ln 2 = \ln e^{0.03t}$$

$$\ln 2 = 0.03t$$

$$\frac{\ln 2}{0.03} = t$$

$$23.10 \approx t$$

It would take about 23.10 years for the value to double.

71. $P = P_0 e^{-0.028t}$

$P = 70e^{-0.028(20)}$

$P = 70e^{-0.56}$

$P \approx 39.98$

After 20 years, about 39.98 grams remain.

72. $P = P_0 e^{-0.028t}$

$P = 200e^{-0.028(40)}$

$P = 200e^{-1.12}$

$P \approx 65.26$

After 40 years, about 65.26 grams remain.

73. $f(t) = 1 - e^{-0.04t}$

  a. $f(t) = 1 - e^{-0.04(50)} = 1 - e^{-2} \approx 0.8647$

   About 86.47% of the target market buys the drink after 50 days of advertising.

  b. $0.75 = 1 - e^{-0.04t}$

   $-0.25 = -e^{-0.04t}$

   $0.25 = e^{-0.04t}$

   $\ln 0.25 = \ln e^{-0.04t}$

   $\ln 0.25 = -0.04t$

   $t = \dfrac{\ln 0.25}{-0.04}$

   $t \approx 34.66$

   About 34.66 days of advertising are needed if 75% of the target market is to buy the soft drink.

74. $g(t) = 300e^{0.07t}$

  a. $t = 2008 - 2005 = 3$

   $g(3) = 300e^{0.07(3)}$

   $= 300e^{0.21}$

   ≈ 370

   There will be about 370 trout in 2008.

  b. $t = 2015 - 2005 = 10$

   $g(10) = 300e^{0.07(10)}$

   $= 300e^{0.7}$

   ≈ 604

   There will be about 604 trout in 2015.

75. $f(P) = 0.37 \ln P + 0.05$

  a. $f(972,000) = 0.37 \ln(972,000) + 0.05$

   $\approx 5.1012311 + 0.05$

   ≈ 5.15

   The average walking speed in Nashville, Tennessee is 5.15 feet per second.

  b. $f(8,567,000) = 0.37 \ln(8,567,000) + 0.05$

   $\approx -5.906 + 0.05$

   ≈ 5.96

   The average walking speed in New York City is 5.96 feet per second.

  c. $5 = 0.37 \ln P + 0.05$

   $4.95 = 0.37 \ln P$

   $13.378378 = \ln P$

   $e^{13.378378} = e^{\ln P}$

   $P = e^{13.378378}$

   $P \approx 646,000$

   The population is about 646,000.

76. $N(a) = 800 + 300 \ln a$

  a. $N(1.5) = 800 + 300 \ln(1.5)$

   $\approx 800 + 300(0.405465) \approx 922$

   About 922 ties were sold.

  b. $1000 = 800 + 300 \ln a$

   $200 = 300 \ln a$

   $\dfrac{2}{3} = \ln a$

   $e^{2/3} = e^{\ln a}$

   $a = e^{2/3} \approx 1.95$

   $1.95 thousand or $1950 must be spent on advertising to sell 1000 ties.

77. $V(t) = 24e^{0.08t}, \quad t = 2008 - 1626 = 382$

$V(377) = 24e^{0.08(382)}$

$\approx 449,004,412,200,000$

The value of Manhattan in 2003 is about $449,004,412,200,000.

78. $P(t) = 1 - e^{-0.22t}$

$P(2) = 1 - e^{-0.22(2)}$

$\quad = 1 - e^{-0.44}$

$\quad \approx 1 - 0.64404$

$\quad \approx 0.356$

The percent of doctors who will prescribe the new drug two months after it has been on the market is about 35.6%.

79. $P(t) = 6.30e^{0.013t}$

a. $\quad t = 2010 - 2003 = 7$

$P(7) = 6.30e^{0.013(7)}$

$\quad = 6.30e^{0.091}$

$\quad \approx 6.9$

The world's population in 2010 is expected to be about 6.9 billion.

b. $2(6.30 \text{ billion}) \Rightarrow 12.60 \text{ billion}$

$12.60 = 6.30e^{0.013t}$

$\dfrac{12.60}{6.30} = \dfrac{6.30e^{0.013t}}{6.30}$

$2 = e^{0.013t}$

$\ln 2 = \ln e^{0.013t}$

$\ln 2 = 0.013t$

$t = \dfrac{\ln 2}{0.013} \approx 53$

The world's population will double in about 53 years.

80. $f(t) = 6.52e^{0.087t}$

a. $\quad t = 2006 - 2001 = 5$

$f(5) = 6.52e^{0.087(5)} = 6.52e^{0.435} \approx 10.07$

According to the trend, there were approximately 1,007,000 prescriptions for generic drugs used by members of the COVA Health Care Plan in 2006.

b. $\quad t = 2008 - 2001 = 7$

$f(7) = 6.52e^{0.087(7)} = 6.52e^{0.609} \approx 11.99$

According to the trend, there will be approximately 1,199,000 prescriptions for generic drugs used by members of the COVA Health Care Plan in 2008.

81. $d(t) = 2.19e^{0.0164t}$

a. $\quad t = 2025 - 2005 = 20$

$d(20) = 2.19e^{0.0164(20)} = 2.19e^{0.328} \approx 3.04$

According to the trend, the demand for nurses in 2025 will be approximately 3.04 million.

b. $\quad t = 2040 - 2005 = 35$

$d(35) = 2.19e^{0.0164(35)} = 2.19e^{0.574} \approx 3.89$

According to the trend, the demand for nurses in 2040 will be approximately 3.89 million.

82. $N(t) = 163.21e^{0.481t}$

a. $\quad t = 2007 - 2000 = 7$

$N(7) = 163.21e^{0.481(7)} = 163.21e^{3.367} \approx 4732$

According to the trend, there will be approximately 4732 new products using Splenda in 2007.

b. $\quad t = 2010 - 2000 = 10$

$N(10) = 163.21e^{0.481(10)} = 163.21e^{4.81} \approx 20,031$

According to the trend, there will be approximately 20,031 new products using Splenda in 2010.

83. $r(t) = 1182.3e^{0.0715t}$

a. $\quad t = 2006 - 1994 = 12$

$r(12) = 1182.3e^{0.0715(12)}$

$\quad = 1182.3e^{0.858} \approx 2788.38$

According to the trend, the average annual tax refund was about $2788.38 in 2006.

b. $\quad t = 2010 - 1994 = 16$

$r(16) = 1182.3e^{0.0715(16)}$

$\quad = 1182.3e^{1.144} \approx 3711.59$

According to the trend, the average annual tax refund will be about $3711.59 in 2010.

84. $y = 3.17 + 7.32 \ln x$

a. $y(18) = 3.17 + 7.32 \ln(18) \approx 24.33 \text{ lb}$

b. $y(30) = 3.17 + 7.32 \ln(30) \approx 28.07 \text{ lb}$

85. $y = 15.29 + 5.93 \ln x$

   a. $y(18) = 15.29 + 5.93 \ln(18) \approx 32.43$ in.

   b. $y(30) = 15.29 + 5.93 \ln(30) \approx 35.46$ in.

86. $A = A_0 e^{-0.00003t}$

   a. Use $t = 100$ and $A_0 = 1000$.

$$A = 1000e^{-0.00003(100)}$$
$$A = 1000e^{-0.003}$$
$$A \approx 997$$

About 997 grams are left after 100 years.

   b. Use $A = 500$ and $A_0 = 1000$.

$$500 = 1000e^{-0.00003t}$$
$$0.5 = e^{-0.00003t}$$
$$\ln 0.5 = \ln e^{-0.00003t}$$
$$\ln 0.5 = -0.00003t$$
$$\frac{\ln 0.5}{-0.00003} = t$$
$$t \approx 23{,}104.91$$

The half-life is about 23,104.91 years.

87. $f(t) = v_0 e^{-0.0001205t}$

   a. Use $f(t) = 9$ and $v_0 = 20$.

$$9 = 20e^{-0.0001205t}$$
$$0.45 = e^{-0.0001205t}$$
$$\ln 0.45 = -0.0001205t$$
$$\frac{\ln 0.45}{-0.0001205} = t$$
$$t \approx 6626.62$$

The bone is about 6626.62 years old.

   b. Let x equal the original amount of carbon 14 then $0.5x$ equals the remaining amount.

$$0.5x = xe^{-0.0001205t}$$
$$\frac{0.5x}{x} = \frac{xe^{-0.0001205t}}{x}$$
$$0.5 = e^{-0.0001205t}$$
$$\ln 0.5 = \ln e^{-0.0001205t}$$
$$\ln 0.5 = -0.0001205t$$
$$\frac{\ln 0.5}{-0.0001205} = t$$
$$t \approx 5752.26$$

If 50% of the carbon 14 remains, the item is about 5752.26 years old.

88. The equation is $P = P_0 e^{kt}$. Let $P = 2P_0$ and $t = 13$ to obtain

$$P = P_0 e^{kt}$$
$$2P_0 = P_0 e^{k \cdot 13}$$
$$2P_0 = P_0 e^{13k}$$
$$2 = e^{13k}$$
$$\ln 2 = \ln e^{13k}$$
$$\ln 2 = 13k$$
$$\frac{\ln 2}{13} = k$$
$$0.0533 \approx k \text{ or}$$
$$k \approx 5.33\%$$

The rate needed is about 5.33%.

89. Let P_0 be the initial investment, then $P = 20{,}000$, $k = 0.06$, and $t = 18$.

$$P = P_0 e^{kt}$$
$$20{,}000 = P_0 e^{0.06(18)}$$
$$20{,}000 = P_0 e^{1.08}$$
$$\frac{20{,}000}{e^{1.08}} = P_0$$
$$6791.91 \approx P_0$$

The initial investment should be $6791.91.

90. $P = 50e^{-0.002t}$

   a. Use $t = 50$.

$$P = 50e^{-0.002(50)}$$
$$P = 50e^{-0.1}$$
$$P \approx 45.24$$

After 50 days, about 45.24 watts remain.

   b. Use $P = 10$.

$$10 = 50e^{-0.002t}$$
$$0.2 = e^{-0.002t}$$
$$\ln 0.2 = \ln e^{-0.002t}$$
$$\ln 0.2 = -0.002t$$
$$\frac{\ln 0.2}{-0.002} = t$$
$$t \approx 804.72$$

There will be 10 watts of power remaining after about 804.72 days.

91. a. Strontium 90 has a higher decay rate so it will decompose more quickly.

b. $P = P_0 e^{-kt}$

$P = P_0 e^{-0.023(50)}$

$= P_0 e^{-1.15}$

$\approx P_0(0.3166)$

About 31.66% of the original amount will remain.

92. $t = \dfrac{t_h}{0.693} \ln\left(\dfrac{N_0}{N}\right)$

$= \dfrac{4.5 \times 10^9}{0.693} \ln\left(\dfrac{5 \times 10^{12}}{4 \times 10^{12}}\right)$

$\approx 1.45 \times 10^9$

The rock is about 1.45×10^9 years old..

93. Answers will vary.

94. Answers will vary.

95. $e^{x-4} = 12\ln(x+2)$

$y_1 = e^{x-4}$

$y_2 = 12\ln(x+2) \cdot$

The intersections are approximately $(-0.999, 0.007)$ and $(7.286, 26.742)$. Therefore, $x \approx -0.999$ or $x \approx 7.286$.

96. $\ln(4-x) = 2\ln x + \ln 2.4$

$y_1 = \ln(4-x)$

$y_2 = 2\ln x + \ln 2.4$

The intersection is approximately $(1.099, 1.065)$. Therefore, $x \approx 1.099$.

97. $3x - 6 = 2e^{0.2x} - 12$

$y_1 = 3x - 6$

$y_2 = 2e^{0.2x} - 12$

The intersections are approximately $(-1.507, -10.520)$ and $(16.659, 43.977)$. Therefore, $x \approx -1.507$ and 16.659.

98. $x = k(\ln I_0 - \ln I)$

$\dfrac{x}{k} = \ln \dfrac{I_0}{I}$

$e^{x/k} = e^{\ln(I_0/I)}$

$e^{x/k} = \dfrac{I_0}{I}$

$Ie^{x/k} = I_0$ or $I_0 = Ie^{x/k}$

99. $x = \dfrac{1}{k}\ln(kv_0 t + 1)$

$xk = \ln(kv_0 t + 1)$

$e^{xk} = e^{\ln(kv_0 t + 1)}$

$e^{xk} = kv_0 t + 1$

$e^{xk} - 1 = kv_0 t$

$\dfrac{e^{xk} - 1}{kt} = v_0$ or $v_0 = \dfrac{e^{xk} - 1}{kt}$

100. $\ln M = \ln Q - \ln(1 - Q)$

$\ln M = \ln \dfrac{Q}{1 - Q}$

$e^{\ln M} = e^{\ln[Q/(1-Q)]}$

$M = \dfrac{Q}{1 - Q}$

$M(1 - Q) = Q$

$M - MQ = Q$

$M = Q + MQ$

$M = Q(1 + M)$

$\dfrac{M}{1 + M} = Q$ or $Q = \dfrac{M}{1 + M}$

101. $\ln i - \ln I = \dfrac{-t}{RC}$

$\ln \dfrac{i}{I} = \dfrac{-t}{RC}$

$e^{\ln(i/I)} = e^{-t/RC}$

$\dfrac{i}{I} = e^{-t/RC}$

$i = Ie^{-t/RC}$

102. $(3xy^2 + y)(4x - 3xy)$

$= 12x^2y^2 - 9x^2y^3 + 4xy - 3xy^2$

$= -9x^2y^3 + 12x^2y^2 - 3xy^2 + 4xy$

103. $4x^2 + bx + 25 = (2x)^2 + bx + (5)^2$ will be

a perfect square trinomial if

$bx = \pm 2(2x)(5) \quad \Rightarrow \quad b = \pm 20$

104. $h(x) = \dfrac{x^2 + 4x}{x + 6}$

   a. $h(-4) = \dfrac{(-4)^2 + 4(-4)}{(-4) + 6} = \dfrac{16 - 16}{2} = \dfrac{0}{2} = 0$

   b. $h\left(\dfrac{2}{5}\right) = \dfrac{\left(\frac{2}{5}\right)^2 + 4\left(\frac{2}{5}\right)}{\left(\frac{2}{5}\right) + 6}$

$= \dfrac{\dfrac{4}{25} + \dfrac{40}{25}}{\dfrac{2}{5} + \dfrac{30}{5}} = \dfrac{\dfrac{44}{25}}{\dfrac{32}{5}}$

$= \dfrac{44}{25} \cdot \dfrac{5}{32} = \dfrac{11}{40}$ or 0.275

105. Let x be the number of adult tickets sold and y be the number of children's tickets sold. The following system describes the situation.

$x + \quad y = 550$

$15x + 11y = 7290$

Solve by elimination.

$-11(x + y = 550) \Rightarrow -11x - 11y = -6050$

$15x + 11y = 7290 \Rightarrow \underline{\quad 15x + 11y = \quad 7290}$

$4x \qquad\qquad = 1240$

$x = 310$

Substitute $x = 310$ into the first equation to find y.

$310 + y = 550 \quad \Rightarrow \quad y = 240$

Thus, 310 adult tickets and 240 children's tickets must be sold.

106. $\sqrt[3]{x}\left(\sqrt[3]{x^2} + \sqrt[3]{x^5}\right) = \sqrt[3]{x} \cdot \sqrt[3]{x^2} + \sqrt[3]{x} \cdot \sqrt[3]{x^5}$

$= \sqrt[3]{x^3} + \sqrt[3]{x^6}$

$= x + x^2$

Chapter 13 Review Exercises

1. $(f \circ g)(x) = (2x - 5)^2 - 3(2x - 5) + 4$

$= 4x^2 - 20x + 25 - 6x + 15 + 4$

$= 4x^2 - 26x + 44$

2. $(f \circ g)(x) = 4x^2 - 26x + 44$

$(f \circ g)(3) = 4(3)^2 - 26(3) + 44$

$= 36 - 78 + 44$

$= 2$

3. $(g \circ f)(x) = 2(x^2 - 3x + 4) - 5$

$= 2x^2 - 6x + 8 - 5$

$= 2x^2 - 6x + 3$

4. $(g \circ f)(x) = 2x^2 - 6x + 3$

$(g \circ f)(-3) = 2(-3)^2 - 6(-3) + 3$

$= 18 + 18 + 3$

$= 39$

5. $(f \circ g)(x) = 6\sqrt{x - 3} + 7, \; x \geq 3$

6. $(g \circ f)(x) = \sqrt{(6x + 7) - 3}$

$= \sqrt{6x + 4}, \; x \geq -\dfrac{2}{3}$

7. This function is one-to-one since it passes the horizontal line test.

8. The function is not one-to-one since the graph does not pass the horizontal line test.

9. Yes, the ordered pairs represent a one-to-one function. For each value of x, there is a unique value for y and each y-value has a unique x-value.

10. No, the ordered pairs do not represent a one-to-one function since the pairs $(0, -2)$ and $(3, -2)$ have different x-values but the same y-value.

11. Yes, the function $y = \sqrt{x+8}$, $x \geq -8$, is a one-to-one function since each output, y, corresponds to exactly one intput, x. The graph passes the horizontal line test.

12. No, $y = x^2 - 9$ is a parabola with vertex at $(0, -9)$. It is not a one-to-one function since it does not pass the horizontal line test. Horizontal lines above $y = -9$ intersect the graph at two points.

13. $f(x)$: Domain: $\{-4, -1, 5, 6\}$
Range: $\{-3, 2, 3, 8\}$
$f^{-1}(x)$: Domain: $\{-3, 2, 3, 8\}$
Range: $\{-4, -1, 5, 6\}$

14. $f(x)$: Domain: $\left\{x \middle| x \geq 0\right\}$
Range: $\left\{y \middle| y \geq 4\right\}$
$f^{-1}(x)$: Domain: $\left\{x \middle| x \geq 4\right\}$
Range: $\left\{y \middle| y \geq 0\right\}$

15. $y = f(x) = 4x - 2$
$x = 4y - 2$
$x + 2 = 4y$
$\dfrac{x+2}{4} = y$ or $y = f^{-1}(x) = \dfrac{x+2}{4}$

x	$f(x)$
0	-2
$\frac{1}{2}$	0

x	$f^{-1}(x)$
0	$\frac{1}{2}$
-2	0

16. $y = f(x) = \sqrt[3]{x-1} = (x-1)^{1/3}$
$x = (y-1)^{1/3}$
$x^3 = [(y-1)^{1/3}]^3$
$x^3 = y - 1$
$x^3 + 1 = y$
$f^{-1}(x) = x^3 + 1$

x	$f(x)$
-7	-2
0	-1
1	0
2	1
9	2

x	$f^{-1}(x)$
-2	-7
-1	0
0	1
1	2
2	9

17. $f(x) = 36x \Rightarrow y = 36x$
$x = 36y \Rightarrow y = \dfrac{x}{36} \Rightarrow f^{-1}(x) = \dfrac{x}{36}$
$f^{-1}(x)$ represents yards and x represents inches.

18. $f(x) = 4x \Rightarrow y = 4x$
$x = 4y \Rightarrow y = \dfrac{x}{4} \Rightarrow f^{-1}(x) = \dfrac{x}{4}$
$f^{-1}(x)$ represents gallons and x represents quarts.

19. $y = 2^x$

x	-2	-1	0	1	2	3
y	$\frac{1}{4}$	$\frac{1}{2}$	1	2	4	8

Domain: $\mathbb{R}$

Range: $\{y \mid y > 0\}$

20. $y = \left(\frac{1}{2}\right)^x$

x	-2	-1	0	1	2
y	4	2	1	$\frac{1}{2}$	$\frac{1}{4}$

Domain: $\mathbb{R}$

Range: $\{y \mid y > 0\}$

21. $f(t) = 7.02e^{0.365t}$

a. $t = 2003 - 1999 = 4$

$$f(4) = 7.02e^{0.365(4)}$$
$$\approx 30.23$$

The worldwide shipment in 2003 is about 30.23 million.

b. $t = 2005 - 1999 = 6$

$$f(6) = 7.02e^{0.365(6)}$$
$$\approx 62.73$$

The worldwide shipment in 2005 will be about 62.73 million.

c. $t = 2008 - 1999 = 9$

$$f(9) = 7.02e^{0.365(9)}$$
$$\approx 187.50$$

The worldwide shipment in 2008 will be about 187.50 million.

22. $8^2 = 64$

$\log_8 64 = 2$

23. $81^{1/4} = 3$

$\log_{81} 3 = \frac{1}{4}$

24. $5^{-3} = \frac{1}{125}$

$\log_5 \frac{1}{125} = -3$

25. $\log_2 32 = 5$

$2^5 = 32$

26. $\log_{1/4} \frac{1}{16} = 2$

$\left(\frac{1}{4}\right)^2 = \frac{1}{16}$

27. $\log_6 \frac{1}{36} = -2$

$6^{-2} = \frac{1}{36}$

28. $3 = \log_4 x$

$x = 4^3$

$x = 64$

29. $4 = \log_a 81$

$a^4 = 81$

$a^4 = 3^4$

$a = 3$

30. $-3 = \log_{1/5} x$

$$x = \left(\frac{1}{5}\right)^{-3}$$

$$x = \frac{1}{\left(\frac{1}{5}\right)^3}$$

$$x = \frac{1}{\frac{1}{125}}$$

$$x = 125$$

31. $y = \log_3 x$

$$x = 3^y$$

x	$\frac{1}{9}$	$\frac{1}{3}$	1	3	9	27
y	-2	-1	0	1	2	3

Domain: $\{x \mid x > 0\}$

Range: $\mathbb{R}$

32. $y = \log_{1/2} x$

$$x = \left(\frac{1}{2}\right)^y$$

x	4	2	1	$\frac{1}{2}$	$\frac{1}{4}$
y	-2	-1	0	1	2

Domain: $\{x \mid x > 0\}$

Range: $\mathbb{R}$

33. $\log_5 17^8 = 8 \log_5 17$

34. $\log_3 \sqrt{x-9} = \log_3 (x-9)^{1/2} = \frac{1}{2} \log_3 (x-9)$

35. $\log \dfrac{6(a+1)}{19} = \log\left[6(a+1)\right] - \log 19$

$$= \log 6 + \log(a+1) - \log 19$$

36. $\log \dfrac{x^4}{7(2x+3)^5} = \log x^4 - \log\left(7(2x+3)^5\right)$

$$= 4\log x - \left[\log 7 + \log(2x+3)^5\right]$$

$$= 4\log x - \left[\log 7 + 5\log(2x+3)\right]$$

$$= 4\log x - \log 7 - 5\log(2x+3)$$

37. $5\log x - 3\log(x+1) = \log x^5 - \log(x+1)^3$

$$= \log \frac{x^5}{(x+1)^3}$$

38. $4\left(\log 2 + \log x\right) - \log y = 4\left(\log(2x)\right) - \log y$

$$= \log(2x)^4 - \log y$$

$$= \log \frac{(2x)^4}{y} \quad \text{or} \quad \log \frac{16x^4}{y}$$

39. $\dfrac{1}{3}[\ln x - \ln(x+2)] - \ln 2$

$$= \frac{1}{3}\left(\ln \frac{x}{x+2}\right) - \ln 2$$

$$= \ln\left(\frac{x}{x+2}\right)^{1/3} - \ln 2$$

$$= \ln \frac{\sqrt[3]{\frac{x}{x+2}}}{2}$$

40. $3\ln x + \dfrac{1}{2}\ln(x+1) - 6\ln(x+4)$

$$= \ln x^3 + \ln(x+1)^{1/2} - \ln(x+4)^6$$

$$= \ln \frac{x^3 \sqrt{x+1}}{(x+4)^6}$$

41. $8^{\log_8 10} = 10$

42. $\log_4 4^5 = 5$

43. $11^{\log_9 81} = 11^{\log_9 9^2}$
$$= 11^2$$
$$= 121$$

44. $9^{\log_8 \sqrt{8}} = 9^{\log_8 8^{1/2}}$
$$= 9^{1/2}$$
$$= \sqrt{9}$$
$$= 3$$

45. $\log 819 = 2.9133$

46. $\ln 0.0281 = -3.5720$

47. antilog $3.159 = 1440$

48. antilog$(-3.157) = 0.000697$

49. $\log N = 4.063$
$$N = \text{antilog } 4.063$$
$$N = 11,600$$

50. $\log N = -1.2262$
$$N = \text{antilog } (-1.2262)$$
$$N = 0.0594$$

51. $\log 10^5 = 5$

52. $10^{\log 9} = 9$

53. $7 \log 10^{3.2} = 7(3.2) = 22.4$

54. $2\left(10^{\log 4.7}\right) = 2(4.7) = 9.4$

55. $625 = 5^x$
$$5^4 = 5^x$$
$$4 = x$$

56. $49^x = \dfrac{1}{7}$
$$(7^2)^x = 7^{-1}$$
$$7^{2x} = 7^{-1}$$
$$2x = -1$$
$$x = -\dfrac{1}{2}$$

57. $2^{3x-1} = 32$
$$2^{3x-1} = 2^5$$
$$3x - 1 = 5$$
$$3x = 6$$
$$x = 2$$

58. $27^x = 3^{2x+5}$
$$(3^3)^x = 3^{2x+5}$$
$$3^{3x} = 3^{2x+5}$$
$$3x = 2x + 5$$
$$x = 5$$

59. $7^x = 152$
$$\log 7^x = \log 152$$
$$x \log 7 = \log 152$$
$$x = \frac{\log 152}{\log 7}$$
$$x \approx 2.582$$

60. $3.1^x = 856$
$$\log 3.1^x = \log 856$$
$$x \log 3.1 = \log 856$$
$$x = \frac{\log 856}{\log 3.1}$$
$$x \approx 5.968$$

61. $12.5^{x+1} = 381$
$$\log 12.5^{x+1} = \log 381$$
$$(x+1) \log 12.5 = \log 381$$
$$x + 1 = \frac{\log 381}{\log 12.5}$$
$$x = \frac{\log 381}{\log 12.5} - 1$$
$$x \approx 1.353$$

62.
$$3^{x+2} = 8^x$$
$$\log 3^{x+2} = \log 8^x$$
$$(x+2)\log 3 = x \log 8$$
$$x \log 3 + 2 \log 3 = x \log 8$$
$$2 \log 3 = x \log 8 - x \log 3$$
$$2 \log 3 = x(\log 8 - \log 3)$$
$$\frac{2 \log 3}{\log 8 - \log 3} = x$$
$$2.240 \approx x$$

63. $\log_7 (2x - 3) = 2$
$$7^2 = 2x - 3$$
$$49 = 2x - 3$$
$$52 = 2x$$
$$26 = x$$

64. $\log x + \log(4x - 19) = \log 5$
$$\log \left(x(4x - 19) \right) = \log 5$$
$$x(4x - 19) = 5$$
$$4x^2 - 19x - 5 = 0$$
$$(4x + 1)(x - 5) = 0$$
$$4x + 1 = 0 \quad \text{or} \quad x - 5 = 0$$
$$x = -\frac{1}{4} \qquad\qquad x = 5$$

Only $x = 5$ checks. $x = -\dfrac{1}{4}$ is an extraneous solution since $\log(4x - 19)$ becomes $\log(-20)$ which is not a real number.

65. $\log_3 x + \log_3 (2x + 1) = 1$
$$\log_3 x(2x + 1) = 1$$
$$3^1 = x(2x + 1)$$
$$0 = 2x^2 + x - 3$$
$$0 = (2x + 3)(x - 1)$$
$$2x + 3 = 0 \quad \text{or} \quad x - 1 = 0$$
$$x = -\tfrac{3}{2} \qquad\qquad x = 1$$

Only $x = 1$ checks. $x = -\dfrac{3}{2}$ is an extraneous solution since $\log_3 x$ becomes $\log_3 \left(-\dfrac{3}{2} \right)$ which is not a real number.

66. $\ln(x + 1) - \ln(x - 2) = \ln 4$
$$\ln \frac{x + 1}{x - 2} = \ln 4$$
$$\frac{x + 1}{x - 2} = 4$$
$$x + 1 = 4(x - 2)$$
$$x + 1 = 4x - 8$$
$$1 = 3x - 8$$
$$9 = 3x$$
$$x = 3$$

67.
$$50 = 25e^{0.6t}$$
$$2 = e^{0.6t}$$
$$\ln 2 = \ln e^{0.6t}$$
$$\ln 2 = 0.6t$$
$$\frac{\ln 2}{0.6} = t$$
$$1.155 \approx t$$

68.
$$100 = A_0 e^{-0.42(3)}$$
$$100 = A_0 e^{-1.26}$$
$$\frac{100}{e^{-1.26}} = A_0$$
$$352.542 \approx A_0$$

69.
$$A = A_0 e^{kt}$$
$$\frac{A}{A_0} = e^{kt}$$
$$\ln \frac{A}{A_0} = \ln e^{kt}$$
$$\ln \frac{A}{A_0} = kt$$
$$\frac{\ln \frac{A}{A_0}}{k} = t$$
$$\frac{\ln A - \ln A_0}{k} = t \text{ or } t = \frac{\ln A - \ln A_0}{k}$$

70.

$$200 = 800e^{kt}$$

$$\frac{200}{800} = e^{kt}$$

$$0.25 = e^{kt}$$

$$\ln 0.25 = \ln e^{kt}$$

$$\ln 0.25 = kt$$

$$\frac{\ln 0.25}{t} = k \text{ or } k = \frac{\ln 0.25}{t}$$

71.

$$\ln y - \ln x = 6$$

$$\ln \frac{y}{x} = 6$$

$$e^{\ln \frac{y}{x}} = e^6$$

$$\frac{y}{x} = e^6$$

$$y = xe^6$$

72. $\ln(y+1) - \ln(x+8) = \ln 3$

$$\ln \frac{y+1}{x+8} = \ln 3$$

$$\frac{y+1}{x+8} = 3$$

$$y+1 = 3(x+8)$$

$$y = 3(x+8) - 1$$

$$y = 3x + 24 - 1$$

$$y = 3x + 23$$

73. $\log_2 196 = \dfrac{\log 196}{\log 2} \approx 7.6147$

74. $\log_3 47 = \dfrac{\log 47}{\log 3} \approx 3.5046$

75. $A = P(1+r)^n$

$$= 12,000(1 + 0.06)^8$$

$$= 12,000(1.06)^8$$

$$= 19,126.18$$

The amount is $19,126.18.

76. $P = P_0 e^{kt}$

$$P_0 = 6,000, k = 0.04, \text{ and } P = 12,000$$

$$12,000 = 12,000e^{(0.04)t}$$

$$2 = e^{0.04t}$$

$$\ln 2 = 0.04t$$

$$t = \frac{\ln 2}{0.04}$$

$$t \approx 17.3$$

It will take about 17.3 years for the $6,000 to double.

77. $N(t) = 2000(2)^{0.05t}$

a. Let $N(t) = 50,000$.

$$50,000 = 2000(2)^{0.05t}$$

$$\frac{50,000}{2000} = 2^{0.05t}$$

$$25 = 2^{0.05t}$$

$$\log 25 = \log 2^{0.05t}$$

$$\log 25 = 0.05t \log 2$$

$$\frac{\log 25}{0.05 \log 2} = t$$

$$92.88 \approx t$$

The time is 92.88 minutes.

b. Let $N(t) = 120,000$.

$$120,000 = 2000(2)^{0.05t}$$

$$\frac{120,000}{2000} = 2^{0.05t}$$

$$60 = 2^{0.05t}$$

$$\log 60 = \log 2^{0.05t}$$

$$\log 60 = 0.05t \log 2$$

$$\frac{\log 60}{0.05 \log 2} = t$$

$$118.14 \approx t$$

The time is 118.14 minutes.

78. $P = 14.7e^{-0.00004x}$

$P = 14.7e^{-0.00004(8842)}$

$P = 14.7e^{-0.35368}$

$P \approx 14.7(0.7021)$

$P \approx 10.32$

The atmospheric pressure is 10.32 pounds per square inch at 8,842 feet above sea level.

79. $A(n) = 72 - 18\log(n+1)$

a. $A(0) = 72 - 18\log(0+1)$

$= 72 - 18\log(1)$

$= 72 - 18(0)$

$= 72$

The original class average was 72.

b. $A(3) = 72 - 18\log(3+1)$

$= 72 - 18\log(4)$

$\approx 72 - 10.8$

$= 61.2$

After 3 months, the class average was 61.2.

c. Let $A(n) = 58.0$.

$58.0 = 72 - 18\log(n+1)$

$-14 = -18\log(n+1)$

$\dfrac{7}{9} = \log(n+1)$

$10^{7/9} = 10^{\log(n+1)}$

$10^{7/9} = n+1$

$10^{7/9} - 1 = n$

$5.0 \approx n$

It takes about 5 months.

Chapter 13 Practice Test

1. a. Yes, $\{(4, 2), (-3, 8), (-1, 3), (6, -7)\}$ is one-to-one.

b. $\{(2, 4), (8, -3), (3, -1), (-7, 6)\}$ is the inverse function.

2. a. $(f \circ g)(x) = f[g(x)]$

$= f(x+2)$

$= (x+2)^2 - 3$

$= x^2 + 4x + 4 - 3$

$= x^2 + 4x + 1$

b. $(f \circ g)(6) = 6^2 + 4(6) + 1$

$= 36 + 24 + 1$

$= 61$

3. a. $(g \circ f)(x) = g[f(x)]$

$= g(x^2 + 8)$

$= \sqrt{x^2 + 8 - 5}$

$= \sqrt{x^2 + 3}$

b. $(g \circ f)(7) = \sqrt{7^2 + 3}$

$= \sqrt{49 + 3}$

$= \sqrt{52}$

$= 2\sqrt{13}$

4. a. $y = f(x) = -3x - 5$

$x = -3y - 5$

$x + 5 = -3y$

$\dfrac{x+5}{-3} = y$

$-\dfrac{1}{3}(x + 5) = y$

$f^{-1}(x) = -\dfrac{1}{3}(x + 5)$

b.

x	$f(x)$
0	-5
$-\frac{5}{3}$	0

x	$f^{-1}(x)$
0	$-\frac{5}{3}$
-5	0

5. a. $y = f(x) = \sqrt{x-1},\ x \geq 1$

$$x = (y-1)^{1/2}$$
$$x^2 = [(y-1)^{1/2}]^2$$
$$x^2 = y - 1$$
$$x^2 + 1 = y$$
$$f^{-1}(x) = x^2 + 1,\ x \geq 0$$

b.

x	$f(x)$
1	0
2	1
5	2

x	$f^{-1}(x)$
0	1
1	2
2	5

6. The domain of $y = \log_5(x)$ is $\{x \mid x > 0\}$.

7. $\log_4 \dfrac{1}{256} = \log_4 4^{-4} = -4$

8. $y = 3^x$

x	-2	-1	0	2	3
y	$\frac{1}{9}$	$\frac{1}{3}$	1	9	27

Domain: $\mathbb{R}$
Range: $\{y \mid y > 0\}$

9. $y = \log_2 x$

$$x = 2^y$$

x	$\frac{1}{4}$	$\frac{1}{2}$	1	2	4
y	-2	-1	0	1	2

Domain: $\{x \mid x > 0\}$
Range: $\mathbb{R}$

10. $2^{-5} = \dfrac{1}{32}$

$$\log_2 \frac{1}{32} = -5$$

11. $\log_5 125 = 3$

$$5^3 = 125$$

12. $4 = \log_2(x+3)$

$$2^4 = x + 3$$
$$16 = x + 3$$
$$13 = x$$

13. $y = \log_{64} 16$

$$64^y = 16$$
$$\left(4^3\right)^y = 4^2$$
$$4^{3y} = 4^2$$
$$3y = 2$$
$$y = \frac{2}{3}$$

14. $\log_2 \dfrac{x^3(x-4)}{x+2}$

$$= \log_2 x^3(x-4) - \log_2(x+2)$$
$$= \log_2 x^3 + \log_2(x-4) - \log_2(x+2)$$
$$= 3\log_2 x + \log_2(x-4) - \log_2(x+2)$$

15. $7\log_6(x-4) + 2\log_6(x+3) - \dfrac{1}{2}\log_6 x$

$= \log_6(x-4)^7 + \log_6(x+3)^2 - \log_6 x^{1/2}$

$= \log_6 \dfrac{(x-4)^7(x+3)^2}{\sqrt{x}}$

16. $10\log_9 \sqrt{9} = 10\log_9 9^{1/2}$

$\qquad\qquad = 10 \cdot \dfrac{1}{2}$

$\qquad\qquad = 5$

17. a. $\log 4620 \approx 3.6646$

b. $\ln 0.0692 \approx -2.6708$

18. $3^x = 19$

$\log 3^x = \log 19$

$x\log 3 = \log 19$

$x = \dfrac{\log 19}{\log 3}$

$x \approx 2.68$

19. $\log 4x = \log(x+3) + \log 2$

$\log 4x = \log 2(x+3)$

$4x = 2(x+3)$

$4x = 2x + 6$

$2x = 6$

$x = 3$

20. $\log(x+5) - \log(x-2) = \log 6$

$\log \dfrac{x+5}{x-2} = \log 6$

$\dfrac{x+5}{x-2} = 6$

$x + 5 = 6x - 12$

$17 = 5x$

$\dfrac{17}{5} = x$

21. $\ln N = 2.79$

$e^{2.79} = N$

$16.2810 \approx N$

22. $\log_6 40 = \dfrac{\log 40}{\log 6} \approx 2.0588$

23. $100 = 250e^{-0.03t}$

$\dfrac{100}{250} = e^{-0.03t}$

$\ln \dfrac{100}{250} = -0.03t$

$\dfrac{\ln \frac{100}{250}}{-0.03} = t$

$t \approx 30.5430$

24. $A = p\left(1 + \dfrac{r}{n}\right)^{nt}$

Use $p = 3500$, $r = 0.04$ and $n = 4$

$t = 10$

$A = 3500\left(1 + \dfrac{0.04}{4}\right)^{4\cdot 10}$

$\quad = 3500(1.01)^{40}$

$\quad = 5211.02$

The amount in the account is \$5211.02.

25. $v = v_0 e^{-0.0001205t}$

Use $v = 40$, and $v_0 = 60$.

$40 = 60e^{-0.0001205t}$

$\dfrac{40}{60} = e^{-0.0001205t}$

$\dfrac{2}{3} = e^{-0.0001205t}$

$\ln \dfrac{2}{3} = \ln e^{-0.0001205t}$

$\ln \dfrac{2}{3} = -0.0001205t$

$\dfrac{\ln \frac{2}{3}}{-0.0001205} = t$

$3364.86 \approx t$

The fossil is approximately 3364.86 years old.

Chapter 13 Cumulative Review Test

1. $$\frac{6-\left|-18\right|\div 3^2-6}{4-\left|-8\right|\div 2^2}=\frac{6-18\div 3^2-6}{4-8\div 2^2}$$

$$=\frac{6-18\div 9-6}{4-8\div 4}$$

$$=\frac{6-2-6}{4-2}$$

$$=\frac{-2}{2}=-1$$

2. $4-(6x+6)=-(-2x+10)$

$\quad 4-6x-6=2x-10$

$\qquad -6x-2=2x-10$

$\qquad\qquad -8x=-8$

$\qquad\qquad\quad x=1$

3. $2x-3y=5$

$\quad -3y=5-2x$

$\quad y=\dfrac{5-2x}{-3}$ or $y=\dfrac{2x-5}{3}$

4. Let r be the tax rate.

$92+92r=98.90$

$\qquad 92r=6.90$

$\qquad\quad r=\dfrac{6.90}{92}$

$\qquad\qquad \approx 0.075$

The tax rate is 7.5%.

5. Let $t=$ the time it takes Kendra to catch up to Jason.

Person	Rate	Time	Distance
Jason	4	$t+0.5$	$4(t+0.5)$
Kendra	5	t	$5t$

a. $4(t+0.5)=5t$

$\quad 4t+2=5t$

$\qquad\quad 2=t$

Kendra will meet Jason after she has jogged for 2 hours.

b. $5(2)=10$ miles

6. Two points on the line are $(0, 3)$ and $(-2,-1)$.

$$m=\frac{y_2-y_1}{x_2-x_1}=\frac{-1-3}{-2-0}=\frac{-4}{-2}=2$$

Use point-slope form with $(0,3)$ and $m=2$.

$y-3=2(x-0)$

$y-3=2x$

$y=2x+3$

7. $$\left(\frac{3x^4y^{-3}}{6xy^4z^2}\right)^{-3}=\left(\frac{x^3}{2y^7z^2}\right)^{-3}=\left(\frac{2y^7z^2}{x^3}\right)^3$$

$$=\frac{8y^{21}z^6}{x^9}$$

8. $$\frac{x^3+3x^2+5x+4}{x+1}$$

Using synthetic division with $c=-1$:

$$
\begin{array}{r|rrrr}
-1 & 1 & 3 & 5 & 4 \\
   &   & -1 & -2 & -3 \\
\hline
   & 1 & 2 & 3 & 1
\end{array}
$$

$$\frac{x^3+3x^2+5x+4}{x+1}=x^2+2x+3+\frac{1}{x+1}$$

9. $12x^2-5xy-3y^2=(4x-3y)(3x+y)$

10. $x^2-2xy+y^2-25=\left(x^2-2xy+y^2\right)-25$

$$=(x-y)^2-5^2$$

$$=(x-y-5)(x-y+5)$$

11. $$\frac{x+1}{x+2}+\frac{x-2}{x-3}=\frac{x^2-4}{x^2-x-6}$$

LCD: $(x+2)(x-3)$

$(x+1)(x-3)+(x-2)(x+2)=x^2-4$

$\qquad x^2-2x-3+x^2-4=x^2-4$

$\qquad\qquad\qquad x^2-2x-3=0$

$\qquad\qquad\qquad (x-3)(x+1)=0$

$\qquad x-3=0$ or $x+1=0$

$\qquad\quad x=3\qquad\qquad x=-1$

We exclude $x=3$ since it is not in the domain of the variable. The solution is $x=-1$.

12. $L = \dfrac{K}{P^2} = \dfrac{100}{4^2} = \dfrac{100}{16} = 6.25$

13. $h(x) = \dfrac{x^2 + 4x}{x+6}$

$h(-3) = \dfrac{(-3)^2 + 4(-3)}{(-3)+6}$

$= \dfrac{9-12}{3} = \dfrac{-3}{3} = -1$

14. $0.4x + 0.6y = 3.2$

$1.4x - 0.3y = 1.6$

Multiply the second equation by 2 and add the equations.

$0.4x + 0.6y = 3.2$

$\underline{2.8x - 0.6y = 3.2}$

$3.2x = 6.4$

$x = 2$

Substitute 2 for x in the first equation and solve for y.

$0.4(2) + 0.6y = 3.2$

$0.8 + 0.6y = 3.2$

$0.6y = 2.4$

$y = 4$

The solution is $(2,4)$.

15. $x + y = 6$

$-2x + y = 3$

Write the augmented matrix.

$\begin{bmatrix} 1 & 1 & | & 6 \\ -2 & 1 & | & 3 \end{bmatrix}$

Use row transformations to write the matrix in triangular form.

$\begin{bmatrix} 1 & 1 & | & 6 \\ 0 & 3 & | & 15 \end{bmatrix} 2R_1 + R_2$

$\begin{bmatrix} 1 & 1 & | & 6 \\ 0 & 1 & | & 5 \end{bmatrix} \frac{1}{3}R_2$

Write the equivalent system of equations.

$x + y = 6$

$y = 5$

Substitute 5 for y in the first equation to find x.

$x + (5) = 6$

$x = 1$

The solution is $(1,5)$.

16. $\begin{vmatrix} 3 & 0 & -1 \\ 2 & 5 & 3 \\ -1 & 4 & 6 \end{vmatrix}$ Expand across row 1

$= 3\begin{vmatrix} 5 & 3 \\ 4 & 6 \end{vmatrix} - 0\begin{vmatrix} 2 & 3 \\ -1 & 6 \end{vmatrix} + (-1)\begin{vmatrix} 2 & 5 \\ -1 & 4 \end{vmatrix}$

$= 3(5 \cdot 6 - 4 \cdot 3) - 0 - (2 \cdot 4 - (-1) \cdot 5)$

$= 3(30 - 12) - (8 + 5)$

$= 3(18) - 13$

$= 54 - 13$

$= 41$

17. $y \le \dfrac{1}{3}x + 6$

Plot a solid line at $y = \dfrac{1}{3}x + 6$.

Use the point $(0, 0)$ as the check point.

$y \le \dfrac{1}{3}x + 6$

$0 \le \dfrac{1}{3}(0) + 6$

$0 \le 6$ True

Therefore, shade the half-plane containing $(0,0)$.

18. $g(x) = x^2 - 4x - 5$

a. $g(x) = x^2 - 4x - 5$

$g(x) = (x^2 - 4x + 4) - 5 - 4$

$g(x) = (x - 2)^2 - 9$

b.

$g(x) = x^2 - 4x - 5$

19. $f(x) = x^3 - 6x^2 + 5x \geq 0$

Factor the left side and set equal to 0.

$$x\left(x^2 - 6x + 5\right) = 0$$

$$x(x-5)(x-1) = 0$$

The left side is 0 when $x = 0$, 5, or 1. Therefore, our intervals are $(-\infty, 0)$, $(0,1)$, $(1,5)$, and $(5,\infty)$.

Interval A	Interval B
test value, -1	test value, 0.5

$f(-1) = -12$ $f(0.5) = \dfrac{9}{8}$

Interval C	Interval D
test value, 2	test value, 6

$f(2) = -6$ $f(6) = 30$

The inequality is satisfied on intervals B and D. The inequality is non-strict, so we also include the endpoints. The solution set, in interval notation, is $[0,1] \cup [5,\infty)$.

20. **a.** $A = 600e^{-0.028t}$

When $t = 60$, we get

$A = 600e^{-0.028(60)} \approx 111.82$

After 60 years there will be about 111.82 grams remaining.

b.   To find the half-life, we are looking for the time required to have half of the initial amount remaining.

$$300 = 600e^{-0.028t}$$

$$\frac{1}{2} = e^{-0.028t}$$

$$\ln\left(\frac{1}{2}\right) = -0.028t$$

$$\frac{\ln\left(\dfrac{1}{2}\right)}{-0.028} = t \quad \text{or} \quad t \approx 24.8$$

The half-life is about 24.8 years.

Chapter 14

Exercise Set 14.1

1.

Parabola   Circle   Ellipse   Hyperbola

2. For an equation of the form $y = ax^2 + bx + c$ or $y = a(x-h)^2 + k$, the parabola opens upward if $a > 0$ and downward if $a < 0$. For an equation of the form $x = ay^2 + by + c$ or $x = a(y-k)^2 + h$, the parabola opens to the right if $a > 0$ and to the left if $a < 0$.

3. Yes, any parabola in the form $y = a(x-h)^2 + k$ is a function because each value of x corresponds to only one value of y. The domain is $\mathbb{R}$, the set of all real numbers. Since the vertex is at (h, k) and $a > 0$, the range is $\{y \mid y \geq k\}$.

4. No, a parabola in the form $x = a(y-k)^2 + h$, $a > 0$, is not a function, because for $x > h$, there are two values of y for each value of x. Since the vertex is at (h, k) and $a > 0$, the domain is $\{x \mid x \geq h\}$ and the range is $\mathbb{R}$, the set of all real numbers.

5. The graphs have the same vertex, $(3, 4)$. The first graph opens upward, and the second one opens downward.

6. $d = \sqrt{(x_2 - x_1)^2 + (y_2 - y_1)^2}$

7. The distance is always a positive number because both distances are squared and we use the principal square root.

8. $\left(\dfrac{x_1 + x_2}{2}, \dfrac{y_1 + y_2}{2} \right)$

9. A circle is the set of all points in a plane that are the same distance from a fixed point.

10. $(x-h)^2 + (y-k)^2 = r^2$, where r is the radius.

11. No, the coefficients of the y^2- term and the x^2- term must both be the same.

12. No, the coefficients of the y^2- term and the x^2- term must both be the same.

13. No, the coefficients of the y^2- term and the x^2- term must both be the same.

14. Yes, this equation can be written in the form $x = a(y-k)^2 + h$.

$$x = y^2 - 6y + 3$$
$$x = \left(y^2 - 6y + 9 \right) + 3 - 9$$
$$x = (y-3)^2 - 6$$

15. No, equations of parabolas do not include both x^2- and y^2- terms.

16. No, equations of parabolas must include either an x^2- term or a y^2- term.

17. $y = (x-2)^2 + 3$

This is a parabola in the form $y = a(x-h)^2 + k$ with $a = 1$, $h = 2$ and $k = 3$. Since $a > 0$, the parabola opens upward. The vertex is $(2, 3)$. The y-intercept is $(0, 7)$. There are no x-intercepts.

18. $y = (x-2)^2 - 3$

This is a parabola in the form $y = a(x-h)^2 + k$ with $a = 1$, $h = 2$ and $k = -3$. Since $a > 0$, the parabola opens upward. The vertex is $(2, -3)$. The y-intercept is $(0, 1)$. The x-intercepts are about $(0.27, 0)$ and $(3.73, 0)$.

19. $y = (x+3)^2 + 2$

This is a parabola in the form $y = a(x-h)^2 + k$ with $a = 1$, $h = -3$ and $k = 2$. Since $a > 0$, the parabola opens upward. The vertex is $(-3, 2)$. The y-intercept is $(0, 11)$. There are no x-intercepts.

20. $y = (x+3)^2 - 2$

This is a parabola in the form $y = a(x-h)^2 + k$ with $a = 1$, $h = -3$ and $k = -2$. Since $a > 0$, the parabola opens upward. The vertex is $(-3, -2)$. The y-intercept is $(0, 7)$. The x-intercepts are about $(-4.41, 0)$ and $(-1.59, 0)$.

21. $y = (x-2)^2 - 1$

This is a parabola in the form $y = a(x-h)^2 + k$ with $a = 1$, $h = 2$ and $k = -1$. Since $a > 0$, the parabola opens upward. The vertex is $(2, -1)$. The y-intercept is $(0, 3)$. The x-intercepts are $(1, 0)$ and $(3, 0)$.

22. $y = (x+2)^2 + 1$

This is a parabola in the form $y = a(x-h)^2 + k$ with $a = 1$, $h = -2$ and $k = 1$. Since $a > 0$, the parabola opens upward. The vertex is $(-2, 1)$. The y-intercept is $(0, 5)$. There are no x-intercepts.

23. $y = -(x-1)^2 + 1$

This is a parabola in the form $y = a(x-h)^2 + k$ with $a = -1$, $h = 1$ and $k = 1$. Since $a < 0$, the parabola opens downward. The vertex is $(1, 1)$. The y-intercept is $(0, 0)$. The x-intercepts are $(0, 0)$ and $(2, 0)$.

$$y = -(x - 1)^2 + 1$$

24. $y = -(x+4)^2 - 5$

This is a parabola in the form $y = a(x-h)^2 + k$ with $a = -1$, $h = -4$ and $k = -5$. Since $a < 0$, the parabola opens downward. The vertex is $(-4, -5)$. The y-intercept is $(0, -21)$. There are no x-intercepts.

$$y = -(x + 4)^2 - 5$$

25. $y = -(x+3)^2 + 4$

This is a parabola in the form $y = a(x-h)^2 + k$ with $a = -1$, $h = -3$ and $k = 4$. Since $a < 0$, the parabola opens downward. The vertex is $(-3, 4)$. The y-intercept is $(0, -5)$. The x-intercepts are $(-5, 0)$ and $(-1, 0)$.

$$y = -(x + 3)^2 + 4$$

26. $y = 2(x+1)^2 - 3$

This is a parabola in the form $y = a(x-h)^2 + k$ with $a = 2$, $h = -1$ and $k = -3$. Since $a > 0$, the parabola opens upward. The vertex is $(-1, -3)$. The y-intercept is $(0, -1)$. The x-intercepts are about $(-2.22, 0)$ and $(0.22, 0)$.

$$y = 2(x + 1)^2 - 3$$

27. $y = -3(x-5)^2 + 3$

This is a parabola in the form $y = a(x-h)^2 + k$ with $a = -3$, $h = 5$ and $k = 3$. Since $a < 0$, the parabola opens downward. The vertex is $(5, 3)$. The y-intercept is $(0, -72)$. The x-intercepts are $(4, 0)$ and $(6, 0)$.

$$y = -3(x - 5)^2 + 3$$

28. $x = (y-1)^2 + 1$

This is a parabola in the form $x = a(y-k)^2 + h$ with $a = 1$, $h = 1$ and $k = 1$. Since $a > 0$, the parabola opens to the right. The vertex is $(1, 1)$. There are no y-intercepts. The x-intercept is $(2, 0)$.

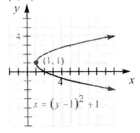

29. $x = (y-4)^2 - 3$

This is a parabola in the form $x = a(y-k)^2 + h$ with $a = 1$, $h = -3$ and $k = 4$. Since $a > 0$, the parabola opens to the right. The vertex is $(-3, 4)$. The y-intercepts are about $(0, 2.27)$ and $(0, 5.73)$. The x-intercept is $(13, 0)$.

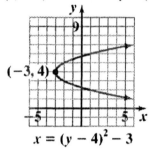

30. $x = -(y-2)^2 + 1$

This is a parabola in the form $x = a(y-k)^2 + h$ with $a = -1$, $h = 1$ and $k = 2$. Since $a < 0$, the parabola opens to the left. The vertex is $(1, 2)$. The y-intercepts are about $(0, 1)$ and $(0, 3)$. The x-intercept is $(-3, 0)$.

31. $x = -(y-5)^2 + 4$

This is a parabola in the form $x = a(y-k)^2 + h$ with $a = -1$, $h = 4$ and $k = 5$. Since $a < 0$, the parabola opens to the left. The vertex is $(4, 5)$. The y-intercepts are $(0, 3)$ and $(0, 7)$. The x-intercept is $(-21, 0)$.

32. $x = -2(y-4)^2 + 4$

This is a parabola in the form $x = a(y-k)^2 + h$ with $a = -2$, $h = 4$ and $k = 4$. Since $a < 0$, the parabola opens to the left. The vertex is $(4, 4)$. The y-intercepts are about $(0, 2.59)$ and $(0, 5.41)$. The x-intercept is $(-28, 0)$.

33. $x = -5(y+3)^2 - 6$

This is a parabola in the form $x = a(y-k)^2 + h$ with $a = -5$, $h = -6$ and $k = -3$. Since $a < 0$, the parabola opens to the left. The vertex is $(-6, -3)$. There are no y-intercepts. The x-intercept is $(-51, 0)$

34. $x = 3(y+1)^2 + 5$

This is a parabola in the form $x = a(y-k)^2 + h$ with $a = 3$, $h = 5$ and $k = -11$. Since $a > 0$, the parabola opens to the right. The vertex is $(5, -1)$. There are no y-intercepts. The x-intercept is $(8, 0)$.

35. $y = -2\left(x + \dfrac{1}{2}\right)^2 + 6$

This is a parabola in the form $y = a(x - h)^2 + k$

with $a = -2$, $h = -\dfrac{1}{2}$ and $k = 6$. Since $a < 0$, the

parabola opens downward. The vertex is

$\left(-\dfrac{1}{2}, 6\right)$. The y-intercept is $\left(0, \dfrac{11}{2}\right)$. The

x-intercepts are about $(-2.23, 0)$ and $(1.23, 0)$.

$$y = -2\left(x + \dfrac{1}{2}\right)^2 + 6$$

36. $y = -\left(x - \dfrac{5}{2}\right)^2 + \dfrac{1}{2}$

This is a parabola in the form $y = a(x - h)^2 + k$

with $a = -1$, $h = \dfrac{5}{2}$ and $k = \dfrac{1}{2}$. Since $a < 0$, the

parabola opens downward. The vertex is

$\left(\dfrac{5}{2}, \dfrac{1}{2}\right)$. The y-intercept is $\left(0, \dfrac{23}{4}\right)$. The

x-intercepts are about $(1.79, 0)$ and $(3.21, 0)$.

$$y = -\left(x - \dfrac{5}{2}\right)^2 + \dfrac{1}{2}$$

37. a. $y = x^2 + 2x$

$y = (x^2 + 2x + 1) - 1$

$y = (x + 1)^2 - 1$

   b. This is a parabola in the form
$y = a(x - h)^2 + k$ with $a = 1$, $h = -1$ and
$k = -1$. Since $a > 0$, the parabola opens
upward. The vertex is $(-1, -1)$. The
y-intercept is $(0, 0)$. The x-intercepts are
$(-2, 0)$ and $(0, 0)$.

38. a. $y = x^2 - 2x$

$y = (x^2 - 2x + 1) - 1$

$y = (x - 1)^2 - 1$

   b. This is a parabola in the form
$y = a(x - h)^2 + k$ with $a = 1$, $h = 1$ and
$k = -1$. Since $a > 0$, the parabola opens
upward. The vertex is $(1, -1)$. The
y-intercept is $(0, 0)$. The x-intercepts are
$(2, 0)$ and $(0, 0)$.

39. a. $y = x^2 + 6x$

$y = (x^2 + 6x + 9) - 9$

$y = (x + 3)^2 - 9$

b. This is a parabola in the form
$y = a(x - h)^2 + k$ with $a = 1$, $h = -3$ and
$k = -9$. Since $a > 0$, the parabola opens
upward. The vertex is $(-3, -9)$. The
y-intercept is $(0, 0)$. The x-intercepts are
$(-6, 0)$ and $(0, 0)$.

40. a. $y = x^2 - 4x$

$y = (x^2 - 4x + 4) - 4$

$y = (x - 2)^2 - 4$

b. This is a parabola in the form
$y = a(x - h)^2 + k$ with $a = 1$, $h = 2$ and
$k = -4$. Since $a > 0$, the parabola opens
upward. The vertex is $(2, -4)$. The
y-intercept is $(0, 0)$. The x-intercepts are
$(0, 0)$ and $(4, 0)$.

$y = x^2 - 4x$

$(2, -4)$

41. a. $x = y^2 + 4y$

$x = (y^2 + 4y + 4) - 4$

$x = (y + 2)^2 - 4$

b. This is a parabola in the form
$x = a(y - k)^2 + h$ with $a = 1$, $h = -4$ and
$k = -2$. Since $a > 0$, the parabola opens to
the right. The vertex is $(-4, -2)$. The
y-intercepts are $(0, -4)$ and $(0, 0)$. The
x-intercept is $(0, 0)$.

42. a. $x = y^2 - 6y$

$x = (y^2 - 6y + 9) - 9$

$x = (y - 3)^2 - 9$

b. This is a parabola in the form
$x = a(y - k)^2 + h$ with $a = 1$, $h = -9$ and
$k = 3$. Since $a > 0$, the parabola opens to the
right. The vertex is $(-9, 3)$. The y-intercepts
are $(0, 6)$ and $(0, 0)$. The x-intercept is $(0, 0)$.

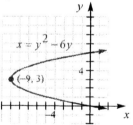

43. a. $y = x^2 + 7x + 10$

$y = \left(x^2 + 7x + \dfrac{49}{4} \right) - \dfrac{49}{4} + 10$

$y = \left(x + \dfrac{7}{2} \right)^2 - \dfrac{9}{4}$

b. This is a parabola in the form

$y = a(x-h)^2 + k$ with $a = 1$, $h = -\dfrac{7}{2}$ and

$k = -\dfrac{9}{4}$. Since $a > 0$, the parabola opens

upward. The vertex is $\left(-\dfrac{7}{2}, -\dfrac{9}{4}\right)$. The

y-intercept is $(0, 10)$. The x-intercepts are
$(-5, 0)$ and $(-2, 0)$.

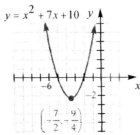

44. a. $y = x^2 + 2x - 7$

$y = (x^2 + 2x + 1) - 1 - 7$

$y = (x+1)^2 - 8$

b. This is a parabola in the form

$y = a(x-h)^2 + k$ with $a = 1$, $h = -1$, and

$k = -8$. Since $a > 0$, the parabola opens
upward. The vertex is $(-1, -8)$. The
y-intercept is $(0, -7)$. The x-intercepts are
about $(-3.83, 0)$ and $(1.83, 0)$.

45. a. $x = -y^2 + 6y - 9$

$x = -(y^2 - 6y) - 9$

$x = -(y^2 - 6y + 9) + 9 - 9$

$x = -(y-3)^2$

b. This is a parabola in the form
$x = a(y-k)^2 + h$ with $a = -1$, $h = 0$ and
$k = 3$. Since $a < 0$, the parabola opens to the
left. The vertex is $(0, 3)$. The y-intercept is
$(0, 3)$. The x-intercept is
$(-9, 0)$.

46. a. $x = -y^2 - 5y - 4$

$x = -\left(y^2 + 5y + \dfrac{25}{4}\right) - 4 + \dfrac{25}{4}$

$x = -\left(y + \dfrac{5}{2}\right)^2 - \dfrac{16}{4} + \dfrac{25}{4}$

$x = -\left(y + \dfrac{5}{2}\right)^2 + \dfrac{9}{4}$

b. This is a parabola in the form

$x = a(y-k)^2 + h$ with $a = -1$, $h = \dfrac{9}{4}$ and

$k = -\dfrac{5}{2}$. Since $a < 0$, the parabola opens to

the left. The vertex is $\left(\dfrac{9}{4}, -\dfrac{5}{2}\right)$. The

y-intercepts are $(0, -4)$ and $(0, -1)$. The
x-intercept is $(-4, 0)$.

47. a.

$$y = -x^2 + 4x - 4$$
$$y = -(x^2 - 4x) - 4$$
$$y = -(x^2 - 4x + 4) + 4 - 4$$
$$y = -(x - 2)^2$$

b. This is a parabola in the form
$y = a(x - h)^2 + k$ with $a = -1$, $h = 2$ and
$k = 0$. Since $a < 0$, the parabola opens
downward. The vertex is (2, 0). The
y-intercept is (0, –4). The x-intercept is
(2, 0).

$$y = -x^2 + 4x - 4$$

48. a.

$$y = 2x^2 - 4x - 4$$
$$y = 2(x^2 - 2x) - 4$$
$$y = 2(x^2 - 2x + 1) - 2 - 4$$
$$y = 2(x - 1)^2 - 6$$

b. This is a parabola in the form
$y = a(x - h)^2 + k$ with $a = 2$, $h = 1$ and
$k = -6$. Since $a > 0$, the parabola opens
upward. The vertex is (1, –6). The
y-intercept is (0, –4). The x-intercepts are
about (–0.73, 0) and (2.73, 0).

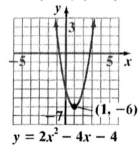

$$y = 2x^2 - 4x - 4$$

49. a.

$$x = -y^2 + 3y - 4$$
$$x = -\left(y^2 - 3y\right) - 4$$
$$x = -\left(y^2 - 3y + \frac{9}{4}\right) + \frac{9}{4} - 4$$
$$x = -\left(y - \frac{3}{2}\right)^2 - \frac{7}{4}$$

b. This is a parabola in the form
$x = a(y - k)^2 + h$ with $a = -1$, $h = -\dfrac{7}{4}$ and

$k = \dfrac{3}{2}$. Since $a < 0$, the parabola opens to

the left. The vertex is $\left(-\dfrac{7}{4}, \dfrac{3}{2}\right)$. There are

no y-intercepts.
The x-intercept is (–4, 0).

50. a.

$$x = 3y^2 - 12y - 36$$
$$x = 3(y^2 - 4y) - 36$$
$$x = 3(y^2 - 4y + 4) - 12 - 36$$
$$x = 3(y - 2)^2 - 48$$

b. This is a parabola in the form
$x = a(y - k)^2 + h$ with $a = 3$, $h = -48$ and
$k = 2$. Since $a > 0$, the parabola opens to the
right. The vertex is (–48, 2).
The y-intercepts are (0, –2) and (0, 6).
The x-intercept is (–36, 0).

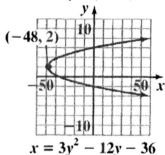

$$x = 3y^2 - 12y - 36$$

51. $d = \sqrt{(x_2 - x_1)^2 + (y_2 - y_1)^2}$

$\quad = \sqrt{(5-5)^2 + \left[-6-(-1)\right]^2}$

$\quad = \sqrt{0^2 + (-5)^2}$

$\quad = \sqrt{0+25}$

$\quad = \sqrt{25}$

$\quad = 5$

52. $d = \sqrt{(x_2 - x_1)^2 + (y_2 - y_1)^2}$

$\quad = \sqrt{\left[-3-(-7)\right]^2 + (2-2)^2}$

$\quad = \sqrt{4^2 + (0)^2}$

$\quad = \sqrt{16+0}$

$\quad = \sqrt{16}$

$\quad = 4$

53. $d = \sqrt{(x_2 - x_1)^2 + (y_2 - y_1)^2}$

$\quad = \sqrt{\left[8-(-1)\right]^2 + (6-6)^2}$

$\quad = \sqrt{9^2 + 0^2}$

$\quad = \sqrt{81+0}$

$\quad = \sqrt{81}$

$\quad = 9$

54. $d = \sqrt{(x_2 - x_1)^2 + (y_2 - y_1)^2}$

$\quad = \sqrt{\left[4-1\right]^2 + \left[12-8\right]^2}$

$\quad = \sqrt{3^2 + 4^2}$

$\quad = \sqrt{9+16}$

$\quad = \sqrt{25}$

$\quad = 5$

55. $d = \sqrt{(x_2 - x_1)^2 + (y_2 - y_1)^2}$

$\quad = \sqrt{\left[4-(-1)\right]^2 + \left[9-(-3)\right]^2}$

$\quad = \sqrt{5^2 + 12^2}$

$\quad = \sqrt{25+144}$

$\quad = \sqrt{169}$

$\quad = 13$

56. $d = \sqrt{(x_2 - x_1)^2 + (y_2 - y_1)^2}$

$\quad = \sqrt{\left[2-(-4)\right]^2 + \left[3-(-5)\right]^2}$

$\quad = \sqrt{6^2 + 8^2}$

$\quad = \sqrt{36+64}$

$\quad = \sqrt{100}$

$\quad = 10$

57. $d = \sqrt{(x_2 - x_1)^2 + (y_2 - y_1)^2}$

$\quad = \sqrt{\left[5-(-4)\right]^2 + \left[-2-(-5)\right]^2}$

$\quad = \sqrt{9^2 + 3^2}$

$\quad = \sqrt{81+9}$

$\quad = \sqrt{90} \approx 9.49$

58. $d = \sqrt{(x_2 - x_1)^2 + (y_2 - y_1)^2}$

$\quad = \sqrt{(11-6)^2 + (0-7)^2}$

$\quad = \sqrt{5^2 + (-7)^2}$

$\quad = \sqrt{25+49}$

$\quad = \sqrt{74} \approx 8.60$

59. $d = \sqrt{(x_2 - x_1)^2 + (y_2 - y_1)^2}$

$\quad = \sqrt{\left(\dfrac{1}{2}-3\right)^2 + \left[4-(-1)\right]^2}$

$\quad = \sqrt{\left(-\dfrac{5}{2}\right)^2 + 5^2}$

$\quad = \sqrt{\dfrac{25}{4} + 25}$

$\quad = \sqrt{\dfrac{125}{4}}$

$\quad \approx 5.59$

60. $d = \sqrt{(x_2 - x_1)^2 + (y_2 - y_1)^2}$

$= \sqrt{\left(-\dfrac{3}{2} - \left(-\dfrac{1}{4}\right)\right)^2 + (6-2)^2}$

$= \sqrt{\left(-\dfrac{5}{4}\right)^2 + 4^2}$

$= \sqrt{\dfrac{25}{16} + 16}$

$= \sqrt{\dfrac{281}{16}}$

≈ 4.19

61. $d = \sqrt{(x_2 - x_1)^2 + (y_2 - y_1)^2}$

$= \sqrt{\left[-4.3 - (-1.6)\right]^2 + (-1.7 - 3.5)^2}$

$= \sqrt{(-2.7)^2 + (-5.2)^2}$

$= \sqrt{7.29 + 27.04}$

$= \sqrt{34.33}$

≈ 5.86

62. $d = \sqrt{(x_2 - x_1)^2 + (y_2 - y_1)^2}$

$= \sqrt{(-1.6 - 5.2)^2 + \left[2.3 - (-3.6)\right]^2}$

$= \sqrt{(-6.8)^2 + 5.9^2}$

$= \sqrt{46.24 + 34.81}$

$= \sqrt{81.05}$

≈ 9.00

63. $d = \sqrt{(x_2 - x_1)^2 + (y_2 - y_1)^2}$

$= \sqrt{\left(0 - \sqrt{7}\right)^2 + \left[0 - \sqrt{3}\right]^2}$

$= \sqrt{\left(-\sqrt{7}\right)^2 + \left(\sqrt{3}\right)^2}$

$= \sqrt{7 + 3}$

$= \sqrt{10}$

≈ 3.16

64. $d = \sqrt{(x_2 - x_1)^2 + (y_2 - y_1)^2}$

$= \sqrt{\left(0 - \left(-\sqrt{2}\right)\right)^2 + \left[0 - \left(-\sqrt{5}\right)\right]^2}$

$= \sqrt{\left(\sqrt{2}\right)^2 + \left(\sqrt{5}\right)^2}$

$= \sqrt{2 + 5}$

$= \sqrt{7}$

≈ 2.65

65. Midpoint $= \left(\dfrac{x_1 + x_2}{2}, \dfrac{y_1 + y_2}{2}\right)$

$= \left(\dfrac{1+5}{2}, \dfrac{9+3}{2}\right)$

$= (3, 6)$

66. Midpoint $= \left(\dfrac{x_1 + x_2}{2}, \dfrac{y_1 + y_2}{2}\right)$

$= \left(\dfrac{0+4}{2}, \dfrac{8+(-6)}{2}\right)$

$= (2, 1)$

67. Midpoint $= \left(\dfrac{x_1 + x_2}{2}, \dfrac{y_1 + y_2}{2}\right)$

$= \left(\dfrac{-7+7}{2}, \dfrac{2+(-2)}{2}\right)$

$= (0, 0)$

68. Midpoint $= \left(\dfrac{x_1 + x_2}{2}, \dfrac{y_1 + y_2}{2}\right)$

$= \left(\dfrac{4+1}{2}, \dfrac{7+(-3)}{2}\right)$

$= \left(\dfrac{5}{2}, 2\right)$

69. Midpoint $= \left(\dfrac{x_1 + x_2}{2}, \dfrac{y_1 + y_2}{2}\right)$

$= \left(\dfrac{-1+4}{2}, \dfrac{4+6}{2}\right)$

$= \left(\dfrac{3}{2}, 5\right)$

70. $\text{Midpoint} = \left(\dfrac{x_1 + x_2}{2}, \dfrac{y_1 + y_2}{2} \right)$

$= \left(\dfrac{-2 + (-6)}{2}, \dfrac{-9 + (-3)}{2} \right)$

$= (-4, -6)$

71. $\text{Midpoint} = \left(\dfrac{x_1 + x_2}{2}, \dfrac{y_1 + y_2}{2} \right)$

$= \left(\dfrac{3 + 2}{2}, \dfrac{\frac{1}{2} + (-4)}{2} \right)$

$= \left(\dfrac{5}{2}, -\dfrac{7}{4} \right)$

72. $\text{Midpoint} = \left(\dfrac{x_1 + x_2}{2}, \dfrac{y_1 + y_2}{2} \right)$

$= \left(\dfrac{\frac{5}{2} + 2}{2}, \dfrac{3 + \frac{9}{2}}{2} \right)$

$= \left(\dfrac{9}{4}, \dfrac{15}{4} \right)$

73. $\text{Midpoint} = \left(\dfrac{x_1 + x_2}{2}, \dfrac{y_1 + y_2}{2} \right)$

$= \left(\dfrac{\sqrt{3} + \sqrt{2}}{2}, \dfrac{2 + 7}{2} \right)$

$= \left(\dfrac{\sqrt{3} + \sqrt{2}}{2}, \dfrac{9}{2} \right)$

74. $\text{Midpoint} = \left(\dfrac{x_1 + x_2}{2}, \dfrac{y_1 + y_2}{2} \right)$

$= \left(\dfrac{-\sqrt{7} + \sqrt{5}}{2}, \dfrac{8 + \sqrt{3}}{2} \right)$

75. $(x - h)^2 + (y - k)^2 = r^2$

$(x - 0)^2 + (y - 0)^2 = 4^2$

$x^2 + y^2 = 16$

76. $(x - h)^2 + (y - k)^2 = r^2$

$(x - 0)^2 + (y - 0)^2 = 7^2$

$x^2 + y^2 = 49$

77. $(x - h)^2 + (y - k)^2 = r^2$

$(x - 2)^2 + (y - 0)^2 = 5^2$

$(x - 2)^2 + y^2 = 25$

78. $(x - h)^2 + (y - k)^2 = r^2$

$(x - (-3))^2 + (y - 0)^2 = 9^2$

$(x + 3)^2 + y^2 = 81$

79. $(x - h)^2 + (y - k)^2 = r^2$

$(x - 0)^2 + (y - 5)^2 = 1^2$

$x^2 + (y - 5)^2 = 1$

80. $(x - h)^2 + (y - k)^2 = r^2$

$(x - 0)^2 + \left[y - (-6) \right]^2 = 6^2$

$x^2 + (y + 6)^2 = 36$

81. $(x - h)^2 + (y - k)^2 = r^2$

$(x - 3)^2 + (y - 4)^2 = (8)^2$

$(x - 3)^2 + (y - 4)^2 = 64$

82. $(x - h)^2 + (y - k)^2 = r^2$

$\left[x - (-5) \right]^2 + (y - 2)^2 = 2^2$

$(x + 5)^2 + (y - 2)^2 = 4$

83. $(x - h)^2 + (y - k)^2 = r^2$

$(x - 7)^2 + \left[y - (-6) \right]^2 = 10^2$

$(x - 7)^2 + (y + 6)^2 = 100$

84. $(x - h)^2 + (y - k)^2 = r^2$

$\left[x - (-6) \right]^2 + \left[y - (-1) \right]^2 = 7^2$

$(x + 6)^2 + (y + 1)^2 = 49$

85. $(x - h)^2 + (y - k)^2 = r^2$

$(x - 1)^2 + (y - 2)^2 = \left(\sqrt{5} \right)^2$

$(x - 1)^2 + (y - 2)^2 = 5$

86. $(x-h)^2+(y-k)^2=r^2$

$$\left[x-(-7)\right]^2+[y-(-2)]^2=\left(\sqrt{13}\right)^2$$

$$(x+7)^2+(y+2)^2=13$$

87. The center is (0, 0) and the radius is 4.

$$(x-h)^2+(y-k)^2=r^2$$

$$(x-0)^2+(y-0)^2=4^2$$

$$x^2+y^2=16$$

88. The center is (–4, 6) and the radius is 2.

$$(x-h)^2+(y-k)^2=r^2$$

$$\left[x-(-4)\right]^2+(y-6)^2=2^2$$

$$(x+4)^2+(y-6)^2=4$$

89. The center is (3, –2) and the radius is 3.

$$(x-h)^2+(y-k)^2=r^2$$

$$(x-3)^2+[y-(-2)]^2=3^2$$

$$(x-3)^2+(y+2)^2=9$$

90. The center is (–5, –3) and the radius is 2.

$$(x-h)^2+(y-k)^2=r^2$$

$$[x-(-5)]^2+[y-(-3)]^2=2^2$$

$$(x+5)^2+(y+3)^2=4$$

91. $x^2+y^2=16$

$$x^2+y^2=4^2$$

The graph is a circle with its center at the origin and radius 4.

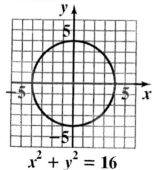

$$x^2+y^2=16$$

92. $x^2+y^2=5$

$$x^2+y^2=\left(\sqrt{5}\right)^2$$

The graph is a circle with its center at the origin and radius $\sqrt{5}$.

93. $x^2+y^2=10$

$$x^2+y^2=\left(\sqrt{10}\right)^2$$

The graph is a circle with its center at the origin and radius $\sqrt{10}$.

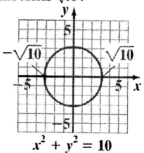

$$x^2+y^2=10$$

94. $(x-1)^2+y^2=7$

$$(x-1)^2+(y-0)^2=\left(\sqrt{7}\right)^2$$

The graph is a circle with its center at (1, 0) and radius $\sqrt{7}$.

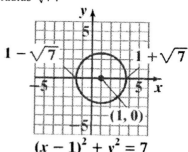

$$(x-1)^2+y^2=7$$

95. $(x+4)^2 + y^2 = 25$

$(x+4)^2 + (y-0)^2 = 5^2$

The graph is a circle with its center at $(-4, 0)$ and radius 5.

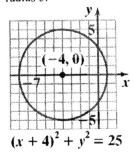

$(x + 4)^2 + y^2 = 25$

96. $x^2 + (y+1)^2 = 9$

$(x-0)^2 + (y+1)^2 = (3)^2$

The graph is a circle with its center at $(0, -1)$ and radius 3.

97. $x^2 + (y-3)^2 = 4$

$(x-0)^2 + (y-3)^2 = (2)^2$

The graph is a circle with its center at $(0, 3)$ and radius 2.

$x^2 + (y - 3)^2 = 4$

98. $(x-2)^2 + (y+3)^2 = 16$

$(x-2)^2 + (y+3)^2 = 4^2$

The graph is a circle with its center at $(2, -3)$ and radius 4.

$(x - 2)^2 + (y + 3)^2 = 16$

99. $(x+8)^2 + (y+2)^2 = 9$

$(x+8)^2 + (y+2)^2 = 3^2$

The graph is a circle with its center at $(-8, -2)$ and radius 3.

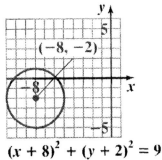

$(x + 8)^2 + (y + 2)^2 = 9$

100. $(x+3)^2 + (y-4)^2 = 36$

$(x+3)^2 + (y-4)^2 = 6^2$

The graph is a circle with its center at $(-3, 4)$ and radius 6.

$(x+3)^2 + (y-4)^2 = 36$

101. $y = \sqrt{25 - x^2}$

If we solve $x^2 + y^2 = 25$ for y, we obtain $y = \pm\sqrt{25 - x^2}$. Therefore, the graph of $y = \sqrt{25 - x^2}$ is the upper half $(y \geq 0)$ of a circle with its center at the origin and radius 5.

102. $y = \sqrt{16 - x^2}$

If we solve $x^2 + y^2 = 16$ for y, we obtain $y = \pm\sqrt{16 - x^2}$. Therefore, the graph of $y = \sqrt{16 - x^2}$ is the upper half $(y \geq 0)$ of a circle with its center at the origin and radius 4.

103. $y = -\sqrt{4 - x^2}$

If we solve $x^2 + y^2 = 4$ for y, we obtain $y = \pm\sqrt{4 - x^2}$. Therefore, the graph of $y = -\sqrt{4 - x^2}$ is the lower half $(y \leq 0)$ of a circle with its center at the origin and radius 2.

104. $y = -\sqrt{49 - x^2}$

If we solve $x^2 + y^2 = 49$ for y, we obtain $y = \pm\sqrt{49 - x^2}$. Therefore, the graph of $y = -\sqrt{49 - x^2}$ is the lower half $(y \leq 0)$ of a circle with its center at the origin and radius 7.

105. a.
$$x^2 + y^2 + 8x + 15 = 0$$
$$x^2 + 8x + y^2 = -15$$
$$(x^2 + 8x + 16) + y^2 = -15 + 16$$
$$(x + 4)^2 + y^2 = 1$$
$$(x + 4)^2 + y^2 = 1^2$$

b. The graph is a circle with center $(-4, 0)$ and radius 1.

106. a.
$$x^2 + y^2 + 4y = 0$$
$$x^2 + (y^2 + 4y + 4) = 4$$
$$x^2 + (y + 2)^2 = 4$$
$$x^2 + (y + 2)^2 = 2^2$$

b. The graph is a circle with center $(0, -2)$ and radius 2.

107. a.
$$x^2 + y^2 + 6x - 4y + 4 = 0$$
$$x^2 + 6x + y^2 - 4y = -4$$
$$(x^2 + 6x + 9) + (y^2 - 4y + 4) = -4 + 9 + 4$$
$$(x + 3)^2 + (y - 2)^2 = 9$$
$$(x + 3)^2 + (y - 2)^2 = 3^2$$

b. The graph is a circle with center (–3, 2) and radius 3.

$$x^2 + y^2 + 6x - 4y + 4 = 0$$

108. a.
$$x^2 + y^2 + 2x - 4y - 4 = 0$$
$$x^2 + 2x + y^2 - 4y = 4$$
$$(x^2 + 2x + 1) + (y^2 - 4y + 4) = 4 + 1 + 4$$
$$(x + 1)^2 + (y - 2)^2 = 9$$
$$(x + 1)^2 + (y - 2)^2 = 3^2$$

b. The graph is a circle with center (–1, 2) and radius 3.

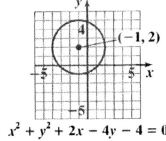

$$x^2 + y^2 + 2x - 4y - 4 = 0$$

109. a.
$$x^2 + y^2 + 6x - 2y + 6 = 0$$
$$x^2 + 6x + y^2 - 2y = -6$$
$$(x^2 + 6x + 9) + (y^2 - 2y + 1) = -6 + 9 + 1$$
$$(x + 3)^2 + (y - 1)^2 = 4$$
$$(x + 3)^2 + (y - 1)^2 = 2^2$$

b. The graph is a circle with center (–3, 1) and radius 2.

$$x^2 + y^2 + 6x - 2y + 6 = 0$$

110. a.
$$x^2 + y^2 + 4x - 6y - 3 = 0$$
$$x^2 + 4x + y^2 - 6y = 3$$
$$(x^2 + 4x + 4) + (y^2 - 6y + 9) = 3 + 4 + 9$$
$$(x + 2)^2 + (y - 3)^2 = 16$$
$$(x + 2)^2 + (y - 3)^2 = 4^2$$

b. The graph is a circle with center (–2, 3) and radius 4.

$$x^2 + y^2 + 4x - 6y - 3 = 0$$

111. a.
$$x^2 + y^2 - 8x + 2y + 13 = 0$$
$$x^2 - 8x + y^2 + 2y = -13$$
$$(x^2 - 8x + 16) + (y^2 + 2y + 1) = -13 + 16 + 1$$
$$(x - 4)^2 + (y + 1)^2 = 4$$
$$(x - 4)^2 + (y + 1)^2 = 2^2$$

b. The graph is a circle with center (4, –1) and radius 2.

$$x^2 + y^2 - 8x + 2y + 13 = 0$$

112. a.
$$x^2 + y^2 - x + 3y - \frac{3}{2} = 0$$

$$x^2 - x + y^2 + 3y = \frac{3}{2}$$

$$\left(x^2 - x + \frac{1}{4}\right) + \left(y^2 + 3y + \frac{9}{4}\right) = \frac{3}{2} + \frac{1}{4} + \frac{9}{4}$$

$$\left(x - \frac{1}{2}\right)^2 + \left(y + \frac{3}{2}\right)^2 = 4$$

$$\left(x - \frac{1}{2}\right)^2 + \left(y + \frac{3}{2}\right)^2 = 2^2$$

b. The graph is a circle with center $\left(\frac{1}{2}, -\frac{3}{2}\right)$ and radius 2.

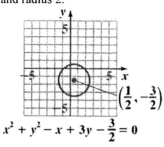

$$x^2 + y^2 - x + 3y - \frac{3}{2} = 0$$

113.
$$(x+4)^2 + y^2 = 25$$

$$(x+4)^2 + (y-0)^2 = 5^2$$

The graph is a circle with its center at $(-4, 0)$ and radius 5.

$$\text{Area} = \pi r^2 = \pi(5)^2 = 25\pi \approx 78.5 \text{ sq. units}$$

114.
$$x^2 + (y-3)^2 = 4$$

$$(x-0)^2 + (y-3)^2 = 2^2$$

The graph is a circle with its center at $(0,3)$ and radius 2.

$$\text{Area} = \pi r^2 = \pi(2)^2 = 4\pi \approx 12.6 \text{ sq. units}$$

115. x-intercept:
$$x = 0^2 - 6(0) - 7$$
$$x = -7$$
The x-intercept is $(-7, 0)$
y-intercepts:
$$0 = y^2 - 6y - 7$$
$$0 = (y+1)(y-7)$$
$$y = -1 \text{ or } y = 7$$
The y-intercepts are $(0, -1)$ and $(0, 7)$.

116. x-intercept:
$$x = -0^2 + 8(0) - 12$$
$$x = -12$$
The x-intercept is $(-12, 0)$.
y-intercepts:
$$0 = -y^2 + 8y - 12$$
$$0 = -(y^2 - 8y + 12)$$
$$0 = -(y-2)(y-6)$$
$$y = 2 \text{ or } y = 6$$
The y-intercepts are $(0, 2)$ and $(0, 6)$.

117. x-intercept:
$$x = 2(0-3)^2 + 6$$
$$x = 24$$
The x-intercept is $(24, 0)$.
y-intercepts:
$$0 = 2(y-3)^2 + 6$$
Since $2(y-3)^2 + 6 \geq 6$ for all real values of y, this equation has no real solutions. There are no y-intercepts.

118. x-intercept:
$$x = -(0+2)^2 - 8$$
$$x = -12$$
The x-intercept is $(-12, 0)$.
y-intercept:
$$0 = -(y+2)^2 - 8$$
Since $-(y+2)^2 - 8 \leq -8$ for all real values of y, this equation has no real solutions. There are no y-intercepts.

119. No. For example, the origin is the midpoint of both the segment from $(1, 1)$ to $(-1, -1)$ and the segment from $(2, 2)$ to $(-2, -2)$, but these segments have different lengths.

120. No. The other endpoint could be any point on a circle whose center is the given endpoint and whose radius is the given distance.

121. The distance from the midpoint (4, –6) to the endpoint (7, –2) is half the length of the line segment.

$$\frac{d}{2} = \sqrt{(7-4)^2 + \left[-2-(-6)\right]^2}$$
$$= \sqrt{3^2 + 4^2}$$
$$= \sqrt{25}$$
$$= 5$$

Since $\frac{d}{2} = 5$, $d = 10$. The length is 10 units.

122. The distance from the midpoint (–2, 4) to the endpoint (3, 6) is half the length of the line segment.

$$\frac{d}{2} = \sqrt{\left[3-(-2)\right]^2 + (6-4)^2}$$
$$= \sqrt{5^2 + 2^2}$$
$$= \sqrt{25+4}$$
$$= \sqrt{29}$$

Since $\frac{d}{2} = \sqrt{29}$, $d = 2\sqrt{29}$. The length is $2\sqrt{29}$ units, or about 10.77 units.

123. Since (–6, 2) is 2 units above the x-axis, the radius is 2.

$$(x-h)^2 + (y-k)^2 = r^2$$
$$(x+6)^2 + (y-2)^2 = 2^2$$
$$(x+6)^2 + (y-2)^2 = 4$$

124. Since (–3, 5) is 3 units to the left of the y-axis, the radius is 3.

$$(x-h)^2 + (y-k)^2 = r^2$$
$$(x+3)^2 + (y-5)^2 = 3^2$$
$$(x+3)^2 + (y-5)^2 = 9$$

125. a. Diameter $= \sqrt{(x_2-x_1)^2 + (y_2-y_1)^2}$
$$= \sqrt{(9-5)^2 + (8-4)^2}$$
$$= \sqrt{4^2 + 4^2}$$
$$= \sqrt{16+16}$$
$$= \sqrt{32}$$
$$= 4\sqrt{2}$$

Since the diameter is $4\sqrt{2}$ units, the radius is $2\sqrt{2}$ units.

b. Midpoint $= \left(\frac{x_1+x_2}{2}, \frac{y_1+y_2}{2}\right)$
$$= \left(\frac{5+9}{2}, \frac{4+8}{2}\right)$$
$$= (7,6)$$
The center is (7, 6).

c. $(x-h)^2 + (y-k)^2 = r^2$
$$(x-7)^2 + (y-6)^2 = \left(2\sqrt{2}\right)^2$$
$$(x-7)^2 + (y-6)^2 = 8$$

126. a. Diameter $= \sqrt{(x_2-x_1)^2 + (y_2-y_1)^2}$
$$= \sqrt{(7-4)^2 + (12-9)^2}$$
$$= \sqrt{3^2 + 3^2}$$
$$= \sqrt{9+9}$$
$$= \sqrt{18}$$
$$= 3\sqrt{2}$$

Since the diameter is $3\sqrt{2}$ units, the radius is $\frac{3}{2}\sqrt{2}$ units.

b. Midpoint $= \left(\frac{x_1+x_2}{2}, \frac{y_1+y_2}{2}\right)$
$$= \left(\frac{4+7}{2}, \frac{9+12}{2}\right)$$
$$= \left(\frac{11}{2}, \frac{21}{2}\right)$$
The center is $\left(\frac{11}{2}, \frac{21}{2}\right)$.

c. $(x-h)^2 + (y-k)^2 = r^2$
$$\left(x-\frac{11}{2}\right)^2 + \left(y-\frac{21}{2}\right)^2 = \left(\frac{3}{2}\sqrt{2}\right)^2$$
$$\left(x-\frac{11}{2}\right)^2 + \left(y-\frac{21}{2}\right)^2 = \frac{9}{2}$$

127. The minimum number is 0 and the maximum number is 4 as shown in the diagrams.

No points of intersection

Four points of intersection

128. a. Area $= \dfrac{1}{2}bh = \dfrac{1}{2}(6)(9) = 27$ square units

b. $(27) \cdot \dfrac{4}{3} = 36$ square units

129. a. Since $150 - 2(68.2) = 13.6$, the clearance is 13.6 feet.

b. Since $150 - 68.2 = 81.8$, the center of the wheel is 81.8 feet above the ground.

c.
$$(x-h)^2 + (y-k)^2 = r^2$$
$$(x-0)^2 + (y-81.8)^2 = 68.2^2$$
$$x^2 + (y-81.8)^2 = 68.2^2$$
$$x^2 + (y-81.8)^2 = 4651.24$$

130. Since the circle has equation $x^2 + y^2 = 9$

(or $x^2 + y^2 = 3^2$), its radius is 3.

Let s be the side length of the square. Since one of the square's diagonals is also a radius of the circle, its length is 3. So, by the Pythagorean theorem,
$$s^2 + s^2 = 3^2$$
$$2s^2 = 9$$
$$s^2 = \dfrac{9}{2}$$

Since s^2 represents the area of the square, the area of the square is 4.5 square units.

131. a. The center of the blue circle is the origin, and the radius is 4.
$$x^2 + y^2 = r^2$$
$$x^2 + y^2 = 4^2$$
$$x^2 + y^2 = 16$$

b. The center of the red circle is (2, 0), and the radius is 2.
$$(x-h)^2 + (y-k)^2 = r^2$$
$$(x-2)^2 + (y-0)^2 = 2^2$$
$$(x-2)^2 + y^2 = 4$$

c. The center of the green circle is (–2, 0), and the radius is 2.
$$(x-h)^2 + (y-k)^2 = r^2$$
$$\left[x-(-2)\right]^2 + (y-0)^2 = 2^2$$
$$(x+2)^2 + y^2 = 4$$

d. Shaded area = (blue circle area) – (red circle area) – (green circle area)
$$= \pi\left(4^2\right) - \pi\left(2^2\right) - \pi\left(2^2\right)$$
$$= 16\pi - 4\pi - 4\pi$$
$$= 8\pi$$

132. Each circle has radius 4, and the centers are (0, 0) and (2, 2), respectively. The distance between the centers is
$$d = \sqrt{(x_2 - x_1)^2 + (y_2 - y_1)^2}$$
$$= \sqrt{(2-0)^2 + (2-0)^2}$$
$$= \sqrt{2^2 + 2^2}$$
$$= \sqrt{4+4}$$
$$= \sqrt{8}$$
$$\approx 2.83$$
Since the circles have the same radius and the distance between the centers is less than twice the radius, there are 2 intersection points.

133. The radii are 4 and 8, respectively. So, the area between the circles is
$$\pi\left(8\right)^2 - \pi\left(4\right)^2 = 64\pi - 16\pi = 48\pi \text{ square units.}$$

134.

In the illustration,
$$d = \sqrt{4^2 + (10+1)^2}$$
$$= \sqrt{16 + 121}$$
$$= \sqrt{137}$$

In order to have 1 foot to spare, the radius should be $\sqrt{137} \approx 11.70$ feet.

135. a. Using $y = ax^2 + bx + c$ we can write an equation for each point (x, y).

$$(0, 12) \rightarrow 12 = a(0)^2 + b(0) + c$$
$$12 = c$$

$$(3, -3) \rightarrow \quad -3 = a(3)^2 + b(3) + c$$
$$-3 = 9a + 3b + c$$

$$(-2, 32) \rightarrow \quad 32 = a(-2)^2 + b(-2) + c$$
$$32 = 4a - 2b + c$$

b. Let $c = 12$ in the second and third equations.
$$-3 = 9a + 3b + 12 \qquad 32 = 4a - 2b + 12$$
$$-15 = 9a + 3b \qquad 20 = 4a - 2b$$
$$-5 = 3a + b \qquad 10 = 2a - b$$

Solving the new first equation for b gives $b = -3a - 5$. Substitute this for b in the new second equation.
$$10 = 2a - b$$
$$10 = 2a - (-3a - 5)$$
$$10 = 2a + 3a + 5$$
$$5 = 5a$$
$$1 = a$$

Now solve for b.
$$b = -3a - 5 = -3(1) - 5 = -8$$

The solution is $(a, b, c) = (1, -8, 12)$.

c. $y = ax^2 + bx + c$
$$y = x^2 - 8x + 12$$

d. $y = x^2 - 8x + 12$
$$y = (x^2 - 8x) + 12$$
$$y = (x^2 - 8x + 16) + 12 - 16$$
$$y = (x - 4)^2 - 4$$

e. $y = (x - 4)^2 - 4$

$$y = (x - 4)^2 - 4$$

(4, −4)

136.
$$\frac{6x^{-3}y^4}{18x^{-2}y^3} = \frac{6}{18}x^{-3-(-2)}y^{4-3}$$
$$= \frac{1}{3}x^{-3+2}y^1$$
$$= \frac{1}{3}x^{-1}y \text{ or } \frac{y}{3x}$$

137. a. area 1: a^2 area 2: ab

area 3: ab area 4: b^2

b. $a^2 + ab + ab + b^2 = a^2 + 2ab + b^2$
$$= (a + b)^2$$

138.
$$\begin{vmatrix} 4 & 0 & 3 \\ 5 & 2 & -1 \\ 3 & 6 & 4 \end{vmatrix} = 4\begin{vmatrix} 2 & -1 \\ 6 & 4 \end{vmatrix} - 5\begin{vmatrix} 0 & 3 \\ 6 & 4 \end{vmatrix} + 3\begin{vmatrix} 0 & 3 \\ 2 & -1 \end{vmatrix}$$
$$= 4(8 + 6) - 5(0 - 18) + 3(0 - 6)$$
$$= 4(14) - 5(-18) + 3(-6)$$
$$= 56 + 90 - 18$$
$$= 128$$

139.
$$-4 < 3x - 4 < 17$$
$$-4 + 4 < 3x - 4 + 4 < 17 + 4$$
$$0 < 3x < 21$$
$$\frac{0}{3} < \frac{3x}{3} < \frac{21}{3}$$
$$0 < x < 7$$

In interval notation: $(0, 7)$

140. This is a parabola in the form $y = a(x-h)^2 + k$ with $a = 1$, $h = 4$ and $k = 1$. Since $a > 0$, the parabola opens upward. The vertex is $(4, 1)$. The y-intercept is $(0, 17)$. There are no x-intercepts.

Exercise Set 14.2

1. An ellipse is a set of points in a plane, the sum of whose distances from two fixed points is constant.

2. $\dfrac{x^2}{a^2} + \dfrac{y^2}{b^2} = 1$

3. $\dfrac{(x-h)^2}{a^2} + \dfrac{(y-k)^2}{b^2} = 1$

4. When $a > b$, the graph is an ellipse with its major axis parallel to the x-axis. When $a < b$, the graph is an ellipse with its major axis parallel to the y-axis. When $a = b$, the graph is a circle.

5. If $a = b$, the formula for a circle is obtained.

6. The x-intercepts are $(\pm a, 0)$ and the y-intercepts are $(0, \pm b)$.

7. First divide both sides by 180.

8. First divide both sides by 225.

9. No, the sign in front of the y^2 is negative.

10. No, the sign in front of the x^2 is negative.

11. $\dfrac{x^2}{4} + \dfrac{y^2}{1} = 1$

   Since $a^2 = 4, a = 2$.
   Since $b^2 = 1, b = 1$.

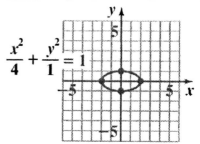

12. $\dfrac{x^2}{1} + \dfrac{y^2}{4} = 1$

   Since $a^2 = 1, a = 1$.
   Since $b^2 = 4, b = 2$.

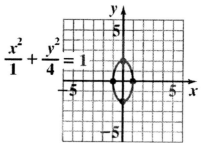

13. $\dfrac{x^2}{4} + \dfrac{y^2}{9} = 1$

   Since $a^2 = 4, a = 2$.
   Since $b^2 = 9, b = 3$.

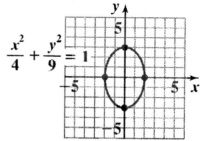

14. $\dfrac{x^2}{9} + \dfrac{y^2}{4} = 1$

Since $a^2 = 9, a = 3$.

Since $b^2 = 4, b = 2$.

15. $\dfrac{x^2}{25} + \dfrac{y^2}{9} = 1$

Since $a^2 = 25, a = 5$.

Since $b^2 = 9, b = 3$.

16. $\dfrac{x^2}{100} + \dfrac{y^2}{16} = 1$

Since $a^2 = 100, a = 10$.

Since $b^2 = 16, b = 4$.

17. $\dfrac{x^2}{16} + \dfrac{y^2}{25} = 1$

Since $a^2 = 16, a = 4$.

Since $b^2 = 25, b = 5$.

18. $\dfrac{x^2}{81} + \dfrac{y^2}{49} = 1$

Since $a^2 = 81, a = 9$.

Since $b^2 = 49, b = 7$.

19. $x^2 + 16y^2 = 16$

$\dfrac{x^2}{16} + \dfrac{16y^2}{16} = 1$

$\dfrac{x^2}{16} + \dfrac{y^2}{1} = 1$

Since $a^2 = 16, a = 4w$.

Since $b^2 = 1, b = 1$.

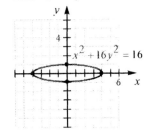

923

20. $x^2 + 25y^2 = 25$

$$\frac{x^2}{25} + \frac{25y^2}{25} = 1$$

$$\frac{x^2}{25} + \frac{y^2}{1} = 1$$

Since $a^2 = 25, a = 5$.

Since $b^2 = 1, b = 1$.

$$x^2 + 25y^2 = 25$$

21. $49x^2 + y^2 = 49$

$$\frac{49x^2}{49} + \frac{y^2}{49} = 1$$

$$\frac{x^2}{1} + \frac{y^2}{49} = 1$$

Since $a^2 = 1, a = 1$.

Since $b^2 = 49, b = 7$.

22. $9x^2 + 25y^2 = 225$

$$\frac{9x^2}{225} + \frac{25y^2}{225} = 1$$

$$\frac{x^2}{25} + \frac{y^2}{9} = 1$$

Since $a^2 = 25, a = 5$.

Since $b^2 = 9, b = 3$.

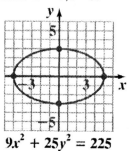

$$9x^2 + 25y^2 = 225$$

23. $9x^2 + 16y^2 = 144$

$$\frac{9x^2}{144} + \frac{16y^2}{144} = 1$$

$$\frac{x^2}{16} + \frac{y^2}{9} = 1$$

Since $a^2 = 16, a = 4$.

Since $b^2 = 9, b = 3$.

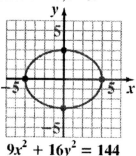

$$9x^2 + 16y^2 = 144$$

24. $25x^2 + 4y^2 = 100$

$$\frac{25x^2}{100} + \frac{4y^2}{100} = 1$$

$$\frac{x^2}{4} + \frac{y^2}{25} = 1$$

Since $a^2 = 4, a = 2$.

Since $b^2 = 25, b = 5$.

25. $25x^2 + 100y^2 = 400$

$$x^2 + 4y^2 = 16$$

$$\frac{x^2}{16} + \frac{4y^2}{16} = 1$$

$$\frac{x^2}{16} + \frac{y^2}{4} = 1$$

Since $a^2 = 16, a = 4$.

Since $b^2 = 4, b = 2$.

26. $100x^2 + 25y^2 = 400$

$$4x^2 + y^2 = 16$$

$$\frac{4x^2}{16} + \frac{y^2}{16} = 1$$

$$\frac{x^2}{4} + \frac{y^2}{16} = 1$$

Since $a^2 = 4, a = 2$.

Since $b^2 = 16, b = 4$.

$$100x^2 + 25y^2 = 400$$

27. $x^2 + 2y^2 = 8$

$$\frac{x^2}{8} + \frac{2y^2}{8} = 1$$

$$\frac{x^2}{8} + \frac{y^2}{4} = 1$$

Since $a^2 = 8, a = \sqrt{8} = 2\sqrt{2} \approx 2.83$.

Since $b^2 = 4, b = 2$.

28. $x^2 + 36y^2 = 36$

$$\frac{x^2}{36} + \frac{36y^2}{36} = 1$$

$$\frac{x^2}{36} + \frac{y^2}{1} = 1$$

Since $a^2 = 36, a = 6$.

Since $b^2 = 1, b = 1$.

$$x^2 + 36y = 36$$

29. $\dfrac{x^2}{16} + \dfrac{(y-2)^2}{9} = 1$

The center is (0, 2).

Since $a^2 = 16, a = 4$.

Since $b^2 = 9, b = 3$.

30. $\dfrac{(x-1)^2}{16}+\dfrac{y^2}{1}=1$

The center is $(1,0)$.

Since $a^2=16, a=4$.

Since $b^2=1, b=1$.

31. $\dfrac{(x-4)^2}{9}+\dfrac{(y+3)^2}{25}=1$

The center is $(4,-3)$.

Since $a^2=9, a=3$.

Since $b^2=25, b=5$.

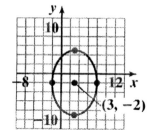

32. $\dfrac{(x-3)^2}{25}+\dfrac{(y+2)^2}{49}=1$

The center is $(3,-2)$.

Since $a^2=25, a=5$.

Since $b^2=49, b=7$.

33. $\dfrac{(x+1)^2}{9}+\dfrac{(y-2)^2}{4}=1$

The center is $(-1,2)$.

Since $a^2=9, a=3$.

Since $b^2=4, b=2$.

34. $\dfrac{(x-3)^2}{16}+\dfrac{(y-4)^2}{25}=1$

The center is $(3,4)$.

Since $a^2=16, a=4$.

Since $b^2=25, b=5$.

35. $(x+3)^2+9(y+1)^2=81$

$\dfrac{(x+3)^2}{81}+\dfrac{9(y+1)^2}{81}=1$

$\dfrac{(x+3)^2}{81}+\dfrac{(y+1)^2}{9}=1$

The center is $(-3,-1)$.

Since $a^2=81, a=9$.

Since $b^2=9, b=3$.

36. $18(x-1)^2 + 2(y+3)^2 = 72$

$$\frac{18(x-1)^2}{72} + \frac{2(y+3)^2}{72} = 1$$

$$\frac{(x-1)^2}{4} + \frac{(y+3)^2}{36} = 1$$

The center is $(1, -3)$.

Since $a^2 = 4, a = 2$.

Since $b^2 = 36, b = 6$.

$18(x-1)^2 + 2(y+3)^2 = 72$

37. $(x-5)^2 + 4(y+4)^2 = 4$

$$\frac{(x-5)^2}{4} + \frac{4(y+4)^2}{4} = 1$$

$$\frac{(x-5)^2}{4} + \frac{(y+4)^2}{1} = 1$$

The center is $(5, -4)$.

Since $a^2 = 4, a = 2$.

Since $b^2 = 1, b = 1$.

38. $4(x-2)^2 + 9(y+2)^2 = 36$

$$\frac{4(x-2)^2}{36} + \frac{9(y+2)^2}{36} = 1$$

$$\frac{(x-2)^2}{9} + \frac{(y+2)^2}{4} = 1$$

The center is $(2, -2)$.

Since $a^2 = 9, a = 3$.

Since $b^2 = 4, b = 2$.

39. $12(x+4)^2 + 3(y-1)^2 = 48$

$$\frac{12(x+4)^2}{48} + \frac{3(y-1)^2}{48} = 1$$

$$\frac{(x+4)^2}{4} + \frac{(y-1)^2}{16} = 1$$

The center is $(-4, 1)$.

Since $a^2 = 4, a = 2$.

Since $b^2 = 16, b = 4$.

40. $16(x-2)^2 + 4(y+3)^2 = 16$

$$\frac{16(x-2)^2}{16} + \frac{4(y+3)^2}{16} = 1$$

$$\frac{(x-2)^2}{1} + \frac{(y+3)^2}{4} = 1$$

The center is $(2, -3)$.

Since $a^2 = 1, a = 1$; Since $b^2 = 4, b = 2$.

927

41. $\dfrac{x^2}{4}+\dfrac{y^2}{1}=1$

Since $a^2=4, a=2$; Since $b^2=1, b=1$.

$$\begin{aligned}\text{Area} &= \pi ab \\ &= \pi(2)(1) \\ &= 2\pi \approx 6.3 \text{ square units}\end{aligned}$$

42. $\dfrac{x^2}{25}+\dfrac{y^2}{9}=1$

Since $a^2=25, a=5$.

Since $b^2=9, b=3$.

$$\begin{aligned}\text{Area} &= \pi ab \\ &= \pi(5)(3) \\ &= 15\pi \approx 47.1 \text{ square units}\end{aligned}$$

43. There is only one point, at $(0, 0)$. Two non-negative numbers can only sum to 0 if they are both 0.

44. It becomes more circular. When $a = b$, the graph is a circle.

45. The center is the origin, $a = 3$, and $b = 4$.

$$\dfrac{x^2}{a^2}+\dfrac{y^2}{b^2}=1$$

$$\dfrac{x^2}{3^2}+\dfrac{y^2}{4^2}=1$$

$$\dfrac{x^2}{9}+\dfrac{y^2}{16}=1$$

46. The center is the origin, $a = 6$, and $b = 5$.

$$\dfrac{x^2}{a^2}+\dfrac{y^2}{b^2}=1$$

$$\dfrac{x^2}{6^2}+\dfrac{y^2}{5^2}=1$$

$$\dfrac{x^2}{36}+\dfrac{y^2}{25}=1$$

47. The center is the origin, $a = 2$, and $b = 3$.

$$\dfrac{x^2}{a^2}+\dfrac{y^2}{b^2}=1$$

$$\dfrac{x^2}{2^2}+\dfrac{y^2}{3^2}=1$$

$$\dfrac{x^2}{4}+\dfrac{y^2}{9}=1$$

48. The center is the origin, $a = 1$, and $b = 7$.

$$\dfrac{x^2}{a^2}+\dfrac{y^2}{b^2}=1$$

$$\dfrac{x^2}{1^2}+\dfrac{y^2}{7^2}=1$$

$$\dfrac{x^2}{1}+\dfrac{y^2}{49}=1$$

49. There are no points of intersection, because the ellipse with $a = 4$ and $b = 5$ is completely inside the circle of radius 7.

50. 2 points of intersection. The parabola's vertex is located at the center of the ellipse, $(2, -3)$.

51.

$$x^2+4y^2+6x+16y-11=0$$

$$x^2+6x+4y^2+16y=11$$

$$(x^2+6x+9)+4(y^2+4y+4)=11+9+16$$

$$\left(x+3\right)^2+4\left(y+2\right)^2=36$$

$$\dfrac{\left(x+3\right)^2}{36}+\dfrac{\left(y+2\right)^2}{9}=1$$

The center is $(-3, -2)$.

52.

$$x^2+4y^2-4x-8y-92=0$$

$$x^2-4x+4y^2-8y=92$$

$$(x^2-4x+4)+4(y^2-2y+1)=92+4+4$$

$$\left(x-2\right)^2+4\left(y-1\right)^2=100$$

$$\dfrac{\left(x-2\right)^2}{100}+\dfrac{\left(y-1\right)^2}{25}=1$$

The center is $(2, 1)$.

53. Since $90.2 - 20.7 = 69.5$, the distance between the foci is 69.5 feet.

54. Since $23{,}200 - 22{,}800 = 400$, the distance is 400 miles.

55. a. Consider the ellipse to be centered at the origin, $(0, 0)$. Here, $a = 10$ and $b = 24$. The equation is

$$\dfrac{x^2}{10^2}+\dfrac{y^2}{24^2}=1 \;\Rightarrow\; \dfrac{x^2}{100}+\dfrac{y^2}{576}=1.$$

b. $$\begin{aligned}\text{Area} &= \pi ab \\ &= \pi(10)(24) \\ &= 240\pi \approx 753.98 \text{ square feet}\end{aligned}$$

c. Area of opening is half the area of ellipse

$$= \frac{\pi ab}{2}$$

$$= \frac{\pi(10)(24)}{2}$$

$$= 120\pi \approx 376.99 \text{ square feet}$$

56. Using $a = 4$ and $b = 2.5$, we may assume that the

ellipse has the equation $\dfrac{x^2}{16} + \dfrac{y^2}{6.25} = 0$ and that

the foci are located at $(\pm c, 0)$. Apply the

definition of an ellipse using the points $(4, 0)$ and $(0, 2.5)$. That is, the distance from $(4, 0)$ to $(-c, 0)$ plus the distance from $(4, 0)$ to $(c, 0)$ is the same as the sum of the distance from $(0, 2.5)$ to $(-c, 0)$ and the distance from $(0, 2.5)$ to $(c, 0)$.

$$\sqrt{[4-(-c)]^2 + (0-0)^2} + \sqrt{(4-c)^2 + (0-0)^2}$$

$$= \sqrt{[0-(-c)]^2 + (2.5-0)^2} + \sqrt{(0-c)^2 + (2.5-0)^2}$$

$$|4+c| + |4-c| = \sqrt{c^2 + 6.25} + \sqrt{(-c)^2 + 6.25}$$

Note that the foci are inside the ellipse, so $4 + c > 0$ and $4 - c > 0$. So, $|4+c| = 4+c$ and

$|4-c| = 4-c$.

$$(4+c) + (4-c) = 2\sqrt{c^2 + 6.25}$$

$$8 = 2\sqrt{c^2 + 6.25}$$

$$4 = \sqrt{c^2 + 6.25}$$

$$16 = c^2 + 6.25$$

$$9.75 = c^2$$

$$c = \pm\sqrt{9.75}$$

The foci are located at $\left(\pm\sqrt{9.75}, 0\right)$.

That is, the foci are $\sqrt{9.75} \approx 3.12$ feet, in both directions, from the center of the ellipse, along the major axis.

57. Using $a = 3$ and $b = 2$, we may assume that the

ellipse has the equation $\dfrac{x^2}{9} + \dfrac{y^2}{4} = 1$ and that the

foci are located at $(\pm c, 0)$. Apply the definition

of an ellipse using the points $(3, 0)$ and $(0, 2)$. That is, the distance from $(3, 0)$ to $(-c, 0)$ plus the distance from $(3, 0)$ to $(c, 0)$ is the same as the sum of the distance from $(0, 2)$ to $(-c, 0)$ and

the distance from $(0, 2)$ to $(c, 0)$.

$$\sqrt{[3-(-c)]^2 + (0-0)^2} + \sqrt{(3-c)^2 + (0-0)^2}$$

$$= \sqrt{[0-(-c)]^2 + (2-0)^2} + \sqrt{(0-c)^2 + (2-0)^2}$$

$$|3+c| + |3-c| = \sqrt{c^2 + 4} + \sqrt{(-c)^2 + 4}$$

Note that the foci are inside the ellipse, so $3 + c > 0$ and $3 - c > 0$. So, $|3+c| = 3+c$ and

$|3-c| = 3-c$.

$$(3+c) + (3-c) = 2\sqrt{c^2 + 4}$$

$$6 = 2\sqrt{c^2 + 4}$$

$$3 = \sqrt{c^2 + 4}$$

$$9 = c^2 + 4$$

$$5 = c^2$$

$$c = \pm\sqrt{5}$$

The foci are located at $\left(\pm\sqrt{5}, 0\right)$. That is, the

foci are $\sqrt{5} \approx 2.24$ feet, in both directions, from the center of the ellipse, along the major axis.

58. Answers will vary.

59. Answers will vary.

60. Answers will vary.

61. Answers will vary.

62. $h = \dfrac{-7+5}{2} = \dfrac{-2}{2} = -1$; $k = \dfrac{5+1}{2} = \dfrac{6}{2} = 3$

Thus, the center is $(-1, 3)$.

$$a = \frac{5-(-7)}{2} = \frac{12}{2} = 6; \quad b = \frac{5-1}{2} = \frac{4}{2} = 2$$

$$\frac{(x-h)^2}{a^2} + \frac{(y-k)^2}{b^2} = 1$$

$$\frac{(x+1)^2}{6^2} + \frac{(y-3)^2}{2^2} = 1$$

$$\frac{(x+1)^2}{36} + \frac{(y-3)^2}{4} = 1$$

63. $h = \dfrac{-3+11}{2} = \dfrac{8}{2} = 4$; $k = \dfrac{5+(-1)}{2} = \dfrac{4}{2} = 2$

Thus, the center is (4, 2).

$a = \dfrac{11-(-3)}{2} = \dfrac{14}{2} = 7$; $b = \dfrac{5-(-1)}{2} = \dfrac{6}{2} = 3$

$\dfrac{(x-h)^2}{a^2} + \dfrac{(y-k)^2}{b^2} = 1$

$\dfrac{(x-4)^2}{7^2} + \dfrac{(y-2)^2}{3^2} = 1$

$\dfrac{(x-4)^2}{49} + \dfrac{(y-2)^2}{9} = 1$

64. a. Since the completed ellipse has a maximum height of 15 feet, the center would be 7.5 feet from the top. The maximum height of the tunnel is 10.5 feet, so the center is $10.5 - 7.5 = 3$ feet above the ground.

b. Since the center is at $(0,3)$ and the maximum height of the ellipse is 15 feet, the y-intercepts occur 7.5 units above and below the center. That is, at the points $(0,10.5)$ and $(0,-4.5)$.

c. The maximum width of the tunnel is 18 feet so we have $a = \dfrac{18}{2} = 9$. This information, along with the information in part (a), gives

$\dfrac{(x-h)^2}{a^2} + \dfrac{(y-k)^2}{b^2} = 1$

$\dfrac{(x-0)^2}{9^2} + \dfrac{(y-3)^2}{7.5^2} = 1$

$\dfrac{x^2}{81} + \dfrac{(y-3)^2}{56.25} = 1$

65. $S = \dfrac{n}{2}(f+l)$, for l

$S = \dfrac{nf}{2} + \dfrac{nl}{2}$

$S - \dfrac{nf}{2} = \dfrac{nl}{2}$

$2\left(S - \dfrac{nf}{2}\right) = 2\left(\dfrac{nl}{2}\right)$

$2S - nf = nl$

$\dfrac{2S - nf}{n} = \dfrac{nl}{n} \implies l = \dfrac{2S-nf}{n}$

66.

$$\begin{array}{r} x + \frac{5}{2} \\ 2x-3\overline{)\,2x^2 + 2x - 7} \\ \underline{2x^2 - 3x} \\ 5x - 7 \\ \underline{5x - \frac{15}{2}} \\ \frac{1}{2} \end{array}$$

$\dfrac{2x^2 + 2x - 7}{2x-3} = x + \dfrac{5}{2} + \dfrac{1}{2(2x-3)}$

67. $\sqrt{3b-2} = 10 - b$

$3b - 2 = (10-b)^2$

$3b - 2 = 100 - 20b + b^2$

$b^2 - 23b + 102 = 0$

$(b-6)(b-17) = 0$

$b - 6 = 0$ or $b - 17 = 0$

$b = 6$ $b = 17$

Upon checking $b = 17$ is extraneous. The solution is $b = 6$.

68. $\dfrac{3x+5}{x-4} \le 0$

$3x + 5 = 0 \implies x = -\dfrac{5}{3}$

$x - 4 = 0 \implies x = 4$

$\dfrac{3x+5}{x-4} \le 0 \implies -\dfrac{5}{3} \le x < 4$ or $\left[-\dfrac{5}{3}, 4\right)$

69. $\log_8 321 = \dfrac{\ln 321}{\ln 8} \approx 2.7755$

Mid-Chapter Test: 14.1 – 14.2

1. This is a parabola in the form $y = a(x-h)^2 + k$ with $a = 1$, $h = 2$, and $k = -1$. Since $a > 0$, the parabola opens upward. The vertex is $(2,8)$. The y-intercept is $(0,3)$. The x-intercepts are $(1,0)$ and $(3,0)$.

$$y = (x - 2)^2 - 1$$

2. This is a parabola in the form $y = a(x-h)^2 + k$ with $a = -1$, $h = -1$, and $k = 3$. Since $a < 0$, the parabola opens downward. The vertex is $(-1,3)$. The y-intercept is $(0,2)$. The x-intercepts are about $(-2.732,0)$ and $(0.732,0)$.

$$y = -(x + 1)^2 + 3$$

3. This is a parabola in the form $x = a(y-k)^2 + h$ with $a = -1$, $h = 1$, and $k = 4$. Since $a < 0$, the parabola opens to the left. The vertex is $(1,4)$. The x-intercept is $(-15,0)$. The y-intercepts are $(0,5)$ and $(0,3)$.

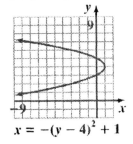
$$x = -(y - 4)^2 + 1$$

4. This is a parabola in the form $x = a(y-k)^2 + h$ with $a = 2$, $h = -2$, and $k = -3$. Since $a > 0$, the parabola opens to the right. The vertex is $(-2,-3)$. The x-intercept is $(16,0)$. The y-intercepts are $(0,-4)$ and $(0,-2)$.

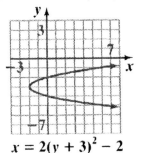
$$x = 2(y + 3)^2 - 2$$

5. $y = x^2 + 6x + 10$
$$= \left(x^2 + 6x\right) + 10$$
$$= \left(x^2 + 6x + 9\right) + 10 - 9$$
$$= (x+3)^2 + 1$$

   This is a parabola in the form $y = a(x-h)^2 + k$ with $a = 1$, $h = -3$, and $k = 1$. Since $a > 0$, the parabola opens upward. The vertex is $(-3,1)$. The y-intercept is $(0,10)$. There are no x-intercepts.

$$y = x^2 + 6x + 10$$

6. $d = \sqrt{(x_2 - x_1)^2 + (y_2 - y_1)^2}$
$$= \sqrt{(-2-(-7))^2 + (-8-4)^2}$$
$$= \sqrt{(5)^2 + (-12)^2}$$
$$= \sqrt{25 + 144}$$
$$= \sqrt{169}$$
$$= 13$$

7. $d = \sqrt{(x_2 - x_1)^2 + (y_2 - y_1)^2}$

    $= \sqrt{(2-5)^2 + (9-(-3))^2}$

    $= \sqrt{(-3)^2 + (12)^2}$

    $= \sqrt{9 + 144}$

    $= \sqrt{153}$

    ≈ 12.37

8. Midpoint $= \left(\dfrac{x_1 + x_2}{2}, \dfrac{y_1 + y_2}{2} \right)$

    $= \left(\dfrac{9 + (-11)}{2}, \dfrac{-1 + 6}{2} \right)$

    $= \left(\dfrac{-2}{2}, \dfrac{5}{2} \right)$

    $= \left(-1, \dfrac{5}{2} \right)$

9. Midpoint $= \left(\dfrac{x_1 + x_2}{2}, \dfrac{y_1 + y_2}{2} \right)$

    $= \left(\dfrac{-\frac{5}{2} + 8}{2}, \dfrac{7 + \frac{1}{2}}{2} \right)$

    $= \left(\dfrac{11}{4}, \dfrac{15}{4} \right)$

10. $(h, k) = (-3, 2)$; $r = 5$

    $(x - h)^2 + (y - k)^2 = r^2$

    $(x - (-3))^2 + (y - 2)^2 = 5^2$

    $(x + 3)^2 + (y - 2)^2 = 25$

11. $x^2 + (y - 1)^2 = 16$

    $x^2 + (y - 1)^2 = 4^2$

    The graph is a circle with its center at $(0, 1)$ and radius 4.

    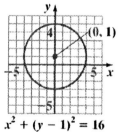

    $x^2 + (y - 1)^2 = 16$

12. $y = \sqrt{36 - x^2}$

    If we solve $x^2 + y^2 = 36$ for y, we obtain $y = \pm\sqrt{36 - x^2}$. Therefore, the graph of $y = \sqrt{36 - x^2}$ is the upper half ($y \geq 0$) of a circle with its center at the origin and radius 6.

13. $x^2 + y^2 - 2x + 4y - 4 = 0$

    Complete the square in both x and y.

    $(x^2 - 2x) + (y^2 + 4y) = 4$

    $(x^2 - 2x + 1) + (y^2 + 4y + 4) = 4 + 1 + 4$

    $(x - 1)^2 + (y + 2)^2 = 9$

    The graph of $x^2 + y^2 - 2x + 4y - 4 = 0$ is a circle with its center at $(1, -2)$ and radius 3.

    $x^2 + y^2 - 2x + 4y - 4 = 0$

14. A circle is defined to be the set of points that are equidistant from a fixed point. This distance is called the radius and the fixed point is called the center.

15. $\dfrac{x^2}{4} + \dfrac{y^2}{9} = 1$

    $a^2 = 4 \rightarrow a = 2$; $b^2 = 9 \rightarrow b = 3$

    The graph of this equation is an ellipse with center at the origin and major axis along the y-axis.

    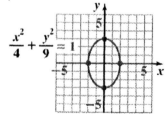

16. $\dfrac{x^2}{81}+\dfrac{y^2}{25}=1$

$a^2=81\rightarrow a=9$; $b^2=25\rightarrow b=5$

The graph of this equation is an ellipse with center at the origin and major axis along the x-axis.

17. $\dfrac{(x-1)^2}{49}+\dfrac{(y+2)^2}{4}=1$

$a^2=49\rightarrow a=7$; $b^2=4\rightarrow b=2$

The graph of this equation is an ellipse with center at $(1,-2)$ and major axis parallel to the x-axis.

$$\dfrac{(x-1)^2}{49}+\dfrac{(y+2)^2}{4}=1$$

18. $36(x+3)^2+(y-4)^2=36$

$$\dfrac{36(x+3)^2}{36}+\dfrac{(y-4)^2}{36}=\dfrac{36}{36}$$

$$\dfrac{(x+3)^2}{1}+\dfrac{(y-4)^2}{36}=1$$

$a^2=1\rightarrow a=1$; $b^2=36\rightarrow b=6$

The graph of this equation is an ellipse with center at $(-3,4)$ and major axis parallel to the y-axis.

$$36(x+3)^2+(y-4)^2=36$$

19. $\dfrac{x^2}{4}+\dfrac{y^2}{9}=1$

Since $a^2=4, a=2$; Since $b^2=9, b=3$.

Area $=\pi ab=\pi(2)(3)$

$\qquad\quad =6\pi\approx 18.85$ square units

20. The center of the ellipse is the origin, $(0,0)$. We have $a=8$ and $b=5$ so $a^2=64$ and $b^2=25$. Thus, the equation of the ellipse is

$$\dfrac{(x-0)^2}{8^2}+\dfrac{(y-0)^2}{5^2}=1$$

$$\dfrac{x^2}{64}+\dfrac{y^2}{25}=1$$

Exercise Set 14.3

1. A hyperbola is the set of points in a plane, the difference of whose distances from two fixed points (called foci) is a constant.

2. The asymptotes of a hyperbola are lines that the hyperbola approaches. The equations of the asymptotes are $y=\pm\dfrac{b}{a}x$.

3. The graph of $\dfrac{x^2}{a^2}-\dfrac{y^2}{b^2}=1$ is a hyperbola with vertices at $(a,0)$ and $(-a,0)$. Its transverse axis lies along the x-axis. The asymptotes are $y=\pm\dfrac{b}{a}x$.

4. The graph of $\dfrac{y^2}{b^2}-\dfrac{x^2}{a^2}=1$ is a hyperbola with vertices at $(0,b)$ and $(0,-b)$. Its transverse axis lies along the y-axis. The asymptotes are $y=\pm\dfrac{b}{a}x$.

5. No, equations of hyperbolas have one positive square term and one negative square term. This equation has two positive square terms.

6. No, equations of hyperbolas have one positive square term and one negative square term. This equation has two negative square terms.

7. Yes, equations of hyperbolas have one positive square term and one negative square term. This equation satisfies that condition.

8. Yes, equations of hyperbolas have one positive square term and one negative square term. This equation satisfies that condition.

9. The first step is to divide both sides by 81 in order to make the right side equal to 1.

10. The first step is to divide both sides by –64 in order to make the right side equal to 1.

11. a. $\dfrac{x^2}{9} - \dfrac{y^2}{4} = 1$

Since $a^2 = 9$ and $b^2 = 4$, $a = 3$ and $b = 2$. The equations of the asymptotes are

$y = \pm\dfrac{b}{a}x$, or $y = \pm\dfrac{2}{3}x$.

b. To graph the asymptotes, plot the points (3, 2), (–3, 2), (3, –2), and (–3, –2). The graph intersects the *x*-axis at (–3, 0) and (3, 0).

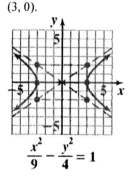

$$\frac{x^2}{9} - \frac{y^2}{4} = 1$$

12. a. $\dfrac{y^2}{4} - \dfrac{x^2}{9} = 1$

Since $a^2 = 9$ and $b^2 = 4$, $a = 3$ and $b = 2$. The equations of the asymptotes are

$y = \pm\dfrac{b}{a}x$, or $y = \pm\dfrac{2}{3}x$.

b. To graph the asymptotes, plot the points (3, 2), (–3, 2), (3, –2), and (–3, –2). The graph intersects the *y*-axis at (0, –2) and (0, 2).

$$\frac{y^2}{4} - \frac{x^2}{9} = 1$$

13. a. $\dfrac{x^2}{4} - \dfrac{y^2}{1} = 1$

Since $a^2 = 4$ and $b^2 = 1$, $a = 2$ and $b = 1$. The equations of the asymptotes are

$y = \pm\dfrac{b}{a}x$, or $y = \pm\dfrac{1}{2}x$.

b. To graph the asymptotes, plot the points (2, 1), (–2, 1), (2, –1), and (–2, –1). The graph intersects the *x*-axis at (–2, 0) and (2, 0).

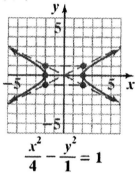

$$\frac{x^2}{4} - \frac{y^2}{1} = 1$$

14. a. $\dfrac{y^2}{1} - \dfrac{x^2}{4} = 1$

Since $a^2 = 4$ and $b^2 = 1$, $a = 2$ and $b = 1$. The equations of the asymptotes are

$y = \pm\dfrac{b}{a}x$, or $y = \pm\dfrac{1}{2}x$.

b. To graph the asymptotes, plot the points (2, 1), (–2, 1), (2, –1), and (–2, –1). The graph intersects the *y*-axis at (0, –1) and (0, 1).

15. a. $\dfrac{x^2}{9} - \dfrac{y^2}{25} = 1$

Since $a^2 = 9$ and $b^2 = 25$, $a = 3$ and $b = 5$. The equations of the asymptotes are

$y = \pm\dfrac{b}{a}x$, or $y = \pm\dfrac{5}{3}x$.

b. To graph the asymptotes, plot the points
(3, 5), (–3, 5), (3, –5), and (–3, –5). The
graph intersects the x-axis at (–3, 0) and
(3, 0).

16. a. $\dfrac{y^2}{25} - \dfrac{x^2}{9} = 1$

Since $a^2 = 9$ and $b^2 = 25$, $a = 3$ and
$b = 5$. The equations of the asymptotes are
$y = \pm\dfrac{b}{a}x$, or $y = \pm\dfrac{5}{3}x$.

b. To graph the asymptotes, plot the points
(3, 5), (–3, 5), (3, –5), and (–3, –5). The
graph intersects the y-axis at (0, –5) and
(0, 5).

17. a. $\dfrac{x^2}{25} - \dfrac{y^2}{16} = 1$

Since $a^2 = 25$ and $b^2 = 16$, $a = 5$ and $b = 4$.
The equations of the asymptotes are
$y = \pm\dfrac{b}{a}x$, or $y = \pm\dfrac{4}{5}x$.

b. To graph the asymptotes, plot the points
(5, 4), (–5, 4), (5, –4), and (–5, –4). The
graph intersects the x-axis at (–5, 0) and
(5, 0).

18. a. $\dfrac{y^2}{16} - \dfrac{x^2}{25} = 1$

Since $a^2 = 25$ and $b^2 = 16$, $a = 5$ and $b = 4$.
The equations of the asymptotes are
$y = \pm\dfrac{b}{a}x$, or $y = \pm\dfrac{4}{5}x$.

b. To graph the asymptotes, plot the points
(5, 4), (–5, 4), (5, –4), and (–5, –4). The
graph intersects the y-axis at (0, –4) and
(0, 4).

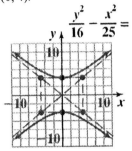

19. a. $\dfrac{y^2}{25} - \dfrac{x^2}{36} = 1$

Since $a^2 = 36$ and $b^2 = 25$, $a = 6$ and
$b = 5$. The equations of the asymptotes are
$y = \pm\dfrac{b}{a}x$, or $y = \pm\dfrac{5}{6}x$.

b. To graph the asymptotes, plot the points
(6, 5), (–6, 5), (6, –5), and (–6, –5). The
graph intersects the y-axis at (0, –5) and
(0, 5).

20. a. $\dfrac{x^2}{36} - \dfrac{y^2}{25} = 1$

Since $a^2 = 36$ and $b^2 = 25$, $a = 6$ and
$b = 5$. The equations of the asymptotes are
$y = \pm\dfrac{b}{a}x$, or $y = \pm\dfrac{5}{6}x$.

b. To graph the asymptotes, plot the points $(6, 5)$, $(-6, 5)$, $(6, -5)$, and $(-6, -5)$. The graph intersects the x-axis at $(6, 0)$ and $(-6, 0)$.

$$\frac{x^2}{36} - \frac{y^2}{25} = 1$$

21. a. $\dfrac{y^2}{9} - \dfrac{x^2}{16} = 1$

Since $a^2 = 16$ and $b^2 = 9$, $a = 4$ and $b = 3$. The equations of the asymptotes are $y = \pm\dfrac{b}{a}x$, or $= y \pm \dfrac{3}{4}x$.

b. To graph the asymptotes, plot the points $(4, 3)$, $(-4, 3)$, $(4, -3)$ and $(-4, -3)$. The graph intersects the y-axis at $(0, -3)$ and $(0, 3)$.

$$\frac{y^2}{9} - \frac{x^2}{16} = 1$$

22. a. $\dfrac{x^2}{16} - \dfrac{y^2}{9} = 1$

Since $a^2 = 16$ and $b^2 = 9$, $a = 4$ and $b = 3$. The equations of the asymptotes are $y = \pm\dfrac{b}{a}x$, or $= y \pm \dfrac{3}{4}x$.

b. To graph the asymptotes, plot the points $(4, 3)$, $(-4, 3)$, $(4, -3)$ and $(-4, -3)$. The graph intersects the x-axis at $(-4, 0)$ and $(4, 0)$.

$$\frac{x^2}{16} - \frac{y^2}{9} = 1$$

23. a. $\dfrac{y^2}{25} - \dfrac{x^2}{4} = 1$

Since $a^2 = 4$ and $b^2 = 25$, $a = 2$ and $b = 5$. The equations of the asymptotes are $y = \pm\dfrac{b}{a}x$ or $y = \pm\dfrac{5}{2}x$.

b. To graph the asymptotes, plot the points $(2, 5)$, $(-2, 5)$, $(2, -5)$ and $(-2, -5)$. The graph intersects the y-axis at $(0, -5)$ and $(0, 5)$.

$$\frac{y^2}{25} - \frac{x^2}{4} = 1$$

24. a. $\dfrac{x^2}{4} - \dfrac{y^2}{25} = 1$

Since $a^2 = 4$ and $b^2 = 25$, $a = 2$ and $b = 5$. The equations of the asymptotes are $y = \pm\dfrac{b}{a}x$ or $y = \pm\dfrac{5}{2}x$.

b. To graph the asymptotes, plot the points $(2, 5)$, $(-2, 5)$, $(2, -5)$ and $(-2, -5)$. The graph intersects the x-axis at $(2, 0)$ and $(-2, 0)$.

$$\frac{x^2}{4} - \frac{y^2}{25} = 1$$

25. a. $\dfrac{x^2}{81} - \dfrac{y^2}{16} = 1$

Since $a^2 = 81$ and $b^2 = 16$, $a = 9$ and $b = 4$. The equations of the asymptotes are $y = \pm\dfrac{b}{a}x$, or $y = \pm\dfrac{4}{9}x$.

b. To graph the asymptotes, plot the points (9, 4), (–9, 4), (9, –4), and (–9, –4). The graph intersects the *x*-axis at (–9, 0) and (9, 0).

26. a. $\dfrac{y^2}{16} - \dfrac{x^2}{81} = 1$

Since $a^2 = 81$ and $b^2 = 16$, $a = 9$ and $b = 4$. The equations of the asymptotes are $y = \pm\dfrac{b}{a}x$, or $y = \pm\dfrac{4}{9}x$.

b. To graph the asymptotes, plot the points (9, 4), (–9, 4), (9, –4), and (–9, –4). The graph intersects the *y*-axis at (0, –4) and (0, 4).

27. a. $x^2 - 25y^2 = 25$

$\dfrac{x^2}{25} - \dfrac{25y^2}{25} = 1$

$\dfrac{x^2}{25} - \dfrac{y^2}{1} = 1$

Since $a^2 = 25$ and $b^2 = 1$, $a = 5$ and $b = 1$. The equations of the asymptotes are $y = \pm\dfrac{b}{a}x$, or $y = \pm\dfrac{1}{5}x$.

b. To graph the asymptotes, plot the points (5, 1), (–5, 1), (5, –1), and (–5, –1). The graph intersects the *x*-axis at (–5, 0), and (5, 0).

28. a. $25y^2 - x^2 = 25$

$\dfrac{25y^2}{25} - \dfrac{x^2}{25} = 1$

$\dfrac{y^2}{1} - \dfrac{x^2}{25} = 1$

Since $a^2 = 25$ and $b^2 = 1$, $a = 5$ and $b = 1$. The equations of the asymptotes are $y = \pm\dfrac{b}{a}x$, or $y = \pm\dfrac{1}{5}x$.

b. To graph the asymptotes, plot the points (5, 1), (–5, 1), (5, –1), and (–5, –1). The graph intersects the *y*-axis at (0, –1), and (0, 1).

29. a. $4y^2 - 16x^2 = 64$

$\dfrac{4y^2}{64} - \dfrac{16x^2}{64} = 1$

$\dfrac{y^2}{16} - \dfrac{x^2}{4} = 1$

Since $a^2 = 4$ and $b^2 = 16$, $a = 2$ and $b = 4$. The equations of the asymptotes are $y = \pm\dfrac{b}{a}x$, or $y = \pm 2x$.

b. To graph the asymptotes, plot (2, 4), (–2, 4), (2 –4), and (–2, –4). The graph intersects the *y*-axis at (0, –4) and (0, 4).

$4y^2 - 16x^2 = 64$

30. a. $16x^2 - 4y^2 = 64$

$$\frac{16x^2}{64} - \frac{4y^2}{64} = 1$$

$$\frac{x^2}{4} - \frac{y^2}{16} = 1$$

Since $a^2 = 4$ and $b^2 = 16$, $a = 2$ and $b = 4$. The equations of the asymptotes are

$y = \pm \dfrac{b}{a} x$, or $y = \pm 2x$.

b. To graph the asymptotes, plot the points (2, 4), (–2, 4), (2 –4), and (–2, –4). The graph intersects the *x*-axis at (–2, 0) and (2, 0).

$16x^2 - 4y^2 = 64$

31. a. $9y^2 - x^2 = 9$

$$\frac{9y^2}{9} - \frac{x^2}{9} = 1$$

$$\frac{y^2}{1} - \frac{x^2}{9} = 1$$

Since $a^2 = 9$ and $b^2 = 1$, $a = 3$ and $b = 1$. The equations of the asymptotes are

$y = \pm \dfrac{b}{a} x$, or $\pm \dfrac{1}{3} x$.

b. To graph the asymptotes, plot the points (3, 1), (–3, 1), (3, –1), and (–3, –1). The graph intersects the *y*-axis at (0, –1) and (0, 1).

$9y^2 - x^2 = 9$

32. a. $x^2 - 9y^2 = 9$

$$\frac{x^2}{9} - \frac{9y^2}{9} = 1$$

$$\frac{x^2}{9} - \frac{y^2}{1} = 1$$

Since $a^2 = 9$ and $b^2 = 1$, $a = 3$ and $b = 1$. The equations of the asymptotes are

$y = \pm \dfrac{b}{a} x$, or $\pm \dfrac{1}{3} x$.

b. To graph the asymptotes, plot the points (3, 1), (–3, 1), (3, –1), and (–3, –1). The graph intersects the *x*-axis at (–3, 0) and (3, 0).

$x^2 - 9y^2 = 9$

33. a. $25x^2 - 9y^2 = 225$

$$\frac{25x^2}{225} - \frac{9y^2}{225} = 1$$

$$\frac{x^2}{9} - \frac{y^2}{25} = 1$$

Since $a^2 = 9$ and $b^2 = 25$, $a = 3$ and $b = 5$. The equations of the asymptotes are

$y = \pm \dfrac{b}{a} x$, or $y = \pm \dfrac{5}{3} x$.

b. To graph the asymptotes, plot the points (3, 5), (–3, 5), (3, –5), and (–3, –5). The graph intersects the *x*-axis at (–3, 0) and (3, 0).

34. a. $9y^2 - 25x^2 = 225$

$$\frac{9y^2}{225} - \frac{25x^2}{225} = 1$$

$$\frac{y^2}{25} - \frac{x^2}{9} = 1$$

Since $a^2 = 9$ and $b^2 = 25$, $a = 3$ and $b = 5$. The equations of the asymptotes are

$$y = \pm\frac{b}{a}x, \text{ or } y = \pm\frac{5}{3}x.$$

b. To graph the asymptotes, plot the points (3, 5), (–3, 5), (3, –5), and (–3, –5). The graph intersects the *y*-axis at (0, –5) and (0, 5).

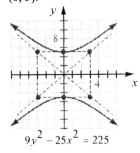

$$9y^2 - 25x^2 = 225$$

35. a. $4y^2 - 36x^2 = 144$

$$\frac{4y^2}{144} - \frac{36x^2}{144} = \frac{144}{144}$$

$$\frac{y^2}{36} - \frac{x^2}{4} = 1$$

Since $a^2 = 4$ and $b^2 = 36$, $a = 2$ and $b = 6$. The equations of the asymptotes are

$$y = \pm\frac{b}{a}x, \text{ or } y = \pm 3x.$$

b. To graph the asymptotes, plot the points (2, 6), (–2, 6), (2, –6), and (–2, –6). The graph intersects the *y*-axis at (0, –6) and (0, 6).

36. a. $64y^2 - 25x^2 = 1600$

$$\frac{64y^2}{1600} - \frac{25x^2}{1600} = 1$$

$$\frac{y^2}{25} - \frac{x^2}{64} = 1$$

Since $a^2 = 64$ and $b^2 = 25$, $a = 8$ and $b = 5$. The equations of the asymptotes are

$$y = \pm\frac{b}{a}x, \text{ or } y = \pm\frac{5}{8}x.$$

b. To graph the asymptotes, plot the points (8, 5), (–8, 5), (8, –5), and (–8, –5). The graph intersects the *y*-axis at (0, –5) and (0, 5).

$$64y^2 - 25x^2 = 1600$$

37. $10x^2 + 10y^2 = 40$

$$\frac{10x^2}{10} + \frac{10y^2}{10} = \frac{40}{10}$$

$$x^2 + y^2 = 4$$

The graph is a circle.

38. $15x^2 - 5y^2 = 75$

$$\frac{15x^2}{75} - \frac{5y^2}{75} = \frac{75}{75}$$

$$\frac{x^2}{5} - \frac{y^2}{15} = 1$$

The graph is a hyperbola.

39. $x^2 + 16y^2 = 64$

$$\frac{x^2}{64} + \frac{16y^2}{64} = \frac{64}{64}$$

$$\frac{x^2}{64} + \frac{y^2}{4} = 1$$

The graph is an ellipse.

40. $x = 5y^2 + 15y + 1$

The graph is a parabola.

41. $4x^2 - 4y^2 = 29$

$$\frac{4x^2}{29} - \frac{4y^2}{29} = \frac{29}{29}$$

$$\frac{x^2}{\frac{29}{4}} - \frac{y^2}{\frac{29}{4}} = 1$$

The graph is a hyperbola.

42. $11x^2 + 11y^2 = 99$

$$\frac{11x^2}{11} + \frac{11y^2}{11} = \frac{99}{11}$$

$$x^2 + y^2 = 9$$

The graph is a circle.

43. $2y = 12x^2 - 8x + 16$

$$y = 6x^2 - 4x + 8$$

The graph is a parabola.

44. $4y^2 - 6x^2 = 72$

$$\frac{4y^2}{72} - \frac{6x^2}{72} = \frac{72}{72}$$

$$\frac{y^2}{18} - \frac{x^2}{12} = 1$$

The graph is a hyperbola.

45. $6x^2 + 9y^2 = 54$

$$\frac{6x^2}{54} + \frac{9y^2}{54} = \frac{54}{54}$$

$$\frac{x^2}{9} + \frac{y^2}{6} = 1$$

The graph is an ellipse.

46. $9.2x^2 + 9.2y^2 = 4.6$

$$\frac{9.2x^2}{9.2} + \frac{9.2y^2}{9.2} = \frac{4.6}{9.2}$$

$$x^2 + y^2 = 0.5$$

The graph is a circle.

47. $3x = -2y^2 + 9y - 15$

$$x = -\frac{2}{3}y^2 + 3y - 5$$

The graph is a parabola.

48. $12x^2 - 3y^2 = 48$

$$\frac{12x^2}{48} - \frac{3y^2}{48} = \frac{48}{48}$$

$$\frac{x^2}{4} - \frac{y^2}{16} = 1$$

The graph is a hyperbola.

49. $6x^2 + 6y^2 = 36$

$$\frac{6x^2}{6} + \frac{6y^2}{6} = \frac{36}{6}$$

$$x^2 + y^2 = 6$$

The graph is a circle.

50. $9x^2 = -9y^2 + 99$

$$9x^2 + 9y^2 = 9$$

$$\frac{9x^2}{9} + \frac{9y^2}{9} = \frac{99}{9}$$

$$x^2 + y^2 = 11$$

The graph is a circle.

51. $14y^2 = 7x^2 + 35$

$$14y^2 - 7x^2 = 35$$

$$\frac{14y^2}{35} - \frac{7x^2}{35} = \frac{35}{35}$$

$$\frac{y^2}{\frac{5}{2}} - \frac{x^2}{5} = 1$$

The graph is a hyperbola.

52.
$$9x^2 = -18y^2 + 36$$
$$9x^2 + 18y^2 = 36$$
$$\frac{9x^2}{36} + \frac{18y^2}{36} = \frac{36}{36}$$
$$\frac{x^2}{4} + \frac{y^2}{2} = 1$$
The graph is an ellipse.

53. $x + y = 2y^2 + 6$
$$x = 2y^2 - y + 6$$
The graph is a parabola.

54.
$$2x^2 = -2y^2 + 32$$
$$2x^2 + 2y^2 = 32$$
$$\frac{2x^2}{2} + \frac{2y^2}{2} = \frac{32}{2}$$
$$x^2 + y^2 = 16$$
The graph is a circle.

55.
$$12x^2 = 4y^2 + 48$$
$$12x^2 - 4y^2 = 48$$
$$\frac{12x^2}{48} - \frac{4y^2}{48} = \frac{48}{48}$$
$$\frac{x^2}{4} - \frac{y^2}{12} = 1$$
The graph is a hyperbola.

56.
$$-8x^2 = -9y^2 - 72$$
$$-8x^2 + 9y^2 = -72$$
$$\frac{-8x^2}{-72} + \frac{9y^2}{-72} = \frac{-72}{-72}$$
$$\frac{x^2}{9} - \frac{y^2}{8} = 1$$
The graph is a hyperbola.

57. $y - x + 4 = x^2$
$$y = x^2 + x - 4$$
The graph is a parabola.

58.
$$17x^2 = -2y^2 + 34$$
$$17x^2 + 2y^2 = 34$$
$$\frac{17x^2}{34} + \frac{2y^2}{34} = \frac{34}{34}$$
$$\frac{x^2}{2} + \frac{y^2}{17} = 1$$
The graph is an ellipse.

59.
$$-3x^2 - 3y^2 = -27$$
$$\frac{-3x^2}{-3} + \frac{-3y^2}{-3} = \frac{-27}{-3}$$
$$x^2 + y^2 = 9$$
The graph is a circle.

60. $x - y^2 = 15$
$$x = y^2 + 15$$
The graph is a parabola.

61. Since the vertices are $(0, \pm 2)$, the hyperbola is of the form $\dfrac{y^2}{b^2} - \dfrac{x^2}{a^2} = 1$ with $b = 2$. Since the asymptotes are $y = \pm\dfrac{1}{2}x$, we have $\dfrac{b}{a} = \dfrac{1}{2}$. Therefore, $\dfrac{2}{a} = \dfrac{1}{2}$, so $a = 4$. The equation of the hyperbola is $\dfrac{y^2}{2^2} - \dfrac{x^2}{4^2} = 1$, or $\dfrac{y^2}{4} - \dfrac{x^2}{16} = 1$.

62. Since the vertices are $(0, \pm 6)$, the hyperbola is of the form $\dfrac{y^2}{b^2} - \dfrac{x^2}{a^2} = 1$ with $b = 6$. Since the asymptotes are $y = \pm\dfrac{3}{2}x$, we have $\dfrac{b}{a} = \dfrac{3}{2}$. Therefore, $\dfrac{6}{a} = \dfrac{3}{2}$, so $a = 4$. The equation of the hyperbola is $\dfrac{y^2}{6^2} - \dfrac{x^2}{4^2} = 1$, or $\dfrac{y^2}{36} - \dfrac{x^2}{16} = 1$.

63. Since the vertices are $(0, \pm 3)$, the hyperbola is

of the form $\dfrac{x^2}{a^2} - \dfrac{y^2}{b^2} = 1$ with $a = 3$. Since the

asymptotes are $y = \pm 2x$, we have $\dfrac{b}{a} = 2$.

Therefore, $\dfrac{b}{3} = 2$, so $b = 6$. The equation of the

hyperbola is $\dfrac{x^2}{3^2} - \dfrac{y^2}{6^2} = 1$, or $\dfrac{x^2}{9} - \dfrac{y^2}{36} = 1$.

64. Since the vertices are $(0, \pm 7)$, the hyperbola is

of the form $\dfrac{x^2}{a^2} - \dfrac{y^2}{b^2} = 1$ with $a = 7$. Since the

asymptotes are $y = \pm \dfrac{4}{7}x$, we have $\dfrac{b}{a} = \dfrac{4}{7}$.

Therefore, $\dfrac{b}{7} = \dfrac{4}{7}$, so $b = 4$. The equation of the

hyperbola is $\dfrac{x^2}{7^2} - \dfrac{y^2}{4^2} = 1$, or $\dfrac{x^2}{49} - \dfrac{y^2}{16} = 1$.

65. Since the transverse axis is along the x-axis, the

equation is of the form $\dfrac{x^2}{a^2} - \dfrac{y^2}{b^2} = 1$ Since the

asymptotes are $y = \pm \dfrac{5}{3}x$, we require $\dfrac{b}{a} = \dfrac{5}{3}$.

Using $a = 3$ and $b = 5$, the equation of the

hyperbola is $\dfrac{x^2}{3^2} - \dfrac{y^2}{5^2} = 1$, or $\dfrac{x^2}{9} - \dfrac{y^2}{25} = 1$.

No, this is not the only possible answer, because
a and b are not uniquely determined.

$\dfrac{x^2}{18} - \dfrac{y^2}{50} = 1$ and others will also work.

66. Since the transverse axis is along the y-axis, the

equation is of the form $\dfrac{y^2}{b^2} - \dfrac{x^2}{a^2} = 1$. Since the

asymptotes are $y = \pm \dfrac{2}{3}x$, we require $\dfrac{b}{a} = \dfrac{2}{3}$.

Using $a = 3$ and $b = 2$, the equation of the

hyperbola is $\dfrac{y^2}{2^2} - \dfrac{x^2}{3^2} = 1$, or $\dfrac{y^2}{4} - \dfrac{x^2}{9} = 1$.

No, this is not the only possible answer, because
a and b are not uniquely determined.

$\dfrac{y^2}{8} - \dfrac{x^2}{18} = 1$ and others will also work.

67. No, for each value of x with $|x| > a$, there are 2
possible values of y.

68. No, for each value of x, there are 2 possible
values of y.

69. $\dfrac{x^2}{25} - \dfrac{y^2}{4} = 1$. This hyperbola has its transverse

axis along the x-axis with vertices at $(\pm 5, 0)$.

Domain: $(-\infty, -5] \cup [5, \infty)$

Range: $\mathbb{R}$

70. $\dfrac{y^2}{36} - \dfrac{x^2}{9} = 1$. This hyperbola has its transverse

axis along the y-axis with vertices at $(0, \pm 6)$.

Domain: $\mathbb{R}$

Range: $(-\infty, -6] \cup [6, \infty)$

71. The equation is changed from $\dfrac{x^2}{a^2} - \dfrac{y^2}{b^2} = 1$ to

$\dfrac{x^2}{b^2} - \dfrac{y^2}{a^2} = 1$. Both graphs have a transverse axis
along the x-axis. The vertices of the second
graph will be closer to the origin, at $(\pm b, 0)$
instead of $(\pm a, 0)$. The second graph will open
wider.

72. The equation is changed from $\dfrac{x^2}{a^2} - \dfrac{y^2}{b^2} = 1$ to

$\dfrac{y^2}{b^2} - \dfrac{x^2}{a^2} = 1$. The transverse axis of the first
graph is along the x-axis. The transverse axis of
the second graph is along the y-axis. The vertices
of the second graph will be closer to the origin,
at $(0, \pm b)$ instead of $(\pm a, 0)$. The second graph
will be wider. Both graphs have the same
asymptotes.

73. Answers will vary.

74. Answers will vary.

75. The points are $(-6,4)$ and $(-2,2)$.

$$m = \frac{y_2 - y_1}{x_2 - x_1} = \frac{2-4}{-2-(-6)} = \frac{-2}{4} = -\frac{1}{2}$$

Use $y - y_1 = m(x - x_1)$, with $m = -\frac{1}{2}$, $(-2, 2)$

$$y - 2 = -\frac{1}{2}\left(x - (-2)\right)$$

$$y - 2 = -\frac{1}{2}x - 1$$

$$y = -\frac{1}{2}x + 1$$

76.
$$\frac{3x}{2x-3} + \frac{2x+4}{2x^2 + x - 6}$$

$$= \frac{3x}{2x-3} + \frac{2x+4}{(2x-3)(x+2)}$$

$$= \frac{3x}{2x-3} \cdot \frac{x+2}{x+2} + \frac{2x+4}{(2x-3)(x+2)}$$

$$= \frac{3x^2 + 6x + 2x + 4}{(2x-3)(x+2)}$$

$$= \frac{3x^2 + 8x + 4}{(2x-3)(x+2)}$$

$$= \frac{(3x+2)(x+2)}{(2x-3)(x+2)}$$

$$= \frac{3x+2}{2x-3}$$

77. $f(x) = 3x^2 - x + 5,\ g(x) = 6 - 4x^2$

$$(f+g)(x) = \left(3x^2 - x + 5\right) + \left(6 - 4x^2\right)$$

$$= -x^2 - x + 11$$

78. $5\left(-4x + 9y = 7\right) \Rightarrow -20x + 45y = 35$

$4\left(5x + 6y = -3\right) \Rightarrow \underline{\quad 20x + 24y = -12}$

$$69y = 23$$

$$y = \frac{1}{3}$$

$$5x + 6\left(\frac{1}{3}\right) = -3 \Rightarrow 5x + 2 = -3 \Rightarrow x = -1$$

The solution is $\left(-1,\ \frac{1}{3}\right)$.

79. $E = \frac{1}{2}mv^2$, for v

$$2E = mv^2$$

$$\frac{2E}{m} = v^2$$

$$\sqrt{\frac{2E}{m}} = v \quad \text{or} \quad v = \sqrt{\frac{2E}{m}}$$

80. $\log(x+4) = \log 5 - \log x$

$$\log(x+4) = \log \frac{5}{x}$$

$$x + 4 = \frac{5}{x}$$

$$x(x+4) = 5$$

$$x^2 + 4x - 5 = 0$$

$$(x+5)(x-1) = 0$$

$$x + 5 = 0 \quad \text{or} \quad x - 1 = 0$$

$$x = -5 \qquad\qquad x = 1$$

Upon checking, $x = -5$ does not satisfy the equation. The solution is $x = 1$.

Exercise Set 14.4

1. A nonlinear system of equations is a system in which at least one equation is nonlinear.

2. To solve a nonlinear system graphically, graph both equations and find points of intersection.

3. Yes

4. Yes

5. Yes

6. Yes

7. $x^2 + y^2 = 18$

$x + y = 0$

Solve $x + y = 0$ for x: $x = -y$.

Substitute $x = -y$ for x in $x^2 + y^2 = 18$.

$x^2 + y^2 = 18$

$(-y)^2 + y^2 = 18$

$y^2 + y^2 = 18$

$2y^2 = 18$

$y^2 = 9$

$y = \pm 3$

$y = 3$ or $y = -3$

$x = -3 \qquad x = 3$

The solutions are $(3, -3)$ and $(-3, 3)$.

8. $x^2 + y^2 = 18$

$x - y = 0$

Solve $x - y = 0$ for x: $x = y$.

Substitute $x = y$ for x in $x^2 + y^2 = 18$.

$x^2 + y^2 = 18$

$(y)^2 + y^2 = 18$

$y^2 + y^2 = 18$

$2y^2 = 18$

$y^2 = 9$

$y = \pm 3$

$y = 3$ or $y = -3$

$x = 3 \qquad x = -3$

The solutions are $(3, 3)$ and $(-3, -3)$.

9. $x^2 + y^2 = 9$

$x + 2y = 3$

Solve $x + 2y = 3$ for x: $x = 3 - 2y$.

Substitute $3 - 2y$ for x in $x^2 + y^2 = 9$.

$x^2 + y^2 = 9$

$(3 - 2y)^2 + y^2 = 9$

$9 - 12y + 4y^2 + y^2 = 9$

$5y^2 - 12y = 0$

$y(5y - 12) = 0$

$y = 0 \qquad$ or $\quad y = \dfrac{12}{5}$

$x = 3 - 2y \qquad\qquad x = 3 - 2y$

$x = 3 - 2(0) \qquad\qquad x = 3 - 2\left(\dfrac{12}{5}\right)$

$x = 3 \qquad\qquad\qquad x = -\dfrac{9}{5}$

The solutions are $(3, 0)$ and $\left(-\dfrac{9}{5}, \dfrac{12}{5}\right)$.

10. $x^2 + y^2 = 4$

$x - 2y = 4$

Solve $x - 2y = 4$ for x: $x = 2y + 4$.

Substitute $2y + 4$ for x in $x^2 + y^2 = 4$.

$x^2 + y^2 = 4$

$(2y + 4)^2 + y^2 = 4$

$4y^2 + 16y + 16 + y^2 = 4$

$5y^2 + 16y + 12 = 0$

$(y + 2)(5y + 6) = 0$

$y = -2 \qquad$ or $\quad y = -\dfrac{6}{5}$

$x = 2y + 4 \qquad\qquad x = 2y + 4$

$x = 2(-2) + 4 \qquad\qquad x = 2\left(-\dfrac{6}{5}\right) + 4$

$x = 0 \qquad\qquad\qquad x = \dfrac{8}{5}$

The solutions are $(0, -2)$ and $\left(\dfrac{8}{5}, -\dfrac{6}{5}\right)$.

11.
$$y = x^2 - 5$$
$$3x + 2y = 10$$
Substitute $x^2 - 5$ for y in $3x + 2y = 10$
$$3x + 2y = 10$$
$$3x + 2(x^2 - 5) = 10$$
$$3x + 2x^2 - 10 = 10$$
$$2x^2 + 3x - 20 = 0$$
$$(x + 4)(2x - 5) = 0$$
$$x = -4 \quad \text{or} \quad x = \frac{5}{2}$$

$$y = x^2 - 5 \qquad\qquad y = x^2 - 5$$
$$y = (-4)^2 - 5 \qquad\quad y = \left(\frac{5}{2}\right)^2 - 5$$
$$y = 11 \qquad\qquad\qquad y = \frac{5}{4}$$

The solutions are $(-4, 11)$ and $\left(\frac{5}{2}, \frac{5}{4}\right)$.

12.
$$x + y = 4$$
$$x^2 - y^2 = 4$$
Solve $x + y = 4$ for y: $y = 4 - x$.
Substitute $4 - x$ for y in $x^2 - y^2 = 4$
$$x^2 - y^2 = 4$$
$$x^2 - (4 - x)^2 = 4$$
$$x^2 - (16 - 8x + x^2) = 4$$
$$-16 + 8x = 4$$
$$8x = 20$$
$$x = \frac{5}{2}$$
$$y = 4 - x$$
$$y = 4 - \frac{5}{2}$$
$$y = \frac{3}{2}$$
The solution is $\left(\frac{5}{2}, \frac{3}{2}\right)$.

13.
$$x^2 + y = 6$$
$$y = x^2 + 4$$
Substitute $x^2 + 4$ for y in $x^2 + y = 6$
$$x^2 + x^2 + 4 = 6$$
$$2x^2 = 2$$
$$x^2 = 1$$
$$x = \pm 1$$
$$y = (1)^2 + 4 \quad \text{or} \quad y = (-1)^2 + 4$$
$$y = 1 + 4 \qquad\qquad y = 1 + 4$$
$$y = 5 \qquad\qquad\quad y = 5$$
The solutions are $(1, 5)$ and $(-1, 5)$.

14.
$$y - x = 2$$
$$x^2 - y^2 = 4$$
Solve $y - x = 2$ for y: $y = x + 2$.
Substitute $x + 2$ for y in $x^2 - y^2 = 4$
$$x^2 - y^2 = 4$$
$$x^2 - (x + 2)^2 = 4$$
$$x^2 - (x^2 + 4x + 4) = 4$$
$$-4x - 4 = 4$$
$$-4x = 8$$
$$x = -2$$
$$y = x + 2$$
$$y = -2 + 2$$
$$y = 0$$
The solution is $(-2, 0)$.

15. $2x^2 + y^2 = 16$

$x^2 - y^2 = -4$

Solve $x^2 - y^2 = -4$ for y^2: $y^2 = x^2 + 4$

Substitute $x^2 + 4$ for y^2 in $2x^2 + y^2 = 16$.

$2x^2 + y^2 = 16$

$2x^2 + (x^2 + 4) = 16$

$3x^2 + 4 = 16$

$3x^2 = 12$

$x^2 = 4$

$x = 2$ or $x = -2$

$y^2 = x^2 + 4$	$y^2 = x^2 + 4$
$y^2 = 2^2 + 4$	$y = (-2)^2 + 4$
$y^2 = 8$	$y = 8$
$y = \pm\sqrt{8} = \pm 2\sqrt{2}$	$y = \pm\sqrt{8} = \pm 2\sqrt{2}$

The solutions are $\left(2, 2\sqrt{2}\right), \left(2, -2\sqrt{2}\right),$

$\left(-2, 2\sqrt{2}\right)$, and $\left(-2, -2\sqrt{2}\right)$.

16. $x + y^2 = 4 \implies y^2 = -x + 4$

$x^2 + y^2 = 6$

Substitute $-x + 4$ for y^2 in $x^2 + y^2 = 6$.

$x^2 + y^2 = 6$

$x^2 + (-x + 4) = 6$

$x^2 - x - 2 = 0$

$(x - 2)(x + 1) = 0$

$x = 2$ or $x = -1$

$y^2 = -x + 4$	$y^2 = -x + 4$
$y^2 = -2 + 4$	$y^2 = -(-1) + 4$
$y^2 = 2$	$y^2 = 5$
$y = \pm\sqrt{2}$	$y = \pm\sqrt{5}$

The solutions are $\left(2, \sqrt{2}\right)$, $\left(2, -\sqrt{2}\right)$, $\left(-1, \sqrt{5}\right)$,

and $\left(-1, -\sqrt{5}\right)$.

17. $x^2 + y^2 = 4$

$y = x^2 - 6 \implies x^2 = y + 6$

Substitute $y + 6$ for x^2 in $x^2 + y^2 = 4$.

$x^2 + y^2 = 4$

$(y + 6) + y^2 = 4$

$y^2 + y + 2 = 0$

$$y = \frac{-1 \pm \sqrt{1^2 - 4(1)(2)}}{2(1)}$$

$$= \frac{-1 \pm \sqrt{-7}}{2}$$

$$= \frac{-1 \pm i\sqrt{31}}{2}$$

There is no real solution.

18. $x^2 - 4y^2 = 36$

$x^2 + 2y^2 = 5$

Solve $x^2 + 2y^2 = 5$ for x^2: $x^2 = 5 - 2y^2$.

Substitute $5 - 2y^2$ for x^2 in $x^2 - 4y^2 = 36$.

$x^2 - 4y^2 = 36$

$(5 - 2y^2) - 4y^2 = 36$

$5 - 6y^2 = 36$

$-6y^2 = 31$

$$y^2 = -\frac{31}{6}$$

There is no real solution.

19. $x^2 + y^2 = 9$

$y = x^2 - 3$

Solve $y = x^2 - 3$ for x^2: $x^2 = y + 3$.

Substitute $y + 3$ for x^2 in $x^2 + y^2 = 9$.

$$x^2 + y^2 = 9$$
$$(y+3) + y^2 = 9$$
$$y^2 + y - 6 = 0$$
$$(y-2)(y+3) = 0$$
$$y = 2 \qquad \text{or} \qquad y = -3$$

$$x^2 = y + 3 \qquad\qquad x^2 = y + 3$$
$$x^2 = 2 + 3 \qquad\qquad x^2 = -3 + 3$$
$$x^2 = 5 \qquad\qquad x^2 = 0$$
$$x = \pm\sqrt{5} \qquad\qquad x = 0$$

The solutions are $(0, -3)$, $\left(\sqrt{5}, 2\right)$, and

$\left(-\sqrt{5}, 2\right)$.

20. $x^2 + y^2 = 16$

$y = x^2 - 4$

Substitute $x^2 - 4$ for y in $x^2 + y^2 = 16$.

$$x^2 + y^2 = 16$$
$$x^2 + \left(x^2 - 4\right)^2 = 16$$
$$x^2 + x^4 - 8x^2 + 16 = 16$$
$$x^4 - 7x^2 = 0$$
$$x^2\left(x^2 - 7\right) = 0$$
$$x^2 = 0 \qquad \text{or} \qquad x^2 - 7 = 0$$
$$x^2 = 7$$
$$x = \pm\sqrt{7}$$

$$y = x^2 - 4 \qquad\qquad y = x^2 - 4$$
$$y = 0 - 4 = -4 \qquad\qquad y = 7 - 4$$
$$y = 3$$

The solutions are $(0, -4)$, $\left(-\sqrt{7}, 3\right)$, and $\left(\sqrt{7}, 3\right)$.

21. $2x^2 - y^2 = -8$

$x - y = 6$

Solve the second equation for y: $y = x - 6$.

Substitute $x - 6$ for y in $2x^2 - y^2 = -8$.

$$2x^2 - y^2 = -8$$
$$2x^2 - \left(x - 6\right)^2 = -8$$
$$2x^2 - (x^2 - 12x + 36) = -8$$
$$2x^2 - x^2 + 12x - 36 = -8$$
$$x^2 + 12x - 28 = 0$$
$$(x-2)(x+14) = 0$$
$$\text{or}$$
$$x = 2 \qquad\qquad x = -14$$

$$y = x - 6 \qquad\qquad y = x - 6$$
$$y = 2 - 6 \qquad\qquad y = -14 - 6$$
$$y = -4 \qquad\qquad y = -20$$

The solutions are $(2, -4)$ and $(-14, -20)$.

22. $x^2 + y^2 = 1$

$y - x = 3 \qquad \Rightarrow \qquad y = x + 3$

Substitute $x + 3$ for y in $x^2 + y^2 = 1$.

$$x^2 + y^2 = 1$$
$$x^2 + (x+3)^2 = 1$$
$$x^2 + x^2 + 6x + 9 = 1$$
$$2x^2 + 6x + 8 = 0$$
$$x^2 + 3x + 4 = 0$$
$$x = \frac{-3 \pm \sqrt{3^2 - 4(1)(4)}}{2(1)}$$
$$= \frac{-3 \pm \sqrt{-7}}{2}$$

There is no real solution.

23.
$$x^2 - y^2 = 4$$
$$\underline{2x^2 + y^2 = 8}$$
$$3x^2 \qquad = 12$$
$$x^2 = 4$$
$$x = 2 \qquad \text{or} \qquad x = -2$$

$$x^2 - y^2 = 4 \qquad\qquad x^2 - y^2 = 4$$
$$2^2 - y^2 = 4 \qquad\qquad \left(-2\right)^2 - y^2 = 4$$
$$y^2 = 0 \qquad\qquad\qquad y^2 = 0$$
$$y = 0 \qquad\qquad\qquad y = 0$$

The solutions are (2, 0) and (−2, 0).

24.
$$x^2 + y^2 = 36$$
$$\underline{x^2 - y^2 = 36}$$
$$2x^2 \qquad = 72$$
$$x^2 = 36$$
$$x = 6 \qquad \text{or} \qquad x = -6$$

$$x^2 - y^2 = 36 \qquad\qquad x^2 - y^2 = 36$$
$$6^2 - y^2 = 36 \qquad\qquad \left(-6\right)^2 - y^2 = 36$$
$$y^2 = 0 \qquad\qquad\qquad y^2 = 0$$
$$y = 0 \qquad\qquad\qquad y = 0$$

The solutions are (6, 0) and (−6, 0).

25.
$$x^2 + y^2 = 16 \ (1)$$
$$2x^2 - 5y^2 = 25 \ (2)$$
$$-2x^2 - 2y^2 = -32 \ (1) \text{ multiplied by } -2$$
$$\underline{2x^2 - 5y^2 = 25 \quad (2)}$$
$$-7y^2 = -7$$
$$y^2 = 1$$
$$y = 1 \qquad \text{or} \qquad y = -1$$

$$x^2 + y^2 = 16 \qquad\qquad x^2 + y^2 = 16$$
$$x^2 + 1^2 = 16 \qquad\qquad x^2 + (-1)^2 = 16$$
$$x^2 = 15 \qquad\qquad\qquad x^2 = 15$$
$$x = \pm\sqrt{15} \qquad\qquad x = \pm\sqrt{15}$$

The solutions are $\left(-\sqrt{15}, 1\right)$, $\left(-\sqrt{15}, -1\right)$, $\left(\sqrt{15}, -1\right)$, and $\left(\sqrt{15}, 1\right)$.

26.
$$x^2 + y^2 = 25 \ (1)$$
$$x^2 - 2y^2 = 7 \quad (2)$$
$$2x^2 + 2y^2 = 50 \ (1) \text{ Multiplied by } 2$$
$$\underline{x^2 - 2y^2 = 7 \quad (2)}$$
$$3x^2 = 57$$
$$x^2 = 19$$
$$x = \sqrt{19} \ \text{ or } \qquad\qquad x = -\sqrt{19}$$

$$x^2 + y^2 = 25 \qquad\qquad x^2 + y^2 = 25$$
$$\left(\sqrt{19}\right)^2 + y^2 = 25 \qquad \left(-\sqrt{19}\right)^2 + y^2 = 25$$
$$y^2 = 6 \qquad\qquad\qquad y^2 = 6$$
$$y = \pm\sqrt{6} \qquad\qquad y = \pm\sqrt{6}$$

The solutions are $\left(\sqrt{19}, \sqrt{6}\right)$, $\left(\sqrt{19}, -\sqrt{6}\right)$, $\left(-\sqrt{19}, \sqrt{6}\right)$, and $\left(-\sqrt{19}, -\sqrt{6}\right)$.

27.
$$3x^2 - y^2 = 4 \ (1)$$
$$x^2 + 4y^2 = 10 \ (2)$$
$$12x^2 - 4y^2 = 16 \ (1) \text{ multiplied by } 4$$
$$\underline{x^2 + 4y^2 = 10 \ (2)}$$
$$13x^2 = 26$$
$$x^2 = 2$$
$$x = \sqrt{2} \qquad \text{or} \qquad x = -\sqrt{2}$$

$$3x^2 - y^2 = 4 \qquad\qquad 3x^2 - y^2 = 4$$
$$3(\sqrt{2})^2 - y^2 = 4 \qquad 3(-\sqrt{2})^2 - y^2 = 4$$
$$6 - y^2 = 4 \qquad\qquad 6 - y^2 = 4$$
$$y^2 = 2 \qquad\qquad\qquad y^2 = 2$$
$$y = \pm\sqrt{2} \qquad\qquad y = \pm\sqrt{2}$$

The solutions are $\left(\sqrt{2}, \sqrt{2}\right)$, $\left(\sqrt{2}, -\sqrt{2}\right)$, $\left(-\sqrt{2}, \sqrt{2}\right)$, and $\left(-\sqrt{2}, -\sqrt{2}\right)$.

28. $3x^2 + 2y^2 = 30$ (1)

$x^2 + y^2 = 13$ (2)

Multiply equation (2) by -2 and add.

$3x^2 + 2y^2 = 30$

$\underline{-2x^2 - 2y^2 = -26}$

$x^2 = 4$

$x = \pm 2$

$x^2 + y^2 = 13$	$x^2 + y^2 = 13$
$(2)^2 + y^2 = 13$	$(-2)^2 + y^2 = 13$
$4 + y^2 = 13$	$4 + y^2 = 13$
$y^2 = 9$	$y^2 = 9$
$y = \pm 3$	$y = \pm 3$

The solutions are $(2,3)$, $(2,-3)$, $(-2,-3)$, and $(-2,3)$.

29. $4x^2 + 9y^2 = 36$

$\underline{2x^2 - 9y^2 = 18}$

$6x^2 = 54$

$x^2 = 9$

$x = 3$ or $x = -3$

$4x^2 + 9y^2 = 36$	$4x^2 + 9y^2 = 36$
$4(3)^2 + 9y^2 = 36$	$4(-3)^2 + 9y^2 = 36$
$9y^2 = 0$	$9y^2 = 0$
$y^2 = 0$	$y^2 = 0$
$y = 0$	$y = 0$

The solutions are $(3, 0)$ and $(-3, 0)$.

30. $x^2 + 4y^2 = 16 \qquad x^2 + 4y^2 = 16$

$-9x^2 + y^2 = 4 \overset{\times(-4)}{\Rightarrow} \underline{36x^2 - 4y^2 = -16}$

$37x^2 \qquad = 0$

$x = 0$

$0^2 + 4y^2 = 16$

$y^2 = 4$

$y = \pm 2$

The solutions are $(0, 2)$ and $(0, -2)$.

31. $2x^2 - y^2 = 7$ (1)

$x^2 + 2y^2 = 6$ (2)

$4x^2 - 2y^2 = 14$ (1) multiplied by 2

$\underline{x^2 + 2y^2 = 6}$ (2)

$5x^2 = 20$

$x^2 = 4$

$x = 2 \qquad$ or $\qquad x = -2$

$2(2)^2 - y^2 = 7$	$2(-2)^2 - y^2 = 7$
$8 - y^2 = 7$	$8 - y^2 = 7$
$y^2 = 1$	$y^2 = 1$
$x = \pm 1$	$x = \pm 1$

The solutions are $(2, 1)$, $(2, -1)$, $(-2, 1)$, and $(-2, -1)$.

32. $5x^2 - 2y^2 = -13$ (1)

$3x^2 + 4y^2 = 39$ (2)

$10x^2 - 4y^2 = -26$ (1) multiplied by 2

$\underline{3x^2 + 4y^2 = 39}$ (2)

$13x^2 = 13$

$x^2 = 1$

$x = 1 \qquad$ or $\qquad x = -1$

$3x^2 + 4y^2 = 39$	$3x^2 + 4y^2 = 39$
$3(1)^2 + 4y^2 = 39$	$3(-1)^2 + 4y^2 = 39$
$4y^2 = 36$	$4y^2 = 36$
$y^2 = 9$	$y^2 = 9$
$y = \pm 3$	$y = \pm 3$

The solutions are $(1, 3)$, $(1, -3)$, $(-1, 3)$, and $(-1, -3)$.

33.
$$x^2 + y^2 = 25 \quad (1)$$
$$2x^2 - 3y^2 = -30 \quad (2)$$
$$3x^2 + 3y^2 = 75 \quad \text{(1) multiplied by 3}$$
$$\underline{2x^2 - 3y^2 = -30} \quad (2)$$
$$5x^2 = 45$$
$$x^2 = 9$$
$$x = 3 \qquad \text{or} \qquad x = -3$$

$$x^2 + y^2 = 25 \qquad x^2 + y^2 = 25$$
$$(3)^2 + y^2 = 25 \qquad (-3)^2 + y^2 = 25$$
$$y^2 = 16 \qquad\qquad y^2 = 16$$
$$y = \pm 4 \qquad\qquad y = \pm 4$$

The solutions are (3, 4), (3, –4), (–3, 4), and (–3, –4).

34.
$$x^2 - 2y^2 = 7 \quad (1)$$
$$x^2 + y^2 = 34 \quad (2)$$
$$-x^2 + 2y^2 = -7 \quad \text{(1) multiplied by –1}$$
$$\underline{x^2 + y^2 = 34} \quad (2)$$
$$3y^2 = 27$$
$$y^2 = 9$$

$$y = 3 \quad \text{or} \quad y = -3$$

$$x^2 + y^2 = 34 \qquad x^2 + y^2 = 34$$
$$x^2 + 3^2 = 34 \qquad x^2 + (-3)^2 = 34$$
$$x^2 = 25 \qquad\qquad x^2 = 25$$
$$x = \pm 5 \qquad\qquad x = \pm 5$$

The solutions are (5, 3), (5, –3), (–5, 3), and (–5, –3).

35.
$$x^2 + y^2 = 9 \quad (1)$$
$$16x^2 - 4y^2 = 64 \quad (2)$$
$$4x^2 + 4y^2 = 36 \quad \text{(1) multiplied by 4}$$
$$\underline{16x^2 - 4y^2 = 64} \quad (2)$$
$$20x^2 = 100$$
$$x^2 = 5$$
$$x = \sqrt{5} \qquad \text{or} \qquad x = -\sqrt{5}$$

$$x^2 + y^2 = 9 \qquad x^2 + y^2 = 9$$
$$\left(\sqrt{5}\right)^2 + y^2 = 9 \qquad \left(-\sqrt{5}\right)^2 + y^2 = 9$$
$$y^2 = 4 \qquad\qquad y^2 = 4$$
$$y = \pm 2 \qquad\qquad y = \pm 2$$

The solutions are $\left(\sqrt{5}, 2\right)$, $\left(\sqrt{5}, -2\right)$, $\left(-\sqrt{5}, 2\right)$, and $\left(-\sqrt{5}, -2\right)$.

36.
$$3x^2 + 4y^2 = 35 \quad (1)$$
$$2x^2 + 5y^2 = 42 \quad (2)$$
$$15x^2 + 20y^2 = 175 \quad \text{(1) multiplied by 5}$$
$$\underline{-8x^2 - 20y^2 = -168} \quad \text{(2) multiplied by –4}$$
$$7x^2 = 7$$
$$x^2 = 1$$
$$x = 1 \qquad \text{or} \qquad x = -1$$

$$3(1)^2 + 4y^2 = 35 \qquad 3(-1)^2 + 4y^2 = 35$$
$$4y^2 = 32 \qquad\qquad 4y^2 = 32$$
$$y^2 = 8 \qquad\qquad y^2 = 8$$
$$y = \pm\sqrt{8} \qquad\qquad y = \pm\sqrt{8}$$
$$y = \pm 2\sqrt{2} \qquad\qquad y = \pm 2\sqrt{2}$$

The solutions are $\left(1, 2\sqrt{2}\right)$, $\left(1, -2\sqrt{2}\right)$, $\left(-1, 2\sqrt{2}\right)$, and $\left(-1, -2\sqrt{2}\right)$.

37.
$$x^2 + y^2 = 4 \quad (1)$$
$$16x^2 + 9y^2 = 144 \quad (2)$$
Multiply the first equation by -16 and add.
$$-16x^2 - 16y^2 = -164$$
$$\underline{16x^2 + 9y^2 = 144}$$
$$7y^2 = -20$$
$$y^2 = -\frac{20}{7}$$
This equation has no real solutions so the system has no real solutions.

38.
$$x^2 + y^2 = 1$$
$$9x^2 - 4y^2 = 36$$
Multiply the first equation by 4 and add.
$$4x^2 + 4y^2 = 4$$
$$\underline{9x^2 - 4y^2 = 36}$$
$$13x^2 = 40$$
$$x^2 = \frac{40}{13}$$
If we substitute $\frac{40}{13}$ for x^2 in the first equation,

we get
$$\frac{40}{13} + y^2 = 1$$
$$y^2 = -\frac{27}{13}$$
which has no real solution. Therefore, the system has no real solution.

39.
$$x^2 + 4y^2 = 4$$
$$10y^2 - 9x^2 = 90$$
Write the equations in standard form.
$$x^2 + 4y^2 = 4$$
$$-9x^2 + 10y^2 = 90$$
Multiply the first equation by -2 and the second equation by 2, then add.
$$-5x^2 - 20y^2 = -20$$
$$\underline{-18x^2 + 20y^2 = 180}$$
$$-23x^2 = 160$$
$$x^2 = -\frac{160}{23}$$
This equation has no real solutions so the system has no real solutions.

40.
$$x^2 + y^2 = 81$$
$$25x^2 + 4y^2 = 100$$
Multiply the first equation by -4 and add.
$$-4x^2 - 4y^2 = -324$$
$$\underline{25x^2 + 4y^2 = 100}$$
$$21x^2 = -224$$
$$x^2 = -\frac{32}{3}$$
This equation has no real solutions so the system has no real solutions.

41. Answers will vary.

42. The maximum number of points of intersection is 4.

43. Let x = length
y = width
$$xy = 440$$
$$2x + 2y = 84$$
Solve $2x + 2y = 84$ for y: $y = 42 - x$.
Substitute $42 - x$ for y in $xy = 440$.
$$xy = 440$$
$$x(42 - x) = 440$$
$$42x - x^2 = 440$$
$$x^2 - 42x + 440 = 0$$
$$(x - 20)(x - 22) = 0$$

$x - 20 = 0$ $\quad$ or $\quad$ $x - 22 = 0$
$\quad x = 20$ $\qquad\qquad\quad x = 22$

$y = 42 - x$ $\qquad\qquad y = 42 - 22$
$y = 42 - 20$ $\qquad\qquad y = 42 - 22$
$y = 22$ $\qquad\qquad\qquad y = 20$

The solutions are (20, 22) and (22, 20).
The dimensions of the dance floor are 20 m by 22 m.

44. $xy = 48$

$2x + y = 20$

Solve $2x + y = 20$ for y: $y = 20 - 2x$.

Substitute $20 - 2x$ for y in $xy = 48$.

$$xy = 48$$
$$x(20 - 2x) = 48$$
$$20x - 2x^2 = 48$$
$$2x^2 - 20x + 48 = 0$$
$$x^2 - 10x + 24 = 0$$
$$(x - 4)(x - 6) = 0$$

$x - 4 = 0$ \quad or \quad $x - 6 = 0$

$\quad x = 4$ \qquad\qquad $x = 6$

$y = 20 - 2x$	$y = 20 - 2x$
$y = 20 - 2(4)$	$y = 20 - 2(6)$
$y = 12$	$y = 8$

The solutions are (4, 12) and (6, 8). The dimensions are 6 ft by 8 ft or 4 ft by 12 ft.

45. Let x = length

$\quad y$ = width

$\quad\quad xy = 270$

$2x + 2y = 78$

Solve $2x + 2y = 78$ for y: $y = 39 - x$.

Substitute $39 - x$ for y in $xy = 270$.

$$xy = 270$$
$$x(39 - x) = 270$$
$$39x - x^2 = 270$$
$$x^2 - 39x + 270 = 0$$
$$(x - 9)(x - 30) = 0$$

$x - 9 = 0$ \qquad or \qquad $x - 30 = 0$

$\quad x = 9$ \qquad\qquad\quad $x = 30$

$y = 39 - x$	$y = 39 - x$
$y = 39 - 9$	$y = 39 - 30$
$y = 30$	$y = 9$

The solutions are (9, 30) and (30, 9). The dimensions of the garden are 9 ft by 30 ft.

46. $xy = 50$

$2x + y = 20$

Solve $2x + y = 20$ for y: $y = 20 - 2x$.

Substitute $20 - 2x$ for y in $xy = 50$.

$$xy = 50$$
$$x(20 - 2x) = 50$$
$$20x - 2x^2 = 50$$
$$2x^2 - 20x + 50 = 0$$
$$x^2 - 10x + 25 = 0$$
$$(x - 5)^2 = 0$$
$$x = 5$$

$$y = 20 - 2x$$
$$y = 20 - 2(5)$$
$$y = 10$$

The solution is (5, 10).
The dimensions are 5 ft by 10 ft.

47. Let x = length

$\quad y$ = width

$\quad\quad xy = 112$

$$x^2 + y^2 = \left(\sqrt{260}\right)^2$$

Solve $xy = 112$ for y: $y = \dfrac{112}{x}$.

$$x^2 + y^2 = 260$$
$$x^2 + \left(\frac{112}{x}\right)^2 = 260$$
$$x^2 + \frac{12{,}544}{x^2} = 260$$
$$x^4 + 12{,}544 = 260x^2$$
$$x^4 - 260x^2 + 12{,}544 = 0$$
$$(x^2 - 64)(x^2 - 196) = 0$$

$x^2 - 64 = 0$ \quad or \quad $x^2 - 196 = 0$

$\quad x^2 = 64$ \qquad\qquad $x^2 = 196$

$\quad x = \pm 8$ \qquad\qquad $x = \pm 14$

Since x must be positive, $x = 8$ or $x = 14$.

If $x = 8$, then $y = \dfrac{112}{8} = 14$.

If $x = 14$, then $y = \dfrac{112}{14} = 8$.

The dimensions of the new bill are 8 cm by 14 cm.

48. Let x = length

$\quad y$ = width

$$xy = 3000$$

$$x^2 + y^2 = 85^2$$

Solve $xy = 3000$ for y: $y = \dfrac{3000}{x}$.

$$x^2 + y^2 = 7225$$

$$x^2 + \left(\frac{3000}{x}\right)^2 = 7225$$

$$x^2 + \frac{9,000,000}{x^2} = 7225$$

$$x^4 + 9,000,000 = 7225x^2$$

$$x^4 - 7225x^2 + 9,000,000 = 0$$

$$(x^2 - 1600)(x^2 - 5625) = 0$$

$$x^2 - 1600 = 0 \quad \text{or} \quad x^2 - 5625 = 0$$

$$x^2 = 1600 \qquad\qquad x^2 = 5625$$

$$x = \pm 40 \qquad\qquad x = \pm 75$$

Since x must be positive, $x = 40$ or $x = 75$.

If $x = 40$, then $y = \dfrac{3000}{40} = 75$.

If $x = 75$, then $y = \dfrac{3000}{75} = 40$.

The dimensions of the rink are 40 ft by 75 ft.

49. Let x = length

$\quad y$ = width

$$x^2 + y^2 = 34^2$$

$$x + y + 34 = 80$$

Solve $x + y + 34 = 80$ for y: $y = 46 - x$.

Substitute $46 - x$ for y in $x^2 + y^2 = 34^2$.

$$x^2 + y^2 = 34^2$$

$$x^2 + (46 - x)^2 = 34^2$$

$$x^2 + (2116 - 92x + x^2) = 1156$$

$$2x^2 - 92 + 2116 = 1156$$

$$2x^2 - 92x + 960 = 0$$

$$x^2 - 46x + 480 = 0$$

$$(x - 16)(x - 30) = 0$$

$$x - 16 = 0 \quad \text{or} \quad x - 30 = 0$$

$$x = 16 \qquad\qquad x = 30$$

$$y = 46 - x \qquad\qquad y = 46 - x$$

$$y = 46 - 16 \qquad\qquad y = 46 - 30$$

$$y = 30 \qquad\qquad y = 16$$

The solutions are (16, 30) and (30, 16).
The dimensions of the piece of wood are 16 in. by 30 in.

50. Let x = length of one leg

$\quad y$ = length of other leg

$$x^2 + y^2 = 15^2$$

$$x + y + 15 = 36$$

Solve $x + y + 15 = 36$ for y: $y = 21 - x$.

Substitute $21 - x$ for y in $x^2 + y^2 = 15^2$.

$$x^2 + y^2 = 15^2$$

$$x^2 + (21 - x)^2 = 15^2$$

$$x^2 + (441 - 42x + x^2) = 225$$

$$2x^2 - 42x + 441 = 225$$

$$2x^2 - 42x + 216 = 0$$

$$x^2 - 21x + 108 = 0$$

$$(x - 9)(x - 12) = 0$$

$$x - 9 = 0 \quad \text{or} \quad x - 12 = 0$$

$$x = 9 \qquad\qquad x = 12$$

$$y = 21 - x \qquad\qquad y = 21 - x$$

$$y = 21 - 9 \qquad\qquad y = 21 - 12$$

$$y = 12 \qquad\qquad y = 9$$

The solutions are (9, 12) and (12, 9). The legs of the triangle measure 9 m and 12 m.

51.
$$d = -16t^2 + 64t$$

$$d = -16t^2 + 16t + 80$$

Substitute $-16t^2 + 64t$ for d in

$d = -16t^2 + 16t + 80$.

$$d = -16t^2 + 16t + 80$$

$$-16t^2 + 64t = -16t^2 + 16t + 80$$

$$64t = 16t + 80$$

$$48t = 80$$

$$t = \frac{80}{48} = \frac{5}{3} \approx 1.67$$

The balls are the same height above the ground at $t \approx 1.67$ sec.

52. $d = -16t^2 - 10t + 950$

$d = -16t^2 + 80t + 750$

Substitute $-16t^2 - 10t + 950$ for d in

$d = -16t^2 + 80t + 750$.

$$d = -16t^2 + 80t + 750$$

$$-16t^2 - 10t + 950 = -16t^2 + 80t + 750$$

$$-10t + 950 = 80t + 750$$

$$200 = 90t$$

$$\frac{200}{90} = t$$

$$t = \frac{200}{90} \approx 2.22$$

The ball and the snowball pass each other at $t \approx 2.22$ sec.

53. Since $t = 1$ year, we may write the formula as $i = pr$.

$7.50 = pr$

$7.50 = (p + 25)(r - 0.01)$

Rewrite the second equation by multiplying the binomials. Then substitute 7.50 for pr and solve for r.

$$7.50 = (p + 25)(r - 0.01)$$

$$7.50 = pr - 0.01p + 25r - 0.25$$

$$7.50 = 7.50 - 0.01p + 25r - 0.25$$

$$0 = -0.01p + 25r - 0.25$$

$$0.01p + 0.25 = 25r$$

$$\frac{0.01p}{25} + \frac{0.25}{25} = \frac{25r}{25}$$

$$r = 0.0004p + 0.01$$

Substitute $0.0004p + 0.01$ for r in $7.50 = pr$.

$7.50 = pr$

$7.50 = p(0.0004p + 0.01)$

$7.50 = 0.0004p^2 + 0.01p$

$0 = 0.0004p^2 + 0.01p - 7.50$

$0 = p^2 + 25p - 18,750$

$0 = (p - 125)(p + 150)$

$p - 125 = 0$ or $p + 150 = 0$

     $p = 125$ $p = -150$

Since the principal must be positive, use $p = 125$.

$r = 0.0004p + 0.01$

$r = 0.0004(125) + 0.01$

$r = 0.06$

The principal is $125 and the interest rate is 6%.

54. Since $t = 1$ year, we may write the formula as $i = pr$.

$72 = pr$

$72 = (p + 120)(r - 0.02)$

Rewrite the second equation by multiplying the binomials. Then substitute 72 for pr and solve for r.

$$72 = (p + 120)(r - 0.02)$$

$$72 = pr - 0.02p + 120r - 2.4$$

$$72 = 72 - 0.02p + 120r - 2.4$$

$$0 = -0.02p + 120r - 2.4$$

$$0.02p + 2.4 = 120r$$

$$\frac{0.02p}{120} + \frac{0.24}{120} = \frac{120r}{120}$$

$$\frac{p}{6000} + 0.02 = r$$

Substitute $\frac{p}{6000} + 0.02$ for r in $72 = pr$.

$72 = pr$

$$72 = p\left(\frac{p}{6000} + 0.02\right)$$

$$72 = \frac{p^2}{6000} + 0.02p$$

$$0 = \frac{p^2}{6000} + 0.02p - 72$$

$$0 = p^2 + 120p - 432,000$$

$$0 = (p - 600)(p + 720)$$

$p - 600 = 0$ or $p + 720 = 0$

     $p = 600$ $p = -720$

Since the principal must be positive, use $p = 600$.

$$r = \frac{p}{6000} + 0.02$$

$$r = \frac{600}{6000} + 0.02$$

$$r = 0.12$$

The principal is $600 and the rate is 12%.

55. $C = 10x + 300$

$R = 30x - 0.1x^2$

$$C = R$$

$$10x + 300 = 30x - 0.1x^2$$

$$0.1x^2 - 20x + 300 = 0$$

$$x = \frac{-b \pm \sqrt{b^2 - 4ac}}{2a}$$

$$= \frac{-(-20) \pm \sqrt{(-20)^2 - 4(0.1)(300)}}{2(0.1)}$$

$$= \frac{20 \pm \sqrt{280}}{0.2}$$

$$x = \frac{20 + \sqrt{280}}{0.2} \approx 183.7$$

or

$$x = \frac{20 - \sqrt{280}}{0.2} \approx 16.3$$

The break-even points are ≈ 16 and ≈ 184.

56. $C = 0.6x^2 + 9$

$R = 12x - 0.2x^2$

$$C = R$$

$$0.6x^2 + 9 = 12x - 0.2x^2$$

$$0.8x^2 - 12x + 9 = 0$$

$$x = \frac{-b \pm \sqrt{b^2 - 4ac}}{2a}$$

$$= \frac{-(-12) \pm \sqrt{(-12)^2 - 4(0.8)(9)}}{2(0.8)}$$

$$= \frac{12 \pm \sqrt{115.2}}{1.6}$$

$$x = \frac{12 + \sqrt{115.2}}{1.6} \approx 14.2$$

or

$$x = \frac{12 - \sqrt{115.2}}{1.6} \approx 0.8$$

The break-even points are ≈ 1 and ≈ 14.

57. $C = 12.6x + 150$

$R = 42.8x - 0.3x^2$

$$C = R$$

$$12.6x + 150 = 42.8x - 0.3x^2$$

$$0.3x^2 - 30.2x + 150 = 0$$

$$x = \frac{-b \pm \sqrt{b^2 - 4ac}}{2a}$$

$$= \frac{-(-30.2) \pm \sqrt{(-30.2)^2 - 4(0.3)(150)}}{2(0.3)}$$

$$= \frac{30.2 \pm \sqrt{732.04}}{0.6}$$

$$x = \frac{30.2 + \sqrt{732.04}}{0.6} \approx 95.4$$

or

$$x = \frac{30.2 - \sqrt{732.04}}{0.6} \approx 5.2$$

The break-even points are ≈ 5 and ≈ 95.

58. $C = 80x + 900$

$R = 120x - 0.2x^2$

$$C = R$$

$$80x + 900 = 120x - 0.2x^2$$

$$0.2x^2 - 40x + 900 = 0$$

$$x = \frac{-b \pm \sqrt{b^2 - 4ac}}{2a}$$

$$= \frac{-(-40) \pm \sqrt{(-40)^2 - 4(0.2)(900)}}{2(0.2)}$$

$$= \frac{40 \pm \sqrt{880}}{0.4}$$

$$x = \frac{40 + \sqrt{880}}{0.4} \approx 174.2$$

or

$$x = \frac{40 - \sqrt{880}}{0.4} \approx 25.8$$

The break-even points are ≈ 26 and ≈ 174.

59. Solve each equation for y.

$$3x - 5y = 12 \qquad x^2 + y^2 = 10$$
$$-5y = -3x + 12 \qquad y^2 = 10 - x^2$$
$$y = \frac{3}{5}x - \frac{12}{5} \qquad y = \pm\sqrt{10 - x^2}$$

Use $y_1 = \frac{3}{5}x - \frac{12}{5}$, $y_2 = \sqrt{10 - x^2}$, and

$y_2 = -\sqrt{10 - x^2}$.

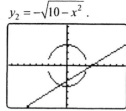

-9.4, 9.4, 1, -6.2, 6.2, 10

Approximate solutions: $(-1, -3)$, $(3.12, -0.53)$

60. Solve each equation for y.

$$y = 2x^2 - x + 2 \qquad 4x^2 + y^2 = 36$$
$$y^2 = 36 - 4x^2$$
$$y = \pm\sqrt{36 - 4x^2}$$

Use $y_1 = 2x^2 - x - 2$, $y_2 = \sqrt{36 - 4x^2}$,

and $y_3 = -\sqrt{36 - 4x^2}$.

-9.4, 9.4, 1, -6.2, 6.2, 10

Approximate solutions: $(1.53, 5.16)$,

$(-1.11, 5.57)$.

61. Let $x =$ length of one leg

$y =$ length of other leg

$$x^2 + y^2 = 26^2$$

$$\frac{1}{2}xy = 120$$

Solve $\frac{1}{2}xy = 120$ for y: $y = \frac{240}{x}$.

Substitute $\frac{240}{x}$ for y in $x^2 + y^2 = 26^2$

$$x^2 + y^2 = 26^2$$
$$x^2 + \left(\frac{240}{x}\right)^2 = 676$$
$$x^2 + \frac{57,600}{x^2} = 676$$
$$x^4 + 57,600 = 676x^2$$
$$x^4 - 676x^2 + 57,600 = 0$$
$$\left(x^2 - 100\right)\left(x^2 - 576\right) = 0$$
$$x^2 - 100 = 0 \quad \text{or} \quad x^2 - 576 = 0$$
$$x^2 = 100 \qquad\qquad x^2 = 576$$
$$x = \pm 10 \qquad\qquad x = \pm 24$$

Since x is a length, x must be positive.

If $x = 10$, then $y = \frac{240}{10} = 24$. If $x = 24$, then

$y = \frac{240}{24} = 10$. The legs have lengths 10 yards

and 24 yards.

62. The radius of the largest circle is $4r$.

$$R = 2r$$

$$\pi\left(4r\right)^2 - 2\pi r^2 - \pi R^2 = 122.5\pi$$

Substitute $2r$ for R in the second equation.

$$\pi\left(4r\right)^2 - 2\pi r^2 - \pi\left(2r\right)^2 = 122.5\pi$$
$$16\pi r^2 - 2\pi r^2 - 4\pi r^2 = 122.5\pi$$
$$10\pi r^2 = 122.5\pi$$
$$r^2 = 12.25$$
$$r = \pm 3.5$$

Since r is a radius, use $r = 3.5$. Then
$R = 2r = 2(3.5) = 7$. So, $r = 3.5$ and $R = 7$.

63. The operations are evaluated in the following order: parentheses, exponents, multiplication or division, addition or subtraction.

64. $\left(x + 1\right)^3 + 1$

$$= \left(x + 1\right)^3 + \left(1\right)^3$$
$$= \left(x + 1 + 1\right)\left(\left(x + 1\right)^2 - \left(x + 1\right)\left(1\right) + \left(1\right)^2\right)$$
$$= \left(x + 2\right)\left(x^2 + 2x + 1 - x - 1 + 1\right)$$
$$= \left(x + 2\right)\left(x^2 + x + 1\right)$$

65. $x = \dfrac{k}{P^2}$

$10 = \dfrac{k}{6^2} \Rightarrow k = 360 \Rightarrow x = \dfrac{360}{P^2}$

$x = \dfrac{360}{20^2} = \dfrac{360}{400} = \dfrac{9}{10}$ or 0.9

66. $\dfrac{5}{\sqrt{x+2}-3} = \dfrac{5}{\sqrt{x+2}-3} \cdot \dfrac{\sqrt{x+2}+3}{\sqrt{x+2}+3}$

$= \dfrac{5\sqrt{x+2}+15}{x+2+3\sqrt{x+2}-3\sqrt{x+2}-9}$

$= \dfrac{5\sqrt{x+2}+15}{x-7}$

67. $A = A_0 e^{kt}$, for k

$\dfrac{A}{A_0} = e^{kt}$

$\ln \dfrac{A}{A_0} = \ln e^{kt}$

$\ln A - \ln A_0 = kt$

$\dfrac{\ln A - \ln A_0}{t} = k$

Chapter 14 Review Exercises

1. $d = \sqrt{(x_2 - x_1)^2 + (y_2 - y_1)^2}$

$= \sqrt{(5-0)^2 + (-12-0)^2}$

$= \sqrt{5^2 + (-12)^2}$

$= \sqrt{25+144}$

$= \sqrt{169}$

$= 13$

$\text{Midpoint} = \left(\dfrac{x_1+x_2}{2}, \dfrac{y_1+y_2}{2} \right)$

$= \left(\dfrac{0+5}{2}, \dfrac{0+(-12)}{2} \right)$

$= \left(\dfrac{5}{2}, -6 \right)$

2. $d = \sqrt{(x_2 - x_1)^2 + (y_2 - y_1)^2}$

$= \sqrt{(-1-(-4))^2 + (5-1)^2}$

$= \sqrt{3^2 + 4^2}$

$= \sqrt{9+16}$

$= \sqrt{25}$

$= 5$

$\text{Midpoint} = \left(\dfrac{x_1+x_2}{2}, \dfrac{y_1+y_2}{2} \right)$

$= \left(\dfrac{-4+(-1)}{2}, \dfrac{1+5}{2} \right)$

$= \left(-\dfrac{5}{2}, 3 \right)$

3. $d = \sqrt{(x_2 - x_1)^2 + (y_2 - y_1)^2}$

$= \sqrt{[-1-(-9)]^2 + [10-(-5)]^2}$

$= \sqrt{(8)^2 + 15^2}$

$= \sqrt{64+225}$

$= \sqrt{289}$

$= 17$

$\text{Midpoint} = \left(\dfrac{x_1+x_2}{2}, \dfrac{y_1+y_2}{2} \right)$

$= \left(\dfrac{-9+(-1)}{2}, \dfrac{-5+10}{2} \right)$

$= \left(-5, \dfrac{5}{2} \right)$

4.
$$d = \sqrt{(x_2 - x_1)^2 + (y_2 - y_1)^2}$$
$$= \sqrt{\left[-2 - (-4)\right]^2 + (5 - 3)^2}$$
$$= \sqrt{2^2 + 2^2}$$
$$= \sqrt{4 + 4}$$
$$= \sqrt{8}$$
$$\approx 2.83$$
$$\text{Midpoint} = \left(\frac{x_1 + x_2}{2}, \frac{y_1 + y_2}{2}\right)$$
$$= \left(\frac{-4 + (-2)}{2}, \frac{3 + 5}{2}\right)$$
$$= (-3, 4)$$

5. $y = (x - 2)^2 + 1$

This is a parabola in the form $y = a(x - h)^2 + k$ with $a = 1$, $h = 2$, and $k = 1$. Since $a > 0$, the parabola opens upward. The vertex is (2, 1). The y-intercept is (0, 5).
There are no x-intercepts.

6. $y = (x + 3)^2 - 4$

This is a parabola in the form $y = a(x - h)^2 + k$ with $a = 1$, $h = -3$, and $k = -4$. Since $a > 0$, the parabola opens upward. The vertex is (-3, -4). The y-intercept is (0, 5).
The x-intercepts are about (-5, 0) and (-1, 0).

7. $x = (y - 1)^2 + 4$

This is a parabola in the form $x = a(y - k)^2 + h$ with $a = 1$, $h = 4$, and $k = 1$. Since $a > 0$, the parabola opens to the right. The vertex is (4, 1). There are no y-intercepts.
The x-intercept is (5, 0).

8. $x = -2(y + 4)^2 - 3$

This is a parabola in the form $x = a(y - k)^2 + h$ with $a = -2$, $h = -3$, and $k = -4$. Since $a < 0$, the parabola opens to the left. The vertex is (-3, -4). There are no y-intercepts.
The x-intercept is (-35, 0).

9. a.
$$y = x^2 - 8x + 22$$
$$y = \left(x^2 - 8x + 16\right) + 22 - 16$$
$$y = \left(x - 4\right)^2 + 6$$

b. This is a parabola in the form $y = a(x - h)^2 + k$ with $a = 1$, $h = 4$, and $k = 6$. Since $a > 0$, the parabola opens upward. The vertex is (4, 6). The y-intercept is (0, 22). There are no y-intercepts.

10. a. $x = -y^2 - 2y + 5$

$x = -(y^2 + 2y) + 5$

$x = -(y^2 + 2y + 1) + 1 + 5$

$x = -(y+1)^2 + 6$

b. This is a parabola in the form
$x = a(y-k)^2 + h$ with $a = -1$, $h = 6$, and
$k = -1$. Since $a < 0$, the parabola opens to
the left. The vertex is $(6, -1)$.
The y-intercepts are about $(0, -3.45)$ and
$(0, 1.45)$. The x-intercept is $(5, 0)$.

11. a. $x = y^2 + 5y + 4$

$x = \left(y^2 + 5y + \dfrac{25}{4}\right) - \dfrac{25}{4} + 4$

$x = \left(y + \dfrac{5}{2}\right)^2 - \dfrac{9}{4}$

b. This is a parabola in the form
$x = a(y-k)^2 + h$ with $a = 1$, $h = -\dfrac{9}{4}$, and

$k = -\dfrac{5}{2}$. Since $a > 0$, the parabola opens to

the right. The vertex is $\left(-\dfrac{9}{4}, -\dfrac{5}{2}\right)$.

The y-intercepts are $(0, -4)$ and $(0, -1)$.
The x-intercept is $(4, 0)$.

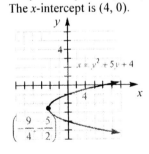

12. a. $y = 2x^2 - 8x - 24$

$y = 2(x^2 - 4x) - 24$

$y = 2(x^2 - 4x + 4) - 8 - 24$

$y = 2(x-2)^2 - 32$

b. This is a parabola in the form
$y = a(x-h)^2 + k$ with $a = 2$, $h = 2$, and
$k = -32$. Since $a > 0$, the parabola opens
upward. The vertex is $(2, -32)$. The y-
intercept is $(0, -24)$. The
x-intercepts are $(-2, 0)$ and $(6, 0)$.

13. a. $(x-h)^2 + (y-k)^2 = r^2$

$(x-0)^2 + (y-0)^2 = 4^2$

$x^2 + y^2 = 4^2$

b. The graph is a circle with center $(0,0)$ and
radius 4.

14. a.
$$(x-h)^2+(y-k)^2=r^2$$
$$\left[x-(-3)\right]^2+(y-4)^2=1^2$$
$$(x+3)^2+(y-4)^2=1^2$$

b. The graph is a circle with center $(-3,4)$ and radius 1.

15. a.
$$x^2+y^2-4y=0$$
$$x^2+(y^2-4y+4)=4$$
$$x^2+(y-2)^2=2^2$$

b. The graph is a circle with center $(0, 2)$ and radius 2.

16. a.
$$x^2+y^2-2x+6y+1=0$$
$$x^2-2x+y^2+6y=-1$$
$$(x^2-2x+1)+(y^2+6y+9)=-1+1+9$$
$$(x-1)^2+(y+3)^2=9$$
$$(x-1)^2+(y+3)^2=3^2$$

b. The graph is a circle with center $(1, -3)$ and radius 3.

17. a.
$$x^2-8x+y^2-10y+40=0$$
$$(x^2-8x+16)+(y^2-10y+25)=-40+16+25$$
$$(x-4)^2+(y-5)^2=1$$
$$(x-4)^2+(y-5)^2=1^2$$

b. The graph is a circle with center $(4, 5)$ and radius 1.

18. a.
$$x^2+y^2-4x+10y+17=0$$
$$x^2-4x+y^2+10y=-17$$
$$(x^2-4x+4)+(y^2+10y+25)=-17+4+25$$
$$(x-2)^2+(y+5)^2=12$$
$$(x-2)^2+(y+5)^2=\left(\sqrt{12}\right)^2$$

b. The graph is a circle with center $(2, -5)$ and radius $\sqrt{12}\approx 3.46$.

19. $y=\sqrt{9-x^2}$

If we solve $x^2+y^2=9$ for y, we obtain $y=\pm\sqrt{9-x^2}$. Therefore, the graph of $y=\sqrt{9-x^2}$ is the upper half $(y\geq 0)$ of a circle with its center at the origin and radius 4.

20. $y = -\sqrt{36-x^2}$

If we solve $x^2 + y^2 = 36$ for y, we obtain

$y = \pm\sqrt{36-x^2}$. Therefore, the graph of

$y = -\sqrt{36-x^2}$ is the lower half $(y \le 0)$ of a

circle with its center at the origin and radius 6.

21. The center is (−1, 1) and the radius is 2.

$(x-h)^2 + (y-k)^2 = r^2$

$[x-(-1)]^2 + (y-1)^2 = 2^2$

$(x+1)^2 + (y-1)^2 = 4$

22. The center is (5, −3) and the radius is 3.

$(x-h)^2 + (y-k)^2 = r^2$

$(x-5)^2 + [y-(-3)]^2 = 3^2$

$(x-5)^2 + (y+3)^2 = 9$

23. $\dfrac{x^2}{4} + \dfrac{y^2}{9} = 1$

Since $a^2 = 4$, $a = 2$.

Since $b^2 = 9$, $b = 3$.

24. $\dfrac{x^2}{36} + \dfrac{y^2}{64} = 1$

Since $a^2 = 36$, $a = 6$.

Since $b^2 = 64$, $b = 8$.

25. $4x^2 + 9y^2 = 36$

$\dfrac{4x^2}{36} + \dfrac{9y^2}{36} = 1$

$\dfrac{x^2}{9} + \dfrac{y^2}{4} = 1$

Since $a^2 = 9$, $a = 3$.

Since $b^2 = 4$, $b = 2$.

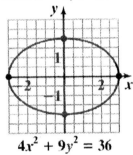

$4x^2 + 9y^2 = 36$

26. $9x^2 + 16y^2 = 144$

$\dfrac{9x^2}{144} + \dfrac{16y^2}{144} = 1$

$\dfrac{x^2}{16} + \dfrac{y^2}{9} = 1$

Since $a^2 = 16$, $a = 4$.

Since $b^2 = 9$, $b = 3$.

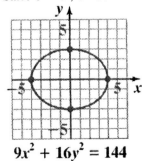

$9x^2 + 16y^2 = 144$

27. $\dfrac{(x-3)^2}{16} + \dfrac{(y+2)^2}{4} = 1$

The center is (3, –2).

Since $a^2 = 16$, $a = 4$.

Since $b^2 = 4$, $b = 2$.

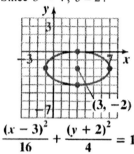

$$\dfrac{(x-3)^2}{16} + \dfrac{(y+2)^2}{4} = 1$$

28. $\dfrac{(x+3)^2}{9} + \dfrac{y^2}{25} = 1$

The center is (–3, 0).

Since $a^2 = 9$, $a = 3$.

Since $b^2 = 25$, $b = 5$.

$$\dfrac{(x+3)^2}{9} + \dfrac{y^2}{25} = 1$$

29. $25(x-2)^2 + 9(y-1)^2 = 225$

$\dfrac{25(x-2)^2}{225} + \dfrac{9(y-1)^2}{225} = 1$

$\dfrac{(x-2)^2}{9} + \dfrac{(y-1)^2}{25} = 1$

The center is (2, 1).

Since $a^2 = 9$, $a = 3$.

Since $b^2 = 25$, $b = 5$.

$$25(x-2)^2 + 9(y-1)^2 = 225$$

30. $\dfrac{x^2}{4} + \dfrac{y^2}{9} = 1$

Since $a^2 = 4$, $a = 2$.

Since $b^2 = 9$, $b = 3$.

Area $= \pi a b = \pi(2)(3) = 6\pi \approx 18.85$ sq. units

31. **a.** $\dfrac{x^2}{4} - \dfrac{y^2}{16} = 1$

Since $a^2 = 4$ and $b^2 = 16$, $a = 2$ and $b = 4$. The equations of the asymptotes are $y = \pm\dfrac{b}{a}x$, or $y = \pm 2x$.

b. To graph the asymptotes, plot the points (2, 4), (–2, 4), (2, –4), and (–2, –4). The graph intersects the x-axis at (–2, 0) and (2, 0).

$$\dfrac{x^2}{4} - \dfrac{y^2}{16} = 1$$

32. **a.** $\dfrac{x^2}{4} - \dfrac{y^2}{4} = 1$

Since $a^2 = 4$ and $b^2 = 4$, $a = 2$ and $b = 2$. The equations of the asymptotes are $y = \pm\dfrac{b}{a}x$, or $y = \pm\dfrac{2}{2}x = \pm x$.

b. To graph the asymptotes, plot the points (2, 2), (–2, 2), (2, –2), and (–2, –2). The graph intersects the x-axis at (–2, 0) and (2, 0).

$$\dfrac{x^2}{4} - \dfrac{y^2}{4} = 1$$

33. a. $\dfrac{y^2}{4} - \dfrac{x^2}{36} = 1$

Since $a^2 = 36$ and $b^2 = 4$, $a = 6$ and $b = 2$. The equations of the asymptotes are

$y = \pm \dfrac{b}{a} x$, or $y = \pm \dfrac{1}{3}$.

b. To graph the asymptotes, plot the points $(6, 2)$, $(6, -2)$, $(-6, 2)$, and $(-6, -2)$. The graph intersects the y-axis at $(0, -2)$ and $(0, 2)$.

$$\dfrac{y^2}{4} - \dfrac{x^2}{36} = 1$$

34. a. $\dfrac{y^2}{25} - \dfrac{x^2}{16} = 1$

Since $a^2 = 16$ and $b^2 = 25$, $a = 4$ and $b = 5$. The equations of the asymptotes are

$y = \pm \dfrac{b}{a} x$, or $y = \pm \dfrac{5}{4} x$.

b. To graph the asymptotes, plot the points $(4, 5)$, $(4, -5)$, $(-4, 5)$, and $(-4, -5)$. The graph intersects the y-axis at $(0, -5)$ and $(0, 5)$.

$$\dfrac{y^2}{25} - \dfrac{x^2}{16} = 1$$

35. a. $x^2 - 9y^2 = 9$

$\dfrac{x^2}{9} - \dfrac{9y^2}{9} = 1$

$\dfrac{x^2}{9} - \dfrac{y^2}{1} = 1$

b. Since $a^2 = 9$ and $b^2 = 1$, $a = 3$ and $b = 1$. The equations of the asymptotes are

$y = \pm \dfrac{b}{a} x$, or $y = \pm \dfrac{1}{3} x$.

c. To graph the asymptotes, plot the points $(3, 1)$, $(-3, 1)$, $(3, -1)$, and $(-3, -1)$. The graph intersects the x-axis at $(-3, 0)$ and $(3, 0)$.

36. a. $25x^2 - 16y^2 = 400$

$\dfrac{25x^2}{400} - \dfrac{16y^2}{400} = 1$

$\dfrac{x^2}{16} - \dfrac{y^2}{25} = 1$

b. Since $a^2 = 16$ and $b^2 = 25$, $a = 4$ and $b = 5$. The equations of the asymptotes are

$y = \pm \dfrac{b}{a} x$, or $y = \pm \dfrac{5}{4} x$.

c. To graph the asymptotes, plot the points $(4, 5)$, $(-4, 5)$, $(4, -5)$, and $(-4, -5)$. The graph intersects the x-axis at $(-4, 0)$ and $(4, 0)$.

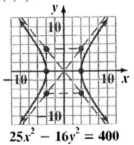

$$25x^2 - 16y^2 = 400$$

37. a. $4y^2 - 25x^2 = 100$

$\dfrac{4y^2}{100} - \dfrac{25x^2}{100} = 1$

$\dfrac{y^2}{25} - \dfrac{x^2}{4} = 1$

b. Since $a^2 = 4$ and $b^2 = 25$, $a = 2$ and
$b = 5$. The equations of the asymptotes are
$y = \pm \dfrac{b}{a} x$, or $y = \pm \dfrac{5}{2} x$.

c. To graph the asymptotes, plot the points
(2, 5), (2, –5), (–2, 5), and (–2, –5). The
graph intersects the y-axis at (0, –5) and
(0, 5).

$$4y^2 - 25x^2 = 100$$

38. a. $49y^2 - 9x^2 = 441$

$$\frac{49y^2}{441} - \frac{9x^2}{441} = 1$$

$$\frac{y^2}{9} - \frac{x^2}{49} = 1$$

b. Since $a^2 = 49$ and $b^2 = 9$, $a = 7$ and $b = 3$.
The equations of the asymptotes are
$y = \pm \dfrac{b}{a} x$, or $y = \pm \dfrac{3}{7} x$.

c. To graph the asymptotes, plot the points
(7, 3), (–7, 3), (7, –3), and (–7, –3). The
graph intersects the y-axis at (0, –3) and
(0, 3).

$$49y^2 - 9x^2 = 441$$

39. $\dfrac{x^2}{49} - \dfrac{y^2}{16} = 1$

The graph is a hyperbola.

40. $4x^2 + 8y^2 = 32$

$$\frac{4x^2}{32} + \frac{8y^2}{32} = \frac{32}{32}$$

$$\frac{x^2}{8} + \frac{y^2}{4} = 1$$

The graph is an ellipse.

41. $5x^2 + 5y^2 = 125$

$$\frac{5x^2}{5} + \frac{5y^2}{5} = \frac{125}{5}$$

$$x^2 + y^2 = 25$$

The graph is a circle.

42. $4x^2 - 25y^2 = 25$

$$\frac{4x^2}{25} - \frac{25y^2}{25} = \frac{25}{25}$$

$$\frac{x^2}{6.25} - \frac{y^2}{1} = 1$$

The graph is a hyperbola.

43. $\dfrac{x^2}{18} + \dfrac{y^2}{9} = 1$

The graph is an ellipse.

44. $y = (x - 2)^2 + 1$

The graph is a parabola.

45. $12x^2 + 9y^2 = 108$

$$\frac{12x^2}{108} + \frac{9y^2}{108} = \frac{108}{108}$$

$$\frac{x^2}{9} + \frac{y^2}{12} = 1$$

The graph is an ellipse.

46. $x = -y^2 + 8y - 9$

The graph is a parabola.

47. $x^2 + 2y^2 = 25$

$x^2 - 3y^2 = 25 \Rightarrow x^2 = 3y^2 + 25$

Substitute $3y^2 + 25$ for x^2 in $x^2 + 2y^2 = 25$.

$x^2 + 2y^2 = 25$

$3y^2 + 25 + 2y^2 = 25$

$5y^2 = 0$

$y^2 = 0$

Substitute 0 for y^2 in $x^2 - 3y^2 = 25$

$x^2 - 0 = 25 \Rightarrow x = \pm 5$

The solutions are $(5, 0)$ and $(-5, 0)$.

48. $x^2 = y^2 + 4$

$x + y = 4$

Solve $x + y = 4$ for y: $y = 4 - x$.

Substitute $4 - x$ for y in $x^2 = y^2 + 4$.

$x^2 = y^2 + 4$

$x^2 = (4 - x)^2 + 4$

$x^2 = (16 - 8x + x^2) + 4$

$8x - 16 = 4$

$8x = 20$

$x = \dfrac{5}{2}$

$y = 4 - x$

$y = 4 - \dfrac{5}{2}$

$y = \dfrac{3}{2}$

The solution is $\left(\dfrac{5}{2}, \dfrac{3}{2} \right)$.

49. $x^2 + y^2 = 9$

$y = 3x + 9$

Substitute $3x + 9$ for y in $x^2 + y^2 = 9$.

$x^2 + y^2 = 9$

$x^2 + (3x + 9)^2 = 9$

$x^2 + 9x^2 + 54x + 81 = 9$

$10x^2 + 54x + 72 = 0$

$5x^2 + 27x + 36 = 0$

$(x + 3)(5x + 12) = 0$

$x + 3 = 0$ or $5x + 12 = 0$

$x = -3$ $x = -\dfrac{12}{5}$

$y = 3x + 9$

$y = 3(-3) + 9$ $y = 3x + 9$

$y = 0$ $y = 3\left(-\dfrac{12}{5} \right) + 9$

                    $y = \dfrac{9}{5}$

The solutions are $(-3, 0)$ and $\left(-\dfrac{12}{5}, \dfrac{9}{5} \right)$.

50. $x^2 + 2y^2 = 9$

$x^2 - 6y^2 = 36$

Solve $x^2 + 2y^2 = 9$ for x^2: $x^2 = 9 - 2y^2$.

Substitute $9 - 2y^2$ for x^2 in $x^2 - 6y^2 = 36$.

$x^2 - 6y^2 = 36$

$(9 - 2y^2) - 6y^2 = 36$

$9 - 8y^2 = 36$

$-8y^2 = 27$

$y^2 = -\dfrac{27}{8}$

There is no real solution to this equation so the system has no real solution.

51. $x^2 + y^2 = 36$

$\underline{x^2 - y^2 = 36}$

$\quad 2x^2 = 72$

$\quad x^2 = 36$

$\quad x = 6$ or $x = -6$

$x^2 + y^2 = 36$ $x^2 + y^2 = 36$

$6^2 + y^2 = 36$ $(-6)^2 + y^2 = 36$

$y^2 = 0$ $y^2 = 0$

$y = 0$ $y = 0$

The solutions are $(6, 0)$ and $(-6, 0)$.

52.
$$x^2 + y^2 = 25 \ (1)$$
$$x^2 - 2y^2 = -2 \ (2)$$
$$2x^2 + 2y^2 = 50 \ (1) \text{ multiplied by 2}$$
$$\underline{x^2 - 2y^2 = -2 \ (2)}$$
$$3x^2 = 48$$
$$x^2 = 16$$
$$x = 4 \quad \text{or} \quad x = -4$$

$$x^2 + y^2 = 25 \qquad x^2 + y^2 = 25$$
$$4^2 + y^2 = 25 \qquad (-4)^2 + y^2 = 25$$
$$y^2 = 9 \qquad\qquad y^2 = 9$$
$$y = \pm 3 \qquad\qquad y = \pm 3$$

The solutions are (4, 3), (4, –3), (–4, 3) and (–4, –3).

53.
$$-4x^2 + y^2 = -15 \ (1)$$
$$8x^2 + 3y^2 = -5 \ (2)$$
$$-8x^2 + 2y^2 = -30 \ (1) \text{ multiplied by 2}$$
$$\underline{8x^2 + 3y^2 = -5 \ (2)}$$
$$5y^2 = -35$$
$$y^2 = -7$$

This equation has no real solution so there is no real solution to the system.

54.
$$3x^2 + 2y^2 = 6 \qquad (1)$$
$$4x^2 + 5y^2 = 15 \qquad (2)$$
$$-12x^2 - 8y^2 = -24 \quad (1) \text{ multiplied by } -4$$
$$\underline{12x^2 + 15y^2 = 45 \quad (2) \text{ multiplied by 3}}$$
$$7y^2 = 21$$
$$y^2 = 3$$
$$y = \pm\sqrt{3}$$
$$3x^2 + 2y^2 = 6$$
$$3x^2 + 2(3) = 6$$
$$3x^2 = 0$$
$$x^2 = 0$$

The solutions are $\left(0, \sqrt{3}\right)$ and $\left(0, -\sqrt{3}\right)$.

55. Let $x = $ length
$$y = \text{ width}$$
$$xy = 45$$
$$2x + 2y = 28$$
Solve $2x + 2y = 28$ for y: $y = 14 - x$.
Substitute $14 - x$ for y in $xy = 45$.
$$xy = 45$$
$$x(14 - x) = 45$$
$$14x - x^2 = 45$$
$$x^2 - 14x + 45 = 0$$
$$(x - 5)(x - 9) = 0$$
$$x - 5 = 0 \quad \text{or} \quad x - 9 = 0$$
$$x = 5 \qquad\qquad x = 9$$

$$y = 14 - x \qquad\qquad y = 14 - x$$
$$y = 14 - 5 \qquad\qquad y = 14 - 9$$
$$y = 9 \qquad\qquad\qquad y = 5$$

The solutions are (5, 9) and (9, 5).
The dimensions of the pool table are 5 feet by 9 feet.

56. $C = 20.3x + 120$
$$R = 50.2x - 0.2x^2$$
$$C = R$$
$$20.3x + 120 = 50.2x - 0.2x^2$$
$$0.2x^2 - 29.9 + 120 = 0$$
$$x = \frac{29.9 \pm \sqrt{(-29.9)^2 - 4(0.2)(120)}}{2(0.2)}$$
$$x = \frac{29.9 \pm \sqrt{798.01}}{0.4}$$
$$x \approx 145 \ \text{or} \ 4$$
The company must sell either 4 bottles or 145 bottles to break even.

57. Since $t = 1$ year, we may rewrite the formula $i = prt$ as $i = pr$.

$$120 = pr$$

$$120 = (p + 2000)(r - 0.01)$$

Rewrite the second equation by multiplying the binomials. Then substitute 120 for pr and solve for r.

$$120 = pr - 0.01p + 2000r - 20$$

$$120 = 120 - 0.01p + 2000r - 20$$

$$0 = -0.01p + 2000r - 20$$

$$0.01p + 20 = 2000r$$

$$\frac{0.01p}{2000} + \frac{20}{2000} = r$$

$$r = 0.000005p + 0.01$$

Substitute $0.000005p + 0.01$ for r in $120 = pr$.

$$120 = pr$$

$$120 = p(0.000005p + 0.01)$$

$$120 = 0.000005p^2 + 0.01p$$

$$0 = 0.000005p^2 + 0.01p - 120$$

$$0 = p^2 + 2000p - 24,000,000$$

$$0 = (p - 4000)(p + 6000)$$

$$p - 4000 = 0 \qquad \text{or} \qquad p + 6000 = 0$$

$$p = 4000 \qquad\qquad\qquad p = -6000$$

The principal must be positive, so use $p = 4000$.

$$r = 0.000005p + 0.01$$

$$r = 0.000005(4000) + 0.01$$

$$r = 0.03$$

The principal is \$4000 and the rate is 3%.

Chapter 14 Practice Test

1. They are formed by cutting a cone or pair of cones.

2. $d = \sqrt{(x_2 - x_1)^2 + (y_2 - y_1)^2}$

$\quad = \sqrt{[6 - (-1)]^2 + (7 - 8)^2}$

$\quad = \sqrt{7^2 + (-1)^2}$

$\quad = \sqrt{49 + 1}$

$\quad = \sqrt{50}$

The length is $\sqrt{50} \approx 7.07$ units.

3. Midpoint $= \left(\dfrac{x_1 + x_2}{2}, \dfrac{y_1 + y_2}{2} \right)$

$\qquad\qquad = \left(\dfrac{-9 + 7}{2}, \dfrac{4 + (-1)}{2} \right)$

$\qquad\qquad = \left(-1, \dfrac{3}{2} \right)$

4. $y = -2(x + 3)^2 + 1$

This is a parabola in the form $y = a(x - h)^2 + k$ with $a = -2$, $h = -3$, and $k = 1$. Since $a < 0$, the parabola opens downward. The vertex is $(-3, 1)$. The y-intercept is $(0, -17)$. The x-intercepts are about $(-3.71, 0)$ and $(-2.29, 0)$.

$$y = -2(x + 3)^2 + 1$$

5. $x = y^2 - 2y + 4$

$\quad x = (y^2 - 2y + 1) - 1 + 4$

$\quad x = (y - 1)^2 + 3$

This is a parabola in the form $x = a(y - k)^2 + h$ with $a = 1$, $h = 3$ and $k = 1$. Since $a > 0$, the parabola opens to the right. The vertex is $(3, 1)$. There is no y-intercept. The x-intercept is $(4, 0)$.

6. $x = -y^2 - 4y - 5$

$x = -(y^2 + 4y) - 5$

$x = -(y^2 + 4y + 4) + 4 - 5$

$x = -(y + 2)^2 - 1$

This is a parabola in the form $x = a(y-k)^2 + h$ with $a = -1$, $h = -1$, and $k = -2$. Since $a < 0$, the parabola opens to the left. The vertex is $(-1, -2)$. There are no y-intercepts. The x-intercept is $(-5, 0)$.

7. $(x-h)^2 + (y-k)^2 = r^2$

$[x-2]^2 + [y-4]^2 = 3^2$

$(x-2)^2 + (y-4)^2 = 9$

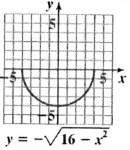

8. $(x+2)^2 + (y-8)^2 = 9$. The graph of this equation is a circle with center $(-2, 8)$ and radius 3.

Area $= \pi r^2$

$\quad = \pi 3^2 = 9\pi \approx 28.27$ sq. units

9. The center is $(3, -1)$ and the radius is 4.

$(x-h)^2 + (y-k)^2 = r^2$

$(x-3)^2 + [y-(-1)]^2 = 4^2$

$(x-3)^2 + (y+1)^2 = 16$

10. $y = -\sqrt{16 - x^2}$

If we solve $x^2 + y^2 = 16$ for y, we obtain $y = \pm\sqrt{16 - x^2}$. Therefore, the graph of $y = -\sqrt{16 - x^2}$ is the lower half ($y \le 0$) of a circle with its center at the origin and radius 4.

$$y = -\sqrt{16 - x^2}$$

11. $x^2 + y^2 + 2x - 6y + 1 = 0$

$x^2 + 2x + y^2 - 6y = -1$

$(x^2 + 2x + 1) + (y^2 - 6y + 9) = -1 + 1 + 9$

$(x+1)^2 + (y-3)^2 = 9$

The graph is a circle with center $(1, 3)$ and radius 3.

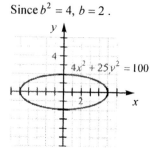

$x^2 + y^2 + 2x - 6y + 1 = 0$

12. $4x^2 + 25y^2 = 100$

$\dfrac{4x^2}{100} + \dfrac{25y^2}{100} = 1$

$\dfrac{x^2}{25} + \dfrac{y^2}{4} = 1$

Since $a^2 = 25$, $a = 5$

Since $b^2 = 4$, $b = 2$.

13. The center is $(-2, -1)$, $a = 4$, and $b = 2$.

$$\frac{(x-h)^2}{a^2} + \frac{(y-k)^2}{b^2} = 1$$

$$\frac{[x-(-2)]^2}{4^2} + \frac{[y-(-1)]^2}{2^2} = 1$$

$$\frac{(x+2)^2}{16} + \frac{(y+1)^2}{4} = 1$$

The values of a^2 and b^2 are switched, so this is not the graph of the given equation. The major axis should be along the y-axis.

14. $4(x-4)^2 + 36(y+2)^2 = 36$

$$\frac{4(x-4)^2}{36} + \frac{36(y+2)^2}{36} = 1$$

$$\frac{(x-4)^2}{9} + \frac{(y+2)^2}{1} = 1$$

The center is $(4, -2)$. Since $a^2 = 9$, $a = 3$

Since $b^2 = 1$, $b = 1$

15. $3(x-8)^2 + 6(y+7)^2 = 18$

$$\frac{3(x-8)^2}{18} + \frac{6(y+7)^2}{18} = \frac{18}{18}$$

$$\frac{(x-8)^2}{6} + \frac{(y+7)^2}{3} = 1$$

The center is $(8, -7)$.

16. The transverse axis lies along the axis corresponding to the positive term of the equation in standard form.

17. $\dfrac{x^2}{16} - \dfrac{y^2}{49} = 1$

Since $a^2 = 16$ and $b^2 = 49$, $a = 4$ and $b = 7$.
The equations of the asymptotes are

$$y = \pm\frac{b}{a}x, \text{ or } y = \pm\frac{7}{4}x.$$

18. $\dfrac{y^2}{25} - \dfrac{x^2}{1} = 1$

Since $a^2 = 1$ and $b^2 = 25$, $a = 1$ and $b = 5$. The equations of the asymptotes are

$$y = \pm\frac{b}{a}x, \text{ or } y = \pm 5x.$$

To graph the asymptotes, plot the points $(1, 5)$, $(-1, 5)$, $(1, -5)$, and $(-1, -5)$.
The graph intersects the y-axis at $(0, -5)$ and $(0, 5)$.

19. $\dfrac{x^2}{4} - \dfrac{y^2}{9} = 1$

Since $a^2 = 4$ and $b^2 = 9$, $a = 2$ and $b = 3$.
The equations of the asymptotes are

$$y = \pm\frac{b}{a}x, \text{ or } y = \pm\frac{3}{2}x.$$

To graph the asymptotes, plot the points $(2, 3)$, $(-2, 3)$, $(2, -3)$, and $(-2, -3)$. The graph intersects the x-axis at $(-2, 0)$ and $(2, 0)$.

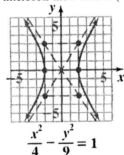

20. $4x^2 - 15y^2 = 30$

$$\frac{4x^2}{30} - \frac{15y^2}{30} = \frac{30}{30}$$

$$\frac{x^2}{\frac{15}{2}} - \frac{y^2}{2} = 1$$

Since the equation is of the form

$$\frac{x^2}{a^2} - \frac{y^2}{b^2} = 1, \text{ the graph is a hyperbola.}$$

21. $25x^2 + 4y^2 = 100$

$$\frac{25x^2}{100} + \frac{4y^2}{100} = \frac{100}{100}$$

$$\frac{x^2}{4} + \frac{y^2}{25} = 1$$

Since the equation is of the form

$\frac{x^2}{a^2} + \frac{y^2}{b^2} = 1$, the graph is an ellipse.

22. $x^2 + y^2 = 7 \overset{\times 3}{\Rightarrow} 3x^2 + 3y^2 = 21$

$$2x^2 - 3y^2 = -1 \qquad \underline{2x^2 - 3y^2 = -1}$$

$$5x^2 \qquad = 20$$

$$x^2 = 4$$

$$x = 2 \qquad \text{or} \qquad x = -2$$

$$x^2 + y^2 = 7 \qquad\qquad x^2 + y^2 = 7$$

$$(2)^2 + y^2 = 7 \qquad\qquad (-2)^2 + y^2 = 7$$

$$4 + y^2 = 7 \qquad\qquad 4 + y^2 = 7$$

$$y^2 = 3 \qquad\qquad y^2 = 3$$

$$y = \pm\sqrt{3} \qquad\qquad y = \pm\sqrt{3}$$

The solutions are $\left(2, \sqrt{3}\right), \left(2, -\sqrt{3}\right),$

$\left(-2, \sqrt{3}\right),$ and $\left(-2, -\sqrt{3}\right)$.

23. $x + y = 8$

$x^2 + y^2 = 4$

Solve $x + y = 8$ for y: $y = 8 - x$.

Substitute $8 - x$ for y in $x^2 + y^2 = 4$.

$$x^2 + y^2 = 4$$

$$x^2 + (8 - x)^2 = 4$$

$$x^2 + 64 - 16x + x^2 = 4$$

$$2x^2 - 16x + 60 = 0$$

$$x^2 - 8x + 30 = 0$$

$$x = \frac{-(-8) \pm \sqrt{(-8)^2 - 4(1)(30)}}{2(1)}$$

$$= \frac{8 \pm \sqrt{-56}}{2} = 4 \pm i\sqrt{14}$$

There is no real solution.

24. Let $x = $ length, $y = $ width.

$$xy = 1500$$

$$2x + 2y = 160$$

Solve $2x + 2y = 160$ for y: $y = 80 - x$.

Substitute $80 - x$ for y in $xy = 1500$.

$$xy = 1500$$

$$x(80 - x) = 1500$$

$$80x - x^2 = 1500$$

$$x^2 - 80x + 1500 = 0$$

$$(x - 30)(x - 50) = 0$$

$$x - 30 = 0 \qquad \text{or} \quad x - 50 = 0$$

$$x = 30 \qquad\qquad x = 50$$

$$y = 80 - 30 \qquad\quad y = 80 - 50$$

$$y = 50 \qquad\qquad y = 30$$

The solutions are (30, 50) and (50, 30).

The dimensions are 30 m by 50 m.

25. Let $x = $ length, $y = $ width

$$xy = 60$$

$$x^2 + y^2 = 13^2$$

Solve $xy = 60$ for y: $y = \frac{60}{x}$.

Substitute $\frac{60}{x}$ for y in $x^2 + y^2 = 13^2$.

$$x^2 + y^2 = 13^2$$

$$x^2 + \left(\frac{60}{x}\right)^2 = 169$$

$$x^2 + \frac{3600}{x^2} = 169$$

$$x^4 + 3600 = 169x^2$$

$$x^4 - 169x^2 + 3600 = 0$$

$$\left(x^2 - 25\right)\left(x^2 - 144\right) = 0$$

$$x^2 - 25 = 0 \quad \text{or} \quad x^2 - 144 = 0$$

$$x^2 = 25 \qquad\qquad x^2 = 144$$

$$x = \pm 5 \qquad\qquad x = \pm 12$$

Since x must be positive, $x = 5$ or $x = 12$.

If $x = 5$, then $y = \frac{60}{5} = 12$. If $x = 12$, then

$y = \frac{60}{12} = 5$. The dimensions of the bed of the

truck are 5 feet by 12 feet

Chapter 14 Cumulative Review Test

1. $4x - 2(3x - 7) = 2x - 5$

$4x - 6x + 14 = 2x - 5$

$-2x + 14 = 2x - 5$

$-4x = -19$

$x = \dfrac{-19}{-4} = \dfrac{19}{4}$

2. $2(x - 5) + 2x = 4x - 7$

$2x - 10 + 2x = 4x - 7$

$4x - 10 = 4x - 7$

$-10 = -7$

This is a contradiction, so the solution set is $\varnothing$.

3. $y = -2x + 2$

The slope is -2 and the y-intercept is $(0, 2)$.

4. $\left(9x^2 y^5\right)\left(-3xy^4\right) = (9)(-3)x^{2+1}y^{5+4} = -27x^3 y^9$

5. $x^4 - x^2 - 42 \qquad$ let $u = x^2$

$= u^2 - u - 42$

$= (u + 6)(u - 7)$

$= \left(x^2 + 6\right)\left(x^2 - 7\right)$

6. Let x be the base of the sign. Then the height can be expressed as $x - 6$.

Area $= \dfrac{1}{2}$ (base $\times$ height)

$56 = \dfrac{1}{2}(x - 6)(x)$

$112 = x^2 - 6x$

$0 = x^2 - 6x - 112$

$0 = (x - 14)(x + 8)$

$x - 14 = 0 \quad$ or $\quad x + 8 = 0$

$x = 14 \qquad\qquad x = -8$

Disregard the negative value. The base of the sign is 14 feet and the height is $14 - 6 = 8$ feet.

7. $\dfrac{3x^2 - x - 4}{4x^2 + 7x + 3} \cdot \dfrac{2x^2 - 5x - 12}{6x^2 + x - 12}$

$= \dfrac{(3x - 4)(x + 1)}{(4x + 3)(x + 1)} \cdot \dfrac{(2x + 3)(x - 4)}{(3x - 4)(2x + 3)}$

$= \dfrac{(3x - 4)(x + 1)(2x + 3)(x - 4)}{(4x + 3)(x + 1)(3x - 4)(2x + 3)}$

$= \dfrac{x - 4}{4x + 3}$

8. $\dfrac{x}{x + 3} - \dfrac{x + 5}{2x^2 - 2x - 24}$

$= \dfrac{x}{x + 3} - \dfrac{x + 5}{2(x + 3)(x - 4)}$

$= \dfrac{2x(x - 4)}{2(x + 3)(x - 4)} - \dfrac{x + 5}{2(x + 3)(x - 4)}$

$= \dfrac{2x^2 - 8x - (x + 5)}{2(x + 3)(x - 4)}$

$= \dfrac{2x^2 - 9x - 5}{2(x + 3)(x - 4)}$

9. $\dfrac{3}{x + 3} + \dfrac{5}{x + 4} = \dfrac{12x + 19}{x^2 + 7x + 12}$

$\left(\dfrac{3}{x + 3} + \dfrac{5}{x + 4} = \dfrac{12x + 19}{(x + 3)(x + 4)}\right)(x + 3)(x + 4)$

$3(x + 4) + 5(x + 3) = 12x + 19$

$3x + 12 + 5x + 15 = 12x + 19$

$8x + 27 = 12x + 19$

$-4x = -8$

$x = 2$

10. $f(x) = x^2 + 3x + 9$

$f(10) = (10)^2 + 3(10) + 9$

$= 100 + 30 + 9$

$= 139$

11. $\frac{1}{2}x - \frac{1}{3}y = 2 \overset{\times(-6)}{\Rightarrow} -3x + 2y = -12$

$\frac{1}{4}x + \frac{2}{3}y = 6 \overset{\times 12}{\Rightarrow} \underline{\quad 3x + 8y = 72\quad}$

$\qquad\qquad\qquad\qquad 10y = 60$

$\qquad\qquad\qquad\qquad\quad y = 6$

Substitute $y = 6$ into $-3x + 2y = -12$

$-3x + 2(6) = -12$

$-3x + 12 = -12$

$-3x = -24$

$x = 8$

The solution is $(8, 6)$.

12. $\qquad |3x + 1| > 4$

$3x + 1 > 4 \qquad 3x + 1 < -4$

$3x > 3 \qquad\quad 3x < -5$

$x > 1 \qquad\qquad x < -\frac{5}{3}$

The solution set is $\left\{ x \mid x < -\frac{5}{3} \text{ or } x > 1 \right\}$

13. $\left(\frac{18x^{1/2}y^3}{2x^{3/2}} \right)^{1/2} = \left(\frac{18}{2}x^{1/2 - 3/2}y^3 \right)^{1/2}$

$= \left(9x^{-1}y^3 \right)^{1/2}$

$= 9^{1/2}x^{-1/2}y^{3/2}$

$= \sqrt{9} \cdot x^{-1/2}y^{3/2}$

$= \frac{3y^{3/2}}{x^{1/2}}$

14. $\frac{6\sqrt{x}}{\sqrt{x} - y} = \frac{6\sqrt{x}}{\sqrt{x} - y} \cdot \frac{\sqrt{x} + y}{\sqrt{x} + y}$

$= \frac{6x + 6y\sqrt{x}}{x + y\sqrt{x} - y\sqrt{x} - y^2}$

$= \frac{6x + 6y\sqrt{x}}{x - y^2}$

15. $3\sqrt[3]{2x + 2} = \sqrt[3]{80x - 24}$

$\left(3\sqrt[3]{2x + 2} \right)^3 = \left(\sqrt[3]{80x - 24} \right)^3$

$27(2x + 2) = (80x - 24)$

$54x + 54 = 80x - 24$

$54x = 80x - 78$

$-26x = -78$

$x = 3$

Check: $3\sqrt[3]{2(3) + 2} \overset{?}{=} \sqrt[3]{80(3) - 24}$

$3\sqrt[3]{8} \overset{?}{=} \sqrt[3]{216}$

$3 \cdot 2 = 6 \quad$ True

The solution is 3.

16. $3x^2 - 4x + 5 = 0$

$x = \frac{-b \pm \sqrt{b^2 - 4ac}}{2a}$

$= \frac{-(-4) \pm \sqrt{(-4)^2 - 4(3)(5)}}{2(3)}$

$= \frac{4 \pm \sqrt{-44}}{6}$

$= \frac{4 \pm 2i\sqrt{11}}{6}$

$= \frac{2 \pm i\sqrt{11}}{3}$

17. $\log(3x - 4) + \log(4) = \log(x + 6)$

$\log 4(3x - 4) = \log(x + 6)$

$\log(12x - 16) = \log(x + 6)$

$12x - 16 = x + 6$

$12x = x + 22$

$11x = 22$

$x = 2$

Check: $\log[3(2) - 4] + \log 4 \overset{?}{=} \log(2 + 6)$

$\log 2 + \log 4 \overset{?}{=} \log 8$

$\log(2 \cdot 4) = \log(8) \quad$ True

The solution is 2.

18.

$$35 = 70e^{-0.3t}$$

$$\frac{1}{2} = e^{-0.3t}$$

$$\ln\frac{1}{2} = \ln e^{-0.3t}$$

$$\ln\frac{1}{2} = -0.3t$$

$$-\frac{1}{0.3}\ln\frac{1}{2} = t$$

$$t = -\frac{1}{0.3}\ln\frac{1}{2} \approx 2.31$$

19. $9x^2 + 4y^2 = 36$

$$\frac{9x^2}{36} + \frac{4y^2}{36} = 1$$

$$\frac{x^2}{4} + \frac{y^2}{9} = 1$$

Since $a^2 = 4$, $a = 2$.

Since $b^2 = 9$, $b = 3$.

20. $\dfrac{y^2}{25} - \dfrac{x^2}{16} = 1$

Since $a^2 = 25$ and $b^2 = 16$, $a = 5$ and $b = 4$

The equations of the asymptotes are $y = \pm\dfrac{b}{a}x$,

or $y = \pm\dfrac{5}{4}x$. To graph the asymptotes, plot the

points $(4, 5)$, $(4, -5)$, $(-4, 5)$, and $(-4, -5)$.
The graph intersects the y-axis at $(0, -5)$ and
$(0, 5)$.

Chapter 15

1. A sequence is a list of numbers arranged in a specific order.

2. An infinite sequence is a function whose domain is the set of natural numbers.

3. A finite sequence is a function whose domain includes only the first n natural numbers.

4. In an increasing sequence, the terms increase.

5. In a decreasing sequence, the terms decrease.

6. In an alternating sequence, the terms alternate in sign.

7. A series is the sum of the terms of a sequence.

8. The nth partial sum is the sum of the first n consecutive terms of a series.

9. $\sum_{i=1}^{5}(i+4)$

   The sum as i goes from 1 to 5 of $i + 4$.

10. $\sum_{i=1}^{5}(k+3)$

    a. 1 is the lower limit.

    b. 5 is the upper limit.

    c. k is the index.

11. The sequence $a_n = 2n - 1$ is an increasing sequence since the coefficient of n is positive.

12. The sequence $a_n = -3n + 7$ is a decreasing sequence since the coefficient of n is negative.

13. Yes, $a_n = 1 + (-2)^n$ is an alternating sequence since $(-2)^n$ alternates between positive and negative values as n alternates from odd to even.

14. No, $a_n = (-1)^{2n}$ is not an alternating sequence because $(-1)^{2n}$ remains a positive value since $2n$ is always an even number.

15. $a_n = 6n$
$$a_1 = 6(1) = 6$$
$$a_2 = 6(2) = 12$$
$$a_3 = 6(3) = 18$$
$$a_4 = 6(4) = 24$$
$$a_5 = 6(5) = 30$$
The terms are 6, 12, 18, 24, 30.

16. $a_n = -5n$
$$a_1 = -5(1) = -5$$
$$a_2 = -5(2) = -10$$
$$a_3 = -5(3) = -15$$
$$a_4 = -5(4) = -20$$
$$a_5 = -5(5) = -25$$
The terms are $-5, -10, -15, -20, -25$.

17. $a_n = 4n - 1$
$$a_1 = 4(1) - 1 = 3$$
$$a_2 = 4(2) - 1 = 7$$
$$a_3 = 4(3) - 1 = 11$$
$$a_4 = 4(4) - 1 = 15$$
$$a_5 = 4(5) - 1 = 19$$
The terms are 3, 7, 11, 15, 19.

18. $a_n = 2n + 5$
$$a_1 = 2(1) + 5 = 7$$
$$a_2 = 2(2) + 5 = 9$$
$$a_3 = 2(3) + 5 = 11$$
$$a_4 = 2(4) + 5 = 13$$
$$a_5 = 2(5) + 5 = 15$$
The terms are 7, 9, 11, 13, 15.

19. $a_n = \dfrac{7}{n}$
$$a_1 = \frac{7}{1} = 7$$
$$a_2 = \frac{7}{2}$$
$$a_3 = \frac{7}{3}$$
$$a_4 = \frac{7}{4}$$
$$a_5 = \frac{7}{5}$$
The terms are $7, \dfrac{7}{2}, \dfrac{7}{3}, \dfrac{7}{4}$, and $\dfrac{7}{5}$.

20. $a_n = \dfrac{8}{n^2}$

$a_1 = \dfrac{8}{1^2} = \dfrac{8}{1} = 8$

$a_2 = \dfrac{8}{2^2} = \dfrac{8}{4} = 2$

$a_3 = \dfrac{8}{3^2} = \dfrac{8}{9}$

$a_4 = \dfrac{8}{4^2} = \dfrac{8}{16} = \dfrac{1}{2}$

$a_5 = \dfrac{8}{5^2} = \dfrac{8}{25}$

The terms are 8, 2, $\dfrac{8}{9}$, $\dfrac{1}{2}$, and $\dfrac{8}{25}$.

21. $a_n = \dfrac{n+2}{n+1}$

$a_1 = \dfrac{1+2}{1+1} = \dfrac{3}{2}$

$a_2 = \dfrac{2+2}{2+1} = \dfrac{4}{3}$

$a_3 = \dfrac{3+2}{3+1} = \dfrac{5}{4}$

$a_4 = \dfrac{4+2}{4+1} = \dfrac{6}{5}$

$a_5 = \dfrac{5+2}{5+1} = \dfrac{7}{6}$

The terms are $\dfrac{3}{2}$, $\dfrac{4}{3}$, $\dfrac{5}{4}$, $\dfrac{6}{5}$, and $\dfrac{7}{6}$.

22. $a_n = \dfrac{n-5}{n+6}$

$a_1 = \dfrac{1-5}{1+6} = \dfrac{-4}{7} = -\dfrac{4}{7}$

$a_2 = \dfrac{2-5}{2+6} = \dfrac{-3}{8} = -\dfrac{3}{8}$

$a_3 = \dfrac{3-5}{3+6} = \dfrac{-2}{9} = -\dfrac{2}{9}$

$a_4 = \dfrac{4-5}{4+6} = \dfrac{-1}{10} = -\dfrac{1}{10}$

$a_5 = \dfrac{5-5}{5+6} = \dfrac{0}{11} = 0$

The terms are $-\dfrac{4}{7}$, $-\dfrac{3}{8}$, $-\dfrac{2}{9}$, $-\dfrac{1}{10}$, and 0.

23. $a_n = (-1)^n$

$a_1 = (-1)^1 = -1$

$a_2 = (-1)^2 = 1$

$a_3 = (-1)^3 = -1$

$a_4 = (-1)^4 = 1$

$a_5 = (-1)^5 = -1$

The terms are -1, 1, -1, 1, -1.

24. $a_n = (-1)^{2n}$

$a_1 = (-1)^{2(1)} = (-1)^2 = 1$

$a_2 = (-1)^{2(2)} = (-1)^4 = 1$

$a_3 = (-1)^{2(3)} = (-1)^6 = 1$

$a_4 = (-1)^{2(4)} = (-1)^8 = 1$

$a_5 = (-1)^{2(5)} = (-1)^{10} = 1$

The terms are 1, 1, 1, 1, 1.

25. $a_n = (-2)^{n+1}$

$a_1 = (-2)^{1+1} = (-2)^2 = 4$

$a_2 = (-2)^{2+1} = (-2)^3 = -8$

$a_3 = (-2)^{3+1} = (-2)^4 = 16$

$a_4 = (-2)^{4+1} = (-2)^5 = -32$

$a_5 = (-2)^{5+1} = (-2)^6 = 64$

The terms are 4, -8, 16, -32, 64.

26. $a_n = 3^{n-1}$

$a_1 = 3^{1-1} = 3^0 = 1$

$a_2 = 3^{2-1} = 3^1 = 3$

$a_3 = 3^{3-1} = 3^2 = 9$

$a_4 = 3^{4-1} = 3^3 = 27$

$a_5 = 3^{5-1} = 3^4 = 81$

The terms are 1, 3, 9, 27, and 81.

27. $a_n = 2n + 7$

$a_{12} = 2(12) + 7 = 24 + 7 = 31$

28. $a_n = 3n + 1$

$a_6 = 3(6) + 2 = 18 + 2 = 20$

29. $a_n = \dfrac{n}{4} + 8$

$a_{16} = \dfrac{16}{4} + 8 = 4 + 8 = 12$

30. $a_n = \dfrac{n}{2} - 13$

$a_{14} = \dfrac{14}{2} - 13 = 7 - 13 = -6$

31. $a_n = (-1)^n$

$a_8 = (-1)^8 = 1$

32. $a_n = (-2)^n$

$a_4 = (-2)^4 = 16$

33. $a_n = n(n+2)$

$a_9 = 9(9+2) = 9(11) = 99$

34. $a_n = (n-1)(n+4)$

$a_5 = (5-1)(5+4) = (4)(9) = 36$

35. $a_n = \dfrac{n^2}{2n+7}$

$a_9 = \dfrac{9^2}{2(9)+7} = \dfrac{81}{18+7} = \dfrac{81}{25}$

36. $a_n = \dfrac{n(n+6)}{n^2}$

$a_9 = \dfrac{10(10+6)}{10^2} = \dfrac{10(16)}{100} = \dfrac{160}{100} = \dfrac{8}{5}$

37. $a_n = 3n - 1$

$a_1 = 3(1) - 1 = 3 - 1 = 2$

$a_2 = 3(2) - 1 = 6 - 1 = 5$

$a_3 = 3(3) - 1 = 9 - 1 = 8$

$s_1 = a_1 = 2$

$s_3 = a_1 + a_2 + a_3 = 2 + 5 + 8 = 15$

38. $a_n = 2n + 3$

$a_1 = 2(1) + 3 = 2 + 3 = 5$

$a_2 = 2(2) + 3 = 4 + 3 = 7$

$a_3 = 2(3) + 3 = 6 + 3 = 9$

$s_1 = a_1 = 5$

$s_3 = a_1 + a_2 + a_3 = 5 + 7 + 9 = 21$

39. $a_n = 2^n + 1$

$a_1 = 2^1 + 1 = 2 + 1 = 3$

$a_2 = 2^2 + 1 = 4 + 1 = 5$

$a_3 = 2^3 + 1 = 8 + 1 = 9$

$s_1 = a_1 = 3$

$s_3 = a_1 + a_2 + a_3 = 3 + 5 + 9 = 17$

40. $a_n = 3^n - 8$

$a_1 = 3^1 - 8 = 3 - 8 = -5$

$a_2 = 3^2 - 8 = 9 - 8 = 1$

$a_3 = 3^3 - 8 = 27 - 8 = 19$

$s_1 = a_1 = -5$

$s_3 = a_1 + a_2 + a_3 = -5 + 1 + 19 = 15$

41. $a_n = \dfrac{n-1}{n+2}$

$a_1 = \dfrac{1-1}{1+2} = \dfrac{0}{3} = 0$

$a_2 = \dfrac{2-1}{2+2} = \dfrac{1}{4}$

$a_3 = \dfrac{3-1}{3+2} = \dfrac{2}{5}$

$s_1 = 0$

$s_3 = 0 + \dfrac{1}{4} + \dfrac{2}{5} = \dfrac{5}{20} + \dfrac{8}{20} = \dfrac{13}{20}$

42. $a_n = \dfrac{n}{n+3}$

$a_1 = \dfrac{1}{1+3} = \dfrac{1}{4}$

$a_2 = \dfrac{2}{2+3} = \dfrac{2}{5}$

$a_3 = \dfrac{3}{3+3} = \dfrac{3}{6} = \dfrac{1}{2}$

$s_1 = a_1 = \dfrac{1}{4}$

$s_3 = a_1 + a_2 + a_3 = \dfrac{1}{4} + \dfrac{2}{5} + \dfrac{1}{2} = \dfrac{5}{20} + \dfrac{8}{20} + \dfrac{10}{20} = \dfrac{23}{20}$

43. $a_n = (-1)^n$

$a_1 = (-1)^1 = -1$

$a_2 = (-1)^2 = 1$

$a_3 = (-1)^3 = -1$

$s_1 = a_1 = -1$

$s_3 = a_1 + a_2 + a_3 = -1 + 1 + -1 = -1$

44. $a_n = (-3)^n$

$a_1 = (-3)^1 = -3$

$a_2 = (-3)^2 = 9$

$a_3 = (-3)^3 = -27$

$s_1 = a_1 = -3$

$s_3 = a_1 + a_2 + a_3 = -3 + 9 + (-27) = -21$

45. $a_n = \dfrac{n^2}{2}$

$a_1 = \dfrac{1^2}{2} = \dfrac{1}{2}$

$a_2 = \dfrac{2^2}{2} = \dfrac{4}{2} = 2$

$a_3 = \dfrac{3^2}{2} = \dfrac{9}{2}$

$s_1 = a_1 = \dfrac{1}{2}$

$s_3 = a_1 + a_2 + a_3 = \dfrac{1}{2} + \dfrac{4}{2} + \dfrac{9}{2} = \dfrac{14}{2} = 7$

46. $a_n = \dfrac{n^2}{n+4}$

$a_1 = \dfrac{1^2}{1+4} = \dfrac{1}{5}$

$a_2 = \dfrac{2^2}{2+4} = \dfrac{4}{6} = \dfrac{2}{3}$

$a_3 = \dfrac{3^2}{3+4} = \dfrac{9}{7}$

$s_1 = a_1 = \dfrac{1}{5}$

$s_3 = a_1 + a_2 + a_3$

$\quad = \dfrac{1}{5} + \dfrac{2}{3} + \dfrac{9}{7} = \dfrac{21}{105} + \dfrac{70}{105} + \dfrac{135}{105} = \dfrac{226}{105}$

47. Each term is twice the preceding term. The next three terms are 64, 128, 256.

48. Each term is 5 more than the previous term. The next three terms are 35, 40, 45.

49. Each term is two more than the preceding term. The next three terms are 17, 19, 21.

50. Each denominator is 1 more than the previous one while each numerator is one. The next three terms are $\dfrac{1}{6}, \dfrac{1}{7}, \dfrac{1}{8}$.

51. Each denominator is one more than the preceding one while each numerator is one. The next three terms are $\dfrac{1}{6}, \dfrac{1}{7}, \dfrac{1}{8}$.

52. The numerators and denominators are both 1 more than the preceding ones. The next three terms are $\dfrac{7}{8}, \dfrac{8}{9}, \dfrac{9}{10}$.

53. Each term is –1 times the previous term. The next three terms are 1, –1, 1.

54. Each term is 10 less than the previous term. The next three terms are –50, –60, –70.

55. Each denominator is three times the previous one while each numerator is one. The next three terms are $\dfrac{1}{81}, \dfrac{1}{243}, \dfrac{1}{729}$.

56. Each numerator is 1 more than the preceding one while the denominators remain at 4. The next three terms are $\dfrac{5}{4}, \dfrac{6}{4}, \dfrac{7}{4}$.

57. Each term is $-\dfrac{1}{2}$ times the preceding term. The next three terms are $\dfrac{1}{16}, -\dfrac{1}{32}, \dfrac{1}{64}$.

58. Each term is $\dfrac{1}{2}$ of the preceding term. The next three terms are $\dfrac{1}{48}, \dfrac{1}{96}, \dfrac{1}{192}$.

59. Each term is 5 less than the preceding term. The next three terms are 17, 12, 7.

60. Each term is eight less than the previous term. The next three terms are –25, –33, –41.

61. $\displaystyle\sum_{i=1}^{5}(3i-1)=\left[3(1)-1\right]+\left[3(2)-1\right]+\left[3(3)-1\right]+\left[3(4)-1\right]+\left[3(5)-1\right]$

$$=2+5+8+11+14$$
$$=40$$

62. $\displaystyle\sum_{i=1}^{4}(4i+5)=\left[4(1)+5\right]+\left[4(2)+5\right]+\left[4(3)+5\right]+\left[4(4)+5\right]$

$$=9+13+17+21$$
$$=60$$

63. $\displaystyle\sum_{i=1}^{6}\left(i^{2}+1\right)=\left(1^{2}+1\right)+\left(2^{2}+1\right)+\left(3^{2}+1\right)+\left(4^{2}+1\right)+\left(5^{2}+1\right)+\left(6^{2}+1\right)$

$$=(1+1)+(4+1)+(9+1)+(16+1)+(25+1)+(36+1)$$
$$=2+5+10+17+26+37$$
$$=97$$

64. $\displaystyle\sum_{i=1}^{5}\left(2i^{2}-7\right)=\left[2(1)^{2}-7\right]+\left[2(2)^{2}-7\right]+\left[2(3)^{2}-7\right]+\left[2(4)^{2}-7\right]+\left[2(5)^{2}-7\right]$

$$=-5+1+11+25+43$$
$$=75$$

65. $\displaystyle\sum_{i=1}^{4}\frac{i^{2}}{2}=\frac{1^{2}}{2}+\frac{2^{2}}{2}+\frac{3^{2}}{2}+\frac{4^{2}}{2}=\frac{1}{2}+\frac{4}{2}+\frac{9}{2}+\frac{16}{2}=\frac{1}{2}+2+\frac{9}{2}+8=\frac{30}{2}=15$

66. $\displaystyle\sum_{i=1}^{3}\frac{i^{2}}{5}=\frac{1^{2}}{5}+\frac{2^{2}}{5}+\frac{3^{2}}{5}=\frac{1}{5}+\frac{4}{5}+\frac{9}{5}=\frac{14}{5}$

67. $\displaystyle\sum_{i=4}^{9}\frac{i^{2}+i}{i+1}=\frac{4^{2}+4}{4+1}+\frac{5^{2}+5}{5+1}+\frac{6^{2}+6}{6+1}+\frac{7^{2}+7}{7+1}+\frac{8^{2}+8}{8+1}+\frac{9^{2}+9}{9+1}$

$$=\frac{20}{5}+\frac{30}{6}+\frac{42}{7}+\frac{56}{8}+\frac{72}{9}+\frac{90}{10}$$
$$=4+5+6+7+8+9$$
$$=39$$

68. $\displaystyle\sum_{i=2}^{5}\frac{i^{3}}{i+1}=\frac{2^{3}}{2+1}+\frac{3^{3}}{3+1}+\frac{4^{3}}{4+1}+\frac{5^{3}}{5+1}$

$$=\frac{8}{3}+\frac{27}{4}+\frac{64}{5}+\frac{125}{6}$$
$$=\frac{160}{60}+\frac{405}{60}+\frac{768}{60}+\frac{1250}{60}$$
$$=\frac{2583}{60}$$
$$=\frac{861}{20}$$

69. $a_n = n + 8$

The fifth partial sum is $\displaystyle\sum_{i=1}^{5}(i + 8)$.

70. $a_n = n^2 + 3$

The fourth partial sum is $\displaystyle\sum_{i=1}^{4}(i^2 + 3)$.

71. $a_n = \dfrac{n^2}{4}$

The third partial sum is $\displaystyle\sum_{i=1}^{3}\dfrac{i^2}{4}$.

72. $a_n = \dfrac{n^2 + 13}{n + 9}$

The third partial sum is $\displaystyle\sum_{i=1}^{3}\dfrac{i^2 + 13}{i + 9}$.

73. $\displaystyle\sum_{i=1}^{5} x_i = x_1 + x_2 + x_3 + x_4 + x_5$

$= 2 + 3 + 5 + (-1) + 4$

$= 13$

74. $\displaystyle\sum_{i=1}^{5}(x_i + 5)$

$= (x_1 + 5) + (x_2 + 5) + (x_3 + 5) + (x_4 + 5) + (x_5 + 5)$

$= (2 + 5) + (3 + 5) + (5 + 5) + (-1 + 5) + (4 + 5)$

$= 7 + 8 + 10 + 4 + 9$

$= 38$

75. $\left(\displaystyle\sum_{i=1}^{5} x_i\right)^2 = (x_1 + x_2 + x_3 + x_4 + x_5)^2$

$= (2 + 3 + 5 + (-1) + 4)^2$

$= 13^2$

$= 169$

76. $\displaystyle\sum_{i=1}^{5} 2x_i = 2x_1 + 2x_2 + 2x_3 + 2x_4 + 2x_5$

$= 2 \cdot 2 + 2 \cdot 3 + 2 \cdot 5 + 2 \cdot (-1) + 2 \cdot 4$

$= 4 + 6 + 10 + (-2) + 8$

$= 26$

77. $\displaystyle\sum_{i=1}^{5} x_i^2 = x_1^2 + x_2^2 + x_3^2 + x_4^2 + x_5^2$

$= 2^2 + 3^2 + 5^2 + (-1)^2 + 4^2$

$= 55$

78. $\displaystyle\sum_{i=1}^{4}(x_i^2 + 3)$

$= (x_1^2 + 3) + (x_2^2 + 3) + (x_3^2 + 3) + (x_4^2 + 3)$

$= (2^2 + 3) + (3^2 + 3) + (5^2 + 3) + \left[(-1)^2 + 3\right]$

$= (4 + 3) + (9 + 3) + (25 + 3) + (1 + 3)$

$= 7 + 12 + 28 + 4$

$= 51$

79. $\bar{x} = \dfrac{15 + 20 + 25 + 30 + 35}{5} = \dfrac{125}{5} = 25$

80. $\bar{x} = \dfrac{16 + 22 + 96 + 18 + 28}{5} = \dfrac{180}{5} = 36$

81. $\bar{x} = \dfrac{72 + 83 + 4 + 60 + 18 + 20}{6} = \dfrac{257}{6} \approx 42.83$

82. $\bar{x} = \dfrac{5 + 13 + 9 + 12 + 23 + 36 + 70}{7} = \dfrac{168}{7} = 24$

83. a. Perimeter of rectangle: $p = 2l + 2w$

$p_1 = 2(1) + 2(2 \cdot 1) = 2 + 4 = 6$

$p_2 = 2(2) + 2(2 \cdot 2) = 4 + 8 = 12$

$p_3 = 2(3) + 2(2 \cdot 3) = 6 + 12 = 18$

$p_4 = 2(4) + 2(2 \cdot 4) = 8 + 16 = 24$

b. $p_n = 2n + 2(2n) = 2n + 4n = 6n$

84. a. Area of rectangle: $a = l \cdot w$

$a_1 = (1)(2 \cdot 1) = 2$

$a_2 = (2)(2 \cdot 2) = 8$

$a_3 = (3)(2 \cdot 3) = 18$

$a_4 = (4)(2 \cdot 4) = 32$

b. $a_n = (n)(2n) = 2n^2$

85 – 87. Answers will vary.

88. a. $\displaystyle\sum_{i=1}^{n} x_i = x_1 + x_2 + x_3 + \cdots + x_n$

b. $\displaystyle\sum_{j=1}^{n} x_j = x_1 + x_2 + x_3 + \cdots + x_n$

c. Yes; only the index differs. The values of the x_i do not change.

89. $\bar{x} = \dfrac{\sum x}{n}$

$n\bar{x} = n \cdot \dfrac{\sum x}{n}$

$n\bar{x} = \sum x$ or $\sum x = n\bar{x}$

90. $\bar{x} = \dfrac{\sum x}{n}$

$n\bar{x} = n \cdot \dfrac{\sum x}{n}$

$n\bar{x} = \sum x$

$\dfrac{n\bar{x}}{\bar{x}} = \dfrac{\sum x}{\bar{x}}$

$n = \dfrac{\sum x}{\bar{x}}$

91. Yes, $\displaystyle\sum_{i=1}^{n} 4x_i = 4\sum_{i=1}^{n} x_i$. Examples will vary.

92. Yes, $\displaystyle\sum_{i=1}^{n} \dfrac{x_i}{3} = \dfrac{1}{3}\sum_{i=1}^{n} x_i$. Examples will vary.

93. a. $\sum x = x_1 + x_2 + x_3 = 3 + 5 + 2 = 10$

b. $\sum y = y_1 + y_2 + y_3 = 4 + 1 + 6 = 11$

c. $\sum x \cdot \sum y = 10 \cdot 11 = 110$

d. $\sum xy = x_1 y_1 + x_2 y_2 + x_3 y_3$
$= 3(4) + 5(1) + 2(6)$
$= 12 + 5 + 12$
$= 29$

e. No, $\sum xy \neq \sum x \cdot \sum y$.

94. $2x^2 + 15 = 13x$

$2x^2 - 13x + 15 = 0$

$(2x - 3)(x - 5) = 0$

$2x - 3 = 0$ or $x - 5 = 0$

$x = \dfrac{3}{2}$ $\qquad x = 5$

The solutions are $\dfrac{3}{2}$ and 5.

95. $6x^2 - 3x - 4 = 2$

$6x^2 - 3x - 6 = 0$

Use the discriminant to determine the number of real solutions:

$a = 6, b = -3, c = -6$.

$b^2 - 4ac = (-3)^2 - 4(6)(-6)$
$= 9 + 144$
$= 153$

Since $153 > 0$, the equation has two real solutions.

96. $\dfrac{x^2}{4} + \dfrac{y^2}{1} = 1$

$\dfrac{x^2}{2^2} + \dfrac{y^2}{1^2} = 1$

$a = 2$ and $b = 1$.

97. $x^2 + y^2 = 5$

$x = 2y$

Use the substitution method. Substitute $2y$ for x in the first equation.

$(2y)^2 + y^2 = 5$

$4y^2 + y^2 = 5$

$5y^2 = 5$

$y^2 = 1$

$y = \pm 1$

Now substitute 1 for y in the second equation and solve for x. Do this again for -1 .

$y = 1 \Rightarrow x = 2(1) = 2$

$y = -1 \Rightarrow x = 2(-1) = -2$

The solutions are $(1, 2)$ and $(-1, -2)$.

Note: Had we substituted $y = \pm 1$ into the first equation, we would have also obtained the solutions $(1, -2)$ and $(-1, 2)$. However, these are extraneous since they do not check when substituted into the second equation.

Exercise Set 15.2

1. In an arithmetic sequence, each term differs by a constant amount.

2. An arithmetic series is the sum of the terms of an arithmetic sequence.

3. It is called the common difference.

4. To find the common difference, subtract any term from the term that directly follows it.

5. The common difference, d, must be a positive number.

6. The common difference, d, must be a negative number.

7. Yes. For example, $-1, -2, -3, -4, \ldots$ is an arithmetic sequence with $a_1 = -1$ and $d = -1$.

8. Yes. For example, $1, 3, 5, 7, \ldots$ is an arithmetic sequence with $a_1 = 1$ and $d = 2$.

9. Yes. For example, $2, 4, 6, 8, \ldots$ is an arithmetic sequence with $a_1 = 2$ and $d = 2$.

10. No. An alternating sequence cannot be an arithmetic sequence.

11. $a_1 = 4$
$a_2 = 4 + (2-1)(3) = 4 + 3 = 7$
$a_3 = 4 + (3-1)(3) = 4 + 2(3) = 4 + 6 = 10$
$a_4 = 4 + (4-1)(3) = 4 + 3(3) = 4 + 9 = 13$
$a_5 = 4 + (5-1)(3) = 4 + 4(3) = 4 + 12 = 16$
The terms are 4, 7, 10, 13, 16. The general term is $a_n = 4 + (n-1)3$ or $a_n = 3n + 1$.

12. $a_1 = -11$
$a_2 = -11 + (2-1)(4) = -11 + 4 = -7$
$a_3 = -11 + (3-1)(4) = -11 + 2(4) = -11 + 8 = -3$
$a_4 = -11 + (4-1)(4) = -11 + 3(4) = -11 + 12 = 1$
$a_5 = -11 + (5-1)(4) = -11 + 4(4) = -11 + 16 = 5$
The terms are $-11, -7, -3, 1, 5$. The general term is $a_n = -11 + (n-1)4$ or $a_n = 4n - 15$.

13. $a_1 = 7$
$a_2 = 7 + (2-1)(-2) = 7 - 2 = 5$
$a_3 = 7 + (3-1)(-2) = 7 + 2(-2) = 7 - 4 = 3$
$a_4 = 7 + (4-1)(-2) = 7 + 3(-2) = 7 - 6 = 1$
$a_5 = 7 + (5-1)(-2) = 7 + 4(-2) = 7 - 8 = -1$
The terms are 7, 5, 3, 1, -1. The general term is $a_n = 7 + (n-1)(-2)$ or $a_n = -2n + 9$.

14. $a_1 = 3$
$a_2 = 3 + (2-1)(-5) = 3 - 5 = -2$
$a_3 = 3 + (3-1)(-5) = 3 + 2(-5) = 3 - 10 = -7$
$a_4 = 3 + (4-1)(-5) = 3 + 3(-5) = 3 - 15 = -12$
$a_5 = 3 + (5-1)(-5) = 3 + 4(-5) = 3 - 20 = -17$
The terms are 3, -2, -7, -12, -17. The general term is $a_n = 3 + (n-1)(-5)$ or $a_n = -5n + 8$.

15. $a_1 = \dfrac{1}{2}$
$a_2 = \dfrac{1}{2} + (2-1)\left(\dfrac{3}{2}\right) = \dfrac{1}{2} + \dfrac{3}{2} = \dfrac{4}{2} = 2$
$a_3 = \dfrac{1}{2} + (3-1)\left(\dfrac{3}{2}\right) = \dfrac{1}{2} + 2\left(\dfrac{3}{2}\right) = \dfrac{1}{2} + \dfrac{6}{2} = \dfrac{7}{2}$
$a_4 = \dfrac{1}{2} + (4-1)\left(\dfrac{3}{2}\right) = \dfrac{1}{2} + 3\left(\dfrac{3}{2}\right) = \dfrac{1}{2} + \dfrac{9}{2} = \dfrac{10}{2} = 5$
$a_5 = \dfrac{1}{2} + (5-1)\left(\dfrac{3}{2}\right) = \dfrac{1}{2} + 4\left(\dfrac{3}{2}\right) = \dfrac{1}{2} + \dfrac{12}{2} = \dfrac{13}{2}$
The terms are $\dfrac{1}{2}, 2, \dfrac{7}{2}, 5, \dfrac{13}{2}$. The general term is
$a_n = \dfrac{1}{2} + (n-1)\dfrac{3}{2}$ or $a_n = \dfrac{3}{2}n - 1$.

16. $a_1 = -\dfrac{5}{3}$
$a_2 = -\dfrac{5}{3} + (2-1)\left(-\dfrac{1}{3}\right)$
$\quad = -\dfrac{5}{3} + \left(-\dfrac{1}{3}\right) = -\dfrac{5}{3} - \dfrac{1}{3} = -\dfrac{6}{3} = -2$
$a_3 = -\dfrac{5}{3} + (3-1)\left(-\dfrac{1}{3}\right)$
$\quad = -\dfrac{5}{3} + 2\left(-\dfrac{1}{3}\right) = -\dfrac{5}{3} - \dfrac{2}{3} = -\dfrac{7}{3}$
$a_4 = -\dfrac{5}{3} + (4-1)\left(-\dfrac{1}{3}\right)$
$\quad = -\dfrac{5}{3} + 3\left(-\dfrac{1}{3}\right) = -\dfrac{5}{3} - \dfrac{3}{3} = -\dfrac{8}{3}$
$a_5 = -\dfrac{5}{3} + (5-1)\left(-\dfrac{1}{3}\right)$
$\quad = -\dfrac{5}{3} + 4\left(-\dfrac{1}{3}\right) = -\dfrac{5}{3} - \dfrac{4}{3} = -\dfrac{9}{3} = -3$
The terms are $-\dfrac{5}{3}, -2, -\dfrac{7}{3}, -\dfrac{8}{3}, -3$. The general term is $a_n = -\dfrac{5}{3} + (n-1)\left(-\dfrac{1}{3}\right)$ or $a_n = -\dfrac{1}{3}n - \dfrac{4}{3}$.

17. $a_1 = 100$

$a_2 = 100 + (2-1)(-5)$

$\quad = 100 + (-5) = 100 - 5 = 95$

$a_3 = 100 + (3-1)(-5)$

$\quad = 100 + 2(-5) = 100 - 10 = 90$

$a_4 = 100 + (4-1)(-5)$

$\quad = 100 + 3(-5) = 100 - 15 = 85$

$a_5 = 100 + (5-1)(-5)$

$\quad = 100 + 4(-5) = 100 - 20 = 80$

The terms are 100, 95, 90, 85, 80. The general term is $a_n = 100 + (n-1)(-5)$ or $a_n = -5n + 105$.

18. $a_1 = \dfrac{7}{4}$

$a_2 = \dfrac{7}{4} + (2-1)\left(-\dfrac{3}{4}\right)$

$\quad = \dfrac{7}{4} + \left(-\dfrac{3}{4}\right) = \dfrac{7}{4} - \dfrac{3}{4} = \dfrac{4}{4} = 1$

$a_3 = \dfrac{7}{4} + (3-1)\left(-\dfrac{3}{4}\right)$

$\quad = \dfrac{7}{4} + 2\left(-\dfrac{3}{4}\right) = \dfrac{7}{4} - \dfrac{6}{4} = \dfrac{1}{4}$

$a_4 = \dfrac{7}{4} + (4-1)\left(-\dfrac{3}{4}\right)$

$\quad = \dfrac{7}{4} + 3\left(-\dfrac{3}{4}\right) = \dfrac{7}{4} - \dfrac{9}{4} = -\dfrac{2}{4} = -\dfrac{1}{2}$

$a_5 = \dfrac{7}{4} + (5-1)\left(-\dfrac{3}{4}\right)$

$\quad = \dfrac{7}{4} + 4\left(-\dfrac{3}{4}\right) = \dfrac{7}{4} - \dfrac{12}{4} = -\dfrac{5}{4}$

The terms are $\dfrac{7}{4}, 1, \dfrac{1}{4}, -\dfrac{1}{2}, -\dfrac{5}{4}$. The general term

is $a_n = \dfrac{7}{4} + (n-1)\left(-\dfrac{3}{4}\right)$ or $a_n = -\dfrac{3}{4}n + \dfrac{5}{2}$.

19. $a_n = a_1 + (n-1)d$

$a_4 = 5 + (4-1)3 = 5 + 3 \cdot 3 = 5 + 9 = 14$

20. $a_n = a_1 + (n-1)d$

$a_5 = 10 + (5-1)(-3) = 10 + 4(-3) = 10 - 12 = -2$

21. $a_n = a_1 + (n-1)d$

$a_{10} = -9 + (10-1)(4) = -9 + 9(4) = -9 + 36 = 27$

22. $a_n = a_1 + (n-1)d$

$a_{12} = -1 + (12-1)(-2)$

$\quad = -1 + 11(-2) = -1 + (-22) = -23$

23. $a_n = a_1 + (n-1)d$

$a_{13} = -8 + (13-1)\left(\dfrac{5}{3}\right)$

$\quad = -8 + 12\left(\dfrac{5}{3}\right) = -8 + 20 = 12$

24. $a_n = a_1 + (n-1)d$

$-21 = 5 + (8-1)d$

$-21 = 5 + 7d$

$-26 = 7d$

$-\dfrac{26}{7} = d$

25. $a_n = a_1 + (n-1)d$

$27 = 11 + (9-1)d$

$27 = 11 + 8d$

$16 = 8d$

$2 = d$

26. $a_n = a_1 + (n-1)d$

$\dfrac{19}{2} = \dfrac{1}{2} + (7-1)d$

$\dfrac{19}{2} = \dfrac{1}{2} + 6d$

$\dfrac{19}{2} - \dfrac{1}{2} = 6d$

$\dfrac{18}{2} = 6d$

$9 = 6d$

$d = \dfrac{9}{6} = \dfrac{3}{2}$

27. $a_n = a_1 + (n-1)d$

$28 = 4 + (n-1)(3)$

$28 = 4 + 3n - 3$

$28 = 1 + 3n$

$27 = 3n$

$9 = n$

28. $a_n = a_1 + (n-1)d$

$-27 = -9 + (n-1)(-3)$

$-27 = -9 - 3n + 3$

$-27 = -6 - 3n$

$-21 = -3n$

$7 = n$

29. $a_n = a_1 + (n-1)d$

$42 = 82 + (n-1)(-8)$

$42 = 82 - 8n + 8$

$42 = 90 - 8n$

$-48 = -8n$

$6 = n$

30. $a_n = a_1 + (n-1)d$

$-\dfrac{14}{3} = -\dfrac{4}{3} + (n-1)\left(-\dfrac{2}{3}\right)$

$-\dfrac{14}{3} = -\dfrac{4}{3} - \dfrac{2}{3}n + \dfrac{2}{3}$

$-\dfrac{14}{3} = -\dfrac{2}{3} - \dfrac{2}{3}n$

$3\left(-\dfrac{14}{3}\right) = 3\left(-\dfrac{2}{3} - \dfrac{2}{3}n\right)$

$-14 = -2 - 2n$

$-12 = -2n$

$6 = n$

31. $s_{10} = \dfrac{10(a_1 + a_{10})}{2} = \dfrac{10(1+19)}{2} = 5(20) = 100$

$a_{10} = a_1 + (10-1)d$

$a_{10} = a_1 + 9d$

$19 = 1 + 9d$

$18 = 9d$

$2 = d$

32. $s_7 = \dfrac{7(a_1 + a_7)}{2} = \dfrac{7(-8+10)}{2} = \dfrac{7(2)}{2} = \dfrac{14}{2} = 7$

$a_7 = a_1 + (7-1)d$

$a_7 = a_1 + 6d$

$10 = -8 + 6d$

$18 = 6d$

$3 = d$

33. $s_8 = \dfrac{8(a_1 + a_8)}{2} = \dfrac{8\left(\frac{3}{5} + 2\right)}{2} = 4\left(\dfrac{3}{5} + 2\right)$

$\quad = 4\left(\dfrac{3}{5} + \dfrac{10}{5}\right) = 4\left(\dfrac{13}{5}\right) = \dfrac{52}{5}$

$a_8 = a_1 + (8-1)d$

$a_8 = a_1 + 7d$

$2 = \dfrac{3}{5} + 7d$

$\dfrac{7}{5} = 7d$

$d = \dfrac{1}{7} \cdot \dfrac{7}{5} = \dfrac{1}{5}$

34. $s_8 = \dfrac{8(a_1 + a_8)}{2} = \dfrac{8[12 + (-23)]}{2} = \dfrac{8(-11)}{2} = -44$

$a_8 = a_1 + (8-1)d$

$a_8 = a_1 + 7d$

$-23 = 12 + 7d$

$-35 = 7d$

$-5 = d$

35. $s_6 = \dfrac{6(a_1 + a_6)}{2} = \dfrac{6(-5 + 13.5)}{2} = \dfrac{6(8.5)}{2} = 25.5$

$a_6 = a_1 + (6-1)d$

$a_6 = a_1 + 5d$

$13.5 = -5 + 5d$

$18.5 = 5d$

$3.7 = d$

36. $s_5 = \dfrac{5(a_1 + a_5)}{2} = \dfrac{5\left(\frac{7}{5} + \frac{23}{5}\right)}{2} = \dfrac{5\left(\frac{30}{5}\right)}{2} = \dfrac{30}{2} = 15$

$a_5 = a_1 + (5-1)d$

$a_5 = a_1 + 4d$

$\dfrac{23}{5} = \dfrac{7}{5} + 4d$

$\dfrac{16}{5} = 4d$

$d = \dfrac{1}{4} \cdot \dfrac{16}{5} = \dfrac{4}{5}$

37. $s_{11} = \dfrac{11(a_1 + a_{11})}{2} = \dfrac{11(7 + 67)}{2} = \dfrac{11(74)}{2} = 407$

$a_{11} = a_1 + (11-1)d$

$a_{11} = a_1 + 10d$

$67 = 7 + 10d$

$60 = 10d$

$6 = d$

38. $s_{31} = \dfrac{31(a_1 + a_{31})}{2} = \dfrac{31(14.25 + 18.75)}{2} = \dfrac{31(33)}{2}$

$\qquad = \dfrac{1023}{2} = 511.5$

$\qquad a_{31} = a_1 + (31-1)d$

$\qquad 18.75 = 14.25 + 30d$

$\qquad 4.50 = 30d$

$\qquad d = \dfrac{4.50}{30} = 0.15$

39. $a_1 = 4$

$\qquad a_2 = 4 + (2-1)(3) = 4 + 3 = 7$

$\qquad a_3 = 4 + (3-1)(3) = 4 + 2(3) = 4 + 6 = 10$

$\qquad a_4 = 4 + (4-1)(3) = 4 + 3(3) = 4 + 9 = 13$

$\qquad$ The terms are 4, 7, 10, 13.

$\qquad a_{10} = 4 + (10-1)(3) = 4 + 9(3) = 4 + 27 = 31$

$\qquad s_{10} = \dfrac{10(4+31)}{2} = \dfrac{10(35)}{2} = 175$

40. $a_1 = 11$

$\qquad a_2 = 11 + (2-1)(-6) = 11 + 1(-6) = 11 - 6 = 5$

$\qquad a_3 = 11 + (3-1)(-6) = 11 + 2(-6) = 11 - 12 = -1$

$\qquad a_4 = 11 + (4-1)(-6) = 11 + 3(-6) = 11 - 18 = -7$

$\qquad$ The terms are 11, 5, –1, –7.

$\qquad a_{10} = 11 + (10-1)(-6) = 11 + 9(-6) = 11 - 54 = -43$

$\qquad s_{10} = \dfrac{10[11+(-43)]}{2} = \dfrac{10(-32)}{2} = -160$

41. $a_1 = -6$

$\qquad a_2 = -6 + (2-1)(2) = -6 + 1(2) = -6 + 2 = -4$

$\qquad a_3 = -6 + (3-1)(2) = -6 + 2(2) = -6 + 4 = -2$

$\qquad a_4 = -6 + (4-1)(2) = -6 + 3(2) = -6 + 6 = 0$

$\qquad$ The terms are –6, –4, –2, 0.

$\qquad a_{10} = -6 + (10-1)(2) = -6 + 9(2) = -6 + 18 = 12$

$\qquad s_{10} = \dfrac{10(-6+12)}{2} = \dfrac{10(6)}{2} = \dfrac{60}{2} = 30$

42. $a_1 = -7$

$\qquad a_2 = -7 + (2-1)(-4) = -7 + 1(-4) = -7 - 4 = -11$

$\qquad a_3 = -7 + (3-1)(-4) = -7 + 2(-4) = -7 - 8 = -15$

$\qquad a_4 = -7 + (4-1)(-4) = -7 + 3(-4) = -7 - 12 = -19$

$\qquad$ The terms are –7, –11, –15, –19.

$\qquad a_{10} = -7 + (10-1)(-4) = -7 + 9(-4) = -7 - 36 = -43$

$\qquad s_{10} = \dfrac{10[-7+(-43)]}{2} = \dfrac{10(-50)}{2} = \dfrac{-500}{2} = -250$

43. $a_1 = -8$

$\qquad a_2 = -8 + (2-1)(-5) = -8 - 5 = -13$

$\qquad a_3 = -8 + (3-1)(-5) = -8 + 2(-5) = -8 - 10 = -18$

$\qquad a_4 = -8 + (4-1)(-5) = -8 + 3(-5) = -8 - 15 = -23$

$\qquad$ The terms are –8, –13, –18, –23.

$\qquad a_{10} = -8 + (10-1)(-5)$

$\qquad = -8 + 9(-5) = -8 - 45 = -53$

$\qquad s_{10} = \dfrac{10[-8+(-53)]}{2} = \dfrac{10(-61)}{2} = \dfrac{-610}{2} = -305$

44. $a_1 = -15$

$\qquad a_2 = -15 + (2-1)(4) = -16 + 1(4) = -15 + 4 = -11$

$\qquad a_3 = -15 + (3-1)(4) = -15 + 2(4) = -15 + 8 = -7$

$\qquad a_4 = -15 + (4-1)(4) = -15 + 3(4) = -15 + 12 = -3$

$\qquad$ The terms are –15, –11, –7, –3.

$\qquad a_{10} = -15 + (10-1)(4)$

$\qquad = -15 + 9(4) = -15 + 36 = 21$

$\qquad s_{10} = \dfrac{10(-15+21)}{2} = \dfrac{10(6)}{2} = \dfrac{60}{2} = 30$

45. $a_1 = \dfrac{7}{2}$

$\qquad a_2 = \dfrac{7}{2} + (2-1)\left(\dfrac{5}{2}\right) = \dfrac{7}{2} + 1\left(\dfrac{5}{2}\right) = \dfrac{7}{2} + \dfrac{5}{2} = \dfrac{12}{2} = 6$

$\qquad a_3 = \dfrac{7}{2} + (3-1)\left(\dfrac{5}{2}\right) = \dfrac{7}{2} + 2\left(\dfrac{5}{2}\right) = \dfrac{7}{2} + \dfrac{10}{2} = \dfrac{17}{2}$

$\qquad a_4 = \dfrac{7}{2} + (4-1)\left(\dfrac{5}{2}\right) = \dfrac{7}{2} + 3\left(\dfrac{5}{2}\right) = \dfrac{7}{2} + \dfrac{15}{2} = \dfrac{22}{2} = 11$

$\qquad$ The terms are $\dfrac{7}{2}$, 6, $\dfrac{17}{2}$, 11.

$\qquad a_{10} = \dfrac{7}{2} + (10-1)\left(\dfrac{5}{2}\right)$

$\qquad = \dfrac{7}{2} + 9\left(\dfrac{5}{2}\right) = \dfrac{7}{2} + \dfrac{45}{2} = \dfrac{52}{2} = 26$

$\qquad s_{10} = \dfrac{10(3.5+26)}{2} = \dfrac{10(29.5)}{2} = 147.5$

46. $a_1 = \dfrac{9}{5}$

$a_2 = \dfrac{9}{5} + (2-1)\left(\dfrac{3}{5}\right) = \dfrac{9}{5} + 1\left(\dfrac{3}{5}\right) = \dfrac{9}{5} + \dfrac{3}{5} = \dfrac{12}{5}$

$a_3 = \dfrac{9}{5} + (3-1)\left(\dfrac{3}{5}\right) = \dfrac{9}{5} + 2\left(\dfrac{3}{5}\right) = \dfrac{9}{5} + \dfrac{6}{5} = \dfrac{15}{5} = 3$

$a_4 = \dfrac{9}{5} + (4-1)\left(\dfrac{3}{5}\right) = \dfrac{9}{5} + 3\left(\dfrac{3}{5}\right) = \dfrac{9}{5} + \dfrac{9}{5} = \dfrac{18}{5}$

The terms are $\dfrac{9}{5}, \dfrac{12}{5}, 3, \dfrac{18}{5}$.

$a_{10} = \dfrac{9}{5} + (10-1)\left(\dfrac{3}{5}\right) = \dfrac{9}{5} + 9\left(\dfrac{3}{5}\right) = \dfrac{9}{5} + \dfrac{27}{5} = \dfrac{36}{5}$

$s_{10} = \dfrac{10\left(\frac{9}{5} + \frac{36}{5}\right)}{2} = 5\left(\dfrac{45}{5}\right) = 45$

47. $a_1 = 100$

$a_2 = 100 + (2-1)(-7)$
$\quad = 100 + 1(-7) = 100 - 7 = 93$

$a_3 = 100 + (3-1)(-7)$
$\quad = 100 + 2(-7) = 100 - 14 = 86$

$a_4 = 100 + (4-1)(-7)$
$\quad = 100 + 3(-7) = 100 - 21 = 79$

The terms are 100, 93, 86, 79.

$a_{10} = 100 + (10-1)(-7)$
$\quad = 100 + 9(-7) = 100 - 63 = 37$

$s_{10} = \dfrac{10(100 + 37)}{2} = \dfrac{10(137)}{2} = 685$

48. $a_1 = 35$

$a_2 = 35 + (2-1)(6) = 35 + 1(6) = 35 + 6 = 41$
$a_3 = 35 + (3-1)(6) = 35 + 2(6) = 35 + 12 = 47$
$a_4 = 35 + (4-1)(6) = 35 + 3(6) = 35 + 18 = 53$

The terms are 35, 41, 47, 53.

$a_{10} = 35 + (10-1)(6) = 35 + 9(6) = 35 + 54 = 89$

$s_{10} = \dfrac{10(35 + 89)}{2} = \dfrac{10(124)}{2} = 620$

49. $d = 4 - 1 = 3$

$a_n = a_1 + (n-1)d$
$43 = 1 + (n-1)(3)$
$43 = 1 + 3n - 3$
$43 = -2 + 3n$
$45 = 3n$
$15 = n$

$s_{15} = \dfrac{15(a_1 + a_{15})}{2} = \dfrac{15(1 + 43)}{2} = \dfrac{15(44)}{2} = 330$

50. $d = -8 - (-10) = -8 + 10 = 2$

$a_n = a_1 + (n-1)d$
$40 = -10 + (n-1)(2)$
$40 = -10 + 2n - 2$
$40 = -12 + 2n$
$52 = 2n$
$26 = n$

$s_{26} = \dfrac{26(a_1 + a_{26})}{2}$
$\quad = \dfrac{26(-10 + 40)}{2} = \dfrac{26(30)}{2} = \dfrac{780}{2} = 390$

51. $d = -5 - (-9) = -5 + 9 = 4$

$a_n = a_1 + (n-1)d$
$31 = -9 + (n-1)(4)$
$31 = -9 + 4n - 4$
$31 = -13 + 4n$
$44 = 4n$
$11 = n$

$s_{10} = \dfrac{11(a_1 + a_{10})}{2} = \dfrac{11(-9 + 31)}{2} = \dfrac{11(22)}{2} = 121$

52. $d = 13 - 6 = 7$

$a_n = a_1 + (n-1)d$
$62 = 6 + (n-1)7$
$62 = 6 + 7n - 7$
$62 = 7n - 1$
$63 = 7n$
$9 = n$

$s_9 = \dfrac{9(a_1 + a_9)}{2} = \dfrac{9(6 + 62)}{2} = \dfrac{9(68)}{2} = \dfrac{612}{2} = 306$

53. $d = \dfrac{2}{2} - \dfrac{1}{2} = \dfrac{1}{2}$

$a_n = \dfrac{1}{2} + (n-1)\left(\dfrac{1}{2}\right)$

$\dfrac{17}{2} = \dfrac{1}{2} + \dfrac{1}{2}n - \dfrac{1}{2}$

$\dfrac{17}{2} = \dfrac{1}{2}n$

$17 = n$

$s_{17} = \dfrac{17(a_1 + a_{17})}{2}$

$\quad = \dfrac{17\left(\frac{1}{2} + \frac{17}{2}\right)}{2} = \dfrac{17\left(\frac{18}{2}\right)}{2} = \dfrac{17(9)}{2} = \dfrac{153}{2}$

54. $d = -\dfrac{7}{6} - \left(-\dfrac{5}{6}\right) = -\dfrac{7}{6} + \dfrac{5}{6} = -\dfrac{2}{6}$

$$a_n = a_1 + (n-1)d$$

$$-\dfrac{21}{6} = -\dfrac{5}{6} + (n-1)\left(-\dfrac{2}{6}\right)$$

$$-\dfrac{21}{6} = -\dfrac{5}{6} - \dfrac{2}{6}n + \dfrac{2}{6}$$

$$-\dfrac{21}{6} = -\dfrac{3}{6} - \dfrac{2}{6}n$$

$$6\left(-\dfrac{21}{6}\right) = 6\left(-\dfrac{3}{6} - \dfrac{2}{6}n\right)$$

$$-21 = -3 - 2n$$

$$-18 = -2n$$

$$9 = n$$

$$s_9 = \dfrac{9(a_1 + a_9)}{2} = \dfrac{9\left[-\frac{5}{6} + \left(-\frac{21}{6}\right)\right]}{2}$$

$$= \dfrac{9\left(-\frac{26}{6}\right)}{2} = 9\left(-\dfrac{26}{6}\right)\left(\dfrac{1}{2}\right) = -\dfrac{39}{2}$$

55. $d = 10 - 7 = 3$

$$a_n = a_1 + (n-1)d$$

$$91 = 7 + (n-1)(3)$$

$$91 = 7 + 3n - 3$$

$$91 = 4 + 3n$$

$$87 = 3n$$

$$29 = n$$

$$s_{29} = \dfrac{29(a_1 + a_{29})}{2} = \dfrac{29(7+91)}{2} = \dfrac{29(98)}{2} = 1421$$

56. $d = -15 - (-11) = -15 + 11 = -4$

$$a_n = a_1 + (n-1)d$$

$$-51 = -11 + (n-1)(-4)$$

$$-51 = -11 - 4n + 4$$

$$-51 = -7 - 4n$$

$$-44 = -4n$$

$$11 = n$$

$$s_{11} = \dfrac{11(a_1 + a_{11})}{2}$$

$$= \dfrac{11[-11 + (-51)]}{2} = \dfrac{11(-62)}{2} = -341$$

57. $s_n = \dfrac{n(a_1 + a_n)}{2}$

$$s_{50} = \dfrac{50(1 + 50)}{2} = \dfrac{50(51)}{2} = 1275$$

58 $s_n = \dfrac{n(a_1 + a_n)}{2}$

$$s_{50} = \dfrac{50(2 + 100)}{2} = \dfrac{50(102)}{2} = 2550$$

59. $s_n = \dfrac{n(a_1 + a_n)}{2}$

$$s_{50} = \dfrac{50(1 + 99)}{2} = \dfrac{50(100)}{2} = 2500$$

60. $s_n = \dfrac{n(a_1 + a_n)}{2}$

$$s_{40} = \dfrac{40(5 + 200)}{2} = \dfrac{40(205)}{2} = 4100$$

61. $s_n = \dfrac{n(a_1 + a_n)}{2}$

$$s_{30} = \dfrac{30(3 + 90)}{2} = \dfrac{30(93)}{2} = 1395$$

62. $s_n = \dfrac{n(a_1 + a_n)}{2}$

Note that there are 101 numbers from 50 to 150.

$$s_{101} = \dfrac{101(50 + 150)}{2} = \dfrac{101(200)}{2} = 10,100$$

63. The smallest number greater than 7 that is divisible by 6 is 12. The largest number less than 1610 that is divisible by 6 is 1608. Now find n in the equation $a_n = a_1 + (n-1)d$.

$$1608 = 12 + (n-1)6$$

$$1596 = 6(n-1)$$

$$266 = n-1$$

$$267 = n$$

There are 267 numbers between 7 and 1610 that are divisible by 6.

64. The smallest number greater than 14 that is divisible by 8 is 16. The largest number less than 1470 that is divisible by 8 is 1464. Now find n in the equation $a_n = a_1 + (n-1)d$.

$$1464 = 16 + (n-1)8$$

$$1448 = 8(n-1)$$

$$181 = n-1$$

$$182 = n$$

There are 182 numbers between 12 and 1470 that are divisible by 8.

65. $a_1 = 20$, $d = 2$, $n = 12$

$a_n = a_1 + (n-1)d$

$a_{12} = 20 + (12-1)(2) = 20 + 11(2) = 20 + 22 = 42$

$S_n = \dfrac{n(a_1 + a_n)}{2}$

$S_{12} = \dfrac{12(20+42)}{2} = \dfrac{12(62)}{2} = \dfrac{744}{2} = 372$

There are 42 seats in the twelfth row and 372 seats in the first twelve rows.

66. $a_1 = 22$, $d = 4$, $n = 9$

$a_n = a_1 + (n-1)d$

$a_9 = 22 + (9-1)(4) = 22 + 8(4) = 22 + 32 = 54$

$S_n = \dfrac{n(a_1 + a_n)}{2}$

$S_9 = \dfrac{9(22+54)}{2} = \dfrac{9(76)}{2} = \dfrac{684}{2} = 342$

There are 54 seats in the ninth row and 342 seats in the first nine rows.

67. $26 + 25 + 24 + \cdots + 1$ or $1 + 2 + 3 + \cdots + 26$

$S_n = \dfrac{n(a_1 + a_n)}{2}$

$S_{26} = \dfrac{26(1+26)}{2} = \dfrac{26(27)}{2} = \dfrac{702}{2} = 351$

There are 351 logs in the pile.

68. $26 + 25 + 24 + \cdots + 8$ or $8 + 9 + 10 + \cdots + 26$

$S_n = \dfrac{n(a_1 + a_n)}{2}$

Note that the number of rows of logs would be $n = 19$.

$S_{19} = \dfrac{19(8+26)}{2} = \dfrac{19(34)}{2} = \dfrac{646}{2} = 323$

There are 323 logs in the pile.

69. $a_1 = 1$, $d = 2$, $n = 14$

$a_n = a_1 + (n-1)d$

$a_{14} = 1 + (14-1)(2) = 1 + 13(2) = 1 + 26 = 27$

$S_n = \dfrac{n(a_1 + a_n)}{2}$

$S_{14} = \dfrac{14(1+27)}{2} = \dfrac{14(28)}{2} = \dfrac{392}{2} = 196$

There are 27 glasses in the 14th row and 196 glasses in all.

70. $a_1 = 1$, $d = 2$, $n = 7$

$a_n = a_1 + (n-1)d$

$a_7 = 1 + (7-1)(2) = 1 + 12 = 13$

$S_n = \dfrac{n(a_1 + a_n)}{2}$

$S_7 = \dfrac{7(1+13)}{2} = \dfrac{7(14)}{2} = \dfrac{98}{2} = 49$

There are 13 candies in the 7th row and 49 candies in all.

71. $1 + 2 + 3 + \cdots + 100$

$= (1+100) + (2+99) + \cdots + (50+51)$

$= 101 + 101 + \cdots + 101$

$= 50(101)$

$= 5050$

72. $101 + 102 + 103 + \cdots + 150$

$= (101+150) + (102+149) + \cdots + (125+126)$

$= 251 + 251 + \cdots + 251$

$= 25(251)$

$= 6275$

73. $S_n = \dfrac{n(a_1 + a_n)}{2}$

$= \dfrac{n[1+(2n-1)]}{2} = \dfrac{n(2n)}{2} = \dfrac{2n^2}{2} = n^2$

74. $S_n = 2 + 4 + 6 + 8 + \cdots + 2n$

$= \dfrac{n(2+2n)}{2} = \dfrac{2n(1+n)}{2} = n(1+n) = n(n+1)$

75. a. $a_1 = 22$, $d = -\dfrac{1}{2}$, $n = 7$

$a_n = a_1 + (n-1)d$

$a_7 = 22 + (7-1)\left(-\dfrac{1}{2}\right) = 22 - 3 = 19$

Her seventh swing is 19 feet.

b. $S_n = \dfrac{n(a_1 + a_n)}{2}$

$S_7 = \dfrac{7(22+19)}{2} = 143.5$

She travels 143.5 feet during the seven swings.

76. a. $a_1 = 6$ feet $= 72$ inches, $d = -2$, $n = 8$

$a_n = a_1 + (n-1)d$

$a_8 = 72 + (8-1)(-2)$

$\quad = 72 + 7(-2) = 72 - 14 = 58$

The eighth swing is 58 inches or $\dfrac{58}{12} = \dfrac{29}{6}$ feet.

b. $S_n = \dfrac{n(a_1 + a_n)}{2}$

$S_8 = \dfrac{8(72+58)}{2} = \dfrac{8(130)}{2} = 520$

The distance traveled in the eight swings is

520 inches or $\dfrac{520}{12} = \dfrac{130}{3} = 43\dfrac{1}{3}$ feet.

77. $d = -6$ in. $= -\dfrac{1}{2}$ ft, $a_1 = 6$

$a_n = a_1 + (n-1)d$

$a_9 = 6 + (9-1)\left(-\dfrac{1}{2}\right) = 6 + 8\left(-\dfrac{1}{2}\right) = 6 - 4 = 2$

The ball bounces 2 feet on the ninth bounce.

78. $d = -3$ in. $= -\dfrac{1}{4}$ ft, $a_1 = 3$

$a_n = a_1 + (n-1)d$

$a_{10} = 3 + (10-1)\left(-\dfrac{1}{4}\right) = 3 + 9\left(-\dfrac{1}{4}\right) = \dfrac{12}{4} - \dfrac{9}{4} = \dfrac{3}{4}$

On the tenth bounce, the ball bounces $\dfrac{3}{4}$ foot or

$12\left(\dfrac{3}{4}\right) = 9$ inches.

79. a. Note that if March 17th is day 1, then March 22nd is day 6.

$a_1 = 105$, $d = 10$, $n = 6$

$a_n = a_1 + (n-1)d$

$a_6 = 105 + (6-1)(10)$

$\quad = 105 + 5(10) = 105 + 50 = 155$

He can prepare 155 packages for shipment on March 22nd.

b. $S_n = \dfrac{n(a_1 + a_n)}{2}$

$S_5 = \dfrac{5(105+155)}{2} = \dfrac{5(260)}{2} = \dfrac{1300}{2} = 650$

He can prepare 650 packages for shipment from March 17th through March 22nd.

80. a. $a_1 = \$37,500$, $d = \$1500$, $n = 10 + 1 = 11$

$a_n = a_1 + (n-1)d$

$a_{10} = 37,500 + (11-1)(1500)$

$\quad = 37,500 + 10(1500)$

$\quad = 37,500 + 15,000$

$\quad = 52,500$

Ten years from now, her salary will be $\$52,500$.

b. $S_n = \dfrac{n(a_1 + a_n)}{2}$

$S_{11} = \dfrac{11(37,500 + 52,500)}{2}$

$\quad = \dfrac{11(90,000)}{2}$

$\quad = 495,000$

During the eleven years she will have earned $\$495,000$.

81. $S_n = \dfrac{n(a_1 + a_n)}{2}$

$S_{31} = \dfrac{31(1+31)}{2} = \dfrac{31(32)}{2} = 496$

On day 31, Craig will have saved $\$496$.

82. $a_{365} = 0.5 + (365-1)(0.5) = 182.50$

$S_n = \dfrac{n(a_1 + a_n)}{2}$

$S_{365} = \dfrac{365(0.5 + 182.50)}{2} = \dfrac{365(183)}{2} = 33,397.5$

By the end of one year, he will have saved $\$33,397.50$.

83. a. $a_{10} = 42,000 + (10-1)(400) = 45,600$

She will receive $\$45,600$ in her tenth year of retirement.

b. $S_{10} = \dfrac{10(42,000 + 45,600)}{2}$

$\quad = \dfrac{10(87,600)}{2}$

$\quad = 438,000$

In her first 10 years, she will receive a total of $\$438,000$.

84. a. $a_{12} = 23,000 + (12-1)(1000) = 33,000$

In year 12, her salary will be $33,000.

b. $s_{12} = \dfrac{12(23,000 + 34,000)}{2}$

$= \dfrac{12(57,000)}{2}$

$= 342,000$

In her first 12 years, she will receive a total of $342,000.

85. $360 - 180 = 180$
$540 - 360 = 180$
$720 - 540 = 180$
The terms form an arithmetic sequence with $d = 180$ and $a_3 = 180$.

$a_n = a_1 + (n-1)d$
$180 = a_1 + (3-1)180$
$180 = a_1 + 360$
$-180 = a_1$

$a_n = a_1 + (n-1)d$
$a_n = -180 + (n-1)(180)$
$= -180 + 180n - 180$
$= 180n - 360$
$= 180(n-2)$

86. $a_n = a_1 + (n-1)d$

$s_n = \dfrac{n(a_1 + a_n)}{2}$

Substitute $a_1 + (n-1)d$ for a_n in the formula for s_n.

$s_n = \dfrac{n\left[a_1 + \left(a_1 + (n-1)d\right)\right]}{2}$

$= \dfrac{n\left[2a_1 + (n-1)d\right]}{2}$

$= \dfrac{n}{2}[2a_1 + (n-1)d]$

87. $\lim\limits_{n \to +\infty} a_n = \lim\limits_{n \to +\infty} \dfrac{1}{n-2} = 0$

88. $\lim\limits_{n \to +\infty} a_n = \lim\limits_{n \to +\infty} \dfrac{n}{n+1} = 1$

89. $\lim\limits_{n \to +\infty} a_n = \lim\limits_{n \to +\infty} \dfrac{1}{n^2 + 2} = 0$

90. $\lim\limits_{n \to +\infty} a_n = \lim\limits_{n \to +\infty} \dfrac{2n+1}{n} = 2$

91. $\lim\limits_{n \to +\infty} a_n = \lim\limits_{n \to +\infty} \dfrac{4n-3}{3n+1} = \dfrac{4}{3}$

92. $\lim\limits_{n \to +\infty} a_n = \lim\limits_{n \to +\infty} \dfrac{n^2}{n+1} = \infty$

93. $A = P + Prt$
$A - P = Prt$
$\dfrac{A-P}{Pt} = r$ or $r = \dfrac{A-P}{Pt}$

94. $12n^2 - 6n - 30n + 15$
$= 3\left(4n^2 - 2n - 10n + 5\right)$
$= 3\left[(4n^2 - 2n) - (10n - 5)\right]$
$= 3\left[2n(2n-1) - 5(2n-1)\right]$
$= 3\left[(2n-1)(2n-5)\right]$
$= 3(2n-1)(2n-5)$

95. $y = 2x + 1$
$3x - 2y = 1$
Substitute $2x+1$ for y in the second equation.
$3x - 2y = 1$
$3x - 2(2x+1) = 1$
$3x - 4x - 2 = 1$
$-x - 2 = 1$
$-x = 3$
$x = -3$
Substitute -3 for x in the first equation.
$y = 2(-3) + 1 = -6 + 1 = -5$
The solution is $(-3, -5)$.

96. $(x+4)^2 + y^2 = 25$
$(x+4)^2 + y^2 = 5^2$
The center is $(-4, 0)$ and the radius is 5.

$(x + 4)^2 + y^2 = 25$

Exercise Set 15.3

1. A geometric sequence is a sequence in which each term after the first is the same multiple of the preceding term.

2. A geometric series is the sum of the terms of a geometric sequence.

3. To find the common ratio, take any term except the first and divide by the term that precedes it.

4. An infinite geometric series is a geometric series that is not finite.

5. r^n approaches 0 as n gets larger and larger when $|r| < 1$.

6. The sum does not exist.

7. Yes

8. Yes

9. Yes, s_∞ exists. $s_\infty = \dfrac{a_1}{1-r} = \dfrac{6}{1-\dfrac{1}{4}} = \dfrac{6}{\dfrac{3}{4}} = 6 \cdot \dfrac{4}{3} = 8$

   This is true since $|r| < 1$.

10. No, s_∞ does not exist since $|r| > 1$.

11. $a_1 = 2$

    $a_2 = 2(3)^{2-1} = 2(3) = 6$
    $a_3 = 2(3)^{3-1} = 2(3)^2 = 2(9) = 18$
    $a_4 = 2(3)^{4-1} = 2(3)^3 = 2(27) = 54$
    $a_5 = 2(3)^{5-1} = 2(3)^4 = 2(81) = 162$
    The terms are 2, 6, 18, 54, 162.

12. $a_1 = 2$

    $a_2 = 2(-3)^{2-1} = 2(-3) = -6$
    $a_3 = 2(-3)^{3-1} = 2(-3)^2 = 2(9) = 18$
    $a_4 = 2(-3)^{4-1} = 2(-3)^3 = 2(27) = -54$
    $a_5 = 2(-3)^{5-1} = 2(-3)^4 = 2(81) = 162$
    The terms are 2, –6, 18, –54, 162.

13. $a_1 = 6$

    $a_2 = 6\left(-\dfrac{1}{2}\right)^{2-1} = 6\left(-\dfrac{1}{2}\right) = -3$
    $a_3 = 6\left(-\dfrac{1}{2}\right)^{3-1} = 6\left(-\dfrac{1}{2}\right)^2 = 6\left(\dfrac{1}{4}\right) = \dfrac{3}{2}$
    $a_4 = 6\left(-\dfrac{1}{2}\right)^{4-1} = 6\left(-\dfrac{1}{2}\right)^3 = 6\left(-\dfrac{1}{8}\right) = -\dfrac{3}{4}$
    $a_5 = 6\left(-\dfrac{1}{2}\right)^{5-1} = 6\left(-\dfrac{1}{2}\right)^4 = 6\left(\dfrac{1}{16}\right) = \dfrac{3}{8}$
    The terms are $6, -3, \dfrac{3}{2}, -\dfrac{3}{4}, \dfrac{3}{8}$.

14. $a_1 = 6$

    $a_2 = 6\left(\dfrac{1}{2}\right)^{2-1} = 6\left(\dfrac{1}{2}\right) = 3$
    $a_3 = 6\left(\dfrac{1}{2}\right)^{3-1} = 6\left(\dfrac{1}{2}\right)^2 = 6\left(\dfrac{1}{4}\right) = \dfrac{3}{2}$
    $a_4 = 6\left(\dfrac{1}{2}\right)^{4-1} = 6\left(\dfrac{1}{2}\right)^3 = 6\left(\dfrac{1}{8}\right) = \dfrac{3}{4}$
    $a_5 = 6\left(\dfrac{1}{2}\right)^{5-1} = 6\left(\dfrac{1}{2}\right)^4 = 6\left(\dfrac{1}{16}\right) = \dfrac{3}{8}$
    The terms are $6, 3, \dfrac{3}{2}, \dfrac{3}{4}, \dfrac{3}{8}$.

15. $a_1 = 72$

    $a_2 = 72\left(\dfrac{1}{3}\right)^{2-1} = 72\left(\dfrac{1}{3}\right) = 24$
    $a_3 = 72\left(\dfrac{1}{3}\right)^{3-1} = 72\left(\dfrac{1}{3}\right)^2 = 72\left(\dfrac{1}{9}\right) = 8$
    $a_4 = 72\left(\dfrac{1}{3}\right)^{4-1} = 72\left(\dfrac{1}{3}\right)^3 = 72\left(\dfrac{1}{27}\right) = \dfrac{8}{3}$
    $a_5 = 72\left(\dfrac{1}{3}\right)^{5-1} = 72\left(\dfrac{1}{3}\right)^4 = 72\left(\dfrac{1}{81}\right) = \dfrac{8}{9}$
    The terms are $72, 24, 8, \dfrac{8}{3}, \dfrac{8}{9}$.

16. $a_1 = \dfrac{1}{8}$

$a_2 = \dfrac{1}{8}(4)^{2-1} = \dfrac{1}{8}(4) = \dfrac{1}{2}$

$a_3 = \dfrac{1}{8}(4)^{3-1} = \dfrac{1}{8}(4)^2 = \dfrac{1}{8}(16) = 2$

$a_4 = \dfrac{1}{8}(4)^{4-1} = \dfrac{1}{8}(4)^3 = \dfrac{1}{8}(64) = 8$

$a_5 = \dfrac{1}{8}(4)^{5-1} = \dfrac{1}{8}(4)^4 = \dfrac{1}{8}(256) = 32$

The terms are $\dfrac{1}{8},\ \dfrac{1}{2},\ 2,\ 8,\ 32$.

17. $a_1 = 90$

$a_2 = 90\left(-\dfrac{1}{3}\right)^{2-1} = 90\left(-\dfrac{1}{3}\right) = -30$

$a_3 = 90\left(-\dfrac{1}{3}\right)^{3-1} = 90\left(-\dfrac{1}{3}\right)^2 = 90\left(\dfrac{1}{9}\right) = 10$

$a_4 = 90\left(-\dfrac{1}{3}\right)^{4-1} = 90\left(-\dfrac{1}{3}\right)^3 = 90\left(-\dfrac{1}{27}\right) = -\dfrac{10}{3}$

$a_5 = 90\left(-\dfrac{1}{3}\right)^{5-1} = 90\left(-\dfrac{1}{3}\right)^4 = 90\left(\dfrac{1}{81}\right) = \dfrac{10}{9}$

The terms are $90,\ -30,\ 10,\ -\dfrac{10}{3},\ \dfrac{10}{9}$.

18. $a_1 = 32$

$a_2 = 32\left(-\dfrac{1}{4}\right)^{2-1} = 32\left(-\dfrac{1}{4}\right)^1 = 32\left(-\dfrac{1}{4}\right) = -8$

$a_3 = 32\left(-\dfrac{1}{4}\right)^{3-1} = 32\left(-\dfrac{1}{4}\right)^2 = 32\left(\dfrac{1}{16}\right) = 2$

$a_4 = 32\left(-\dfrac{1}{4}\right)^{4-1} = 32\left(-\dfrac{1}{4}\right)^3 = 32\left(-\dfrac{1}{64}\right) = -\dfrac{1}{2}$

$a_5 = 32\left(-\dfrac{1}{4}\right)^{5-1} = 32\left(-\dfrac{1}{4}\right)^4 = 32\left(\dfrac{1}{128}\right) = \dfrac{1}{4}$

The terms are $32, -8, 2, -\dfrac{1}{2}, \dfrac{1}{4}$.

19. $a_1 = -1$

$a_2 = -1(3)^{2-1} = -1(3) = -3$

$a_3 = -1(3)^{3-1} = -1(3)^2 = -1(9) = -9$

$a_4 = -1(3)^{4-1} = -1(3)^3 = -1(27) = -27$

$a_5 = -1(3)^{5-1} = -1(3)^4 = -1(81) = -81$

The terms are $-1, -3, -9, -27, -81$.

20. $a_1 = -1$

$a_2 = -1(-3)^{2-1} = -1(-3) = 3$

$a_3 = -1(-3)^{3-1} = -1(-3)^2 = -1(9) = -9$

$a_4 = -1(-3)^{4-1} = -1(-3)^3 = -1(-27) = 27$

$a_5 = -1(-3)^{5-1} = -1(-3)^4 = -1(81) = -81$

The terms are $-1, 3, -9, 27, -81$.

21. $a_1 = 5$

$a_2 = 5(-2)^{2-1} = 5(-2)^1 = 5(-2) = -10$

$a_3 = 5(-2)^{3-1} = 5(-2)^2 = 5(4) = 20$

$a_4 = 5(-2)^{4-1} = 5(-2)^3 = 5(-8) = -40$

$a_5 = 5(-2)^{5-1} = 5(-2)^4 = 5(16) = 80$

The terms are $5, -10, 20, -40, 80$.

22. $a_1 = -13$

$a_2 = -13(-1)^{2-1} = -13(-1)^1 = 13$

$a_3 = -13(-1)^{3-1} = -13(-1)^2 = -13$

$a_4 = -13(-1)^{4-1} = -13(-1)^3 = 13$

$a_5 = -13(-1)^{5-1} = -13(-1)^4 = -13$

The terms are $-13, 13, -13, 13, -13$.

23. $a_1 = \dfrac{1}{3}$

$a_2 = \dfrac{1}{3}\left(\dfrac{1}{2}\right)^{2-1} = \dfrac{1}{3}\left(\dfrac{1}{2}\right) = \dfrac{1}{6}$

$a_3 = \dfrac{1}{3}\left(\dfrac{1}{2}\right)^{3-1} = \dfrac{1}{3}\left(\dfrac{1}{2}\right)^2 = \dfrac{1}{3}\left(\dfrac{1}{4}\right) = \dfrac{1}{12}$

$a_4 = \dfrac{1}{3}\left(\dfrac{1}{2}\right)^{4-1} = \dfrac{1}{3}\left(\dfrac{1}{2}\right)^3 = \dfrac{1}{3}\left(\dfrac{1}{8}\right) = \dfrac{1}{24}$

$a_5 = \dfrac{1}{3}\left(\dfrac{1}{2}\right)^{5-1} = \dfrac{1}{3}\left(\dfrac{1}{2}\right)^4 = \dfrac{1}{3}\left(\dfrac{1}{16}\right) = \dfrac{1}{48}$

The terms are $\dfrac{1}{3}, \dfrac{1}{6}, \dfrac{1}{12}, \dfrac{1}{24}, \dfrac{1}{48}$.

24. $a_1 = \dfrac{1}{2}$

$a_2 = \dfrac{1}{2}\left(-\dfrac{1}{3}\right)^{2-1} = \dfrac{1}{2}\left(-\dfrac{1}{3}\right) = -\dfrac{1}{6}$

$a_3 = \dfrac{1}{2}\left(-\dfrac{1}{3}\right)^{3-1} = \dfrac{1}{2}\left(-\dfrac{1}{3}\right)^2 = \dfrac{1}{2}\left(\dfrac{1}{9}\right) = \dfrac{1}{18}$

$a_4 = \dfrac{1}{2}\left(-\dfrac{1}{3}\right)^{4-1} = \dfrac{1}{2}\left(-\dfrac{1}{3}\right)^3 = \dfrac{1}{2}\left(-\dfrac{1}{27}\right) = -\dfrac{1}{54}$

$a_5 = \dfrac{1}{2}\left(-\dfrac{1}{3}\right)^{5-1} = \dfrac{1}{2}\left(-\dfrac{1}{3}\right)^4 = \dfrac{1}{2}\left(\dfrac{1}{81}\right) = \dfrac{1}{162}$

The terms are $\dfrac{1}{2}, -\dfrac{1}{6}, \dfrac{1}{18}, -\dfrac{1}{54}, \dfrac{1}{162}$.

25. $a_1 = 3$

$$a_2 = 3\left(\frac{3}{2}\right)^{2-1} = 3\left(\frac{3}{2}\right) = \frac{9}{2}$$

$$a_3 = 3\left(\frac{3}{2}\right)^{3-1} = 3\left(\frac{3}{2}\right)^2 = 3\left(\frac{9}{4}\right) = \frac{27}{4}$$

$$a_4 = 3\left(\frac{3}{2}\right)^{4-1} = 3\left(\frac{3}{2}\right)^3 = 3\left(\frac{27}{8}\right) = \frac{81}{8}$$

$$a_5 = 3\left(\frac{3}{2}\right)^{5-1} = 3\left(\frac{3}{2}\right)^4 = 3\left(\frac{81}{16}\right) = \frac{243}{16}$$

The terms are $3, \dfrac{9}{2}, \dfrac{27}{4}, \dfrac{81}{8}, \dfrac{243}{16}$.

26. $a_1 = 60$

$$a_2 = 60\left(-\frac{2}{5}\right)^{2-1} = 60\left(-\frac{2}{5}\right) = -24$$

$$a_3 = 60\left(-\frac{2}{5}\right)^{3-1} = 60\left(-\frac{2}{5}\right)^2 = 60\left(\frac{4}{25}\right) = \frac{48}{5}$$

$$a_4 = 60\left(-\frac{2}{5}\right)^{4-1} = 60\left(-\frac{2}{5}\right)^3 = 60\left(-\frac{8}{125}\right) = -\frac{96}{25}$$

$$a_5 = 60\left(-\frac{2}{5}\right)^{5-1} = 60\left(-\frac{2}{5}\right)^4 = 60\left(\frac{16}{625}\right) = \frac{192}{125}$$

The terms are $60, -24, \dfrac{48}{5}, -\dfrac{96}{25}, \dfrac{192}{125}$.

27. $a_6 = a_1 r^{6-1}$

$$a_6 = 4(2)^{6-1} = 4(2)^5 = 4(32) = 128$$

28. $a_6 = a_1 r^{6-1}$

$$a_6 = 4(-2)^{6-1} = 4(-2)^5 = 4(-32) = -128$$

29. $a_9 = a_1 r^{9-1}$

$$a_9 = -12\left(\frac{1}{2}\right)^{9-1} = -12\left(\frac{1}{2}\right)^8 = -12\left(\frac{1}{256}\right) = -\frac{3}{64}$$

30. $a_7 = a_1 r^{7-1}$

$$a_7 = 27\left(\frac{1}{3}\right)^{7-1} = 27\left(\frac{1}{3}\right)^6 = 27\left(\frac{1}{729}\right) = \frac{1}{27}$$

31. $a_{10} = a_1 r^{10-1}$

$$a_{10} = \frac{1}{4}(2)^{10-1} = \frac{1}{4}(2)^9 = \frac{1}{4}(512) = 128$$

32. $a_6 = a_1 r^{6-1}$

$$a_6 = 3(3)^{6-1} = 3(3)^5 = 3(243) = 729$$

33. $a_{12} = a_1 r^{12-1}$

$$a_{12} = -3(-2)^{12-1} = -3(-2)^{11} = -3(-2048) = 6144$$

34. $a_{10} = a_1 r^{10-1}$

$$a_{10} = -10(-2)^{10-1} = -10(-2)^9 = -10(-512) = 5,120$$

35. $a_8 = a_1 r^{8-1}$

$$a_8 = 2\left(\frac{1}{2}\right)^{8-1} = 2\left(\frac{1}{2}\right)^7 = 2\left(\frac{1}{128}\right) = \frac{1}{64}$$

36. $a_9 = a_1 r^{9-1}$

$$a_9 = 5\left(\frac{2}{3}\right)^{9-1} = 5\left(\frac{2}{3}\right)^8 = 5\left(\frac{256}{6561}\right) = \frac{1280}{6561}$$

37. $a_7 = a_1 r^{7-1}$

$$a_7 = 50\left(\frac{1}{3}\right)^{7-1} = 50\left(\frac{1}{3}\right)^6 = 50\left(\frac{1}{729}\right) = \frac{50}{729}$$

38. $a_7 = a_1 r^{7-1}$

$$a_7 = -7\left(-\frac{3}{4}\right)^{7-1}$$

$$= -7\left(-\frac{3}{4}\right)^6 = -7\left(\frac{729}{4096}\right) = -\frac{5103}{4096}$$

39. $s_5 = \dfrac{a_1(1-r^5)}{1-r}$

$$s_5 = \frac{5(1-2^5)}{1-2} = \frac{5(1-32)}{-1} = \frac{5(-31)}{-1} = \frac{-155}{-1} = 155$$

40. $s_5 = \dfrac{a_1(1-r^5)}{1-r}$

$$s_5 = \frac{7\left(1-(-3)^5\right)}{1-(-3)} = \frac{7(1+243)}{4} = \frac{7(244)}{4} = 427$$

41. $s_6 = \dfrac{a_1(1-r^6)}{1-r}$

$$s_6 = \frac{2(1-5^6)}{1-5} = \frac{2(1-15,625)}{-4} = \frac{2(-15,624)}{-4} = 7812$$

42. $s_6 = \dfrac{a_1(1-r^6)}{1-r}$

$s_6 = \dfrac{9\left[1-\left(\frac{1}{2}\right)^6\right]}{1-\frac{1}{2}}$

$= \dfrac{9\left(1-\frac{1}{64}\right)}{\frac{1}{2}} = \dfrac{9\left(\frac{63}{64}\right)}{\frac{1}{2}} = 9\left(\dfrac{63}{64}\right)(2) = \dfrac{9(63)}{32} = \dfrac{567}{32}$

43. $s_7 = \dfrac{a_1(1-r^7)}{1-r}$

$s_7 = \dfrac{80(1-2^7)}{1-2}$

$= \dfrac{80(1-128)}{-1} = \dfrac{80(-127)}{-1} = \dfrac{-10,160}{-1} = 10,160$

44. $s_{12} = \dfrac{a_1(1-r^{12})}{1-r}$

$s_{12} = \dfrac{2\left[1-(-2)^{12}\right]}{1-(-2)}$

$= \dfrac{2(1-4096)}{3} = \dfrac{2(-4095)}{3} = -\dfrac{8190}{3} = -2730$

45. $s_9 = \dfrac{a_1(1-r^9)}{1-r}$

$s_9 = \dfrac{-15\left[1-\left(-\frac{1}{2}\right)^9\right]}{1-\left(-\frac{1}{2}\right)}$

$= \dfrac{-15\left[1-\left(-\frac{1}{512}\right)\right]}{\frac{3}{2}}$

$= \dfrac{-15\left(1+\frac{1}{512}\right)}{\frac{3}{2}}$

$= \dfrac{-15\left(\frac{513}{512}\right)}{\frac{3}{2}}$

$= -15\left(\dfrac{513}{512}\right)\left(\dfrac{2}{3}\right)$

$= -\dfrac{2565}{256}$

46. $s_7 = \dfrac{a_1(1-r^7)}{1-r}$

$s_7 = \dfrac{\frac{3}{4}(1-3^7)}{1-3}$

$= \dfrac{3(1-2187)}{4(1-3)} = \dfrac{3(-2186)}{4(-2)} = \dfrac{-6558}{-8} = \dfrac{3279}{4}$

47. $s_5 = \dfrac{a_1(1-r^5)}{1-r}$

$s_5 = \dfrac{-9\left[1-\left(\frac{2}{5}\right)^5\right]}{1-\frac{2}{5}} = \dfrac{-9\left(1-\frac{32}{3125}\right)}{\frac{3}{5}}$

$= \dfrac{-9\left(\frac{3093}{3125}\right)}{\frac{3}{5}} = -9\left(\dfrac{3093}{3125}\right)\left(\dfrac{5}{3}\right) = -\dfrac{9279}{625}$

48. $s_{12} = \dfrac{a_1(1-r^{12})}{1-r}$

$s_{12} = \dfrac{35\left[1-\left(\frac{1}{5}\right)^{12}\right]}{1-\frac{1}{5}} = \dfrac{35\left(1-\frac{1}{244,140,625}\right)}{\frac{4}{5}}$

$= 35\left(\dfrac{244,140,624}{244,140,625}\right)\left(\dfrac{5}{4}\right)$

$= \dfrac{427,246,092}{9,765,625} \approx 43.75$

49. $r = \dfrac{3}{2} \div 3 = \dfrac{3}{2} \cdot \dfrac{1}{3} = \dfrac{1}{2}$

$a_n = 3\left(\dfrac{1}{2}\right)^{n-1}$

50. $r = -\dfrac{3}{2} \div 3 = -\dfrac{3}{2} \cdot \dfrac{1}{3} = -\dfrac{1}{2}$

$a_n = 3\left(-\dfrac{1}{2}\right)^{n-1}$

51. $r = 18 \div 9 = 2$

$a_n = 9(2)^{n-1}$

52. $r = \dfrac{6}{2} = 3$

$a_n = 2(3)^{n-1}$

53. $r = -6 \div 2 = -3$

$a_n = 2(-3)^{n-1}$

54. $r = -3 \div (-1) = 3$

$a_n = -1(3)^{n-1}$

55. $r = \dfrac{1}{2} \div \dfrac{3}{4} = \dfrac{1}{2} \cdot \dfrac{4}{3} = \dfrac{2}{3}$

$a_n = \dfrac{3}{4}\left(\dfrac{2}{3}\right)^{n-1}$

56. $r = \dfrac{8}{3} \div \dfrac{4}{3} = \dfrac{8}{3} \cdot \dfrac{3}{4} = 2$

$a_n = \dfrac{4}{3}(2)^{n-1}$

57. $r = \dfrac{1}{2} \div 1 = \dfrac{1}{2}$

$s_\infty = \dfrac{1}{1-\frac{1}{2}} = \dfrac{1}{\frac{1}{2}} = 1\left(\dfrac{2}{1}\right) = 2$

58. $r = -\dfrac{1}{2} \div 1 = -\dfrac{1}{2}$

$s_\infty = \dfrac{1}{1-\left(-\frac{1}{2}\right)} = \dfrac{1}{\frac{3}{2}} = 1\left(\dfrac{2}{3}\right) = \dfrac{2}{3}$

59. $r = \dfrac{1}{5} \div 1 = \dfrac{1}{5}$

$s_\infty = \dfrac{1}{1-\frac{1}{5}} = \dfrac{1}{\frac{4}{5}} = 1\left(\dfrac{5}{4}\right) = \dfrac{5}{4}$

60. $r = -\dfrac{1}{5} \div 1 = -\dfrac{1}{5}$

$s_\infty = \dfrac{1}{1-\left(-\frac{1}{5}\right)} = \dfrac{1}{\frac{6}{5}} = 1\left(\dfrac{5}{6}\right) = \dfrac{5}{6}$

61. $r = 3 \div 6 = \dfrac{1}{2}$

$s_\infty = \dfrac{6}{1-\frac{1}{2}} = \dfrac{6}{\frac{1}{2}} = 6\left(\dfrac{2}{1}\right) = 12$

62. $r = \dfrac{1}{9} \div \dfrac{1}{3} = \dfrac{1}{9} \cdot \dfrac{3}{1} = \dfrac{1}{3}$

$s_\infty = \dfrac{\frac{1}{3}}{1-\frac{1}{3}} = \dfrac{\frac{1}{3}}{\frac{2}{3}} = \dfrac{1}{3} \cdot \dfrac{3}{2} = \dfrac{1}{2}$

63. $r = 2 \div 5 = \dfrac{2}{5}$

$s_\infty = \dfrac{5}{1-\frac{2}{5}} = \dfrac{5}{\frac{3}{5}} = 5\left(\dfrac{5}{3}\right) = \dfrac{25}{3}$

64. $r = -\dfrac{4}{9} \div \left(-\dfrac{4}{3}\right) = -\dfrac{4}{9}\left(-\dfrac{3}{4}\right) = \dfrac{1}{3}$

$s_\infty = \dfrac{-\frac{4}{3}}{1-\frac{1}{3}} = \dfrac{-\frac{4}{3}}{\frac{2}{3}} = -\dfrac{4}{3} \cdot \dfrac{3}{2} = -2$

65. $s_n = \dfrac{a_1(1-r^n)}{1-r}$

$93 = \dfrac{3(1-2^n)}{1-2}$

$93 = \dfrac{3(1-2^n)}{-1}$

$93 = -3(1-2^n)$

$-31 = 1-2^n$

$-32 = -2^n$

$32 = 2^n$

$n = 5$ since $2^5 = 32$

66. $s_n = \dfrac{a_1(1-r^n)}{1-r}$

$80 = \dfrac{2(1-3^n)}{1-3}$

$80 = \dfrac{2(1-3^n)}{-2}$

$80 = -1(1-3^n)$

$80 = -1+3^n$

$81 = 3^n$

$n = 4$ since $3^4 = 81$

67. $s_n = \dfrac{a_1(1-r^n)}{1-r}$

$\dfrac{189}{32} = \dfrac{3\left[1-\left(\frac{1}{2}\right)^n\right]}{1-\frac{1}{2}}$

$\dfrac{189}{32} = \dfrac{3\left(1-\left(\frac{1}{2}\right)^n\right)}{\frac{1}{2}}$

$\dfrac{1}{2} \cdot \dfrac{1}{3} \cdot \dfrac{189}{32} = 1-\left(\dfrac{1}{2}\right)^n$

$\dfrac{63}{64} = 1-\left(\dfrac{1}{2}\right)^n$

$-\dfrac{1}{64} = -\left(\dfrac{1}{2}\right)^n$

$\dfrac{1}{64} = \left(\dfrac{1}{2}\right)^n$

$n = 6$ since $\left(\dfrac{1}{2}\right)^6 = \dfrac{1}{64}$

68. $s_n = \dfrac{a_1(1-r^n)}{1-r}$

$\dfrac{121}{9} = \dfrac{9\left[1-\left(\frac{1}{3}\right)^n\right]}{1-\frac{1}{3}}$

$\dfrac{121}{9} = \dfrac{9\left(1-\left(\frac{1}{3}\right)^n\right)}{\frac{2}{3}}$

$\dfrac{2}{3} \cdot \dfrac{1}{9} \cdot \dfrac{121}{9} = 1-\left(\dfrac{1}{3}\right)^n$

$\dfrac{242}{243} = 1-\left(\dfrac{1}{3}\right)^n$

$-\dfrac{1}{243} = -\left(\dfrac{1}{3}\right)^n$

$\dfrac{1}{243} = \left(\dfrac{1}{3}\right)^n$

$n = 5$ since $\left(\dfrac{1}{3}\right)^5 = \dfrac{1}{243}$

69. $r = 1 \div 2 = \dfrac{1}{2}$

$s_\infty = \dfrac{2}{1-\frac{1}{2}} = \dfrac{2}{\frac{1}{2}} = 2\left(\dfrac{2}{1}\right) = 4$

70. $r = 4 \div 8 = \dfrac{1}{2}$

$s_\infty = \dfrac{8}{1-\frac{1}{2}} = \dfrac{8}{\frac{1}{2}} = 8\left(\dfrac{2}{1}\right) = 16$

71. $r = \dfrac{16}{3} \div 8 = \dfrac{16}{3}\left(\dfrac{1}{8}\right) = \dfrac{2}{3}$

$s_\infty = \dfrac{8}{1-\frac{2}{3}} = \dfrac{8}{\frac{1}{3}} = 8\left(\dfrac{3}{1}\right) = 24$

72. $r = -2 \div 6 = \dfrac{-2}{6} = -\dfrac{1}{3}$

$s_\infty = \dfrac{6}{1-\left(-\frac{1}{3}\right)} = \dfrac{6}{1+\frac{1}{3}} = \dfrac{6}{\frac{4}{3}} = 6\left(\dfrac{3}{4}\right) = \dfrac{9}{2}$

73. $r = 20 \div -60 = \dfrac{20}{-60} = -\dfrac{1}{3}$

$s_\infty = \dfrac{-60}{1-\left(-\frac{1}{3}\right)} = \dfrac{-60}{1+\frac{1}{3}} = \dfrac{-60}{\frac{4}{3}} = -60\left(\dfrac{3}{4}\right) = -45$

74. $r = \dfrac{4}{3} \div 2 = \dfrac{4}{3} \cdot \dfrac{1}{2} = \dfrac{2}{3}$

$s_\infty = \dfrac{2}{1-\frac{2}{3}} = \dfrac{2}{\frac{1}{3}} = 2\left(\dfrac{3}{1}\right) = 6$

75. $r = -\dfrac{12}{5} \div -12 = -\dfrac{12}{5}\left(-\dfrac{1}{12}\right) = \dfrac{1}{5}$

$s_\infty = \dfrac{-12}{1-\frac{1}{5}} = \dfrac{-12}{\frac{4}{5}} = -12\left(\dfrac{5}{4}\right) = -15$

76. $r = -1 \div 5 = -\dfrac{1}{5}$

$s_\infty = \dfrac{5}{1-\left(-\frac{1}{5}\right)} = \dfrac{5}{1+\frac{1}{5}} = \dfrac{5}{\frac{6}{5}} = 5\left(\dfrac{5}{6}\right) = \dfrac{25}{6}$

77. $0.242424... = 0.24 + 0.0024 + 0.000024 + \cdots$

$\qquad = 0.24 + 0.24(0.01) + 0.24(0.01)^2 + \cdots$

$r = 0.01$ and $a_1 = 0.24$

$s_\infty = \dfrac{0.24}{1-0.01} = \dfrac{0.24}{0.99} = \dfrac{24}{99} = \dfrac{8}{33}$

78. $0.454545... = 0.45 + 0.0045 + 0.000045 + \cdots$

$\qquad = 0.45 + 0.45(0.01) + 0.45(0.01)^2 + \cdots$

$r = 0.01$ and $a_1 = 0.45$

$s_\infty = \dfrac{0.45}{1-0.01} = \dfrac{0.45}{0.99} = \dfrac{45}{99} = \dfrac{5}{11}$

79. $0.8888\ldots = 0.8 + 0.08 + 0.008 + \cdots$

$\qquad = 0.8 + 0.8(0.1) + 0.8(0.1)^2 + \cdots$

$r = 0.1$ and $a_1 = 0.8$

$s_\infty = \dfrac{0.8}{1-0.1} = \dfrac{0.8}{0.9} = \dfrac{8}{9}$

80. $0.375375\cdots$

$\quad = 0.375 + 0.000375 + 0.000000375 + \cdots$

$\quad = 0.375 + 0.375(0.001) + 0.375(0.001)^2 + \cdots$

$r = 0.001$ and $a_1 = 0.375$

$s_\infty = \dfrac{0.375}{1-0.001} = \dfrac{0.375}{0.999} = \dfrac{375}{999} = \dfrac{125}{333}$

81. $0.515151\cdots = 0.51 + 0.0051 + 0.000051 + \cdots$

$\qquad = 0.51 + 0.51(0.01) + 0.51(0.01)^2 + \cdots$

$r = 0.01$ and $a_1 = 0.51$

$s_\infty = \dfrac{0.51}{1-0.01} = \dfrac{0.51}{0.99} = \dfrac{51}{99} = \dfrac{17}{33}$

82. $0.742742\cdots$

$= 0.742 + 0.000742 + 0.000000742 + \cdots$

$= 0.742 + 0.742(0.001) + 0.742(0.001)^2 + \cdots$

$r = 0.001$ and $a_1 = 0.742$

$$s_\infty = \frac{0.742}{1-0.001} = \frac{0.742}{0.999} = \frac{742}{999}$$

83. Consider a new series $b_1, b_2, b_3, \ldots$ where $b_1 = 15$ and $b_4 = 405$. Now $b_4 = b_1 r^{4-1}$ becomes

$405 = 15r^3$

$\dfrac{405}{15} = r^3$

$27 = r^3$

$\sqrt[3]{27} = r$

$3 = r$

From the original series, $a_1 = \dfrac{a_2}{r} = \dfrac{15}{3} = 5$.

84. Consider a new series $b_1, b_2, b_3, \ldots$ with $b_1 = 27$ and $b_4 = 1$. Now $b_4 = b_1 r^{4-1}$ becomes

$1 = 27r^3$

$\dfrac{1}{27} = r^3$

$\sqrt[3]{\dfrac{1}{27}} = r$

$\dfrac{1}{3} = r$

From the original series,

$a_1 = \dfrac{a_2}{r} = \dfrac{27}{\frac{1}{3}} = 27 \cdot \dfrac{3}{1} = 81$.

85. Consider a new series $b_1, b_2, b_3, \ldots$ where $b_1 = 28$ and $b_3 = 112$. Now $b_3 = b_1 r^{3-1}$ becomes

$112 = 28r^2$

$\dfrac{112}{28} = r^2$

$4 = r^2$

so that $r = 2$ or $r = -2$. From the original series

$a_1 = \dfrac{a_3}{r^2} = \dfrac{28}{4} = 7$.

86. Consider a new series $b_1, b_2, b_3, \ldots$ where $b_1 = 12$ and $b_4 = -324$. Now $b_4 = b_1 r^{4-1}$ becomes

$-324 = 12r^3$

$\dfrac{-324}{12} = r^3$

$-27 = r^3$

$\sqrt[3]{-27} = r$

$-3 = r$

From the original series, $a_1 = \dfrac{a_2}{r} = \dfrac{12}{-3} = -4$.

87. $a_1 = 1.40$, $n = 9$, $r = 1.03$

$a_n = a_1 r^{n-1}$

$a_9 = 1.4(1.03)^{9-1} = 1.4(1.03)^8 \approx 1.77$

In 8 years, a loaf of bread would cost \$1.77.

88. $a_1 = 400$, $n = 13$, $r = 1.04$

$a_n = a_1 r^{n-1}$

$a_{13} = 400(1.04)^{13-1} = 400(1.04)^{12} \approx 640.41$

In 12 years, the bike would cost \$640.41.

89. $r = \dfrac{1}{2}$. Let a_n be the amount left after the nth day. After 1 day there are $600\left(\dfrac{1}{2}\right) = 300$ grams left, so $a_1 = 300$.

a. $37.5 = 300\left(\dfrac{1}{2}\right)^{n-1}$

$\dfrac{37.5}{300} = \left(\dfrac{1}{2}\right)^{n-1}$

$\dfrac{1}{8} = \left(\dfrac{1}{2}\right)^{n-1}$

$\left(\dfrac{1}{2}\right)^3 = \left(\dfrac{1}{2}\right)^{n-1}$

$n - 1 = 3$

$n = 4$

37.5 grams are left after 4 days.

b. $a_9 = 300\left(\dfrac{1}{2}\right)^{9-1} = 300\left(\dfrac{1}{256}\right) \approx 1.172$

After 9 days, about 1.172 grams of the substance remain.

90. Let n stand for the hour that the bacteria have a given population. Use $a_1 = 1000$, $a_n = 64,000$, and $r = 2$. $a_n = a_1 r^{n-1}$ becomes

$$64,000 = 1000(2)^{n-1}$$
$$64 = 2^{n-1}$$
$$2^6 = 2^{n-1}$$
$$6 = n-1$$
$$7 = n$$

After 6 hours (as the beginning of the 7th hour) the population will be 64,000.

91. After ten years will be at the beginning of the eleventh year. If the population increases by 1.1% each year, then the population at the beginning of a year will be 1.011 times the population at the beginning of the previous year.

a. Use $a_1 = 296.5$, $r = 1.011$, and $n = 11$.

$$a_{11} = a_1 r^{11-1} = 296.5(1.011)^{10} \approx 330.78$$

After ten years (the beginning of the eleventh year), the population is about 330.78 million people.

b. $a_n = 2(296.5) = 593$

Now, use $a_n = a_1 r^{n-1}$

$$593 = 296.5(1.011)^{n-1}$$
$$\frac{593}{296.5} = (1.011)^{n-1}$$
$$2 = (1.011)^{n-1}$$

Now, use logarithms.

$$\log 2 = \log(1.011)^{n-1}$$
$$\log 2 = (n-1)\log 1.011$$
$$\frac{\log 2}{\log 1.011} = n-1$$
$$63.4 \approx n-1$$
$$64.4 \approx n$$

The population will be double at the beginning of the 64.4 year, which is the end of the 63.4 year.

92. After 4 years will be the beginning of the fifth year. If the equipment decreases in value 15% per year, then it is worth 85% of its previous value every year. Use $a_1 = 105,000$, $r = 0.85$, and $n = 5$.

$$a_5 = 105,000(0.85)^{5-1}$$
$$= 105,000(0.85)^4$$
$$\approx 54,810.66$$

The equipment is worth $54.810.66 after 4 years.

93. a. After 1 meter there is $\frac{1}{2}$ of the original light remaining, so $a_1 = \frac{1}{2}$.

$$a_1 = \frac{1}{2}$$
$$a_2 = \frac{1}{2}\left(\frac{1}{2}\right)^{2-1} = \left(\frac{1}{2}\right)\left(\frac{1}{2}\right) = \frac{1}{4}$$
$$a_3 = \frac{1}{2}\left(\frac{1}{2}\right)^{3-1} = \left(\frac{1}{2}\right)\left(\frac{1}{4}\right) = \frac{1}{8}$$
$$a_4 = \frac{1}{2}\left(\frac{1}{2}\right)^{4-1} = \left(\frac{1}{2}\right)\left(\frac{1}{8}\right) = \frac{1}{16}$$
$$a_5 = \frac{1}{2}\left(\frac{1}{2}\right)^{5-1} = \left(\frac{1}{2}\right)\left(\frac{1}{16}\right) = \frac{1}{32}$$

b. $a_n = \frac{1}{2}\left(\frac{1}{2}\right)^{n-1} = \left(\frac{1}{2}\right)^n$

c. $a_7 = \left(\frac{1}{2}\right)^7 = \frac{1}{128} \approx 0.0078$ or 0.78%

94. $r = 0.8$ and $a_1 = 10$

$$s_\infty = \frac{10}{1-0.8} = \frac{10}{0.2} = 50$$

The pendulum travels a total distance of 50 feet.

95. After 8 years will be the beginning of the ninth year. In any given year (except the first) there will be 106% of the previous amount in the account. Use $a_1 = 10,000$, $r = 1.06$, and $n = 9$

$$a_9 = 10,000(1.06)^{9-1}$$
$$\approx 10,000(1.5938481)$$
$$\approx 15,938.48$$

At the end of 8 years, there is $15,938.48 in the account.

96. After 1 hour there is $\frac{2}{3}$ of the original dye left, so $a_1 = \frac{2}{3}$. Also, $r = \frac{2}{3}$ and $n = 10$.

$$a_{10} = \frac{2}{3}\left(\frac{2}{3}\right)^{10-1} = \frac{2}{3}\left(\frac{2}{3}\right)^9 = \left(\frac{2}{3}\right)^{10} \approx 0.017$$

About 0.017 or 1.7% of the dye remains after 10 hours.

97. a. $a_1 = 0.6(220) = 132$, $r = 0.6$

$a_n = a_1 r^{n-1}$

$a_4 = 132(0.6)^{4-1} = 132(0.6)^3 = 28.512$

The height of the fourth bounce is 28.512 feet.

b. $s_\infty = \dfrac{a_1}{1-r} = \dfrac{220}{1-0.6} = \dfrac{220}{0.4} = 550$

She travels a total of 550 feet in the downward direction.

98. $s_\infty = \dfrac{a_1}{1-r} = \dfrac{132}{1-0.6} = 330$

She travels a total of 330 feet in the upward direction.

99. a. $a_1 = 30(0.7) = 21$, $r = 0.7$

$a_n = a_1 r^{n-1}$

$a_3 = 21(0.7)^{3-1} = 21(0.7)^2 = 10.29$

The ball will bounce 10.29 inches on the third bounce.

b. $s_\infty = \dfrac{a_1}{1-r} = \dfrac{30}{1-0.7} = \dfrac{30}{0.3} = 100$

The ball travels a total of 100 inches in the downward direction.

100. $s_\infty = \dfrac{a_1}{1-r} = \dfrac{21}{1-0.7} = \dfrac{21}{0.3} = 70$

The ball travels a total of 70 inches in the upward direction.

101. Blue: $a_1 = 1$, $r = 2$

Red: $a_1 = 1$, $r = 3$

$a_6 = a_1 r^{6-1} = a_1 r^5$

Blue: $a_6 = 1(2)^5 = 32$

Red: $a_6 = 1(3)^5 = 243$

$243 - 32 = 211$

There are 211 more chips in the sixth stack of red chips.

102. Let n stand for the day in which you have more than \$1,000,000. Use $a_1 = 1$, $a_n = 1,000,000$, and $r = 2$. Then $a_n < a_1 r^{n-1}$ becomes

$1,000,000 < 1 \cdot 2^{n-1}$ or $1,000,000 < 2^{n-1}$. Observe that $2^{20} = 1,048,576$. Make this substitution on the left side: $1,000,000 < 2^{20} < 2^{n-1}$

$20 = n-1$

$21 = n$

Thus, it takes 21 days.

103. Let $a_n = $ value left after the nth year. After the first year there is $15000\left(\dfrac{4}{5}\right) = 12000$ of the value left, so $a_1 = 12000$, $r = \dfrac{4}{5}$.

$a_2 = 12000\left(\dfrac{4}{5}\right)^{2-1} = 12000\left(\dfrac{4}{5}\right) = 9600$

$a_3 = 12000\left(\dfrac{4}{5}\right)^{3-1} = 12000\left(\dfrac{16}{25}\right) = 7680$

$a_4 = 12000\left(\dfrac{4}{5}\right)^{4-1} = 12000\left(\dfrac{64}{125}\right) = 6144$

a. \$12,000, \$9,600, \$7,680, \$6,144

b. $a_n = 12000\left(\dfrac{4}{5}\right)^{n-1}$

c. $a_5 = 12000\left(\dfrac{4}{5}\right)^{5-1} = 12000\left(\dfrac{256}{625}\right) = 4915.20$

After 5 years, the value of the car is \$4,915.20.

104. a. According to Exercise 103(c), the value of the car after 5 years is \$4,915.20.

b. Use $c = 15000$, $r = \dfrac{1}{5}$ and $n = 5$ to obtain

$S = c(1-r)^n$

$= 15000\left(1 - \dfrac{1}{5}\right)^5$

$= 15000\left(\dfrac{4}{5}\right)^5$

$= 15000\left(\dfrac{1024}{3125}\right)$

$= 4915.2$

The scrap value after 5 years is \$4,915.20. The two answers agree.

105. Each time the ball bounces it goes up and then comes down the same distance. Therefore, the total vertical distance will be twice the height it rises after each bounce plus the initial 10 feet. The heights after each bounce form an infinite geometric sequence with $r = 0.9$ and $a_1 = 9$.

$s_\infty = \dfrac{9}{1-0.9} = \dfrac{9}{0.1} = 90$

Total distance: 6

$2(s_\infty) + 10 = 2(90) + 10 = 190$

The total vertical distance is 190 feet.

106. The total distance is
$$1 + \left[1 - (-0.50)\right] + \left[0.25 - (-0.50)\right]$$
$$+ \left[0.25 - (-0.125)\right] + \cdots$$
$$= 1 + \underbrace{1.50 + 0.75 + 0.375 + \cdots}$$

The part above the bracket is an infinite geometric

sequence. Using $a_1 = 1.50$ and $r = \dfrac{0.75}{1.50} = 0.50$,

the sum is $s_\infty = \dfrac{a_1}{1-r} = \dfrac{1.50}{1-0.5} = \dfrac{1.5}{0.50} = 3$. Thus

the total distance is $1 + s_\infty = 1 + 3 = 4$ feet.

107. a. y_2 goes up more steeply.

  b.

  $$-10, \ 10, \ 1, \ -1, \ 19, \ 1$$

  From the graph y_2 goes up more steeply,
  which agrees with our answer to part (a).

108. $100 = 3 \cdot 2^{n-1}$

$y_1 = 100$, $y_2 = 3 \cdot 2^{n-1}$

  Intersection
  X=6.0588937   Y=100
  $$-10, \ 10, \ 1, \ -20, \ 120, \ 10$$
  $n \approx 6.06$

109. This is a geometric sequence with $r = \dfrac{2}{1} = 2$.

Also, $a_n = 1{,}048{,}576 = 2^{20}$. Using $a_n = a_1 r^{n-1}$
gives
$$2^{20} = 1(2)^{n-1}$$
$$2^{20} = 2^{n-1}$$
$$20 = n - 1$$
$$21 = n$$
Thus, there are 21 terms in the sequence.
$$s_{21} = \frac{a_1(1 - r^{21})}{1 - r} = \frac{1(1 - 2^{21})}{1 - 2}$$
$$= \frac{1 - 2{,}097{,}152}{-1} = \frac{-2{,}097{,}151}{-1} = 2{,}097{,}151$$

110. $(4x^2 - 3x + 6)(2x - 3)$
$$= 8x^3 - 12x^2 - 6x^2 + 9x + 12x - 18$$
$$= 8x^3 - 18x^2 + 21x - 18$$

111.
$$\begin{array}{r} 8x - 15 \\ 2x + 5 \overline{)\, 16x^2 + 10x - 18} \\ \underline{16x^2 + 40x} \\ -30x - 18 \\ \underline{-30x - 75} \\ 57 \end{array}$$

$$(16x^2 + 10x - 18) \div (2x + 5) = 8x - 15 + \frac{57}{2x + 5}$$

112. Let x = the time it takes Mr. Donovan to load the
truck by himself. Then $2x$ = the time it take Mrs.
Donovan to load the truck by herself.

	Rate of Work	Time Worked	Part of Task
Mr. Donovan	$\dfrac{1}{x}$	8	$\dfrac{8}{x}$
Mrs. Donovan	$\dfrac{1}{2x}$	8	$\dfrac{8}{2x}$

$$\frac{8}{x} + \frac{8}{2x} = 1$$
$$2x\left(\frac{8}{x} + \frac{8}{2x}\right) = 2x(1)$$
$$16 + 8 = 2x$$
$$24 = 2x$$
$$12 = x$$

Mr. Donovan will need 12 hours to load the truck
by himself.

113. $\left(\dfrac{9}{100}\right)^{-1/2} = \left(\dfrac{100}{9}\right)^{1/2} = \sqrt{\dfrac{100}{9}} = \dfrac{\sqrt{100}}{\sqrt{9}} = \dfrac{10}{3}$

114. $\sqrt[3]{9x^2 y}\left(\sqrt[3]{3x^4 y^6} - \sqrt[3]{8xy^4}\right)$
$$= \sqrt[3]{9x^2 y}\left(3x^4 y^6\right) - \sqrt[3]{9x^2 y}\left(8xy^4\right)$$
$$= \sqrt[3]{27x^6 y^7} - \sqrt[3]{72x^3 y^5}$$
$$= \sqrt[3]{27x^6 y^6 y} - \sqrt[3]{8 \cdot 9 x^3 y^3 y^2}$$
$$= 3x^2 y^2 \sqrt[3]{y} - 2xy\sqrt[3]{9y^2}$$

115. $x\sqrt{y} - 2\sqrt{x^2 y} + \sqrt{4x^2 y}$
$$= x\sqrt{y} - 2x\sqrt{y} + 2x\sqrt{y}$$
$$= x\sqrt{y}$$

116. $\sqrt{a^2 + 9a + 3} = -a$

$\left(\sqrt{a^2 + 9a + 3}\right)^2 = (-a)^2$

$a^2 + 9a + 3 = a^2$

$9a = -3$

$a = \dfrac{-3}{9} = -\dfrac{1}{3}$

Check: $\sqrt{\left(-\dfrac{1}{3}\right)^2 + 9\left(-\dfrac{1}{3}\right) + 3} =^? -\left(-\dfrac{1}{3}\right)$

$\sqrt{\dfrac{1}{9} - 3 + 3} =^? \dfrac{1}{3}$

$\sqrt{\dfrac{1}{9}} =^? \dfrac{1}{3}$

$\dfrac{1}{3} = \dfrac{1}{3}$ True

The solution is $-\dfrac{1}{3}$.

Mid-Chapter Test: 15.1-15.3

1. $a_n = -3n + 5$

$a_1 = -3(1) + 5 = -3 + 5 = 2$

$a_2 = -3(2) + 5 = -6 + 5 = -1$

$a_3 = -3(3) + 5 = -9 + 5 = -4$

$a_4 = -3(4) + 5 = -12 + 5 = -7$

$a_5 = -3(5) + 5 = -15 + 5 = -10$

The terms are $2, -1, -4, -7, -10$.

2. $a_n = n(n + 6)$

$a_7 = 7(7 + 6) = 7(13) = 91$

3. $a_n = 2^n - 1$

$a_1 = 2^1 - 1 = 2 - 1 = 1$

$a_2 = 2^2 - 1 = 4 - 1 = 3$

$a_3 = 2^3 - 1 = 8 - 1 = 7$

$s_1 = a_1 = 1$

$s_3 = a_1 + a_2 + a_3 = 1 + 3 + 7 = 11$

4. Each term is 4 less than the previous term. The next three terms are $-15, -19, -23$.

5. $\displaystyle\sum_{i=1}^{5}(4i - 3)$

$= [4(1) - 3] + [4(2) - 3] + [4(3) - 3]$

$\quad + [4(4) - 3] + [4(5) - 3]$

$= [4 - 3] + [8 - 3] + [12 - 3] + [16 - 3] + [20 - 3]$

$= 1 + 5 + 9 + 13 + 17$

$= 45$

6. $a_n = \dfrac{1}{3}n + 7$

The fifth partial sum is $\displaystyle\sum_{i=1}^{5}\left(\dfrac{1}{3}i + 7\right)$.

7. $a_1 = -6$

$a_2 = -6 + (2 - 1)(5) = -6 + 1(5) = -6 + 5 = -1$

$a_3 = -6 + (3 - 1)(5) = -6 + 2(5) = -6 + 10 = 4$

$a_4 = -6 + (4 - 1)(5) = -6 + 3(5) = -6 + 15 = 9$

$a_5 = -6 + (5 - 1)(5) = -6 + 4(5) = -6 + 20 = 14$

The terms are $-6, -1, 4, 9, 14$. The general term is $a_n = -6 + (n - 1)5$ or $a_n = 5n - 11$.

8. $a_n = a_1 + (n - 1)d$

$-\dfrac{1}{2} = \dfrac{11}{2} + (7 - 1)d$

$-\dfrac{1}{2} = \dfrac{11}{2} + 6d$

$-\dfrac{12}{2} = 6d$

$-6 = 6d$

$-1 = d$

9. $a_n = a_1 + (n - 1)d$

$-3 = 22 + (n - 1)(-5)$

$-3 = 22 - 5n + 5$

$-3 = 27 - 5n$

$-30 = -5n$

$6 = n$

10. $a_n = a_1 + (n - 1)d$

$7 = -8 + (6 - 1)d$

$7 = -8 + 5d$

$15 = 5d$

$3 = d$

$s_6 = \dfrac{6(a_1 + a_6)}{2} = \dfrac{6(-8 + 7)}{2} = \dfrac{6(-1)}{2} = \dfrac{-6}{2} = -3$

11. $a_n = a_1 + (n - 1)d$

$a_{10} = \dfrac{5}{2} + (10 - 1)\left(\dfrac{1}{2}\right) = \dfrac{5}{2} + 9\left(\dfrac{1}{2}\right) = \dfrac{5}{2} + \dfrac{9}{2} = \dfrac{14}{2} = 7$

$s_{10} = \dfrac{10(a_1 + a_{10})}{2}$

$\quad = \dfrac{10\left(\frac{5}{2} + 7\right)}{2} = \dfrac{25 + 70}{2} = \dfrac{95}{2} = 47\dfrac{1}{2}$

12. $d = 0 - (-7) = 0 + 7 = 7$

$a_n = a_1 + (n-1)d$

$63 = -7 + (n-1)(7)$

$63 = -7 + 7n - 7$

$63 = 7n - 14$

$77 = 7n$

$11 = n$

There are 11 terms in the sequence.

13. $16 + 15 + 14 + \cdots + 1$ or $1 + 2 + 3 + \cdots + 16$

$$s_n = \frac{n(a_1 + a_n)}{2}$$

$$s_{16} = \frac{16(1+16)}{2} = \frac{16(17)}{2} = \frac{272}{2} = 136$$

There are 136 logs in the pile.

14. $a_1 = 80$

$$a_2 = 80\left(-\frac{1}{2}\right)^{2-1} = 80\left(-\frac{1}{2}\right) = -40$$

$$a_3 = 80\left(-\frac{1}{2}\right)^{3-1} = 80\left(-\frac{1}{2}\right)^2 = 80\left(\frac{1}{4}\right) = 20$$

$$a_4 = 80\left(-\frac{1}{2}\right)^{4-1} = 80\left(-\frac{1}{2}\right)^3 = 80\left(-\frac{1}{8}\right) = -10$$

$$a_5 = 80\left(-\frac{1}{2}\right)^{5-1} = 80\left(-\frac{1}{2}\right)^4 = 80\left(\frac{1}{16}\right) = 5$$

The terms are 80, –40, 20, –10, 5.

15. $a_7 = a_1 r^{7-1}$

$$a_7 = 81\left(\frac{1}{3}\right)^{7-1} = 81\left(\frac{1}{3}\right)^6 = 81\left(\frac{1}{729}\right) = \frac{1}{9}$$

16. $$s_6 = \frac{a_1(1-r^6)}{1-r}$$

$$s_6 = \frac{5(1-2^6)}{1-2} = \frac{5(1-64)}{-1} = \frac{5(-63)}{-1} = 315$$

17. $r = -\frac{16}{3} \div 8 = -\frac{16}{3} \cdot \frac{1}{8} = -\frac{2}{3}$

18. $r = 4 \div 12 = \frac{4}{12} = \frac{1}{3}$

$$s_\infty = \frac{a_1}{1-r} = \frac{12}{1-\frac{1}{3}} = \frac{12}{\frac{2}{3}} = 12\left(\frac{3}{2}\right) = 18$$

19. $0.878787\ldots = 0.87 + 0.0087 + 0.000087 + \cdots$

$$= 0.87 + 0.87(0.01) + 0.87(0.01)^2 + \cdots$$

$r = 0.01$ and $a_1 = 0.87$

$$s_\infty = \frac{0.87}{1-0.01} = \frac{0.87}{0.99} = \frac{87}{99} = \frac{29}{33}$$

20. a. A sequence is a list of numbers arranged in a specific order.

b. An arithmetic sequence is a sequence where each term differs by a constant amount.

c. A geometric sequence is a sequence in which each term after the first is the same multiple of the preceding term.

d. A series is the sum of the terms of a sequence.

Exercise Set 15.4

1. Answers will vary. One possibility follows. The first and last numbers in each row are 1 and the inner numbers are obtained by adding the two numbers in the row above (to the right and left).

2. $n! = n(n-1)(n-2)\cdots(1)$

3. $1! = 1$

4. $0! = 1$

5. No. Factorials are only defined for nonnegative integers.

6. No. Factorials are only defined for nonnegative integers.

7. The expansion of $(a+b)^{13}$ has 14 terms, one more than the power to which the binomial is raised.

8. The expansion of $(a+b)^{20}$ has 21 terms, one more than the power to which the binomial is raised.

9. $\dbinom{5}{2} = \dfrac{5!}{2!\,(5-2)!}$

$= \dfrac{5!}{2!\,3!}$

$= \dfrac{5 \cdot 4 \cdot 3 \cdot 2 \cdot 1}{(2 \cdot 1)(3 \cdot 2 \cdot 1)}$

$= \dfrac{20}{2}$

$= 10$

10. $\dbinom{6}{3} = \dfrac{6!}{3!\,(6-3)!}$

$= \dfrac{6!}{3!\,3!}$

$= \dfrac{6 \cdot 5 \cdot 4 \cdot 3 \cdot 2 \cdot 1}{(3 \cdot 2 \cdot 1)(3 \cdot 2 \cdot 1)}$

$= \dfrac{120}{6}$

$= 20$

11. $\dbinom{5}{5} = \dfrac{5!}{5!(5-5)!} = \dfrac{5!}{5! \cdot 0!} = \dfrac{1}{0!} = \dfrac{1}{1} = 1$

12. $\dbinom{9}{3} = \dfrac{9!}{3!\,(9-3)!}$

$= \dfrac{9!}{3!\,6!}$

$= \dfrac{9 \cdot 8 \cdot 7 \cdot 6 \cdot 5 \cdot 4 \cdot 3 \cdot 2 \cdot 1}{(3 \cdot 2 \cdot 1)(6 \cdot 5 \cdot 4 \cdot 3 \cdot 2 \cdot 1)}$

$= \dfrac{504}{6}$

$= 84$

13. $\dbinom{7}{0} = \dfrac{7!}{0!(7-0)!} = \dfrac{7!}{0! \cdot 7!} = \dfrac{7!}{0! \cdot 7!} = \dfrac{1}{0!} = \dfrac{1}{1} = 1$

14. $\dbinom{10}{7} = \dfrac{10!}{7!\,(10-7)!}$

$= \dfrac{10!}{7!\,3!}$

$= \dfrac{10 \cdot 9 \cdot 8 \cdot 7 \cdot 6 \cdot 5 \cdot 4 \cdot 3 \cdot 2 \cdot 1}{(7 \cdot 6 \cdot 5 \cdot 4 \cdot 3 \cdot 2 \cdot 1)(3 \cdot 2 \cdot 1)}$

$= \dfrac{720}{6}$

$= 120$

15. $\dbinom{8}{4} = \dfrac{8!}{4!\,(8-4)!}$

$= \dfrac{8!}{4!\,4!}$

$= \dfrac{8 \cdot 7 \cdot 6 \cdot 5 \cdot 4 \cdot 3 \cdot 2 \cdot 1}{(4 \cdot 3 \cdot 2 \cdot 1)(4 \cdot 3 \cdot 2 \cdot 1)}$

$= \dfrac{1680}{24}$

$= 70$

16. $\dbinom{12}{3} = \dfrac{12!}{3!\,(12-3)!}$

$= \dfrac{12!}{3!\,9!}$

$= \dfrac{12 \cdot 11 \cdot 10 \cdot 9 \cdot 8 \cdot 7 \cdot 6 \cdot 5 \cdot 4 \cdot 3 \cdot 2 \cdot 1}{(3 \cdot 2 \cdot 1)(9 \cdot 8 \cdot 7 \cdot 6 \cdot 5 \cdot 4 \cdot 3 \cdot 2 \cdot 1)}$

$= \dfrac{1320}{6}$

$= 220$

17. $\dbinom{8}{2} = \dfrac{8!}{2!\,(8-2)!}$

$= \dfrac{8!}{2!\,6!}$

$= \dfrac{8 \cdot 7 \cdot 6 \cdot 5 \cdot 4 \cdot 3 \cdot 2 \cdot 1}{(2 \cdot 1) \cdot (6 \cdot 5 \cdot 4 \cdot 3 \cdot 2 \cdot 1)}$

$= \dfrac{56}{2}$

$= 28$

18. $\dbinom{11}{4} = \dfrac{11!}{4!\,(11-7)!}$

$= \dfrac{11!}{4!\,7!}$

$= \dfrac{11 \cdot 10 \cdot 9 \cdot 8 \cdot 7 \cdot 6 \cdot 5 \cdot 4 \cdot 3 \cdot 2 \cdot 1}{(4 \cdot 3 \cdot 2 \cdot 1)(7 \cdot 6 \cdot 5 \cdot 4 \cdot 3 \cdot 2 \cdot 1)}$

$= \dfrac{7920}{24}$

$= 330$

19. $(x+4)^3$

$= \dbinom{3}{0}x^3 4^0 + \dbinom{3}{1}x^2 4^1 + \dbinom{3}{2}x^1 4^2 + \dbinom{3}{3}x^0 4^3$

$= 1x^3(1) + 3x^2(4) + 3x(16) + 1(1)64$

$= x^3 + 12x^2 + 48x + 64$

20. $(x-4)^3 = \binom{3}{0}x^3(-4)^0 + \binom{3}{1}x^2(-4)^1 + \binom{3}{2}x^1(-4)^2 + \binom{3}{3}x^0(-4)^3$

$\qquad = 1x^3(1) + 3x^2(-4) + 3x(16) + 1(1)(-64)$

$\qquad = x^3 - 12x^2 + 48x - 64$

21. $(2x-3)^3 = \binom{3}{0}(2x)^3(-3)^0 + \binom{3}{1}(2x)^2(-3)^1 + \binom{3}{2}(2x)^1(-3)^2 + \binom{3}{3}(2x)^0(-3)^3$

$\qquad = 1(8x^3)(1) + 3(4x^2)(-3) + 3(2x)(9) + 1(1)(-27)$

$\qquad = 8x^3 - 36x^2 + 54x - 27$

22. $(2x+3)^3 = \binom{3}{0}(2x)^3(3)^0 + \binom{3}{1}(2x)^2(3)^1 + \binom{3}{2}(2x)^1(3)^2 + \binom{3}{3}(2x)^0(3)^3$

$\qquad = 1(8x^3)(1) + 3(4x^2)(3) + 3(2x)(9) + 1(1)(27)$

$\qquad = 8x^3 + 36x^2 + 54x + 27$

23. $(a-b)^4 = \binom{4}{0}a^4(-b)^0 + \binom{4}{1}a^3(-b)^1 + \binom{4}{2}a^2(-b)^2 + \binom{4}{3}a^1(-b)^3 + \binom{4}{4}a^0(-b)^4$

$\qquad = 1a^4(1) + 4a^3(-b) + 6a^2b^2 + 4a(-b^3) + 1(1)b^4$

$\qquad = a^4 - 4a^3b + 6a^2b^2 - 4ab^3 + b^4$

24. $(2r+s^2)^4 = \binom{4}{0}(2r)^4(s^2)^0 + \binom{4}{1}(2r)^3(s^2)^1 + \binom{4}{2}(2r)^2(s^2)^2 + \binom{4}{3}(2r)^1(s^2)^3 + \binom{4}{4}(2r)^0(s^2)^4$

$\qquad = 1(16r^4)(1) + 4(8r^3)(s^2) + 6(4r^2)(s^4) + 4(2r)(s^6) + 1(1)(s^8)$

$\qquad = 16r^4 + 32r^3s^2 + 24r^2s^4 + 8rs^6 + s^8$

25. $(3a-b)^5 = \binom{5}{0}(3a)^5(-b)^0 + \binom{5}{1}(3a)^4(-b)^1 + \binom{5}{2}(3a)^3(-b)^2 + \binom{5}{3}(3a)^2(-b)^3 + \binom{5}{4}(3a)^1(-b)^4 + \binom{5}{5}(3a)^0(-b)^5$

$\qquad = 1(243a^5)(1) + 5(81a^4)(-b) + 10(27a^3)b^2 + 10(9a^2)(-b^3) + 5(3a)b^4 + 1(1)(-b^5)$

$\qquad = 243a^5 - 405a^4b + 270a^3b^2 - 90a^2b^3 + 15ab^4 - b^5$

26. $(x+2y)^5 = \binom{5}{0}(x)^5(2y)^0 + \binom{5}{1}(x)^4(2y)^1 + \binom{5}{2}(x)^3(2y)^2 + \binom{5}{3}(x)^2(2y)^3 + \binom{5}{4}(x)^1(2y)^4 + \binom{5}{5}(x)^0(2y)^5$

$\qquad = 1(x^5)(1) + 5(x^4)(2y) + 10(x^3)(4y^2) + 10(x^2)(8y^3) + 5(x)(16y^4) + 1(1)(32y^5)$

$\qquad = x^5 + 10x^4y + 40x^3y^2 + 80x^2y^3 + 80xy^4 + 32y^5$

27. $\left(2x+\dfrac{1}{2}\right)^4 = \binom{4}{0}(2x)^4\left(\dfrac{1}{2}\right)^0 + \binom{4}{1}(2x)^3\left(\dfrac{1}{2}\right)^1 + \binom{4}{2}(2x)^2\left(\dfrac{1}{2}\right)^2 + \binom{4}{3}(2x)^1\left(\dfrac{1}{2}\right)^3 + \binom{4}{4}(2x)^0\left(\dfrac{1}{2}\right)^4$

$\qquad = 1(16x^4)(1) + 4(8x^3)\left(\dfrac{1}{2}\right) + 6(4x^2)\left(\dfrac{1}{4}\right) + 4(2x)\left(\dfrac{1}{8}\right) + 1(1)\left(\dfrac{1}{16}\right)$

$\qquad = 16x^4 + 16x^3 + 6x^2 + x + \dfrac{1}{16}$

28. $\left(\dfrac{2}{3}x+\dfrac{3}{2}\right)^{4} = \binom{4}{0}\left(\dfrac{2}{3}x\right)^{4}\left(\dfrac{3}{2}\right)^{0} + \binom{4}{1}\left(\dfrac{2}{3}x\right)^{3}\left(\dfrac{3}{2}\right)^{1} + \binom{4}{2}\left(\dfrac{2}{3}x\right)^{2}\left(\dfrac{3}{2}\right)^{2} + \binom{4}{3}\left(\dfrac{2}{3}x\right)^{1}\left(\dfrac{3}{2}\right)^{3} + \binom{4}{4}\left(\dfrac{2}{3}x\right)^{0}\left(\dfrac{3}{2}\right)^{4}$

$= 1\left(\dfrac{16}{81}x^{4}\right)(1) + 4\left(\dfrac{8}{27}x^{3}\right)\left(\dfrac{3}{2}\right) + 6\left(\dfrac{4}{9}x^{2}\right)\left(\dfrac{9}{4}\right) + 4\left(\dfrac{2}{3}x\right)\left(\dfrac{27}{8}\right) + 1(1)\left(\dfrac{81}{16}\right)$

$= \dfrac{16}{81}x^{4} + \dfrac{16}{9}x^{3} + 6x^{2} + 9x + \dfrac{81}{16}$

29. $\left(\dfrac{x}{2}-3\right)^{4} = \binom{4}{0}\left(\dfrac{x}{2}\right)^{4}(-3)^{0} + \binom{4}{1}\left(\dfrac{x}{2}\right)^{3}(-3)^{1} + \binom{4}{2}\left(\dfrac{x}{2}\right)^{2}(-3)^{2} + \binom{4}{3}\left(\dfrac{x}{2}\right)^{1}(-3)^{3} + \binom{4}{4}\left(\dfrac{x}{2}\right)^{0}(-3)^{4}$

$= 1\left(\dfrac{x^{4}}{16}\right)(1) + 4\left(\dfrac{x^{3}}{8}\right)(-3) + 6\left(\dfrac{x^{2}}{4}\right)(9) + 4\left(\dfrac{x}{2}\right)(-27) + 1(1)(81)$

$= \dfrac{x^{4}}{16} - \dfrac{3x^{3}}{2} + \dfrac{27x^{2}}{2} - 54x + 81$

30. $(3x^{2}+y)^{5} = \binom{5}{0}(3x^{2})^{5}(y)^{0} + \binom{5}{1}(3x^{2})^{4}(y)^{1} + \binom{5}{2}(3x^{2})^{3}(y)^{2} + \binom{5}{3}(3x^{2})^{2}(y)^{3} + \binom{5}{4}(3x^{2})^{1}(y)^{4} + \binom{5}{5}(3x^{2})^{0}(y)^{5}$

$= (1)(243x^{10})(1) + 5(81x^{8})(y) + 10(27x^{6})(y^{2}) + 10(9x^{4})(y^{3}) + 5(3x^{2})(y^{4}) + 1(1)(y^{5})$

$= 243x^{10} + 405x^{8}y + 270x^{6}y^{2} + 90x^{4}y^{3} + 15x^{2}y^{4} + y^{5}$

31. $(x+10)^{10} = \binom{10}{0}x^{10}(10)^{0} + \binom{10}{1}x^{9}(10)^{1} + \binom{10}{2}x^{8}(10)^{2} + \binom{10}{3}x^{7}(10)^{3} + \cdots$

$= 1x^{10}(1) + \dfrac{10}{1}x^{9}(10) + \dfrac{10\cdot9}{2\cdot1}x^{8}(100) + \dfrac{10\cdot9\cdot8}{3\cdot2\cdot1}x^{7}(1000) + \cdots$

$= x^{10} + 100x^{9} + 4{,}500x^{8} + 120{,}000x^{7} + \cdots$

32. $(2x+3)^{8} = \binom{8}{0}(2x)^{8}(3)^{0} + \binom{8}{1}(2x)^{7}(3)^{1} + \binom{8}{2}(2x)^{6}(3)^{2} + \binom{8}{3}(2x)^{5}(3)^{3} + \cdots$

$= (1)(256x^{8})(1) + \dfrac{8}{1}(128x^{7})(3) + \dfrac{8\cdot7}{2\cdot1}(64x^{6})(9) + \dfrac{8\cdot7\cdot6}{3\cdot2\cdot1}(32x^{5})(27) + \cdots$

$= 256x^{8} + 8(128x^{7})(3) + 28(64x^{6})(9) + 56(32x^{5})(27) + \cdots$

$= 256x^{8} + 3072x^{7} + 16{,}128x^{6} + 48{,}384x^{5} + \cdots$

33. $(3x-y)^{7} = \binom{7}{0}(3x)^{7}(-y)^{0} + \binom{7}{1}(3x)^{6}(-y)^{1} + \binom{7}{2}(3x)^{5}(-y)^{2} + \binom{7}{3}(3x)^{4}(-y)^{3} + \cdots$

$= 1(2187x^{7})(1) + \dfrac{7}{1}(729x^{6})(-y) + \dfrac{7\cdot6}{2\cdot1}(243x^{5})(y^{2}) + \dfrac{7\cdot6\cdot5}{3\cdot2\cdot1}(81x^{4})(-y^{3}) + \cdots$

$= 2187x^{7} + 7(729x^{6})(-y) + 21(243x^{5})(y^{2}) + 35(81x^{4})(-y^{3}) + \cdots$

$= 2187x^{7} - 5103x^{6}y + 5103x^{5}y^{2} - 2835x^{4}y^{3} + \cdots$

34. $(3p-2q)^{11} = \binom{11}{0}(3p)^{11}(-2q)^{0} + \binom{11}{1}(3p)^{10}(-2q)^{1} + \binom{11}{2}(3p)^{9}(-2q)^{2} + \binom{11}{3}(3p)^{8}(-2q)^{3} + \cdots$

$= 1(3p)^{11}(1) + \dfrac{11}{1}(3p)^{10}(-2q)^{1} + \dfrac{11\cdot10}{2\cdot1}(3p)^{9}(-2q)^{2} + \dfrac{11\cdot10\cdot9}{3\cdot2\cdot1}(3p)^{8}(-2q)^{3} + \cdots$

$= 3^{11}p^{11} + 11(3^{10}p^{10})(-2q) + 55(3^{9}p^{9})(4q^{2}) + 165(3^{8}p^{8})(-8q^{3}) + \cdots$

$= 3^{11}p^{11} - (22)3^{10}p^{10}q + (220)3^{9}p^{9}q^{2} - (1320)3^{8}p^{8}q^{3} + \cdots$

35. $(x^2 - 3y)^8 = \binom{8}{0}(x^2)^8(-3y)^0 + \binom{8}{1}(x^2)^7(-3y)^1 + \binom{8}{2}(x^2)^6(-3y)^2 + \binom{8}{3}(x^2)^5(-3y)^3 + \cdots$

$= 1(x^{16})(1) + \frac{8}{1}(x^{14})(-3y) + \frac{8 \cdot 7}{2 \cdot 1}(x^{12})(9y^2) + \frac{8 \cdot 7 \cdot 6}{3 \cdot 2 \cdot 1}(x^{10})(-27y^3) + \cdots$

$= x^{16} + 8(x^{14})(-3y) + 28(x^{12})(9y^2) + 56(x^{10})(-27y^3) + \cdots$

$= x^{16} - 24x^{14}y + 252x^{12}y^2 - 1512x^{10}y^3 + \cdots$

36. $\left(2x + \frac{y}{7}\right)^9 = \binom{9}{0}(2x)^9\left(\frac{y}{7}\right)^0 + \binom{9}{1}(2x)^8\left(\frac{y}{7}\right)^1 + \binom{9}{2}(2x)^7\left(\frac{y}{7}\right)^2 + \binom{9}{3}(2x)^6\left(\frac{y}{7}\right)^3 + \cdots$

$= 1(512x^9)(1) + \frac{9}{1}(256x^8)\left(\frac{y}{7}\right) + \frac{9 \cdot 8}{2 \cdot 1}(128x^7)\left(\frac{y^2}{49}\right) + \frac{9 \cdot 8 \cdot 7}{3 \cdot 2 \cdot 1}(64x^6)\left(\frac{y^3}{343}\right) + \cdots$

$= 512x^9 + 9(256x^8)\left(\frac{y}{7}\right) + 36(128x^7)\left(\frac{y^2}{49}\right) + 84(64x^6)\left(\frac{y^3}{343}\right) + \cdots$

$= 512x^9 + \frac{2304}{7}x^8y + \frac{4608}{49}x^7y^2 + \frac{5376}{343}x^6y^3 + \cdots$

---

37. Yes, $n! = n \cdot (n-1)!$

$4! = 4 \cdot 3 \cdot 2 \cdot 1$

$= 4 \cdot (3 \cdot 2 \cdot 1)$

$= 4 \cdot (3)!$

$= 4 \cdot (4-1)!$

38. Yes, $(n+1)! = (n+1) \cdot n!$

$(4+1)! = 5!$

$= 5 \cdot 4 \cdot 3 \cdot 2 \cdot 1$

$= 5 \cdot (4 \cdot 3 \cdot 2 \cdot 1)$

$= 5 \cdot 4!$

$= (4+1) \cdot 4!$

39. Yes, $(n-3)! = (n-3)(n-4)(n-5)!$ for $n \geq 5$.

Let $n = 7$:

$(7-3)! = (7-3)(7-4)(7-5)!$ or

$4! = 4 \cdot 3 \cdot 2! = 4 \cdot 3 \cdot 2 \cdot 1 = 4!$

40. Yes, $(n+2)! = (n+2)(n+1)(n)(n-1)!$ for $n \geq 1$.

Let $n = 5$:

$(n+2)! \overset{?}{=} (n+2)(n+1)(n)(n-1)!$

$(5+2)! \overset{?}{=} (5+2)(5+1)(5)(5-1)!$

$(7)! \overset{?}{=} (7)(6)(5)(4)!$

$(7)! = (7)!$ True

41. $\binom{n}{m} = 1$ when either $n = m$ or $m = 0$.

42. No. $\binom{n}{m}$ must always be 1 or larger.

43. $(x + 3)^8$

First term is $\binom{8}{0}(x)^8(3)^0 = 1(x^8)(1) = x^8$.

Second term is $\binom{8}{1}(x)^7(3)^1 = 8(x^7)(3) = 24x^7$.

Next to last term is

$\binom{8}{7}(x)^1(3)^7 = 8(x)(2187) = 17,496x$.

Last term is $\binom{8}{8}(x)^0(3)^8 = 1(1)(6561) = 6561$.

44. $(2x + 5)^6$

First term is

$\binom{6}{0}(2x)^6(5)^0 = 1(64x^6)(1) = 64x^6$.

Second term is

$\binom{6}{1}(2x)^5(5)^1 = \frac{6}{1}(32x^5)(5) = 960x^5$.

Next to last term is

$\binom{6}{5}(2x)^1(5)^5 = \frac{6}{1}(2x)(3125) = 37,500x$.

Last term is

$\binom{6}{6}(2x)^0(5)^6 = 1(1)(15,625) = 15,625$.

45. $(a+b)^n = \sum_{i=0}^{n}\binom{n}{i}a^{n-i}b^i$

46. $\binom{n}{r} = \dfrac{n!}{r!(n-r)!}$

$= \dfrac{n!}{(n-r)![n-(n-r)]!}$

$= \binom{n}{n-r}$

47. Let $x = 0$.

$2x + y = 10$

$2(0) + y = 6$

$y = 6$

The y-intercept is $(0, 10)$.

48. $x(x-11) = -18$

$x^2 - 11x + 18 = 0$

$(x-9)(x-2) = 0$

$x - 9 = 0$ or $x - 2 = 0$

$x = 9$ $x = 2$

49. $\dfrac{1}{5}x + \dfrac{1}{2}y = 4 \overset{\times(-10)}{\Rightarrow} -2x - 5y = -40$ (1)

$\dfrac{2}{3}x - y = \dfrac{8}{3} \overset{\times 3}{\Rightarrow} \underline{\quad 2x - 3y = \;\; 8 \quad}$ (2)

$-8y = -32$

$y = 4$

Substitute $y = 4$ into equation (2):

$2x - 3(4) = 8$

$2x = 20$

$x = 10$

The solution is $(10, 4)$.

50. $\sqrt{20xy^4}\sqrt{6x^5y^7} = \sqrt{120x^6y^{11}}$

$= \sqrt{4x^6y^{10}\cdot 30y}$

$= 2x^3y^5\sqrt{30y}$

51. $f(x) = 3x + 8$

$y = 3x + 8$

$x = 3y + 8$

$3y = x - 8$

$y = \dfrac{x-8}{3}$

$f^{-1}(x) = \dfrac{x-8}{3}$

Chapter 15 Review Exercises

1. $a_n = n + 5$

$a_1 = 1 + 5 = 6$

$a_2 = 2 + 5 = 7$

$a_3 = 3 + 5 = 8$

$a_4 = 4 + 5 = 9$

$a_5 = 5 + 5 = 10$

The terms are 6, 7, 8, 9, 10.

2. $a_n = n^2 + n - 3$

$a_1 = 1^2 + 1 - 3 = -1$

$a_2 = 2^2 + 2 - 3 = 3$

$a_3 = 3^2 + 3 - 3 = 9$

$a_4 = 4^2 + 4 - 3 = 17$

$a_5 = 5^2 + 5 - 3 = 27$

The terms are $-1, 3, 9, 17, 27$.

3. $a_n = \dfrac{6}{n}$

$a_1 = \dfrac{6}{1} = 6$

$a_2 = \dfrac{6}{2} = 3$

$a_3 = \dfrac{6}{3} = 2$

$a_4 = \dfrac{6}{4} = \dfrac{3}{2}$

$a_5 = \dfrac{6}{5}$

The terms are $6, 3, 2, \dfrac{3}{2}, \dfrac{6}{5}$.

4. $a_n = \dfrac{n^2}{n+4}$

$a_1 = \dfrac{1^2}{1+4} = \dfrac{1}{5}$

$a_2 = \dfrac{2^2}{2+4} = \dfrac{4}{6} = \dfrac{2}{3}$

$a_3 = \dfrac{3^2}{3+4} = \dfrac{9}{7}$

$a_4 = \dfrac{4^2}{4+4} = \dfrac{16}{8} = 2$

$a_5 = \dfrac{5^2}{5+4} = \dfrac{25}{9}$

The terms are $\dfrac{1}{5}, \dfrac{2}{3}, \dfrac{9}{7}, 2, \dfrac{25}{9}$.

5. $a_n = 3n - 10$

$a_7 = 3(7) - 10 = 21 - 10 = 11$

6. $a_n = (-1)^n + 5$

$a_7 = (-1)^7 + 5 = -1 + 5 = 4$

7. $a_n = \dfrac{n+17}{n^2}$

$a_9 = \dfrac{9+17}{9^2} = \dfrac{26}{81}$

8. $a_n = (n)(n-3)$

$a_{11} = (11)(11-3) = (11)(8) = 88$

9. $a_n = 2n + 5$

$a_1 = 2(1) + 5 = 2 + 5 = 7$

$a_2 = 2(2) + 5 = 4 + 5 = 9$

$a_3 = 2(3) + 5 = 6 + 5 = 11$

$s_1 = a_1 = 7$

$s_3 = a_1 + a_2 + a_3 = 7 + 9 + 11 = 27$

10. $a_n = n^2 + 8$

$a_1 = (1)^2 + 8 = 1 + 8 = 9$

$a_2 = (2)^2 + 8 = 4 + 8 = 12$

$a_3 = (3)^2 + 8 = 9 + 8 = 17$

$s_1 = a_1 = 9$

$s_3 = a_1 + a_2 + a_3 = 9 + 12 + 17 = 38$

11. $a_n = \dfrac{n+3}{n+2}$

$a_1 = \dfrac{1+3}{1+2} = \dfrac{4}{3}$

$a_2 = \dfrac{2+3}{2+2} = \dfrac{5}{4}$

$a_3 = \dfrac{3+3}{3+2} = \dfrac{6}{5}$

$s_1 = a_1 = \dfrac{4}{3}$

$s_3 = a_1 + a_2 + a_3$

$= \dfrac{4}{3} + \dfrac{5}{4} + \dfrac{6}{5}$

$= \dfrac{80}{60} + \dfrac{75}{60} + \dfrac{72}{60}$

$= \dfrac{227}{60}$

12. $a_n = (-1)^n (n+8)$

$a_1 = (-1)^1(1+8) = (-1)(9) = -9$

$a_2 = (-1)^2(2+8) = 1(10) = 10$

$a_3 = (-1)^3(3+8) = -1(11) = -11$

$s_1 = a_1 = -9$

$s_3 = a_1 + a_2 + a_3 = -9 + 10 - 11 = -10$

13. This is a geometric sequence with $r = 4 \div 2 = 2$ and $a_1 = 2$.

$a_5 = 2(2)^{5-1} = 2 \cdot 2^4 = 32$

$a_6 = 2(2)^{6-1} = 2 \cdot 2^5 = 64$

$a_7 = 2(2)^{7-1} = 2 \cdot 2^6 = 128$

The terms are 32, 64, 128.

$a_n = 2(2)^{n-1} = 2^1 2^{n-1} = 2^n$

14. This is a geometric sequence with

$r = 9 \div (-27) = \dfrac{9}{-27} = -\dfrac{1}{3}$ and $a_1 = -27$.

$a_5 = -27\left(-\dfrac{1}{3}\right)^4 = -27\left(\dfrac{1}{81}\right) = -\dfrac{1}{3}$

$a_6 = -27\left(-\dfrac{1}{3}\right)^5 = -27\left(-\dfrac{1}{243}\right) = \dfrac{1}{9}$

$a_5 = -27\left(-\dfrac{1}{3}\right)^6 = -27\left(\dfrac{1}{729}\right) = -\dfrac{1}{27}$

The terms are $-\dfrac{1}{3}, \dfrac{1}{9}, -\dfrac{1}{27}$.

$a_n = -27\left(-\dfrac{1}{3}\right)^{n-1}$ or $a_n = (-1)^n \left(3^{4-n}\right)$

15. This is a geometric sequence with

$r = \dfrac{2}{7} \div \dfrac{1}{7} = \dfrac{2}{7} \cdot \dfrac{7}{1} = 2$ and $a_1 = \dfrac{1}{7}$.

$a_5 = \dfrac{1}{7}(2)^{5-1} = \dfrac{2^4}{7} = \dfrac{16}{7}$

$a_6 = \dfrac{1}{7}(2)^{6-1} = \dfrac{2^5}{7} = \dfrac{32}{7}$

$a_7 = \dfrac{1}{7}(2)^{7-1} = \dfrac{2^6}{7} = \dfrac{64}{7}$

The terms are $\dfrac{16}{7}, \dfrac{32}{7}, \dfrac{64}{7}$.

$a_n = \dfrac{1}{7}(2)^{n-1} = \dfrac{2^{n-1}}{7}$

16. This is an arithmetic sequence with
$d = 9 - 13 = -4$ and $a_1 = 13$.
$a_5 = 13 + (5-1)(-4) = 13 - 16 = -3$
$a_6 = 13 + (6-1)(-4) = 13 - 20 = -7$
$a_7 = 13 + (7-1)(-4) = 13 - 24 = -11$
The terms are $-3, -7, -11$.
$a_n = a_1 + (n-1)d$
$= 13 + (n-1)(-4)$
$= 13 - 4n + 4$
$= 17 - 4n$

17. $\sum_{i=1}^{3}(i^2 + 9) = (1^2 + 9) + (2^2 + 9) + (3^2 + 9)$
$= (1+9) + (4+9) + (9+9)$
$= 10 + 13 + 18$
$= 41$

18. $\sum_{i=1}^{4} i(i+5)$
$= 1(1+5) + 2(2+5) + 3(3+5) + 4(4+5)$
$= 1(6) + 2(7) + 3(8) + 4(9)$
$= 6 + 14 + 24 + 36$
$= 80$

19. $\sum_{i=1}^{5}\frac{i^2}{6} = \frac{1^2}{6} + \frac{2^2}{6} + \frac{3^2}{6} + \frac{4^2}{6} + \frac{5^2}{6}$
$= \frac{1}{6} + \frac{4}{6} + \frac{9}{6} + \frac{16}{6} + \frac{25}{6}$
$= \frac{55}{6}$

20. $\sum_{i=1}^{4}\frac{i}{i+1} = \frac{1}{1+1} + \frac{2}{2+1} + \frac{3}{3+1} + \frac{4}{4+1}$
$= \frac{1}{2} + \frac{2}{3} + \frac{3}{4} + \frac{4}{5}$
$= \frac{163}{60}$

21. $\sum_{i=1}^{4} x_i = x_1 + x_2 + x_3 + x_4 = 3 + 9 + 7 + 10 = 29$

22. $\sum_{i=1}^{4}(x_i)^2 = x_1^2 + x_2^2 + x_3^2 + x_4^2$
$= 3^2 + 9^2 + 7^2 + 10^2$
$= 9 + 81 + 49 + 100$
$= 239$

23. $\sum_{i=2}^{3}(x_i^2 + 1) = (x_2^2 + 1) + (x_3^2 + 1)$
$= (9^2 + 1) + (7^2 + 1)$
$= (81 + 1) + (49 + 1)$
$= 82 + 50$
$= 132$

24. $\left(\sum_{i=1}^{4} x_i\right)^2 = (x_1 + x_2 + x_3 + x_4)^2$
$= (3 + 9 + 7 + 10)^2$
$= (29)^2$
$= 841$

25. a. perimeter of rectangle: $p = 2l + 2w$
$p_1 = 2(1) + 2(1+3) = 2 + 8 = 10$
$p_2 = 2(2) + 2(2+3) = 4 + 10 = 14$
$p_3 = 2(3) + 2(3+3) = 6 + 12 = 18$
$p_4 = 2(4) + 2(4+3) = 8 + 14 = 22$

b. $p_n = 2n + 2(n+3) = 2n + 2n + 6 = 4n + 6$

26. a. area of rectangle: $a = l \cdot w$
$a_1 = 1(1+3) = 4$
$a_2 = 2(2+3) = 10$
$a_3 = 3(3+3) = 18$
$a_4 = 4(4+3) = 28$

b. $a_n = n(n+3) = n^2 + 3n$

27. $a_1 = 5$
$a_2 = 5 + (2-1)(3) = 5 + 1(3) = 5 + 3 = 8$
$a_3 = 5 + (3-1)(3) = 5 + 2(3) = 5 + 6 = 11$
$a_4 = 5 + (4-1)(3) = 5 + 3(3) = 5 + 9 = 14$
$a_5 = 5 + (5-1)(3) = 5 + 4(3) = 5 + 12 = 17$
The terms are 5, 7, 9, 11, 13.

28. $a_1 = 5$
$a_2 = 5 + (2-1)\left(-\frac{1}{3}\right) = 5 + 1\left(-\frac{1}{3}\right) = \frac{15}{3} - \frac{1}{3} = \frac{14}{3}$
$a_3 = 5 + (3-1)\left(-\frac{1}{3}\right) = 5 + 2\left(-\frac{1}{3}\right) = \frac{15}{3} - \frac{2}{3} = \frac{13}{3}$
$a_4 = 5 + (4-1)\left(-\frac{1}{3}\right) = 5 + 3\left(-\frac{1}{3}\right) = 5 - 1 = 4$
$a_5 = 5 + (5-1)\left(-\frac{1}{3}\right) = 5 + 4\left(-\frac{1}{3}\right) = \frac{15}{3} - \frac{4}{3} = \frac{11}{3}$
The terms are $5, \frac{14}{3}, \frac{13}{3}, 4, \frac{11}{3}$.

29. $a_1 = \dfrac{1}{2}$

$a_2 = \dfrac{1}{2} + (2-1)(-2) = \dfrac{1}{2} - 2 = -\dfrac{3}{2}$

$a_3 = \dfrac{1}{2} + (3-1)(-2) = \dfrac{1}{2} - 4 = -\dfrac{7}{2}$

$a_4 = \dfrac{1}{2} + (4-1)(-2) = \dfrac{1}{2} - 6 = -\dfrac{11}{2}$

$a_5 = \dfrac{1}{2} + (5-1)(-2) = \dfrac{1}{2} - 8 = -\dfrac{15}{2}$

The terms are $\dfrac{1}{2}, -\dfrac{3}{2}, -\dfrac{7}{2}, -\dfrac{11}{2}, -\dfrac{15}{2}$.

30. $a_1 = -100$

$a_2 = -100 + (2-1)\left(\dfrac{1}{5}\right) = -100 + \dfrac{1}{5} = -\dfrac{499}{5}$

$a_3 = -100 + (3-1)\left(\dfrac{1}{5}\right) = -100 + \dfrac{2}{5} = -\dfrac{498}{5}$

$a_4 = -100 + (4-1)\left(\dfrac{1}{5}\right) = -100 + \dfrac{3}{5} = -\dfrac{497}{5}$

$a_5 = -100 + (5-1)\left(\dfrac{1}{5}\right) = -100 + \dfrac{4}{5} = -\dfrac{496}{5}$

The terms are $-100, -\dfrac{499}{5}, -\dfrac{498}{5}, -\dfrac{497}{5}, -\dfrac{496}{5}$.

31. $a_9 = a_1 + (9-1)d$

$a_9 = 6 + (9-1)(3) = 6 + 8(3) = 6 + 24 = 30$

32. $a_7 = a_1 + (7-1)d$

$-14 = 10 + 6d$

$-24 = 6d$

$-4 = d$

33. $a_{11} = a_1 + (11-1)d$

$2 = -3 + 10d$

$5 = 10d$

$d = \dfrac{5}{10} = \dfrac{1}{2}$

34. $a_n = a_1 + (n-1)d$

$-3 = 22 + (n-1)(-5)$

$-3 = 22 - 5n + 5$

$-3 = 27 - 5n$

$-30 = -5n$

$6 = n$

35. $a_8 = a_1 + (8-1)d$

$21 = 7 + 7d$

$14 = 7d$

$2 = d$

$S_8 = \dfrac{8(a_1 + a_8)}{2} = \dfrac{8(7+21)}{2} = \dfrac{8(28)}{2} = \dfrac{224}{2} = 112$

36. $a_7 = a_1 + (7-1)d$

$-48 = -12 + 6d$

$-36 = 6d$

$-6 = d$

$S_7 = \dfrac{7(a_1 + a_7)}{2} = \dfrac{7(-12-48)}{2} = \dfrac{7(-60)}{2} = -210$

37. $a_6 = a_1 + (6-1)d$

$\dfrac{13}{5} = \dfrac{3}{5} + 5d$

$\dfrac{13}{5} - \dfrac{3}{5} = 5d$

$\dfrac{10}{5} = 5d$

$2 = 5d$

$\dfrac{2}{5} = d$

$S_6 = \dfrac{6(a_1 + a_6)}{2}$

$= \dfrac{6\left(\frac{3}{5} + \frac{13}{5}\right)}{2} = \dfrac{6\left(\frac{16}{5}\right)}{2} = 6\left(\dfrac{16}{5}\right)\left(\dfrac{1}{2}\right) = \dfrac{48}{5}$

38. $a_9 = a_1 + (9-1)d$

$-6 = -\dfrac{10}{3} + 8d$

$-6 + \dfrac{10}{3} = 8d$

$-\dfrac{8}{3} = 8d$

$d = \dfrac{1}{8}\left(-\dfrac{8}{3}\right) = -\dfrac{1}{3}$

$S_9 = \dfrac{9(a_1 + a_n)}{2}$

$= \dfrac{9\left(-\frac{10}{3} - 6\right)}{2} = \dfrac{9\left(-\frac{28}{3}\right)}{2} = 9\left(-\dfrac{28}{3}\right)\left(\dfrac{1}{2}\right) = -42$

39. $a_1 = -7$

$a_2 = -7 + (2-1)(4) = -7 + 1(4) = -7 + 4 = -3$

$a_3 = -7 + (3-1)(4) = -7 + 2(4) = -7 + 8 = 1$

$a_4 = -7 + (4-1)(4) = -7 + 3(4) = -7 + 12 = 5$

The terms are $-7, -3, 1, 5$.

$a_{10} = -7 + (10-1)(4) = -7 + 9(4) = -7 + 36 = 29$

$S_{10} = \dfrac{10(-7+29)}{2} = \dfrac{10(22)}{2} = \dfrac{220}{2} = 110$

40. $a_1 = 4$

$a_2 = 4 + (2-1)(-3) = 4 + 1(-3) = 4 - 3 = 1$

$a_3 = 4 + (3-1)(-3) = 4 + 2(-3) = 4 - 6 = -2$

$a_4 = 4 + (4-1)(-3) = 4 + 3(-3) = 4 - 9 = -5$

The terms are $4, 1, -2, -5$.

$a_{10} = 4 + (10-1)(-3) = 4 + 9(-3) = 4 - 27 = -23$

$S_{10} = \dfrac{10[4+(-23)]}{2} = \dfrac{10(-19)}{2} = \dfrac{-190}{2} = -95$

41. $a_1 = \dfrac{5}{6}$

$a_2 = \dfrac{5}{6} + (2-1)\left(\dfrac{2}{3}\right) = \dfrac{5}{6} + \dfrac{2}{3} = \dfrac{9}{6} = \dfrac{3}{2}$

$a_3 = \dfrac{5}{6} + (3-1)\left(\dfrac{2}{3}\right) = \dfrac{5}{6} + 2\left(\dfrac{2}{3}\right) = \dfrac{5}{6} + \dfrac{4}{3} = \dfrac{13}{6}$

$a_4 = \dfrac{5}{6} + (4-1)\left(\dfrac{2}{3}\right) = \dfrac{5}{6} + 3\left(\dfrac{2}{3}\right) = \dfrac{5}{6} + \dfrac{6}{3} = \dfrac{17}{6}$

The terms are $\dfrac{5}{6}, \dfrac{3}{2}, \dfrac{13}{6}, \dfrac{17}{6}$.

$a_{10} = \dfrac{5}{6} + (10-1)\left(\dfrac{2}{3}\right) = \dfrac{5}{6} + 9\left(\dfrac{2}{3}\right) = \dfrac{5}{6} + 6 = \dfrac{41}{6}$

$S_{10} = \dfrac{10\left(\frac{5}{6}+\frac{41}{6}\right)}{2} = \dfrac{10\left(\frac{46}{6}\right)}{2} = 5\left(\dfrac{46}{6}\right) = 5\left(\dfrac{23}{3}\right) = \dfrac{115}{3}$

42. $a_1 = -60$

$a_2 = -60 + (2-1)(5) = -60 + 1(5) = -60 + 5 = -55$

$a_3 = -60 + (3-1)(5) = -60 + 2(5) = -60 + 10 = -50$

$a_4 = -60 + (4-1)(5) = -60 + 3(5) = -60 + 15 = -45$

The terms are $-60, -55, -50, -45$.

$a_{10} = -60 + (10-1)(5) = -60 + 45 = -15$

$S_{10} = \dfrac{10(-60-15)}{2} = 5(-75) = -375$

43. $d = 9 - 4 = 5$

$a_n = a_1 + (n-1)d$

$64 = 4 + (n-1)5$

$64 = 4 + 5n - 5$

$64 = 5n - 1$

$65 = 5n$

$13 = n$

$S_{13} = \dfrac{13(a_1 + a_{13})}{2} = \dfrac{13(4+64)}{2} = \dfrac{13(68)}{2} = 442$

44. $d = -4 - (-7) = -4 + 7 = 3$

$a_n = a_1 + (n-1)d$

$11 = -7 + (n-1)3$

$11 = -7 + 3n - 3$

$11 = 3n - 10$

$21 = 3n$

$7 = n$

$S_7 = \dfrac{7(a_1 + a_7)}{2} = \dfrac{7(-7+11)}{2} = \dfrac{7(4)}{2} = \dfrac{28}{2} = 14$

45. $d = \dfrac{9}{10} - \dfrac{6}{10} = \dfrac{3}{10}$

$a_n = a_1 + (n-1)d$

$\dfrac{36}{10} = \dfrac{6}{10} + (n-1)\dfrac{3}{10}$

$\dfrac{36}{10} = \dfrac{6}{10} + \dfrac{3}{10}n - \dfrac{3}{10}$

$\dfrac{36}{10} = \dfrac{3}{10} + \dfrac{3}{10}n$

$\dfrac{33}{10} = \dfrac{3}{10}n$

$n = \dfrac{10}{3}\left(\dfrac{33}{10}\right) = 11$

$S_{11} = \dfrac{11(a_1 + a_{11})}{2}$

$= \dfrac{11\left(\frac{6}{10}+\frac{36}{10}\right)}{2} = \dfrac{11\left(\frac{42}{10}\right)}{2} = 11\left(\dfrac{42}{10}\right)\left(\dfrac{1}{2}\right) = \dfrac{231}{10}$

46. $d = -3 - (-9) = -3 + 9 = 6$

$a_n = a_1 + (n-1)d$

$45 = -9 + (n-1)6$

$45 = -9 + 6n - 6$

$45 = -15 + 6n$

$60 = 6n$

$10 = n$

$S_{10} = \dfrac{10(a_1 + a_{10})}{2} = \dfrac{10(-9+45)}{2} = \dfrac{10(36)}{2} = 180$

47. $a_1 = 6$

$a_2 = 6(2)^{2-1} = 6(2) = 12$

$a_3 = 6(2)^{3-1} = 6(2)^2 = 6(4) = 24$

$a_4 = 6(2)^{4-1} = 6(2)^3 = 6(8) = 48$

$a_5 = 6(2)^{5-1} = 6(2)^4 = 6(16) = 96$

The terms are 6, 12, 24, 48, 96.

48. $a_1 = -12$

$a_2 = -12\left(\dfrac{1}{2}\right)^{2-1} = -12\left(\dfrac{1}{2}\right) = -6$

$a_3 = -12\left(\dfrac{1}{2}\right)^{3-1} = -12\left(\dfrac{1}{4}\right) = -3$

$a_4 = -12\left(\dfrac{1}{2}\right)^{4-1} = -12\left(\dfrac{1}{8}\right) = -\dfrac{3}{2}$

$a_5 = -12\left(\dfrac{1}{2}\right)^{5-1} = -12\left(\dfrac{1}{16}\right) = -\dfrac{3}{4}$

The terms are $-12, -6, -3, -\dfrac{3}{2}, -\dfrac{3}{4}$.

49. $a_1 = 20$

$a_2 = 20\left(-\dfrac{2}{3}\right)^{2-1} = 20\left(-\dfrac{2}{3}\right) = -\dfrac{40}{3}$

$a_3 = 20\left(-\dfrac{2}{3}\right)^{3-1} = 20\left(-\dfrac{2}{3}\right)^2 = 20\left(\dfrac{4}{9}\right) = \dfrac{80}{9}$

$a_4 = 20\left(-\dfrac{2}{3}\right)^{4-1} = 20\left(-\dfrac{2}{3}\right)^3 = 20\left(-\dfrac{8}{27}\right) = -\dfrac{160}{27}$

$a_5 = 20\left(-\dfrac{2}{3}\right)^{5-1} = 20\left(-\dfrac{2}{3}\right)^4 = 20\left(\dfrac{16}{81}\right) = \dfrac{320}{81}$

The terms are $20, -\dfrac{40}{3}, \dfrac{80}{9}, -\dfrac{160}{27}, \dfrac{320}{81}$.

50. $a_1 = -20$

$a_2 = -20\left(\dfrac{1}{5}\right)^{2-1} = -20\left(\dfrac{1}{5}\right) = -4$

$a_3 = -20\left(\dfrac{1}{5}\right)^{3-1} = -20\left(\dfrac{1}{25}\right) = -\dfrac{4}{5}$

$a_4 = -20\left(\dfrac{1}{5}\right)^{4-1} = -20\left(\dfrac{1}{125}\right) = -\dfrac{4}{25}$

$a_5 = -20\left(\dfrac{1}{5}\right)^{5-1} = -20\left(\dfrac{1}{625}\right) = -\dfrac{4}{125}$

The terms are $-20, -4, -\dfrac{4}{5}, -\dfrac{4}{25}, -\dfrac{4}{125}$.

51. $a_5 = a_1 \cdot r^{5-1} = 6\left(\dfrac{1}{3}\right)^{5-1} = 6\left(\dfrac{1}{3}\right)^4 = 6\left(\dfrac{1}{81}\right) = \dfrac{2}{27}$

52. $a_6 = a_1 \cdot r^{6-1} = 15(2)^{6-1} = 15(2)^5 = 15(32) = 480$

53. $a_4 = -8(-3)^{4-1} = -8(-3)^3 = -8(-27) = 216$

54. $a_5 = \dfrac{1}{12}\left(\dfrac{2}{3}\right)^{5-1} = \dfrac{1}{12}\left(\dfrac{2}{3}\right)^4 = \dfrac{1}{12}\left(\dfrac{16}{81}\right) = \dfrac{4}{243}$

55. $s_6 = \dfrac{6(1-2^6)}{1-2} = \dfrac{6(1-64)}{-1} = \dfrac{6(-63)}{-1} = 378$

56. $s_5 = \dfrac{-84\left[1-\left(-\frac{1}{4}\right)^5\right]}{1-\left(-\frac{1}{4}\right)}$

$= \dfrac{-84\left[1-\left(-\frac{1}{1024}\right)\right]}{1+\frac{1}{4}}$

$= \dfrac{-84\left(1+\frac{1}{1024}\right)}{\frac{5}{4}}$

$= -84 \cdot \left(\dfrac{1025}{1024}\right) \cdot \dfrac{4}{5}$

$= -\dfrac{4305}{64}$

57. $s_4 = \dfrac{9\left[1-\left(\frac{3}{2}\right)^4\right]}{1-\frac{3}{2}} = \dfrac{9\left(1-\frac{81}{16}\right)}{-\frac{1}{2}} = 9\left(-\dfrac{65}{16}\right)\left(-\dfrac{2}{1}\right) = \dfrac{585}{8}$

58. $s_7 = \dfrac{8\left[1-\left(\frac{1}{2}\right)^7\right]}{1-\frac{1}{2}} = \dfrac{8\left(1-\frac{1}{128}\right)}{\frac{1}{2}} = 8\left(\dfrac{127}{128}\right)\left(\dfrac{2}{1}\right) = \dfrac{127}{8}$

59. $r = 12 \div 6 = 2$

$a_n = 6(2)^{n-1}$

60. $r = -20 \div (-4) = 5$

$a_n = -4(5)^{n-1}$

61. $r = \dfrac{10}{3} \div 10 = \dfrac{10}{3} \cdot \dfrac{1}{10} = \dfrac{1}{3}$

$a_n = 10\left(\dfrac{1}{3}\right)^{n-1}$

62. $r = \dfrac{18}{15} \div \dfrac{9}{5} = \dfrac{18}{15} \cdot \dfrac{5}{9} = \dfrac{2}{3}$

$a_n = \dfrac{9}{5}\left(\dfrac{2}{3}\right)^{n-1}$

63. $r = \dfrac{5}{2} \div 5 = \dfrac{5}{2} \cdot \dfrac{1}{5} = \dfrac{1}{2}$

$S_\infty = \dfrac{5}{1-\frac{1}{2}} = \dfrac{5}{\frac{1}{2}} = 5\left(\dfrac{2}{1}\right) = 10$

64. $r = 1 \div \dfrac{5}{2} = 1\left(\dfrac{2}{5}\right) = \dfrac{2}{5}$

$S_\infty = \dfrac{\frac{5}{2}}{1-\frac{2}{5}} = \dfrac{\frac{5}{2}}{\frac{3}{5}} = \dfrac{5}{2}\left(\dfrac{5}{3}\right) = \dfrac{25}{6}$

65. $r = \dfrac{8}{3} \div (-8) = \dfrac{8}{3}\left(-\dfrac{1}{8}\right) = -\dfrac{1}{3}$

$S_\infty = \dfrac{-8}{1-\left(-\frac{1}{3}\right)} = \dfrac{-8}{\frac{4}{3}} = -8\left(\dfrac{3}{4}\right) = -6$

66. $r = -4 \div -6 = \dfrac{-4}{-6} = \dfrac{2}{3}$

$S_\infty = \dfrac{-6}{1-\frac{2}{3}} = \dfrac{-6}{\frac{1}{3}} = -6\left(\dfrac{3}{1}\right) = -18$

67. $r = 8 \div 16 = \dfrac{8}{16} = \dfrac{1}{2}$

$S_\infty = \dfrac{16}{1-\frac{1}{2}} = \dfrac{16}{\frac{1}{2}} = 16\left(\dfrac{2}{1}\right) = 32$

68. $r = \dfrac{9}{3} \div 9 = \dfrac{9}{3} \cdot \dfrac{1}{9} = \dfrac{1}{3}$

$S_\infty = \dfrac{9}{1-\frac{1}{3}} = \dfrac{9}{\frac{2}{3}} = 9\left(\dfrac{3}{2}\right) = \dfrac{27}{2}$

69. $r = -1 \div 5 = -\dfrac{1}{5}$

$S_\infty = \dfrac{5}{1-\left(-\frac{1}{5}\right)} = \dfrac{5}{\frac{6}{5}} = 5\left(\dfrac{5}{6}\right) = \dfrac{25}{6}$

70. $r = -\dfrac{8}{3} \div -4 = -\dfrac{8}{3}\left(-\dfrac{1}{4}\right) = \dfrac{2}{3}$

$S_\infty = \dfrac{-4}{1-\frac{2}{3}} = \dfrac{-4}{\frac{1}{3}} = -4\left(\dfrac{3}{1}\right) = -12$

71. $0.363636... = 0.36 + 0.0036 + 0.000036 + ...$

$\qquad = 0.36 + 0.36(0.01) + 0.36(0.01)^2 + \cdots$

$a_1 = 0.36$ and $r = 0.01$

$S_\infty = \dfrac{0.36}{1-0.01} = \dfrac{0.36}{0.99} = \dfrac{36}{99} = \dfrac{4}{11}$

72. $0.621621...$

$= 0.621 + 0.000621 + 0.000000621 + \cdots$

$= 0.621 + 0.621(0.001) + 0.621(0.001)^2 + \cdots$

$a_1 = 0.621$ and $r = 0.001$

$S_\infty = \dfrac{0.621}{1-0.001} = \dfrac{0.621}{0.999} = \dfrac{621}{999} = \dfrac{23}{37}$

---

73. $(3x+y)^4 = \binom{4}{0}(3x)^4(y)^0 + \binom{4}{1}(3x)^3(y)^1 + \binom{4}{2}(3x)^2(y)^2 + \binom{4}{3}(3x)^1(y)^3 + \binom{4}{4}(3x)^0(y)^4$

$= 1(81x^4)(1) + 4(27x^3)(y) + 6(9x^2)(y^2) + 4(3x)(y^3) + 1(1)(y^4)$

$= 81x^4 + 108x^3y + 54x^2y^2 + 12xy^3 + y^4$

74. $(2x-3y^2)^3 = \binom{3}{0}(2x)^3(-3y^2)^0 + \binom{3}{1}(2x)^2(-3y^2)^1 + \binom{3}{2}(2x)^1(-3y^2)^2 + \binom{3}{3}(2x)^0(-3y^2)^3$

$= 1(8x^3)(1) + 3(4x^2)(-3y^2) + 3(2x)(9y^4) + 1(1)(-27y^6)$

$= 8x^3 - 36x^2y^2 + 54xy^4 - 27y^6$

75. $(x-2y)^9 = \binom{9}{0}(x)^9(-2y)^0 + \binom{9}{1}(x)^8(-2y)^1 + \binom{9}{2}(x)^7(-2y)^2 + \binom{9}{3}(x)^6(-2y)^3 + \cdots$

$= 1(x^9)(1) + 9(x^8)(-2y) + 36(x^7)(4y^2) + 84(x^6)(-8y^3) + \cdots$

$= x^9 - 18x^8y + 144x^7y^2 - 672x^6y^3 + \cdots$

76. $(2a^2+3b)^8 = \binom{8}{0}(2a^2)^8(3b)^0 + \binom{8}{1}(2a^2)^7(3b)^1 + \binom{8}{2}(2a^2)^6(3b)^2 + \binom{8}{3}(2a^2)^5(3b)^3 + \cdots$

$$= 1(256a^{16})(1) + 8(128a^{14})(3b) + 28(64a^{12})(9b^2) + 56(32a^{10})(27b^3) + \cdots$$

$$= 256a^{16} + 3072a^{14}b + 16,128a^{12}b^2 + 48,384a^{10}b^3 + \cdots$$

---

77. This is an arithmetic series with $d = 1$, $a_1 = 101$, and $a_n = 200$.

$a_n = a_1 + (n-1)d$

$200 = 101 + (n-1)(1)$

$200 = 101 + n - 1$

$200 = n + 100$

$100 = n$

The sum is

$s_{100} = \dfrac{n(a_1 + a_{100})}{2}$

$= \dfrac{100(101 + 200)}{2}$

$= \dfrac{100(301)}{2}$

$= 15,050$

78. $21 + 20 + 19 + \cdots + 1$ or $1 + 2 + 3 + \cdots + 21$

$s_n = \dfrac{n(a_1 + a_n)}{2}$

$s_{21} = \dfrac{21(1+21)}{2} = \dfrac{21(22)}{2} = \dfrac{462}{2} = 231$

There are 231 barrels in the stack.

79. This is an arithmetic sequence with $d = 1000$

a. $a_1 = 36,000$

$a_2 = 36,000 + (2-1)(1000)$

$= 36,000 + 1000$

$= 37,000$

$a_3 = 36,000 + (3-1)(1000)$

$= 36,000 + 2000$

$= 38,000$

$a_4 = 36,000 + (4-1)(1000)$

$= 36,000 + 3000$

$= 39,000$

Ahmed's salaries for the first four years are $36,000, $37,000, $38,000, and $39,000.

b. $a_n = 36,000 + (n-1)(1000)$

$= 36,000 + 1000n - 1000$

$= 35,000 + 1000n$

c. $a_6 = 35,000 + 1000(6)$

$= 35,000 + 6,000$

$= 41,000$

In the 6th year, his salary would be $41,000.

d. $a_{11} = 36,000 + (11-1)1000 = 46,000$

$s_n = \dfrac{n(a_1 + a_n)}{2}$

$s_{11} = \dfrac{11(36,000 + 46,000)}{2}$

$= \dfrac{11(82,000)}{2}$

$= 451,000$

Ahmed will make a total of $451,000 in his first 11 years.

80. This is a geometric series with $r = 2$, $a_1 = 100$, and $n = 11$. (Note: There are 11 terms here since 200 represents the first doubling.)

$a_{11} = a_1 \cdot r^{11-1}$

$= 100(2)^{11-1} = 100(2)^{10} = 100(1024) = 102,400$

You would have $102,400.

81. $a_1 = 1600$, $r = 1.04$, $a_n = a_1 r^{n-1}$

a. July is the 7th month, so $n = 7$.

$a_7 = 1600(1.04)^{7-1} = 1600(1.04)^6 \approx 2024.51$

Gertrude's salary will be $2,024.51 in July.

b. December is the 12th month, so $n = 12$.

$a_{12} = 1600(1.04)^{12-1} = 1600(1.04)^{11} \approx 2463.13$

Gertrude's salary will be $2,463.13 in December.

c. $s_n = \dfrac{a_1(1-r^n)}{1-r}$, $n = 12$

$s_{12} = \dfrac{1600\left[1 - (1.04)^{12}\right]}{1 - 1.04} \approx 24,041.29$

Gertrude will make $24,041.29 in 2006.

82. Each year, the cost of the object will be 1.08 times greater than the previous year. After 12 years will be the 13th year. Therefore,
$$a_{13} = 200(1.08)^{13-1} \approx 200(2.51817) \approx 503.63$$
The item would cost $503.63.

83. This is an infinite geometric series with $r = 0.92$ and $a_1 = 12$.
$$s_\infty = \frac{12}{1-0.92} = \frac{12}{0.08} = 150$$
The pendulum travels a total distance of 150 feet.

Chapter 15 Practice Test

1. A series is the sum of the terms of a sequence

2. a. An arithmetic sequence is one whose terms differ by a constant amount.

b. A geometric sequence is one whose terms differ by a common multiple.

3. $a_n = \dfrac{n-2}{3n}$

$a_1 = \dfrac{1-2}{3(1)} = \dfrac{-1}{3} = -\dfrac{1}{3}$

$a_2 = \dfrac{2-2}{3(2)} = \dfrac{0}{6} = 0$

$a_3 = \dfrac{3-2}{3(3)} = \dfrac{1}{9}$

$a_4 = \dfrac{4-2}{3(4)} = \dfrac{2}{12} = \dfrac{1}{6}$

$a_5 = \dfrac{5-2}{3(5)} = \dfrac{3}{15} = \dfrac{1}{5}$

The terms are $-\dfrac{1}{3}$, 0, $\dfrac{1}{9}$, $\dfrac{1}{6}$, $\dfrac{1}{5}$.

4. $a_n = \dfrac{2n+1}{n^2}$

$a_1 = \dfrac{2(1)+1}{1^2} = \dfrac{2+1}{1} = 3$

$a_2 = \dfrac{2(2)+1}{2^2} = \dfrac{4+1}{4} = \dfrac{5}{4}$

$a_3 = \dfrac{2(3)+1}{3^2} = \dfrac{6+1}{9} = \dfrac{7}{9}$

$s_1 = a_1 = 3$

$s_3 = a_1 + a_2 + a_3 = 3 + \dfrac{5}{4} + \dfrac{7}{9} = \dfrac{181}{36}$

5. $\displaystyle\sum_{i=1}^{5}(2i^2 + 3)$

$= [2(1)^2 + 3] + [2(2)^2 + 3] + [2(3)^2 + 3]$
$\qquad + [2(4)^2 + 3] + [2(5)^2 + 3]$

$= (2+3) + (8+3) + (18+3) + (32+3) + (50+3)$

$= 5 + 11 + 21 + 35 + 53$

$= 125$

6. $\displaystyle\sum_{i=1}^{4}(x_i)^2 = x_1^2 + x_2^2 + x_3^2 + x_4^2$

$= 4^2 + 2^2 + 8^2 + 10^2$

$= 16 + 4 + 64 + 100$

$= 184$

7. $d = \dfrac{2}{3} - \dfrac{1}{3} = \dfrac{1}{3}$

$a_n = a_1 + (n-1)d$

$= \dfrac{1}{3} + (n-1)\left(\dfrac{1}{3}\right) = \dfrac{1}{3} + \dfrac{1}{3}n - \dfrac{1}{3} = \dfrac{1}{3}n$

8. $r = 10 \div 5 = \dfrac{10}{5} = 2$

$a_n = a_1 r^{n-1} = 5(2)^{n-1}$

9. $a_1 = 15$

$a_2 = 15 + (2-1)(-6) = 15 + 1(-6) = 15 - 6 = 9$

$a_3 = 15 + (3-1)(-6) = 15 + 2(-6) = 15 - 12 = 3$

$a_4 = 15 + (4-1)(-6) = 15 + 3(-6) = 15 - 18 = -3$

The terms are 15, 9, 3, –3.

10. $a_1 = \dfrac{5}{12}$

$a_2 = a_1 r^1 = \dfrac{5}{12}\left(\dfrac{2}{3}\right)^1 = \dfrac{5}{12}\left(\dfrac{2}{3}\right) = \dfrac{5}{18}$

$a_3 = a_1 r^2 = \dfrac{5}{12}\left(\dfrac{2}{3}\right)^2 = \dfrac{5}{12}\left(\dfrac{4}{9}\right) = \dfrac{5}{27}$

$a_4 = a_1 r^3 = \dfrac{5}{12}\left(\dfrac{2}{3}\right)^3 = \dfrac{5}{12}\left(\dfrac{8}{27}\right) = \dfrac{10}{81}$

The terms are $\dfrac{5}{12}$, $\dfrac{5}{18}$, $\dfrac{5}{27}$, $\dfrac{10}{81}$.

11. $a_{11} = a_1 + 10d = 40 + (10)(-8) = 40 - 80 = -40$

12. $s_8 = \dfrac{8(a_1 + a_8)}{2} = \dfrac{8[7 + (-12)]}{2} = \dfrac{8(-5)}{2} = -20$

13. $d = -16 - (-4) = -16 + 4 = -12$

$a_n = a_1 + (n-1)d$

$-136 = -4 + (n-1)(-12)$

$-136 = -4 - 12n + 12$

$-136 = 8 - 12n$

$-144 = -12n$

$12 = n$

14. $a_6 = a_1 r^5 = 8\left(\dfrac{2}{3}\right)^5 = 8\left(\dfrac{32}{243}\right) = \dfrac{256}{243}$

15. $s_7 = \dfrac{a_1\left(1-r^7\right)}{1-r}$

$= \dfrac{\frac{3}{5}\left[1-(-5)^7\right]}{1-(-5)}$

$= \dfrac{\frac{3}{5}\left[1-(-78,125)\right]}{1-(-5)}$

$= \dfrac{\frac{3}{5}(1+78,125)}{1+5}$

$= \dfrac{\frac{3}{5}(78,126)}{6}$

$= \dfrac{3(78,126)}{5 \cdot 6}$

$= \dfrac{78,126}{5 \cdot 2}$

$= \dfrac{39,063}{5}$

16. $r = 5 \div 15 = \dfrac{5}{15} = \dfrac{1}{3}$

$a_n = a_1 r^{n-1} = 15\left(\dfrac{1}{3}\right)^{n-1}$

17. $r = \dfrac{8}{3} \div 4 = \dfrac{8}{3} \cdot \dfrac{1}{4} = \dfrac{2}{3}$

$s_\infty = \dfrac{a_1}{1-r} = \dfrac{4}{1-\frac{2}{3}} = \dfrac{4}{\frac{1}{3}} = 4 \cdot \dfrac{3}{1} = 12$

18. $0.3939\cdots = 0.39 + 0.0039 + 0.000039 + \cdots$

$\qquad = 0.39 + 0.39(0.01) + 0.39(0.01)^2 + \cdots$

$r = 0.01$ and $a_1 = 0.39$

$s_\infty = \dfrac{0.39}{1-0.01} = \dfrac{0.39}{0.99} = \dfrac{39}{99} = \dfrac{13}{33}$

19. $\dbinom{8}{3} = \dfrac{8!}{3!(8-3)!}$

$= \dfrac{8!}{3!5!}$

$= \dfrac{8 \cdot 7 \cdot 6 \cdot \cancel{5 \cdot 4 \cdot 3 \cdot 2 \cdot 1}}{(3 \cdot 2 \cdot 1)(\cancel{5 \cdot 4 \cdot 3 \cdot 2 \cdot 1})}$

$= \dfrac{336}{6}$

$= 56$

20. $(x+2y)^4 = \dbinom{4}{0}(x)^4(2y)^0 + \dbinom{4}{1}(x)^3(2y)^1 + \dbinom{4}{2}(x)^2(2y)^2 + \dbinom{4}{3}(x)^1(2y)^3 + \dbinom{4}{4}(x)^0(2y)^4$

$\qquad = 1(x^4)(1) + 4(x^3)(2y) + 6(x^2)(4y^2) + 4(x)(8y^3) + 1(1)(16y^4)$

$\qquad = x^4 + 8x^3 y + 24x^2 y^2 + 32xy^3 + 16y^4$

21. $\bar{x} = \dfrac{\sum x}{n} = \dfrac{76+93+83+87+71}{5} = \dfrac{410}{5} = 82$

22. $13+12+11+\cdots+1$ or $1+2+3+\cdots+13$

$s_n = \dfrac{n(a_1 + a_n)}{2}$

$s_{13} = \dfrac{13(1+13)}{2} = \dfrac{13(14)}{2} = \dfrac{182}{2} = 91$

There are 91 logs in the pile.

23. $a_1 = 1000$, $n = 20$

$a_n = a_1 + (n-1)d$

$a_{20} = 1000 + (20-1)(1000) = 20,000$

$s_{20} = \dfrac{20(1000+20,000)}{2} = \dfrac{20(21,000)}{2} = 210,000$

After 20 years, she will have saved \$210,000.

24. $a_1 = 700, \quad r = 1.04, \quad a_n = a_1 r^{n-1}$

$a_6 = 700(1.04)^{6-1} = 700(1.04)^5 \approx 851.66$

She will be making about $851.66 in the sixth week.

25. $r = 3, \quad a_1 = 500(3) = 1500$

$a_6 = 1500(3)^{6-1} = 1500(3)^5 = 364,500$

At the end of the sixth hour, there will be 364,500 bacteria in the culture.

Chapter 15 Cumulative Review Test

1. $A = \dfrac{1}{2}bh, \quad \text{for } b$

$2A = bh$

$\dfrac{2A}{h} = \dfrac{bh}{h}$

$\dfrac{2A}{h} = b$

2. $m = \dfrac{y_2 - y_1}{x_2 - x_1} = \dfrac{9 - (-2)}{1 - 4} = \dfrac{11}{-3} = -\dfrac{11}{3}$

Use the point-slope equation with $m = -\dfrac{11}{3}$ and $(4, -2)$.

$y - y_1 = m(x - x_1)$

$y - (-2) = -\dfrac{11}{3}(x - 4)$

$y + 2 = -\dfrac{11}{3}x + \dfrac{44}{3}$

$y = -\dfrac{11}{3}x + \dfrac{44}{3} - 2$

$y = -\dfrac{11}{3}x + \dfrac{38}{3}$

3.
$$
\begin{array}{r}
5x^3 + 4x^2 - 6x + 2 \\
\hline
x + 5 \overline{) } \\
\end{array}
$$

$5x^4 + 4x^3 - 6x^2 + 2x$

$\underline{25x^3 + 20x^2 - 30x + 10}$

$5x^4 + 29x^3 + 14x^2 - 28x + 10$

4. $x^3 + 2x - 5x^2 - 10 = (x^3 + 2x) - (5x^2 + 10)$

$ = x(x^2 + 2) - 6(x^2 + 2)$

$ = (x^2 + 2)(x - 6)$

5. $(a+b)^2 + 8(a+b) + 16 \qquad$ [Let $u = a + b$.]

$= u^2 + 8u + 16$

$= (u + 4)(u + 4)$

$= (u + 4)^2 \qquad$ [Back substitute $a + b$ for u.]

$= (a + b + 4)^2$

6. $5 - \dfrac{x - 1}{x^2 + 3x - 10} = 5 - \dfrac{x - 1}{(x + 5)(x - 2)}$

$= \dfrac{5(x + 5)(x - 2)}{(x + 5)(x - 2)} - \dfrac{x - 1}{(x + 5)(x - 2)}$

$= \dfrac{5x^2 + 15x - 50}{(x + 5)(x - 2)} - \dfrac{x - 1}{(x + 5)(x - 2)}$

$= \dfrac{5x^2 + 15x - 50 - (x - 1)}{(x + 5)(x - 2)}$

$= \dfrac{5x^2 + 15x - 50 - x + 1}{(x + 5)(x - 2)}$

$= \dfrac{5x^2 + 14x - 49}{(x + 5)(x - 2)}$

7. $y = kz^2$

$80 = k(20)^2$

$80 = 400k$

$k = \dfrac{80}{400} = 0.2$

$y = 0.2z^2$

Let $z = 50$: $\quad y = 0.2(50)^2 = 0.2(2500) = 500$

8. $x + y + z = 1 \quad$ (1)

$2x + 2y + 2z = 2 \quad$ (2)

$3x + 3y + 3z = 3 \quad$ (3)

Notice that if you multiply equation (1) by 2, the result is exactly the same as equation (2). This implies that this is a dependent system and therefore has infinitely many solutions.

9. $f(x) = 3\sqrt[3]{x - 2}, \quad g(x) = \sqrt[3]{7x - 14}$

$f(x) = g(x)$

$2\sqrt[3]{x - 3} = \sqrt[3]{5x - 15}$

$\left(2\sqrt[3]{x - 3}\right)^3 = \left(\sqrt[3]{5x - 15}\right)^3$

$8(x - 3) = 5x - 15$

$8x - 24 = 5x - 15$

$3x = 9$

$x = 3$

10. $\sqrt{6x-5}-\sqrt{2x+6}-1=0$

$\sqrt{6x-5}=1+\sqrt{2x+6}$

$\left(\sqrt{6x-5}\right)^2=\left(1+\sqrt{2x+6}\right)^2$

$6x-5=1+2\sqrt{2x+6}+2x+6$

$4x-12=2\sqrt{2x+6}$

$2x-6=\sqrt{2x+6}$

$(2x-6)^2=\left(\sqrt{2x+6}\right)^2$

$4x^2-24x+36=2x+6$

$4x^2-26x+30=0$

$2\left(2x^2-13x+15\right)=0$

$2(2x-3)(x-5)=0$

$2x-3=0 \quad \text{or} \quad x-5=0$

$x=\dfrac{3}{2} \qquad\qquad x=5$

Upon checking, $x=\dfrac{3}{2}$ is an extraneous solution.

The solution is $x=5$.

11. $x^2+2x+15=0$

$x^2+2x \quad\quad =-15$

$x^2+2x+1=-15+1$

$(x+1)^2=-14$

$x+1=\pm\sqrt{-14}$

$x+1=\pm i\sqrt{14}$

$x=-1\pm i\sqrt{14}$

12. $x^2-\dfrac{x}{5}-\dfrac{1}{3}=0$

$15\left(x^2-\dfrac{x}{5}-\dfrac{1}{3}\right)=15(0)$

$15x^2-3x-5=0$

$x=\dfrac{-b\pm\sqrt{b^2-4ac}}{2a}$

$=\dfrac{-(-3)\pm\sqrt{(-3)^2-4(15)(-5)}}{2(15)}$

$=\dfrac{3\pm\sqrt{9+300}}{30}$

$=\dfrac{3\pm\sqrt{309}}{30}$

13. Let x be the number. Then

$2x^2-9x=5$

$2x^2-9x-5=0$

$(2x+1)(x-5)=0$

$2x+1=0 \quad \text{or} \quad x-5=0$

$x=-\dfrac{1}{2} \qquad\qquad x=5$

Since the number must be positive, disregard

$x=-\dfrac{1}{2}$. The number is 5.

14. $y=2^x-1$

15. $\log_a \dfrac{1}{64}=6$

$a^6=\dfrac{1}{64}$

$a^6=\left(\dfrac{1}{2}\right)^6$

$a=\dfrac{1}{2}$

16. $y=x^2-4x$

$y=\left(x^2-4x+4\right)-4$

$y=(x-2)^2-4$

The vertex is $(2,-4)$.

17. $(h,k)=(-6,2),\ r=7$

$(x-h)^2+(y-k)^2=r^2$

$\left(x-(-6)\right)^2+\left(y-2\right)^2=7^2$

$(x+6)^2+(y-2)^2=49$

18. $(x+3)^2 + (y+1)^2 = 16$

$(x+3)^2 + (y+1)^2 = 4^2$

center: $(-3,-1)$ radius: 4

$(x+3)^2 + (y+1)^2 = 16$

19. $9x^2 + 16y^2 = 144$

$$\frac{9x^2}{144} + \frac{16y^2}{144} = 1$$

$$\frac{x^2}{16} + \frac{y^2}{9} = 1$$

$$\frac{x^2}{4^2} + \frac{y^2}{3^2} = 1 \implies a = 4 \text{ and } b = 3$$

$9x^2 + 16y^2 = 144$

20. $r = 4 \div 6 = \dfrac{4}{6} = \dfrac{2}{3}$

$$s_\infty = \frac{a_1}{1-r} = \frac{6}{1-\frac{2}{3}} = \frac{6}{\frac{1}{3}} = 6 \cdot \frac{3}{1} = 18$$